APOSTLES' CREED

May replace the Nicene Creed

I believe in God,
the Father almighty,
Creator of heaven and earth,
and in Jesus Christ, his only Son, our Lord,

All bow at the following words up to and including:
    the Virgin Mary,

who was conceived by the Holy Spirit,
born of the Virgin Mary,
suffered under Pontius Pilate,
was crucified, died and was buried;
he descended into hell;
on the third day he rose again from the dead;
he ascended into heaven,
and is seated at the right hand
    of God the Father almighty;
from there he will come to judge
    the living and the dead.

I believe in the Holy Spirit,
the holy catholic Church,
the communion of saints,
the forgiveness of sins,
the resurrection of the body,
and life everlasting. Amen.

INVITATION TO PRAYER

Priest: Pray... the almighty Father.
Assembly: May the Lord accept the
            sacrifice at your hands
            for the praise and glory of his name,
            for our good
            and the good of all his holy Church.

PREFACE DIALOGUE

Priest: The Lord be with you.
Assembly: And with your spirit.
Priest: Lift up your hearts.
Assembly: We lift them up to the Lord.
Priest: Let us give thanks to the Lord
          our God.
Assembly: It is right and just.

HOLY, HOLY, HOLY

Holy, Holy, Holy Lord God of hosts.
Heaven and earth are full of your glory.
Hosanna in the highest.
Blessed is he who comes
    in the name of the Lord.
Hosanna in the highest.

MEMORIAL ACCLAMATION A

We proclaim your Death, O Lord,
and profess your Resurrection
until you come again.

MEMORIAL ACCLAMATION B

When we eat this Bread and drink this Cup,
we proclaim your Death, O Lord,
until you come again.

MEMORIAL ACCLAMATION C

Save us, Savior of the world,
for by your Cross and Resurrection
you have set us free.

SIGN OF PEACE

Priest: The peace of the Lord be with you
          always.
Assembly: And with your spirit.

INVITATION TO COMMUNION

Priest: Behold... supper of the Lamb.
Assembly: Lord, I am not worthy
            that you should enter under my roof,
            but only say the word
            and my soul shall be healed.

DISMISSAL

Priest: The Lord be with you.
Assembly: And with your spirit.

RITUAL**SONG**
SECOND EDITION

GIA PUBLICATIONS, INC.
CHICAGO

G-9000R
Copyright © 2016 by GIA Publications, Inc.
7404 South Mason Avenue, Chicago, Illinois 60638
www.giamusic.com

PREFACE

In 1996, GIA Publications, Inc. published *RitualSong*, a hymnal and service book for Roman Catholics. This hymnal responded to the growing need for a single worship resource that offered an eclectic mix of musical forms and styles reflective of the diversity of many Sunday assemblies in the United States. Furthermore, as suggested by its name, it reflected a particular emphasis on the inclusion of music that would allow communities to sing the rites of the Church. Twenty years later, committed to the vision of the original publication, GIA is pleased to release *Ritual Song—Second Edition*.

At the core of *Ritual Song—Second Edition* is a collection of nearly six hundred hymns, songs, and short refrains drawn from a wide range of traditions, cultures, eras, and publishers. As the first GIA hymnal compiled and edited after the full implementation of the *Roman Missal, Third Edition*, it captures the best and most used new and revised mass settings created in the years following the release of the Revised Order of Mass. It includes the largest amount of service music and liturgical settings ever found in a GIA hymnal. And like its predecessor, it offers a substantial amount of music for the rites of the Church.

One of the most compelling elements of the original edition was its robust offering of psalmody. *Ritual Song—Second Edition* contains an even richer offering of psalmody. The first complete lectionary psalter utilizes the now-classic refrains that have appeared in GIA hymnals since 1975; these refrains are paired with psalm verses set to the timeless Gelineau tones as well as

psalms tones that originated in the monastic tradition. A second complete lectionary psalter features the refrains and tones of Michel Guimont. These two lectionary psalters utilize *The Revised Grail Psalms* of 2010, one of two translations authorized for lectionary use and the only translation used in the Roman Catholic Church's new and forthcoming ritual books. A generous amount of lyric psalmody in a variety of styles is found in the front of the hymnal. No Roman Catholic hymnal offers as many possibilities for singing the psalms.

The overarching principles that guided the design, repertoire selections, and new features of this edition were carefully developed by a committee of skilled pastoral musicians, each of whom embrace a wide diversity of music and texts in liturgical worship. Its contents have been selected by seasoned practitioners who value the primacy of the assembly's song. The committee carefully discerned the merits of each item found in this hymnal through the prism of their individual experiences and areas of expertise and with a deep consideration for the musical, liturgical, and pastoral judgments that should always guide the selection of post-conciliar liturgical music.

A team of readers provided invaluable comments, insights, suggestions, and affirmations for which we are grateful: Frank Brownstead, Chris de Silva, Lena Gokelman, David Haas, Marty Haugen, Rachelle Kramer, Judith Kubicki, Meg Matuska, John Miller, Gerardo Ramos, John Romeri, Wendy Barton Silhavy, Angela Stramaglia, Timothy Westerhaus, Kate Williams, and Robert Wolf.

The production of a hymnal is a significant undertaking for any publisher; *Ritual Song—Second Edition* honors the legacy of past GIA hymnals through the continued use of Michael Tapia's iconic book design first used in *Worship—Third Edition*. Similarly, Gabe Huck's liturgical commentary has helped form thousands of worshipers over several decades. The quality of this hymnal is due in large part to a dedicated team of employees who have mastered the art of hymnal production: Jeffry Mickus (production coordinator, engraver, editor, indexer, layout), Gail Gillispie (typesetting and layout), Sabina L. Lilly (proofreading), Michael Boschert (permissions editor), Andrew Schultz (logo design), Suzanne Orland (marketing), and Matthew Merz (marketing). The committee also wishes to acknowledge the work of Victoria Zibell for her meticulous record keeping and careful capturing of information. Finally, we are grateful to Alec Harris, president of GIA Publications, Inc., for his eager desire to see this hymnal come to fruition.

Ritual Song—Second Edition
Hymnal Committee
  Michael Silhavy
    Senior Editor
  David Anderson
    Editor-at-Large
  Tony Alonso
  Jennifer Kerr Budziak
  Heather Martin Cooper
  Thomas Stehle

Contents

Lectionary

Indexes

Liturgy of the Hours

When darkness gives way before the sun's light and a new day begins, people of all religions have had their rites of morning: words and songs and gestures with which to pray. It has been the same at the end of the day's light, and again in the last moments before sleep.

Christians, following the example of their Jewish ancestors, continued to pray at morning and evening and night. These moments are the hinges of daily life. As they came round each day they have been occasions to repeat what every child has learned by heart: words to praise God for a new morning, to thank the Father for Christ who is our light as evening comes, to invoke God's strong protection through the hours of night.

The daily prayers of Christians were fashioned at first from very simple things: the sign of the cross, the Lord's Prayer, a few verses and songs and short psalms, intercessions. And for most Christians morning and night remain times for such simple prayers always said by heart.

The pages of this section offer a form of daily prayer that grew from this same tradition. When Christians have gathered in the early morning, at day's end, just before retiring, the simple prayers for the individual have grown more elaborate. The daily assemblies of Christians gave shape to what became known as the divine office or "liturgy of the hours." In recent times, these prayers have been restored to some of their original simplicity and are again being prayed in parish churches and Christian households.

In using and in adapting the forms of morning, evening and night prayer given below, two things are especially important. First, these are not to be prayers which could be prayed any time. Rather, they are prayers (in word, song, gesture, silence) which are prompted by the morning itself, by the evening, by the night. Their content and pace should reflect what is unique to each of these moments. Second, the assembly's parts in these prayers should be gradually learned by heart. Simplicity, repetition and care for times of silence make it possible for these prayers to belong fully to those who assemble.

2 INVITATORY

The invitatory belongs at the very beginning of each day's prayer. It precedes either the Office of Readings or Morning Prayer. It consists of the dialogue below followed by Psalm 24, 67, 95, or 100. Settings of Psalm 95 are found at nos. 76 and 77, and below; settings of Psalm 100 are found at nos. 81–83.

Stand. All make the sign of the cross on their lips.

O Lord, ✠ o - pen my lips.   And my mouth will pro - claim your praise.

3 PSALM 95

The psalm may begin with an appropriate antiphon.

Antiphon I – Advent

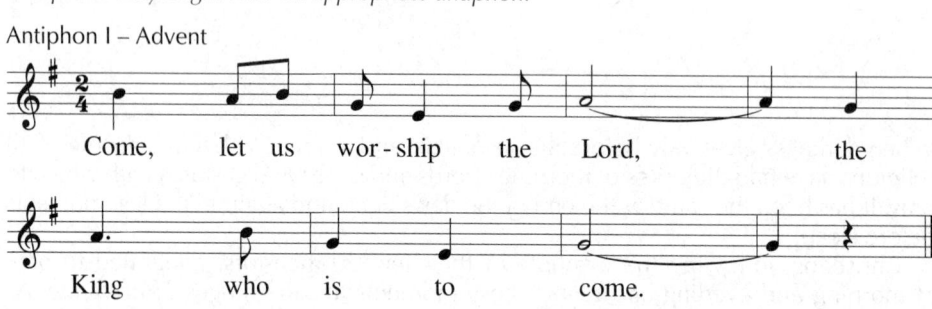

Come, let us wor - ship the Lord, the

King who is to come.

Antiphon II – Christmas

Christ is born for us; come, let us a - dore him.

Antiphon III – Lent

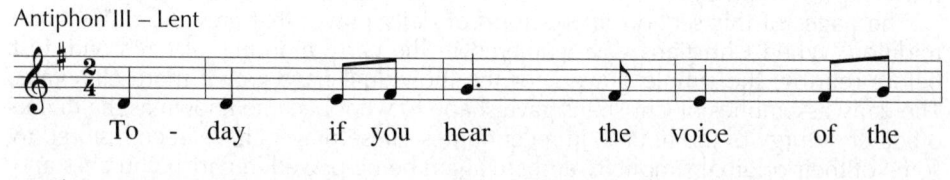

To - day if you hear the voice of the

Lord, hard - en not your hearts.

Antiphon IV – Easter

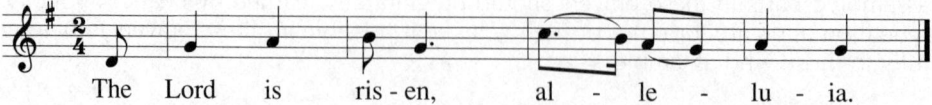

The Lord is ris - en, al - le - lu - ia.

Antiphon V – General

Cry out with joy to the Lord, all the earth; serve the Lord with glad - ness.

Psalm Tone

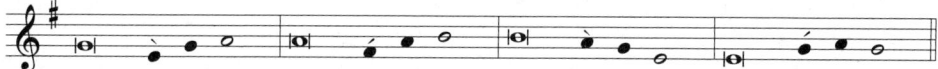

Verses

1. Come, ring out our joy tò the LORD;
   hail the róck who saves us.
   Let us come before God, gìving thanks,
   with songs let us háil the Lord.

2. A mighty God is the LORD, a great king abòve all gods,
   in whose hands are the depths of the earth; the heights of the mountáins as well.
   The sea belongs to Gòd, who made it
   and the dry land shaped bý his hands.

3. Come in; let us bow ànd bend low;
   let us kneel before the Gód who made us
   for this is our God and we the people who belong tò his pasture,
   the flock that is led bý his hand.

4. O that today you would listen tò God's voice!
   "Harden not your hearts ás at Meribah,
   as on that day at Massah in the desert when your ancestors put me tò the test;
   when they tried me, though they sáw my work.

5. "For forty years I was wearied of these people and I said: 'Their hearts àre astray,
   these people do not knów my ways.'
   Then I took an oath ìn my anger:
   'Never shall they entér my rest.'"

6. Give praise to the Fathèr almighty,
   to his Son, Jesus Chríst the Lord,
   to the Spirit who dwells ìn our hearts,
   both now and for evér. Amen.

Text: Antiphons, © 1974, ICEL; Psalm 95, © 1963, 1993, The Grail, GIA Publications, Inc., agent
Music: Howard Hughes, SM, © 1974, ICEL

4 Morning Prayer / Lauds

The Church's sense for how to pray in the morning comes from our Jewish heritage. Whatever the day, whatever the difficulties, the tradition has been to begin the day with praise for the Creator. The sign of the cross, first traced on the Christian at baptism, is again made to begin the new day and its prayer. In the hymn and the psalms, in the scripture and intercessions, each one who prays and the community together finds what it is to stand at the beginning of a new day as a Christian. The morning's prayer gives the day its meaning when, through the years, these prayers become one's own.

The following verse and response are omitted when the hour begins with the invitatory.

Stand. All make the sign of the cross.

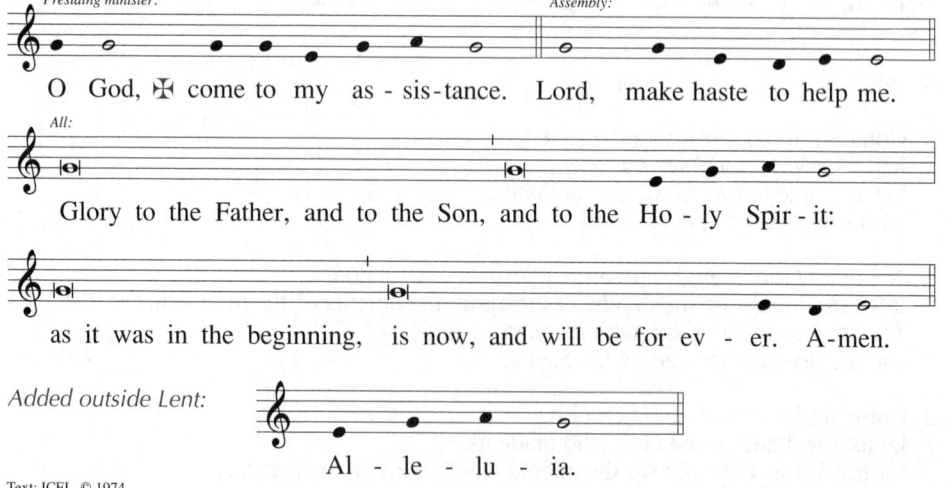

Presiding minister: O God, ✠ come to my as-sis-tance. *Assembly:* Lord, make haste to help me.

All: Glory to the Father, and to the Son, and to the Ho-ly Spir-it:

as it was in the beginning, is now, and will be for ev-er. A-men.

Added outside Lent: Al - le - lu - ia.

Text: ICEL, © 1974

5 HYMN

This or another morning hymn (see nos. 942 to 945), or one related to the season or feast, may be sung.

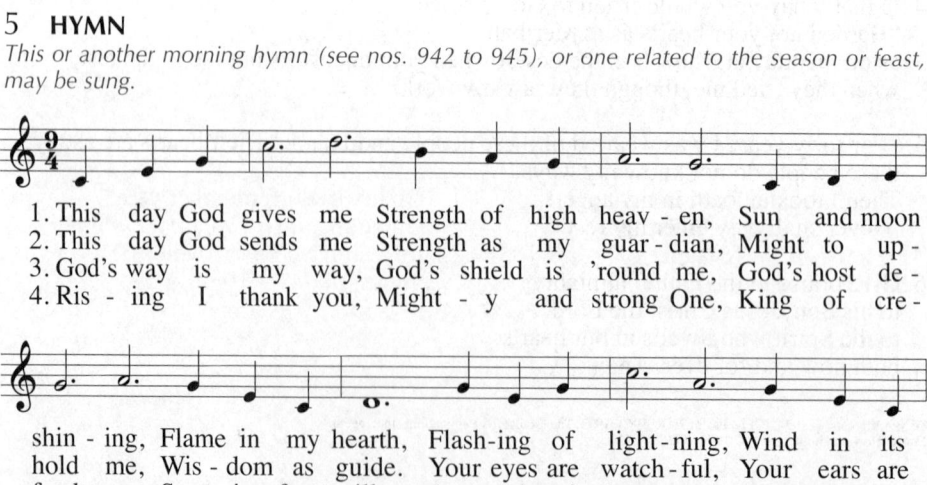

1. This day God gives me Strength of high heav-en, Sun and moon shin-ing, Flame in my hearth, Flash-ing of light-ning, Wind in its
2. This day God sends me Strength as my guar-dian, Might to up-hold me, Wis-dom as guide. Your eyes are watch-ful, Your ears are
3. God's way is my way, God's shield is 'round me, God's host de-fends me, Sav-ing from ill. An-gels of heav-en, Drive from me
4. Ris-ing I thank you, Might-y and strong One, King of cre-a-tion, Giv-er of rest, Firm-ly con-fess-ing Three-ness of

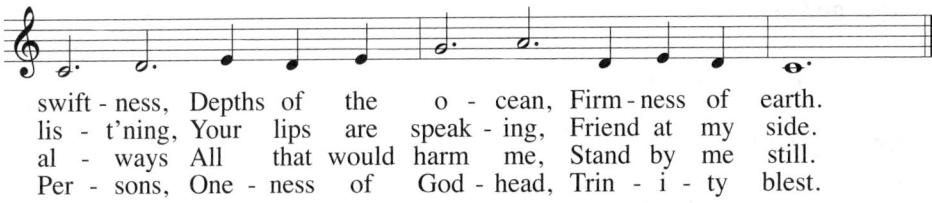

swift - ness, Depths of the o - cean, Firm - ness of earth.
lis - t'ning, Your lips are speak - ing, Friend at my side.
al - ways All that would harm me, Stand by me still.
Per - sons, One - ness of God - head, Trin - i - ty blest.

Text: Ascribed to St. Patrick; James Quinn, SJ, 1919–2010, © 1969, James Quinn, SJ. Published by OCP.
Tune: BUNESSAN, 5 5 5 4 D; Gaelic melody; acc. by Marty Haugen, b.1950, © 1987, GIA Publications, Inc.

PSALMODY

The singing of one or more psalms is a central part of morning prayer. Psalm 63 is one of the premier morning psalms. Psalm 51 is commonly substituted for Psalm 63 on Wednesday and Friday, as well as during Lent. Other appropriate psalms for morning are Psalms 8, 33, 42, 47, 66, 72, 80, 85, 95, 98, 100, 118, and 150.

Sit

PSALM 63   6

Antiphon

In the morn-ing I will sing, will sing glad songs of praise to you.

Text: *Praise God in Song*
Music: David Clark Isele
© 1979, GIA Publications, Inc.

Psalm Tone

Music: A. Gregory Murray, OSB, © Downside Abbey

Gelineau Tone

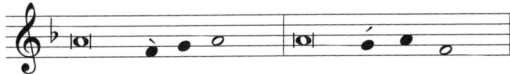

Music: Joseph Gelineau, SJ, © 1963, The Grail, GIA Publications, Inc., agent

² O **God**, you are my **God**, for yòu I **long**;
for **you** my **sóul** is **thirst**ing.
My **bod**y **pìnes** for **you**
like a **dry**, weary **land** wíthout **wa**ter.
³ So I **gaze** on **you** ìn the **sanc**tuary
to **see** your **strength** ánd your **glory**.

⁴ For your **love** is **bet**tèr than **life**,
my **lips** will **spéak** your **praise**.
⁵ So I will **bless** you àll my **life**,
in your **name** I will **lift** úp my **hands**.
⁶ My **soul** shall be **filled** as wìth a **ban**quet,
my **mouth** shall **praise** yóu with **joy**.

⁷ On my **bed** I remèm**ber you**.
On **you** I **muse** thróugh the **night**
for **you** have **bèen** my **help**;
⁸ in the **shad**ow of your **wings** Í re**joice**.
My **soul clìngs** to **you**;
⁹ your **right** hand **hólds** me **fast**.

Give **praise** to the **Fa**thèr Al**might**y,
to his **Son**, Jesus **Chríst** the **Lord**,
to the **Spir**it who **dwells** ìn our **hearts**,
both **now** and for **evér**. **Amen**.

Text: Psalm 63:2–9; The Grail, © 1963, 1993, The Grail, GIA Publications, Inc., agent

PSALM PRAYER

After each psalm a moment of silence is observed. This may be followed by a psalm prayer, to which all respond: **Amen.**

WORD OF GOD

A period of silence may follow the reading.

7 RESPONSE TO THE WORD OF GOD

A. ADVENT

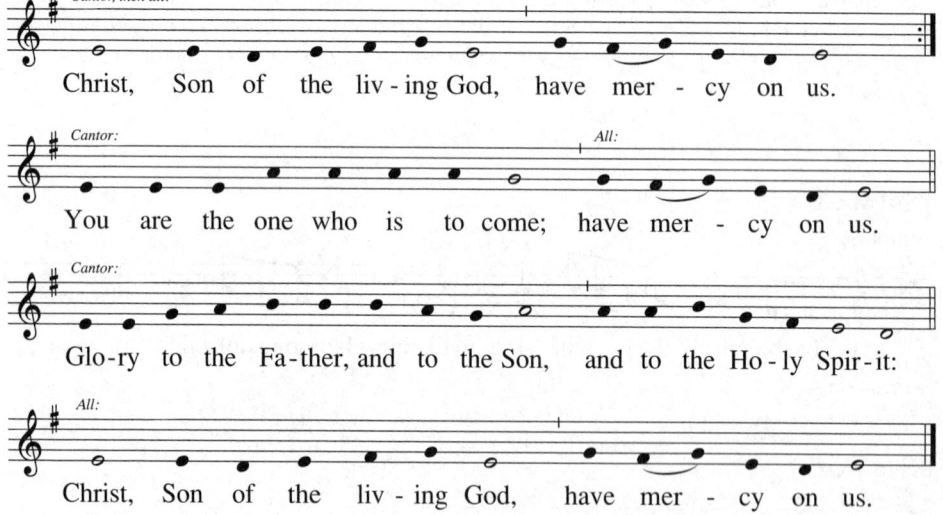

Cantor, then all:
Christ, Son of the liv-ing God, have mer-cy on us.

Cantor: You are the one who is to come; *All:* have mer-cy on us.

Cantor: Glo-ry to the Fa-ther, and to the Son, and to the Ho-ly Spir-it:

All: Christ, Son of the liv-ing God, have mer-cy on us.

B. CHRISTMAS

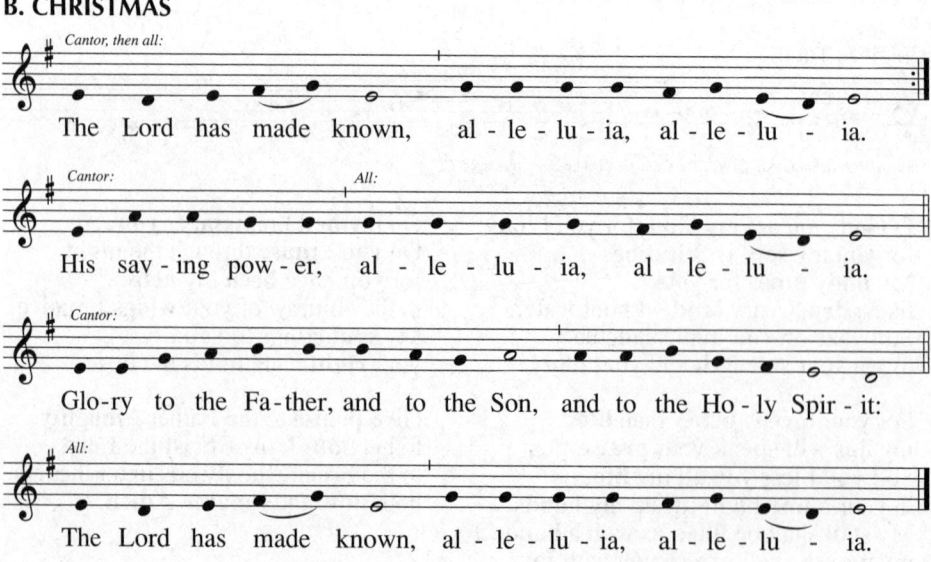

Cantor, then all:
The Lord has made known, al-le-lu-ia, al-le-lu-ia.

Cantor: His sav-ing pow-er, *All:* al-le-lu-ia, al-le-lu-ia.

Cantor: Glo-ry to the Fa-ther, and to the Son, and to the Ho-ly Spir-it:

All: The Lord has made known, al-le-lu-ia, al-le-lu-ia.

C. LENT

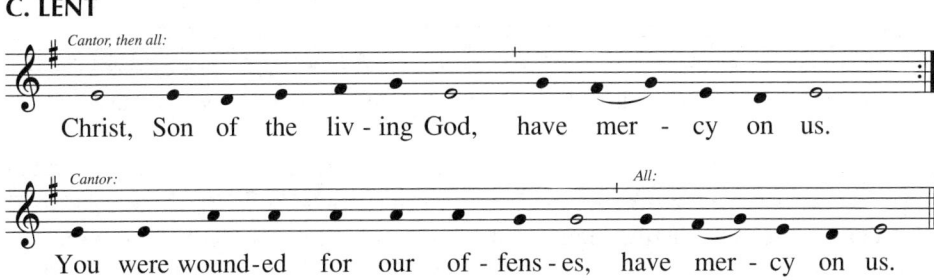

Christ, Son of the liv-ing God, have mer - cy on us.

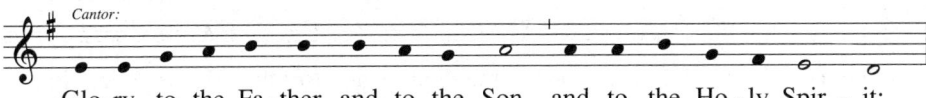

You were wound-ed for our of - fens - es, have mer - cy on us.

Glo-ry to the Fa-ther, and to the Son, and to the Ho-ly Spir - it:

Christ, Son of the liv - ing God, have mer - cy on us.

D. EASTER

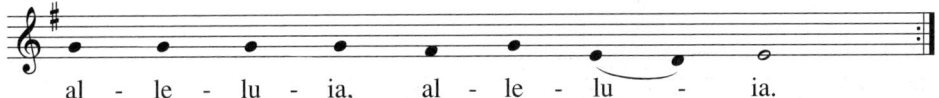

Christ, Son of the liv - ing God, have mer - cy on us,

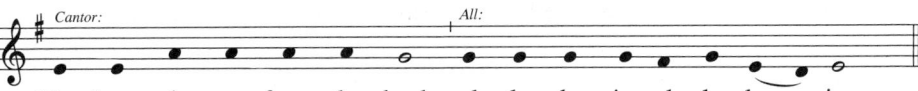

al - le - lu - ia, al - le - lu - ia.

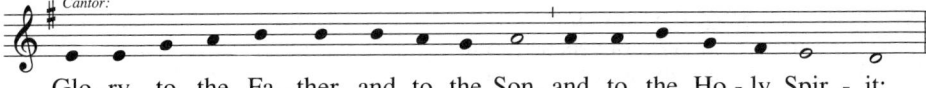

You have ris - en from the dead, al - le - lu - ia, al - le - lu - ia.

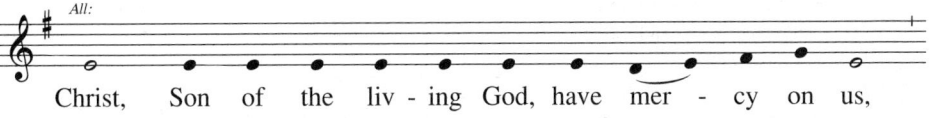

Glo-ry to the Fa - ther, and to the Son, and to the Ho - ly Spir - it:

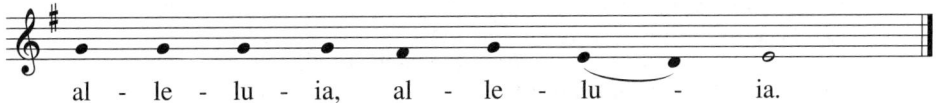

Christ, Son of the liv - ing God, have mer - cy on us,

al - le - lu - ia, al - le - lu - ia.

E. GENERAL

Cantor, then all:

Christ, Son of the liv-ing God, have mer-cy on us.

Cantor: *All:*

You are seat-ed at the right hand of the Fa-ther, have mer-cy on us.

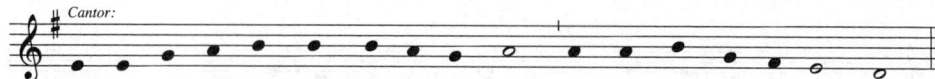

Cantor:

Glo-ry to the Fa-ther, and to the Son, and to the Ho-ly Spir-it:

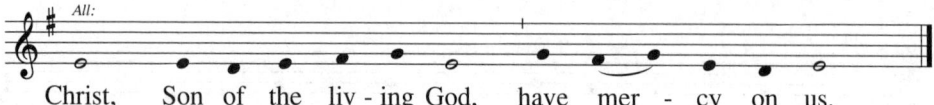

All:

Christ, Son of the liv-ing God, have mer-cy on us.

Text: *Liturgy of the Hours,* © 1974, ICEL
Tune: Robert LeBlanc, © 1986, GIA Publications, Inc.

8 GOSPEL CANTICLE

Stand

Antiphon

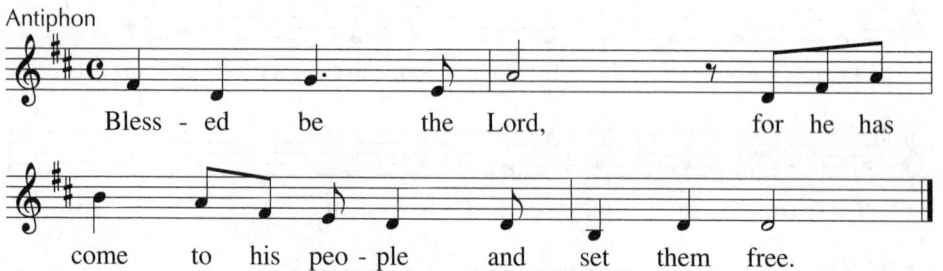

Bless - ed be the Lord, for he has

come to his peo - ple and set them free.

Verses *All make the sign of the cross.*

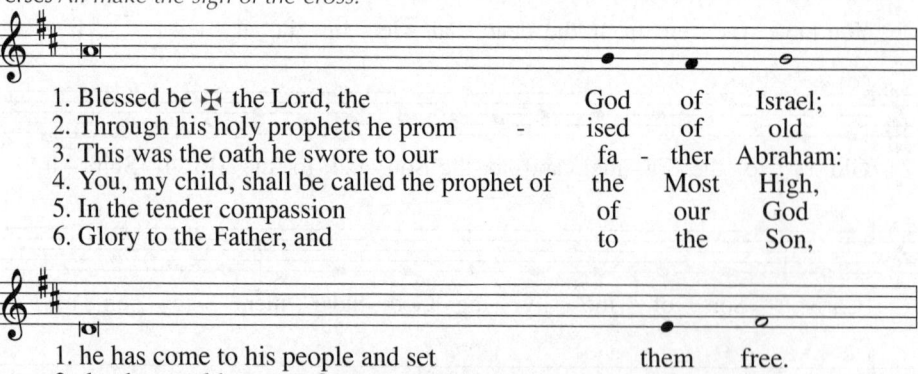

1. Blessed be ✠ the Lord, the God	of	Israel;
2. Through his holy prophets he prom - ised	of	old
3. This was the oath he swore to our fa - ther	Abraham:	
4. You, my child, shall be called the prophet of the Most	High,	
5. In the tender compassion of our	God	
6. Glory to the Father, and to the	Son,	

1. he has come to his people and set   them   free.
2. that he would save us from our enemies,
                from the hands of all who   hate us.
3. to set us free from the hands of   our   enemies,
4. for you will go before the Lord to prepare   his   way,
5. the dawn from on high shall break   up - on us,
6. and to the Ho -   ly   Spirit:

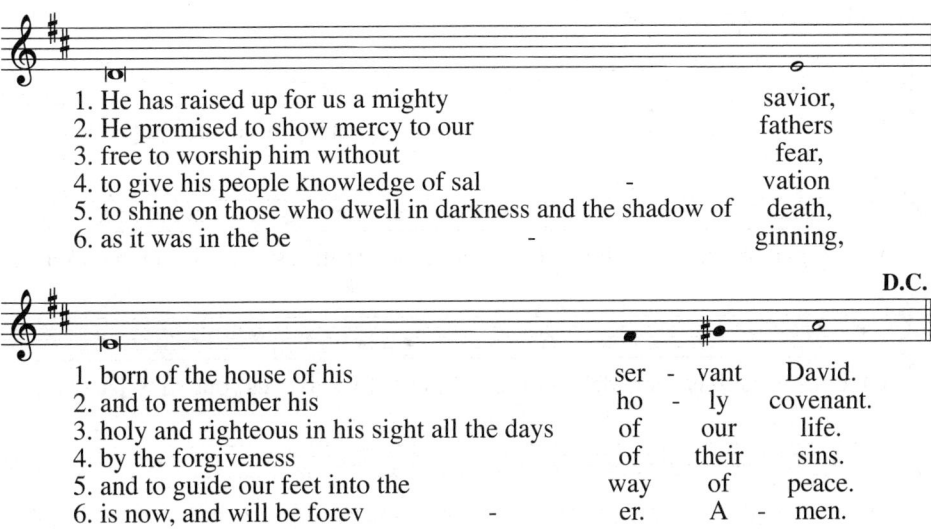

1. He has raised up for us a mighty   savior,
2. He promised to show mercy to our   fathers
3. free to worship him without   fear,
4. to give his people knowledge of sal   -   vation
5. to shine on those who dwell in darkness and the shadow of   death,
6. as it was in the be   -   ginning,

D.C.

1. born of the house of his   ser - vant   David.
2. and to remember his   ho - ly   covenant.
3. holy and righteous in his sight all the days   of   our   life.
4. by the forgiveness   of   their   sins.
5. and to guide our feet into the   way   of   peace.
6. is now, and will be forev   -   er.   A - men.

Text: Luke 1:68–79; *International Consultation on English Texts*
Music: Refrain, Ronald F. Krisman, © 2011, GIA Publications, Inc.; verses, Michel Guimont, © 1994, 1998, GIA Publications, Inc.

INTERCESSIONS   9

The following intercessions or similar ones may be used.

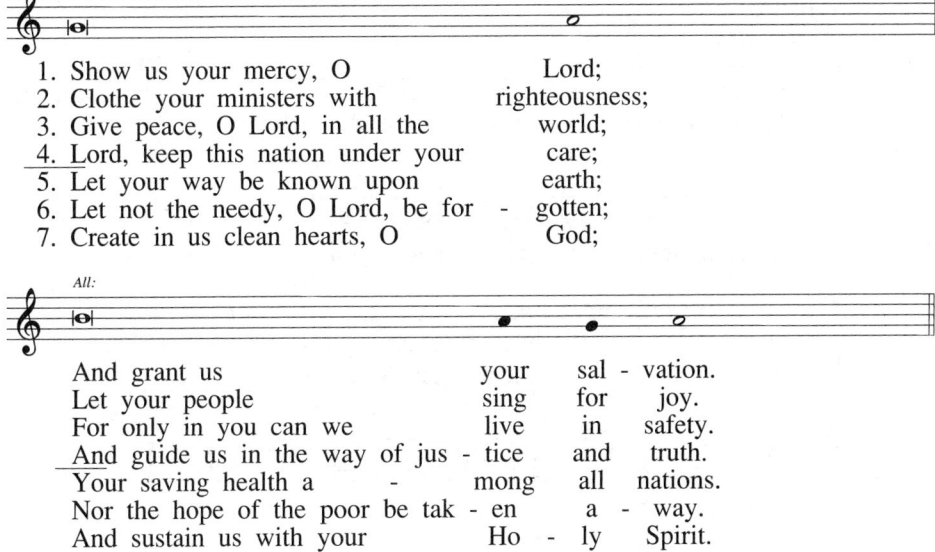

Cantor or presiding minister:

1. Show us your mercy, O   Lord;
2. Clothe your ministers with   righteousness;
3. Give peace, O Lord, in all the   world;
4. Lord, keep this nation under your   care;
5. Let your way be known upon   earth;
6. Let not the needy, O Lord, be for - gotten;
7. Create in us clean hearts, O   God;

All:

And grant us   your   sal - vation.
Let your people   sing   for   joy.
For only in you can we   live   in   safety.
And guide us in the way of jus - tice   and   truth.
Your saving health a   -   mong   all   nations.
Nor the hope of the poor be tak - en   a - way.
And sustain us with your   Ho - ly   Spirit.

Text: *The Book of Common Prayer*
Music: *Praise God in Song*, © 1979, GIA Publications, Inc.

10 THE LORD'S PRAYER

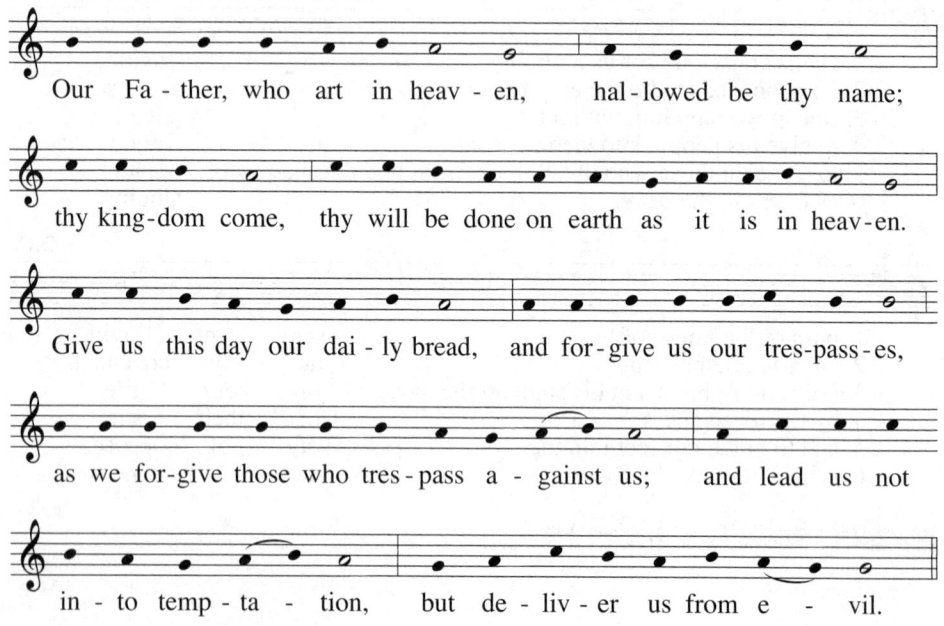

Our Fa - ther, who art in heav - en, hal - lowed be thy name;

thy king-dom come, thy will be done on earth as it is in heav-en.

Give us this day our dai - ly bread, and for - give us our tres-pass-es,

as we for-give those who tres - pass a - gainst us; and lead us not

in - to temp - ta - tion, but de - liv - er us from e - vil.

Music: Traditional chant, adapt. by Robert Snow, 1964; acc. by Robert J. Batastini, © 1975, 1993, GIA Publications, Inc.

CONCLUDING PRAYER
All respond: **Amen.**

11 DISMISSAL

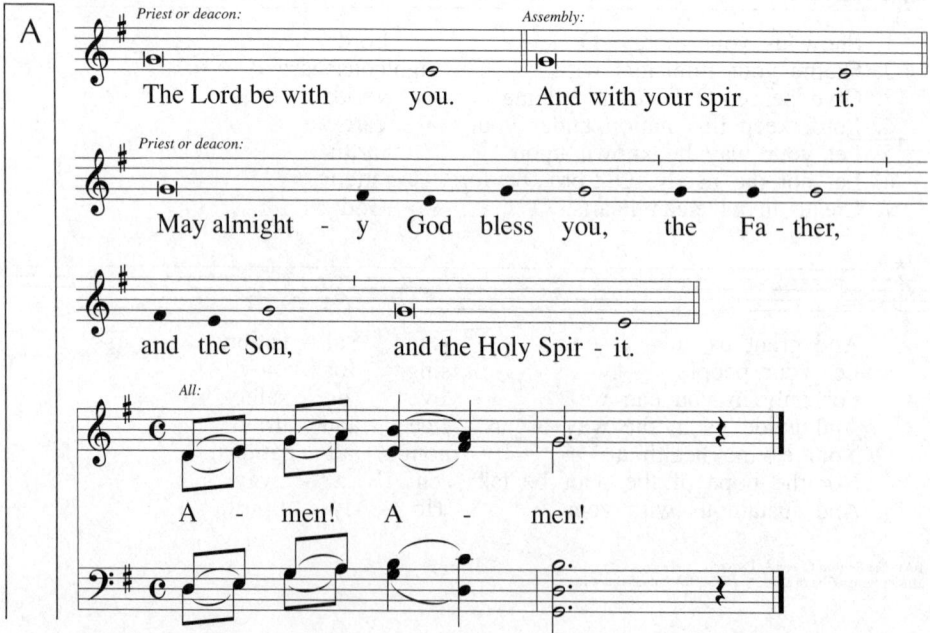

A

Priest or deacon:

The Lord be with you. *Assembly:* And with your spir - it.

Priest or deacon:

May almight - y God bless you, the Fa - ther,

and the Son, and the Holy Spir - it.

All:

A - men! A - men!

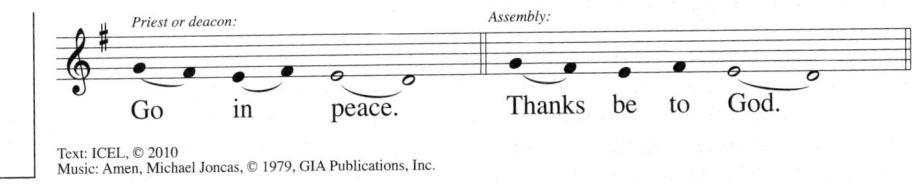

Priest or deacon: Go in peace. *Assembly:* Thanks be to God.

Text: ICEL, © 2010
Music: Amen, Michael Joncas, © 1979, GIA Publications, Inc.

Dismissal, if the leader is not a priest or deacon:

12

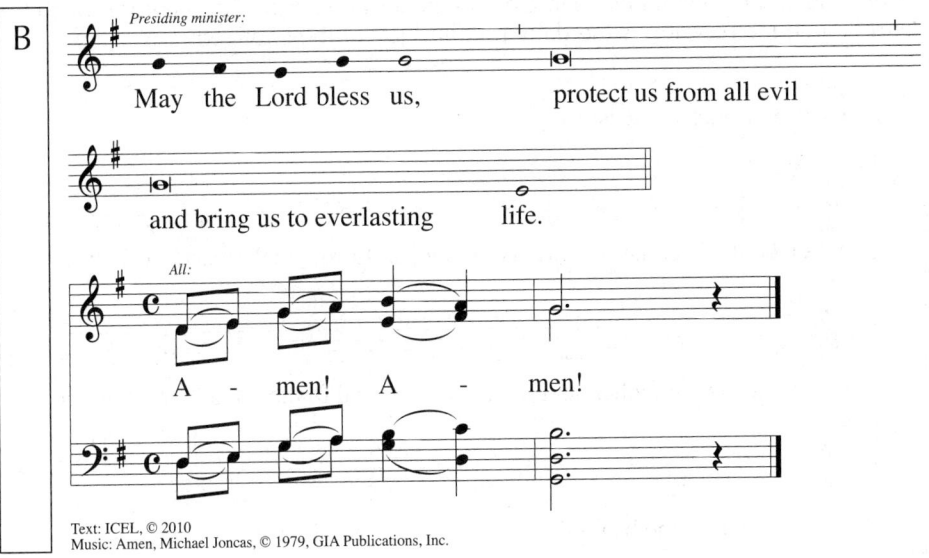

Presiding minister: May the Lord bless us, protect us from all evil and bring us to everlasting life.

All: A - men! A - men!

Text: ICEL, © 2010
Music: Amen, Michael Joncas, © 1979, GIA Publications, Inc.

All may conclude the celebration by exchanging a sign of peace.

13 Evening Prayer / Vespers

The Church gathers in the evening to give thanks for the day that is ending. In the earliest tradition, this began with the lighting of the lamps as darkness fell and with the hymn of praise of Christ who is "radiant Light . . . of God the Father's deathless face." The evening psalms and the Magnificat bring the day just past to focus for the Christian: "God has cast down the mighty from their thrones, and has lifted up the lowly"; "God has remembered the promise of mercy, the promise made to our ancestors." Prayers of intercession are almost always part of the Church's liturgy, but those which conclude evening prayer are especially important. As day ends, the Church again and again lifts up to God the needs and sorrows and failures of all the world. Such intercession is the daily task and joy of the baptized.

Stand. All make the sign of the cross.

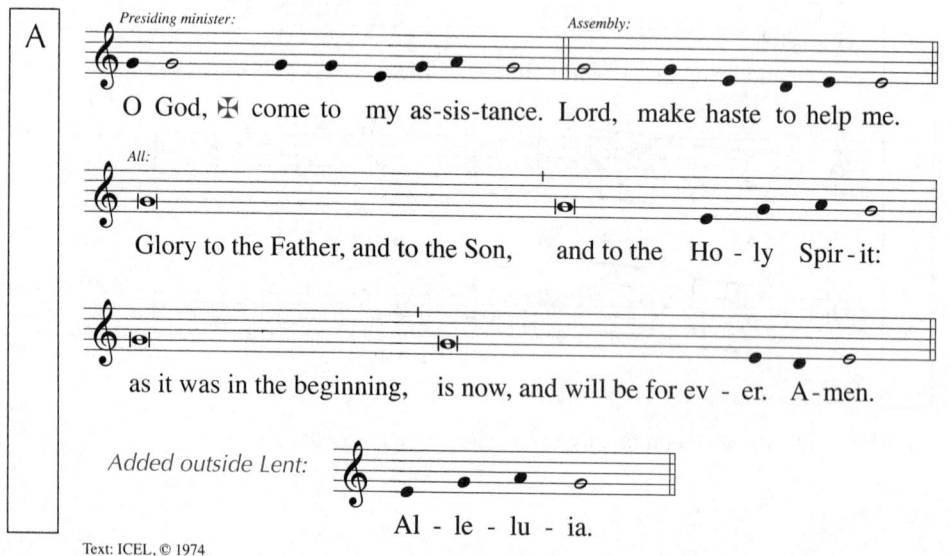

Text: ICEL, © 1974

If Evening Prayer begins with a service of light (lucernarium), the following greeting may be used:

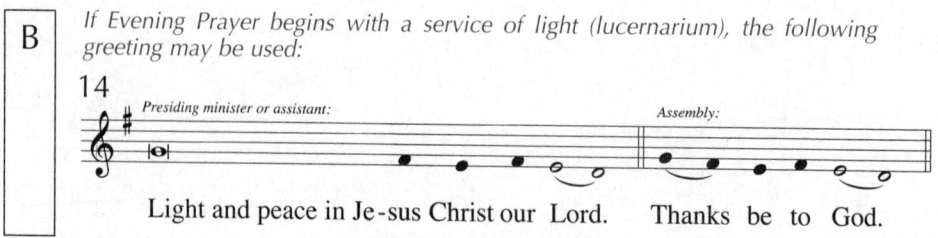

HYMN

This or another evening hymn (see nos. 946 to 953), or one related to the season or feast, may be sung.

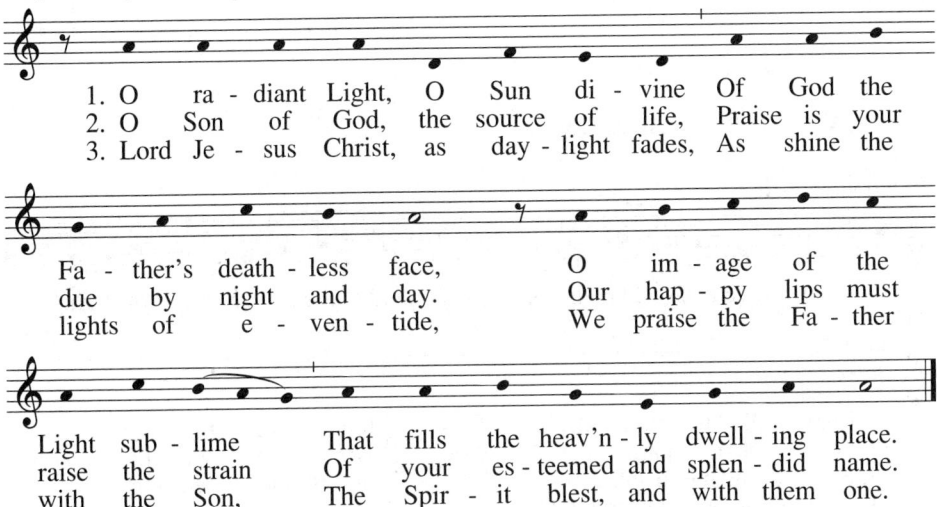

1. O ra - diant Light, O Sun di - vine Of God the
2. O Son of God, the source of life, Praise is your
3. Lord Je - sus Christ, as day - light fades, As shine the

Fa - ther's death - less face, O im - age of the
due by night and day. Our hap - py lips must
lights of e - ven - tide, We praise the Fa - ther

Light sub - lime That fills the heav'n - ly dwell - ing place.
raise the strain Of your es - teemed and splen - did name.
with the Son, The Spir - it blest, and with them one.

Text: *Phos Hilaron*, Greek, c.200; tr. by William G. Storey, ©
Music: JESU DULCIS MEMORIA, LM; Mode I; acc. by Richard Proulx, © 1975, GIA Publications, Inc.

If the lucernarium is celebrated, the evening thanksgiving may be sung:

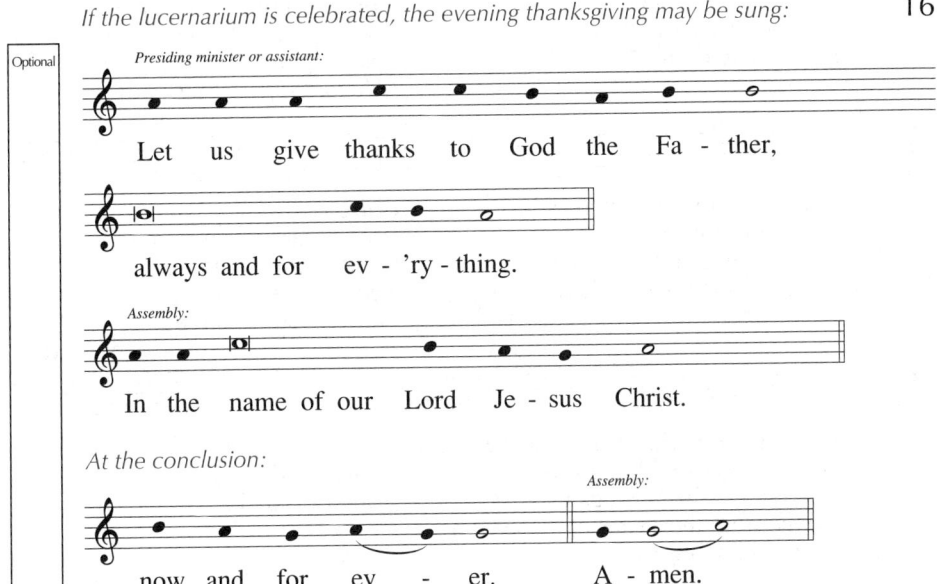

Optional

Presiding minister or assistant:

Let us give thanks to God the Fa - ther,

always and for ev - 'ry - thing.

Assembly:

In the name of our Lord Je - sus Christ.

At the conclusion:

Assembly:

...now and for ev - er. A - men.

PSALMODY

The singing of one or more psalms is a central part of evening prayer. Psalm 141 is one of the premier evening psalms. It is customary to use incense as it is sung. Other appropriate psalms for evening are Psalms 4, 19, 23, 27, 84, 91, 104, 110, 111, 118, 121, 122, 130, and 145.

Sit

17 PSALM 141/INCENSE PSALM

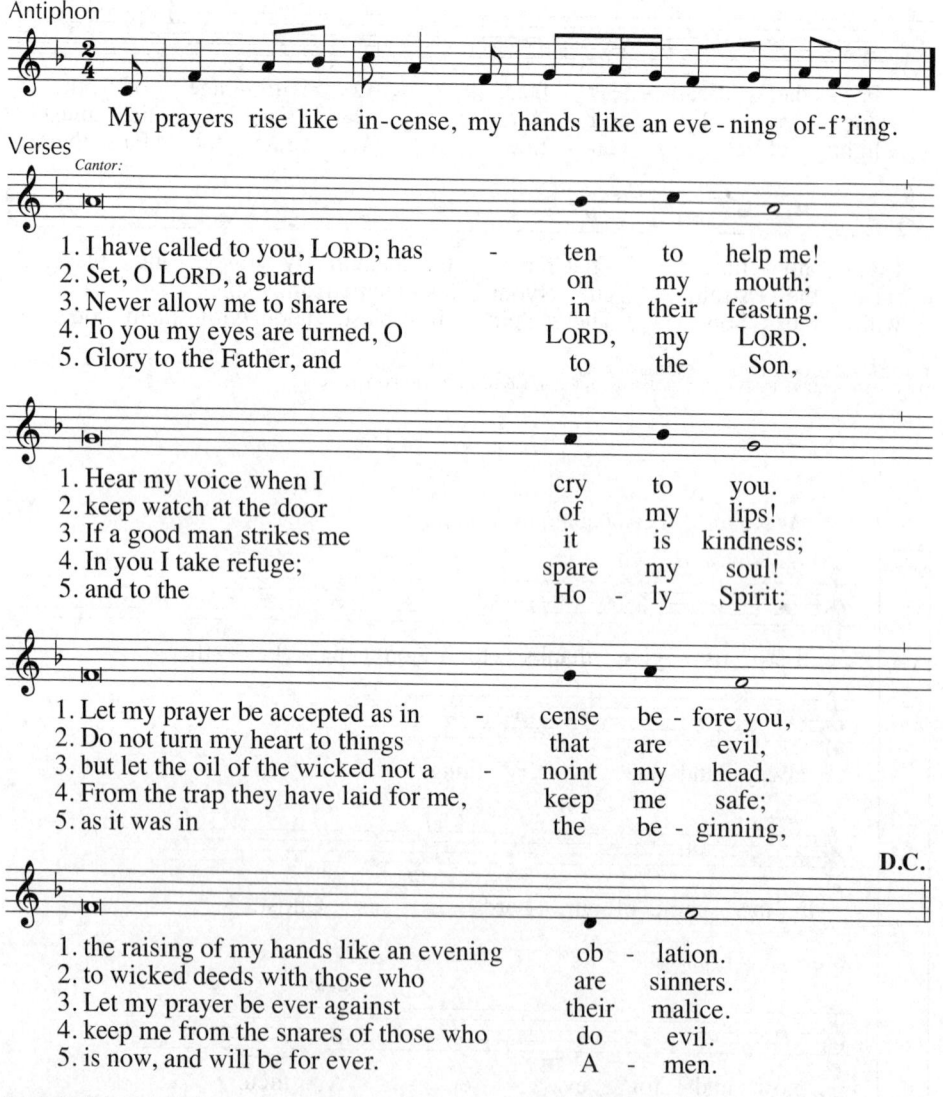

Antiphon

My prayers rise like in-cense, my hands like an eve-ning of-f'ring.

Verses

Cantor:

1. I have called to you, LORD; has - ten to help me!
2. Set, O LORD, a guard on my mouth;
3. Never allow me to share in their feasting.
4. To you my eyes are turned, O LORD, my LORD.
5. Glory to the Father, and to the Son,

1. Hear my voice when I cry to you.
2. keep watch at the door of my lips!
3. If a good man strikes me it is kindness;
4. In you I take refuge; spare my soul!
5. and to the Ho - ly Spirit:

1. Let my prayer be accepted as in - cense be - fore you,
2. Do not turn my heart to things that are evil,
3. but let the oil of the wicked not a - noint my head.
4. From the trap they have laid for me, keep me safe;
5. as it was in the be - ginning,

D.C.

1. the raising of my hands like an evening ob - lation.
2. to wicked deeds with those who are sinners.
3. Let my prayer be ever against their malice.
4. keep me from the snares of those who do evil.
5. is now, and will be for ever. A - men.

Text: Psalm 141:1–2, 3–4, 5, 8–9; *The Revised Grail Psalms*, © 2010, Conception Abbey and The Grail, admin. by GIA Publications, Inc.
Music: Howard Hughes, SM, © 1979, GIA Publications, Inc.

PSALM PRAYER

After each psalm a moment of silence is observed. This may be followed by a psalm prayer, to which all respond: **Amen.**

WORD OF GOD

A period of silence may follow the reading.

RESPONSE TO THE WORD OF GOD

A. ADVENT

Cantor, then all:
Lord, show us your mer-cy and love.

Cantor:
And grant us your sal-va-tion,

All:
your mer-cy and love.

Cantor:
Glo-ry to the Fa-ther, and to the Son,

All:
and to the Ho-ly Spir-it: Lord, show us your mer-cy and love.

B. CHRISTMAS

Cantor, then all:
The Word was made man, al-le-lu-ia, al-le-lu-ia.

Cantor: *All:*
He lived a-mong us, al-le-lu-ia, al-le-lu-ia.

Cantor:
Glo-ry to the Fa-ther, and to the Son, and to the Ho-ly Spir-it:

All:
The Word was made man, al-le-lu-ia, al-le-lu-ia.

C. LENT

Cantor, then all:
Listen to us, O Lord, and have mer-cy, for we have sinned a-gainst you.

Cantor: *All:*
Christ Jesus, hear our hum-ble pe-ti-tions for we have sinned a-gainst you.

Cantor:
Glo-ry to the Fa-ther, and to the Son, and to the Ho-ly Spir-it:

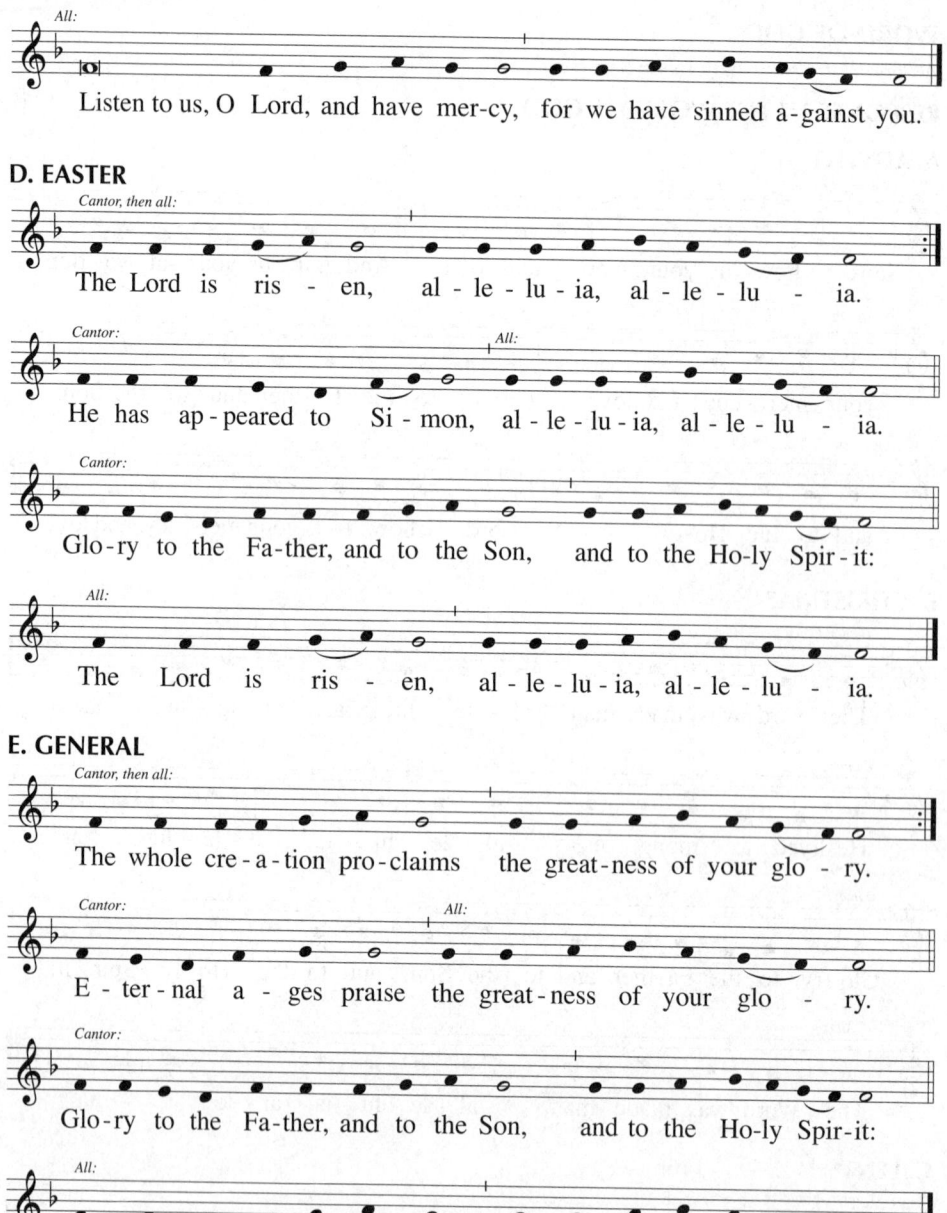

All:

Listen to us, O Lord, and have mer-cy, for we have sinned a-gainst you.

D. EASTER

Cantor, then all:

The Lord is ris - en, al - le - lu - ia, al - le - lu - ia.

Cantor: ... *All:*

He has ap - peared to Si - mon, al - le - lu - ia, al - le - lu - ia.

Cantor:

Glo-ry to the Fa-ther, and to the Son, and to the Ho-ly Spir-it:

All:

The Lord is ris - en, al - le - lu - ia, al - le - lu - ia.

E. GENERAL

Cantor, then all:

The whole cre - a - tion pro - claims the great-ness of your glo - ry.

Cantor: ... *All:*

E - ter - nal a - ges praise the great-ness of your glo - ry.

Cantor:

Glo-ry to the Fa-ther, and to the Son, and to the Ho-ly Spir-it:

All:

The whole cre - a - tion pro - claims the great-ness of your glo - ry.

Text: *Liturgy of the Hours,* © 1974, ICEL
Music: Robert LeBlanc, © 1986, GIA Publications, Inc.

GOSPEL CANTICLE

Stand

Antiphon

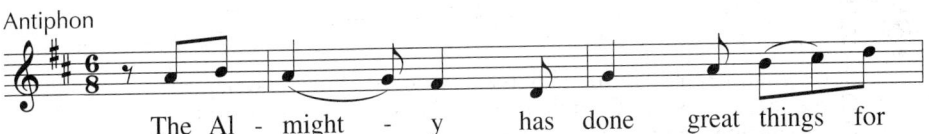

The Al - might - y has done great things for

me, and ho - ly is his Name.

Verses *All make the sign of the cross.*

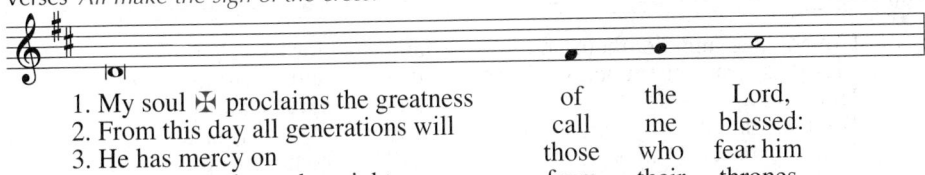

1. My soul ✠ proclaims the greatness of the Lord,
2. From this day all generations will call me blessed:
3. He has mercy on those who fear him
4. He has cast down the mighty from their thrones,
5. He has come to the help of his ser - vant Israel
6. Glory to the Father, and to the Son,

1. my spirit rejoices in God my Savior
2. the Almighty has done great things for me,
3. in every gen - er - ation.
4. and has lifted up the lowly.
5. for he has remembered his prom - ise of mercy,
6. and to the Ho - ly Spirit:

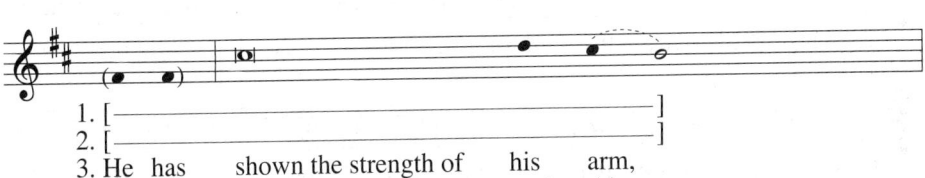

1. [———————————————]
2. [———————————————]
3. He has shown the strength of his arm,
4. He has filled the hungry with good things,
5. the promise he made to our fa - thers,
6. as it was in the beginning, is now,

D.C.

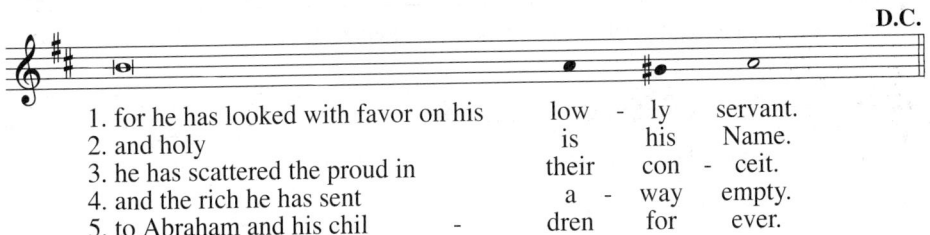

1. for he has looked with favor on his low - ly servant.
2. and holy is his Name.
3. he has scattered the proud in their con - ceit.
4. and the rich he has sent a - way empty.
5. to Abraham and his chil - dren for ever.
6. and will be for ev - er. A - men.

Text: Luke 1:46–55; *International Consultation on English Texts*
Music: Refrain, Ronald F. Krisman, © 2011, GIA Publications, Inc.; verses, Michel Guimont, © 1994, 1998, GIA Publications, Inc.

20   INTERCESSIONS

The following intercessions or similar ones may be used.

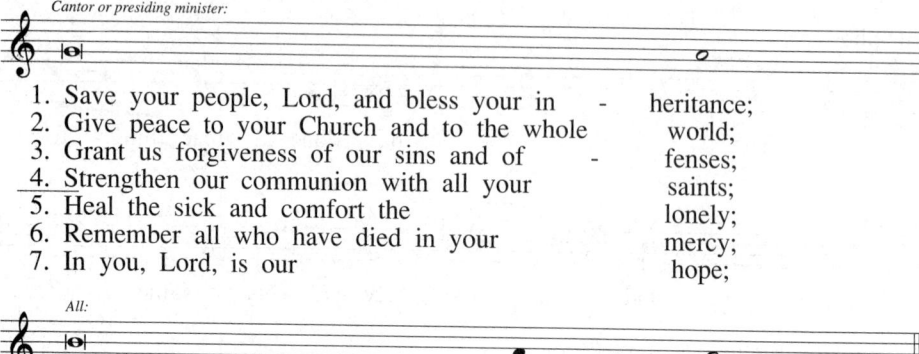

Cantor or presiding minister:

1. Save your people, Lord, and bless your in - heritance;
2. Give peace to your Church and to the whole world;
3. Grant us forgiveness of our sins and of - fenses;
4. Strengthen our communion with all your saints;
5. Heal the sick and comfort the lonely;
6. Remember all who have died in your mercy;
7. In you, Lord, is our hope;

All:

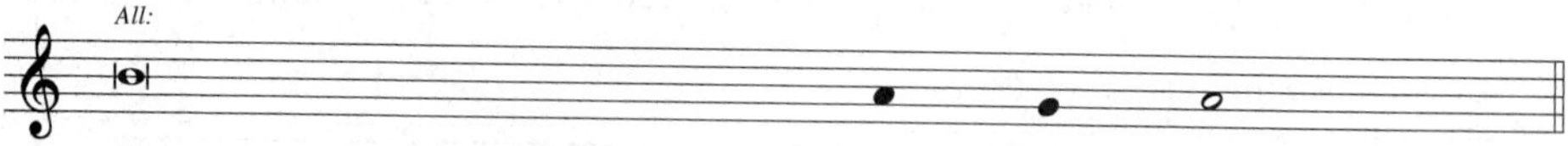

Govern and uphold them, now   and   for - ever.
Make us your instruments of jus - tice   and   truth.
Have mercy on us,   Lord,   have   mercy.
Bind us together by your   Ho - ly   Spirit.
Relieve the sufferings of   all   your   people.
Welcome them into the light   of   your   kingdom.
And we shall never   hope   in   vain.

Text: Adapted from *The Book of Common Prayer*
Music: *Praise God in Song,* © 1979, GIA Publications, Inc.

21   THE LORD'S PRAYER

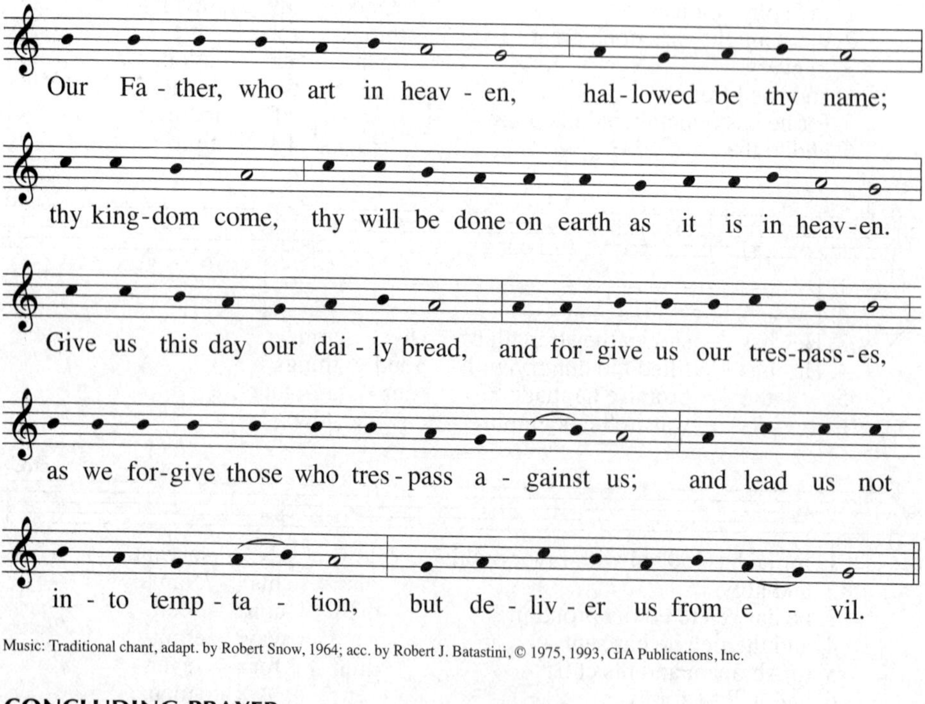

Our Fa - ther, who art in heav - en, hal - lowed be thy name;

thy king-dom come, thy will be done on earth as it is in heav - en.

Give us this day our dai - ly bread, and for - give us our tres-pass - es,

as we for-give those who tres - pass a - gainst us; and lead us not

in - to temp - ta - tion, but de - liv - er us from e - vil.

Music: Traditional chant, adapt. by Robert Snow, 1964; acc. by Robert J. Batastini, © 1975, 1993, GIA Publications, Inc.

CONCLUDING PRAYER

All respond: **Amen.**

DISMISSAL

A

Priest or deacon: *Assembly:*

The Lord be with you. And with your spir - it.

Priest or deacon:

May almight - y God bless you, the Fa - ther,

and the Son, and the Holy Spir - it.

All:

A - men! A - men!

Priest or deacon: *Assembly:*

Go in peace. Thanks be to God.

Text: ICEL, © 2010
Music: Amen, Michael Joncas, © 1979, GIA Publications, Inc.

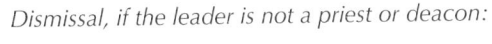

Dismissal, if the leader is not a priest or deacon:

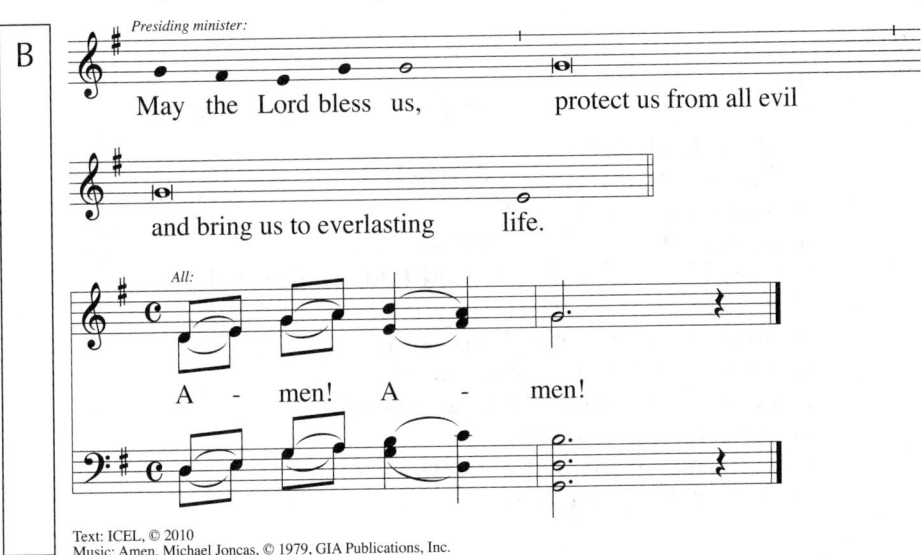

B

Presiding minister:

May the Lord bless us, protect us from all evil

and bring us to everlasting life.

All:

A - men! A - men!

Text: ICEL, © 2010
Music: Amen, Michael Joncas, © 1979, GIA Publications, Inc.

All may conclude the celebration by exchanging a sign of peace.

24 Night Prayer / Compline

The Church's prayers at night are direct and simple. The Christian remembers with sorrow the day's evil and failure, and places this before the mercy of God. Before surrendering to sleep, there is prayer for God's protection through the night and an expression of acceptance: "Now, Lord, you may dismiss your servant." The night prayer concludes by binding together the sleep of this night with the final falling asleep in the Lord: "May the all-powerful Lord grant us a restful night and a peaceful death." Night's last words are often a gentle invocation of our mother, "When this exile is ended, show us your womb's blessed fruit, Jesus."

Stand. All make the sign of the cross.

Presiding minister: O God, ✠ come to my as-sis-tance. *Assembly:* Lord, make haste to help me.

All: Glory to the Father, and to the Son, and to the Ho-ly Spir-it: as it was in the beginning, is now, and will be for ev-er. A-men.

Added outside Lent: Al-le-lu-ia.

Text: ICEL, © 1974

A brief examination of conscience may be made. At its conclusion, the following may be said:

Optional	**I confess to almighty God** **and to you, my brothers and sisters,** **that I have greatly sinned,** **in my thoughts and in my words,** **in what I have done and in what I have failed to do,** *All strike their breast as they say:* **through my fault, through my fault,** **through my most grievous fault;** **therefore I ask blessed Mary ever-Virgin,** **all the Angels and Saints,** **and you, my brothers and sisters,** **to pray for me to the Lord our God.**

HYMN

This or another evening hymn (see nos. 946 to 953), or one related to the season or feast, may be sung.

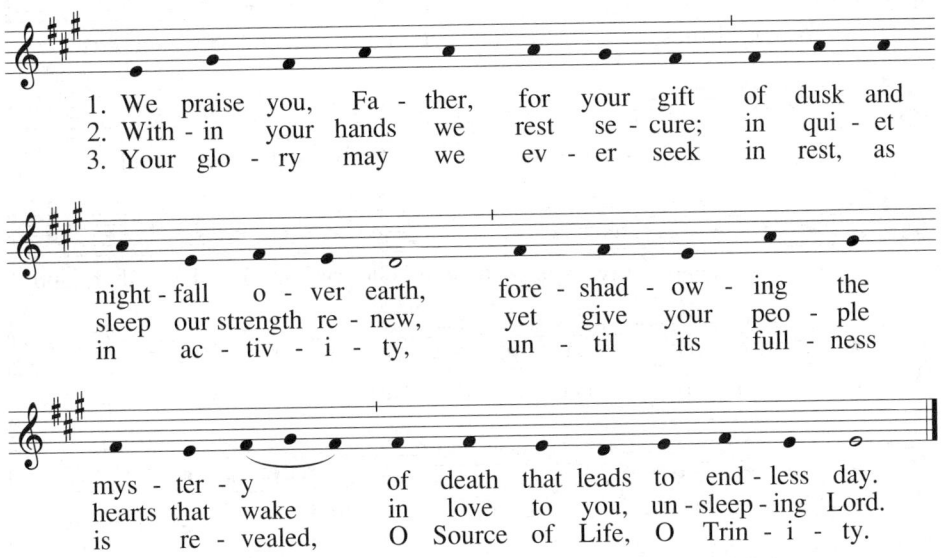

1. We praise you, Fa - ther, for your gift of dusk and night - fall o - ver earth, fore - shad - ow - ing the mys - ter - y of death that leads to end - less day.
2. With - in your hands we rest se - cure; in qui - et sleep our strength re - new, yet give your peo - ple hearts that wake in love to you, un - sleep - ing Lord.
3. Your glo - ry may we ev - er seek in rest, as in ac - tiv - i - ty, un - til its full - ness is re - vealed, O Source of Life, O Trin - i - ty.

Text: Benedictine Nuns of St. Mary's Abbey, West Malling, Kent, © 1967
Music: TE LUCIS ANTE TERMINUM, LM; adapt. by Howard Hughes, SM, © 1982, GIA Publications, Inc.

PSALMODY

The psalms for Night Prayer include Psalms 4, 16, 31, 91, 130, and 134.

Sit

PSALM 134

Antiphon

In the si - lent hours of night, bless the Lord.

Verses

1. O come, bless the LORD,
   all you who serve the LORD,
   who stand in the house of the LORD,
   in the courts of the house of our God.

2. Lift up your hands to the holy place
   and bless the LORD through the night.

3. May the LORD bless you from Zion,
   God who made both heaven and earth.

4. Glory to the Father, and the Son,
   and to the Holy Spirit:
   as it was in the beginning, is now,
   and will be for ever. Amen.

Text: Psalm 134; The Grail, © 1963, 1993, GIA Publications, Inc., agent; refrain text, from *Praise God in Song,* © 1979, GIA Publications, Inc.
Music: Howard Hughes, SM, © 1979, GIA Publications, Inc.

After the psalm a moment of silence is observed.

WORD OF GOD

A period of silence may follow the reading.

27 RESPONSORY

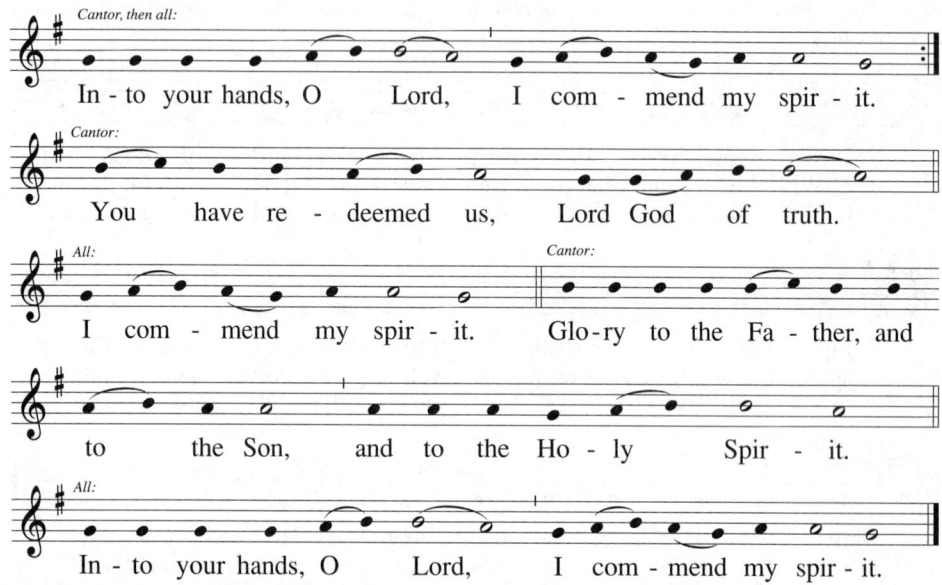

Cantor, then all:
In - to your hands, O Lord, I com - mend my spir - it.

Cantor:
You have re - deemed us, Lord God of truth.

All:
I com - mend my spir - it. *Cantor:* Glo - ry to the Fa - ther, and

to the Son, and to the Ho - ly Spir - it.

All:
In - to your hands, O Lord, I com - mend my spir - it.

Text: *Liturgy of the Hours,* © 1974, ICEL
Music: Sarum tone, adapt. by Richard Proulx, © 1986, GIA Publications, Inc.

28 GOSPEL CANTICLE

Stand

Antiphon

Pro - tect us, Lord, as we stay a - wake; watch o - ver us

as we sleep, that a - wake we may keep watch with Christ,

and, a - sleep, rest in his peace.

Verse 1 *All make the sign of the cross.*

1. Lord, ✠ now you let your ser - vant go in peace:

your word has been ful - filled. *Verse 2* 2. My own eyes have

seen the sal - va - tion which you have prepared in the sight of

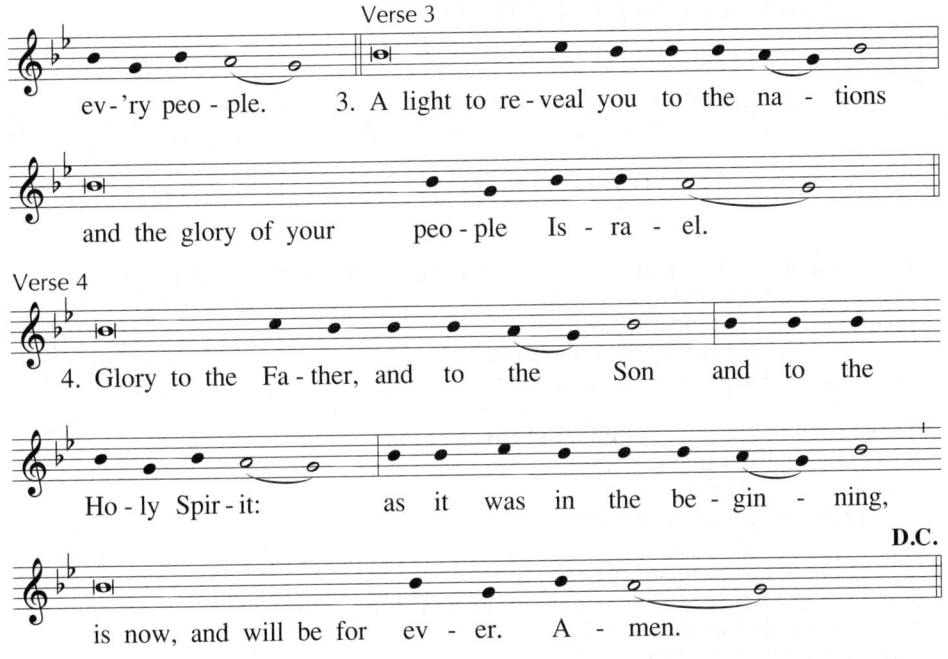

Verse 3

ev-'ry peo-ple. 3. A light to re-veal you to the na - tions

and the glory of your peo-ple Is - ra - el.

Verse 4

4. Glory to the Fa-ther, and to the Son and to the

Ho - ly Spir-it: as it was in the be - gin - ning,

D.C.

is now, and will be for ev - er. A - men.

Text: Antiphon from *Liturgy of the Hours*, © 1974, ICEL; verses, Luke 2:29–32; *International Consultation on English Texts*
Music: Sarum tone, adapt. by Richard Proulx, © 1986, GIA Publications, Inc.

CONCLUDING PRAYER
All respond: **Amen.**

CONCLUSION   29

May the all-powerful Lord grant us a restful night and a peaceful death.

A - men! A - men!

Text: ICEL, © 1974
Music: Amen, Michael Joncas, © 1979, GIA Publications, Inc.

The Marian antiphon, "Salve Regina," no. 1000, or during Easter season, "Regina Caeli," no. 615, may follow.

30 Psalm 1: Blessed Are They

Refrain

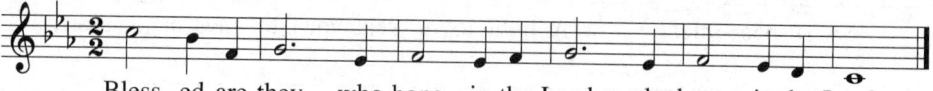

Bless-ed are they who hope in the Lord, who hope in the Lord.

Verses

1. Blessed indeed is the man who follows not the counsel of the wicked,
   nor stands in the path with sinners,
   nor abides in the company of scorners,
   but whose delight is the law of the LORD,
   and who ponders his law day and night.

2. He is like a tree that is planted beside the flowing waters,
   that yields its fruit in due season,
   and whose leaves shall never fade;
   and all that he does shall prosper.

3. Not so are the wicked, not so!
   For they, like winnowed chaff, shall be driven away by the wind;
   for the LORD knows the way of the just,
   but the way of the wicked will perish.

Text: Psalm 1:1–2, 3, 4 and 6; *The Revised Grail Psalms,* © 2010, Conception Abbey and The Grail, admin. by GIA Publications, Inc.;
refrain trans., © 1969, ICEL
Music: Tony E. Alonso, © 2012, GIA Publications, Inc.

31 Psalm 4

Antiphon

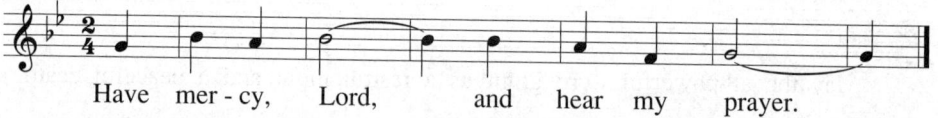

Have mer-cy, Lord, and hear my prayer.

Text: *Liturgy of the Hours,* © 1974, ICEL
Music: Eugene Englert, © 1986, GIA Publications, Inc.

Psalm Tone

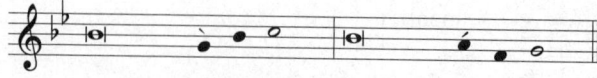

Music: A. Gregory Murray, OSB, © Downside Abbey

Gelineau Tone

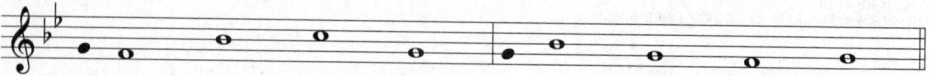

Music: Joseph Gelineau, SJ, © 1963, The Grail, GIA Publications, Inc., agent

Cum invocarem

2 O **God** of my **right**eousness, give **an**swer whèn I **call**;
   from **an**guish you re**leased** me, have **mer**cy, héar my **prayer**!

3 O you **peo**ple, how **long** will my **glo**ry bè dis**hon**ored,
   will you **love** what is **fu**tile and **seek** whát is **false**?

4 **Know** that the LORD works **won**ders fòr the **faith**ful;
   the LORD will **hear** me when**ev**er Í call **out**.

5 Tremble, **do** not sìn: **pon**der on your **bed** ànd be **still**.
6 Offer a **right**eous **sac**rifice, and **trust** ín the LORD.

7 "O that **we** might **see** better **times**," màny **say**.
   Lift up the **light** of your **face** on **ús**, O LORD.

8 You have **put** into my **heart** a **grèa**ter **joy**
   than a**bun**dance of **grain** and new **wine** cán pro**vide**.

9 In **peace** I will lie **down** and **fàll** a**sleep**,
   for **you** alone, O LORD, make me **dwéll** in **safe**ty.

   Give **praise** to the **Fa**ther, the **Son** and Hòly **Spir**it,
   both **now** and for **ag**es un**end**íng. **Amen**.

Text: Psalm 4; *The Ecumenical Grail Psalter*, © 2015, Conception Abbey and The Grail, admin. by GIA Publications, Inc.

Psalm 8: How Glorious Is Your Name   32

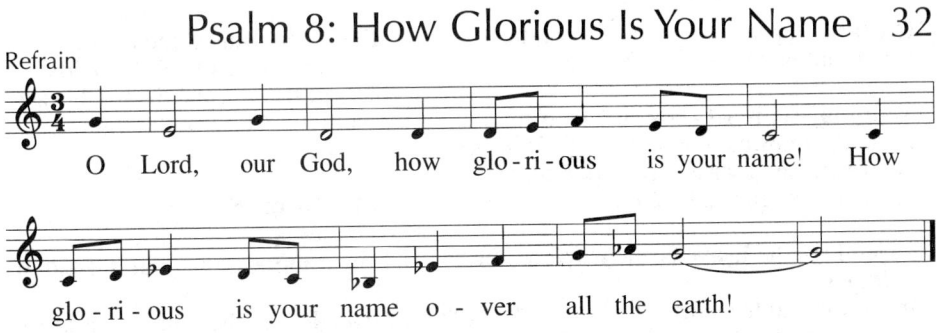

Refrain

O Lord, our God, how glo-ri-ous is your name! How
glo-ri-ous is your name o-ver all the earth!

Verses

1. When I see the heavens, the work of your hands,
   the moon and the stars which you arranged,
   What are we that you keep us in mind?
   Your children that you remember them at all?

2. Yet you have made us little less than gods, with glory and honor you crowned us,
   Gave us pow'r over the work of your hands, dominion over all that you have made.

3. All sheep and oxen, birds of the air, all things that swim in the sea.
   Beasts without number, life without names, you have placed under our feet.

Text: Psalm 8:4–5, 6–7, 8–9; Rory Cooney
Music: Rory Cooney
© 1990, GIA Publications, Inc.

33 Psalm 8

Antiphon I

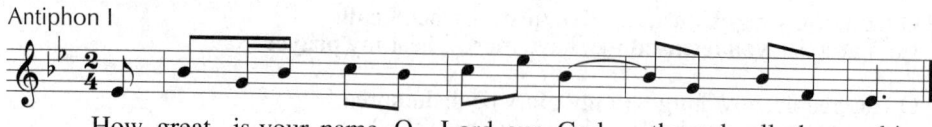

How great is your name, O Lord our God, through all the earth!

Text: The Grail
Music: A. Gregory Murray, OSB
© 1963, The Grail, GIA Publications, Inc., agent

Antiphon II

From the voic-es of chil-dren, Lord, comes the sound of your praise.

Text: The Grail
Music: A. Gregory Murray, OSB
© 1963, The Grail, GIA Publications, Inc., agent

Conception Abbey Tone

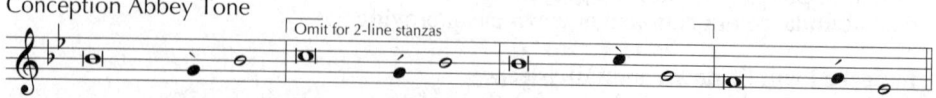

Music: Gregory J. Polan, OSB, © 2010, Conception Abbey, admin. by GIA Publications, Inc.

Gelineau Tone

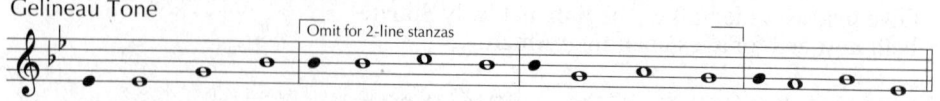

Music: Joseph Gelineau, SJ, © 1963, The Grail, GIA Publications, Inc., agent

Domine, Dominus noster

*2 O **LORD**, our **Sovereign**, how màjestic
is your **name** through all thé **earth**!

Your **majesty** is **set** above thè **heav**ens.
3 From the **mouths** of **child**ren and óf **babes**
you **fash**ioned praise to **foil** yòur **en**emy,
to **silence** the **foe** and thé **reb**el.

4 When I see the **heav**ens, the **work** of yòur
fingers,
the **moon** and the **stars** which you árranged,
5 what are human **be**ings that you **keep** them
in **mind**,
mortal **crea**tures that you **care** fór **them**?

6 Yet you have **made** them little **low**er than
thè **an**gels;
with **glory** and **hon**or yóu **crowned** them,
7 gave them **pow**er over the **works** of yòur
hands:
you put **all** things **un**der théir **feet**,

8 **All** of them, **sheep** ànd **oxen**,
yes, **even** the **cattle** of thé **fields**,
9 birds of the **air**, and **fish** of thè **sea**
that **make** their **way** through thé
seas.

*10 O **LORD**, our **Sovereign**, how
màjestic
is your **name** through all thé **earth**!

Give **glory** to the **Father** Àlmighty,
to his **Son**, Jesus **Christ** thé **Lord**,
to the **Spir**it who **dwells** in òur
hearts,
both **now** and for **ever**. Ámen.

Omitted when Antiphon I is used.

Text: Psalm 8; *The Ecumenical Grail Psalter*, © 2015, Conception Abbey and The Grail, admin. by GIA Publications, Inc.

Psalm 16: You Are My Inheritance   34

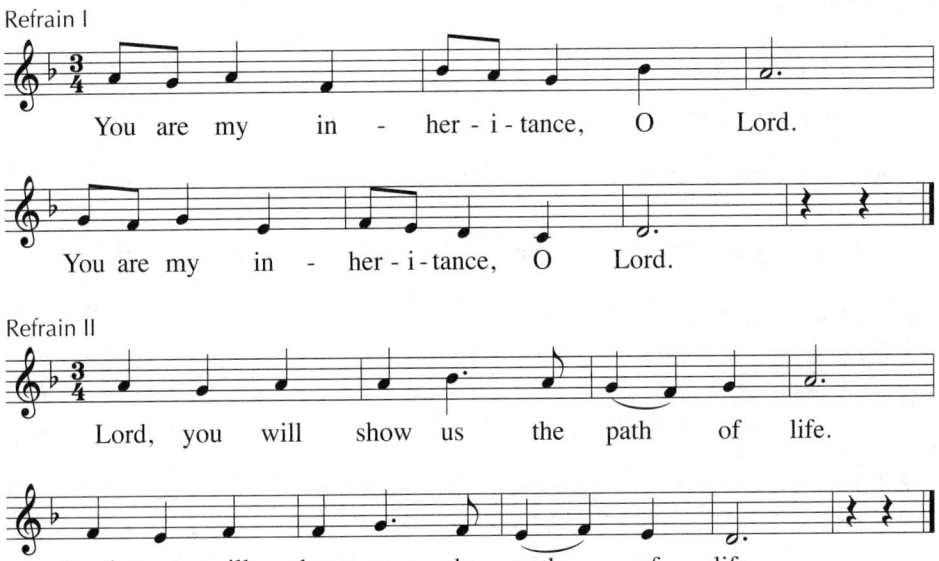

Refrain I

You are my in - her - i - tance, O Lord.

You are my in - her - i - tance, O Lord.

Refrain II

Lord, you will show us the path of life.

Lord, you will show us the path of life.

Verses

1. Preserve me, O God, for in you I take refuge.
   I say to the LORD, "You are my Lord."
   O LORD, it is you who are my portion and cup;
   you yourself who secure my lot.

2. I will bless the LORD who gives me counsel,
   who even at night directs my heart.
   I keep the LORD before me always;
   with him at my right hand, I shall not be moved.

3. And so, my heart rejoices, my soul is glad;
   even my flesh shall rest in hope.
   For you will not abandon my soul to hell,
   nor let your holy one see corruption.

4. You will show me the path of life,
   the fullness of joy in your presence,
   at your right hand, bliss forever,
   at your right hand, bliss forever.

Text: Psalm 16:1–2a and 5, 7–8, 9–10, 11; *The Revised Grail Psalms,* © 2010, Conception Abbey and The Grail, admin. by GIA Publications, Inc.;
refrains trans., © 1969, ICEL
Music: Tony E. Alonso, © 2013, GIA Publications, Inc.

35 Psalm 19: Lord, You Have the Words

Refrain I (Vss. 1–4)

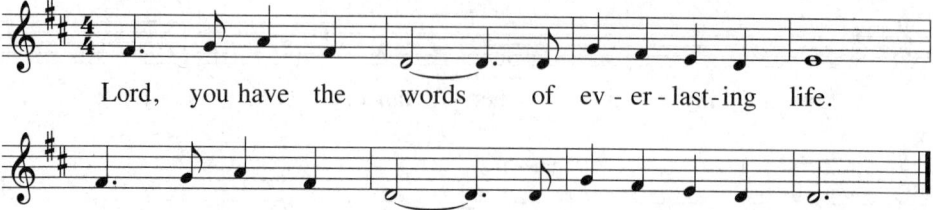

Lord, you have the words of ev - er - last-ing life.

Lord, you have the words of ev - er - last-ing life.

Refrain II (Vss. 1, 3, 5, 6)

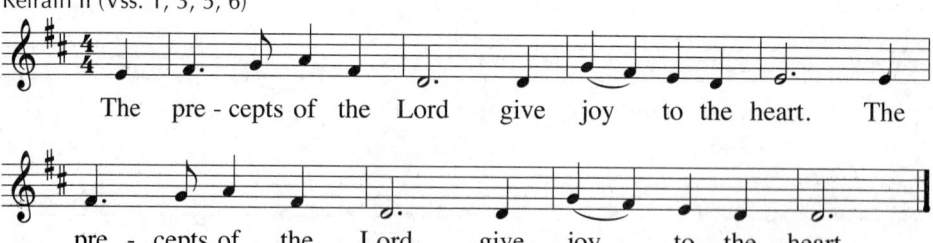

The pre - cepts of the Lord give joy to the heart. The

pre - cepts of the Lord give joy to the heart.

Refrain III (Vss. 1–4 or 1–3, 7)

Your words, Lord, are Spir-it and life, your words are Spir-it and life.

Verses

1. The law of the LORD is perfect; it revives the soul.
   The decrees of the LORD are steadfast; they give wisdom to the simple.

2. The precepts of the LORD are right; they gladden the heart.
   The command of the LORD is clear; it gives light to the eyes.

3. The fear of the LORD is pure, abiding forever.
   The judgments of the LORD are true; they are, all of them, just.

4. They are more to be desired than gold, than quantities of gold.
   And sweeter are they than honey, than honey flowing from the comb.

5. So in them your servant finds instruction; great reward is in their keeping.
   But who can detect their own errors? From hidden faults acquit me.

6. From presumption restrain your servant; may it not rule me.
   Then shall I be blameless, clean from grave sin.

7. May the spoken words of my mouth, the thoughts of my heart,
   win favor in your sight, O LORD, my rock and my redeemer!

Text: Psalm 19:8, 9, 10, 11, 12–13, 14, 15; *The Revised Grail Psalms*, © 2010, Conception Abbey and The Grail, admin. by GIA Publications, Inc.; refrains trans., © 1969, ICEL
Music: Tony E. Alonso, © 2003, 2012, GIA Publications, Inc.

Psalm 19: Lord, You Have the Words 36

Refrain

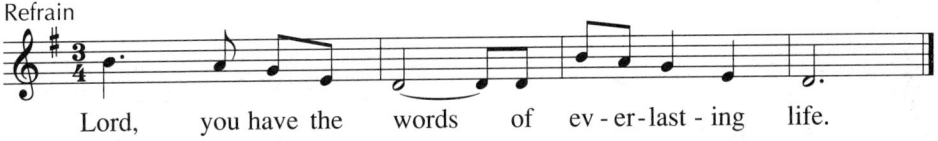

Lord, you have the words of ev-er-last-ing life.

Verses

1. The law of the Lord is perfect, refreshing the soul;
   the Lord's rule is to be trusted, the simple find wisdom.

2. The fear of the Lord is holy, abiding for ever;
   the decrees of the Lord are true, all of them just.

3. The precepts of the Lord are right, they gladden the heart,
   the command of the Lord is clear, giving light to the eye.

4. They are worth more than gold, than the finest gold,
   sweeter than honey, than honey from the comb.

Text: Psalm 19:8, 9, 10, 11; David Haas, © 1983, GIA Publications, Inc.; refrain trans., © 1969, ICEL
Music: David Haas, © 1983, GIA Publications, Inc.

Psalm 22: My God, My God 37

Refrain

My God, my God, why have you a-ban-doned me?

Verses

1. All who see me deride me;
   they curl their lips, they toss their heads:
   "He trusted in the LORD, let him save him;
   let him release him, for in him he delights."

2. For dogs have surrounded me;
   a band of the wicked besets me.
   They tear holes in my hands and my feet;
   I can count every one of my bones.

3. They divide my clothing among them,
   they cast lots for my robe.
   But you, O LORD, do not stay afar off;
   my strength, make haste to help me!

4. I will tell of your name to my kin,
   and praise you in the midst of the assembly;
   You who fear the LORD, give him praise;
   all descendants of Jacob, give him glory;
   revere him, all you descendants of Israel.

Text: Psalm 22:8–9, 17–18a, 19–20, 23–24; *The Revised Grail Psalms,* © 2010, Conception Abbey and The Grail, admin. by GIA Publications, Inc.;
refrain trans., © 1969, ICEL
Music: Paul A. Tate, © 2013, 2014, GIA Publications, Inc.

38 Psalm 22: My God, My God

Refrain

My God, my God, O why have you a-ban-doned me?

Verses

1. All who see me laugh at me, they mock me and they shake their heads:
   "He relied on the Lord, let the Lord be his refuge."

2. As dogs around me, they circle me about.
   Wounded me and pierced me, I can number all my bones.

3. My clothing they divided, for my garments casting lots,
   O Lord, do not desert me, but hasten to my aid.

4. I will praise you to my people, and proclaim you in their midst,
   O fear the Lord, my people, give glory to God's name.

Text: Psalm 22:8–9, 17–18, 19–20, 23–24; Marty Haugen, © 1983, GIA Publications, Inc.; refrain trans., © 1969, ICEL
Music: Marty Haugen, © 1983, GIA Publications, Inc.

39 Psalm 23: Shepherd Me, O God

Refrain

Shep-herd me, O God, be-yond my wants, be-

yond my fears, from death in-to life.

Verses

1. God is my shepherd, so nothing shall I want;
   I rest in the meadows of faithfulness and love;
   I walk by the quiet waters of peace.

2. Gently you raise me and heal my weary soul;
   you lead me by pathways of righteousness and truth;
   my spirit shall sing the music of your name.

3. Though I should wander the valley of death,
   I fear no evil, for you are at my side;
   your rod and your staff, my comfort and my hope.

4. You have set me a banquet of love in the face of hatred,
   crowning me with love beyond my pow'r to hold.

5. Surely your kindness and mercy follow me all the days of my life;
   I will dwell in the house of my God forevermore.

Text: Psalm 23; Marty Haugen
Music: Marty Haugen
© 1986, GIA Publications, Inc.

Psalm 23: Nada Me Falta / 40
My Shepherd Is the Lord

Estribillo / Refrain*

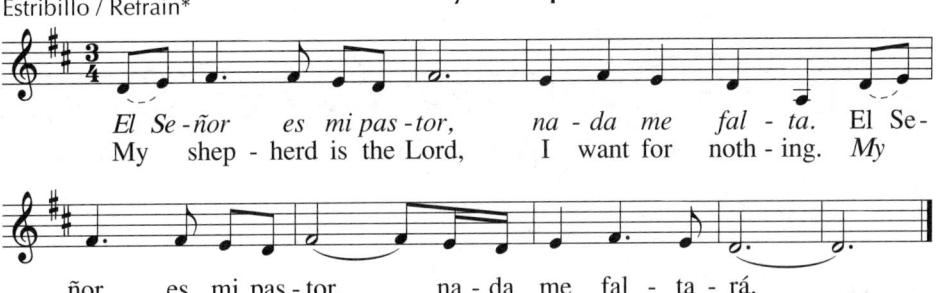

El Se-ñor es mi pas-tor, na - da me fal - ta. El Se-
My shep - herd is the Lord, I want for noth - ing. My

ñor es mi pas-tor, na - da me fal - ta - rá.
shep - herd is the Lord, noth-ing more shall I need.

Estrofas / Verses

1. El Señor es mi pastor, nada me falta: en verdes praderas me hace recostar;
   me conduce hacia fuentes tranquilas y repara mis fuerzas.

2. Él me guía por senderos justos, por el honor de su nombre.
   Aunque camine por cañadas oscuras, nada temo: tú vas conmigo;
   tu vara y tu cayado me sosiegan.

3. Tú preparas una mesa delante de mí, enfrente de mis enemigos;
   tú me unges la cabeza con perfume, y mi copa rebosa.

4. Tu bondad y tu clemencia, ellas me acompañan todos los días de mi vida,
   y habitaré en la casa, la casa del Señor por siempre.

1. My shepherd is the Lord; I have all I need:
   green are the pastures where he gives me repose,
   calm and soothing are the waters where he leads me to revive my spirit.

2. He guides me in paths of righteousness, true to his name.
   Though I walk in death's dark valley, no evil will I fear.
   You are with me by my side; your rod and your staff give me comfort.

3. You prepare a lavish feast, spreading it before me,
   while my enemies are there looking on.
   You anoint my head with oil; you fill my cup so full it runs over.

4. May goodness and loving-kindness, these alone, pursue me each day,
   each moment that I have to live.
   In the house of the Lord I will dwell for ever and ever.

*For a bilingual refrain, sing the text in italics.

Text: Psalm 23, alt.; © 1970, Conferencia Episcopal Española; English tr. by Ronald F. Krisman, © 2012, GIA Publications, Inc.
Music: Donna Peña; acc. by Diana Kodner, © 1988, 1993, GIA Publications, Inc.

41   Psalm 23

Antiphon I

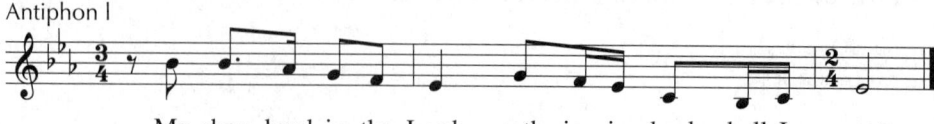

My shep-herd is the Lord,   noth-ing in-deed shall I   want.

Text: Psalm 23; The Grail
Music: Joseph Gelineau, SJ
© 1963, The Grail, GIA Publications, Inc., agent

Antiphon II

His good-ness shall fol-low me al-ways to the   end of my days.

Text: Psalm 23; The Grail
Music: A. Gregory Murray, OSB
© 1963, The Grail, GIA Publications, Inc., agent

Antiphon III

The   Lord   is   my   shep-herd,   noth-ing shall I   want: he

leads   me   by   safe   paths,   noth-ing shall I   fear.

Text: Psalm 23; The Grail
Music: A. Gregory Murray, OSB
© 1963, The Grail, GIA Publications, Inc., agent

Antiphon IV

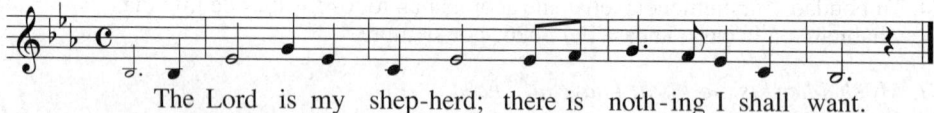

The   Lord   is   my   shep-herd; there is   noth-ing I shall want.

Text: Psalm 23; The Grail, © 1963, The Grail, GIA Publications, Inc., agent
Music: Richard Proulx, © 1975, GIA Publications, Inc.

Antiphon V

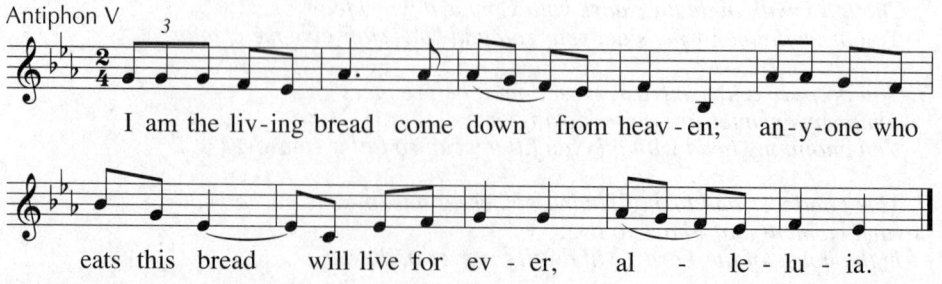

I am the liv-ing bread   come down   from heav-en;   an-y-one who

eats this   bread   will live for ev-er,   al - le-lu - ia.

Text: *Liturgy of the Hours,* © 1974, ICEL
Music: Ronald F. Krisman, © 2011, GIA Publications, Inc.

Psalm Tone

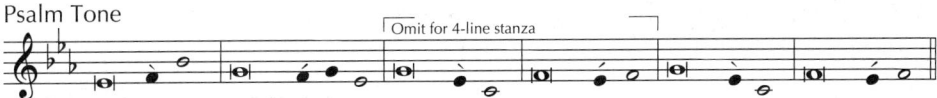

Omit for 4-line stanza

Music: Richard Proulx, © 1975, GIA Publications, Inc.

Gelineau Tone

Omit for 4-line stanzas

Music: Joseph Gelineau, SJ, © 1963, The Grail, GIA Publications, Inc., agent

Dominus pascit me

The **LORD** is mỳ **shep**herd;
there is **noth**ing Í shall **want**.
[2] **Fresh** and **green** are thè **pastures**
where you **give** me ré**pose**.
Near **rest**ful **wa**ters yòu **lead** me;
[3] **to** re**vive** mý **soul**.

You **guide** me a**long** the rìght **path**,
for the **sake** óf your **name**.
[4] **Though** I should **walk** in thè **val**ley
of the **shad**ow óf **death**,
no **e**vil would I **fear**, for you àre **with** me.
Your **crook** and your **staff** will give mé **com**fort.

[5] You have pre**pared** a **ta**ble bè**fore** me
in the **sight** óf my **foes**.
My **head** you have a**noint**ed wìth **oil**;
my **cup** is ové**rflowing**.

[6] Surely **good**ness and **kind**ness shàll **fol**low me
all the **days** óf my **life**.
In the **LORD's** own **house** shall Ì **dwell**
for **length** of days ú**nending**.

To the **Fa**ther and **Son** gìve **glo**ry,
give **glo**ry tó the **Spir**it.
To God who **is**, who **was**, and whò **will** be,
for **ev**er ánd **ever**.

Text: Psalm 23; *The Ecumenical Grail Psalter*, © 2015, Conception Abbey and The Grail, admin. by GIA Publications, Inc.

42   Psalm 25: To You, O Lord

Refrain I

To you, O Lord, I lift my soul, to you, I lift my soul.

Refrain II

Your ways, O Lord, are love and truth, to

those who keep your cov - e - nant.

Verses

1. Lord, make me know your ways, teach me your paths
   and keep me in the way of your truth, for you are God, my Savior.

2. For the Lord is good and righteous, revealing the way to those who wander,
   gently leading the poor and the humble.

3. To the ones who seek the Lord, who look to God's word, who live God's love,
   God will always be near, and will show them mercy.

Text: Psalm 25:4–5, 8–9, 12–14; Marty Haugen, © 1982, GIA Publications, Inc.; refrains trans., © 1969, ICEL
Music: Marty Haugen, © 1982, GIA Publications, Inc.

43   Psalm 27: The Lord Is My Light

Refrain

The Lord is my light and my sal - va - tion, of

whom should I be a - fraid, of whom should I be a - fraid?

Verses

1. The Lord is my light and my help; whom should I fear?
   The Lord is the stronghold of my life; before whom should I shrink?

2. There is one thing I ask of the Lord; for this I long:
   to live in the house of the Lord all the days of my life.

3. I believe I shall see the goodness of the Lord in the land of the living;
   hope in God, and take heart. Hope in the Lord!

Text: Psalm 27:1–2, 4, 13–14; David Haas
Music: David Haas
© 1983, GIA Publications, Inc.

Psalm 27: The Lord Is My Light   44

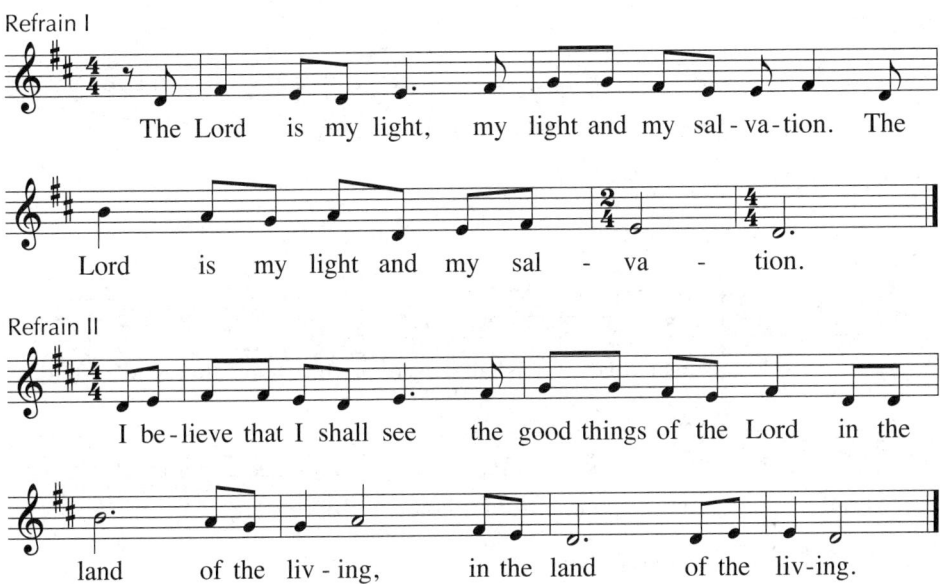

Refrain I

The Lord is my light, my light and my sal-va-tion. The
Lord is my light and my sal - va - tion.

Refrain II

I be-lieve that I shall see the good things of the Lord in the
land of the liv-ing, in the land of the liv-ing.

Verses

1. The LORD is my light and my salvation;
   whom shall I fear, whom shall I fear?
   The LORD is the stronghold of my life; whom should I dread?

2. There is one thing I ask of the LORD, only this do I seek:
   to live in the house of the LORD all the days of my life,
   to gaze on the beauty of the LORD, to inquire at his temple.

3. O LORD, hear my voice when I call; have mercy and answer me.
   Of you my heart has spoken, "Seek his face."
   It is your face, O LORD, that I seek.

4. Hide not your face from me. Dismiss not your servant in anger;
   you have been my help. Do not abandon or forsake me.

5. I believe I shall see the LORD's goodness in the land of the living.
   Wait for the LORD; be strong; be stouthearted, and wait for the LORD!

Text: Psalm 27:1, 4, 7–8, 9abcd, 13–14; *The Revised Grail Psalms*, © 2010, Conception Abbey and The Grail, admin. by GIA Publications, Inc.;
refrains trans., © 1969, ICEL
Music: Tony E. Alonso, © 2012, GIA Publications, Inc.

45   Psalm 27

Antiphon I

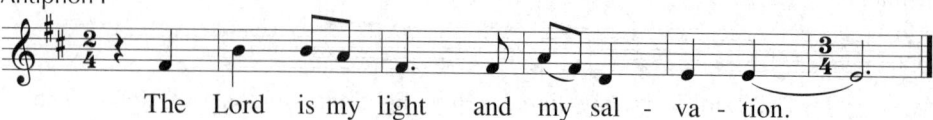

The Lord is my light and my sal - va - tion.

Text: *Lectionary for Mass*, © 1969, 1981, 1997, ICEL
Music: Richard Proulx, © 1975, GIA Publications, Inc.

Antiphon II

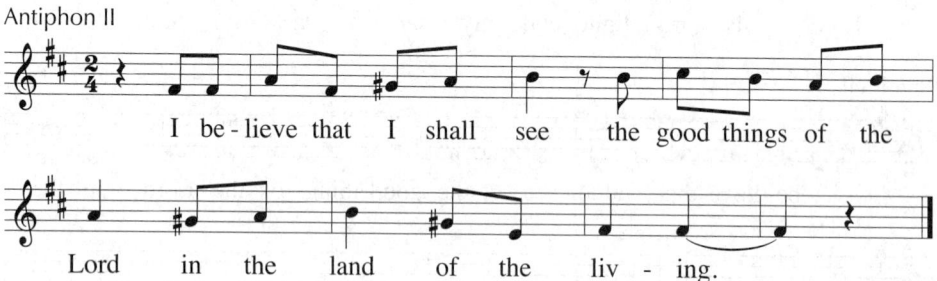

I be - lieve that I shall see the good things of the

Lord in the land of the liv - ing.

Text: *Lectionary for Mass*, © 1969, 1981, 1997, ICEL
Music: Columba Kelly, OSB, © 1975, GIA Publications, Inc.

Antiphon III

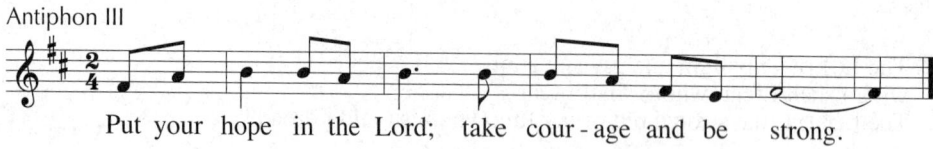

Put your hope in the Lord; take cour - age and be strong.

Text: *Lectionary for Mass*, © 1969, 1981, 1997, ICEL
Music: Howard Hughes, SM, © 1975, GIA Publications, Inc.

Antiphon IV

I will sing and make mu - sic for the Lord.

Text: Psalm 27:6e
Music: Ingrid Brustle
© 1963, The Grail, GIA Publications, Inc., agent

Psalm Tone

Repeat for 6-line stanzas   Repeat for 5-line stanza

Music: Laurence Bevenot, OSB, © 1969, Ampleforth Abbey Trustees

Gelineau Tone

Music: Joseph Gelineau, SJ, © 1963, The Grail, GIA Publications, Inc., agent

Dominus illuminatio mea

The **LORD** is my **light** and mỳ salvation;
whom sháll I **fear**?
The **LORD** is the **strong**hold òf my **life**;
whom shóuld I **dread**?

2 When **those** who do evìl draw **near**
to devóur my **flesh**,
it is **they**, my enemìes and **foes**,
who **stum**blé and **fall**.

3 Though an **army** encàmp against me,
my **heart** wóuld not **fear**.
Though **war** break òut against me,
even **then** wóuld I **trust**.

4 There is **one** thing I **ask** òf the **LORD**,
only **this** dó I **seek**:
to **live** in the **house** òf the **LORD**
all the **days** óf my **life**,
to **gaze** on the **beau**ty òf the **LORD**,
to in**quire** át his **temple**.

5 For **there** I am sàfely **shel**tered
in the **dáy** of e**vil**;
God **hides** me under **cov**er òf a **tent**;
setting me **high** upón a **rock**.

6 And **now** my **head** shàll be **raised**
above my **foes** whó sur**round** me,
and I shall **of**fer withìn God's **tent**
sacrifices **full** of èxul**ta**tion.
I will **sing** and make **mu**sic fór the **LORD**.

7 O **LORD**, hear my **voice** whèn I **call**;
have **mer**cý and **an**swer me.
8 Of **you** my **hèart** has **spo**ken,
"Seek the **fáce** of **God**."

It is your **face**, O **LORD**, thàt I **seek**;
9 hide not your **fáce** from **me**.
Dis**miss** not your **serv**ànt in **anger**;
you have béen my **help**.

Do not a**ban**don òr for**sake** me,
O **Gód**, my **Savior**!
10 Though **father** and **mothèr** for**sake** me,
the **LORD** wíll re**ceive** me.

11 In**struct** me, **LORD**, ìn your **way**;
on an e**vén** path **lead** me
be**cause** òf my e**nemies**.
12 Do not **leave** me to the **will** óf my **foes**,
for false **wit**nesses rise **ùp** a**gainst** me,
and they **bréathe** out **violence**.

13 I believe I shall **see** the **good**ness òf
the **LORD**
in the **land** óf the **living**.
14 **Wait** for the **LÒRD**; be **strong**;
be stout**heart**ed, and **wait** fór the **LORD**!

Praise the **Father**, **Son** and Hòly **Spir**it,
both **now** ánd for **ever**,
the God who **is**, who **was**, and ìs to **come**,
at the **end** óf the **ages**.

Text: Psalm 27: *The Ecumenical Grail Psalter*, © 2015, Conception Abbey and The Grail, admin. by GIA Publications, Inc.

46　Psalm 30: I Will Praise You, Lord

Refrain

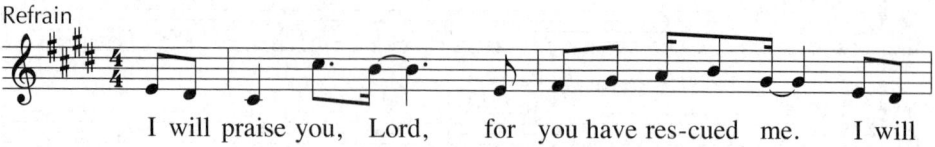

I will praise you, Lord, for you have res-cued me. I will

praise you, Lord, for you have res-cued me.

Verses

1. I will extol you, LORD, for you have raised me up,
   and have not let my enemies rejoice over me.
   O LORD, you have lifted up my soul from the grave,
   restored me to life from those who sink into the pit.

2. Sing psalms to the LORD, you faithful ones;
   give thanks to his holy name.
   His anger lasts a moment; his favor all through life.
   At night come tears, but dawn brings joy.

3. Hear, O LORD, and have mercy on me;
   be my helper, O LORD.
   You have changed my mourning into dancing.
   O LORD my God, I will thank you forever.

Text: Psalm 30:2 and 4, 5–6, 11 and 12a and 13b, *The Revised Grail Psalms*, © 2010, Conception Abbey and The Grail, admin. by
GIA Publications, Inc.; refrain trans., © 1969, ICEL
Music: Norah Duncan IV, © 2012, GIA Publications, Inc.

47　Psalm 31: Father, into Your Hands

Refrain

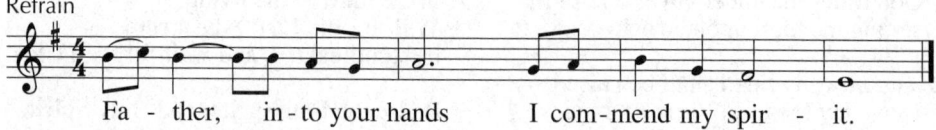

Fa - ther, in-to your hands I com-mend my spir - it.

Verses

1. In you, O LORD, I take refuge.
   Let me never be put to shame.
   In your justice, set me free.
   Into your hands I commend my spirit.
   You will redeem me, O LORD, O faithful God.

2. Because of all my foes I have become a reproach,
   an object of scorn of my neighbors and of fear to my friends.
   Those who see me in the street flee from me.
   I am forgotten, like someone dead,
   and have become like a broken vessel.

3. But as for me, I trust in you, O LORD;
   I say, "You are my God.
   My lot is in your hands, deliver me
   from the hands of my enemies and those who pursue me."

4. "Let your face shine on your servant.
   Save me in your merciful love."
   Be strong, let your heart take courage,
   all who hope in the LORD.

Text: Psalm 31:2 and 6, 12–13, 15–16, 17 and 25; *The Revised Grail Psalms*, © 2010, Conception Abbey and The Grail, admin. by GIA Publications, Inc.; refrain trans., © 1969, ICEL
Music: Stephen Pishner, © 2013, GIA Publications, Inc.

Psalm 32: I Turn to You, Lord   48

Refrain I (Vss. 1, 2, 4)

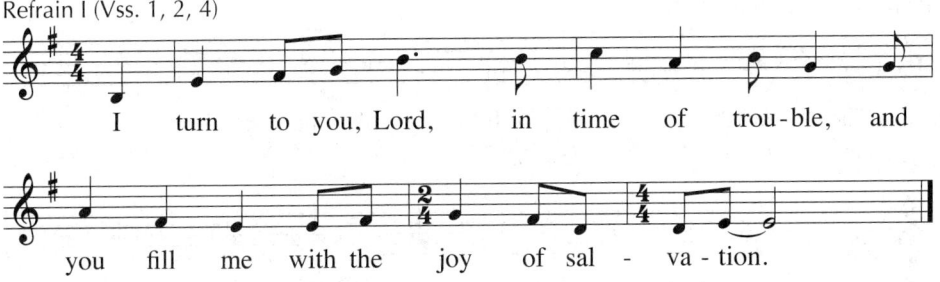

I turn to you, Lord, in time of trou-ble, and you fill me with the joy of sal - va - tion.

Refrain II (Vss. 1–4)

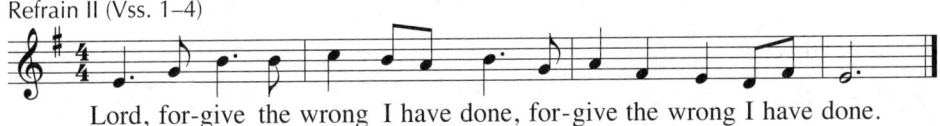

Lord, for-give the wrong I have done, for-give the wrong I have done.

Verses

1. Blessed is he whose transgression is forgiven,
   whose sin is remitted.
   Blessed the man to whom the LORD imputes no guilt,
   in whose spirit is no guile.

2. To you I have acknowledged, acknowledged my sin;
   my guilt I did not hide.
   I said, "I will confess my transgression to the LORD."
   And you have forgiven the guilt of my sin.

3. You are a hiding place for me;
   you keep me safe from distress;
   you surround me with cries, with cries of deliverance,
   you surround me with cries of deliverance.

4. Rejoice in the LORD; exult, you just! Rejoice in the LORD.
   Ring out your joy, all you upright of heart! Ring out your joy!

Text: Psalm 32:1–2, 5, 7, 11; *The Revised Grail Psalms*, © 2010, Conception Abbey and The Grail, admin. by GIA Publications, Inc.; refrains trans., © 1969, ICEL
Music: Tony E. Alonso, © 2014, GIA Publications, Inc.

49 Psalm 33: Let Your Mercy Be on Us / Señor, Que Tu Misericordia

Refrain / Estribillo I

Let your mer - cy be on us, O God,
Se - ñor, que tu mi - se - ri - cor - dia

as we place our trust in you.
ven - ga so - bre no - so - tros.

Refrain / Estribillo II

The earth is full of the good-ness of
La mi - se - ri - cor - dia de nues - tro

God, the good - ness of our God.
Dios lle - na la tie - rra.

Refrain / Estribillo III

Hap - py are the peo - ple the Lord has
Di - cho - so el pue - blo que_el Se - ñor se_es - co -

cho - sen, cho - sen to be his own.
gió co - mo he - re - dad.

Verses / Estrofas

1. Your words, O God, are truth indeed, and all your works are ever faithful;
   you love justice and right, your compassion fills all creation.

2. See how the eye of God is watching, ever guarding all who wait in hope,
   to deliver them from death and sustain them in time of famine.

3. Exult, you just, in the Lord, for praise is the song of the righteous!
   How happy the people of God, the ones whom God has chosen!

4. Our soul is waiting for God, for God is our help and our shield.
   May your kindness, O God, be upon us who place our hope in you.

1. *La palabra del Señor es recta, y todas sus acciones son leales;*
la justicia él ama, y la tierra su gracia llena.

2. *Los ojos de Dios ven a sus fieles, los que esperan su misericordia;*
los rescata de la muerte y sacia en tiempo de hambre.

3. *Festejen, justos, al Señor, es propio de los buenos alabarlo.*
Dichoso el pueblo de Dios, que él se escogió como heredad.

4. *Aguardamos al Señor: él es nuestro auxilio y escudo;*
que tu amor, Señor, esté con nosotros, como lo esperamos de ti.

Text: Psalm 33:1, 4–5, 12, 18–19, 20, 22; Marty Haugen; Spanish tr. by Ronald F. Krisman, © 1987, 2011, GIA Publications, Inc.; English refrain III trans., © 1969, ICEL
Music: Marty Haugen, © 1987, 1994, GIA Publications, Inc.

Psalm 34: Taste and See 50

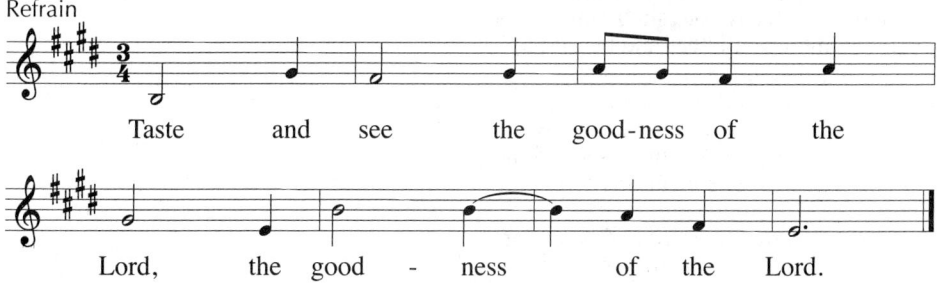

Refrain

Taste and see the good-ness of the Lord, the good - ness of the Lord.

Verses

1. I will bless the Lord at all times, God's praise ever in my mouth.
Glory in the Lord for ever, and the lowly will hear and be glad.

2. Glory in the Lord with me, let us together extol God's name.
I sought the Lord, who answered me and delivered me from all my fears.

3. Look to God that you might be radiant with joy,
and your faces free from all shame.
The Lord hears the suffering souls, and saves them from all distress.

Text: Psalm 34:2–3, 4–5, 6–7; Marty Haugen, © 1980, GIA Publications, Inc.; refrain trans., © 1969, ICEL
Music: Marty Haugen, © 1980, GIA Publications, Inc.

51 Psalm 34: Taste and See

Antiphon I

Taste and see the good - ness of the Lord.

Antiphon II

I will bless the Lord at all times.

Antiphon III

Taste and see, taste and see the good-ness of the Lord. Lord.

Guimont Tone

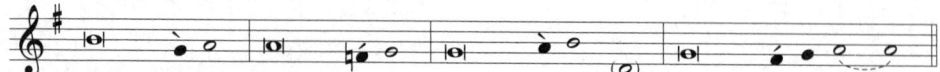

Benedicam Dominum

1. ² I will bless the LORD at àll times;
   praise is always in mý mouth.
   ³ In the LORD my soul shall make ìts boast;
   the humble shall hear ánd be glad.

2. ⁴ Glorify the LORD wìth me;
   together let us praise Gód's name.
   ⁵ I sought the LORD, whò answered me,
   and set me free from áll my terrors.

3. ⁶ Look towards the Lord and bè radiant;
   let your faces not be ábashed.
   ⁷ When the lowly call out, the LÒRD hears,
   and rescues them from all théir distress.

4. ⁸ The angel of the LORD is èncamped
   around those who are reverent, tó rescue them.
   ⁹ Taste and see that the LORD ìs good.
   Blessed are they who seek refúge in him.

5. ¹⁰ Fear the LORD, yòu holy ones.
   They lack nothing, those who féar God.
   ¹¹ The rich suffer want and gò hungry,
   but those who seek the LORD láck no blessing.

6. [12] Come, children, ànd hear me,
    that I may teach you the fear of thé LORD.
    [13] Who is eager fòr life
    and longs to see prospérous days?

7. [14] Guard your tongue fròm evil,
    and your lips from speaking déceit.
    [15] Turn aside from evil and dò good.
    Seek after peace, ánd pursue it.

8. [16] The eyes of the LORD are on thè righteous;
    God's ears are open to théir cry.
    [17] The LORD's face is turned against thè wicked
    to cut off their remembrance fróm the earth.

9. [18] When the righteous cry out, the LÒRD hears,
    and rescues them in all their dístress.
    [19] The LORD is close to the brokènhearted,
    and saves those whose spirít is crushed.

10. [20] Many are the trials of thè righteous,
    but from them all the LORD wíll rescue them,
    [21] God keeps guard over all thèir bones;
    not one of their bones sháll be broken.

11. [22] Evil brings death to thè wicked;
    those who hate the righteous áre doomed.
    [23] The souls of those who serve the LORD àre ransomed.
    None who trust in God shall bé condemned.

12. Give praise to the Father Àlmighty,
    to his Son, Jesus Christ thé Lord,
    to the Spirit who dwells in òur hearts,
    both now and for evér. Amen.

Text: Psalm 34; *The Ecumenical Grail Psalter*, © 2015, Conception Abbey and The Grail, admin. by GIA Publications, Inc.; antiphons trans.,
© 1969, ICEL
Music: Michel Guimont, antiphon I and verses, © 1995, and antiphons II and III, © 2011, GIA Publications, Inc.

52 Psalm 34: The Cry of the Poor

Refrain

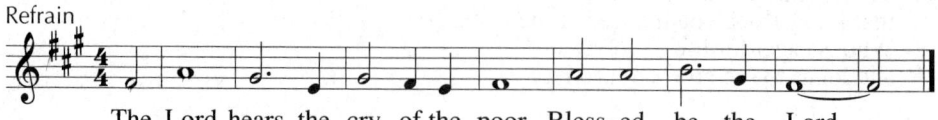

The Lord hears the cry of the poor. Bless-ed be the Lord.

Verses

1. I will bless the Lord at all times, with praise ever in my mouth.
   Let my soul glory in the Lord, who will hear the cry of the poor.

2. Let the lowly hear and be glad: the Lord listens to their pleas;
   and to hearts broken, God is near, who will hear the cry of the poor.

3. Every spirit crushed, God will save; will be ransom for their lives;
   will be safe shelter for their fears, and will hear the cry of the poor.

4. We proclaim your greatness, O God, your praise ever in our mouth;
   every face brightened in your light, for you hear the cry of the poor.

Text: Psalm 34:2–3, 6–7, 18–19, 23; John Foley, SJ
Music: John Foley, SJ
© 1978, John B. Foley, SJ, and OCP

53 Psalm 40: Here I Am

Refrain

Here I am, Lord, here I am. I come to do your will.

Verses

1. Long was I waiting for God, and then he heard my cry.
   It was he who taught this song to me, a song of praise to God.

2. You asked me not for sacrifice, for slaughtered goats or lambs.
   No, my heart, you gave me ears to hear you, then I said, "Here I am."

3. You wrote it in the scrolls of law what you would have me do.
   Doing that is what has made me happy, your law is in my heart.

4. I spoke before your holy people, the good news that you save.
   Now you know that I will not be silent, I'll always sing your praise.

Text: Psalm 40:2 and 4, 7–8a, 8b–9, 10; Rory Cooney, © 1971, 1991, OCP; refrain trans., © 1969, ICEL
Music: Rory Cooney, © 1971, 1991, OCP

Psalm 40: Here Am I   54

Refrain (Vss. 1–4 or 2–5)

Here am I, Lord, here am I; I come to do your will.

Here am I, Lord, here am I; I come to do your will.

Verses

1. I waited, I waited for the LORD, and he stooped down to me.
   He put a new song into my mouth, praise of our God.

2. You delight not in sacrifice and offerings, but in an open ear.
   You do not ask for holocaust and victim. Then I said, "See, I have come."

3. In the scroll of the book it stands written of me:
   "I delight to do your will, O my God;
   your instruction lies deep within me, your instruction lies deep within me."

4. Your justice I have proclaimed in the great assembly.
   My lips I have not sealed; you know it, O LORD.

5. Your saving help I have not hidden in my heart;
   of your faithfulness and salvation I have spoken.
   I made no secret of your merciful love and your faithfulness
   to the great assembly.

Text: Psalm 40:2ab and 4ab, 7–8a, 8b–9, 10, 11; *The Revised Grail Psalms*, © 2010, Conception Abbey and The Grail, admin. by GIA Publications, Inc.; refrain trans., © 1969, ICEL
Music: Tony E. Alonso, © 2013, GIA Publications, Inc.

55 Psalm 42–43: As the Deer Longs

Refrain

As the deer longs for run - ning streams, so I long,

so I long, so I long for you.

Verses*

1. Athirst my soul for you, the God who is my life!
   When shall I see, when shall I see, see the face of God?

2. Continually the foe delights in taunting me:
   "Where is God, where is your God?" Where, O where are you?

3. Defend me, God; send forth your light and your truth.
   They will lead me to your holy mountain, to your dwelling place.

4. Then I shall go unto the altar of my God.
   Praising you, O my joy and gladness, I shall praise your name.

*Beginning with verse 2, refrain and verse may be sung together.

Text: Psalm 42:2, 3, 4; 43:3, 4; Bob Hurd
Music: Bob Hurd; arr. by Craig S. Kingsbury
© 1988, Bob Hurd. Published by OCP.

56 Psalm 45: The Queen Stands at Your Right Hand

Refrain

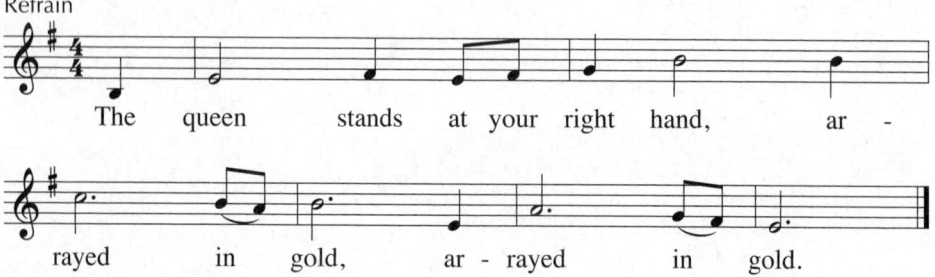

The queen stands at your right hand, ar -

rayed in gold, ar - rayed in gold.

Verses

1. The daughters of kings are those whom you favor.
   On your right stands the queen in gold of Ophir.

2. Listen, O daughter; pay heed and give ear:
   forget your own people and your father's house.

3. So will the king desire your beauty.
   He is your lord, pay homage to him.

4. They are escorted amid gladness and joy;
   they pass within the palace of the king.

Text: Psalm 45:10, 11, 12ab, 16; *The Revised Grail Psalms,* © 2010, Conception Abbey and The Grail, admin. by GIA Publications, Inc.; refrain trans., © 1969, ICEL
Music: Tony E. Alonso, © 2012, GIA Publications, Inc.

Psalm 47: God Mounts His Throne   57

Refrain

God   mounts his throne   to   shouts   of   joy;   a

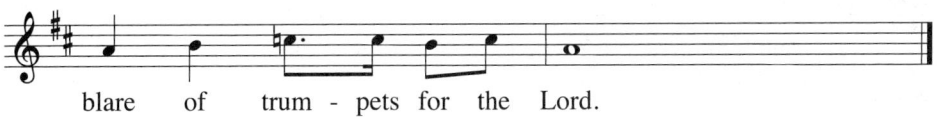

blare   of   trum - pets for   the   Lord.

Verses

1. All peoples, clap your hands.
   Cry to God with shouts of joy!
   For the LORD, the Most High, is awesome,
   the great King over all the earth.

2. God goes up with shouts of joy.
   The LORD goes up with trumpet blast.
   Sing praise for God; sing praise!
   Sing praise to our king; sing praise!

3. God is King of all the earth.
   Sing praise with all your skill.
   God reigns over the nations.
   God sits upon his holy throne.

Text: Psalm 47:2–3, 6–7, 8–9, *The Revised Grail Psalms,* © 2010, Conception Abbey and The Grail, admin. GIA Publications, Inc.; refrain trans., © 1969, ICEL
Tune: James J. Chepponis, © 1994, 2011, GIA Publications, Inc.

58 Psalm 47

Antiphon I

Sing praise to our king, sing praise: for God is king of all the earth.

Text: Psalm 47:7; The Grail
Music: A. Gregory Murray, OSB
© 1963, The Grail, GIA Publications, Inc., agent

Antiphon II

God mounts his throne to shouts of joy, to shouts, to shouts of joy.

Text: *Lectionary for Mass,* © 1969, 1981, 1997, ICEL
Music: Richard Proulx, © 1975, GIA Publications, Inc.

Antiphon III

Christ is the light of the na - tions, to bring sal -

va - tion to the ends of the earth.

Text: *Simple Gradual,* © 1968, ICEL
Music: John R. Ainslie, © 1969, Geoffrey Chapman Ltd.

Conception Abbey Tone

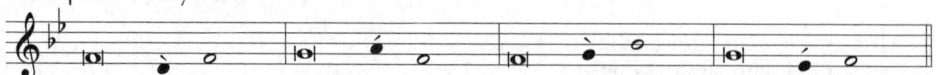

Music: Gregory J. Polan, OSB, © 2010, Conception Abbey, admin. by GIA Publications, Inc.

Gelineau Tone

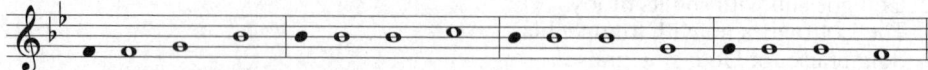

Music: Joseph Gelineau, SJ, © 1963, The Grail, GIA Publications, Inc., agent

Omnes gentes plaudite

2 All **peoples, clap** yòur **hands.**
Cry to **God** with **shouts** óf **joy!**
3 For the **LÓRD,** the Most **High,** ìs
awesome,
the great **king** over **all** thé **earth.**

4 God **humbles** peoplès **un**der us
and **nations un**der óur **feet.**
5 Our **her**itage God **chose** fòr **us,**
the **pride** of **Ja**cob the **bé**loved.

⁶ God has gone **up** with **shouts** òf **joy**.
  The LORD goes **up** with **trump**ét **blast**.
⁷ Sing **praise** for **God**; sìng **praise**!
  Sing **praise** to our **king**; síng **praise**!

⁸ For God is **king** of **all** thè **earth**.
  Sing praise with á **hymn**.
⁹ **God** is **reign**ing ovèr **nations**,
  God **sits** upon a **holý throne**.

¹⁰ The **lead**ers of the **peo**ples are àss**em**bled
  with the **peo**ple of the **God** óf **Abraham**.
  For the **rul**ers of the **earth** belong tò **God**,
  who is **great**ly éxalted.

Give **praise** to the **Father** Àl**mighty**,
to his **Son**, Jesus **Christ** thé **Lord**,
to the **Spir**it who **dwells** in òur **hearts**,
both **now** and for **ever**. Ámen.

Text: Psalm 47; *The Ecumenical Grail Psalter*, © 2015, Conception Abbey and The Grail, admin. by GIA Publications, Inc.

59 Psalm 47: God Mounts His Throne

Ostinato Refrain*

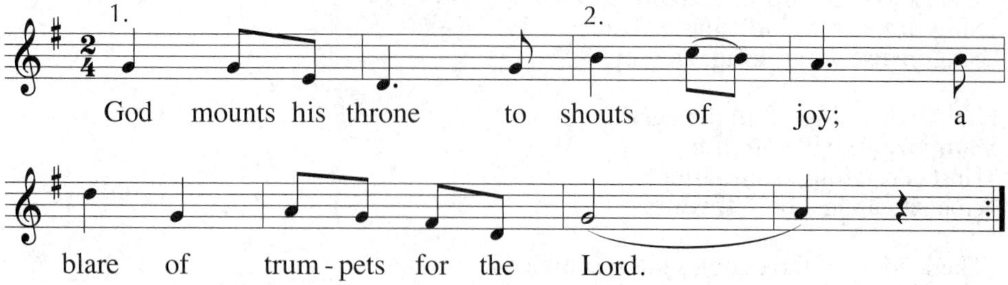

God mounts his throne to shouts of joy; a

blare of trum-pets for the Lord.

Verses

1. All you peoples, clap your hands, shout to God in gladness,
   the Lord we must fear, king of all the earth.

2. God goes up to shouts of joy, sound the trumpet blast.
   Sing praise to our God, praise unto our king!

3. God is king of all the earth, sing with all your skill
   to the king of all nations, God enthroned on high!

May be sung in canon.

Text: Psalm 47:2–3, 6–7, 8–9; Marty Haugen, © 1983, GIA Publications, Inc.; refrain trans., © 1969, ICEL
Music: Marty Haugen, © 1983, GIA Publications, Inc.

60 Psalm 51: Be Merciful, O Lord

Refrain

Be mer-ci-ful, O Lord, for we have sinned; be

mer-ci-ful, O Lord, for we have sinned.

Verses

1. Have mercy on me, God, in your kindness,
   in your compassion, blot out my offense.
   O wash me more and more from my guilt and my sorrow,
   and cleanse me from all of my sin.

2. My offenses, truly I know them, and my sins are always before me;
   against you alone have I sinned, O Lord, what is evil in your sight I have done.

3. Create in me a clean heart, O God, put your steadfast spirit in my soul.
   Cast me not away from your presence, O Lord, and take not your spirit from me.

4. Give back to me the joy of your salvation, let your willing spirit bear me up
   and I shall teach your way to the ones who have wandered,
   and bring them all home to your side.

Text: Psalm 51:3–4, 5–6, 12–13, 14–15; Marty Haugen, © 1983, GIA Publications, Inc.; refrain trans., © 1969, ICEL
Music: Marty Haugen, © 1983, GIA Publications, Inc.

Psalm 51: Be Merciful, O Lord 61

Refrain

Be mer - ci - ful, O Lord; be mer - ci - ful, O Lord. Be

mer - ci - ful, O Lord, for we have sinned.

Verses

1. Have mercy on me, God, in your kindness.
   In your compassion blot out my offense.
   O wash me more and more from my guilt
   and cleanse me from my sin.

2. My offenses truly I know them;
   my sin is always before me.
   Against you, you alone, have I sinned;
   what is evil in your sight I have done.

3. A pure heart create for me, O God,
   put a steadfast spirit within me.
   Do not cast me away from your presence,
   nor deprive me of your holy spirit.

4. Give me again the joy of your help;
   with a spirit of fervor sustain me.
   O Lord, open my lips
   and my mouth shall declare your praise.

Text: Psalm 51:3–4, 5–6a, 12–13, 14 and 17; The Grail, © 1986, The Grail, GIA Publications, Inc., agent; refrain trans., © 1969, ICEL
Music: Michael Joncas, © 1989, GIA Publications, Inc.

62 Psalm 51: Have Mercy, Lord

Antiphon I

Have mer - cy, Lord, cleanse me from all my sins.

Text: Psalm 51; The Grail
Music: Joseph Gelineau, SJ
© 1963, 1993, The Grail, GIA Publications, Inc., agent

Antiphon II

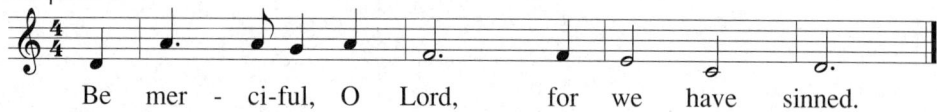

Be mer - ci-ful, O Lord, for we have sinned.

Text: *Lectionary for Mass*, © 1969, 1981, 1997, ICEL
Music: Patricia Craig, © 1975, GIA Publications, Inc.

Antiphon III

Lord, if you will, you can make me clean.

Text: A. Gregory Murray, OSB
Music: A. Gregory Murray, OSB
© 1963, The Grail, GIA Publications, Inc., agent

Antiphon IV

Give back to me the joy of your sal - va - tion.

Text: *Rite of Penance*, © 1975, ICEL
Music: Howard Hughes, SM, © 1975, GIA Publications, Inc.

Psalm Tone

Repeat for 5-line stanzas
Repeat for 6-line stanzas

Music: Chrysogonus Waddell, OCSO, © Gethsemani Abbey

Gelineau Tone
4 and 5 lines

Repeat for vs. 16ab   Repeat for vss. 19ab and 21ab

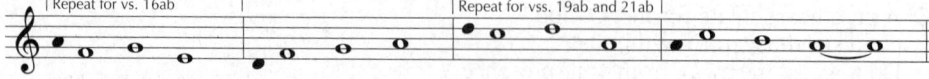

6 lines

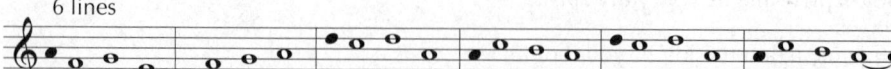

Music: Joseph Gelineau, SJ, © 1963, 1993, The Grail, GIA Publications, Inc., agent

Miserere mei Deus

³ Have **mercy** on **mè, O God,**
   ac**cord**ing to your **mer**cif**úl love;**
   ac**cord**ing to your **great** cò**mpas**sion,
   blot out **my** tráns**gres**sions.
⁴ O **wash** me com**plete**ly from m**y guilt,**
   and **cleanse** me **from** m**ý sin.**

⁵ My trans**gres**sions, **trul**ỳ I **know** them;
   my **sin** is **al**ways bé**fore** me.
⁶ Against **you,** you a**lone,** have **Ì sinned;**
   what is **e**vil in your **sight** I **háve done.**
   So **you** are **just** in yòur **sen**tence,
   with**out** re**proach** in yóur **judg**ment.

⁷ Be**hold,** in **guilt Ì** was **born,**
   a **sin**ner when my **moth**er cón**ceived** me.
⁸ Behold, you de**light** in sin**cer**ity ò**f heart;**
   in **se**cret you **teach** mé **wis**dom.
⁹ Cleanse me with **hys**sop, and **I** shall
   bè **pure;**
   wash me, and **I** shall be **whit**er thán **snow.**

¹⁰ Let me **hear** re**joic**ìng and **glad**ness,
   that the **bones** you have **crushed** may
   é**xult.**
¹¹ **Turn** away your **face** from m**y sins,**
   and **blot** out **all** mý **guilt.**

¹² Cre**ate** a pure **heart** for **mè, O God;**
   renew a **stead**fast **spir**it w**íth**in me.
¹³ Do not **cast** me a**way** from yòur
   presence;
   take not your **ho**ly **spir**it fróm **me.**

¹⁴ Re**store** in me the **joy** of yòur
   sal**va**tion;
   sus**tain** in me a **will**íng **spir**it.
¹⁵ I will **teach** trans**gres**sors yòur **ways,**
   that **sin**ners may re**turn** tó **you.**

¹⁶ **Res**cue me from **blood**shèd, **O God,**
   O God of **my** sál**va**tion,
   and then my **tongue** shall ring **out**
   yòur **right**eousness.
¹⁷ O **LORD,** o**pen** m**y lips**
   and my **mouth** shall pro**claim** yóur
   praise.

¹⁸ For in **sac**rifice you **take** nò de**light;**
   burnt **off**ering from **me** would nót
   please you.
¹⁹ My **sac**rifice to **God,** a brokèn **spir**it:
   a **brok**en and **hum**blèd **heart,**
   you **will** not **spurn, Ó God.**

²⁰ In your good **pleas**ure, show **favò**r to
   Zion;
   re**build** the **walls** of Jéru**sa**lem.
²¹ **Then** you will de**light** in rightèous
   sacrifice,
   burnt **off**erings **whol**ly còn**sumed.**
   Then you will be **off**ered young **bulls**
   on yóur **al**tar.

Give **glo**ry to the **Fathèr Al**might**y,**
   to his **Son,** Jesus **Christ** thé **Lord,**
   to the **Spir**it who **dwells** in òur **hearts,**
   both **now** and for**ev**er. Á**men.**

Text: Psalm 51; *The Ecumenical Grail Psalter,* © 2015, Conception Abbey and The Grail, admin. by GIA Publications, Inc.

63 Psalm 63: My Soul Is Thirsting

Refrain

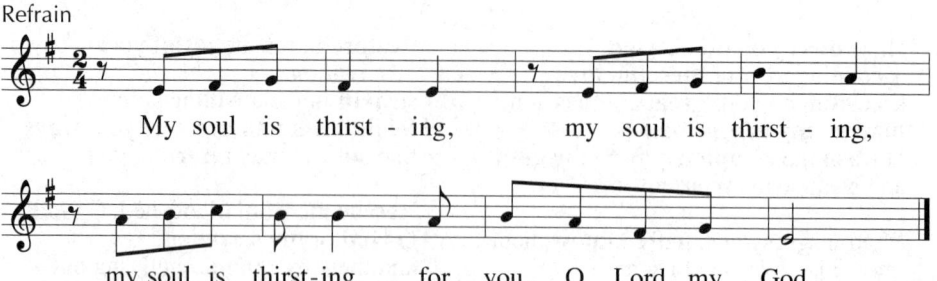

My soul is thirst - ing, my soul is thirst - ing,

my soul is thirst-ing for you, O Lord my God.

Verses

1. O God, you are my God whom I seek;
   O God, you are my God whom I seek;
   for you my flesh pines, my soul thirsts like the earth,
   parched, lifeless, without water.

2. Thus have I gazed toward you in your holy place
   to see your power and your glory.
   Your kindness is a greater good than life itself;
   my lips will glorify you.

3. Thus will I bless you while I live;
   Lifting up my hands I will call upon your name.
   As with a banquet shall my soul be satisfied;
   with exultant lips my mouth shall praise you.

4. For you have been my help, you have been my help;
   in the shadow of your wings I shout for joy.
   My soul clings fast to you; your right hand holds me firm;
   in the shadow of your wings I sing for joy.

Text: Psalm 63:2, 3–4, 5–6, 8–9; verses adapt. © 1970, Confraternity of Christian Doctrine, Inc.; refrain by Michael Joncas, © 1987,
   GIA Publications, Inc.
Music: Michael Joncas, © 1987, GIA Publications, Inc.

Psalm 63: As Morning Breaks 64

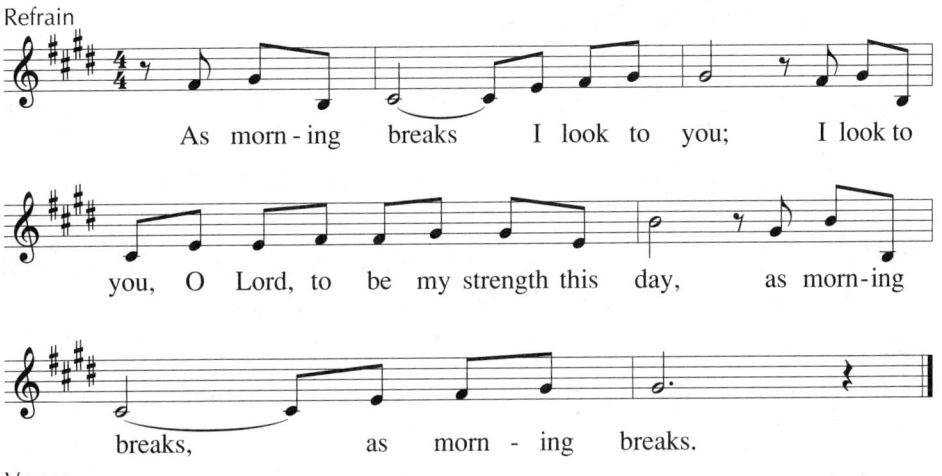

Refrain

As morn-ing breaks I look to you; I look to you, O Lord, to be my strength this day, as morn-ing breaks, as morn-ing breaks.

Verses

1. O God, you are my God, for you I long; for you my soul is thirsting.
   My body pines for you like a dry, weary land without water.
   So I gaze on you in your holy place to see your strength and your glory.

2. For your love is better than life, my lips will speak your praise.
   So I will bless you all my life, in your name I will lift up my hands.
   My soul shall be filled as with a banquet, my mouth shall praise you with joy.

3. On my bed I remember you. On you I muse through the night
   for you have been my help; in the shadow of your wings I rejoice.
   My soul clings to you; your right hand holds me fast.

4. Glory to the Father, and to the Son, and to the Holy Spirit;
   as it was in the beginning, is now, and will be forever. Amen.

Text: Psalm 63:2–3, 4–6, 7–9; © 1963, 1986, The Grail, GIA Publications, Inc., agent; refrain trans. © 1974, ICEL
Music: Michael Joncas, © 1985, Michael Joncas. Published by OCP.

65 Psalm 63: Mi Alma Está Sedienta / My Soul Is Thirsting

Bilingual Refrain

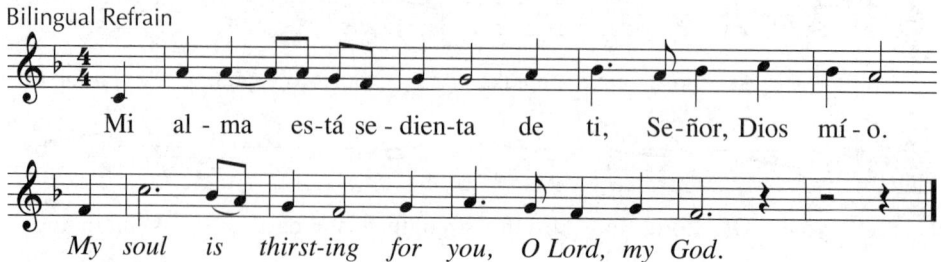

Mi al - ma es-tá se - dien-ta de ti, Se-ñor, Dios mí - o.

My soul is thirst-ing for you, O Lord, my God.

Estrofas / Verses

1. Oh Dios, tú eres mi Dios,
   por ti madrugo,
   mi alma está sedienta de ti;
   mi carne tiene ansia de ti, como tierra reseca, agostada, sin agua.

2. Cómo te contemplaba en el santuario
   viendo tu fuerza y tu gloria.
   Tu gracia vale más que la vida,
   te alabarán mis labios.

3. Toda mi vida te bendeciré y alzaré las manos invocándote.
   Me saciaré como de enjundia y de manteca,
   y mis labios te alabarán jubilosos.

4. Porque fuiste mi auxilio,
   y a la sombra de tus alas canto con júbilo;
   mi alma está unida a ti,
   y tu diestra me sostiene, me sostiene.

1. *O God, you are my God,*
   for you I long;
   for you my soul is thirsting.
   My body pines for you like a dry, weary land without water.

2. *So I gaze on you in the sanctuary*
   to see your strength and your glory.
   For your love is better than life,
   my lips will speak your praise, speak your praise.

3. *So I will bless you all my life,*
   in your name I will lift up my hands.
   My soul shall be filled as with a banquet,
   my mouth shall praise you with joy.

4. *For you have been my help;*
   in the shadow of your wings I rejoice.
   My soul clings to you;
   your right hand holds me fast, holds me fast!

Text: Psalm 63:2, 3–4, 5–6, 8–9; *Leccionario, Edición Hispanoamerérica*, © 1970, 1972, Conferencia Episcopal Española;
English tr., The Grail, © 1963, 1993, The Grail, GIA Publications, Inc., agent
Music: Tony E. Alonso, © 2008, GIA Publications, Inc.

Psalm 67: May God Bless Us in His Mercy   66

Refrain I

May God bless us in his mer - cy.

May God bless us in his mer - cy.

Refrain II

O God, let all the na-tions praise you!   O

God, let all the na - tions praise you!

Verses

1. O God, be gracious and bless us
   and let your face shed its light upon us.
   So will your ways be known upon earth
   and all nations learn your salvation.

2. Let the nations be glad and shout for joy,
   with uprightness you rule the peoples;
   you guide the nations, the nations on earth,
   you guide the nations on earth.

3. Let the peoples praise you, O God;
   let all the peoples praise you.
   May God still give us his blessing
   that all the ends of the earth may revere him.

Text: Psalm 67:2–3, 5, 6 and 8; *The Revised Grail Psalms,* © 2010, Conception Abbey and The Grail, admin. by GIA Publications, Inc.;
refrain trans., © 1969, ICEL
Music: Tony E. Alonso, © 2012, GIA Publications, Inc.

67 Psalm 71: I Will Sing of Your Salvation

Refrain I

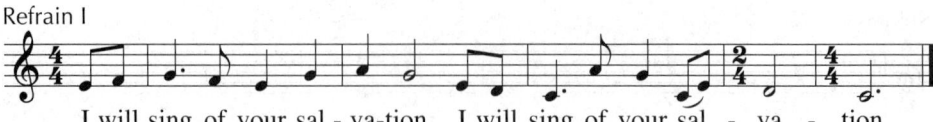

I will sing of your sal - va-tion. I will sing of your sal - va - tion.

Refrain II

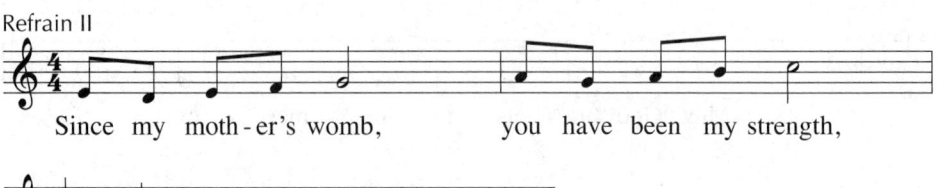

Since my moth - er's womb, you have been my strength,

you have been my strength.

Verses

1. In you, O LORD, I take refuge;
   let me never be put to shame.
   In your justice, rescue me, free me;
   incline your ear to me and save me.

2. Be my rock, my constant refuge,
   a mighty stronghold to save me,
   for you are my rock, my stronghold.
   My God, free me from the hand of the wicked.

3. It is you, O LORD, who are my hope,
   my trust, O LORD, from my youth.
   On you I have leaned from my birth;
   from my mother's womb, you have been my help.

4. My mouth will tell of your justice,
   and all the day long of your salvation.
   O God, you have taught me from my youth,
   and I proclaim your wonders still.

Text: Psalm 71:1–2, 3–4a, 5–6ab, 15ab and 17; *The Revised Grail Psalms*, © 2010, Conception Abbey and The Grail, admin. by GIA Publications, Inc.;
refrains trans., © 1969, ICEL
Music: Tony E. Alonso, © 2012, GIA Publications, Inc.

68 Psalm 72: Every Nation on Earth

Refrain I

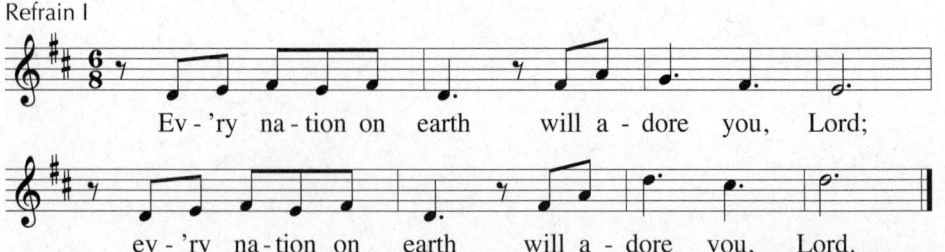

Ev - 'ry na - tion on earth will a - dore you, Lord;

ev - 'ry na - tion on earth will a - dore you, Lord.

Refrain II

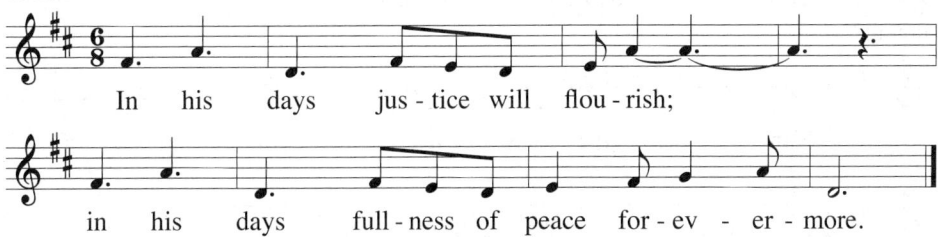

In his days jus - tice will flou - rish;

in his days full - ness of peace for - ev - er - more.

Verses

1. O God, with your judgment endow the king; with your justice endow the
king's son.
With justice he will govern your people, your afflicted ones with right judgment.

2. Justice shall flow'r in his days, lasting peace 'til the moon be no more.
May he rule from sea to sea, from the river to the ends of the earth.

3. The kings of Tarshish and the Isles offer gifts, those from Seba and Arabia bring
tribute.
All kings shall pay him their homage, all nations shall serve him.

4. He rescues the poor when they cry out, the afflicted with no one to help.
The lowly and poor he shall pity, the lives of the poor he will save.

Text: Psalm 72:1–2, 7–8, 10–11, 12–13; Michael Joncas
Music: Michael Joncas
© 1987, 1994, GIA Publications, Inc.

Psalm 80: Lord, Make Us Turn to You   69

Refrain

Lord, make us turn to you, Lord, make us turn to you;

let us see your face and we shall be saved.

Verses

1. O shepherd of Israel, hear us,
enthroned on the cherubim, shine forth.
Rouse up your might and come to save us.

2. God of hosts, turn again, we implore; look down from heaven and see.
Visit this vine and protect it, the vine your right hand has planted,
the son of man you have claimed for yourself.

3. May your hand be on the man at your right hand,
the son of man you have confirmed as your own.
And we shall never forsake you again;
give us life that we may call upon your name.

Text: Psalm 80:2ac and 3b, 15–16, 18–19; The Revised Grail Psalms, © 2010, Conception Abbey and The Grail, admin. by GIA Publications, Inc.;
refrain trans., © 1969, ICEL
Music: Marty Haugen, © 2012, GIA Publications, Inc.

70 Psalm 84: Happy Are They

Refrain*

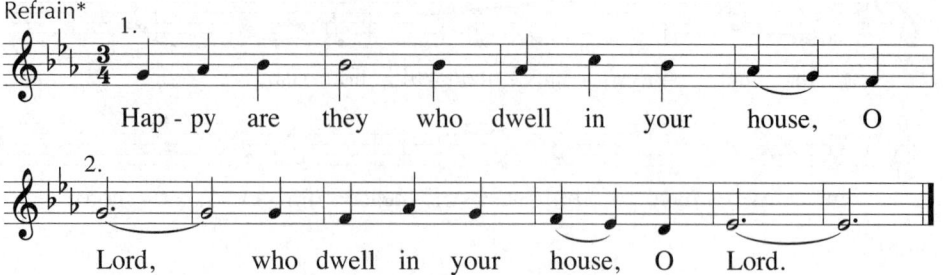

Hap-py are they who dwell in your house, O
Lord, who dwell in your house, O Lord.

Verses

1. My soul yearns and pines for the courts of the Lord.
   My heart and my flesh cry to the living God.

2. The sparrow finds a home and the swallow a nest;
   Your altars, O Lord, my King and my God.

3. Happy are they who abide in your house.
   You are their strength, your praises they will sing.

May be sung as a canon.

Text: Psalm 84:2, 3, 4, 5–6; Thomas J. Porter
Music: Thomas J. Porter
© 1987, GIA Publications, Inc.

71 Psalm 85: Lord, Let Us See Your Kindness

Refrain

Lord, let us see your kind-ness;
Lord, let us see your kind-ness.

Verses

1. Let us hear what our God proclaims: Peace to the people of God,
   salvation is near to the ones who fear God.

2. Kindness and truth, justice and peace;
   truth shall spring up as the water from the earth,
   justice shall rain from the heavens.

3. The Lord will come and you shall know his love,
   justice shall walk in his pathways, salvation the gift that he brings.

Text: Psalm 85:9–10, 11–12, 13–14; Marty Haugen, © 1983, GIA Publications, Inc.; refrain trans. © 1969, ICEL
Music: Marty Haugen, © 1983, GIA Publications, Inc.

Refrain

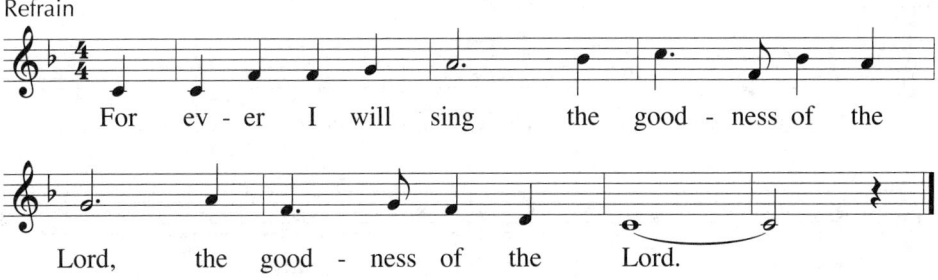

For ev - er I will sing the good - ness of the
Lord, the good - ness of the Lord.

Verses

1. "With my chosen one I have made a covenant; I have sworn to David my servant:
   I will establish your dynasty forever and set up your throne through all ages."

2. Happy the people who acclaim such a God,
   who walk, O Lord, in the light of your face,
   who find their joy ev'ry day in your name,
   who make your justice the source of their bliss.

3. He will say to me: "You are my father, my God, the rock who saves me!"
   I will keep my love for him always; with him my covenant shall last.

Alternate Verses

1. I have found David my servant,
   with my holy oil I have anointed him,
   that my hand may ever be with him
   and my arm make him strong.

2. My faithfulness and love shall be with you,
   in my Name your name will be exalted.

3. He shall cry to me, "My God, my rock of salvation, my salvation."

Text: Psalm 89: 4–5, 16–17, 27–29, © 1963, 1993, The Grail, GIA Publications, Inc., agent; alt. verses 21–22, 25, 27, Marty Haugen, © 1988, 1994,
    GIA Publications, Inc.; refrain trans. © 1969, ICEL
Music: Marty Haugen, © 1988, 1994, GIA Publications, Inc.

73 Psalm 90: Fill Us with Your Love, O Lord

Refrain

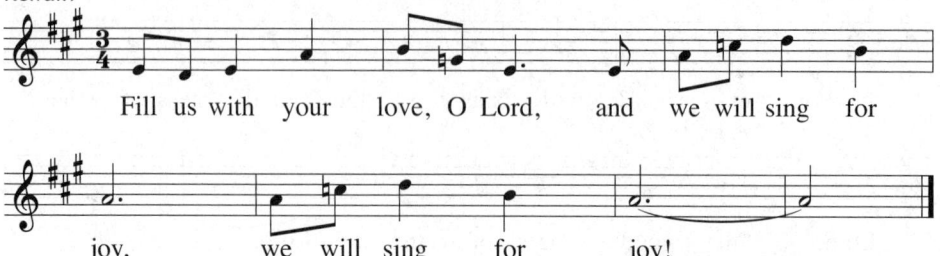

Fill us with your love, O Lord, and we will sing for joy, we will sing for joy!

Verses

1. Teach us to number our days,
   that we may gain wisdom of heart.
   Turn back, O LORD! How long?
   Show pity to your servants.

2. At dawn, fill us with your merciful love;
   we shall exult and rejoice all our days.
   Give us joy for the days of our affliction,
   for the years when we looked upon evil.

3. Let your deed be seen by your servants,
   and your glorious pow'r by their children.
   Let the favor of the LORD our God be upon us;
   give success to the work of our hands.
   O give success to the work of our hands.

Text: Psalm 90:12–13, 14–15, 16–17; *The Revised Grail Psalms,* © 2010, Conception Abbey and The Grail, admin. by GIA Publications, Inc.; refrain trans., © 1969, ICEL
Music: Marty Haugen, © 2012, 2014, GIA Publications, Inc.

74 Psalm 91

Antiphon I

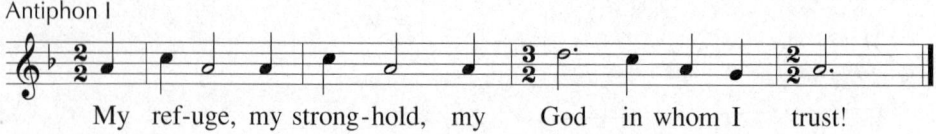

My ref-uge, my strong-hold, my God in whom I trust!

Text: The Grail
Music: A. Gregory Murray, OSB
© 1963, The Grail, GIA Publications, Inc., agent

Antiphon II

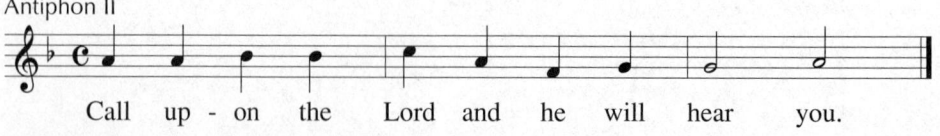

Call up - on the Lord and he will hear you.

Text: The Grail
Music: Joseph Gelineau, SJ
© 1963, The Grail, GIA Publications, Inc., agent

Antiphon III

Night holds no ter-rors for me sleep-ing un-der God's wings.

Text: *Liturgy of the Hours,* © 1974, ICEL
Music: Peter Hallock, acc. by Michael Connolly, © 1986, GIA Publications, Inc.

Psalm Tone

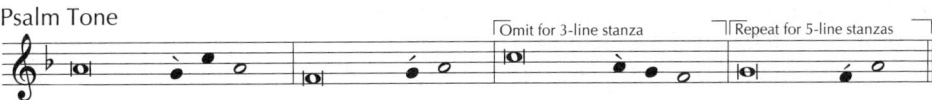

Music: Richard Proulx, © 1986, GIA Publications

Gelineau Tone

Music: Joseph Gelineau, SJ, © 1963, The Grail, GIA Publications, Inc., agent

Qui habitat in adiutorio

¹ You who **dwell** in the Most **High's**
   hìdden **place**,
   and a**bide** in the **shade** of the Ál**mighty**,
² **say** to the **LÒRD**, "My **ref**uge,
   my **strong**hold, my **God** in whom Í
   trust!"

³ The Lord will **free** you from the **snare**
   òf the **fow**ler,
   from the des**truc**tíve **plague**.
⁴ The **pin**ions of **God** wìll con**ceal** you,
   under **wings** of the **Lord** you will fínd
   refuge.
   God's **faith**fulness is **buck**ler ánd **shield**.

⁵ You will not **fear** the **ter**ror òf the **night**,
   nor the **ar**row that **flies** bý **day**,
⁶ nor the **plague** that **prowls** ìn the
   darkness,
   nor the **scourge** that lays **waste** át **noon**.

⁷ A **thous**and may **fall** àt your **side**,
   ten **thous**and **fall** at yóur **right**:
   you it will **nev**er áp**proach**.

⁸ Your **eyes** have onlỳ to **look**
   to **see** how the **wick**ed are ré**paid**.
⁹ For **you**, O **LORD**, àre my **ref**uge.
   You have **made** the Most **High** yóur
   dwelling.

¹⁰ Upon **you** no **ev**ìl shall **fall**,
   no **plague** ap**proach** yóur **tent**.
¹¹ For **you** has God com**mand**èd the
   angels
   to **keep** you in **all** yóur **ways**.

¹² They shall **bear** you upòn their **hands**,
   lest you **strike** your **foot** against á **stone**.
¹³ On the **lion** and the **vip**er yòu will **tread**,
   and **tram**ple the young **lion** and thé
   serpent.

¹⁴ Since you **cling** to me in **love**, Ì will
   free you,
   pro**tect** you, for you **know** mý **name**.
¹⁵ When you **call** on **me**, Ì will **an**swer
   you;
   I will **be** with **you** in dís**tress**;
   I will de**liv**er you, and **give** yóu **glo**ry.

¹⁶ With **length** of **days** I wìll con**tent**
   you;
   I will **show** you my sav**íng pow**er.
   To the **Fa**ther, the **Son** and Hòly
   Spirit
   give **praise** for **ever**. Á**men**.

Text: Psalm 91; *The Ecumenical Grail Psalter,* © 2015, Conception Abbey and The Grail, admin. by GIA Publications, Inc.

75 Psalm 91: Be with Me, Lord

Refrain

Be with me, Lord, when I am in trou-ble, be with me, Lord, I pray.

Verses

1. You who dwell in the shelter of the Lord, Most High,
   who abide in the shadow of our God,
   say to the Lord: "My refuge and fortress, the God in whom I trust."

2. No evil shall befall you, no pain come near,
   for the angels stand close by your side,
   guarding you always and bearing you gently, watching over your life.

3. Those who cling to the Lord live secure in God's love,
   lifted high, those who trust in God's name,
   call on the Lord, who will never forsake you.
   God will bring you salvation and joy.

Text: Psalm 91:1–2, 10–11, 14–15; Marty Haugen
Music: Marty Haugen
© 1980, GIA Publications, Inc.

76 Psalm 95: If Today You Hear God's Voice

Refrain

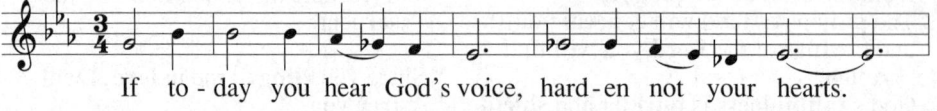

If to-day you hear God's voice, hard-en not your hearts.

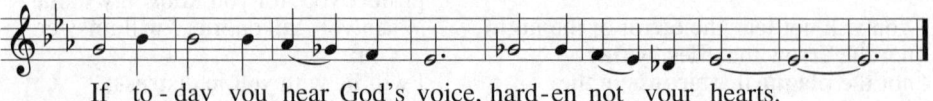

If to-day you hear God's voice, hard-en not your hearts.

Verses

1. Come, ring out our joy to the Lord, hail the rock who saves us,
   let us come now before our God, with songs let us hail the Lord.

2. Come, let us bow and bend low, let us kneel before God who made us,
   for here is our God; we the people, the flock that is led by God's hand.

3. O that today you would hear God's voice, "Harden not your hearts,
   as on that day in the desert, when your parents put me to the test."

Text: Psalm 95:1–2, 6–7, 8–9; David Haas
Music: David Haas
© 1983, 1994, GIA Publications, Inc.

Psalm 95: If Today You Hear His Voice   77

Refrain

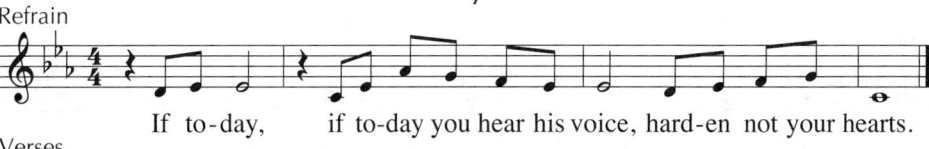

If to-day, if to-day you hear his voice, hard-en not your hearts.

Verses

1. Come, let us ring out our joy to the LORD; hail the rock who saves us.
   Let us come into his presence, giving thanks; let us hail him with a song of praise.

2. O come; let us bow and bend low.
   Let us kneel before the God who made us, for he is our God and we
   the people who belong to his pasture, the flock that is led by his hand.

3. O that today you would listen to his voice!
   "Harden not your hearts as at Meribah, as on that day at Massah in the desert
   when your forebears put me to the test;
   when they tried me, though they saw my work."

Text: Psalm 95:1–2, 6–7, 8–9; *The Revised Grail Psalms,* © 2010, Conception Abbey and The Grail, admin. by GIA Publications, Inc.; refrain trans., © 1969, ICEL
Music: Paul A. Tate, © 2013, GIA Publications, Inc.

Psalm 96: Today Is Born Our Savior   78

Refrain

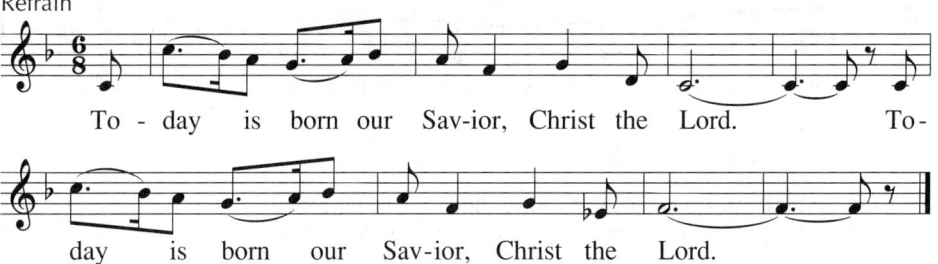

To - day   is   born   our   Sav-ior,   Christ   the   Lord.   To-

day   is   born   our   Sav-ior,   Christ   the   Lord.

Verses

1. Sing to the Lord a new song;
   sing to the Lord, all you lands.
   Sing to the Lord; bless his name.

2. Announce his salvation, day after day.
   Tell his glory among the nations;
   Among all peoples, his wondrous deeds.

3. Let the heavens be glad and the earth rejoice;
   let the sea and what fills it resound;
   let the plains be joyful and all that is in them!
   Then shall all the trees of the forest exult.

4. They shall exult before the Lord, for he comes;
   for he comes to rule the earth.
   He shall rule the world with justice
   and the peoples with his constancy.

Text: Psalm 96; verses trans., © 1970, Confraternity of Christian Doctrine, Inc.; refrain trans., © 1969, ICEL
Music: Howard Hughes, SM, © 1976, GIA Publications, Inc.

79   Psalm 96: Proclaim to All the Nations

Refrain I

Pro - claim   to   all   the   na - tions   the
mar - vel-ous deeds of the   Lord!   Pro - claim   to   all   the
na - tions   the   mar - vel-ous deeds of   the Lord!

Refrain II

Give   the Lord   glo - ry and   hon - or.

Give   the Lord   glo - ry   and   hon - or.

Verses

1. Sing to the Lord a new song. Sing to the Lord all you lands!
   Sing to the Lord with all your heart, and bless God's name!

2. Announce salvation day by day, God's glory throughout the earth!
   Among all the people in every land, God's wondrous deeds!

3. Give to the Lord, you nations, praise to the Lord of all!
   Sing glory and praise and sing to the name, above all names!

4. Worship the Lord, and tremble, proclaim the one who reigns!
   Say to the nations: "The Lord is King;" who rules with justice!

Text: Psalm 96:1–2, 3, 7–8, 9–10; David Haas, © 1989, GIA Publications, Inc.; refrains trans., © 1969, ICEL
Music: Marty Haugen; refrain I, David Haas; refrain II adapt. by Diana Kodner; © 1989, 1994, GIA Publications, Inc.

Psalm 98: All the Ends of the Earth   80

Refrain I

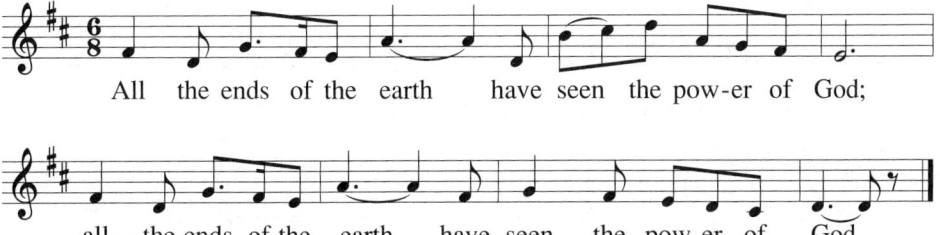

All the ends of the earth have seen the pow-er of God;

all the ends of the earth have seen the pow-er of God.

Refrain II

Sing to the Lord a new song, for God has done won-der-ful deeds.

Sing to the Lord a new song, for God has done won-der-ful deeds.

Refrain III

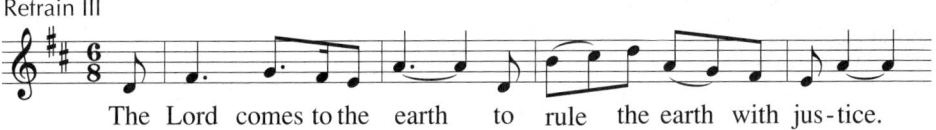

The Lord comes to the earth to rule the earth with jus-tice.

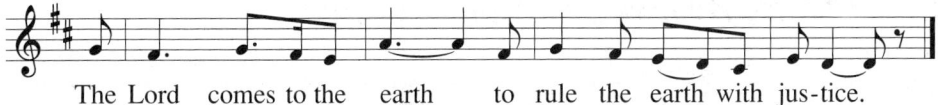

The Lord comes to the earth to rule the earth with jus-tice.

Verses

1. Sing to the Lord a new song, for God has done wondrous deeds;
   whose right hand has won the victory for us, God's holy arm.

2. The Lord has made salvation known, and justice revealed to all,
   remembering kindness and faithfulness to Israel.

3. All of the ends of earth have seen salvation by our God.
   Joyfully sing out all you lands, break forth in song.

4. Sing to the Lord with harp and song, with trumpet and with horn.
   Sing in your joy before the king, the king, our Lord.

Text: Psalm 98:1, 2–3, 3–4, 5–6; David Haas, Marty Haugen
Music: David Haas, Marty Haugen; refrain II, III adapt. by Diana Kodner
© 1983, 1994, GIA Publications, Inc.

81 Psalm 100: We Are God's People

Ostinato Refrain

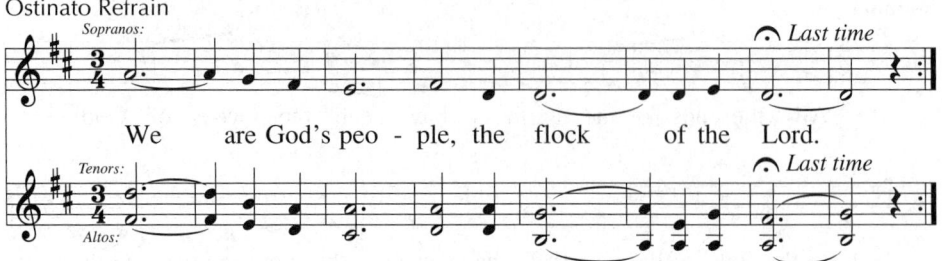

We are God's peo - ple, the flock of the Lord.

Verses

1. Cry out with joy to the Lord, all you lands, all you lands.
   Serve the Lord now with gladness, come before God singing for joy!

2. Know that the Lord is God! Know that the Lord is God,
   who made us, to God we belong, God's people, the sheep of the flock!

3. Go, now within the gates giving thanks, giving thanks.
   Enter the courts singing praise, give thanks and bless God's name!

4. Indeed, how good is the Lord, whose mercy endures for ever,
   for the Lord is faithful, is faithful from age to age!

Text: Psalm 100:1–2, 3, 4, 5; David Haas
Music: David Haas
© 1983, GIA Publications, Inc.

82 Psalm 100: We Are His People

Refrain

We are his peo - ple, the sheep of his flock.

We are his peo - ple, the sheep of his flock.

Verses

1. Cry out with joy to the LORD, all the earth. Serve the LORD with gladness.
   Come before him, singing for joy, come before him, singing for joy.

2. Know that he, the LORD, is God. He made us; we belong to him.
   We are his people, the sheep of his flock, his people, the sheep of his flock.

3. Indeed, how good, how good is the LORD, eternal his merciful love.
   He is faithful from age to age, he is faithful from age to age.

Text: Psalm 100:1–2, 3, 5; *The Revised Grail Psalms,* © 2010, Conception Abbey and The Grail, admin. by GIA Publications, Inc.;
   refrain trans., © 1969, ICEL
Music: Tony E. Alonso, © 2012, GIA Publications, Inc.

Psalm 100   83

Antiphon I

A - rise, come to your God, sing him your songs of re - joic - ing.

Text: Joseph Gelineau, SJ
Music: Joseph Gelineau, SJ
© 1963, The Grail, GIA Publications, Inc., agent

Antiphon II

Al - le - lu - ia,   al - le - lu - ia,   al - le - lu - ia.

Music: A. Gregory Murray, OSB, © 1963, The Grail, GIA Publications, Inc., agent

Conception Abbey Tone

Music: Gregory J. Polan, OSB, © 2010, Conception Abbey, admin. by GIA Publications, Inc.

Gelineau Tone

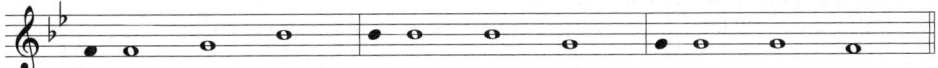

Music: Joseph Gelineau, SJ, © 1963, The Grail, GIA Publications, Inc., agent

Jubilate Deo

Cry out with **joy** to the **LORD**, all thè **earth.**
[2] **Serve** the **LORD** wíth **glad**ness.
Come be**fore** God, **sing**ing fòr **joy.**

[3] **Know** that the **LORD** ìs **God,**
who **made** us, to **whom** we bélong.
We are God's **peo**ple, the **sheep** of Gòd's **flock.**

[4] Enter the **tem**ple **gates** with thànks**giv**ing
and its **courts** with **songs** óf **praise.**
Give **thanks** and **bless** Gòd's **name.**

[5] **Indeed**, how **good** is thè **LORD,**
eter**nal** God's **mer**cifúl **love.**
God is **faith**ful from **age** tò **age.**

Give **praise** to the **Father** Àl**might**y,
to his **Son**, Jesus **Christ** thé **Lord,**
to the **Spir**it who **dwells** in òur **hearts.**

Text: Psalm 100; *The Ecumenical Grail Psalter,* © 2015, Conception Abbey and The Grail, admin. by GIA Publications, Inc.

84 Psalm 103: The Lord Is Kind and Merciful

Refrain

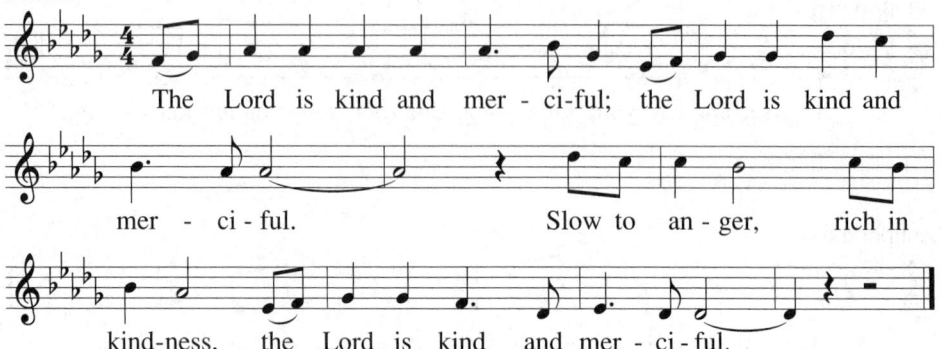

The Lord is kind and mer-ci-ful; the Lord is kind and mer-ci-ful. Slow to an-ger, rich in kind-ness, the Lord is kind and mer-ci-ful.

Verses

1. Bless the Lord, O my soul; all my being bless God's name.
   Bless the Lord, O my soul; forget not all God's blessings.

2. The Lord is gracious and merciful, slow to anger, full of kindness.
   God is good to all creation, full of compassion.

3. The goodness of God is from age to age,
   blessing those who choose to love.
   And justice toward God's children; on all who keep the covenant.

Text: Psalm 103; Jeanne Cotter
Music: Jeanne Cotter
© 1993, GIA Publications, Inc.

85 Psalm 103

Antiphon I

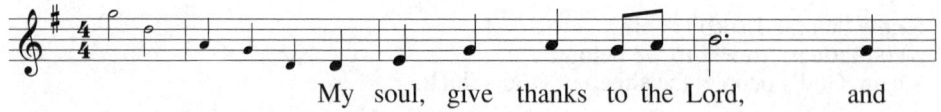

My soul, give thanks to the Lord, and bless God's ho-ly name.

Text: Psalm 103:1; © 1963, 1993, The Grail, GIA Publications, Inc., agent
Music: Richard Proulx, © 1975, GIA Publications, Inc.

Antiphon II

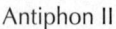

The Lord is kind and mer-ci-ful.

Text: *Lectionary for Mass*, © 1969, 1981, 1997, ICEL
Music: David Haas, © 1986, GIA Publications, Inc.

Conception Abbey Tone

Music: Gregory J. Polan, OSB, © 2010, Conception Abbey, admin. by GIA Publications, Inc.

Gelineau Tone

Music: Joseph Gelineau, SJ, © 1963, The Grail, GIA Publications, Inc., agent

Benedic anima mea, et omnia

Bless the **LORD**, O mỳ **soul**,
and all with**in** me, the **ho**ly name óf
God.
2 **Bless** the **LORD**, O mỳ **soul**,
and **never** for**get** all Gód's **ben**efits.

3 It is the **LORD** who for**gives** all yòur
sins,
who **heals** every **one** of yóur **ills**,
4 who re**deems** your **life** from thè **grave**,
who **crowns** you with **love** and
cóm**pas**sion,
5 who **fills** your **life** with gòod **things**,
re**new**ing your **youth** like án **eag**le's.

6 The **LORD** does **right**èous **deeds**,
gives full **jus**tice to **all** who are
óp**pressed**.
7 The Lord made **known** divine **ways** tò
Moses,
and wondrous **deeds** to the **chil**dren óf
Israel.

8 The **LORD** is com**pas**sionate ànd
gracious,
slow to **an**ger and a**bound**ing ín **love**,
9 not **al**ways find**ìng** **fault**,
nor per**sist**ing in **an**ger fórever.
10 God does not **treat** us ac**cord**ing to
òur **sins**,
nor re**pay** us ac**cord**ing to óur **faults**.

11 For as the **heav**ens are **high** above thè
earth,
so strong the **mer**cy for **those** who
féar **God**.
12 As **far** as the **east** is from thè **west**,
so far from **us** does God re**move** our
tráns**gres**sions.

13 As a **fa**ther has com**pas**sion on hìs
children,
divine com**pas**sion is on **those** who
fear thé **LORD**,
14 who **knows** of **what** we àre **made**,
who re**mem**bers that **we** áre **dust**.

15 Human **be**ings, their **days** are lìke **grass**;
they **flow**er like the **flow**er of thé **field**.
16 The wind **blows**, and it **is** nò **more**,
and its **place** never **sees** it **a**gain.

17 But the **love** of the **LORD** is evèr**last**ing
upon **those** who re**vere** godlý **ways**,
upon **chil**dren's **chil**dren divìne
righteousness
18 for **those** who **keep** thé **cov**enant,
and re**mem**ber to ful**fill** its cóm**mands**.

19 The **LORD** has **fixed** a **throne** ìn **heav**en,
and God's **king**dom is **rul**ing ovér **all**.
20 Bless the **LORD**, all you **an**gels òf
heaven,
mighty in **pow**er, ful**fill**ing Gód's **word**,
who **heed** the **voice** of Gód's **word**.

21 **Bless** the **LORD**, all yòu **hosts**,
you **ser**vants, who **do** Gód's **will**.
22 **Bless** the **LORD**, all yòu **crea**tures,
in **every** **place** of God's dó**main**.
Bless the **LORD**, O mý **soul**!

Give **praise** to the Father Àl**might**y,
to his **Son**, Jesus **Christ** thé **Lord**,
to the **Spir**it who **dwells** in òur **hearts**,
both **now** and for **ever**. Á**men**.

Text: Psalm 103; *The Ecumenical Grail Psalter*, © 2015, Conception Abbey and The Grail, admin. by GIA Publications, Inc.

86 Psalm 104: Lord, Send Out Your Spirit

Refrain*

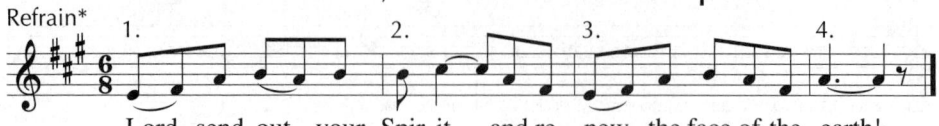

Lord, send out your Spir-it, and re - new the face of the earth!

Verses

1. Bless the Lord, O my soul; O Lord, my God, you are great indeed!
   How manifold are your works, O Lord! The earth is full of your creatures!

2. If you take away their breath, they die and they return to their dust.
   When you send forth your Spirit of life, they are created in your sight!

3. May his glory last for all time; may the Lord be glad in his works.
   Pleasing to him will be my theme; I will be glad in the Lord!

May be sung as a canon.

Text: Psalm 104:1, 24, 29–30, 31, 34; Paul Lisicky, © 1985, GIA Publications, Inc.; refrain trans. © 1969, ICEL
Music: Paul Lisicky, © 1985, GIA Publications, Inc.

87 Psalm 104: Lord, Send Out Your Spirit on Us

Refrain

Lord, send out your Spir-it on us; re-new the face of the earth.

Verses

1. Bless the LORD, O my soul!
   O LORD my God, how great you are!
   How many are your works, O LORD!
   The earth is full of your creatures.

2. You take away their breath, they die,
   returning to the dust from which they came.
   You send forth your Spirit, and they are created,
   and you renew the face of the earth.

3. May the glory of the LORD last forever!
   May the LORD rejoice in his works!
   May my thoughts be pleasing to him.
   I will rejoice in the LORD.

Text: Psalm 104:1, 24, 29–30, 31, 34; *The Revised Grail Psalms,* © 2010, Conception Abbey and The Grail, admin. GIA Publications, Inc.
Tune: James J. Chepponis, © 1994, 2011, GIA Publications, Inc.

Psalm 104: Send Forth Your Spirit 88

Text: Psalm 104; Marty Haugen
Music: Marty Haugen
© 2007, GIA Publications, Inc.

Refrain*

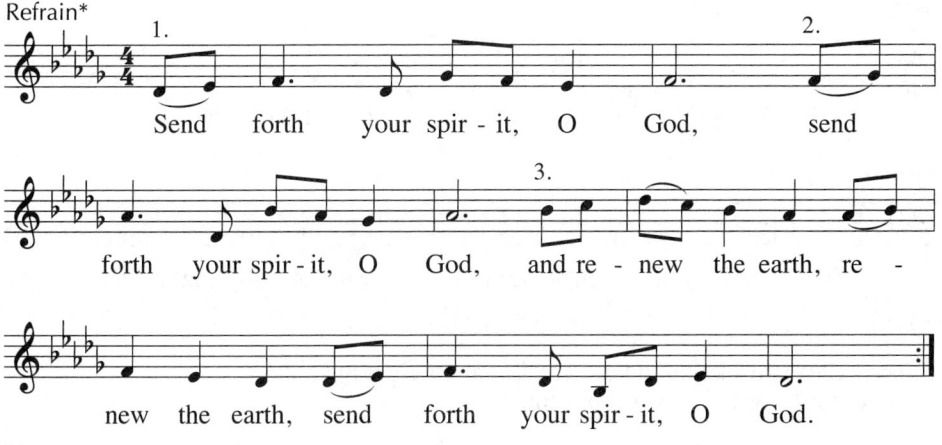

Send forth your spir - it, O God, send
forth your spir - it, O God, and re - new the earth, re -
new the earth, send forth your spir - it, O God.

Verses

1. Bless the Lord, O my soul. O God, you are great indeed!
   You are clothed in majesty and splendor, and adorned in a robe of light.

2. You spread the heavens out like a tent, you set your palace on the waters above.
   You have fashioned the clouds as your chariot and you ride upon the wings of
   the wind.

3. You have fixed the earth on its foundation and the seas that clothe it like a
   garment.
   At the sound of your voice they rush and tumble; you have marked the bound'ries
   of their breadth.

4. You make springs break forth in the valleys, giving drink to the beasts of the field,
   birds that sing from the trees by living waters, rains from heaven's height that
   nourish the earth.

5. You give plants for the life of your creatures, food for strength, wine for joy,
   oil for gladness;
   mighty trees, the cedars of Lebanon, where the birds and storks shall make
   their home.

6. You have made the moon to mark the seasons, told the sun when to rise and
   when to set.
   You make night for the creatures of the forest, they seek food from the hand of
   their God.

7. O God, how countless are your works! By your wisdom you fashioned them all.
   All the earth is filled with your creatures, oceans teem with the life you made.

May be sung in canon.

89 Psalm 110: You Are a Priest for Ever

Refrain I

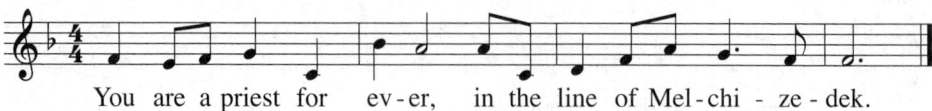

You are a priest for ev-er, in the line of Mel-chi - ze - dek.

Refrain II

The Lord said to my lord: "Sit at my right hand."

Verses

1. The LORD's revelation to my lord: "Sit at my right hand,
   until I make your foes your footstool."

2. The LORD will send from Sion your scepter of pow'r:
   rule in the midst of your foes.

3. With you is princely rule on the day of your pow'r.
   In holy splendor, from the womb before the dawn, I have begotten you.

4. The LORD has sworn an oath he will not change:
   "You are a priest forever, in the line of Melchizedek."

Text: Psalm 110:1, 2, 3, 4; *The Revised Grail Psalms*, © 2010, Conception Abbey and The Grail, admin. by GIA Publications, Inc.;
refrains trans., © 1969, ICEL
Music: Tony E. Alonso, © 2012, 2016, GIA Publications, Inc.

90 Psalm 116: Our Blessing-Cup / El Cáliz que Bendecimos

Bilingual Refrain

Our bless-ing - cup is a com-mun - ion with the

Blood of Christ the Lord. El cá -liz que ben-de-

ci-mos es la co-mu-nión de la san - gre de Cris -to.

Verses / Estrofas

1. How can I repay the Lord the goodness God has shown to me?
   The cup of blessing I raise; I call upon God's name.

2. Painful to the eyes of God, the death of faithful servants.
   I am your servant, your child; you rescued me from death.

3. Thanks and praise I will offer God, and call upon your name, Lord.
   I will fulfill my vows to the Lord in the presence of God's people.

1. *¿Cómo le pagaré al Señor, mi Dios, todo_el bien que me ha hecho?*
   Alzaré la copa de la salvación, e_invocaré el nombre del Señor.

2. *Al Señor, que penosa es la muerte de sus fieles.*
   Soy tu sirviente, tu hijo: rompiste mis cadenas.

3. *Te_ofreceré mis gracias, Dios, invocando tu nombre.*
   Cumpliré mis promesas al Señor en presencia de todo su pueblo.

Text: Psalm 116:12–13, 15–16bc, 17–18; Tony E. Alonso, © 2003, GIA Publications, Inc.; Spanish refrain trans. © 1970, Conferencia Episcopal Española
Music: Tony E. Alonso, © 2003, GIA Publications, Inc.

Psalm 116: The Name of God   91

Refrain I

I will take the cup of life, I will call God's name all my days.

Refrain II

Our bless-ing-cup is a com-mun-ion with the Blood of Christ.

Refrain III

In the land of the liv-ing, I will walk with God all my days.

Verses

1. How can I make a return for the goodness of God?
   This saving cup I will bless and sing, and call the name of God!

2. The dying of those who keep faith is precious to our God.
   I am your servant called from your hands, you have set me free!

3. To you I will offer my thanks and call upon your name.
   You are my promise for all to see. I love your name, O God!

Text: Psalm 116:12–13, 15–16, 17–18; David Haas, © 1987, GIA Publications, Inc.; refrain II trans., © 1969, ICEL
Music: David Haas, © 1987, GIA Publications, Inc.

92 Psalm 116: Our Blessing-Cup

Refrain

Our bless-ing-cup is a com-mun-ion with the Blood of the Lord.

Verses

1. How can I make a return to the Lord for all God has done for me?
The cup of salvation I will take up, I will call on the name of the Lord.

2. Precious, indeed, in the sight of the Lord is the death of the faithful ones;
and I am your servant, your chosen one, for you have set me free.

3. Unto your name I will offer my thanks for the debt that I owe to you.
In the presence of all who have called on your name,
in the courts of the house of the Lord.

Text: Psalm 116:12–13, 15–16, 17–19; Marty Haugen
Music: Marty Haugen
© 1983, GIA Publications, Inc.

93 Psalm 116: I Will Take the Cup of Salvation

Refrain

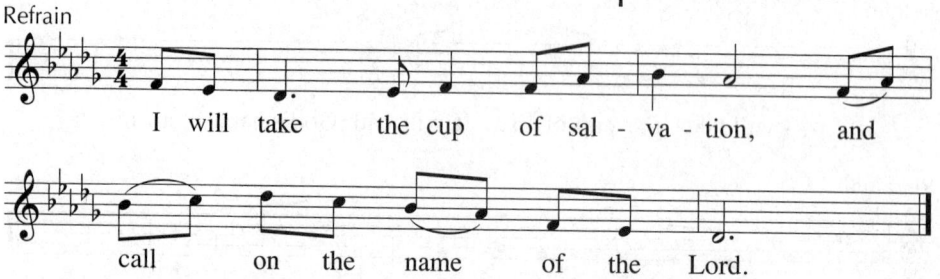

I will take the cup of sal - va - tion, and

call on the name of the Lord.

Verses

1. How can I repay the LORD
for all his goodness to me, for all his goodness to me?
The cup of salvation I will raise;
I will call on the name of the LORD.

2. How precious in the eyes of the LORD
is the death of his faithful, is the death of his faithful.
Your servant am I, the son of your handmaid;
you have loosened my bonds.

3. A thanksgiving sacrifice I make;
I will call on the name, on the name of the LORD.
My vows to the LORD I will fulfill before all his people.

Text: Psalm 116:12–13, 15–16bc, 17–18; The Revised Grail Psalms, © 2010, Conception Abbey and The Grail, admin. by GIA Publications, Inc.;
refrain trans., © 1969, ICEL
Music: Tony E. Alonso, © 2014, GIA Publications, Inc.

Psalm 118: Let Us Rejoice / Éste Es el Día 94

Refrain

[1.]
*This is the day the Lord has made, let us re-
*Al - le - lu - ia,† al - le - lu - ia! Al - le-
Give thanks to the Lord for he is good, his love is

[2.] *To verses*
joice and be glad; let us re-joice and be glad!
lu - ia! Al - le - lu - ia!
ev - er - last - ing. Give love is ev - er - last - ing.

Estribillo

[1.]
És-te es el dí - a que hi-zo el Se - ñor: sea nues-tra a-le-grí-a y

[2.] *A las estrofas*
go - zo. nues-tra a-le-grí-a y go - zo.

Verses / Estrofas

1. Give thanks to the Lord, for God is good; God's mercy endures for ever.
   Let the house of Israel say: "God's mercy endures for ever."

2. The hand of the Lord has struck with power, God's right hand is exalted.
   I shall not die, but live anew, declaring the works of the Lord.

3. The stone which the builders rejected has become the cornerstone.
   The Lord of love and mercy has brought wonder to our eyes!

1. *Den gracias a Dios, el buen Señor, eterna es su misericordia.*
   Diga la casa de Israel: "Eterna es su misericordia."

2. *La diestra de Dios es excelsa, la diestra de Dios es potente.*
   No he de morir, yo viviré; las obras de Dios contaré.

3. *La piedra que fue desechada es ahora la piedra angular.*
   El Señor es quien lo ha hecho, y es un milagro patente.

*For a bilingual refrain, sing the English through the first ending, followed by the Spanish
 with the second ending.*
†Or: ¡Aleluya!

Text: Psalm 118:1–2, 16–17, 22–23, Marty Haugen, © 1983, GIA Publications, Inc.; English refrains trans., © 1969, ICEL; Spanish tr. by
    Ronald F. Krisman, © 2012, GIA Publications, Inc.
Music: Marty Haugen, © 1983, GIA Publications, Inc.

95 Psalm 118: This Is the Day

Refrain

This is the day the Lord has made; let us re-joice and be glad.

Verses

1. Give praise to the LORD, for he is good;
his mercy endures forever.
Let the house of Israel say,
"His mercy endures forever."

2. "The LORD's right hand has done
mighty deeds;
his right hand is exalted."
I shall not die, I shall live
and recount the deeds of the LORD.

3. The stone that the builders rejected
has become the cornerstone.
By the LORD has this been done,
a marvel in our eyes.

Text: Psalm 118:1–2, 16–17, 22–23, *The Revised Grail Psalms,* © 2010, Conception Abbey and The Grail, admin. GIA Publications, Inc.; refrain trans. © 1969, ICEL
Tune: James J. Chepponis, © 1994, 2011, GIA Publications, Inc.

96 Psalm 118: This Is the Day

Refrain

This is the day the Lord has made; let us re-joice and be glad.

This is the day the Lord has made; let us re-joice and be glad.

Verses

1. Give thanks to the LORD for he is good,
his mercy endures for ever;
let the house of Israel say:
"His mercy endures for ever."

2. The LORD's right hand has struck with power,
the LORD's right hand is exalted;
I shall not die, but live
and declare the works of the LORD.

3. The stone which the builders rejected
has become the cornerstone.
By the LORD has this been done;
it is wonderful in our eyes!

Text: Psalm 118:1–2, 16–17, 22–23; © Confraternity of Christian Doctrine, Inc., alt.; refrain trans., © 1969, ICEL
Music: Michael Joncas, © 1988, Jan Michael Joncas Trust. Published by OCP.

Psalm 118: This Is the Day   97

Refrain

This is the day the Lord has made; let us re-joice and be
glad in it! This is the day the Lord has made;
let us be glad, be glad, be glad, be glad and re-joice in it!

Verses

1. Give praise to the LORD, for he is good;
   his mercy endures forever.
   Let the house of Israel say,
   "His mercy endures forever."

2. "The LORD's right hand has done mighty deeds;
   his right hand is exalted."
   I shall not die, I shall live
   and recount the deeds of the LORD.

3. The stone that the builders rejected
   has become the cornerstone.
   By the LORD has this been done,
   a marvel in our eyes.

Text: Psalm 118:1–2, 16–17, 22–23; *The Revised Grail Psalms,* © 2010, Conception Abbey and The Grail, admin. by GIA Publications, Inc.;
refrain trans., © 1969, ICEL
Music: Refrain, Leon C. Roberts, © 1997, GIA Publications, Inc.; verses, Leon C. Roberts, adapt. by Kelly Dobbs Mickus, © 2012, GIA Publications, Inc.

98　Psalm 121: Our Help Comes from the Lord

Refrain

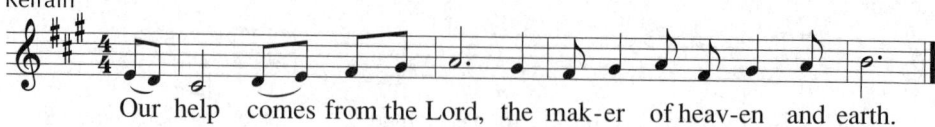

Our help comes from the Lord, the mak-er of heav-en and earth.

Verses

1. I lift up my eyes to the mountains: from where shall come my help?
   My help shall come from the Lord who made heaven and earth.

2. May God never allow you to stumble! Let God sleep not, your guard.
   Neither sleeping nor slumbering, God, Israel's guard.

3. The Lord is your guard and your shade: and at your right side stands,
   By day the sun shall not smite you nor the moon in the night.

4. The Lord will guard you from evil: God will guard your soul.
   The Lord will guard your going and coming both now and for ever.

5. Glory to the Father, and to the Son, and to the Holy Spirit:
   as it was in the beginning, is now, and will be for ever. Amen.

99　Psalm 122: Let Us Go Rejoicing

Refrain

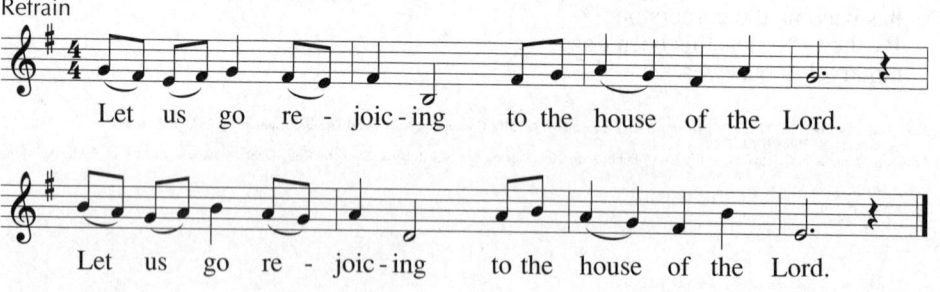

Let us go re-joic-ing to the house of the Lord.

Let us go re-joic-ing to the house of the Lord.

Verses

1. I rejoiced when I heard them say: "Let us go to the house of the Lord,"
   and now our feet are standing within your gates, O Jerusalem.

2. Jerusalem is a city built with unity and strength.
   It is there, it is there that the tribes go up, the tribes of the Lord.

3. For Israel's law is to praise God's name and there to give God thanks.
   There are set the judgment thrones for all of David's house.

4. Pray for the peace of Jerusalem! "May those who love you prosper;
   May peace ever reign within your walls, and wealth within your buildings!"

5. For love of my family and love of my friends, I pray that peace be yours.
   For love of the house of the Lord our God I pray for your good.

Text: Psalm 122; Michael Joncas, © 1987, GIA Publications, Inc.; refrain trans., © 1969, ICEL
Music: Michael Joncas, © 1987, GIA Publications, Inc.

Psalm 122: Let Us Go Rejoicing   100

Refrain

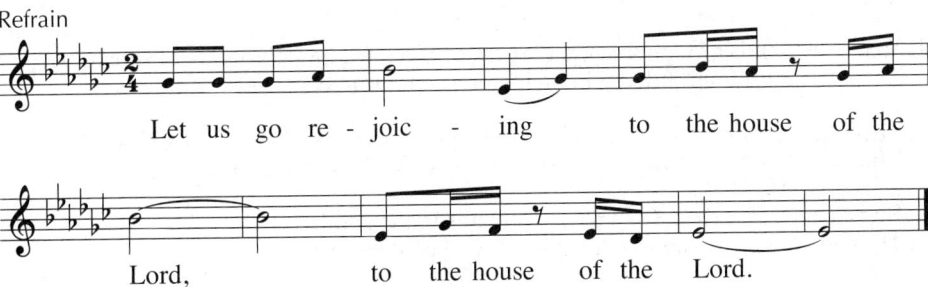

Let us go re - joic - ing to the house of the Lord, to the house of the Lord.

Verses

1. I rejoiced when they said to me,
   "Let us go to the house of the LORD."
   And now our feet are standing
   within your gates, O Jerusalem.

2. Jerusalem is built as a city
   bonded as one together.
   It is there that the tribes go up,
   the tribes of the LORD.

3. For Israel's witness it is
   to praise the name of the LORD.
   There were set the thrones for judgment,
   the thrones of the house of David.

4. For the peace of Jerusalem pray,
   "May they prosper, those who love you."
   May peace abide in your walls,
   and security be in your towers.

5. For the sake of my family and friends,
   let me say, "Peace upon you."
   For the sake of the house of the LORD, our God,
   I will seek good things for you.

Text: Psalm 122:1–2, 3–4ab, 4cd–5, 6–7, 8–9; *The Revised Grail Psalms*, © 2010, Conception Abbey and The Grail, admin. by
   GIA Publications, Inc.; refrain trans., © 1969, ICEL
Music: Refrain, Leon C. Roberts, © 1981, 1997, GIA Publications, Inc.; verses, Stanbrook Abbey, © 1984, Benedictine Sisters
   of Stanbrook Abbey

101 Psalm 126: The Lord Has Done Great Things

Refrain

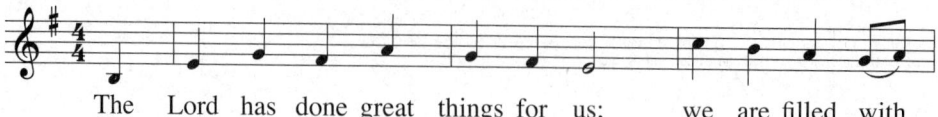

The Lord has done great things for us; we are filled with

joy, we are filled with joy.

Verses

1. When the LORD brought back the exiles of Sion, we thought we were dreaming.
   Then was our mouth filled with laughter; on our tongues, songs of joy.

2. Then the nations themselves said, "What great deeds the LORD worked for them!"
   What great deeds the LORD worked for us! Indeed, we were glad.

3. Bring back our exiles, O LORD, as streams in the south.
   Those who are sowing in tears will sing when they reap.

4. They go out, they go out, full of tears, bearing seed for the sowing;
   they come back, they come back with a song, bearing their sheaves.

Text: Psalm 126:1–2ab, 2cd–3, 4–5, 6; *The Revised Grail Psalms,* © 2010, Conception Abbey and The Grail, admin. by GIA Publications, Inc.;
refrain trans., © 1969, ICEL
Music: Tony E. Alonso, © 2012, GIA Publications, Inc.

102 Psalm 128: Blest Are Those Who Love You

Refrain I

Blest are those who love you, hap - py those who

fol-low you, blest are those who seek you, O God.

Refrain II

May the Lord bless us, may the Lord pro -

tect us, all the days, all the days of our life.

Verses

1. Happy all those who fear the Lord, and walk in God's pathway;
   you will find what you long for: the riches of our God.

2. Your spouse shall be like a fruitful vine in the midst of your home,
   your children flourish like olive plants rejoicing at your table.

3. May the blessings of God be yours all the days of your life,
   may the peace and the love of God live always in your heart.

Text: Psalm 128:1–2, 3, 5; Marty Haugen
Music: Marty Haugen; refrain II adapt. by Diana Kodner
© 1987, 1993, GIA Publications, Inc.

Psalm 128: Blessed Are Those Who Fear the Lord   103

Refrain I (Vss. 1–3)

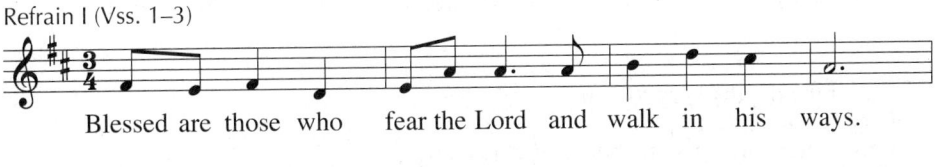

Blessed are those who fear the Lord and walk in his ways.

Blessed are those who fear the Lord and walk in his ways.

Refrain II

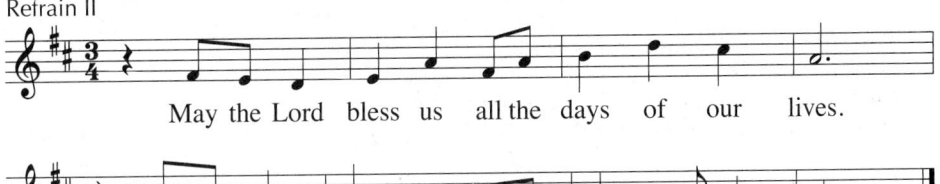

May the Lord bless us all the days of our lives.

May the Lord bless us all the days of our lives.

Verses

1. Blessed are all who fear the LORD, and walk in his ways!
   By the labor of your hands you shall eat.
   You will be blessed and prosper.

2. Your wife like a fruitful vine in the heart of your house;
   your children like shoots of the olive around your table.

3. Indeed thus shall be blessed the man who fears the LORD.
   May the LORD bless you from Sion.
   May you see Jerusalem prosper all the days of your life!

4. May you see your children's children. On Israel, peace!

Text: Psalm 128:1–2, 3, 4–5, 6; *The Revised Grail Psalms*, © 2010, Conception Abbey and The Grail, admin. by GIA Publications, Inc.;
    refrains trans., © 1969, ICEL
Music: Tony E. Alonso, © 2012, 2014, GIA Publications, Inc.

104 Psalm 130: With the Lord There Is Mercy

Refrain

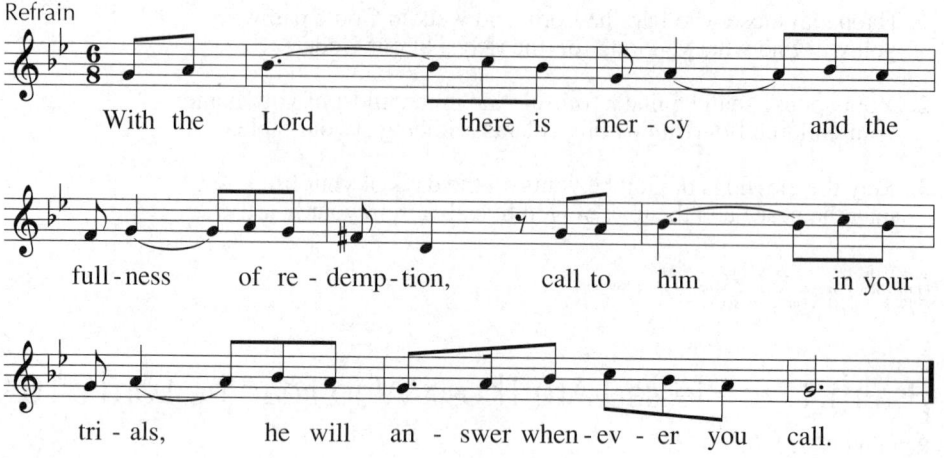

With the Lord there is mer-cy and the full-ness of re-demp-tion, call to him in your tri-als, he will an-swer when-ev-er you call.

Verses

1. Out of the depths I cry to you,
   I cry to you, O Lord.
   Lord, open your ears and hear my voice,
   attend to the sound of my plea.

2. If you, O Lord, should mark our guilt,
   then, Lord, who could hope to survive?
   But with you is found forgiveness of sin,
   and mercy that we might revere you.

3. Trust in the Lord, count on his word,
   wait for the Lord, my soul.
   I will wait for the Lord all the days of my life
   as sentinels wait for the dawn.

4. More than the sentinels wait for the dawn,
   let Israel wait for the Lord.
   For kindness is his, redemption for all,
   forgiveness of sins for his people.

Text: Psalm 130; Michael Joncas
Music: Michael Joncas
© 1983, OCP

Psalm 130: With the Lord There Is Mercy 105

Refrain

With the Lord there is mer-cy, and full-ness of re-demp-tion.

Verses

1. From out of the depths, I cry unto you,
   Lord, hear my voice, come hear my prayer;
   O let your ear be open to my pleading.

2. If you, O Lord, should mark our guilt,
   then who could stand within your sight?
   But in you is found forgiveness for our failings.

3. Just as those who wait for the morning light,
   even more I long for the Lord, my God,
   whose word to me shall ever be my comfort.

Text: Psalm 130:1–2, 3–4, 5–6; Marty Haugen, © 1983, GIA Publications, Inc.; refrain trans. © 1969, ICEL
Music: Marty Haugen, © 1983, GIA Publications, Inc.

Psalm 131: My Soul Is Still 106

Refrain

In you, O Lord, I have found my

peace, I have found my peace.

Verses

1. My heart is not proud, my eyes not above you;
   You fill my soul. I am not filled with great things,
   nor with thoughts beyond me.

2. My soul is still, my soul stays quiet,
   longing for you like a weaned child
   in its mother's arms; so is my soul a child with you.

Text: Psalm 131:1, 2; David Haas, © 1985, GIA Publications, Inc.; refrain trans. © 1969, ICEL
Music: David Haas, © 1985, GIA Publications, Inc.

107   Psalm 137: Let My Tongue Be Silenced

Refrain

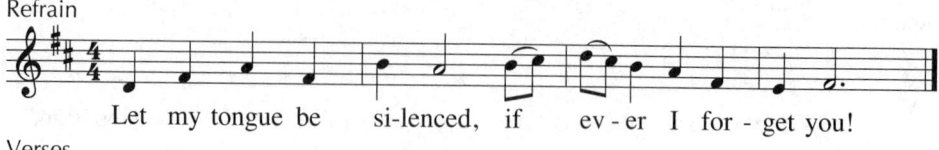

Let my tongue be si-lenced, if ev-er I for-get you!

Verses

1. By the streams of Babylon, we sat and wept rememb'ring Zion.
   On the willows of that land we hung our harps.

2. There our captors asked of us the hymns of Zion.
   Our tormentors cried out, "Sing for us!"

3. How shall we sing God's song in a foreign land?
   If I forget you, Jerusalem, let my right hand be forgotten.

4. Let my tongue be silenced if ever I forget you;
   if I prize not Jerusalem above all joy.

Text: Psalm 137, Jeanne Cotter, © 1989, GIA Publications, Inc.; refrain trans., © 1969, ICEL
Music: Jeanne Cotter, © 1989, GIA Publications, Inc.

108   Psalm 138: Lord, I Thank You

Refrains I, II (Vss. 1–3 or 1–3, 5)

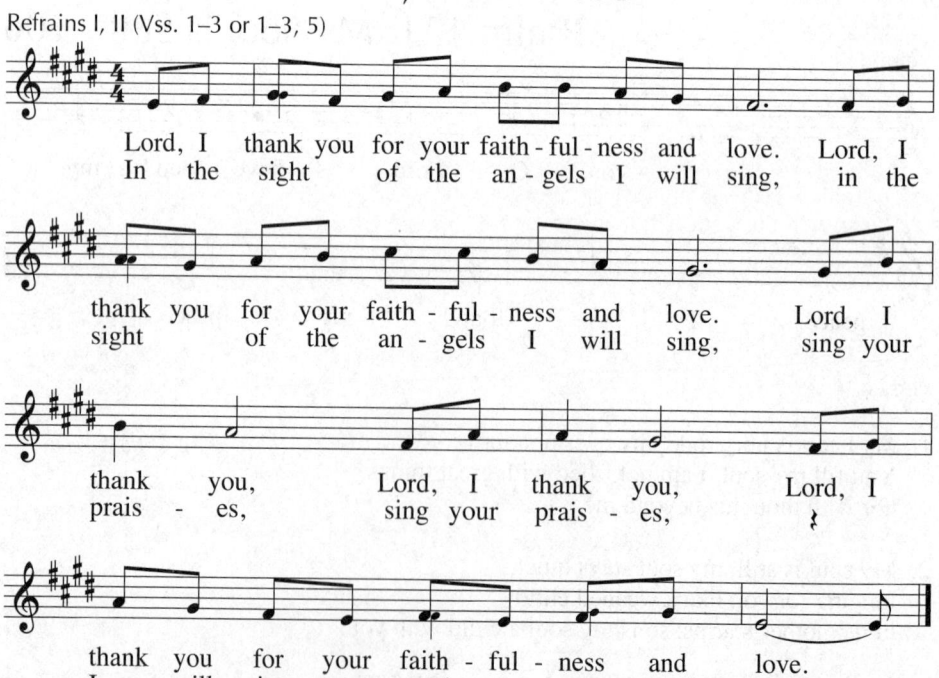

Lord, I thank you for your faith-ful-ness and love. Lord, I
In the sight of the an-gels I will sing, in the

thank you for your faith-ful-ness and love. Lord, I
sight of the an-gels I will sing, Lord, I

thank you, Lord, I thank you, Lord, I
prais-es, sing your prais-es,

thank you for your faith-ful-ness and love.
I will sing your prais-es, Lord.

Refrain III (Vss. 1, 2, 4, 5)

Lord, on the day I called for help, you an - swered me, you an - swered me.

Refrain IV (Vss. 1, 2, 4, 5)

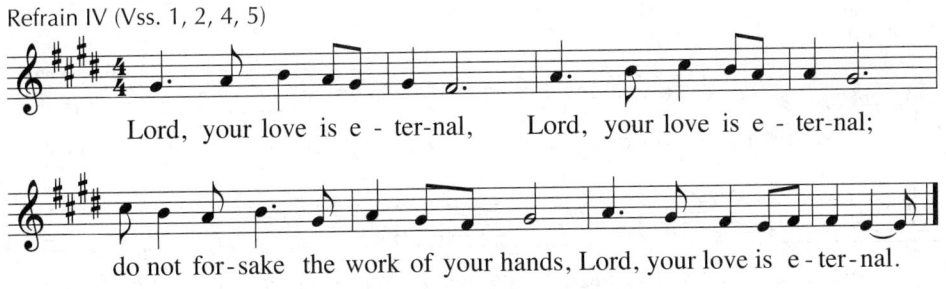

Lord, your love is e - ter-nal, Lord, your love is e - ter-nal; do not for-sake the work of your hands, Lord, your love is e - ter-nal.

Verses

1. I thank you, LORD, with all my heart; you have heard the words of my mouth.
   In the presence of the angels I praise you. I bow down toward your holy temple.

2. I give thanks to your name for your merciful love and your faithfulness.
   On the day I called, you answered me; you increased the strength of my soul.

3. All earth's kings shall thank you, O LORD, when they hear the words of your mouth.
   They shall sing of the ways of the LORD, "How great is the glory of the LORD!"

4. The LORD is high, yet he looks on the lowly, and the haughty he knows from afar.
   You give me life though I walk amid affliction;
   you stretch out your hand against the anger of my foes.

5. With your right hand you save me; the LORD will accomplish this for me.
   O LORD, your merciful love is eternal; discard not the work of your hands.

Text: Psalm 138:1–2a, 2bc and 3, 4–5, 6–7ab, 7c–8; *The Revised Grail Psalms*, © 2010, Conception Abbey and The Grail, admin. by
GIA Publications, Inc.; refrains trans., © 1969, ICEL
Music: Tony E. Alonso, © 2012, 2013, GIA Publications, Inc.

109 Psalm 141: Let My Prayer Rise Up / Suba Mi Oración

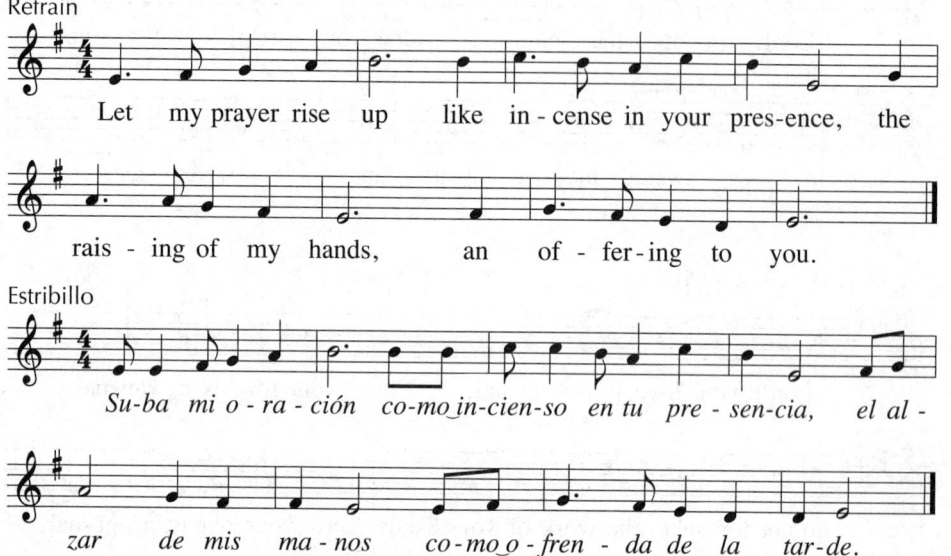

Refrain

Let my prayer rise up like in-cense in your pres-ence, the
rais-ing of my hands, an of-fer-ing to you.

Estribillo

Su-ba mi o-ra-ción co-mo_in-cien-so en tu pre-sen-cia, el alzar de mis ma-nos co-mo_o-fren-da de la tar-de.

Verses / Estrofas

1. I have called to you, O God, come quickly to help me.
   Hear my voice when I call to you.
   Let my prayer rise up like incense before you,
   and my hands like an evening off'ring.

2. Set a guard on my mouth and guide my ev'ry word,
   keep watch on the door of my lips.
   Let me never turn my heart toward evil or revenge,
   nor join the evil in their feasting.

3. When the just correct me, I take their words as kindness,
   but the oil of the wicked will not touch me.
   So I pray to you, O God, I pray to you, O God,
   against their hateful ways.

4. To you, O God, I turn my eyes,
   in you I find refuge and safety.
   From the trap that has been set by those who wish me harm,
   keep me safe, O God.

5. Glory to the Father, glory to the Son,
   and glory to the Holy Spirit.
   As it was in the beginning, is now and ever shall be,
   world without end. Amen.

1. *Señor, te llamo, ven a mí.*
   Escucha mi voz cuando te_invoco.
   Suba mi_oración como_incienso_en tu presencia,
   como_incienso_en tu presencia.

2. *Coloca, Señor, una guardia en mi boca,*
   y vigilia la puerta de mis labios.
   No me dejes inclinarme a la maldad,
   ni comer con los hombres malvados.

3. *Que_el justo me golpee, que_el bueno me reprenda,*
   es un gran favor, oh Señor.
   Pero que_el óleo del impío no perfume mi cabeza;
   seguiré rezando_en sus desgracias.

4. *Mis ojos, Señor, están vueltos a ti.*
   Señor, en ti me refugio.
   Guarda mi vida, líbrame, Señor,
   de la trampa de los malhechores.

5. *Gloria al Padre, gloria al Hijo,*
   y gloria_al Espíritu Santo,
   como era_en el principio, ahora y siempre,
   por los siglos de los siglos. Amén.

Text: Psalm 141, Tony E. Alonso, © 2008, GIA Publications, Inc.; Spanish refrain, *Liturgia de la Horas*, © 1981, Comisión Episcopal
Española de Liturgia
Music: Tony E. Alonso, © 2008, GIA Publications, Inc.

Psalm 141: My Prayers Rise Like Incense 110

Antiphon

My prayers rise like in - cense, my hands like the eve-ning of - f'ring.

Verses

1. I have called to you, LORD; O hasten to help me!
   Hear my voice when I cry to you.
   Let my prayer be as incense before you,
   the raising of my hands like an evening oblation.

2. Set, O LORD, a guard on my mouth;
   keep watch at the door of my lips!
   Do not turn my heart to things that are evil,
   to wicked deeds with those who are sinners.

3. Never allow me to share in their feasting.
   If someone righteous strikes me it is kindness;
   but let the oil of the wicked not anoint my head.
   Let my prayer be ever against their malice.

4. To you my eyes are turned, O LORD, my Lord.
   In you I take refuge; spare my soul!
   Give praise to the Father, the Son and Holy Spirit,
   both now and for ages unending. Amen.

Text: Psalm 141:1–2, 3–4, 4–5, 8; *The Ecumenical Grail Psalter*, © 2015, Conception Abbey and The Grail, admin. by GIA Publications, Inc.
Music: Tonus Peregrinus; acc. by Robert LeBlanc, OSB, © 1986, GIA Publications, Inc.

111 Psalm 141: Let My Prayer Rise Like Incense

Antiphon

Be gracious, O Lord! Let my prayer rise like in-cense,

my hands like an evening sac - ri - fice.

Verses

1. I have called to you, LORD, has - ten to help me!
3. Set, O LORD, a guard o - ver my mouth;
5. Never al - low me to share in their feasting.
7. Their leaders were thrown down by the side of the rock;
9. To you, LORD God, my eyes are turned;
11. Let the wicked fall into the traps they have set

1. Hear my voice when I cry to you.
3. keep watch, O Lord, at the door of my lips!
5. If the upright strike or reprove me it is kind - ness;
7. then they understood that my words were kind.
9. in you I take refuge; spare my soul!
11. whilst I pursue my way un - harmed.

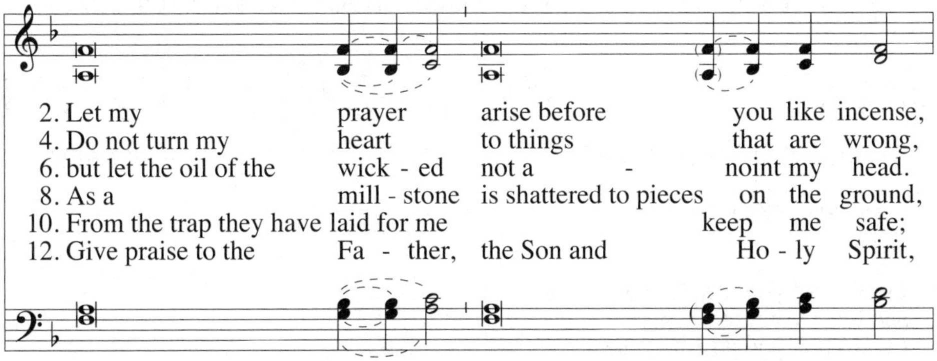

2. Let my prayer arise before you like incense,
4. Do not turn my heart to things that are wrong,
6. but let the oil of the wick - ed not a - noint my head.
8. As a mill - stone is shattered to pieces on the ground,
10. From the trap they have laid for me keep me safe;
12. Give praise to the Fa - ther, the Son and Ho - ly Spirit,

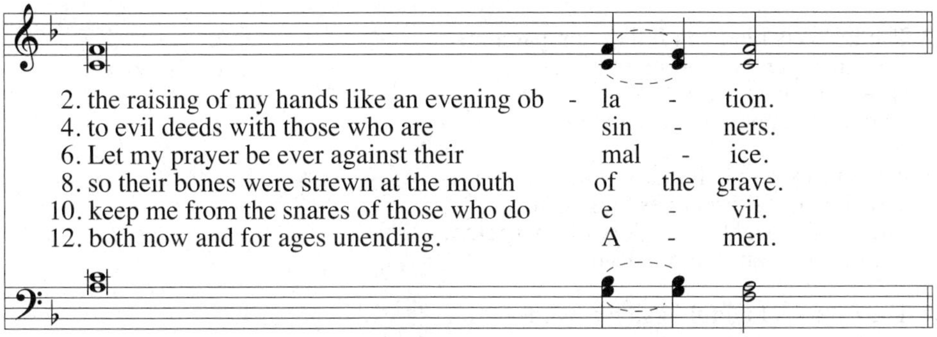

2. the raising of my hands like an evening ob - la - tion.
4. to evil deeds with those who are sin - ners.
6. Let my prayer be ever against their mal - ice.
8. so their bones were strewn at the mouth of the grave.
10. keep me from the snares of those who do e - vil.
12. both now and for ages unending. A - men.

Text: Psalm 141; © 1963, 1993, The Grail, GIA Publications, Inc., agent
Music: KONTAKION; Russian Orthodox Liturgy, adapt. by Richard Proulx, © 1985, GIA Publications, Inc.

Psalm 145: I Will Praise Your Name   112

Refrain

I will praise your name, my King and my God.   King and my God.

Verses

1. I will give you glory, my God above, and I will bless your name for ever.
   Ev'ry day I will bless and praise your name for ever.

2. The Lord is full of grace and mercy, who is kind and slow to anger.
   God is good in ev'ry way, and full of compassion.

3. Let all your works give you thanks, O Lord,
   and let all the faithful bless you.
   Let them speak of your might, O Lord, the glory of your kingdom.

4. The Lord is faithful in word and deed,
   and always near, his name is holy.
   Lifting up all those who fall, God raises up the lowly.

Text: Psalm 145:1–2, 8–9, 10–11, 13b–14; David Haas
Music: David Haas
© 1983, GIA Publications, Inc.

113   Psalm 145: I Will Praise Your Name for Ever

Refrain

I will praise your name for ev - er, my King and my God.

Text: *Lectionary for Mass,* © 1969, 1981, 1997, ICEL
Music: Leon Roberts, © 1987, GIA Publications, Inc.

Verses

1. I will extol you, my God and king,
   and bless your name forever and ever.
   I will bless you day after day,
   and praise your name forever and ever.

2. The LORD is kind and full of compassion,
   slow to anger, abounding in mercy.
   How good is the LORD to all,
   compassionate to all his creatures.

3. All your works shall thank you, O LORD,
   and all your faithful ones bless you.
   They shall speak of the glory of your reign,
   and declare your mighty deeds.

4. The LORD is faithful in all his words,
   and holy in all his deeds.
   The LORD supports all who fall,
   and raises up all who are bowed down.

Text: Psalm 145:1–2, 8–9, 10–11, 13cd–14; *The Revised Grail Psalms,* © 2010, Conception Abbey and The Grail, admin. by GIA Publications, Inc.
Music: Paschal Jordan, OSB, © 1986, GIA Publications, Inc.

114   Psalm 145: I Will Praise Your Name

Refrain I (Vss. 1, 3, 4, 6 or 3–5)

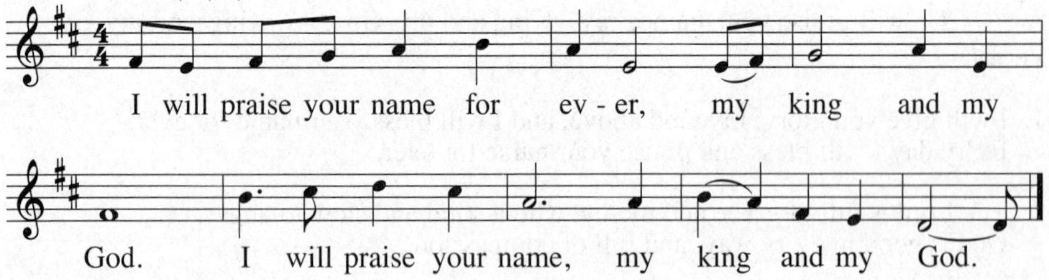

I will praise your name for ev - er, my king and my

God.   I will praise your name, my king and my God.

Refrain II (Vss. 3, 7, 8)

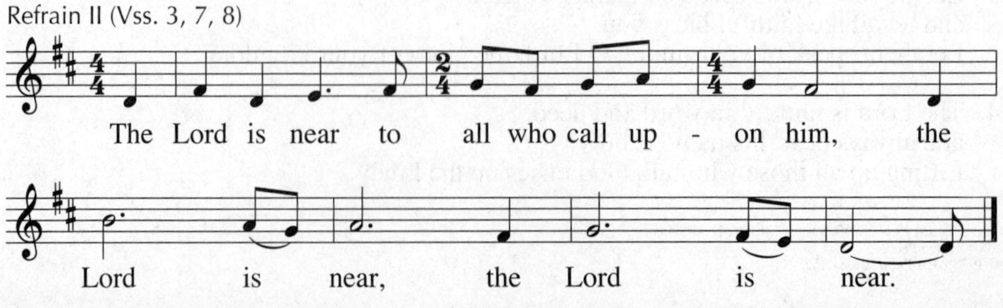

The Lord is near to all who call up - on him, the

Lord is near, the Lord is near.

Refrain III (Vss. 2, 3, 8)

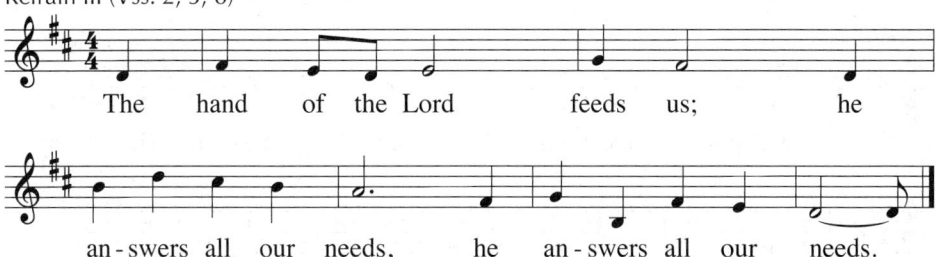

The hand of the Lord feeds us; he an-swers all our needs, he an-swers all our needs.

Verses

1. I will extol you, my God and king,
    and bless your name forever and ever.
    I will bless you day after day,
    and praise your name forever and ever.

2. I will bless you day after day,
    and praise your name forever and ever.
    The LORD is great and highly to be praised;
    his greatness cannot be measured.

3. The LORD is kind and full of compassion,
    slow to anger, abounding in mercy.
    How good is the LORD to all,
    compassionate to all his creatures.

4. All your works shall thank you, O LORD,
    and all your faithful ones bless you.
    They shall speak of the glory of your reign,
    and declare your mighty deeds.

5. To make known your might to the children of men,
    and the glorious splendor of your reign.
    Your kingdom is an everlasting kingdom;
    your rule endures for all generations.

6. The LORD is faithful in all his words,
    and holy in all his deeds.
    The LORD supports all who fall,
    and raises up all who are bowed down.

7. The eyes of all look to you,
    and you give them their food in due season.
    You open your hand and satisfy
    the desire of ev'ry living thing.

8. The LORD is just in all his ways,
    and holy in all his deeds.
    The LORD is close to all who call him,
    who call on him in truth.

Text: Psalm 145:1–2, 2–3, 8–9, 10–11, 12–13ab, 13cd–14, 15–16, 17–18; *The Revised Grail Psalms,* © 2010, Conception Abbey and The Grail, admin. by GIA Publications, Inc.; refrains trans., © 1969, ICEL
Music: Tony E. Alonso, © 2012, 2013, GIA Publications, Inc.

115   Psalm 146: I Will Praise the Lord

Refrain

I will praise the Lord all my days, make mu-sic to my
God while I live, make mu-sic to my God while I live.

Verses

1. Put no trust in the powerful,
   mere mortals in whom there is no help.
   Take their breath, they return to clay,
   and their plans that day come to nothing.
   They are happy who are helped by Jacob's God,
   whose hope is in the Lord their God,
   who alone made heaven and earth, the seas and all they contain.

2. It is the Lord who keeps faith for ever, who is just to the oppressed.
   It is God who gives bread to the hungry,
   the Lord, who sets prisoners free.
   It is the Lord who gives sight to the blind,
   who raises up those who are bowed down,
   the Lord who protects the stranger, and upholds the widow and orphan.

3. It is the Lord who loves the just but thwarts the path of the wicked.
   The Lord will reign for ever, Zion's God from age to age.

Text: Psalm 146; The Grail, © 1963, 1993, The Grail, GIA Publications, Inc., agent
Music: Michael Joncas, © 1990, GIA Publications, Inc.

Psalm 150: Praise God in This Holy Dwelling 116

Al-le-lu - ia! Al - le-lu - ia! Al-le-lu - ia!

1. Praise God in this ho - ly dwell-ing; Praise God on the
2. Praise God with the blast of trum - pet; Bring praise now with
3. Praise God with re - sound-ing cym - bals; With cym - bals that
4. Praise God, the al - might - y Fa - ther; Praise Christ, the be -

might - y throne; Prais - ing for all won - der-ful
lyre and harp; Prais - ing with the tim - brel and
crash, give praise; O let ev - 'ry-thing that has
lov - ed Son; Give praise to the Spir - it of

deeds; Sing praise to our Sov - 'reign Maj - es - ty.
dance; With the gen-tle sound of string and reed.
breath, Let all liv - ing crea - tures praise the Lord.
love; For ev - er the Tri - une God be praised.

Al - le - lu - ia! Al - le - lu - ia!

1.–3.
Al - le - lu - ia!

4.
lu - ia!

Text: Psalm 150:1–2, 3–4, 5–6; adapt. by Omer Westendorf
Music: Jan M. Vermulst; arr. by Charles G. Frischmann
© 1964, World Library Publications

117   Exodus 15: Song of Moses

Refrain

Cantor:

I will sing,   I will sing   to the God who sets me free!   I will

sing,   I will sing   to the   God who sets me free!   Phar-aoh's

ar - my and his char - i - ots God   cast in - to the sea!   Phar-aoh's

ar - my and his char - i - ots God   cast in - to   the   sea!

Verses

1. The Lord is my strength, my protection and my shield;
   Pharaoh's army and his chariots God cast into the sea.
   Our God is a warrior whose name is "the Lord,"
   God of might, God of victory!

2. The brave and the mighty, the pride of Pharaoh's army,
   God plunged them to the bottom of the sea like a stone.
   The hand of the Lord is magnificent in power;
   the Lord has crushed our foes!

3. O God who redeems, who delivers us from slavery,
   you set us on the mountain of your holy place.
   Your throne and your temple shall endure for all time;
   your reign shall never end!

Text: Exodus 15; Scott Soper
Music: Scott Soper
© 1997, GIA Publications, Inc.

Exodus 15: Let Us Sing to the Lord   118

Refrain

Let us sing to the Lord; Let us sing to the Lord; he has
cov-ered him-self in glo-ry; he has cov-ered him-self in glo-ry!

Verses

1. I will sing to the LORD, for he is gloriously triumphant;
   horse and chariot he has cast into the sea.
   My strength and my courage is the the LORD,
   and he has been my savior.
   He is my God, I praise him;
   the God of my father, I extol him.

2. The LORD is a warrior, LORD is his name!
   Pharaoh's chariots and army he hurled into the sea.
   At a breath of your anger the waters piled up,
   the flowing waters stood like a mound,
   the flood waters congealed in the midst of the sea.

3. The enemy boasted, "I will pursue and overtake them;
   I will divide the spoils and have my fill of them;
   I will draw my sword; my hand shall despoil them!
   When your wind blew, the sea covered them;
   like lead they sank in the mighty waters.

4. Who is like to you among the gods, O LORD?
   Who is like to you, magnificent in holiness?
   O terrible in renown, worker of wonders,
   when you stretched out your right hand,
   the earth swallowed them!

5. In your mercy you led the people you redeemed;
   in your strength you guided them to your holy dwelling.
   And you brought them in and planted them
   on the mountain of your inheritance —
   the place where you made your seat, O LORD,
   the sanctuary, O LORD, which your hands established.
   The LORD shall reign for ever and ever.

6. Glory to the Father, and to the Son,
   and to the Holy Spirit.
   As it was in the beginning, is now
   and will be for ever. Amen.

Text: Exodus 15, *New American Bible*, © 1970, Confraternity of Christian Doctrine, Inc.
Music: Howard Hughes, SM, © 1979, 1988, GIA Publications, Inc.

119 Isaiah 12: You Will Draw Water Joyfully / Sacarán Aguas con Alegría

Bilingual Refrain

Verses / Estrofas

1. God indeed is my Savior; I am confident and fearless.
   My courage is the Lord, for God has been my savior!

2. Proclaim God's name to the nations, tell the world of God's works.
   Praise the Lord, all you people, how glorious is God's name!

3. Sing the wonders God works, make them known in ev'ry land.
   O people of Zion, shout: the holy one is among you.

1. *Vean al Dios que me salva, con él estoy seguro.*
   ¡Mi fuerza y protección, el Señor es mi salvación!

2. *¡Denle las gracias a Dios, invoquen su nombre,*
   proclamen sus hazañas, a todos proclamen su nombre!

3. *Canten a Dios por sus proezas, anúncienlas a toda la tierra.*
   Habitantes de Sión se alegran: "Contigo está el Dios de Israel."

Text: Isaiah 12:2–3, 4bcd, 5–6, adapt. and tr. by Tony E. Alonso, © 2003, GIA Publications, Inc.; English refrain trans., © 1969, ICEL
Music: Tony E. Alonso, © 2003, GIA Publications, Inc.

Daniel 3:57–88 / O All You Works of the Lord   120

Benedicite omnia opera Domini

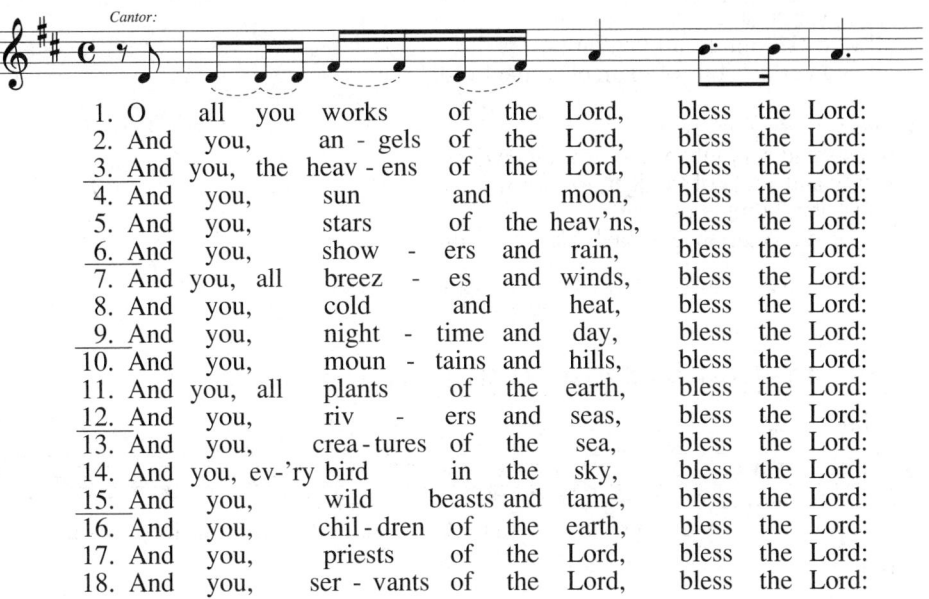

Text: Daniel 3:57–88; The Grail
Music: A. Gregory Murray, OSB
© 1963, The Grail, GIA Publications, Inc., agent

121   Daniel 3:57–88 / Canticle of Daniel

Refrain

God is praised and ex - alt - ed a - bove all for - ev - er.

Verses

1. Angels of the Lord, *Response*
   you heavens, *Response*
   all waters above the heavens, *Response*
   all you hosts of the Lord, sun and moon,
   stars of heaven, bless the Lord!

2. Every shower and dew, *Response*
   all wind and heat, *Response*
   cold and chill, dew and rain, *Response*
   ice and snow, nights and days,
   lights and darkness and clouds, bless the Lord!

3. Mountains and hills, *Response*
   everything growing from the earth, *Response*
   springs, seas and rivers, *Response*
   all water creatures, all you birds,
   all you beasts, sons of man, bless the Lord!

4. O Israel, *Response*
   priests and servants of the Lord, *Response*
   spirits and souls of the just, *Response*
   holy men, humble of heart,
   Hananiah, Azariah, Mishael, bless the Lord!

Assembly Response

Bless   the   Lord!

Text: Daniel 3:57–88; adapt. from the *New American Bible*, © 1970, Confraternity of Christian Doctrine, Inc.
Music: John Angotti; arr. by Paul A. Tate, © 2002, World Library Publications

122   Daniel 3:57–87 / Benedicite

Antiphon

Praise and ex-alt him for   ev - er, O praise and ex-alt him for   ev-er.

Verses

1. Bless the Lord, all you works of the Lord,
   angels of the Lord, bless the Lord.

2. Heavens above, bless the Lord,
   waters o'er the heavens, bless the Lord.

3. All you hosts of the Lord, bless the Lord,
   sun and moon, bless the Lord.

4. Stars of heaven, bless the Lord,
   showers and dews, bless the Lord.

5. All you winds, bless the Lord,
   fire and heat, bless the Lord.

6. Cold and chill, bless the Lord,
   dew and rain, bless the Lord.

7. Ice and snow, bless the Lord,
   frost and chill, bless the Lord.

8. Nights and days, bless the Lord,
   light and darkness, bless the Lord.

9. Lightning and clouds, bless the Lord,
   let all the earth, bless the Lord.

10. Mountains and hills, bless the Lord,
    all growing things, bless the Lord.

11. Flowing springs, bless the Lord,
    seas and rivers, bless the Lord.

12. Dolphins and sea creatures, bless the Lord,
    birds of the skies, bless the Lord.

13. All you beasts, wild and tame,
    children of the Lord, bless the Lord.

14. Israel, bless the Lord,
    servants of the Lord, bless the Lord.

15. Souls of the just, bless the Lord,
    humble hearts, bless the Lord.

Text: Daniel 3:57–87, *New American Bible,* © 1970, Confraternity of Christian Doctrine, Inc.
Music: Robert M. Hutmacher, OFM, © 1984, GIA Publications, Inc.

Luke 1:46–55 / Holy Is Your Name   123

Verse 1

1. My soul is filled with joy as I sing to God my savior:
   you have looked upon your servant, you have visited your people.

Refrain

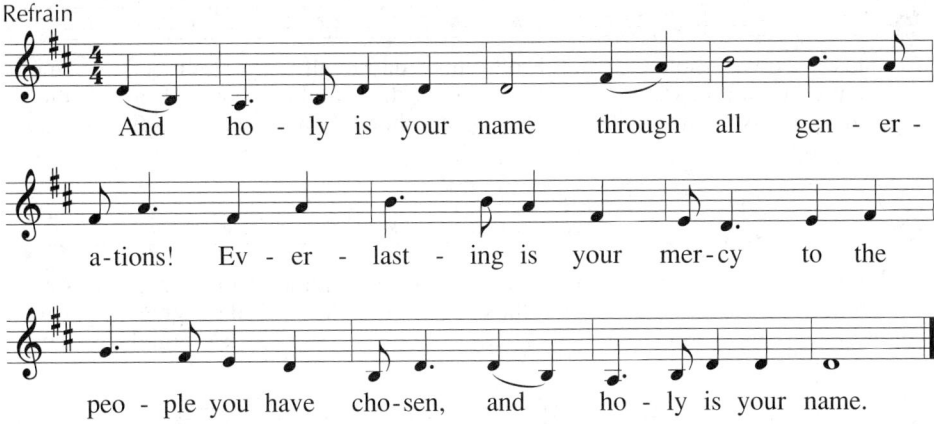

And ho-ly is your name through all gen-er-a-tions! Ev-er-last-ing is your mer-cy to the peo-ple you have cho-sen, and ho-ly is your name.

Verses 2–5

2. I am lowly as a child, but I know from this day forward
   that my name will be remembered, for all will call me blessed.

3. I proclaim the pow'r of God, you do marvels for your servants;
   though you scatter the proud hearted, and destroy the might of princes.

4. To the hungry you give food, send the rich away empty.
   In your mercy you are mindful of the people you have chosen.

5. In your love you now fulfill what you promised to your people.
   I will praise you Lord, my savior, everlasting is your mercy.

Text: Luke 1:46–55, David Haas
Music: WILD MOUNTAIN THYME, Irregular; Irish traditional; arr. by David Haas
© 1989, GIA Publications, Inc.

124 Luke 1:46–53 / My Soul Gives Glory to the Lord

1. My soul gives glo - ry to the Lord, In
2. His mer - cy goes to all who fear, From
3. He raised his ser - vant Is - ra - el, Re -

God my Sav - ior I re - joice. My low - li -
age to age and to all parts. His arm of
mem - b'ring his e - ter - nal grace, As from of

ness he did re - gard, Ex - alt - ing me by
strength to all is near; He scat - ters those who
old he did fore - tell To A - bra - ham and

his own choice. From this day all shall call me
have proud hearts. He casts the might - y from their
all his race. O Fa - ther, Son and Spir - it

blest, For he has done great things for me, Of
throne And rais - es those of low de - gree; He
blest, In three - fold Name are you a - dored, To

all great names his is the best, For
feeds the hun - gry as his own, The
you be ev - 'ry prayer ad - dressed, From

it is ho - ly; strong is he.
rich de - part in pov - er - ty.
age to age the on - ly Lord.

Text: Luke 1:46–55; J.T. Mueller, 1885–1967, alt.
Tune: MAGNIFICAT, LMD; Michael Joncas, b.1951, © 1979, 1988, GIA Publications, Inc.

Luke 1:46–53 / My Soul Gives Glory to My God 125

1. My soul gives glory to my God,
   Who reaches down with loving grace
   To lift me from my low estate
   And set me in the highest place.
   Magníficat, magníficat!
   With all my heart, I answer Yes
   When God announces wondrous news.
   And ev'ry age shall call me blest.

2. God's mercy comforts all who fear,
   Embracing with a steadfast arm
   That casts the mighty from their thrones,
   But keeps the humble safe from harm.
   Magníficat, magníficat!
   The weak find strength; the weary, rest.
   God's promise sounds from age to age:
   The needy of the world are blest.

3. God's justice sends the rich away,
   But feeds the poor with lavish things.
   Each hungry soul now fills with joy
   And joins the song that Mary sings:
   Magníficat, magníficat!
   To God, Creator, Christ, the Son;
   And Holy Spirit— triune God:
   All praises to the Three in One.

Text: Luke 1:46–53; Mary Louise Bringle, © 2004, GIA Publications, Inc.

Luke 1:46–55 / Proclaim the Greatness of God 126

Refrain

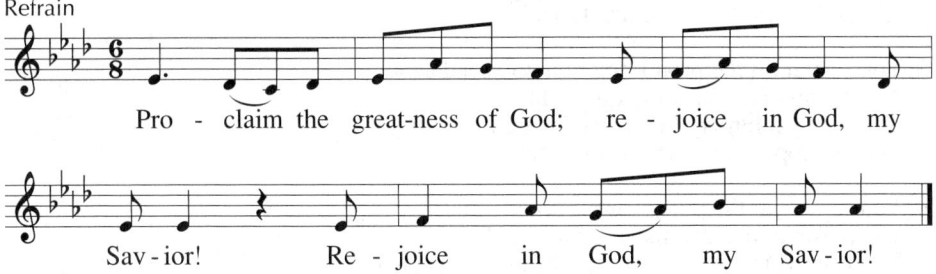

Pro - claim the great-ness of God; re - joice in God, my Sav - ior! Re - joice in God, my Sav - ior!

Verses

1. For he has favored his lowly one, and all shall call me blessed.
   The almighty has done great things for me, and holy is his name.

2. He favors those who fear his name, in ev'ry generation.
   He has shown the might and strength of his arm,
   and scattered the proud of heart.

3. He has cast the mighty from their thrones, and lifted up the lowly.
   He has filled the hungry with all good gifts, and sent the rich away.

4. He has helped his servant Israel, remembering his mercy.
   He promised his mercy to Abraham and his children for evermore.

Text: Luke 1:46–55; James J. Chepponis
Music: James J. Chepponis
© 1980, GIA Publications, Inc.

127　Luke 1:46–55 / Magnificat

Refrain

Ma - gní - fi-cat, ma - gní - fi-cat á - ni-ma me - a

Dó - mi-num. Ma - gní - fi-cat, ma - gní - fi-cat

á - ni - ma   me - a Dó - mi - num.

Verses

1. I sing with all my heart, my spirit leaps for joy.
   Who am I that you should honor me?
   By your saving grace, all will call me blest,
   and proclaim the greatness of your name.

2. How great your gifts to us, how wonderful your works!
   With your pow'r you strengthen all the weak.
   Your mery will endure, steadfast is your love.
   All the faithful follow and believe.

3. You scatter all the proud, the rich you send away.
   All the mighty vanish in your sight.
   You fill each hungry heart, raising up the least.
   You are hope for all who are in need.

4. You rescue all the poor, your servant Israel,
   you preserve the promise long foretold.
   You keep your saving word; faithful is your name.
   Ev'ry generation sings your praise!

Text: Luke 1:46–55; Lori True
Music: Lori True
© 2004, GIA Publications, Inc.

Luke 1:68–79 / Now Bless the God of Israel 128

1. Now bless the God of Is - ra - el, Who
2. Re - mem - ber - ing the cov - e - nant, God
3. In ten - der mer - cy, God will send The

comes in love and pow'r, Who rais - es from the
res - cues us from fear, That we might serve in
day - spring from on high, Our ris - ing sun, the

roy - al house De - liv - 'rance in this hour. Through
ho - li - ness And peace from year to year; And
light of life For those who sit and sigh. God

ho - ly proph - ets God has sworn To
you, my child, shall go be - fore To
comes to guide our way to peace, That

free us from a - larm, To save us from the
preach, to proph - e - sy, That all may know the
death shall reign no more. Sing prais - es to the

heav - y hand Of all who wish us harm.
ten - der love, The grace of God most high.
Ho - ly One! O wor - ship and a - dore!

Text: *Benedictus*, Luke 1:68–79; Ruth Duck, © 1992, GIA Publications, Inc.
Tune: FOREST GREEN, CMD; English; harm. by Michael Joncas, © 1987, GIA Publications, Inc.

129 Luke 1:67–79 / The Rising Sun

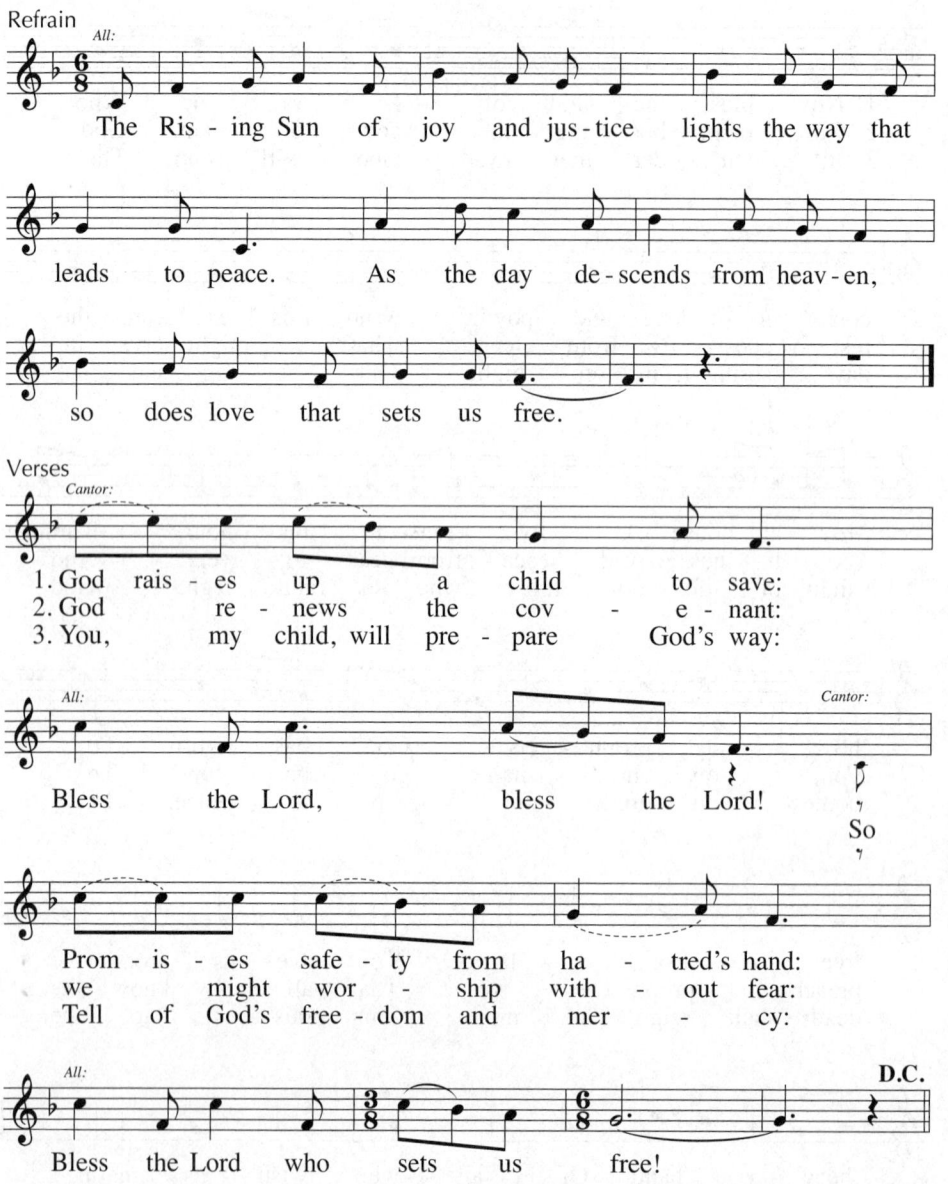

Refrain (All:)

The Ris-ing Sun of joy and jus-tice lights the way that leads to peace. As the day de-scends from heav-en, so does love that sets us free.

Verses (Cantor:)

1. God rais-es up a child to save:
2. God re-news the cov - e-nant:
3. You, my child, will pre-pare God's way:

(All:)

Bless the Lord, bless the Lord!

(Cantor:) So

Prom-is-es safe-ty from ha - tred's hand:
we might wor - ship with - out fear:
Tell of God's free-dom and mer - cy:

(All:)

Bless the Lord who sets us free!

D.C.

Text: *Benedictus*, Luke 1:67–79; Tony E. Alonso
Music: Tony E. Alonso
© 2004, GIA Publications, Inc.

Luke 1:68–79 / Blest Be the Lord 130

1. Blest be the Lord, the God of Is - ra - el,
2. The proph - ets tell a sto - ry just be - gun
3. This is the oath once sworn to A - bra - ham:
4. And you, my child, this day you shall be called
5. The ten - der love God prom - ised from our birth
6. All glo - ry be to God, Cre - a - tor blest,

Who brings the dawn and dark - est night dis - pels,
Of van - quished foe and glo - rious vic - t'ry won,
All shall be free to dwell up - on the land,
The prom - ised one, the proph - et of our God,
Is soon to dawn up - on this shad - owed earth,
To Je - sus Christ, God's love made man - i - fest,

Who rais - es up a might - y Sav - ior from the earth,
Of prom - ise made to all who keep the law as guide:
Free now to praise, un - harmed by the op - pres - sor's rod,
For you will go be - fore the Lord to clear the way,
To shine on those whose sor - rows seem to nev - er cease,
And to the Ho - ly Spir - it, gen - tle Com - fort - er,

Of Da - vid's line, a son of roy - al birth.
God's faith - ful love and mer - cy will a - bide.
Ho - ly and right - eous in the sight of God.
And shep - herd all in - to the light of day.
To guide our feet in - to the path of peace.
All glo - ry be, both now and ev - er - more.

Text: *Benedictus*, Luke 1:68–79; Owen Alstott, © 1991, Owen Alstott
Music: Bernadette Farrell, © 1993, Bernadette Farrell
Published by OCP.

131   Luke 2:29 / Nunc Dimittis

Ostinato Refrain

Nunc di - mít - tis ser - vum tu - um, Dó - mi -
Let your ser - vant now go in peace, O

ne, se - cún - dum ver - bum
Lord, now go in peace ac -

ne, Dó - mi - ne,
Lord, O Lord,

pa - ce.
word.

tu - um in pa - ce, Dó - mi - ne. Nunc di -
cord - ing to your word, to your word. Let your

Last time

Text: Luke 2:29; Taizé Community, 1980
Tune: Jacques Berthier, 1923–1994

Luke 2:29–35 / Lord, Bid Your Servant Go 132
in Peace

1. Lord, bid your ser - vant go in peace, Your
2. This is the Sav - ior of the world, The
3. This Child shall see in Is - ra - el, So
4. His moth - er's soul a sword shall pierce, Of
5. Blessed be the Fa - ther, who has giv'n His

word is now ful - filled. These eyes have seen sal -
Gen - tiles' prom - ised light, God's glo - ry dwell - ing
man - y rise or fall: God's sign raised high for
sor - row, keen and deep. From man - y hearts their
Son to be our Lord; Blessed too that Son, and

va - tion's dawn, This Child so long fore - told.
in our midst, The joy of Is - ra - el.
all to see, Which yet shall be de - nied.
se - cret thoughts Through him shall be re - vealed.
with them both The Spir - it of their love.

Text: *Nunc dimittis*; Luke 2:29–32, 34–35; James Quinn, SJ, 1919–2010, © 1969, 1989, James Quinn, SJ. Published by OCP.
Tune: MORNING SONG, CM; Wyeth's *Repository of Sacred Music*, 1813; harm. by Richard Proulx, 1937–2010, © 1975, GIA Publications, Inc.

133 Luke 2:29–34 / Nunc Dimittis

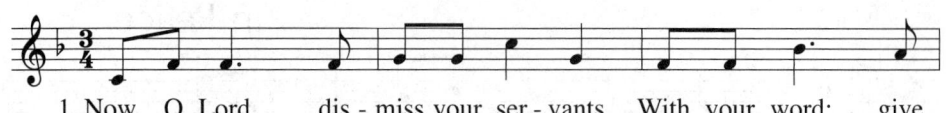

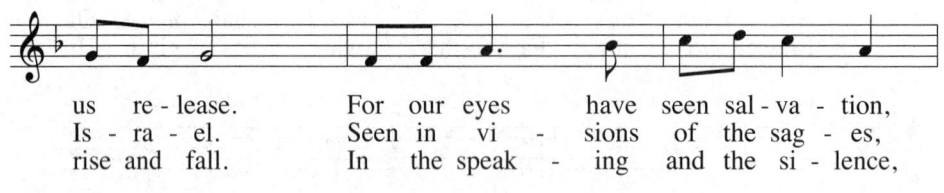

1. Now, O Lord, dis - miss your ser - vants With your word; give
2. Light, en - light - 'ning ev - 'ry peo - ple, Glo - ry of your
3. Child of Mar - y, sign of won - der, By you, man - y

us re - lease. For our eyes have seen sal - va - tion,
Is - ra - el. Seen in vi - sions of the sag - es,
rise and fall. In the speak - ing and the si - lence,

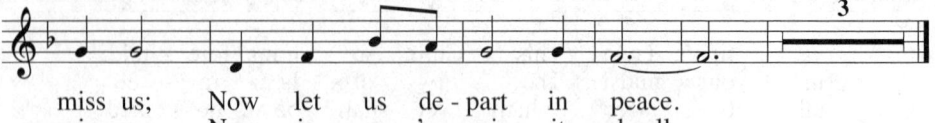

Prom - ised ev - er to in - crease. Lord, dis - miss us, Lord, dis-
Heard in what the proph - ets tell. Lord, dis - miss us, Lord, dis-
Pierce our hearts and break our walls. Lord, dis - miss us, Lord, dis-

miss us; Now let us de - part in peace.
miss us; Now in ev - 'ry spir - it dwell.
miss us; Now, our God, our life, our all.

Text: *Nunc dimittis*, Luke 2:29–34; Sylvia Dunstan, © 1995, GIA Publications, Inc.
Music: PEACETIME, 8 7 8 7 8 7; David Haas, © 2003, GIA Publications, Inc.

Philippians 2:6–11 134

Qui cum in forma Dei

Cantor: Though he was in the form of God,
Jesus did not deem equality with God something to be grasped at.

JE-SUS CHRIST IS LORD! JE-SUS CHRIST IS LORD!

Cantor: Rather, he emptied himself and took the form of a slave,
being born in the likeness of men.

JE-SUS CHRIST IS LORD! JE-SUS CHRIST IS LORD!

Cantor: He was known to be of human estate, and it was thus that he humbled himself,
obediently accepting even death, death on a cross!

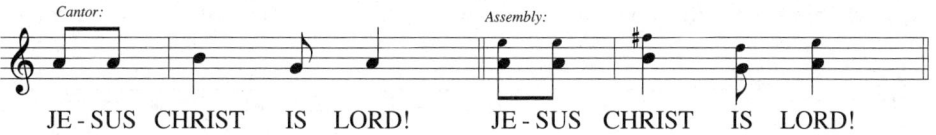

JE-SUS CHRIST IS LORD! JE-SUS CHRIST IS LORD!

Cantor: Because of this, God highly exalted him
and bestowed on him the name above ev'ry other name,

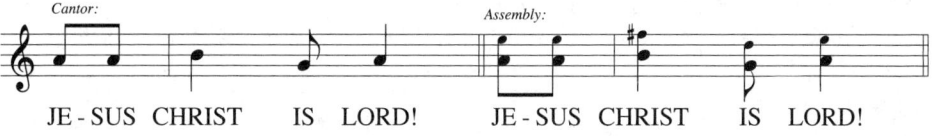

JE-SUS CHRIST IS LORD! JE-SUS CHRIST IS LORD!

Cantor: so that at Jesus' name ev'ry knee must bend in the heav'ns, on the earth,
and under the earth, and every tongue proclaim to the glory of God the Father:

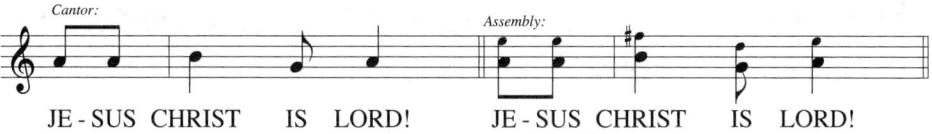

JE-SUS CHRIST IS LORD! JE-SUS CHRIST IS LORD!

Cantor: Glory to the Father, and to the Son, and to the Holy Spirit:
as it was in the beginning, is now, and will be for ever. Amen.

JE-SUS CHRIST IS LORD! JE-SUS CHRIST IS LORD!

Text: Philippians 2:6–11; *New American Bible,* © 1970, Confraternity of Christian Doctrine, Inc.
Music: Howard Hughes, SM, © 1985, GIA Publications, Inc.

135   1 Peter 2:21–24 / By Your Wounds, O Christ

Antiphon

By your wounds, O Christ, we have been healed.

Psalm Tone

Omit for stanza 1

In hoc enim

1. Christ suf-fèred for you, and left you án ex-am-ple,
to have you fol-low in hís foot-steps. 2. He dìd no wrong,
no de-ceit was found in hís mouth. When he was ìn-sult-ed,
he re-turned nó in-sult. 3. When he was màde to suf-fer,
he did not coun-ter wíth threats. In-stead he de-liv-ered him-sèlf up
to the One who judg-és just-ly. 4. In his own bod-y
he brought your sins tò the Cross, so that all of us, dead tó sin,
could live in ac-cord with Gòd's will. By his wounds you áre healed.

Text: 1 Peter 2:21–24; *New American Bible*, © 1970, Confraternity of Christian Doctrine, Inc.
Music: Richard Proulx, © 1986, GIA Publications, Inc.

Revelation 19: All Power Is Yours 136

Antiphon

All pow'r is yours, Lord God, our might-y King, al-le-lu-ia!

Refrain I

Al - le - lu - ia, al - le - lu - ia!

Verses
Cantor: Refrain II

Al - le - lu - ia!

Cantor: Refrain I

Al - le - lu - ia, al - le - lu - ia!

Salus et gloria

1. Salvation, glory and pòwer to our Gód: (Alleluia!)
   his judgments are hònest and trúe. (Alleluia, alleluia!)

2. Sing praise to our God, àll you his sérvants, (Alleluia!)
   all who worship him reverently, grèat and smáll. (Alleluia, alleluia!)

3. The Lord our all-powerful Gòd is Kíng; (Alleluia!)
   let us rejoice, sing pràise, and give him glóry. (Alleluia, alleluia!)

4. The wedding feast of the Làmb has begún, (Alleluia!)
   and his bride is prepàred to wélcome him. (Alleluia, alleluia!)

5. Glory to the Father, and to the Sòn, and to the Holy Spírit, (Alleluia!)
   as it was in the beginning, is now, and will be for èver. Amén. (Alleluia, alleluia!)

Text: Revelation 19:1–7; *The Liturgy of the Hours*, © 1974, ICEL
Music: Howard Hughes, SM, © 1976, 1978, ICEL

Rites of the Church

137 Christian Initiation of Adults

The passage of an adult into the Christian community takes place over an extended period of time. The members of the local Church, the catechists and sponsors, the clergy and the diocesan bishop take part in the journey from inquiry through the catechumenate to baptism, confirmation and eucharist. With their example the candidates are invited to pray, to reflect on the word of God, to fast and to join in the community's practice of charity. They are to learn the way of Jesus from the members of the Church.

This journey of the candidates and community is marked by liturgical rites; thus the community publicly acknowledges, encourages and strengthens the candidates. The first of these is the rite of becoming catechumens. It concludes the sometimes lengthy period during which those who have come to ask about the way of the Church and the life of a Christian have heard the gospel proclaimed and seen it practiced. Those who then feel called to walk in this way of Christ's Church ask to begin the journey toward baptism. If the Church judges the inquirers ready, they are accepted into the order of catechumens.

Those who have entered the catechumenate are already part of the household of Christ. During this time the catechumens are to hear and reflect on God's word, to learn the teachings and practices of the Church, to become gradually accustomed to the ways of prayer and discipline in the Church, to observe and to join in the good works of Christians. Ordinarily the catechumens are present on Sunday for the liturgy of the word and may be dismissed after the homily—to continue prayer and study with their catechists—since they cannot join in the Eucharist.

Rites of exorcism and blessing may be celebrated during the catechumenate. Through such rites the Church prays that the catechumens will be purified, strengthened against all evil and thus eagerly grow in faith and good works. The very presence of the catechumens—at the Sunday liturgy, in these special rites and in everyday life—is itself a source of strength and blessing to the faithful.

Each year as Lent begins, the bishop, with the help of the local pastor and others involved with the catechumens, is to call those catechumens who are judged ready to prepare themselves for baptism at the Easter Vigil. Thus the catechumens become the "elect," the chosen, and for the forty days of Lent they make preparations: praying, fasting, doing good works. All the faithful join them in this. On several Sundays in Lent the rites of scrutiny take place when the assembled Church prays over the elect. During Lent also the catechumens may publicly receive the words of the Church's creed and of the Lord's Prayer.

Good Friday and Holy Saturday are days of prayer, fasting and preparation for the rites of the Easter Vigil. On the night between Saturday and Sunday, the Church assembles to keep vigil and listen to many readings from Scripture. Then the catechumens are called forward for baptism and confirmation. These rites are found in the Easter Vigil.

The newly baptized, now called neophytes, take a special place in the Sunday Eucharist throughout the fifty days of Eastertime. This is a time for deepening their incorporation into the Church.

All of these stages of initiation take place in the midst of the community. In various rites, the faithful show the Christian life to the inquirers and catechumens. In turn, the faithful are strengthened and challenged in their faith by the presence of the catechumens.

Those who seek to belong to the Roman Catholic Church and who are already baptized may participate in the catechesis and in some of the rites of the catechumenate but they are not baptized again. Rather, they are received into the full communion of the Roman Catholic Church.

ACCEPTANCE INTO THE ORDER OF CATECHUMENS 138

INTRODUCTORY RITES

The priest greets the assembly: candidates, sponsors, members of the parish. The candidates are asked what it is that they seek and each replies. After each candidate has responded, one of the following may be sung:

139

We stand with you, we pray for you, O ho-ly child of God!

Text: David Haas
Music: David Haas
© 1988, GIA Publications, Inc.

140

We praise you, Lord, we praise you, Lord,

we praise you, Lord, and we bless you.

Text: ICEL, © 1985
Music: Marty Haugen, © 1995, GIA Publications, Inc.

CANDIDATES' FIRST ACCEPTANCE OF THE GOSPEL

The priest solemnly asks if the candidates are ready to begin walking the way of the gospel. The sponsors and all present are asked if they stand ready to assist the candidates as they strive to know and follow Christ. All respond: **We are.**

SIGNING OF THE CANDIDATES WITH THE CROSS

The sign of the cross marks the candidates for their new way of life. The priest signs each on the forehead saying:

N., receive the cross on your forehead.
It is Christ himself who now strengthens you
with this sign of his love.
Learn now to know him and follow him.

Sponsors and others also sign the candidates. Ears and eyes and other senses may also be signed. The priest prays that the catechumens may share in the saving power of the cross.

One of the following musical settings with assembly acclamations may be used:

141

Priest: Receive the sign of the cross....

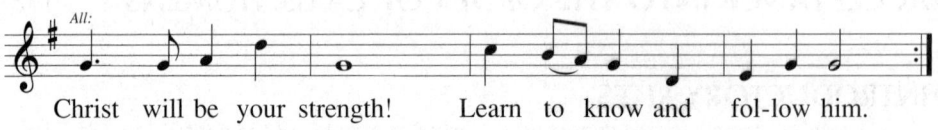

Christ will be your strength! Learn to know and fol-low him.

Music: David Haas, © 1988, GIA Publications, Inc.

142

Refrain I

In the cross of Christ, our glo - ry,

Christ, our sto - ry, Christ, our song.

Refrain II

Glo - ry and praise to you, Lord Je - sus Christ!

Text: ICEL, © 1969
Music: Marty Haugen, © 1995, GIA Publications, Inc.

INVITATION TO THE CELEBRATION OF THE WORD OF GOD

If the assembly processes to the place for the liturgy of the word, an appropriate psalm or hymn may be sung.

143 LITURGY OF THE WORD

There may be one or more readings from Scripture, together with a responsorial psalm. After the homily, a Bible may be given to the new catechumens for their study and prayer throughout the time of the catechumenate.

INTERCESSIONS FOR THE CATECHUMENS

All join in prayer for the new catechumens. All respond with: **Lord, hear our prayer**, *or a similar response. If the Eucharist is to be celebrated, the catechumens are first dismissed. For music to accompany the dismissal, see below.*

RITES OF THE CATECHUMENATE   144

DISMISSAL OF THE CATECHUMENS

When the catechumens are present at Mass, they are usually dismissed after the homily. Only when they have been baptized are they able to join the faithful in the reception of the eucharist. After their dismissal, the catechumens remain together and are joined by their catechists or others to pray and reflect on the scripture readings.

One of the following may be sung to accompany the dismissal:

145

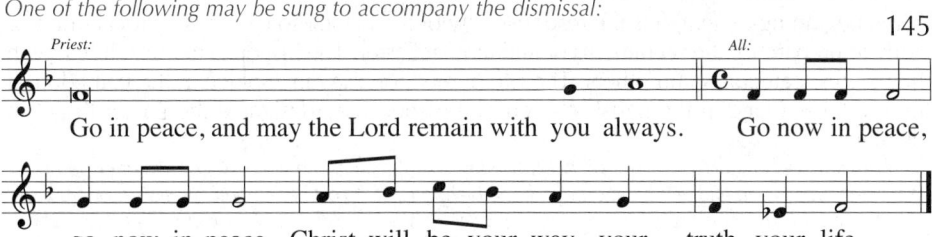

Go in peace, and may the Lord remain with you always. Go now in peace, go now in peace, Christ will be your way, your truth, your life.

Text: *Rite of Christian Initiation of Adults,* © 1985, ICEL
Music: Lynn Trapp, © 1991, Birnamwood Publications (ASCAP). A division of MorningStar Music Publishers, Inc.

146

Go in peace, the peace of Christ, and learn the ways of God.

Text: Marty Haugen
Music: Marty Haugen
© 1997, GIA Publications, Inc.

147

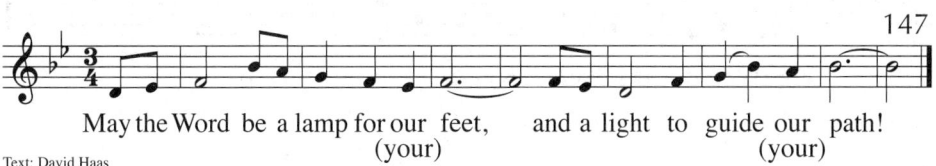

May the Word be a lamp for our feet, and a light to guide our path!
(your)   (your)

Text: David Haas
Music: David Haas
© 1991, GIA Publications, Inc.

CELEBRATIONS OF THE WORD OF GOD

On Sundays, after the catechetical sessions, before the beginning of a new liturgical season, and at other times the catechumens and others may join for liturgy: song, reading of Scripture, psalmody, prayer and silence are normally part of such a service.

MINOR EXORCISMS

At appropriate times during the catechumenate, the catechists or other approved ministers may lead the community in prayers of exorcism over the catechumens. These prayers acknowledge the struggle against evil and ask that God strengthen the catechumens.

BLESSINGS OF THE CATECHUMENS

Prayers of blessing and the laying on of hands may take place whenever the catechumens gather for instruction or other purposes. Catechists or other approved ministers ask these blessings over the catechumens.

ANOINTINGS AND PRESENTATIONS

During the catechumenate or during Lent, the candidates may be anointed with the oil of catechumens as a sign of strength given for their struggle to live the gospel. At some point in this time they are publicly presented with the Church's treasury of prayer and faith, the Lord's Prayer and the Creed.

RITE OF ELECTION OR ENROLLMENT OF NAMES

At the beginning of Lent, it is the responsibility of the bishop to call those who are judged ready to prepare for the sacraments of initiation at Easter. The bishop is to consult first with the pastors, catechists and others. The rite of election may take place at the cathedral. If the rite takes place in the parish church, the bishop may designate the pastor to act in his place.

This rite is also called the "Enrollment of Names." Each candidate now gives his/her name, or writes it down. When all have been enrolled, the bishop says: "You have been chosen to be initiated into the sacred mysteries at the Easter Vigil." He then speaks to them and to their sponsors about their lenten preparation for baptism.

While or immediately after the candidates have signed their names, an appropriate hymn or acclamation may be sung, for example, Blessed Be God, Who Chose You in Christ, no. 1013.

SCRUTINIES

The scrutinies occur on the Third, Fourth and Fifth Sundays of Lent. The elect are called before the community for exorcism and prayer. If the Intercessions for the Elect are chanted, the assembly may respond with one of the following:

148

Ký-ri-e, e-lé-i-son, Ký-ri-e, e-lé-i-son.

Music: Jacques Berthier, © 1998, Les Presses de Taizé, GIA Publications, Inc., agent

149

First Scrutiny: 1. We thirst for liv-ing wa-ter,
Second Scrutiny: 2. We search for light in dark-ness, de-liv-er us, O Lord.
Third Scrutiny: 3. We long to rise to new life,

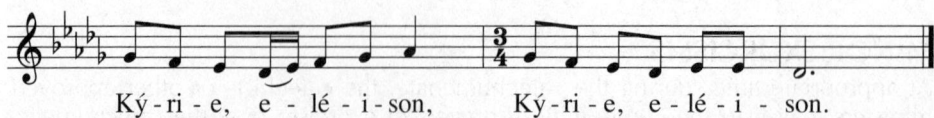

Ký-ri-e, e-lé-i-son, Ký-ri-e, e-lé-i-son.

Text: Carol Browning
Music: Carol Browning
© 2011, GIA Publications, Inc.

Refrain

150

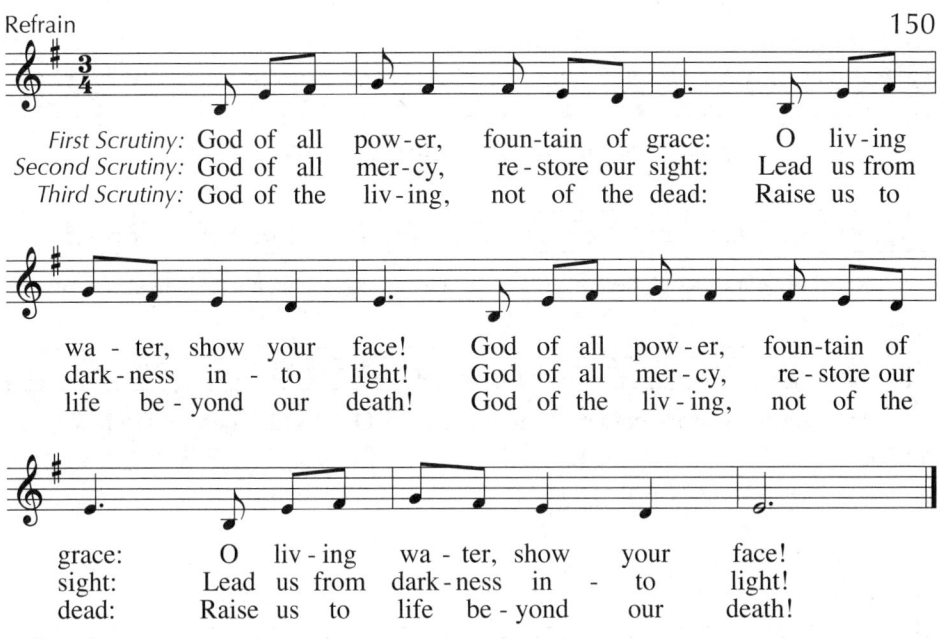

First Scrutiny: God of all pow-er, foun-tain of grace: O liv-ing wa-ter, show your face! God of all pow-er, foun-tain of grace: O liv-ing wa-ter, show your face!

Second Scrutiny: God of all mer-cy, re-store our sight: Lead us from dark-ness in-to light! God of all mer-cy, re-store our sight: Lead us from dark-ness in-to light!

Third Scrutiny: God of the liv-ing, not of the dead: Raise us to life be-yond our death! God of the liv-ing, not of the dead: Raise us to life be-yond our death!

Text: David Haas
Music: David Haas
© 1988, GIA Publications, Inc.

PREPARATORY RITES

Various preparation rites take place during the day on Holy Saturday. These include prayer, recitation of the Creed, and the rite of Ephphetha (opening of ears and mouth).

SACRAMENTS OF INITIATION

The sacraments of initiation take place at the Easter Vigil.

PERIOD OF MYSTAGOGIA

"Mystagogia" refers to the fifty-day period of postbaptismal catechesis and celebration when the newly baptized are gradually drawn by the community into the fullness of Christian life and prayer. The newly baptized retain a special place in the assembly and are mentioned in the prayers of intercession. A special celebration, on Pentecost or just before, may mark the conclusion of the whole period of initiation.

ADDITIONAL REPERTOIRE

These acclamations may be incorporated into the various Rites of Christian Initiation of Adults.

151

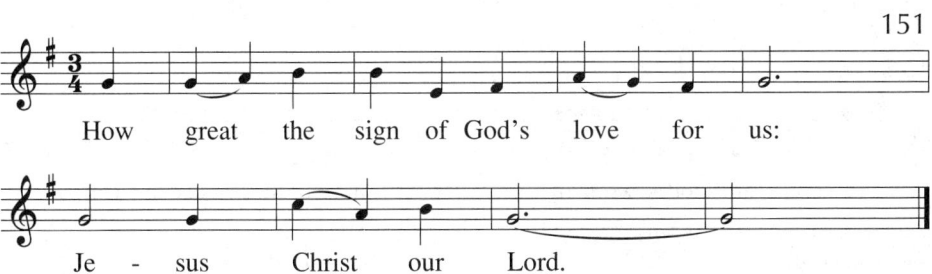

How great the sign of God's love for us: Je-sus Christ our Lord.

Text: *Rite of Christian Initiation of Adults,* © 1985, ICEL
Music: Paul M. French, © 2011, GIA Publications, Inc.

152

O - pen *their minds to know you, Lord; o - pen their ears to hear your voice; o - pen their hearts now to your Word; come to us now, O Lord, our God.

*Or: our

Text: David Haas, © 1991, GIA Publications, Inc.
Tune: OLD HUNDREDTH, LM; Louis Bourgeois, c.1510–1561

153

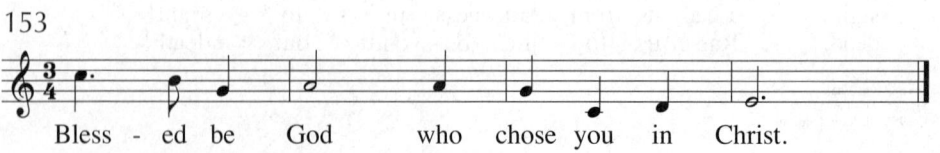

Bless - ed be God who chose you in Christ.

Text: *Rite of Baptism for Children*, © 1969, ICEL
Music: Eugene Englert, © 1986, GIA Publications, Inc.

154

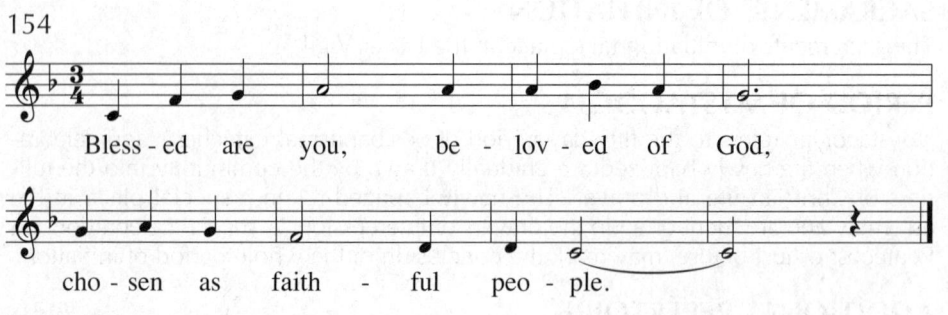

Bless - ed are you, be - lov - ed of God, cho - sen as faith - ful peo - ple.

Text: Jeanne Cotter
Music: Jeanne Cotter
© 1991, GIA Publications, Inc.

155

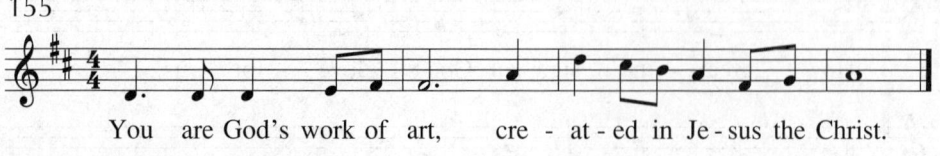

You are God's work of art, cre - at - ed in Je - sus the Christ.

Text: Ephesians 2:10, *Rite of Baptism*, David Haas, b.1957
Tune: David Haas, b.1957
© 1988, GIA Publications, Inc.

Baptism of Children 156

Children are baptized in the faith of the Church: of parents, godparents, the local parish, the Church throughout the world, the saints. Bringing their children for baptism, the parents profess their commitment to make a home where the gospel is lived. And the godparents and all members of the community promise to support the parents in this. Thus the children enter the waters of baptism and so are joined to this people, all baptized into the death and resurrection of Christ.

Baptism is celebrated above all at the Easter Vigil, but also on other Sundays, for Sunday is the Lord's Day, the day when the Church gathers to proclaim the paschal mystery. Baptism is always celebrated in an assembly of members of the Church and may take place at Sunday Mass.

RECEPTION OF THE CHILDREN 157

The people may sing a psalm or hymn suitable for the occasion as the priest/deacon goes to meet the parents and godparents at the entrance of the church, or as all process into the church.

The parents and godparents are welcomed by all. The priest/deacon asks the names of the children and questions the parents about their own expectations and willingness to take on the responsibilities this baptism brings. The godparents are asked if they are ready to assist the parents in their responsibilities as Christian mothers and fathers.

With joy, then, the priest/deacon, the parents and godparents make the sign of the cross on the child's forehead as the priest or deacon says: "I claim you for Christ our Savior by the sign of his cross."

If there is to be a procession to the place where Scripture will be read, the following antiphon, or a hymn, may be sung:

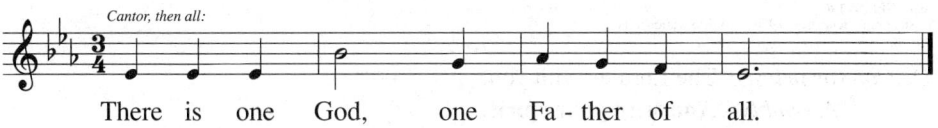

Cantor, then all:

There is one God, one Fa - ther of all.

Text: *Rite of Baptism for Children,* © 1969, ICEL
Music: Robert J. Batastini, © 2011, GIA Publications, Inc.

LITURGY OF THE WORD 158

FIRST READINGS

One or more passages from Scripture are read. At the conclusion of each:

Reader: The word of the Lord.
Assembly: **Thanks be to God.**

RESPONSORIAL PSALM

The following psalm, or a setting of Psalm 23 or 34, may follow the first reading:

Refrain

The Lord is my light and my sal - va - tion.

Text: *Lectionary for Mass,* © 1969, ICEL
Music: Howard Hughes, SM, © 1985, GIA Publications, Inc.

Verses

The LORD is my light and my salvation; whom shall I fear?

The LORD is the stronghold of my life; whom should I dread? ℟.

There is one thing I ask of the Lord,
only this do I seek:
to live in the house of the Lord
all the days of my life,
to gaze on the beauty of the Lord,
to inquire at his temple. ℟.

I believe I shall see the Lord's goodness
in the land of the living.
Wait for the Lord; be strong;
be stouthearted, and wait for the Lord! ℟.

Text: Psalm 27:1, 4, 13–14, *The Revised Grail Psalms*, © 2010, Conception Abbey and The Grail, admin. by GIA Publications, Inc.
Music: Michel Guimont, © 1995, GIA Publications, Inc.

159 GOSPEL

Before the gospel reading, an acclamation is sung:

Al - le - lu - ia,   al - le - lu - ia,   al - le - lu - ia.

Music: Chant Mode VI; acc. by Richard Proulx, © 1985, GIA Publications, Inc.

During Lent:

Praise to you, Lord Je - sus Christ,   King of end - less glo - ry!

Text: ICEL, © 1969
Music: Frank Schoen, © 1970, GIA Publications, Inc.

Deacon (or priest): The Lord be with you.
    Assembly: **And with your spirit.**
      Deacon: A reading from the holy Gospel according to N.
    Assembly: **Glory to you, O Lord.**

After the reading:

    Deacon: The Gospel of the Lord.
    Assembly: **Praise to you, Lord Jesus Christ.**

INTERCESSIONS

All join in prayer for the Church, the needs of the world, the poor, the children to be baptized and their parents. All respond with: **Lord, hear our prayer**, *or a similar response.*

160 *This prayer concludes with the litany of the saints, which may include the patron saints of the children and of the local Church.*

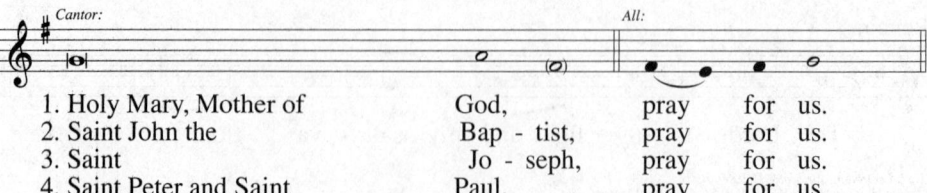

1. Holy Mary, Mother of   God,   pray   for us.
2. Saint John the   Bap - tist,   pray   for us.
3. Saint   Jo - seph,   pray   for us.
4. Saint Peter and Saint   Paul,   pray   for us.

The names of other saints may be added here. The litany concludes:

5. All holy men and women, Saints of God,   pray   for us.

PRAYER OF EXORCISM AND ANOINTING 161

The priest/deacon stands before the parents with their infants and prays that God deliver these children from the power of evil. The children may be anointed with the oil of catechumens, an anointing which makes them strong for their struggle against evil in their lives. Or, the priest/deacon may lay hands on each child to show the love and concern the Church has for them. If there is a procession to the baptistry, the following may be sung:

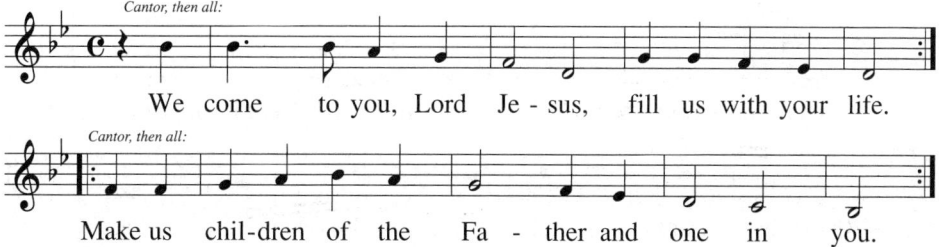

Text: *Rite of Baptism for Children,* © 1969, ICEL
Music: Ronald Arnatt, © 1984, GIA Publications, Inc.

SACRAMENT OF BAPTISM 162

BLESSING AND INVOCATION OF GOD OVER BAPTISMAL WATER

When all are gathered at the font, the priest/deacon leads a blessing of the water, unless the baptismal water has already been blessed. The following response may be sung:

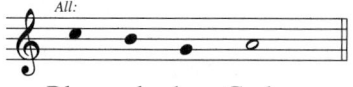

RENUNCIATION OF SIN AND PROFESSION OF FAITH 163

The priest/deacon then questions the parents and godparents, and they make a renunciation of sin and evil and profess their faith. The assembly listens to their responses. The priest/ deacon then invites all to give their assent to this profession of faith, using the following formulary, a similar one, or a suitable song by which the community expresses its faith with a single voice.

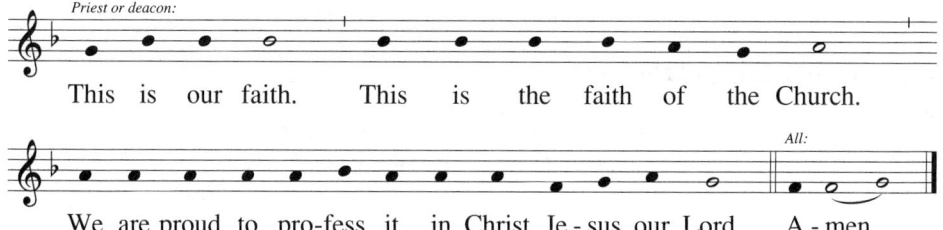

Text: *Rite of Baptism for Children,* © 1969, ICEL

164 BAPTISM

One by one, the infants are brought to the font by their parents. There the parents express their desire to have their child baptized in the faith of the Church which they have professed. The infant is then immersed in the water three times (or water is poured over the infant's head three times) as the priest/deacon says: "N., I baptize you in the name of the Father, and of the Son, and of the Holy Spirit." All may respond to each baptism with an acclamation.

You have put on Christ, in him you have been bap - tized.

Al - le - lu - ia, al - le - lu - ia.

*May be sung in canon.

Text: *Rite of Baptism for Children*, © 1969, ICEL
Music: Howard Hughes, SM, © 1977, ICEL

During Lent:

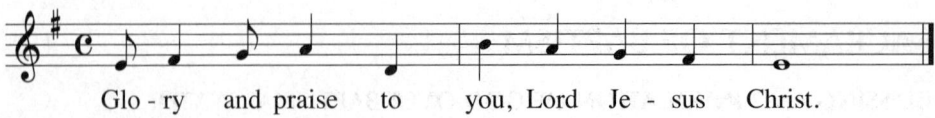

Glo - ry and praise to you, Lord Je - sus Christ.

Text: *Rite of Christian Initiation of Adults*, © 1969, ICEL
Music: Marty Haugen, © 1995, GIA Publications, Inc.

165 ANOINTING WITH CHRISM

The priest/deacon anoints each child on the crown of the head with holy chrism, a mixture of oil and perfume. The word "Christ" means "anointed." The baptized child has been "Christ-ed" and the sweet smell of the anointing reminds all of this.

CLOTHING WITH THE BAPTISMAL GARMENT AND GIVING OF THE CANDLE

The infants are then clothed in baptismal garments and a candle for each of the newly bap-tized is lighted from the paschal candle.

(Optional) EPHPHETHA

The priest/deacon may touch the ears and mouth of each child: "May Jesus soon touch your ears to receive his word, and your mouth to proclaim his faith."

CONCLUSION AND BLESSING

If baptism is celebrated at Mass, the liturgy continues with the Eucharist. Otherwise, all process to the altar, carrying lighted candles. The above acclamation may be sung again dur-ing this procession. All then pray the Lord's Prayer, the parents are blessed, after which all respond: **Amen***, and the liturgy concludes with a hymn of praise and thanksgiving.*

ADDITIONAL REPERTOIRE

These acclamations may be incorporated into the various Rites of Baptism.

166

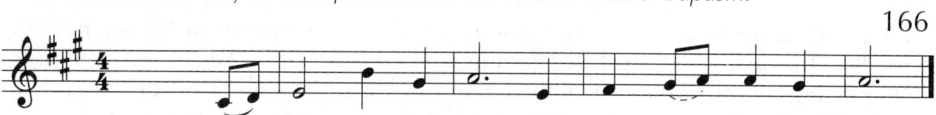

Anointing after baptism: Re - joice, Child of God! Be sealed in the life of Christ!
Baptismal garment: Re - joice, Child of God! Be clothed in the love of Christ!
Presentation of candle: Re - joice, Child of God! Re - ceive the Light of Christ!

Text: David Haas
Music: David Haas
© 1991, GIA Publications, Inc.

167

Cantor: There is one God, one Fa - ther of all. There is

one God, one Fa-ther of all. *Cantor:* He is o - ver all, and

through all, he lives in all of us. *Assembly:* There is one God, one

Fa-ther of all. *Cantor:* All of us are one, u - nit-ed in Christ

Assembly: Je - sus. There is one God, one Fa-ther of all.

Text: *Rite of Baptism for Children*, © 1969, ICEL
Music: Calvin Hampton; acc. by Chris DeBlasio, © 1986, GIA Publications, Inc.

168 Confirmation

Along with baptism and eucharist, confirmation is a sacrament of Christian initiation. It is the seal of baptism, the giving of the Holy Spirit. Adults are confirmed immediately after their baptism at the Easter Vigil. Children who have been baptized as infants are confirmed some years later. The bishop or his delegate presides over the celebration. The rite is usually celebrated within Mass; the introductory rites are done in the usual way.

169 LITURGY OF THE WORD

FIRST READINGS

One or more passages from Scripture are read. At the conclusion of each:

Reader: The word of the Lord.
Assembly: **Thanks be to God.**

RESPONSORIAL PSALM

The following psalm, or a setting of Psalm 23 or 96, may follow the first reading:

Refrain

Lord, send out your Spir-it, and re-new the face of the earth.

Text: *Lectionary for Mass*, © 1969, 1981, 1997, ICEL
Music: Richard Proulx, © 1975, GIA Publications, Inc.

Verses

Bless the LORD, O my soul!
O LORD my God, how great you are.
How many are your works, O LORD!
In wisdom you have made them all.
The earth is full of your creatures. ℟.

You send forth your spirit, and they
   are created,
and you renew the face of the earth.
May the glory of the LORD last forever!
May the LORD rejoice in his works! ℟.

All of these look to you
to give them their food in due season.
You give it, they gather it up;
you open wide your hand, they are well
   filled. ℟.

I will sing to the LORD all my life,
sing psalms to my God while I live.
May my thoughts be pleasing to him.
I will rejoice in the LORD. ℟.

Text: Psalm 104:1 and 24, 27–28, 30–31, 33–34, *The Revised Grail Psalms*, © 2010, Conception Abbey and The Grail, admin. by
   GIA Publications, Inc.
Music: Joseph Gelineau, SJ, © 1963, The Grail, GIA Publications, Inc., agent

170 GOSPEL

Before the gospel reading, an acclamation is sung:

Cantor, then all:

Al - le - lu - ia, al - le - lu - ia, al - le - lu - ia.

Music: Chant Mode VI; acc. by Richard Proulx, © 1985, GIA Publications, Inc.

During Lent:

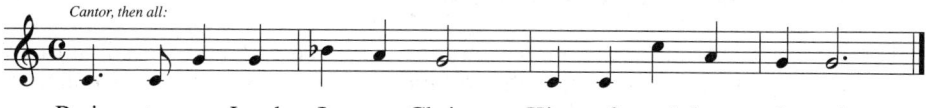

Praise to you, Lord Je - sus Christ, King of end - less glo - ry!

Text: ICEL, © 1969
Music: Frank Schoen, © 1970, GIA Publications, Inc.

Deacon (or priest): The Lord be with you.
 Assembly: **And with your spirit.**
  Deacon: A reading from the holy Gospel according to N.
 Assembly: **Glory to you, O Lord.**

After the reading:

  Deacon: The Gospel of the Lord.
 Assembly: **Praise to you, Lord Jesus Christ.**

SACRAMENT OF CONFIRMATION   171

PRESENTATION OF THE CANDIDATES
The pastor or another minister calls the candidates by name to come forward. Sponsors may accompany candidates.

HOMILY

RENEWAL OF BAPTISMAL PROMISES   172
The bishop leads the candidates in the renunciation of sin and evil and the profession of their faith. When the candidates have responded, the bishop invites all to give their assent to this profession of faith, using the following formulary, a similar one, or a suitable song by which the community expresses its faith with a single voice.

This is our faith. This is the faith of the Church.

We are proud to pro-fess it in Christ Je - sus our Lord. A - men.

Text: *Rite of Baptism for Children*, © 1969, ICEL

LAYING ON OF HANDS
Over and over the Church makes this gesture in the sacraments as a blessing, a sign of solidarity and love. Here the bishop prays for the coming of the Holy Spirit on those confirmed.

ANOINTING WITH CHRISM
Chrism is a mixture of olive oil and perfume that has been consecrated by the bishop at the end of Lent. The meaning of "Christ" is "the anointed," so in this gesture the candidate is anointed, sealed, to follow in the way of Christ. The bishop rubs the chrism into the forehead of each candidate and says: "N., be sealed with the gift of the Holy Spirit," and the newly confirmed person responds, "Amen." The bishop then says, "Peace be with you," and the newly confirmed person responds, "And with your spirit." The assembly may join in song during the anointing. Suitable songs include Veni Sancte Spiritus, no. 647, Holy Spirit, Come to Us, no. 644, Veni Creator Spiritus, no. 650, and Take, O Take Me As I Am, no. 764.

  After the anointing the liturgy continues with the prayer of the faithful and the liturgy of the eucharist. If confirmation is celebrated apart from Mass, the intercessions are followed by the Lord's Prayer (see no. 244), the blessing, and the concluding hymn.

173 Holy Communion outside Mass

When for good reason Communion cannot be received at Mass, the faithful may share in the paschal mystery through the liturgy of the word and the reception of Holy Communion.

174 INTRODUCTORY RITES

An appropriate hymn or psalm may be sung.

GREETING

If the minister is a priest or deacon, the usual form of greeting is used:

Assembly: **And with your spirit.**

If the minister is not a priest or deacon, another form of greeting may be used:

Assembly: **Blessed be God for ever.**

PENITENTIAL ACT

The minister invites silent reflection and repentance. After some silence:

Assembly: **I confess to almighty God**
and to you, my brothers and sisters,
that I have greatly sinned,
in my thoughts and in my words,
in what I have done and in what I have failed to do,
All strike their breast as they say:
through my fault, through my fault,
through my most grievous fault;
therefore I ask blessed Mary ever-Virgin,
all the Angels and Saints,
and you, my brothers and sisters,
to pray for me to the Lord our God.

The forms found at nos. 229 and 230 may also be used.

175 CELEBRATION OF THE WORD OF GOD

FIRST READINGS

One or more passages from Scripture are read. At the conclusion of each:

Reader: The word of the Lord.
Assembly: **Thanks be to God.**

RESPONSORIAL PSALM

An appropriate psalm may follow the first reading.

GOSPEL 176

Before the gospel reading, an alleluia or Lenten acclamation is sung.

⎡*Deacon (or priest):* The Lord be with you.⎤
⎣   *Assembly:* **And with your spirit.**⎦
   Reader: A reading from the holy Gospel according to N.
   Assembly: **Glory to you, O Lord.**

After the reading:

   Reader: The Gospel of the Lord.
   Assembly: **Praise to you, Lord Jesus Christ.**

INTERCESSIONS

The assembly joins in prayer for the needs of the world, of the poor, and of the Church.

HOLY COMMUNION 177

The minister invites all to join in the Lord's Prayer, then to exchange a sign of peace. The minister then raises the eucharistic bread and all respond to the invitation.

Assembly: **Lord, I am not worthy**
that you should enter under my roof,
but only say the word
and my soul shall be healed.

A psalm or hymn may be sung during Communion. Afterwards, there may be a period of silence or the singing of a psalm or hymn. The minister then recites a concluding prayer.

CONCLUDING RITE

All are blessed and dismissed.

Presiding minister: Go in the peace of Christ.
   Assembly: **Thanks be to God.**

178 Eucharistic Exposition and Benediction

"Exposition of the holy eucharist . . . is intended to acknowledge Christ's marvelous presence in the sacrament. Exposition invites us to the spiritual union with him that culminates in sacramental communion. Thus it fosters very well the worship which is due to Christ in spirit and in truth.

   This kind of exposition must clearly express the cult of the blessed sacrament in its relationship to the Mass. The plan of the exposition should carefully avoid anything which might somehow obscure the principal desire of Christ in instituting the eucharist, namely, to be with us as food, medicine, and comfort" (*Holy Communion and Worship of the Eucharist outside of Mass*, #82).

179 EXPOSITION

As the priest or deacon prepares the holy eucharist for adoration, the following or another suitable song is sung:

1. O Sav - ing Vic - tim, o - p'ning wide The gate of heav'n to us be - low! Our foes press on from ev - 'ry side: Your aid sup - ply, your strength be - stow.
2. To your great name be end - less praise, Im - mor - tal God-head, One in Three; O grant us end - less length of days When our true na - tive land we see.

1. O sa - lu - tá - ris hó - sti - a, Quae cae - li pan - dis ó - sti - um: Bel - la pre - munt ho - stí - li - a, Da ro - bur fer au - xí - li - um.
2. U - ni tri - nó - que Dó - mi - no Sit sem - pi - tér - na gló - ri - a: Qui vi - tam si - ne tér - mi - no No - bis do - net in pá - tri - a.

Text: Thomas Aquinas, c.1225–1274; tr. by Edward Caswall, 1814–1878 and John Mason Neale, 1818–1866, alt.
Tune: DUGUET, LM; Dieudonné Duguet, 1794–1849

180 ADORATION

During the adoration there are prayers, songs, scripture readings, and possibly a homily to develop a better understanding of the eucharistic mystery. Silent prayer is also encouraged. If time allows, the Liturgy of the Hours may be celebrated here.

181 BENEDICTION

As the priest or deacon incenses the Blessed Sacrament, the following or another appropriate hymn or song may be sung:

1. Come a - dore this won - drous pres - ence; Bow to Christ, the
2. Glo - ry be to God the Fa - ther, Praise to his co -
1. *Tan - tum er - go Sa - cra - mén - tum Ve - ne - ré - mur*
2. *Ge - ni - tó - ri, Ge - ni - tó - que Laus et ju - bi -*

source of grace. Here is kept the an - cient prom - ise
e - qual Son, Ad - o - ra - tion to the Spir - it,
cér - nu - i: Et an - tí - quum do - cu - mén - tum
lá - ti - o, Sa - lus, ho - nor, vir - tus quo - que

Of God's earth - ly dwell - ing - place. Sight is blind be -
Bond of love, in God - head one. Blest be God by
No - vo ce - dat rí - tu - i: Prae - stet fi - des
Sit et be - ne - dí - cti - o: Pro - ce - dén - ti

fore God's glo - ry, Faith a - lone may see his face.
all cre - a - tion Joy - ous - ly while a - ges run.
sup - ple - mén - tum Sén - su - um de - fé - ctu - i.
ab u - tró - que Com - par sit lau - dá - ti - o.

Text: Thomas Aquinas, c.1225–1274; tr. by James Quinn, SJ, 1919–2010, © 1969, James Quinn, SJ. Published by OCP.
Tune: ST. THOMAS (Wade), 8 7 8 7 8 7; John F. Wade, 1711–1786

After a prayer, the priest or deacon blesses the assembly with the Blessed Sacrament.

REPOSITION 182

As the priest or deacon replaces the Sacrament in the tabernacle, the assembly may sing or say the following acclamations:

Blessed be God.
Blessed be his holy name.
Blessed be Jesus Christ, true God and true man.
Blessed be the name of Jesus.
Blessed be his most sacred heart.
Blessed be his most precious blood.
Blessed be Jesus in the most holy sacrament of the altar.
Blessed be the Holy Spirit, the Paraclete.
Blessed be the great Mother of God, Mary most holy.
Blessed be her holy and immaculate conception.
Blessed be her glorious assumption.
Blessed be the name of Mary, virgin and mother.
Blessed be Saint Joseph, her most chaste spouse.
Blessed be God in his angels and in his saints.

183 Reconciliation of Several Penitents

The sacrament of penance, also called the sacrament of reconciliation, may be celebrated with one penitent or with many. The latter form, the communal penance service, is a gathering of a few or a large number of Christians. Together they listen to Scripture, sing psalms and hymns, pray, individually confess their sins and receive absolution, then praise God whose mercy and love are greater than our evil. In the rite of penance, the members of the Church confront the struggle that was entered at baptism. There has been failure, evil done and good undone, but the penitent Church comes again and again to name and renounce its sins and to return to the way of the Lord.

184 INTRODUCTORY RITES

An appropriate hymn or psalm may be sung (see nos. 1060–1069).

GREETING

The priest greets the assembly, using these or other words:

> *Priest:* Grace to you and peace from God our Father
> and the Lord Jesus Christ.
> *Assembly:* **And with your spirit.**

OPENING PRAYER

After silent prayer, the priest concludes the gathering rite with a solemn prayer.

185 CELEBRATION OF THE WORD OF GOD

FIRST READINGS

One or more passages from Scripture are read. At the conclusion of each:

> *Reader:* The word of the Lord.
> *Assembly:* **Thanks be to God.**

RESPONSORIAL PSALM

The following psalm, or a setting of Psalm 25, 51, or 90, may follow the first reading:

Refrain

With the Lord there is mer-cy, and full-ness of re-demp-tion.

Verses

Out of the depths I cry to you, O Lord;
Lord, hear my voice!
O let your ears be attentive
to the sound of my pleadings. ℟.

If you, O Lord, should mark iniquities,
Lord, who could stand?
But with you is found forgiveness,
that you may be revered. ℟.

I long for you, O Lord,
my soul longs for his word.
My soul hopes in the Lord
more than watchmen for daybreak. ℟.

For with the Lord there is mercy,
in him is plentiful redemption.
It is he who will redeem Israel
from all its iniquities. ℟.

Text: Psalm 130:1–2, 3–4, 5–6, 7–8; *The Revised Grail Psalms*, © 2010, Conception Abbey and The Grail, admin. by GIA Publications, Inc.;
   refrain trans., © 1969, ICEL
Music: Michel Guimont, © 1995, GIA Publications, Inc.

GOSPEL   186

Before the gospel reading, an acclamation is sung:

Al - le - lu - ia,   al - le - lu - ia,   al - le - lu - ia.

Music: Chant Mode VI; acc. by Richard Proulx, © 1985, GIA Publications, Inc.

During Lent:

Praise   to you, Lord   Je - sus Christ,   King of end - less   glo - ry!

Text: ICEL, © 1969
Music: Frank Schoen, © 1970, GIA Publications, Inc.

Deacon (or priest): The Lord be with you.
     Assembly: **And with your spirit.**
       Deacon: A reading from the holy Gospel according to N.
     Assembly: **Glory to you, O Lord.**

After the reading:

       Deacon: The Gospel of the Lord.
     Assembly: **Praise to you, Lord Jesus Christ.**

HOMILY

EXAMINATION OF CONSCIENCE

In silence or through some other manner all reflect on their lives with sorrow for their sins.

SACRAMENT OF PENANCE   187

GENERAL CONFESSION OF SINS

Kneeling (or with another posture that expresses sorrow), all join in confession.
This form may be used:

Assembly: **I confess to almighty God**
        and to you, my brothers and sisters,
        that I have greatly sinned,
        in my thoughts and in my words,
        in what I have done and in what I have failed to do,
        All strike their breast as they say:
        through my fault, through my fault,
        through my most grievous fault;

> **therefore I ask blessed Mary ever-Virgin,
> all the Angels and Saints,
> and you, my brothers and sisters,
> to pray for me to the Lord our God.**

188

Standing, all join in a litany using one of the following responses, or a song asking God's mercy. The Lord's Prayer is then recited or sung (see no. 244).

A	**We pray you, hear us.**
B	**Lord, be merciful to me, a sinner.**
C	**Lord, have mercy.**

189   INDIVIDUAL CONFESSION AND ABSOLUTION

One by one the penitents approach the priest confessors. All confess their sins, accept some fitting act of satisfaction and the counsel of the confessor. Then the priest extends his hands over the penitent's head and speaks the prayer of absolution, concluding: "Through the ministry of the Church may God give you pardon and peace, and I absolve you from your sins in the name of the Father, and of the Son, and of the Holy Spirit." The penitent responds, "Amen." (Note: On those occasions when general absolution is permitted, the rest of the rite remains the same.)

190   PROCLAMATION OF PRAISE FOR GOD'S MERCY

The priest invites all to give thanks and to show by their lives—and in the life of the whole community—the grace of repentance. A psalm, canticle or hymn may be sung to proclaim God's mercy.

Refrain

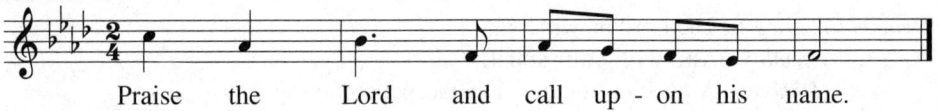

Praise the Lord and call up-on his name.

Text: *Rite of Penance,* © 1975, ICEL
Music: Robert J. Batastini, © 1986, GIA Publications, Inc.

Verses

I thank you, Lord, you were angry with me
but your anger has passed and you give me
   comfort. ℟.

Truly, God is my salvation,
I trust, I shall not fear.
For the Lord is my strength, my song,
he became my savior.
With joy you will draw water
from the wells of salvation. ℟.

Give thanks to the Lord, give praise to his
   name!
Make his mighty deeds known to the peoples!
Declare the greatness of his name,
sing a psalm to the Lord!
For he has done glorious deeds,
make them known to all the earth! ℟.

People of Zion, sing and shout for joy
for great in your midst is the Holy One of
   Israel. ℟.

Text: Isaiah 12:1–6; The Grail, © 1963, The Grail, GIA Publications, Inc., agent
Music: Michel Guimont, © 1995, GIA Publications, Inc.

CONCLUDING PRAYER OF THANKSGIVING

This prayer is spoken by the priest.

BLESSING AND DISMISSAL

The priest blesses all present and the deacon or other minister dismisses the assembly.
All respond: **Thanks be to God.**

Anointing of the Sick 191

The sacrament of the anointing of the sick is celebrated when a Christian's health is seriously impaired by sickness or old age. Through the anointing with the blessed oil of the sick, the Church supports those who struggle against illness or injury and continues the healing work of Christ. The anointing is intended to bring hope and comfort to those anointed and, to the gathered assembly of family and friends, a spirit of support and sharing in the sufferings of their brothers and sisters.

The anointing may be celebrated within Mass or outside Mass. In either case a liturgy of the word precedes the anointing. Following is the rite of anointing within Mass.

INTRODUCTORY RITES 192

An appropriate hymn or psalm may be sung (see nos. 1052–1059).

GREETING

After all make the sign of the cross, the priest greets the assembly, using these or other words.

> *Priest:* The grace of our Lord Jesus Christ,
> and the love of God,
> and the communion of the Holy Spirit
> be with you all.
>
> *Assembly:* **And with your spirit.**

The priest introduces the celebration, and the penitential act may follow (see Order of Mass, nos. 229 and 230). Then, after a period of silence, he says the opening prayer, to which all respond: **Amen**.

LITURGY OF THE WORD 193

FIRST READINGS

One or more passages from Scripture are read. At the conclusion of each:

> *Reader:* The word of the Lord.
> *Assembly:* **Thanks be to God.**

RESPONSORIAL PSALM

The following psalm, or a setting of Psalm 25, 27, 34, 42, 63, 90, or 103, may follow the first reading:

Refrain

My God, my God, come quick-ly to help me.

Verses

In you, O Lord, I take refuge;
let me never be put to shame.
In your justice, rescue me, free me;
incline your ear to me and save me. ℟.

It is you, O Lord, who are my hope,
my trust, O Lord, from my youth.
On you I have leaned from my birth;
from my mother's womb, you have
been my help. ℟.

My mouth is filled with your praise,	But as for me, I will always hope,
with your glory, all the day long.	and praise you more and more.
Do not reject me now that I am old;	My mouth will tell of your justice,
when my strength fails do not forsake me. ℟.	and all the day long of your salvation. ℟.

Text: Psalm 71:1–2, 5–6, 8–9, 14–15, *The Revised Grail Psalms*, © 2010, Conception Abbey and The Grail, admin. by GIA Publications, Inc.;
refrain from *Pastoral Care of the Sick: Rites of Anointing and Viaticum*, © 1982, ICEL
Music: Paul M. French, © 2011, GIA Publications, Inc.

194 GOSPEL

Before the gospel reading, an acclamation is sung:

Al - le - lu - ia,   al - le - lu - ia,   al - le - lu - ia.

Music: Chant Mode VI; acc. by Richard Proulx, © 1985, GIA Publications, Inc.

During Lent:

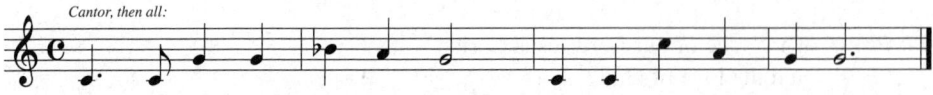

Praise to you, Lord   Je - sus Christ,   King of end - less   glo - ry!

Text: ICEL, © 1969
Music: Frank Schoen, © 1970, GIA Publications, Inc.

Deacon (or priest): The Lord be with you.
    Assembly: **And with your spirit.**
     Deacon: A reading from the holy Gospel according to N.
    Assembly: **Glory to you, O Lord.**

After the reading:

     Deacon: The Gospel of the Lord.
    Assembly: **Praise to you, Lord Jesus Christ.**

HOMILY

195 LITURGY OF ANOINTING

LITANY

The assembly joins in prayers for the sick and for those who care for them. Each petition concludes with "Lord, have mercy," and all repeat:

Lord, have mer - cy.

LAYING ON OF HANDS

The priest silently lays hands on the head of each sick person in a gesture of prayer, healing and solidarity.

PRAYER OVER THE OIL   196

If the oil is already blessed, the priest leads a prayer of thanksgiving over it.
After each invocation:

Bless - ed   be   God   who   heals   us   in   Christ.

Text: *Pastoral Care of the Sick: Rites of Anointing and Viaticum,* © 1982, ICEL
Music: Paul M. French, © 2011, GIA Publications, Inc.

If the oil is not blessed, the priest says the prayer of blessing.

ANOINTING   197

The priest anoints each sick person on the forehead, saying:

Through this holy anointing may the Lord in his love and mercy help you with the grace of the Holy Spirit.

Assembly: **Amen.**

The priest anoints the hands of each sick person, saying:

May the Lord who frees you from sin save you and raise you up.

Assembly: **Amen.**

The priest may anoint other parts of the body.

PRAYER AFTER ANOINTING

The priest prays for those who have been anointed. Then the liturgy of the eucharist is celebrated with special prayers for the sick (see Order of Mass, no. 237).

If the rite of anointing is celebrated outside Mass, the liturgy begins with the greeting, introduction, and penitential act (or sacrament of penance). After the scripture readings a period of silence is observed, or the priest gives a brief homily. The liturgy of anointing is celebrated as above. Then the Lord's Prayer is recited or sung, the liturgy of Holy Communion may follow, and a final blessing is given.

198 Marriage

The mutual and lifelong commitment of a man and a woman in marriage is viewed by the Church as a sacred covenant. When two Christians marry, it is also a sacrament, an effective sign of the presence of God in the world and a symbol of Christ's love for his Church. In the sacrament of matrimony God's special graces are given to the couple to live out "in mutual and lasting fidelity" the vows they make to each other and to God in the presence of the Christian community.

At their wedding the bride and groom themselves are the ministers of the sacrament to each other; the priest or deacon who presides over the wedding serves as the authorized witness of the Church and prays the nuptial blessing of the Church over the spouses.

The rite of marriage may be celebrated at Mass or outside of Mass. In either case the rite begins with a liturgy of the word: the proclamation of God's faithful love by means of readings from Scripture and a reflection on them (the homily). The following elements are included in all celebrations.

199 INTRODUCTORY RITES

An appropriate hymn or psalm may be sung during the procession or immediately after it (see nos. 1070–1077).

GREETING

After all make the sign of the cross, the priest or deacon greets the assembly, using these or other words.

> *Priest:* The grace of our Lord Jesus Christ,
> and the love of God,
> and the communion of the Holy Spirit
> be with you all.
> *Assembly:* **And with your spirit.**

GLORY TO GOD

The Gloria is sung.

OPENING PRAYER

The priest or deacon introduces the celebration and, after a period of silence, says the opening prayer, to which all respond: **Amen**. *All then sit.*

200 LITURGY OF THE WORD

FIRST READINGS

One or more passages from Scripture are read. At the conclusion of each:

> *Reader:* The word of the Lord.
> *Assembly:* **Thanks be to God.**

RESPONSORIAL PSALM

The following psalm, or a setting of Psalm 33, 103, or 128, may follow the first reading:

Refrain

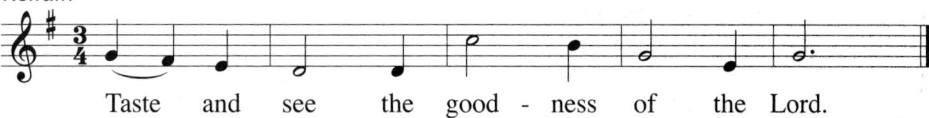

Taste and see the good - ness of the Lord.

Verses

I will bless the LORD at all times;
praise of him is always in my mouth.
In the LORD my soul shall make its boast;
the humble shall hear and be glad. ℟.

Glorify the LORD with me;
together let us praise his name.
I sought the LORD, and he answered me;
from all my terrors he set me free. ℟.

Look toward him and be radiant;
let your faces not be abashed.
This lowly one called; the LORD heard,
and rescued him from all his distress. ℟.

The angel of the LORD is encamped
around those who fear him, to rescue them.
Taste and see that the LORD is good.
Blessed the man who seeks refuge in
him. ℟.

Text: Psalm 34:2–9, *The Revised Grail Psalms*, © 2010, Conception Abbey and The Grail, admin. by GIA Publications, Inc.; refrain trans. © 1969,
ICEL
Music: Michel Guimont, © 2004, GIA Publications, Inc.

GOSPEL   201

Before the gospel reading, all stand as an acclamation is sung:

Al - le - lu - ia,   al - le - lu - ia,   al - le - lu - ia.

Music: Chant Mode VI; acc. by Richard Proulx, © 1985, GIA Publications, Inc.

During Lent:

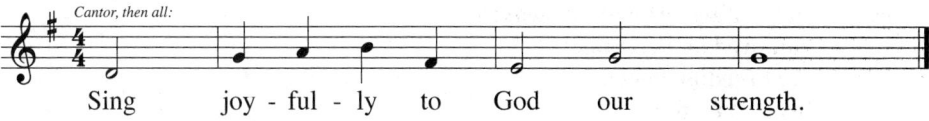

Sing   joy - ful - ly   to   God   our   strength.

Text: ICEL, © 2013
Music: Kyle Cothern, © 2016, GIA Publications, Inc.

Deacon (or priest): The Lord be with you.
Assembly: **And with your spirit.**
Deacon: A reading from the holy Gospel according to N.
Assembly: **Glory to you, O Lord.**

After the reading:

Deacon: The Gospel of the Lord.
Assembly: **Praise to you, Lord Jesus Christ.**

HOMILY *(All sit)*

202 THE CELEBRATION OF MATRIMONY
Stand

QUESTIONS BEFORE CONSENT
The couple is questioned about their freedom of choice, fidelity to each other, and the acceptance and upbringing of children.

CONSENT
The couple declares their consent to one another.

RECEPTION OF THE CONSENT
The priest or deacon addresses the couple, and then invites all present to praise God for this couple. The following, or a similar response, may be sung:

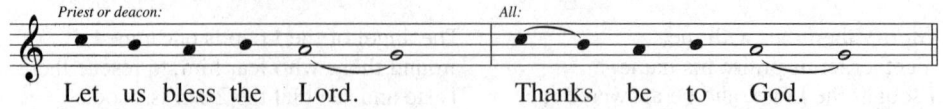

Let us bless the Lord.   Thanks be to God.

BLESSING AND GIVING OF RINGS
Wedding rings are blessed, and then exchanged by the couple. The blessing and giving of the arras (coins) may take place following the blessing and giving of rings. Likewise, the crowning of the bride or veiling of the spouses may take place.

In the prayer of the faithful the Church prays for the needs of the world, the local community, and the newly married couple. A common response to each petition is: **Lord, hear our prayer.**

If the liturgy of the eucharist does not follow the rite of marriage, the priest or deacon prays the nuptial blessing at the end of the prayer of the faithful. The celebration concludes with the Lord's Prayer and a final blessing.

When the liturgy of the eucharist follows the rite of marriage, the nuptial blessing is given after the Lord's Prayer before Holy Communion. Everything else follows the Order of Mass, beginning with the presentation and preparation of the gifts. The bride and groom may bring the bread and wine to the altar (see Order of Mass, no. 237).

203 THE LORD'S PRAYER
Assembly: **Our Father, who art in heaven,**
          hallowed be thy name;
          thy kingdom come,
          thy will be done
          on earth as it is in heaven.
          Give us this day our daily bread,
          and forgive us our trespasses,
          as we forgive those who trespass against us;
          and lead us not into temptation,
          but deliver us from evil.

BLESSING AND DISMISSAL
All respond to each part of the blessing: **Amen.**

   Deacon or priest: Go in peace.
      Assembly: **Thanks be to God.**

A hymn or instrumental music may follow.

Order of Christian Funerals 204

The rites which surround the death of a Christian extend from Viaticum (the last Holy Communion) and final prayers before death through the wake service and funeral liturgy to the burial of the body or cremated remains. In all of this the community affirms its faith in the communion of saints and the resurrection of the dead. The family and friends are helped in their time of sorrow with prayer and song. Thus they express present grief even as they hold to the Church's lasting hope.

I. Vigil For The Deceased

The Vigil for the Deceased, commonly known as a wake service, provides an opportunity for the gathered community and family to pray for the deceased, share remembrances of the deceased, and comfort one another. Commonly celebrated in a funeral home the day and evening before the funeral Mass, the vigil may also be celebrated in the church immediately before the funeral Mass.

INTRODUCTORY RITES 205

GREETING

SPRINKLING WITH HOLY WATER AND PLACING OF CHRISTIAN SYMBOLS
When the Vigil for the Deceased is celebrated in the church immediately prior to the funeral Mass, the coffin may be sprinkled with holy water. The pall may also be placed on the coffin; likewise, Christian symbols may be placed on the coffin.

INVITATION TO PRAYER
All are invited to pray silently.

OPENING PRAYER
At the conclusion of the prayer all respond: **Amen.**

LITURGY OF THE WORD 206

FIRST READINGS
One or more passages from Scripture are read. At the conclusion of each:

Reader: The word of the Lord.
Assembly: **Thanks be to God.**

RESPONSORIAL PSALM
The following psalm may follow the first reading:

Refrain

The Lord is my light and my sal - va - tion.

Text: *Lectionary for Mass,* © 1969, 1981, 1997, ICEL
Music: Richard Proulx, © 1975, GIA Publications, Inc.

Verses

The LORD is my light and my salvation;
whom shall I fear?

The LORD is the stronghold of my life;
whom should I dread? ℟.

There is one thing I ask of the LORD,
only this do I seek:
to live in the house of the LORD
all the days of my life,
to gaze on the beauty of the LORD,
to inquire at his temple. ℟.

O LORD, hear my voice when I call;

have mercy and answer me.
Of you my heart has spoken,
"Seek his face." ℟.

I believe I shall see the LORD's goodness
in the land of the living.
Wait for the LORD; be strong;
be stouthearted, and wait for the LORD! ℟.

Text: Psalm 27:1, 4, 7–8, 13–14, *The Revised Grail Psalms*, © 2010, Conception Abbey and The Grail, admin. by GIA Publications, Inc.
Music: Joseph Gelineau, SJ, © 1963, The Grail, GIA Publications, Inc., agent

207 GOSPEL

Before the gospel reading, all stand as an acclamation is sung:

Al - le - lu - ia,   al - le - lu - ia,   al - le - lu - ia.

Music: Chant Mode VI; acc. by Richard Proulx, © 1985, GIA Publications, Inc.

During Lent:

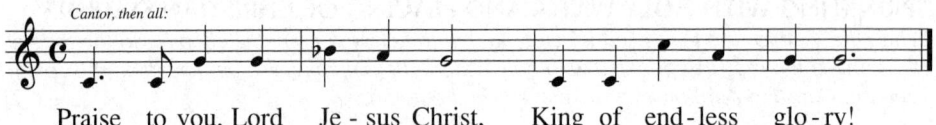

Praise to you, Lord Je - sus Christ, King of end - less glo - ry!

Text: ICEL, © 1969
Music: Frank Schoen, © 1970, GIA Publications, Inc.

Deacon (or priest): The Lord be with you.
Assembly: **And with your spirit.**
Deacon: A reading from the holy Gospel according to N.
Assembly: **Glory to you, O Lord.**

After the reading:

Deacon: The Gospel of the Lord.
Assembly: **Praise to you, Lord Jesus Christ.**

HOMILY
A priest or deacon may offer a brief homily, or a parish staff member or other minister may offer a brief reflection on the readings.

208 PRAYER OF INTERCESSION

LITANY
All respond with: **Lord, hear our prayer**, *or a similar response.*

THE LORD'S PRAYER

Assembly: **Our Father, who art in heaven,**
hallowed be thy name;
thy kingdom come,
thy will be done
on earth as it is in heaven.
Give us this day our daily bread,
and forgive us our trespasses,
as we forgive those who trespass against us;
and lead us not into temptation,
but deliver us from evil.

CONCLUDING PRAYER

At the conclusion of the prayer, all respond: **Amen.** *A member or friend of the family may speak in remembrance of the deceased.*

CONCLUDING RITES 209

BLESSING

The leader prays a short prayer and then says:

> *Leader:* Eternal rest grant unto him/her, Lord.
> *Assembly:* **And let perpetual light shine upon him/her.**
> *Leader:* May his/her soul and the souls of all the faithful departed,
> through the mercy of God, rest in peace.
> *Assembly:* **Amen.**

A final prayer is prayed and at its conclusion all respond: **Amen.**

II. Funeral Mass 210

The funeral liturgy may be celebrated within Mass or outside Mass. In either case the rite begins with a liturgy of the word. The following elements are included in all celebrations.

INTRODUCTORY RITES 211

GREETING

All stand as the priest (or deacon) greets the assembly at the door, using these or other words.

> *Priest:* Grace to you and peace from God our Father
> and the Lord Jesus Christ.
> *Assembly:* **And with your spirit.**

The body is sprinkled with holy water, a reminder of baptism. The family or pall bearers spread the pall, a garment like that which the Christian received at baptism, over the body. The funeral procession then moves into the church accompanied by an appropriate hymn or psalm.

Refrain

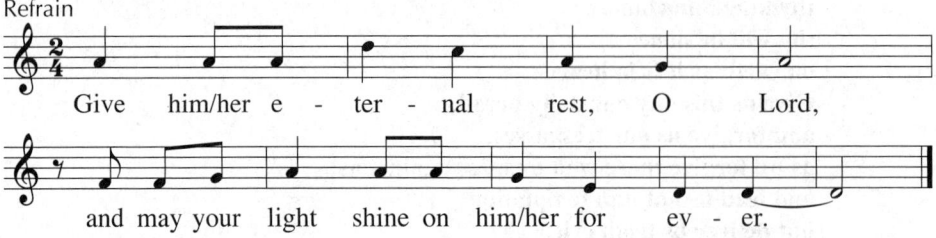

Give him/her e - ter - nal rest, O Lord, and may your light shine on him/her for ev - er.

Text: *Order of Christian Funerals*, © 1985, ICEL
Music: Robert J. Batastini, © 1986, GIA Publications, Inc.

Verses

I love the LORD, for he has heard
my voice, my appeal;
for he has turned his ear to me
whenever I call. ℟.

They surrounded me, the snares of death;
the anguish of the grave has found me;
anguish and sorrow I found.
I called on the name of the LORD:
"Deliver my soul, O LORD!" ℟.

How gracious is the LORD, and just;
our God has compassion.

The LORD protects the simple;
I was brought low, and he saved me. ℟.

Turn back, my soul, to your rest,
for the LORD has been good to you;
he has kept my soul from death,
my eyes from tears, and my feet from
    stumbling. ℟.

I will walk in the presence of the LORD
in the land of the living.
Praise the Father, the Son and Holy Spirit,
for ever and ever. ℟.

Text: Psalm 116A, *The Revised Grail Psalms*, © 2010, Conception Abbey and The Grail, admin. by GIA Publications, Inc.
Music: Joseph Gelineau, SJ, © 1963, The Grail, GIA Publications, Inc., agent

OPENING PRAYER
After silent prayer, the priest concludes the introductory rites with a solemn prayer, to which all respond: **Amen.**

212 LITURGY OF THE WORD

FIRST READINGS
One or more passages from Scripture are read. At the conclusion of each:
   Reader: The word of the Lord.
Assembly: **Thanks be to God.**

RESPONSORIAL PSALM
The following psalm, or a setting of Psalm 25, 27, 42, 63, 103, 116, 122, or 130, may follow the first reading:

Refrain

The Lord is my shep-herd; there is noth-ing I shall want.

Text: *Lectionary for Mass*, © 1969, 1981, 1997, ICEL
Music: Richard Proulx, © 1975, GIA Publications, Inc.

Verses

The L̲ord is my shepherd;
there is nothing I shall want.
Fresh and green are the pastures
where he gives me repose.
Near restful waters he leads me;
he revives my soul. ℟.

He guides me along the right path,
for the sake of his name.
Though I should walk in the valley
    of the shadow of death,
no evil would I fear, for you are with me.

Your crook and your staff will give
    me comfort. ℟.

You have prepared a table before me
in the sight of my foes.
My head you have anointed with oil;
my cup is overflowing. ℟.

Surely goodness and mercy shall follow me
all the days of my life.
In the L̲ord's own house shall I dwell
for length of days unending. ℟.

Text: Psalm 23, *The Revised Grail Psalms*, © 2010, Conception Abbey and The Grail, admin. by GIA Publications, Inc.
Music: Joseph Gelineau, SJ, © 1963, The Grail, GIA Publications, Inc., agent

GOSPEL   213

Before the gospel reading, all stand as an acclamation is sung:

Al - le - lu - ia,   al - le - lu - ia,   al - le - lu - ia.

Music: Chant Mode VI; acc. by Richard Proulx, © 1985, GIA Publications, Inc.

During Lent:

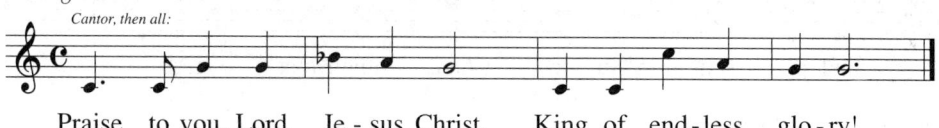

Praise to you, Lord Je - sus Christ, King of end - less glo - ry!

Text: ICEL, © 1969
Music: Frank Schoen, © 1970, GIA Publications, Inc.

Deacon (or priest): The Lord be with you.
   Assembly: **And with your spirit.**
    Deacon: A reading from the holy Gospel according to N.
   Assembly: **Glory to you, O Lord.**

After the reading:

    Deacon: The Gospel of the Lord.
   Assembly: **Praise to you, Lord Jesus Christ.**

HOMILY *(All sit)*

PRAYER OF THE FAITHFUL
*All join in prayer for the deceased, for grieving family members and friends, and for the needs
of the Church and the world. All respond with:* **Lord, hear our prayer***, or a similar response.*

If the funeral liturgy is celebrated within Mass, the liturgy of the eucharist follows (see Order of Mass, no. 237). During the eucharistic prayer, special remembrance is made of the deceased. Following the prayer after communion, the funeral liturgy concludes with the final commendation (below).

When the funeral liturgy is celebrated outside Mass, the final commendation follows the prayer of the faithful.

214 FINAL COMMENDATION

The ministers and assembly gather around the body of the deceased. After an invitation to prayer, all pray silently. The coffin may then be sprinkled with holy water and incensed, or this may take place during or after the song of farewell.

215 SONG OF FAREWELL

One of the following or another appropriate responsory (see nos. 1084 and 1085) or song may be sung.

Refrain

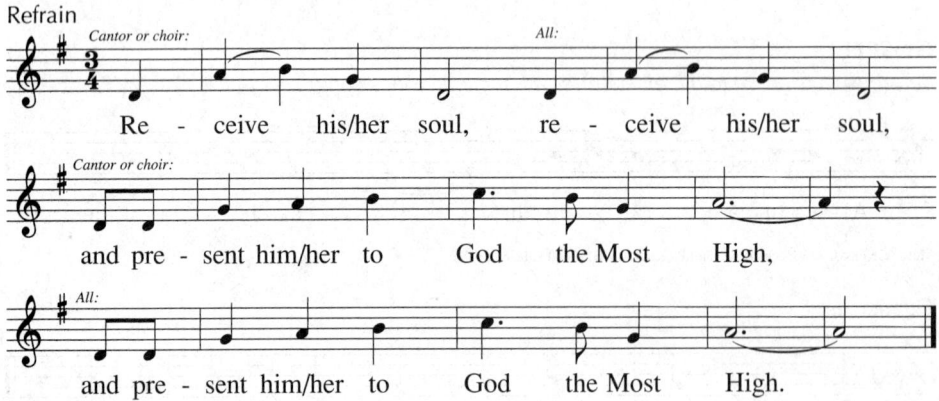

Re - ceive his/her soul, re - ceive his/her soul, and pre - sent him/her to God the Most High, and pre - sent him/her to God the Most High.

Text: *Order of Christian Funerals,* © 1985, ICEL
Music: Steven R. Janco, © 1990, GIA Publications, Inc.

216

Refrain

Re - ceive her/his soul and pre - sent her/him to God,

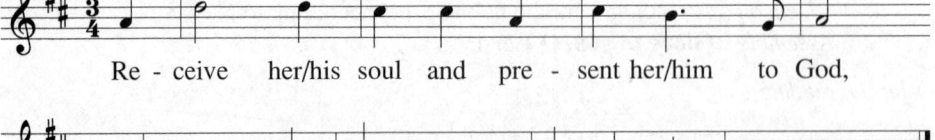

pre - sent this soul to God most high.

Text: *Order of Christian Funerals;* para. by David Haas
Music: David Haas
© 1990, GIA Publications, Inc.

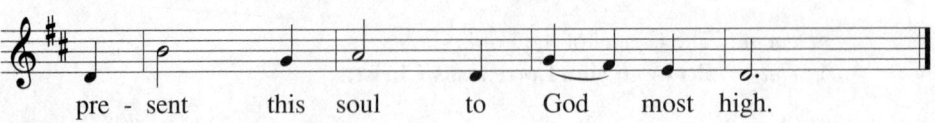

1. Saints of God, come to his/her aid!
2. May Christ who called you, take you to him - self;
3. Give him/her e - ter - nal rest, O Lord,

Come to meet him,/her, an - gels of the
may an - gels lead you to A - bra - ham's
and may your light shine on him/her for

Lord!
side. Re - ceive his/her soul and pre -
ev - er.

sent him/her to God, to God the Most High.

All:

Re - ceive his/her soul and pre - sent him/her to

God, to God the Most High.

Text: *Order of Christian Funerals*; alt. by Richard Proulx
Music: Richard Proulx
© 1975, GIA Publications, Inc.

PRAYER OF COMMENDATION
At the conclusion of the prayer all respond: **Amen.**

PROCESSION TO THE PLACE OF COMMITTAL 218
The deacon or priest says: In peace let us take our brother/sister to his/her place of rest.

SONG

As the assembly leaves the church, one of the following or another appropriate responsory (see nos. 1078 and 1082) or song may be sung.

219

In pa - ra - dí - sum de - dú - cant te án - ge - li:
May choirs of an - gels es - cort you in - to par - a - dise:

in tu - o ad - vén - tu su - scí - pi - ant te
and at your ar - ri - val may the mar - tyrs re - ceive

már - ty - res, et per - dú - cant te in
and wel - come you; may they bring you home in -

ci - vi - tá - tem san - ctam Je - rú - sa - lem.
to the ho - ly cit - y, Je - ru - sa - lem.

Cho - rus an - ge - ló - rum te su -
May the ho - ly an - gels wel -

scí - pi - at, et cum Lá - za - ro quon - dam
come you, and with Laz - a - rus, who lived in

páu - pe - re ae - tér - nam
pov - er - ty, may you have

há - be - as ré - qui - em.
ev - er - last - ing rest.

Text: *In paradisum* and *Chorus angelorum*, tr. © 1986, GIA Publications, Inc.
Tune: Mode VII; acc. by Richard Proulx, 1937–2010, © 1986, GIA Publications, Inc.

220

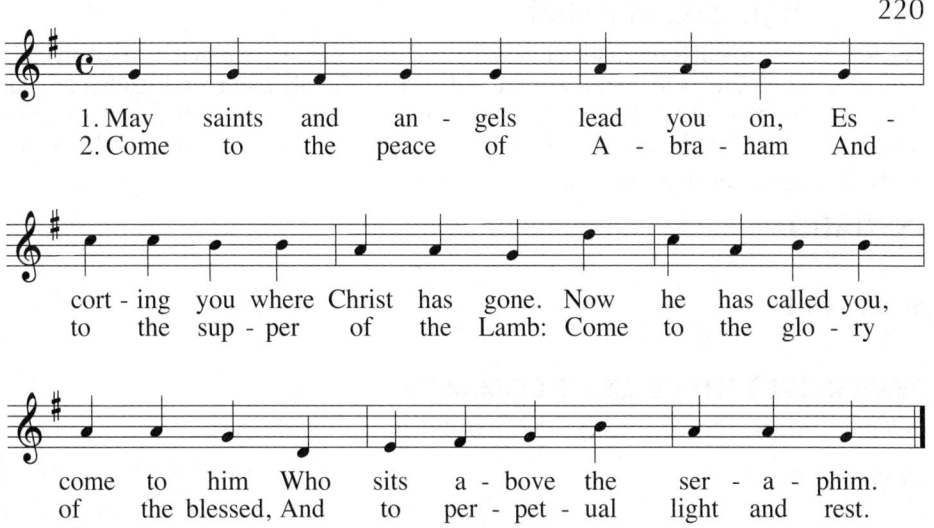

1. May saints and an - gels lead you on, Es -
2. Come to the peace of A - bra - ham And

cort - ing you where Christ has gone. Now he has called you,
to the sup - per of the Lamb: Come to the glo - ry

come to him Who sits a - bove the ser - a - phim.
of the blessed, And to per - pet - ual light and rest.

Text: *In paradisum,* © 1985, ICEL
Tune: TALLIS' CANON, LM; Thomas Tallis, c.1505–1585

221

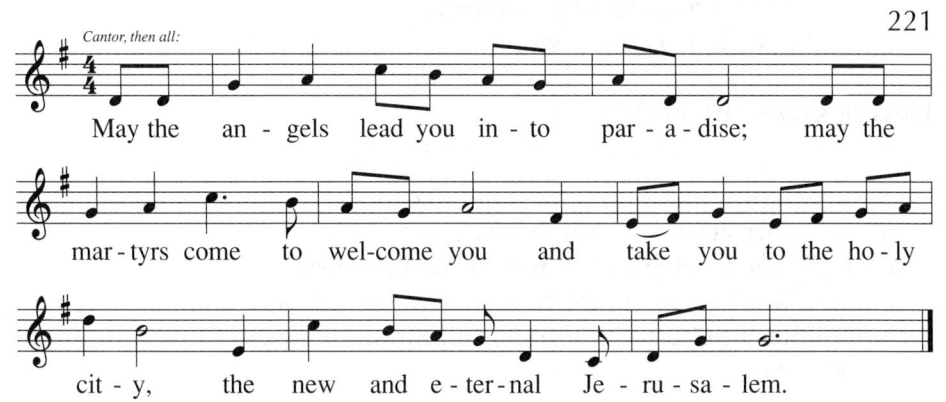

Cantor, then all:

May the an - gels lead you in - to par - a - dise; may the

mar - tyrs come to wel - come you and take you to the ho - ly

cit - y, the new and e - ter - nal Je - ru - sa - lem.

Text: *Order of Christian Funerals,* © 1985, ICEL
Music: Steven R. Janco, © 1990, GIA Publications, Inc.

222 III. Rite of Committal

The Rite of Committal is normally celebrated at the site of the grave in the cemetery. It is the last of the Church's funeral rites for the deceased. Family and friends gather to take the deceased to his or her final resting place. The celebration also honors the place of interment, where family and friends will continue to visit and remember the deceased.

As the family and friends gather, a song may be sung.

INVITATION
All are invited to pray.

SCRIPTURE
A brief Scripture passage is read.

PRAYER OVER THE PLACE OF COMMITAL
At the conclusion of the prayer all respond: **Amen.**

COMMITTAL
The body or cremated remains is placed in its final resting place.

INTERCESSIONS
All respond: **Lord, have mercy.**

THE LORD'S PRAYER
Assembly: **Our Father, who art in heaven,
hallowed be thy name;
thy kingdom come,
thy will be done on earth as it is in heaven.
Give us this day our daily bread,
and forgive us our trespasses,
as we forgive those who trespass against us;
and lead us not into temptation,
but deliver us from evil.**

PRAYER OVER THE PEOPLE
At the conclusion of the prayer all respond: **Amen.**

The leader then says the following:

Leader: Eternal rest grant unto him/her, Lord.
Assembly: **And let perpetual light shine upon him/her.**
Leader: May his/her soul and the souls of all the faithful departed, through the mercy of God, rest in peace.
Assembly: **Amen.**

A final prayer is prayed and at its conclusion all respond: **Amen.**

The service concludes:

Leader: Go in the peace of Christ.
Assembly: **Thanks be to God.**

If customary, flowers or soil may be placed be placed on the coffin. A song may be sung at this time.

Stations of the Cross

INTRODUCTION
All make the sign of the cross.

Leader: Lord Jesus,
We seek to follow you in all we do.
As we walk these stations of the cross,
make us aware of your great love for us.
Set us out on a path of loving service
as we journey through life
to the kingdom of your Easter glory.

All: **Amen**.

PROCESSION
The introductory stanza and stanza one (below) are sung during the procession to the first station. The leader is accompanied by a cross bearer and candle bearers. All who are gathered, or a small group, may join in the procession.

When the procession arrives at each station, it is announced, followed by:

Leader: We adore you, O Christ, and we praise you.
All genuflect and say: **Because by your holy cross**
you have redeemed the world.

A brief reflection may be read or silence may be observed. During the procession to the next station, the corresponding stanza is sung.

HYMN 224

*Je - sus kneels, in sor - row pray - ing, Knows his fate, God's
1. Meet - ing Pi - late's earth - ly pow - er, Je - sus lives these
2. In the weight of cross-beams wood - en Je - sus feels the
3. Stum - bling un - der weight so crush - ing, Jeer - ing crowds up -

will o - bey - ing: "Let your will, not mine, be done."
fi - nal ho - urs Con - fi - dent in heav - en's might.
heav - y bur - den Of our frail hu - man - i - ty.
on him rush - ing, Je - sus falls, re - turns to dust.

*Introductory stanza

1. Jesus is condemned

2. Jesus carries his cross

3. Jesus falls the first time

4. Jesus meets his mother
She who knew her heart in sorrow
Would be pierced, here bravely follows
In her Son's distress and pain.

5. Simon helps Jesus carry his cross
Simon, one with Jesus bearing,
Shows the way of our own sharing,
Taking up our daily cross.

6. Veronica wipes the face of Jesus
Boldly facing disapproval
She, in cleansing, seeks removal
Of the stains of agony.

7. Jesus falls a second time
Falling once again, Lord Jesus
Shows the suffering that frees us
As we struggle on our way.

8. Jesus meets the women of Jerusalem
Israel's own daughters, weeping
Come to Jesus, comfort seeking
In the time of their distress.

9. Jesus falls the third time
Jesus weakened, bruised and feeble,
Falls again, appears unable
To complete his painful road.

10. Jesus is stripped of his garments
Naked, stark, in desolation,
Jesus knows humiliation,
Robbed of his last dignity.

11. Jesus is nailed to the cross
Hands which heal and bless and feed us,
Feet which to the kingdom lead us,
Now are pierced with brutal steel.

12. Jesus dies on the cross
There between the earth and heaven
Death appears, in triumph, proven:
Jesus draws his dying breath.

13. Jesus is taken down from the cross
Oh, what sorrow, pain and anguish
Comes to those who saw him perish
As they take his body down.

14. Jesus is laid in the tomb
Some believe the awful journey
Finishes all bleak and stony,
Yet a new life will arise.

Concluding stanza
Let us walk with Christ while praying
As he did, God's will obeying,
"Let your will, not mine, be done."

Text: Alan J. Hommerding, b.1956, © 2000, World Library Publications
Tune: STABAT MATER, 88 7; Mainz *Gesangbuch*, 1661; harm. by Richard Proulx, 1937–2010, © 1986, GIA Publications, Inc.

An alternate setting is found at no. 571.

The following refrain may be used instead of the previous hymn. Other suitable songs include the refrain of Now We Remain, *no. 889, or* Jesus, Remember Me, *no. 842.*

225 In the Cross of Christ

In the cross of Christ, our glo-ry, Christ, our sto-ry, Christ, our song.

Text: Marty Haugen, b.1950
Tune: Marty Haugen, b.1950
© 1995, GIA Publications, Inc.

Praying with the Songs of the Taizé Community

Taizé is a small village in the Burgundy region of France and home to an ecumenical community of brothers in the monastic tradition founded during the Second World War by Brother Roger Schütz. Life at Taizé revolves around prayer, work and hospitality. Since the 1960s, the hospitality has taken the form of welcoming large numbers of young adults—sometimes several thousand at a time—to stay for week-long meetings.

In order to accommodate the large number of visitors speaking various languages, composers began creating simple, repetitive musical refrains for use in worship. Many of the refrains are in Latin; in Taizé itself, numerous languages are used in prayer. In a local community, it may be disconcerting to use foreign languages without a particular reason, and so it is better to choose songs in English, the local language, or possibly in Latin. One or two well-known local songs or hymns can also be included.

The songs of Taizé are meant to help people take time in God's presence. They should be long enough to allow distracted thoughts to calm down and for the words to sink in: each song is typically repeated for about four to eight minutes. Gathered in the presence of Christ, these uncomplicated, repetitive songs, uncluttered by too many words, allow the mystery of God to become tangible through the beauty of simplicity. A few words sung over and over again reinforce the meditative quality of prayer. They express a basic reality of faith that can quickly be grasped by the intellect and that gradually penetrates the whole being.

In the spirit of this ecumenical community, it is both appropriate and encouraged to invite and welcome Christians of all traditions to come together for this time of prayer, word and song.

GATHERING SONGS
To begin the prayer, choose one or two songs of praise (see nos. 644, 732, 739, and 846). You may sing the melody or sing in harmony as you wish.

PSALM
Jesus prayed these age-old prayers of his people; Christians have always found in them a wellspring of life. The psalms place us in the great communion of all believers. An alleluia (see nos. 415, 419, and 422) is often used as an acclamation between verses.

SONG OF LIGHT (Optional)
An additional song may be sung (see nos. 695 and 950) celebrating the Light of Christ.

FIRST BIBLE READING
Christ is made present in the proclamation of the Scriptures.

SONG
A song after the reading, somewhat prolonged, can help to let the Word of God sink in and lead into a time of silence (see nos. 502, 748, and 917).

SECOND BIBLE READING (Optional)

SILENCE

When we try to express communication with God in words, we rapidly reach the end of our capacities. A fairly long period of silence (five to ten minutes) to listen to the voice of God deep within, therefore, is essential in discovering the heart of prayer.

INTERCESSIONS OR LITANY OF PRAISE

We pray that God will grant us what we ask, as well as what we need. A sung Kyrie eleison follows each petition or acclamation of praise (see nos. 433 and 439). After the prepared petitions or acclamations are finished, time may be left for people to pray spontaneously in their own words.

THE LORD'S PRAYER

CONCLUDING PRAYER

CONCLUDING SONGS

At the end of the prayer, the singing may continue for an extended time (see nos. 712, 713, and 846).

On certain nights, ideally Friday and Saturday, the following options may be observed.

PRAYER AROUND THE CROSS

The icon of the cross or cross is laid down flat in the center of the prayer space resting on several cushions or stools. While the meditative singing continues (see nos. 572, 590, 592, 602, and 842), those who wish may come up to the cross to pray. We can make a gesture, such as kissing, touching, or placing the forehead on the wood of the cross, as a sign that we are entrusting silently to Christ all that burdens us. Those who wish to leave may do so at any time. Others may wish to remain in prayer and song. There is no dismissal.

CELEBRATION OF THE RESURRECTION

The resurrection of Christ is the promise of our own resurrection and can be celebrated by a festival of the light of Christ, which is also a sign of our identity as Christians as children of the light. While a resurrection song is sung (see nos. 624, 628, and 729) each person's candle is lit (each person receives a taper candle as they enter the church), until the whole space is full of light. Perhaps children can help with the passing of the light. Then, a Gospel of the resurrection can be read, followed by more meditative singing.

Mass

Order of Mass

The Church gathers on the Lord's Day to listen to Scripture, to offer prayers, to give thanks and praise to God while recalling God's gifts in creation and saving deeds in Jesus, and to share in Holy Communion.

In these rites of word and eucharist, the Church keeps Sunday as the Lord's Day, the day of creation and resurrection, the "eighth day" when the fullness of God's kingdom is anticipated. The Mass or eucharistic celebration of the Christian community has rites of gathering, of word, of eucharist, of dismissal. All those who gather constitute the assembly. One member of this assembly who has been ordained to the presbyterate or episcopate, the priesthood, leads the opening and closing prayers and the eucharistic prayer, and presides over the whole assembly. A member ordained to the diaconate may assist, read the gospel, and preach. Other members of the assembly are chosen and trained for various ministries: These are the readers, servers, ushers, musicians, communion ministers. All of these assist the assembly. It is the assembly itself, all those present, that does the liturgy.

The Order of Mass which follows is familiar to all who regularly join in this assembly. It is learned through repetition. This Order of Mass leaves many decisions to the local community, and others are determined by the various seasons of the liturgical year.

INTRODUCTORY RITES
The rites which precede the liturgy of the word assist the assembly to gather as a community. They prepare that community to listen to Scripture and to celebrate the Eucharist together. The procession and entrance song are ways of expressing the unity and spirit of the assembly.

GREETING
All make the sign of the cross.

Priest: In the name of the Father, and of the Son, and of the Holy Spirit.

A - men.

After the sign of the cross one of the greetings is given.

A   *Priest:* The grace of our Lord Jesus Christ,
and the love of God,
and the communion of the Holy Spirit
be with you all.

B   *Priest:* Grace to you and peace from God our Father
and the Lord Jesus Christ.

C   *Priest:* The Lord be with you. (*Bishop:* Peace be with you.)

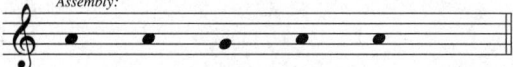

And with your spir - it.

228 BLESSING AND SPRINKLING OF HOLY WATER

On Sundays, especially during the season of Easter, instead of the penitential act below, the blessing and sprinkling of holy water may take place.

229 PENITENTIAL ACT

The priest invites all to be mindful of their sins and of the great mercy of God. After a time of silence, one of the following forms is used.

A   *Assembly:* **I confess to almighty God
and to you, my brothers and sisters,
that I have greatly sinned,
in my thoughts and in my words,
in what I have done and in what I have failed to do,**
All strike their breast as they say:
**through my fault, through my fault,
through my most grievous fault;
therefore I ask blessed Mary ever-Virgin,
all the Angels and Saints,
and you, my brothers and sisters,
to pray for me to the Lord our God.**

B

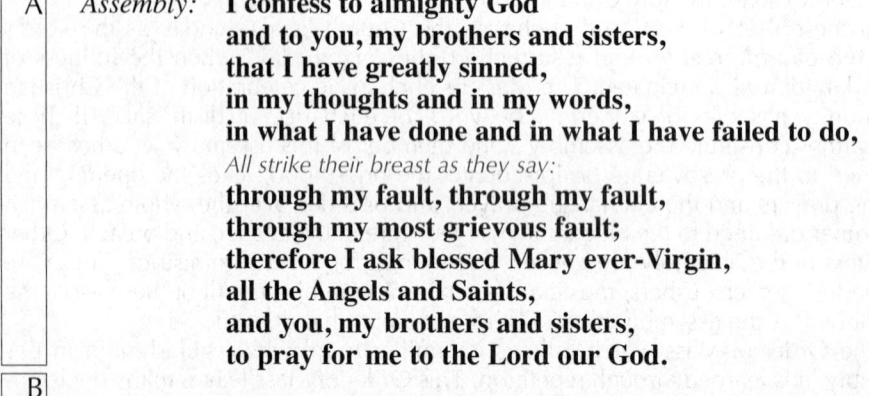

Have mercy on us, O Lord.   For we have sinned a - gainst you.

Show us, O Lord, your mer - cy.   And grant us your sal - va - tion.

C

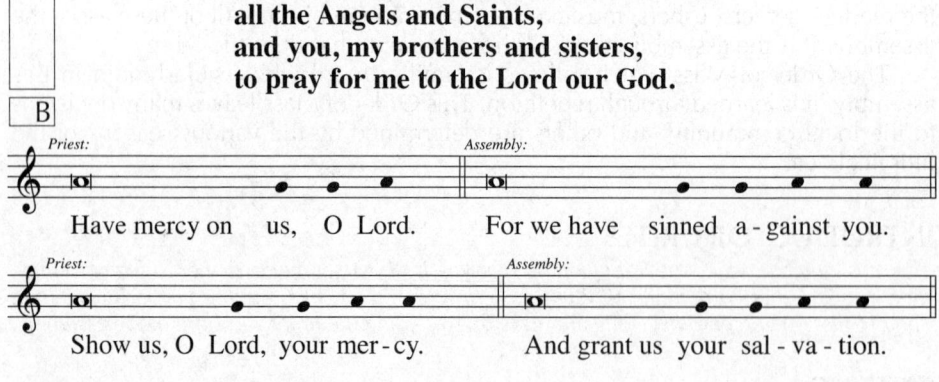

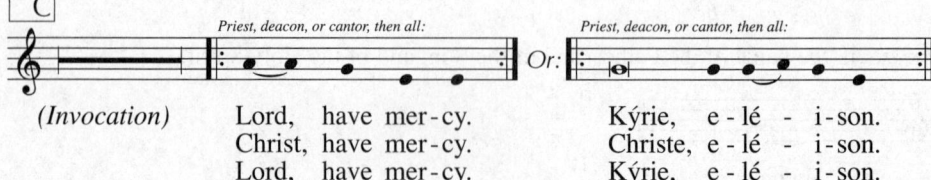

(*Invocation*)   Lord, have mer - cy.   Kýrie, e - lé - i - son.
Christ, have mer - cy.   Christe, e - lé - i - son.
Lord, have mer - cy.   Kýrie, e - lé - i - son.

Priest: May almighty God…everlasting life.

A - men.

KYRIE 230

Unless form C of the penitential act has been used, the Kyrie follows.

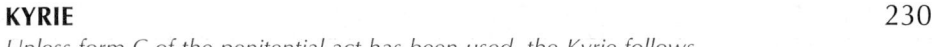

Ký - ri - e, e - lé - i - son. Chri - ste, e - lé - i - son.

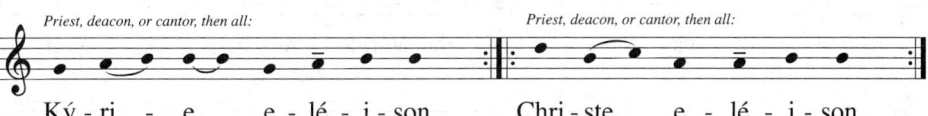

Ký-ri - e, e - lé - i-son. Ký-ri - e, e - lé - i - son.

Or:

Lord, have mer - cy. Christ, have mer - cy.

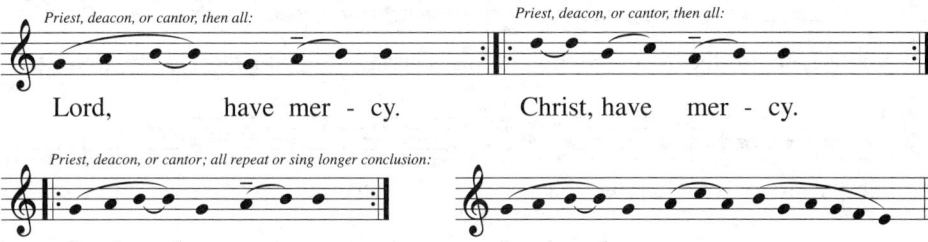

Lord, have mer - cy. Lord, have mer - cy.

GLORIA 231

The Gloria is omitted during Advent, Lent, and most weekdays.

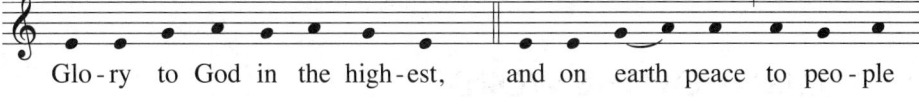

Glo - ry to God in the high-est, and on earth peace to peo - ple

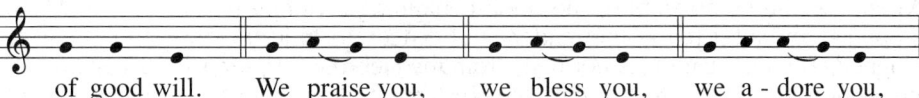

of good will. We praise you, we bless you, we a - dore you,

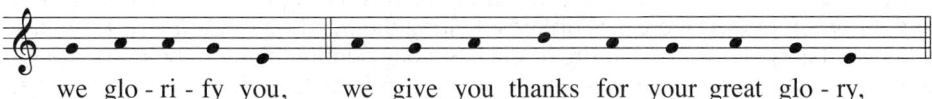

we glo - ri - fy you, we give you thanks for your great glo - ry,

Lord God, heav - en - ly King, O God, al - might - y Fa - ther.

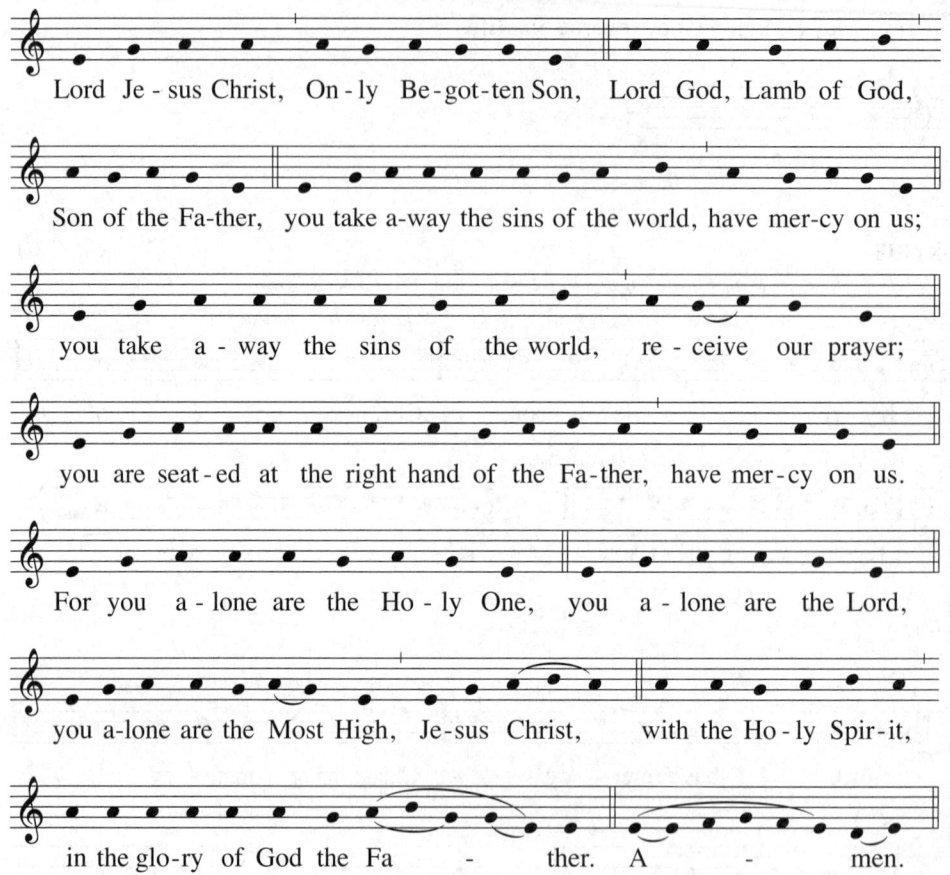

Lord Je-sus Christ, On-ly Be-got-ten Son, Lord God, Lamb of God,

Son of the Fa-ther, you take a-way the sins of the world, have mer-cy on us;

you take a-way the sins of the world, re-ceive our prayer;

you are seat-ed at the right hand of the Fa-ther, have mer-cy on us.

For you a-lone are the Ho-ly One, you a-lone are the Lord,

you a-lone are the Most High, Je-sus Christ, with the Ho-ly Spir-it,

in the glo-ry of God the Fa - ther. A - men.

COLLECT

After the invitation from the priest, all pray in silence for a while. The introductory rites conclude with the proper opening prayer to which all respond: **Amen.**

232 LITURGY OF THE WORD

When the Church assembles, the book containing Scripture (*Lectionary for Mass*) is opened and all listen as the readers and deacon (or priest) read from the places assigned. The first reading is normally from the Hebrew Scriptures (Old Testament), the second from the letters of the New Testament, and the third from the Book of Gospels. Over a three-year cycle, the Church reads through the letters and gospels and a portion of the Hebrew Scriptures. During the Sundays of Ordinary Time, the letters and gospels are read in order, each Sunday continuing near the place where the previous Sunday's readings ended. During Advent/Christmas and Lent/Easter, the readings are those which are traditional and appropriate to these seasons.

The Church listens to and—through the weeks and years—is shaped by the word of God. Those who have gathered for the Sunday liturgy are to give their full attention to the words of the reader. A time of silence and reflection follows each of the first two readings. After the first reading, this reflection continues in the singing of the psalm. A homily, bringing together the scripture readings and the life of the community, follows the gospel. The liturgy of the word concludes with the dismissal of the catechumens, the creed and the prayers of intercession. In the latter, the assembly continues its constant work of recalling and praying for the universal Church and all those in need.

This reading and hearing of the word—simple things that they are—are the foundation of the liturgical celebration. The public reading of Scripture and the rituals which surround this—silence and psalm and acclamation, posture and gesture, preaching and litany of intercession—gather the Church generation after generation. They gather and sustain and gradually make of us the image of Christ.

FIRST READING

After the reading:

The word of the Lord. Thanks be to God.

After a period of silence, the responsorial psalm is sung.

SECOND READING

After the reading:

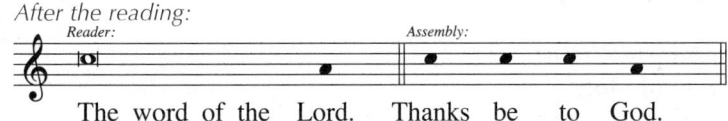

The word of the Lord. Thanks be to God.

A time of silence follows the reading.

GOSPEL   233

Before the gospel, an acclamation is sung.

Al - le - lú - ia, al - le - lú - ia, al - le - lú - ia.

During Lent:

Praise and hon - or to you, O Lord Je - sus Christ.

Before the gospel:

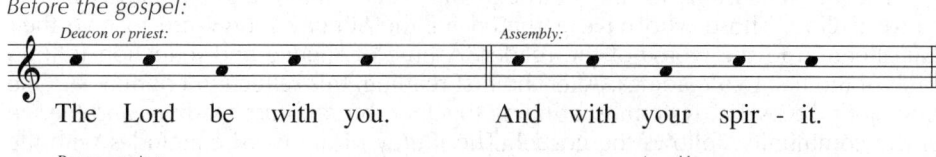

After the reading:

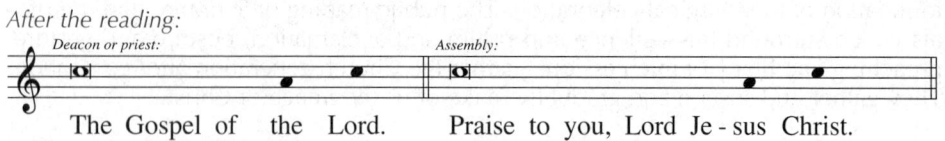

HOMILY

234 PROFESSION OF FAITH
Musical settings can be found at nos. 251 and 431.

I believe in one God,
the Father almighty,
maker of heaven and earth,
of all things visible and invisible.

I believe in one Lord Jesus Christ,
the Only Begotten Son of God,
born of the Father before all ages.
God from God, Light from Light,
true God from true God,
begotten, not made, consubstantial with the Father;
through him all things were made.
For us men and for our salvation
he came down from heaven,
All bow at the following words up to: and became man.
and by the Holy Spirit was incarnate of the Virgin Mary,
and became man.

For our sake he was crucified under Pontius Pilate,
he suffered death and was buried,
and rose again on the third day
in accordance with the Scriptures.
He ascended into heaven
and is seated at the right hand of the Father.
He will come again in glory
to judge the living and the dead
and his kingdom will have no end.

I believe in the Holy Spirit, the Lord, the giver of life,
who proceeds from the Father and the Son,
who with the Father and the Son is adored and glorified,
who has spoken through the prophets.

I believe in one, holy, catholic and apostolic Church.
I confess one Baptism for the forgiveness of sins
and I look forward to the resurrection of the dead
and the life of the world to come. Amen.

Instead of the Nicene Creed, especially during Lent and the Easter season,   235
the Apostles' Creed may be used:

I believe in God,
the Father almighty,
Creator of heaven and earth,
and in Jesus Christ, his only Son, our Lord,
All bow at the following words up to: the Virgin Mary.
who was conceived by the Holy Spirit,
born of the Virgin Mary,
suffered under Pontius Pilate,
was crucified, died and was buried;
he descended into hell;
on the third day he rose again from the dead;
he ascended into heaven,
and is seated at the right hand of God the Father almighty;
from there he will come to judge the living and the dead.

I believe in the Holy Spirit,
the holy catholic Church,
the communion of saints,
the forgiveness of sins,
the resurrection of the body,
and life everlasting. Amen.

PRAYER OF THE FAITHFUL   236

The people respond to each petition as follows, or according to local practice.

Deacon or cantor: Let us pray to the Lord.

Lord, hear our prayer.

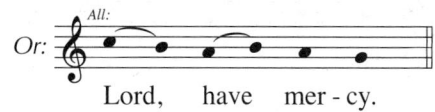
Lord, have mer-cy.

237 LITURGY OF THE EUCHARIST

To celebrate the Eucharist means to give God thanks and praise. When the altar has been prepared with the bread and wine, the assembly joins the priest in remembering the gracious gifts of God in creation and God's saving deeds. The center of this is the paschal mystery, the death of our Lord Jesus Christ which destroyed the power of death and his rising which brings us life. That mystery into which we were baptized we proclaim each Sunday at the Eucharist. It is the very shape of Christian life. We find this in the simple bread and wine which stir our remembering and draw forth our prayer of thanksgiving. "Fruit of the earth and work of human hands," the bread and wine become our Holy Communion in the Body and Blood of the Lord. We eat and drink and so proclaim that we belong to one another and to the Lord.

The members of the assembly quietly prepare themselves even as the table is prepared. The priest then invites all to lift up their hearts and join in the eucharistic prayer. All do this by giving their full attention and by singing the acclamations from the "Holy, Holy, Holy" to the great "Amen." Then the assembly joins in the Lord's Prayer, the sign of peace and the "Lamb of God" litany which accompanies the breaking of bread. Ministers of communion assist the assembly to share the Body and Blood of Christ. A time of silence and prayer concludes the liturgy of the eucharist.

PRESENTATION AND PREPARATION OF THE GIFTS

Bread and wine are brought to the altar and the deacon or priest prepares these gifts. If there is no music, the prayers may be said aloud, and all may respond: **Blessed be God for ever.** *The priest then invites all to pray.*

Priest: Pray, brethren (brothers and sisters),
that my sacrifice and yours
may be acceptable to God, the almighty Father.

The people rise and reply:

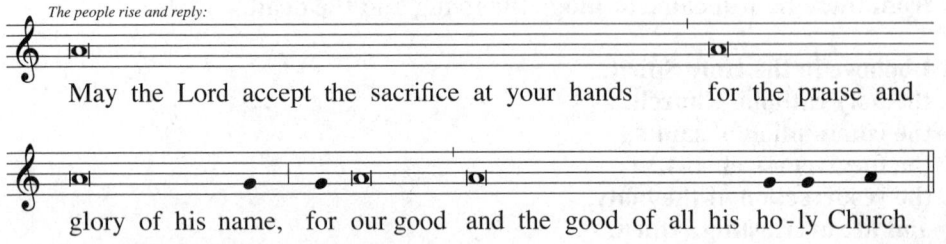

May the Lord accept the sacrifice at your hands   for the praise and glory of his name,   for our good   and the good of all his ho-ly Church.

The priest says the prayer over the offerings and all respond: **Amen.**

238 EUCHARISTIC PRAYER

The central prayer of the Mass begins with this dialogue between priest and assembly.

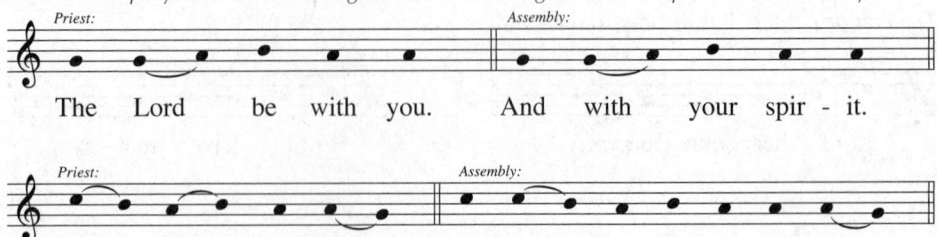

Priest: The Lord be with you. *Assembly:* And with your spir - it.

Priest: Lift up your hearts. *Assembly:* We lift them up to the Lord.

Priest: Let us give thanks to the Lord our God. *Assembly:* It is right and just.

The Holy, Holy, Holy acclamation is sung to conclude the introduction to the eucharistic prayer. 239

Ho-ly, Ho-ly, Ho-ly Lord God of hosts. Heav-en and earth are full of your glo-ry. Ho-san-na in the high-est. Bless-ed is he who comes in the name of the Lord. Ho-san-na in the high-est.

One of the following acclamations follows the priest's invitation: "The mystery of faith." 240

A

We pro-claim your Death, O Lord, and pro-fess your Res-ur-rec-tion un-til you come a-gain.

B 241

When we eat this Bread and drink this Cup, we pro-claim your Death, O Lord, un-til you come a-gain.

C 242

Save us, Sav-ior of the world, for by your Cross and Res-ur-rec-tion you have set us free.

243 *The eucharistic prayer concludes:*
Priest: Through him, and with him, and in him,
O God, almighty Father,
in the unity of the Holy Spirit,
all glory and honor is yours,
for ever and ever.

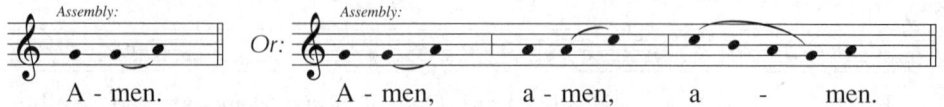

244 COMMUNION RITE

The priest invites all to join in the Lord's Prayer.

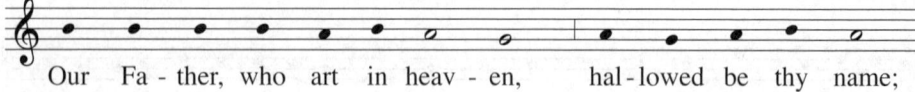

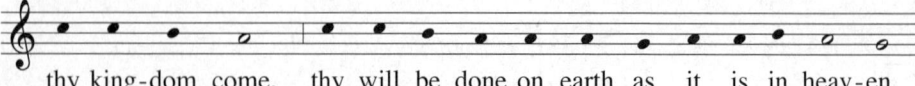

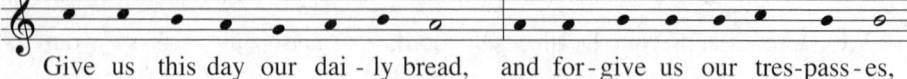

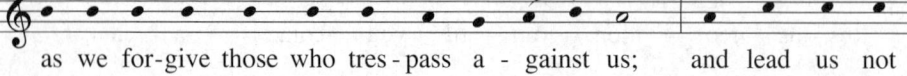

Priest: Deliver us, Lord…and the coming of our Savior, Jesus Christ.

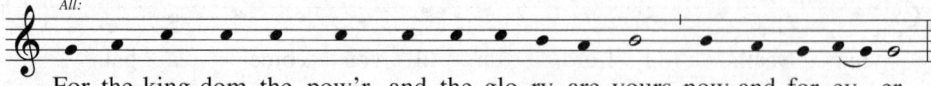

SIGN OF PEACE

Priest: Lord Jesus Christ, who said…for ever and ever.

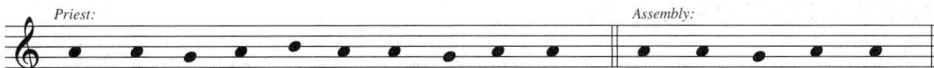

Priest: ... *Assembly:*

The peace of the Lord be with you al-ways. And with your spir - it.

Deacon or priest: Let us offer each other the sign of peace.

All exchange a sign of peace.

Then the eucharistic bread is solemnly broken and the consecrated bread and wine are prepared for Holy Communion. The litany "Lamb of God" is sung during the breaking of the bread. **245**

Lamb of God, you take a-way the sins of the world, have mer - cy on us.

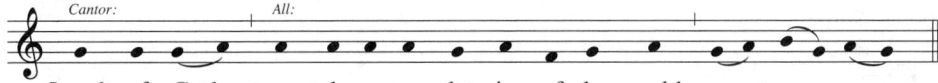

Lamb of God, you take a-way the sins of the world, grant us peace.

The priest then invites all to share in Holy Communion. **246**

Priest: Behold the Lamb of God,
behold him who takes away the sins of the world.
Blessed are those called to the supper of the Lamb.

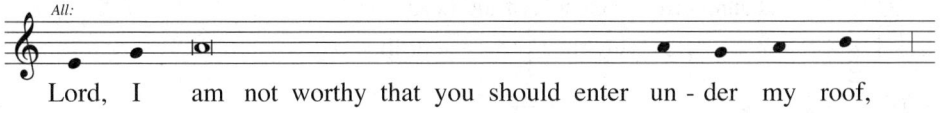

Lord, I am not worthy that you should enter un - der my roof,

but only say the word and my soul shall be healed.

Minister of communion: The Body (Blood) of Christ.
Communicant: **Amen.**

While the priest is receiving the Body of Christ, the communion song or psalm begins. After communion, a time of silence is observed or a song of thanksgiving is sung. The rite concludes with the prayer after communion to which all respond: **Amen.**

CONCLUDING RITES   247
The liturgy of the eucharist ends very simply. There may be announcements of events and concerns for the community, then the priest gives a blessing and the assembly is dismissed.

GREETING AND FINAL BLESSING

Priest: The Lord be with you. *Assembly:* And with your spir - it.

When a bishop blesses the people, he adds the following:

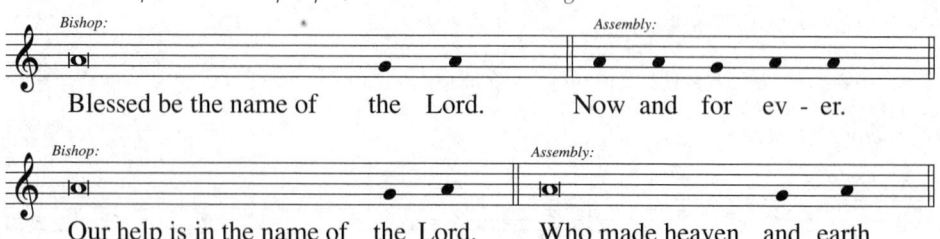

Bishop: Blessed be the name of the Lord. *Assembly:* Now and for ev - er.

Bishop: Our help is in the name of the Lord. *Assembly:* Who made heaven and earth.

The blessing may be in a simple or solemn form. All respond to the blessing or to each part of the blessing:

Assembly: A - men.

DISMISSAL

The deacon or priest then dismisses the assembly:

A	Go forth, the Mass is ended.
B	Go and announce the Gospel of the Lord.
C	Go in peace, glorifying the Lord by your life.

Assembly: Thanks be to God.

| D |

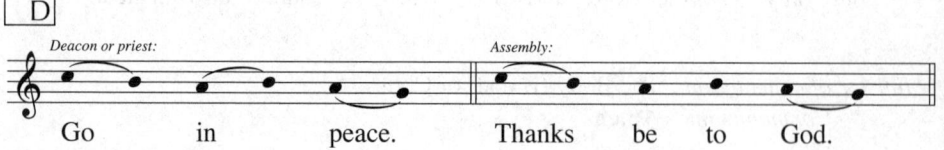

Deacon or priest: Go in peace. *Assembly:* Thanks be to God.

EASTER DISMISSAL

The deacon or priest then dismisses the assembly:

| A | Go forth, the Mass is ended, alleluia, alleluia. |
| B | Go in peace, alleluia, alleluia. |

Assembly: Thanks be to God, al - le - lú - ia, al - le - lú - ia.

Additional Chants

SIMPLE CHANTS

GREETING   248

Priest: In the name of the Father, and of the Son, and of the Holy Spirit.

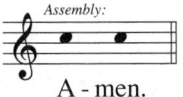

A - men.

A	*Priest:*	The grace of our Lord Jesus Christ, and the love of God, and the communion of the Holy Spirit be with you all.
B	*Priest:*	Grace to you and peace from God our Father and the Lord Jesus Christ.
C	*Priest:*	The Lord be with you. (*Bishop:* Peace be with you.)

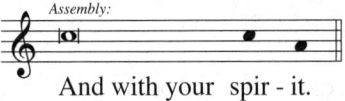

And with your spir - it.

PENITENTIAL ACT   249

B

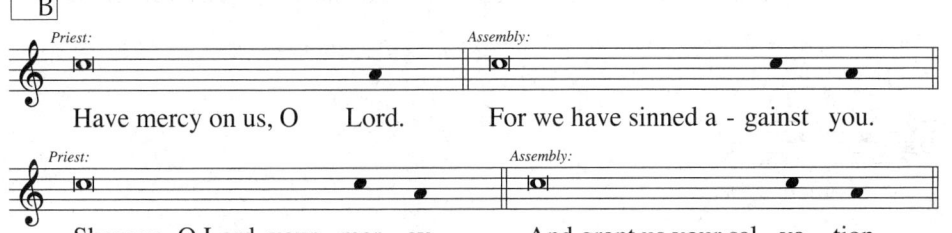

Have mercy on us, O Lord.   For we have sinned a - gainst you.

Show us, O Lord, your mer - cy.   And grant us your sal - va - tion.

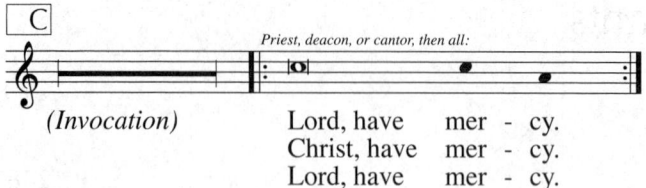

(*Invocation*)

Lord, have mer - cy.
Christ, have mer - cy.
Lord, have mer - cy.

Priest: May almighty God…everlasting life.

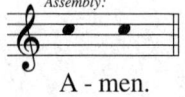

A - men.

250 GREETING AND FINAL BLESSING

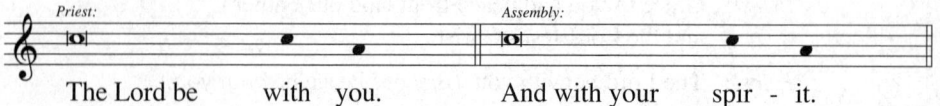

The Lord be with you.   And with your spir - it.

When a bishop blesses the people, he adds the following:

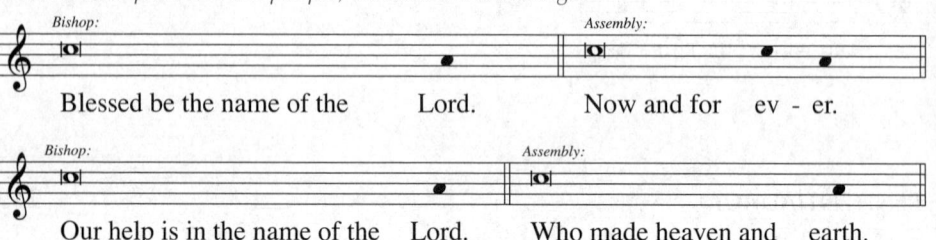

Blessed be the name of the Lord.   Now and for ev - er.

Our help is in the name of the Lord.   Who made heaven and earth.

The blessing may be in a simple or solemn form. All respond to the blessing or to each part of the blessing:

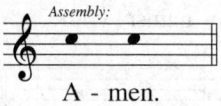

A - men.

CREDO I

I be-lieve in one God, the Fa-ther al-might-y, mak-er of

heav-en and earth, of all things vis - i-ble and in-vis - i-ble.

I be-lieve in one Lord Je - sus Christ, the Only Be - got-ten

Son of God, born of the Father be - fore all a - ges.

God from God, Light from Light, true God from true God,

be - got-ten, not made, con - sub - stan - tial with the Fa - ther;

through him all things were made. For us men and for our sal-va-tion

All bow

he came down from heav-en, and by the Ho-ly Spir-it was in-car-nate

of the Vir - gin Mar - y, and be - came man.

For our sake he was cru - ci - fied un - der Pon-tius Pi - late,

he suffered death and was bur-ied, and rose a-gain on the third day

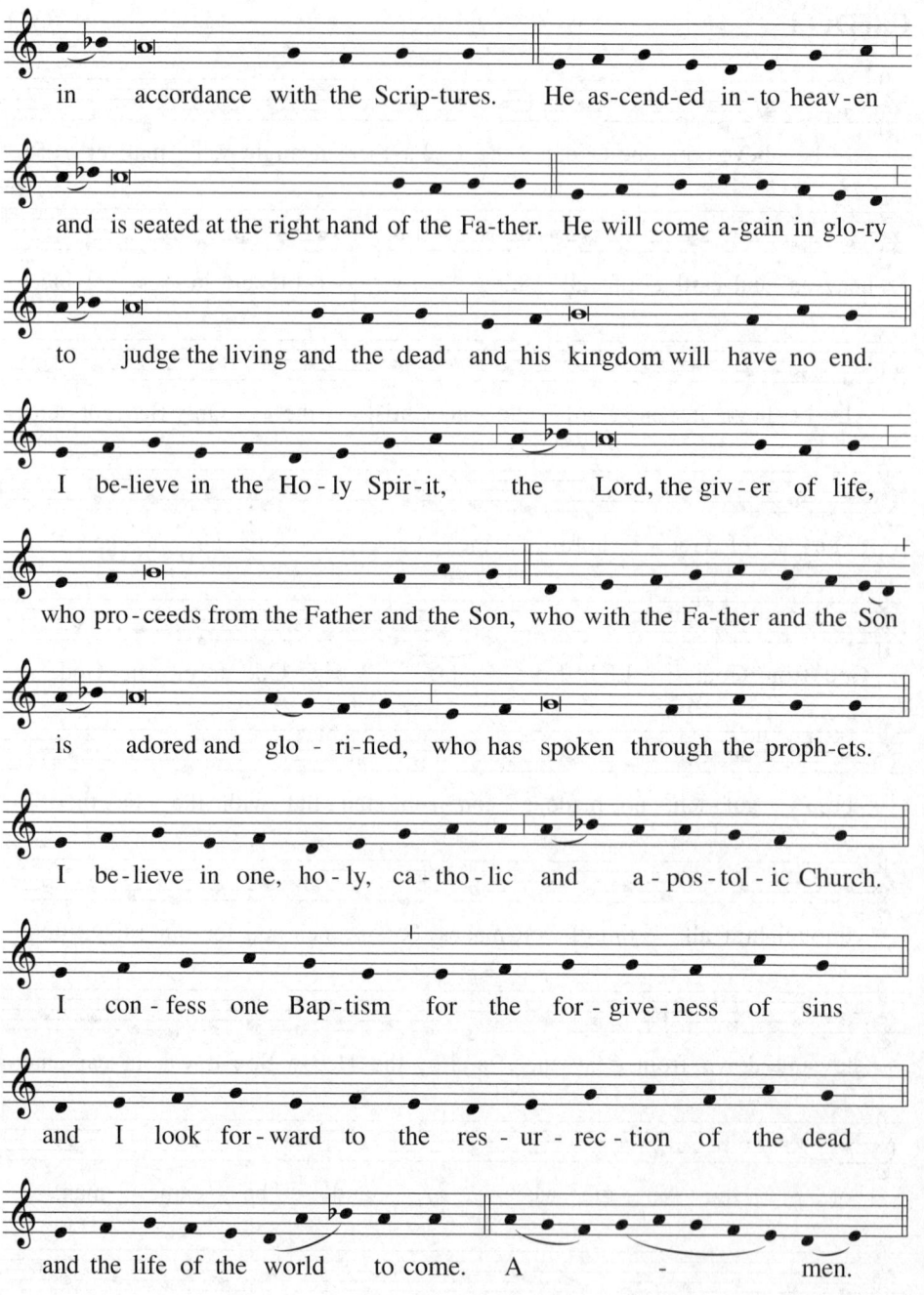

in accordance with the Scrip-tures. He as-cend-ed in-to heav-en

and is seated at the right hand of the Fa-ther. He will come a-gain in glo-ry

to judge the living and the dead and his kingdom will have no end.

I be-lieve in the Ho-ly Spir-it, the Lord, the giv-er of life,

who pro-ceeds from the Father and the Son, who with the Fa-ther and the Son

is adored and glo-ri-fied, who has spoken through the proph-ets.

I be-lieve in one, ho-ly, ca-tho-lic and a-pos-tol-ic Church.

I con-fess one Bap-tism for the for-give-ness of sins

and I look for-ward to the res-ur-rec-tion of the dead

and the life of the world to come. A - men.

Setting One: Mass of Creation /
Misa de la Creación

PENITENTIAL ACT

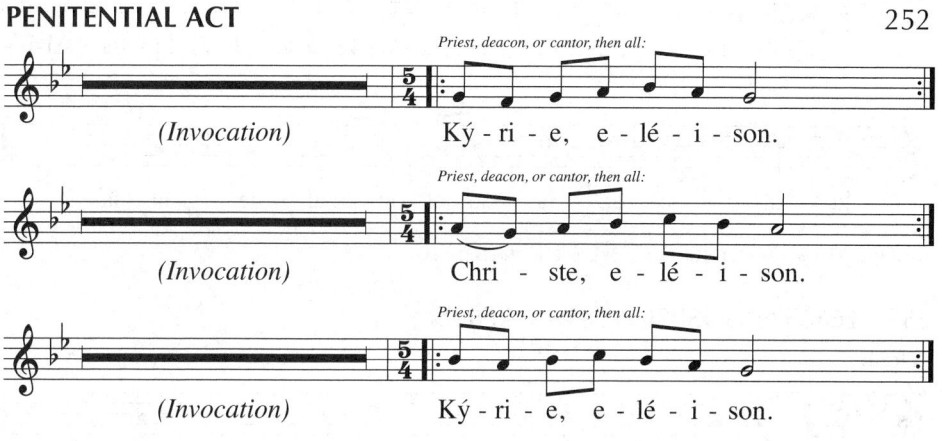

Priest, deacon, or cantor, then all:

(Invocation)   Ký - ri - e, e - lé - i - son.

Priest, deacon, or cantor, then all:

(Invocation)   Chri - ste, e - lé - i - son.

Priest, deacon, or cantor, then all:

(Invocation)   Ký - ri - e, e - lé - i - son.

Priest: May almighty God...everlasting life.

Cantor, then all:

A - men.

Music: *Mass of Creation,* Marty Haugen, © 2010, GIA Publications, Inc.

GLORIA

Refrain

Glo - ry to God in the high-est, and on earth

peace to peo - ple of good will.

Verses

1. We praise you,
   we bless you,
   we adore you,
   we glorify you,
   we give you thanks for your great glory,
   Lord God, heavenly King,
   O God, almighty Father.

2. Lord Jesus Christ, Only Begotten Son,
   Lord God, Lamb of God, Son of the
     Father,
   you take away the sins of the world,
   have mercy on us;

   you take away the sins of the world,
   receive our prayer;
   you are seated at the right hand of the
     Father,
   have mercy on us.

3. For you alone are the Holy One,
   you alone are the Lord,
   you alone are the Most High,
   Jesus Christ,
   with the Holy Spirit,
   in the glory of God the Father.
   Amen.

Text: ICEL, © 2010
Music: *Mass of Creation,* Marty Haugen, © 1984, 1985, 2010, GIA Publications, Inc.

254 GOSPEL ACCLAMATION

Refrain

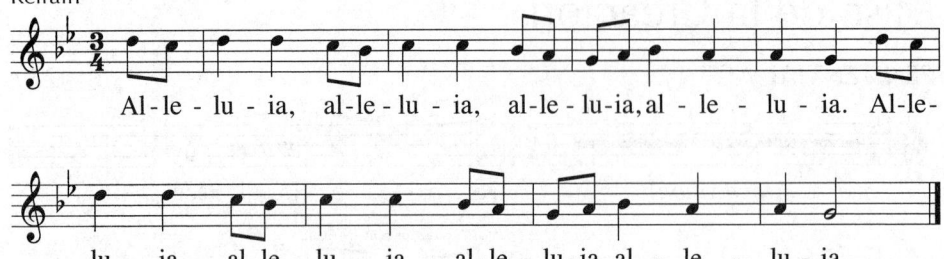

Al-le-lu-ia, al-le-lu-ia, al-le-lu-ia, al-le-lu-ia. Al-le-lu-ia, al-le-lu-ia, al-le-lu-ia, al-le-lu-ia.

Music: *Mass of Creation*, Marty Haugen, © 1984, 1985, 2010, GIA Publications, Inc.

255 LENTEN GOSPEL ACCLAMATION

Refrain

Praise to you, Lord   Je-sus Christ,   King of end-less   glo-ry!

Text: ICEL, © 1969
Music: *Mass of Creation*, Marty Haugen, © 1984, 1985, GIA Publications, Inc.

256 PRAYER OF THE FAITHFUL

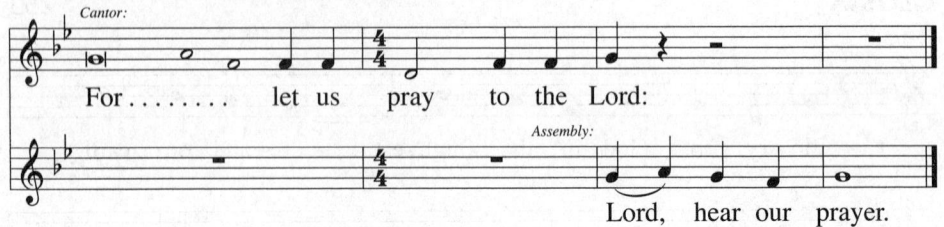

Cantor:

For . . . .   let us   pray   to   the Lord:

Assembly:

Lord,   hear   our   prayer.

Music: *Mass of Creation*, Marty Haugen, © 1984, 1985, GIA Publications, Inc.

257 PREFACE DIALOGUE

Priest: The Lord be with you.   All: And with your spir-it.

Priest: Lift up your hearts.   All: We lift them up to the Lord.

Priest: Let us give thanks to the Lord our God.   All: It is right and just.

Text: ICEL, © 2010
Music: *Mass of Creation*, Marty Haugen, © 1984, 1985, 2010, GIA Publications, Inc.

CHILDREN'S ACCLAMATION 1  258

Ho-san-na in the high-est, ho-san-na in the high-est.

Text: ICEL, © 1975
Music: Eucharistic Prayer for Children, *Mass of Creation*, Marty Haugen, adapt. by Rob Glover, © 1989, GIA Publications, Inc.

HOLY, HOLY, HOLY 259

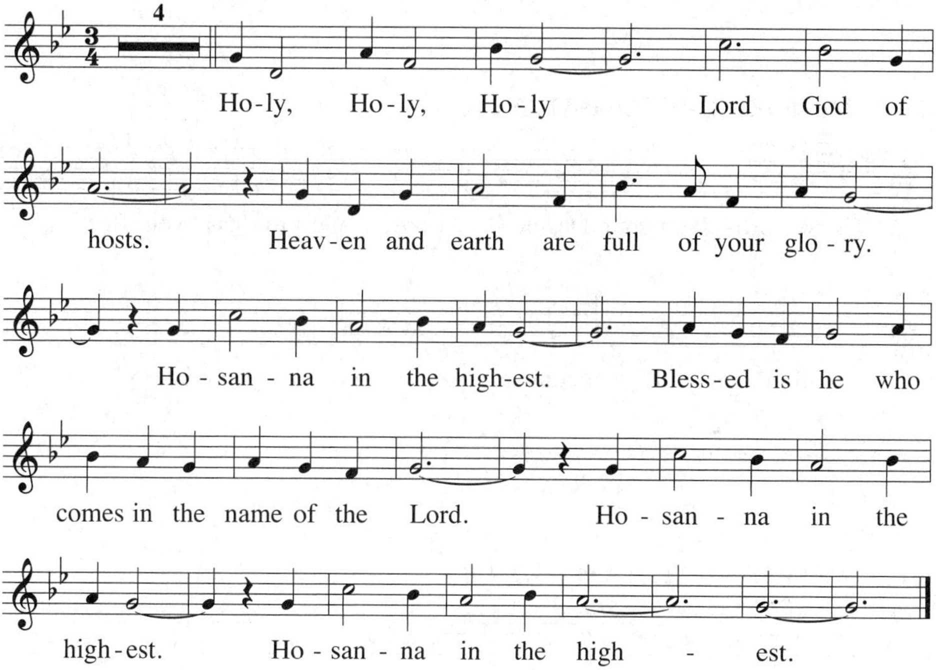

Ho-ly, Ho-ly, Ho-ly Lord God of

hosts. Heav-en and earth are full of your glo-ry.

Ho - san - na in the high-est. Bless-ed is he who

comes in the name of the Lord. Ho - san - na in the

high-est. Ho - san - na in the high - est.

Text: ICEL, © 2010
Music: *Mass of Creation*, Marty Haugen, © 1984, 1985, 2010, GIA Publications, Inc.

260 CHILDREN'S ACCLAMATION 2

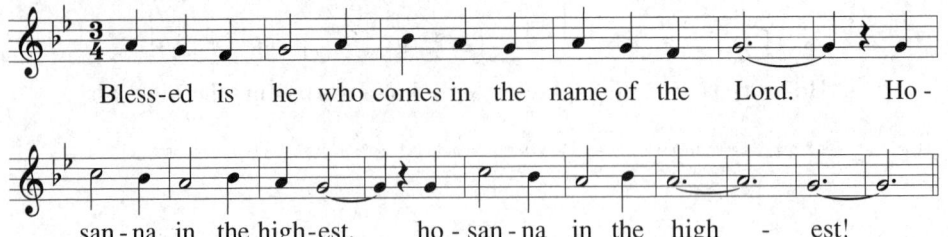

Bless-ed is he who comes in the name of the Lord. Ho-

san-na in the high-est, ho-san-na in the high - est!

Text: ICEL, © 1975
Music: Eucharistic Prayer for Children, *Mass of Creation*, Marty Haugen, adapt. by Rob Glover, © 1989, GIA Publications, Inc.

In Eucharistic Prayer 1, this acclamation precedes the Holy, Holy, Holy.

261 MEMORIAL ACCLAMATION A

We pro-claim your Death, O Lord, and pro-fess your Res-ur-

rec-tion un-til you come a-gain, un-til you come a-gain.

Text: ICEL, © 2010
Music: *Mass of Creation*, Marty Haugen, © 2010, GIA Publications, Inc.

262 MEMORIAL ACCLAMATION B

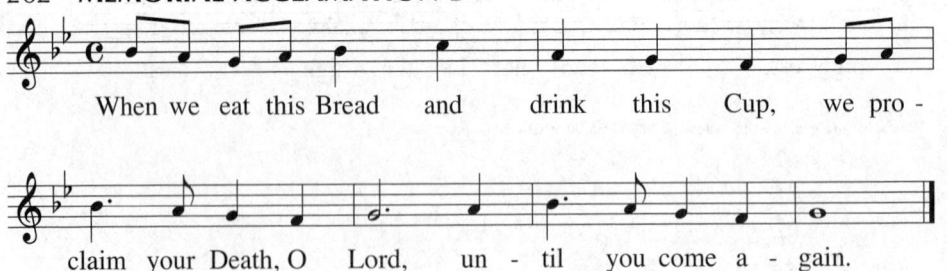

When we eat this Bread and drink this Cup, we pro-

claim your Death, O Lord, un-til you come a-gain.

Text: ICEL, © 2010
Music: *Mass of Creation*, Marty Haugen, © 2010, GIA Publications, Inc.

MEMORIAL ACCLAMATION C

263

Save us, Sav-ior of the world, for by your Cross and Res-ur-rec-tion you have set us free, you have set us free.

Text: ICEL, © 2010
Music: *Mass of Creation,* Marty Haugen, © 2010, GIA Publications, Inc.

CHILDREN'S ACCLAMATION 3

264

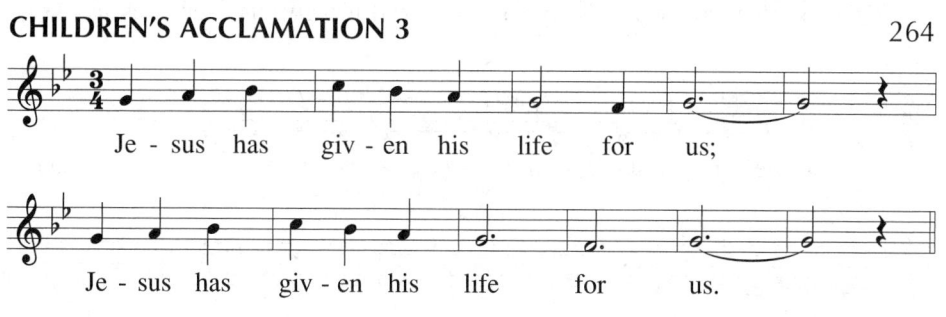

Je - sus has giv-en his life for us;
Je - sus has giv-en his life for us.

Text: ICEL, © 1975
Music: Eucharistic Prayer for Children, *Mass of Creation,* Marty Haugen, adapt. by Rob Glover, © 1989, GIA Publications, Inc.

CHILDREN'S ACCLAMATION 4

265

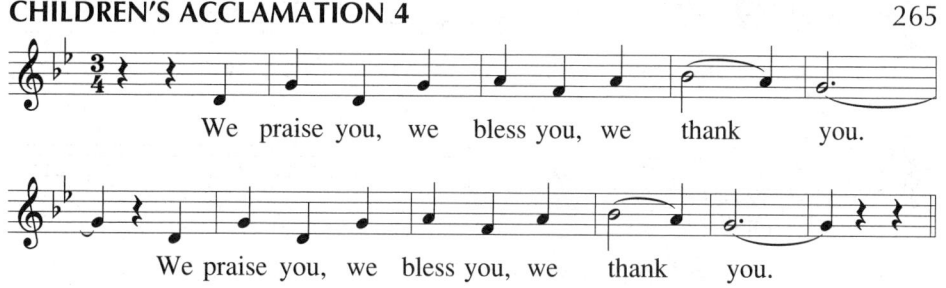

We praise you, we bless you, we thank you.
We praise you, we bless you, we thank you.

Text: ICEL, © 1975
Music: Eucharistic Prayer for Children, *Mass of Creation,* Marty Haugen, adapt. by Rob Glover, © 1989, GIA Publications, Inc.

AMEN

266

A - men, a - men, a - men!

Music: *Mass of Creation,* Marty Haugen, © 1984, 1985, GIA Publications, Inc.

267 THE LORD'S PRAYER

Our Fa - ther, who art in heav-en, hal-low-ed be thy name; thy

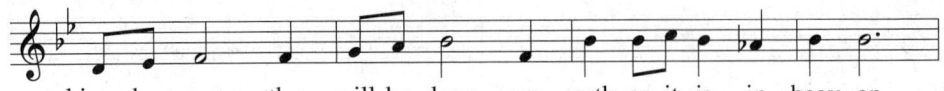

king-dom come, thy will be done on earth as it is in heav-en.

Give us this day our dai-ly bread, and for-give us our tres-pass-es,

as we for-give those who tres - pass a-gainst us; and

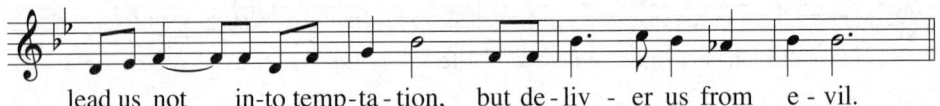

lead us not in-to temp-ta - tion, but de-liv - er us from e - vil.

Priest: Deliver us, Lord... and the coming of our Savior, Jesus Christ.

For the king - dom, the pow-er and the glo-ry are yours

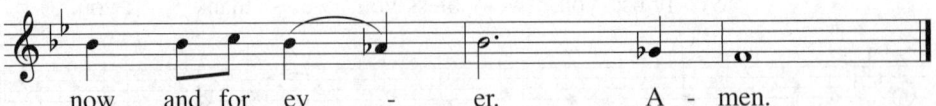

now and for ev - er. A - men.

Music: *Mass of Creation*, Marty Haugen, © 1984, 1985, GIA Publications, Inc.

268 LAMB OF GOD

Cantor:

Lamb of God, you take a-way the sins of the

Assembly:

To repeat

world, have mer - cy on us.

world,   grant   us   peace.

Music: *Mass of Creation,* Marty Haugen, © 1984, 1985, GIA Publications, Inc.

GLORIA 269

Refrain / Estribillo

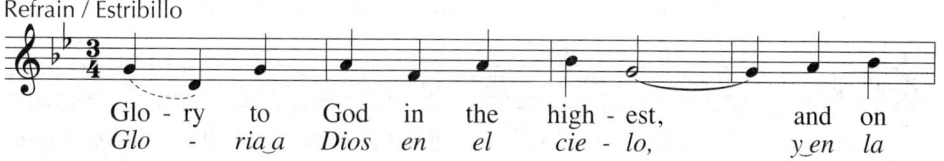

Glo - ry   to   God   in   the   high - est,   and   on
Glo - ria_a   Dios   en   el   cie - lo,   y_en   la

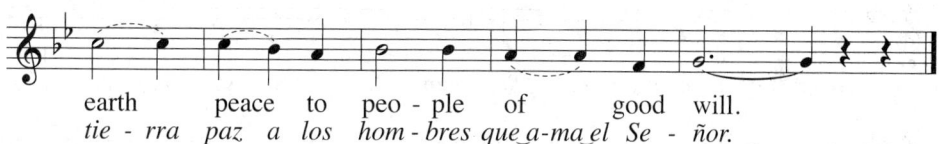

earth   peace   to   peo - ple   of   good   will.
tie - rra   paz   a   los   hom - bres   que_a-ma_el   Se - ñor.

Verses / Estrofas

1. We praise you,
   we bless you,
   we adore you,
   we glorify you,
   we give you thanks for your great glory,
   Lord God, heavenly King,
   O God, almighty Father.

2. Lord Jesus Christ, Only Begotten Son,
   Lord God, Lamb of God, Son of the
       Father,
   you take away the sins of the world,
   have mercy on us;
   you take away the sins of the world,
   receive our prayer;
   you are seated at the right hand of the
       Father,
   have mercy on us.

3. For you alone are the Holy One,
   you alone are the Lord,
   you alone are the Most High,
   Jesus Christ,
   with the Holy Spirit,
   in the glory of God the Father.
   Amen.

1. *Por tu_inmensa gloria te_alabamos,*
   te bendecimos,
   te_adoramos,
   te glorificamos,
   te damos gracias,
   Señor Dios, Rey celestial,
   Dios Padre todopoderoso.

2. *Señor, Hijo único, Jesucristo,*
   Señor Dios, Cordero de Dios, Hijo
       del Padre;
   tú que quitas el pecado del mundo,
   ten piedad de nosotros;
   tú que quitas el pecado del mundo,
   a tiende nuestra súplica;
   tú que_estás sentado_a la derecha
       del Padre,
   ten piedad de nosotros.

3. *Porque sólo tú_eres Santo,*
   sólo tú Señor,
   sólo tú Altísimo,
   Jesucristo,
   con el Espíritu Santo
   en la gloria de Dios Padre.
   Amén.

Text: English, ICEL, © 2010
Music: *Mass of Creation,* Marty Haugen; adapt. by Tony E. Alonso, © 1984, 1985, 2010, 2013, GIA Publications, Inc.

270 SANTO, SANTO, SANTO — HOLY, HOLY, HOLY

San-to, San-to, San-to es el Se-ñor, Dios del

U-ni-ver-so. Heav-en and earth are full of your

glo-ry. Ho-san-na in the high-est. Ben-di-to el que

vie-ne en nom-bre del Se-ñor. Ho-san-na en el

cie-lo. Ho-san-na in the high - est.

Text: English, ICEL, © 2010
Music: *Mass of Creation,* Marty Haugen; adapt. by Tony E. Alonso, © 1984, 1985, 2010, 2013, GIA Publications, Inc.

271 MEMORIAL ACCLAMATION A — ACLAMACIÓN AL MEMORIAL A

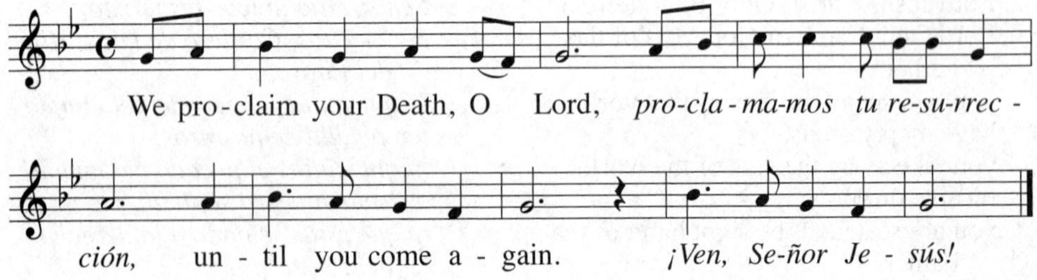

We pro-claim your Death, O Lord, *pro-cla-ma-mos tu re-su-rrec-*

ción, un - til you come a - gain. *¡Ven, Se-ñor Je - sús!*

Text: English, ICEL, © 2010
Music: *Mass of Creation,* Marty Haugen; adapt. by Tony E. Alonso, © 2010, 2013, GIA Publications, Inc.

MEMORIAL ACCLAMATION B   ACLAMACIÓN AL MEMORIAL B   272

When we eat this Bread and drink this Cup, *a-nun-cia-mos tu*

muer-te, Se-ñor, *has-ta que vuel-vas,* un-til you come a-gain.

Text: English, ICEL, © 2010
Music: *Mass of Creation,* Marty Haugen; adapt. by Tony E. Alonso, © 2010, 2013, GIA Publications, Inc.

MEMORIAL ACCLAMATION C   ACLAMACIÓN AL MEMORIAL C   273

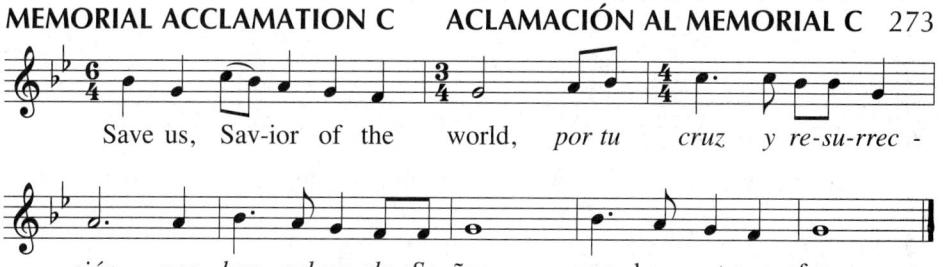

Save us, Sav-ior of the world, *por tu* *cruz* *y re-su-rrec-*

ción *nos has sal-va-do, Se-ñor,* you have set us free.

Text: English, ICEL, © 2010
Music: *Mass of Creation,* Marty Haugen; adapt. by Tony E. Alonso, © 2010, 2013, GIA Publications, Inc.

AMÉN   274

A - mén, a - mén, a - mén!

Music: *Mass of Creation,* Marty Haugen, © 1984, 1985, GIA Publications, Inc.

Setting Two: A Community Mass

275 KYRIE

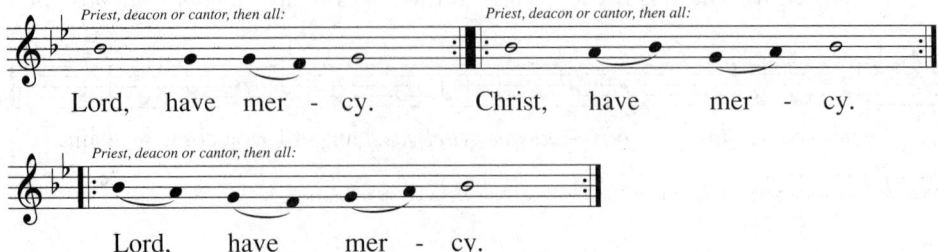

Priest, deacon or cantor, then all:

Lord, have mer - cy. Christ, have mer - cy.

Priest, deacon or cantor, then all:

Lord, have mer - cy.

Music: *Litany of the Saints;* adapt. by Richard Proulx, © 1971, GIA Publications, Inc.

Or:

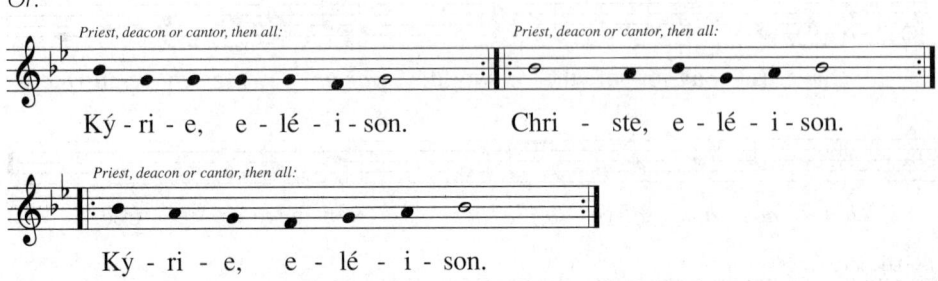

Priest, deacon or cantor, then all:

Ký - ri - e, e - lé - i - son. Chri - ste, e - lé - i - son.

Priest, deacon or cantor, then all:

Ký - ri - e, e - lé - i - son.

Music: *Litany of the Saints;* adapt. by Richard Proulx, © 1971, GIA Publications, Inc.

276 GLORIA

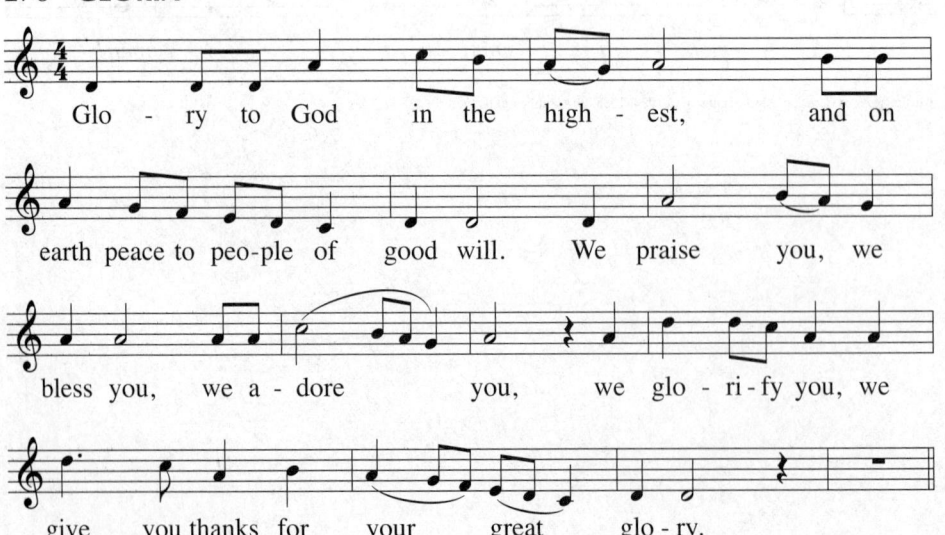

Glo - ry to God in the high - est, and on

earth peace to peo-ple of good will. We praise you, we

bless you, we a - dore you, we glo - ri-fy you, we

give you thanks for your great glo - ry.

Lord God, heav'n-ly King, O God, al-might-y Fa-ther. Lord Je-sus Christ, On-ly Be-got-ten Son, Lord God, Lamb of God, Son of the Fa - ther, you take a-way the sins of the world, have mer-cy on us; you take a-way the sins of the world, re - ceive our prayer; you are seat-ed at the right hand of the Fa-ther, have mer-cy on us. For you a-lone are the Ho-ly One, you a-lone are the Lord, you a-lone are the Most High, Je-sus Christ, with the Ho-ly Spir-it, in the glo-ry of God the Fa-ther. A - men, a - men.

Text: ICEL, © 2010
Music: *A Community Mass*, Richard Proulx, © 1971, 1977, 2006, 2010, GIA Publications, Inc.

277 HOLY, HOLY, HOLY

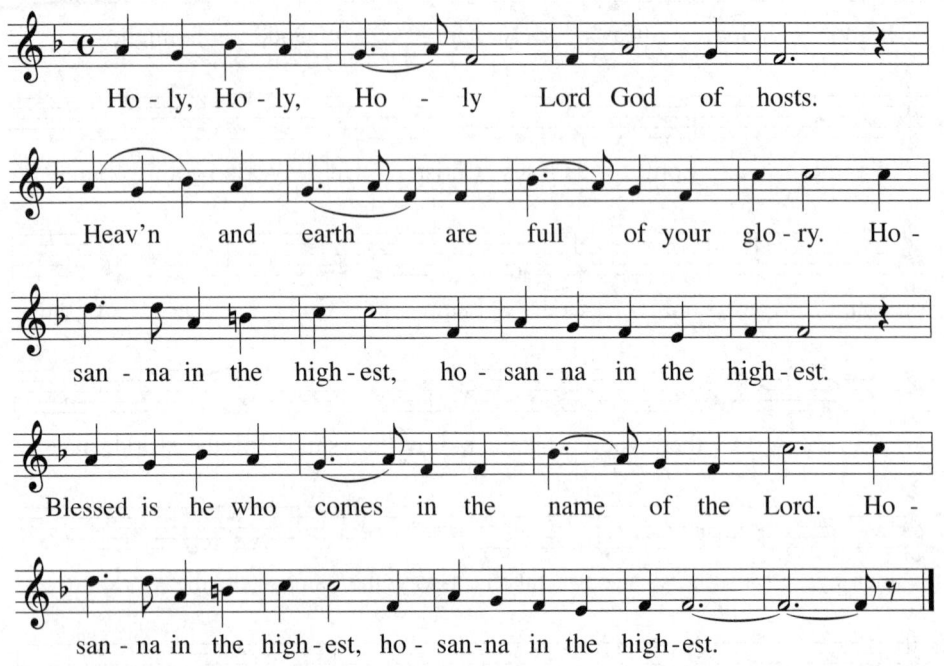

Ho - ly, Ho - ly, Ho - ly Lord God of hosts.

Heav'n and earth are full of your glo - ry. Ho -

san - na in the high - est, ho - san - na in the high - est.

Blessed is he who comes in the name of the Lord. Ho -

san - na in the high - est, ho - san - na in the high - est.

Text: ICEL, © 2010
Music: *A Community Mass,* Richard Proulx, © 1971, GIA Publications, Inc.

278 MEMORIAL ACCLAMATION A

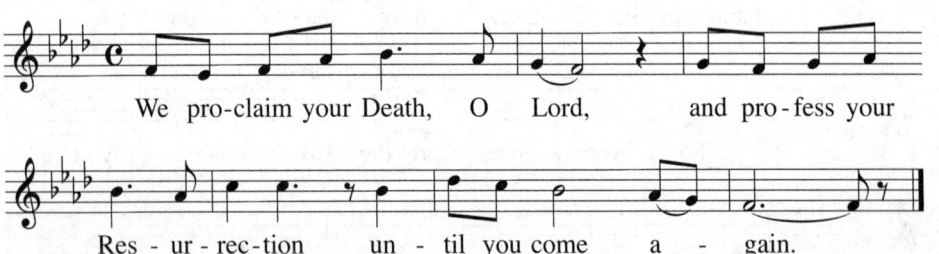

We pro-claim your Death, O Lord, and pro-fess your

Res - ur - rec - tion un - til you come a - gain.

Text: ICEL, © 2010
Music: *A Community Mass,* Richard Proulx, © 2010, GIA Publications, Inc.

279 AMEN

A - men, a - men, a - men.

Music: *A Community Mass,* Richard Proulx, © 1971, 1977, GIA Publications, Inc.

MEMORIAL ACCLAMATION B

280

When we eat this Bread and drink this Cup, we pro-
claim your Death, O Lord, un - til you come a - gain.

Text: ICEL, © 2010
Music: *A Community Mass,* Richard Proulx, © 1988, 2010, GIA Publications, Inc.

MEMORIAL ACCLAMATION C

281

Save us, Sav-ior of the world, for by your Cross and
Res - ur - rec-tion you have set us free.

Text: ICEL, © 2010
Music: *A Community Mass,* Richard Proulx, © 1985, 2010, GIA Publications, Inc.

AMEN

282

A - men, a - men, a - men.

Music: *A Community Mass,* Richard Proulx (adapt.), © 1971, 2011, GIA Publications, Inc.

LAMB OF GOD

283

Lamb of God, you take a - way the sins of the
world, have mer - cy on us. Lamb of God, you
take a - way the sins of the world, grant us peace.

Music: *A Community Mass,* Richard Proulx, © 1971, 1977, GIA Publications, Inc.

Setting Three: Mass of Joy and Peace

284 SPRINKLING SONG

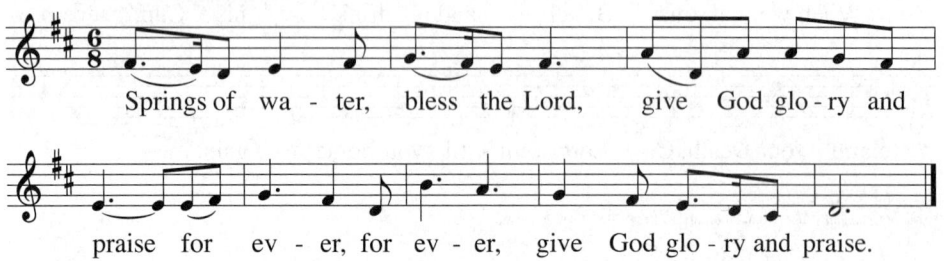

Springs of wa - ter, bless the Lord, give God glo - ry and
praise for ev - er, for ev - er, give God glo - ry and praise.

Music: *Mass of Joy and Peace,* Tony E. Alonso, © 2010, GIA Publications, Inc.

285 PENITENTIAL ACT

Priest, deacon, or cantor, then all:

(*Invocation*) Ký - ri - e, e - lé - i - son.

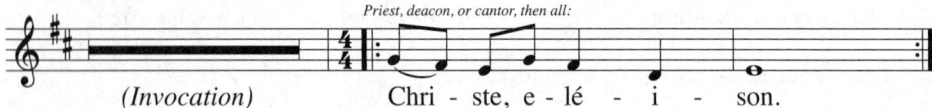

Priest, deacon, or cantor, then all:

(*Invocation*) Chri - ste, e - lé - i - son.

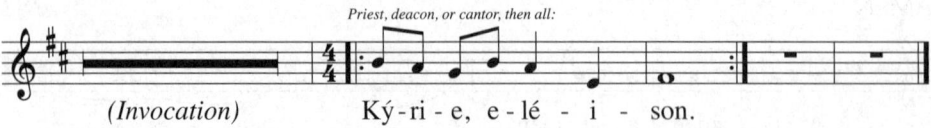

Priest, deacon, or cantor, then all:

(*Invocation*) Ký - ri - e, e - lé - i - son.

Music: *Mass of Joy and Peace,* Tony E. Alonso, © 2010, GIA Publications, Inc.

286 GLORIA

Refrain

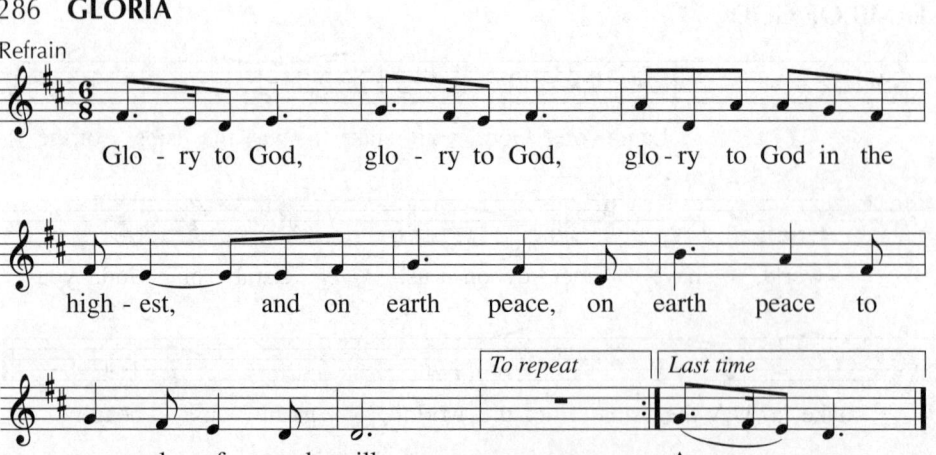

Glo - ry to God, glo - ry to God, glo - ry to God in the
high - est, and on earth peace, on earth peace to
peo - ple of good will.

To repeat | *Last time*

A - men.

SETTING THREE

Verses

1. We praise you,
   we bless you,
   we adore you,
   we glorify you,
   we give you thanks for your great glory,
   Lord God, heavenly King,
   O God, almighty Father.

2. Lord Jesus Christ, Only Begotten Son,
   Lord God, Lamb of God, Son of the Father,
   you take away the sins of the world,
   have mercy on us;
   you take away the sins of the world,
   receive our prayer;
   you are seated at the right hand of the Father,
   have mercy on us.

3. For you alone are the Holy One,
   you alone are the Lord,
   you alone are the Most High,
   Jesus Christ,
   with the Holy Spirit,
   in the glory of God the Father.
   Amen.

Text: ICEL, © 2010
Music: *Mass of Joy and Peace,* Tony E. Alonso, © 2010, GIA Publications, Inc.

GOSPEL ACCLAMATION 287

Music: *Mass of Joy and Peace,* Tony E. Alonso, © 2010, GIA Publications, Inc.

288 LENTEN GOSPEL ACCLAMATION

Refrain

Glo - ry to you, Word of God, Lord Je - sus Christ!

Glo - ry to you, Word of God, Lord Je-sus Christ!

Text: ICEL, © 1969
Music: *Mass of Joy and Peace*, Tony E. Alonso, © 2010, GIA Publications, Inc.

289 PRAYER OF THE FAITHFUL

Cantor, then all:

God of mer - cy, hear our prayer. *(Intercessions)*

Response

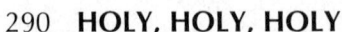

Cantor: *All:*

We pray to the Lord: God of mer - cy, hear our prayer.

Music: *Mass of Joy and Peace*, Tony E. Alonso, © 2010, GIA Publications, Inc.

290 HOLY, HOLY, HOLY

Ho - ly, Ho - ly, Ho - ly Lord God of hosts.

Heav - en and earth are full of your glo - ry. Ho -

san - na in the high - est, ho - san - na in the

high - est. Bless - ed is he, bless - ed is he who

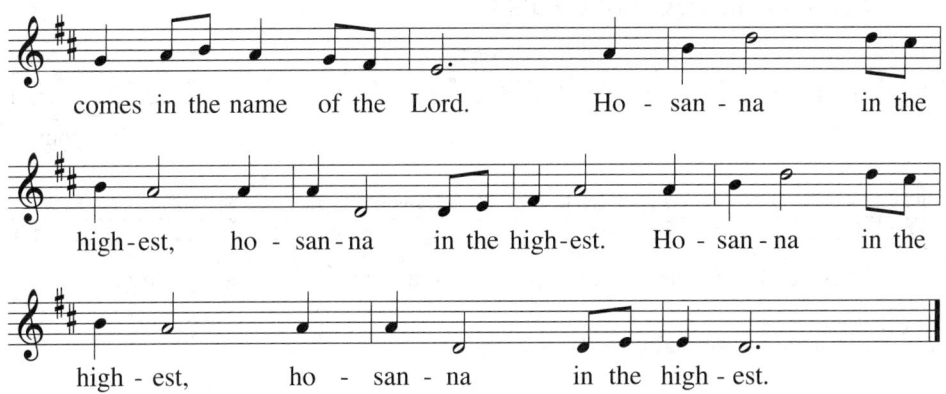

comes in the name of the Lord. Ho - san - na in the high-est, ho - san - na in the high-est. Ho - san - na in the high - est, ho - san - na in the high - est.

Text: ICEL, © 2010
Music: *Mass of Joy and Peace,* Tony E. Alonso, © 2010, GIA Publications, Inc.

MEMORIAL ACCLAMATION A 291

We pro - claim your Death, O Lord, and pro - fess your Res - ur - rec - tion un - til you come a - gain.

Text: ICEL, © 2010
Music: *Mass of Joy and Peace,* Tony E. Alonso, © 2010, GIA Publications, Inc.

MEMORIAL ACCLAMATION B 292

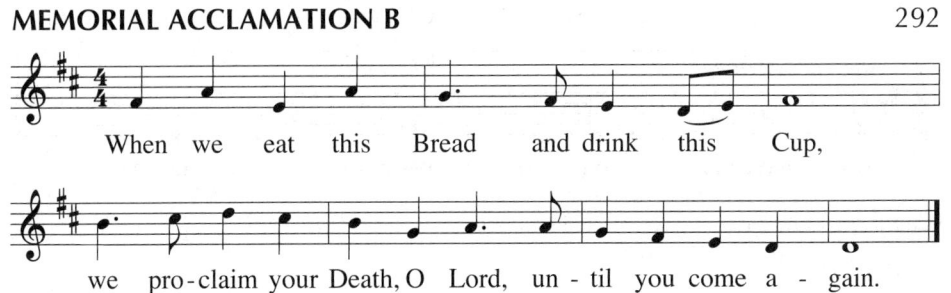

When we eat this Bread and drink this Cup, we pro-claim your Death, O Lord, un - til you come a - gain.

Text: ICEL, © 2010
Music: *Mass of Joy and Peace,* Tony E. Alonso, © 2010, GIA Publications, Inc.

293 MEMORIAL ACCLAMATION C

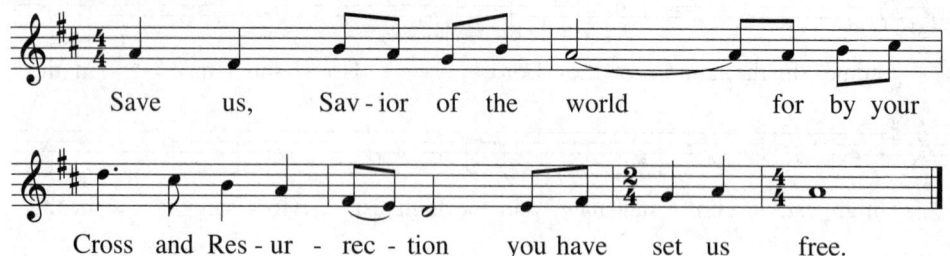

Save us, Sav-ior of the world for by your

Cross and Res-ur - rec - tion you have set us free.

Text: ICEL, © 2010
Music: *Mass of Joy and Peace,* Tony E. Alonso, © 2010, GIA Publications, Inc.

294 AMEN

A - men, a - men, a - men, a -

men. A - men, a - men, a - men, a - men.

Music: *Mass of Joy and Peace,* Tony E. Alonso, © 2010, GIA Publications, Inc.

295 LAMB OF GOD

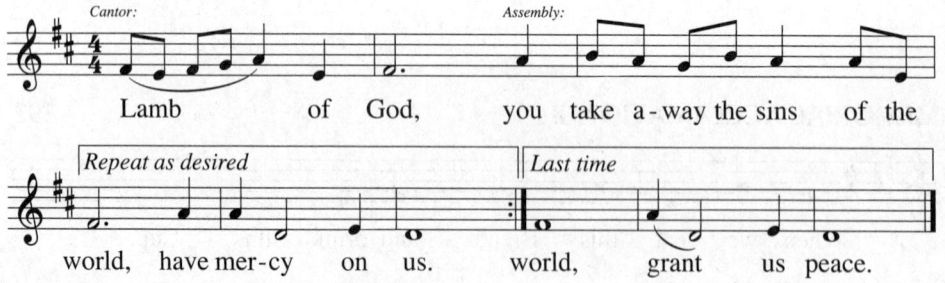

Cantor: *Assembly:*

Lamb of God, you take a - way the sins of the

Repeat as desired   *Last time*

world, have mer-cy on us. world, grant us peace.

Music: *Mass of Joy and Peace,* Tony E. Alonso, © 2010, GIA Publications, Inc.

Setting Four: Mass of the Angels and Saints

PENITENTIAL ACT 296

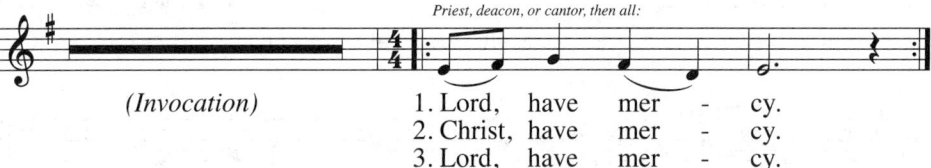

Priest, deacon, or cantor, then all:

(Invocation)
1. Lord, have mer - cy.
2. Christ, have mer - cy.
3. Lord, have mer - cy.

Priest: May almighty God...everlasting life.

Assembly:

A - men.

Music: *Mass of the Angels and Saints,* Steven R. Janco, © 1996, GIA Publications, Inc.

GLORIA 297

Refrain

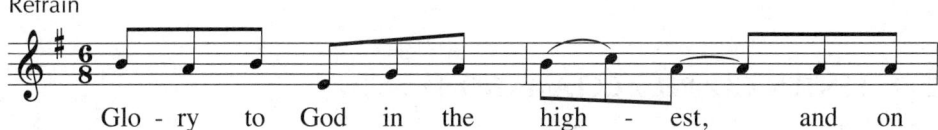

Glo - ry to God in the high - est, and on

To verses

earth peace to peo - ple of good will.

Cantor, then all: (Last time)

A - men.

Verses

1. We praise you, we bless you, we adore you, we glorify you,
   we give you thanks for your great glory,
   Lord God, heavenly King, O God, almighty Father.

2. Lord Jesus Christ, Only Begotten Son,
   Lord God, Lamb of God, Son of the Father,
   you take away the sins of the world, have mercy on us;
   you take away the sins of the world, receive our prayer;
   you are seated at the right hand of the Father, have mercy on us.

3. For you alone are the Holy One, you alone are the Lord,
   you alone are the Most High, Jesus Christ,
   with the Holy Spirit, in the glory of God the Father.

Text: ICEL, © 2010
Music: *Mass of the Angels and Saints,* Steven R. Janco, © 1996, 2010, GIA Publications, Inc.

298 GOSPEL ACCLAMATION

Refrain

Al - le - lu - ia, al - le - lu - ia, al - le - lu - ia.

Al - le - lu - ia, al - le - lu - ia, al - le - lu - ia.

Verse Response

After first phrase: *After second phrase:*   **D.C.**

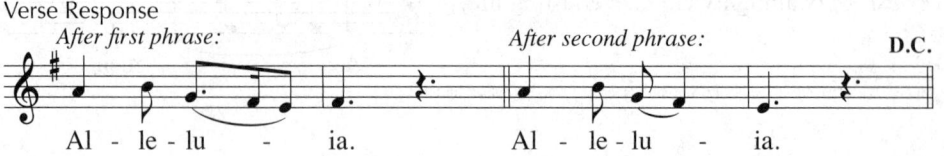

Al - le - lu - ia.   Al - le - lu - ia.

Music: *Mass of the Angels and Saints,* Steven R. Janco, © 1996, 2010, GIA Publications, Inc.

299 LENTEN GOSPEL ACCLAMATION

Glo - ry, praise and hon - or to you, Lord Je - sus Christ.

Text: ICEL, © 2010
Music: *Mass of the Angels and Saints,* Steven R. Janco, © 2010, GIA Publications, Inc.

300 PRAYER OF THE FAITHFUL

Cantor: *All:*

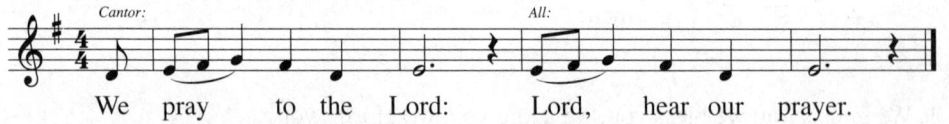

We pray to the Lord: Lord, hear our prayer.

Alternate Responses

A

Lord, have mer - cy.

B

Gra - cious-ly hear us.

Music: *Mass of the Angels and Saints,* Steven R. Janco, © 2010, GIA Publications, Inc.

CHILDREN'S ACCLAMATION 1   301

Ho - san - na, ho - san - na, ho - san - na in the high - est.

Text: ICEL, © 1975
Music: *Mass of the Angels and Saints,* Steven R. Janco, © 1996, 2010, GIA Publications, Inc.

HOLY, HOLY, HOLY   302

Ho - ly, Ho - ly, Ho - ly   Lord   God of   hosts.

Heav'n and earth   are   full of your glo - ry.   Ho -

san - na,   ho - san - na,   ho - san - na   in the

high - est,   ho - san - na,   ho - san - na,   ho -

san - na   in the high - est. Bless - ed is he   who comes in the

name   of the   Lord.   Ho - san - na,   ho -

san - na,   ho - san - na   in the   high - est,   ho -

san - na,   ho - san - na,   ho - san - na   in the high - est.

Text: ICEL, © 2010
Music: *Mass of the Angels and Saints,* Steven R. Janco, © 1996, 2010, GIA Publications, Inc.

303 CHILDREN'S ACCLAMATION 2

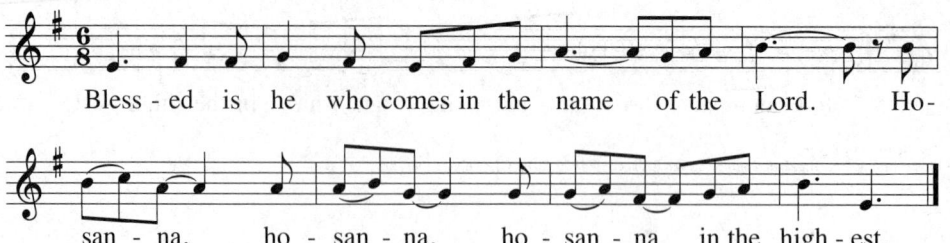

Bless - ed is he who comes in the name of the Lord. Ho-
san - na, ho - san - na, ho - san - na in the high - est.

Text: ICEL, © 1975
Music: *Mass of the Angels and Saints,* Steven R. Janco, © 1996, 2010, GIA Publications, Inc.

In Eucharistic Prayer 1, this acclamation precedes the Holy, Holy, Holy.

304 MEMORIAL ACCLAMATION A

We pro - claim your Death, O Lord, and pro -
fess your Res - ur - rec - tion un - til you come a - gain.

Text: ICEL, © 2010
Music: *Mass of the Angels and Saints,* Steven R. Janco, © 1996, 2010, GIA Publications, Inc.

305 MEMORIAL ACCLAMATION B

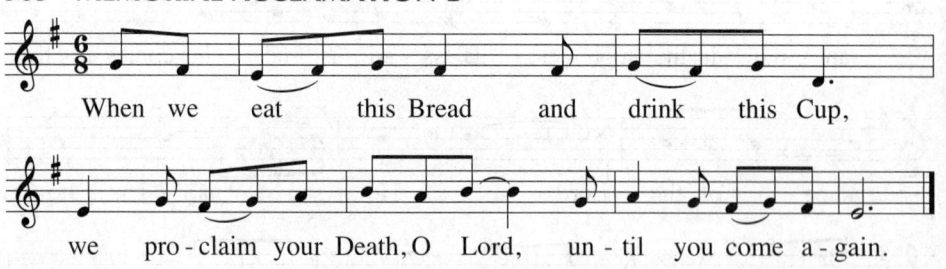

When we eat this Bread and drink this Cup,
we pro - claim your Death, O Lord, un - til you come a - gain.

Text: ICEL, © 2010
Music: *Mass of the Angels and Saints,* Steven R. Janco, © 1996, 2010, GIA Publications, Inc.

MEMORIAL ACCLAMATION C 306

Save us, Sav - ior of the world, for by your Cross and Res - ur - rec - tion you have set us free.

Text: ICEL, © 2010
Music: *Mass of the Angels and Saints,* Steven R. Janco, © 2010, GIA Publications, Inc.

CHILDREN'S ACCLAMATION 3 307

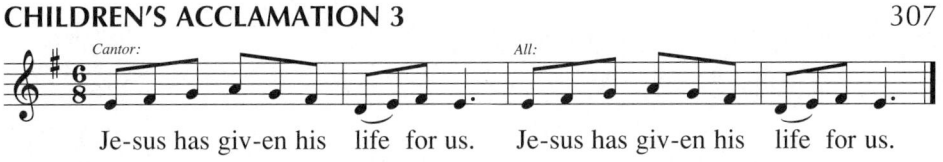

Cantor: Je-sus has giv-en his life for us. *All:* Je-sus has giv-en his life for us.

Text: ICEL, © 1975
Music: *Mass of the Angels and Saints,* Steve R. Janco, © 2000, GIA Publications, Inc.

CHILDREN'S ACCLAMATION 4 308

Cantor: We praise you, we bless you, we thank you.

All: We praise you, we bless you, we thank you.

Text: ICEL, © 1975
Music: *Mass of the Angels and Saints,* Steve R. Janco, © 2000, GIA Publications, Inc.

AMEN 309

A - men, a - men, a - men.

A - men, a - men, a - men.

Music: *Mass of the Angels and Saints,* Steven R. Janco, © 1996, GIA Publications, Inc.

310 **LAMB OF GOD**

Have mer - cy on us. Have mer - cy on us.

Grant us peace. Grant us peace.

Music: *Mass of the Angels and Saints*, Steven R. Janco, © 1996, GIA Publications, Inc.

Setting Five: Mass for a Servant Church

PENITENTIAL ACT 1

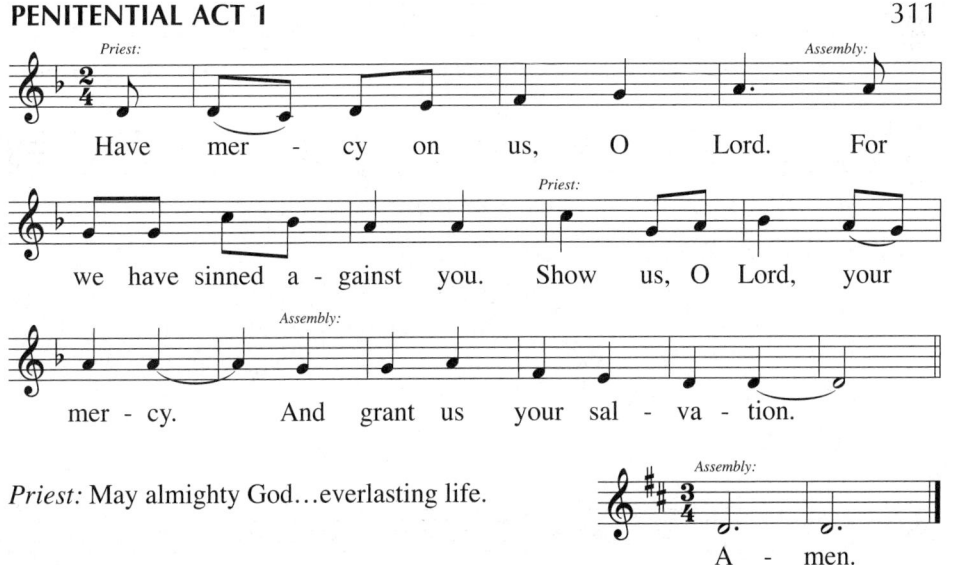

Have mer - cy on us, O Lord. For we have sinned a - gainst you. Show us, O Lord, your mer - cy. And grant us your sal - va - tion.

Priest: May almighty God...everlasting life.

A - men.

Text: ICEL, © 2010
Music: *Mass for a Servant Church*, Michel Guimont, © 2010, GIA Publications, Inc.

PENITENTIAL ACT 2

(Invocation) Ký - ri - e, e - lé - i - son.
Lord, have mer - cy.

(Invocation) Chri - ste, e - lé - i - son.
Christ, have mer - cy.

(Invocation) Ký - ri - e, e - lé - i - son.
Lord, have mer - cy.

Last time

Priest: May almighty God...everlasting life.

A - men.

Music: *Mass for a Servant Church*, Michel Guimont, © 2010, GIA Publications, Inc.

313 KYRIE

Ký - ri - e, e - lé - i - son. Chri - ste, e -
lé - i - son. Ký - ri - e, e - lé - i - son.

Music: *Mass for a Servant Church,* Michel Guimont, © 2010, GIA Publications, Inc.

314 GLORIA

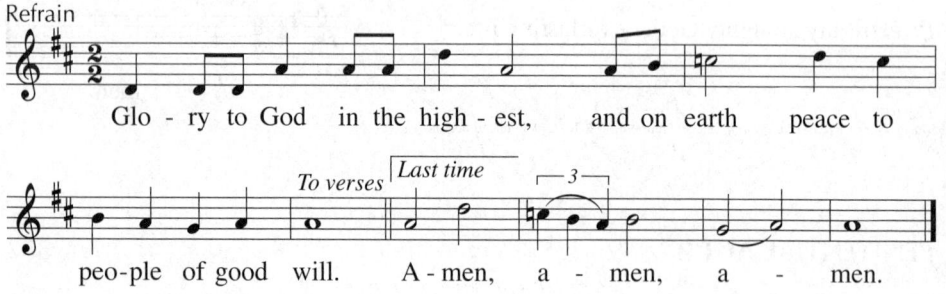

Glo - ry to God in the high - est, and on earth peace to
peo - ple of good will. A - men, a - men, a - men.

Verses

1. We praise you,
   we bless you,
   we adore you,
   we glorify you,
   we give you thanks for your great glory,
   Lord God, heavenly King,
   O God, almighty Father.

2. Lord Jesus Christ, Only Begotten Son,
   Lord God, Lamb of God, Son of the Father,
   you take away the sins of the world,

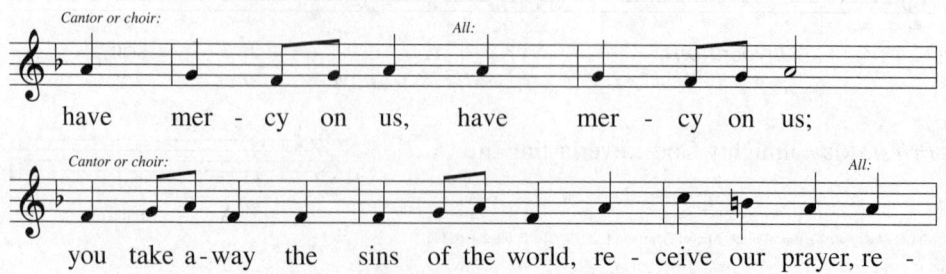

have mer - cy on us, have mer - cy on us;
you take a - way the sins of the world, re - ceive our prayer, re -

ceive our prayer; you are seat - ed at the right hand of the

All: D.C.

Fa - ther, have mer - cy on us, have mer - cy on us.

3. For you alone are the Holy One,
   you alone are the Lord,
   you alone are the Most High,
   Jesus Christ,
   with the Holy Spirit,
   in the glory of God the Father.
   Amen.

Text: ICEL, © 2010
Music: *Mass for a Servant Church,* Michel Guimont, © 2010, GIA Publications, Inc.

HOLY, HOLY, HOLY 315

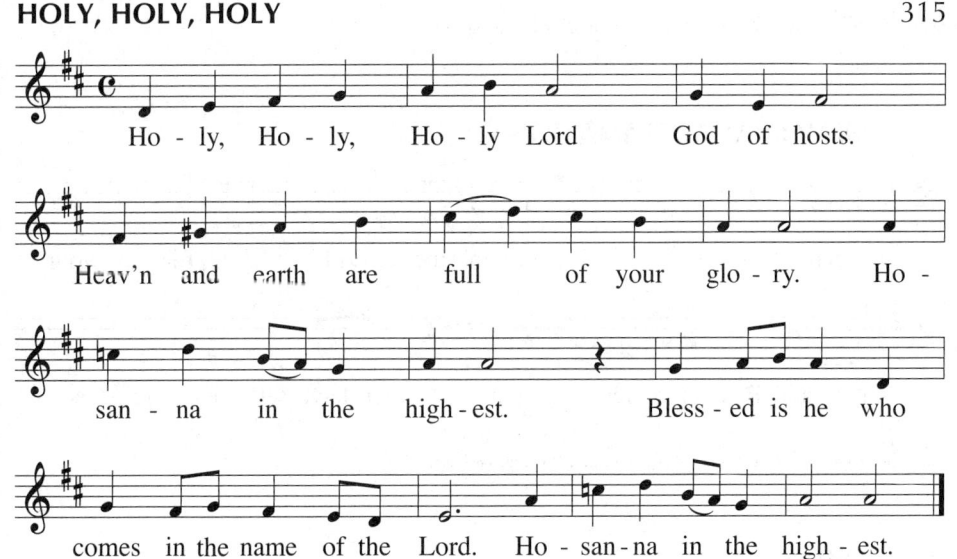

Ho - ly, Ho - ly, Ho - ly Lord God of hosts.

Heav'n and earth are full of your glo - ry. Ho -

san - na in the high - est. Bless - ed is he who

comes in the name of the Lord. Ho - san - na in the high - est.

Text: ICEL, © 2010
Music: *Mass for a Servant Church,* Michel Guimont, © 2010, GIA Publications, Inc.

316 MEMORIAL ACCLAMATION A

We pro - claim your Death, O Lord, and pro - fess your Res - ur - rec - tion un - til you come a - gain.

Text: ICEL, © 2010
Music: *Mass for a Servant Church,* Michel Guimont, © 2010, GIA Publications, Inc.

317 MEMORIAL ACCLAMATION B

When we eat this Bread and drink this Cup, we pro - claim your Death, O Lord, un - til you come a - gain.

Text: ICEL, © 2010
Music: *Mass for a Servant Church,* Michel Guimont, © 2010, GIA Publications, Inc.

318 MEMORIAL ACCLAMATION C

Save us, Sav - ior of the world, for by your Cross and Res - ur - rec - tion you have set us free.

Text: ICEL, © 2010
Music: *Mass for a Servant Church,* Michel Guimont, © 2010, GIA Publications, Inc.

319 AMEN

A - men, a - men, a - men.

Music: *Mass for a Servant Church,* Michel Guimont, © 2010, GIA Publications, Inc.

LAMB OF GOD

320

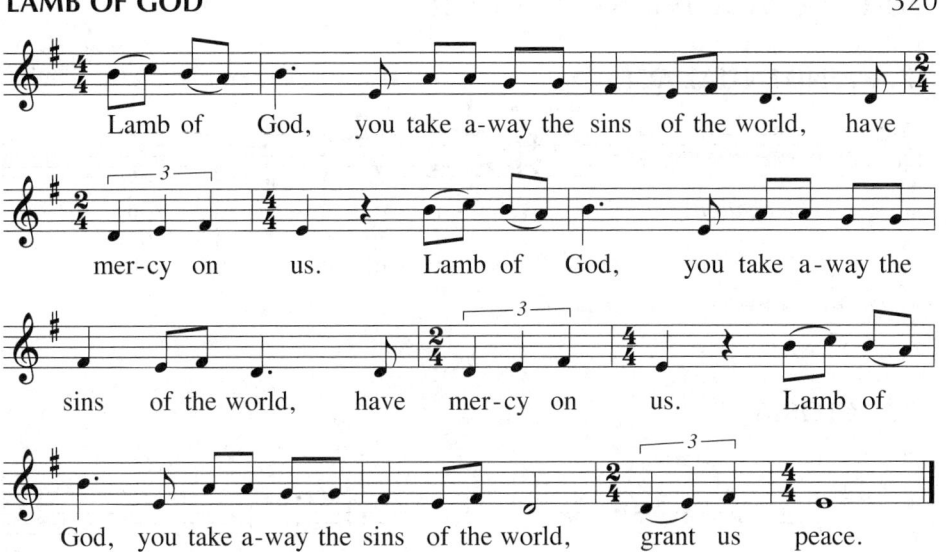

Lamb of God, you take a-way the sins of the world, have mer-cy on us. Lamb of God, you take a-way the sins of the world, have mer-cy on us. Lamb of God, you take a-way the sins of the world, grant us peace.

Music: *Mass for a Servant Church,* Michel Guimont, © 2010, GIA Publications, Inc.

Setting Six: Mass of Light

321 PENITENTIAL ACT

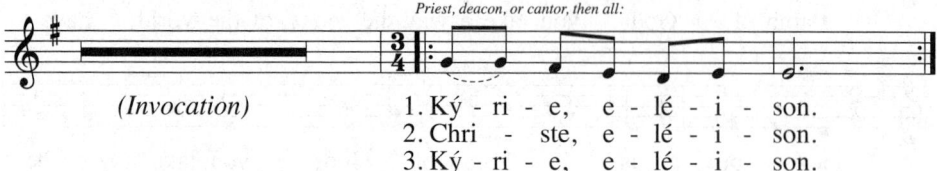

Priest, deacon, or cantor, then all:

(Invocation)

1. Ký - ri - e, e - lé - i - son.
2. Chri - ste, e - lé - i - son.
3. Ký - ri - e, e - lé - i - son.

Music: *Mass of Light,* David Haas, © 1988, GIA Publications, Inc.

322 GLORIA

Refrain

Glo - ry to God in the high - est, glo - ry to

God, and on earth peace to peo - ple, to

peo - ple of good will.

Verses

1. We praise you,
   we bless you,
   we adore you,
   we glorify you,
   we give you thanks for your great glory,
   Lord God, heavenly King,
   O God, almighty Father.

2. Lord Jesus Christ, Only Begotten Son,
   Lord God, Lamb of God, Son of the Father,
   you take away the sins of the world,
   have mercy on us;
   you take away the sins of the world,
   receive our prayer;
   you are seated at the right hand of the Father,
   have mercy on us.

3. For you alone are the Holy One,
   you alone are the Lord,
   you alone are the Most High,
   Jesus Christ,

with the Ho - ly Spir - it, in the

D.C.

glo - ry of God the Fa - ther. A - men.

Text: ICEL, © 2010
Music: *Mass of Light,* David Haas, © 1988, 2010, GIA Publications, Inc.

GOSPEL ACCLAMATION 323

Refrain

Al - le - lu - ia, al - le - lu - ia, al - le - lu - ia!
Lent: Glo-ry to you, O Word of God, Lord Je - sus Christ.

Text: ICEL, © 1969
Music: *Mass of Light,* David Haas, © 1988, GIA Publications, Inc.

HOLY, HOLY, HOLY 324

Ho - ly, Ho - ly, Ho - ly Lord

God of hosts. Heav-en and earth are full of your

glo - ry. Ho - san - na in the high - est.

Bless-ed is he who comes in the name of the Lord. Ho -

san - na in the high - est. Ho -

san - na in the high - est.

Text: ICEL, © 2010
Music: *Mass of Light,* David Haas, © 1988, 2010, GIA Publications, Inc.

325 MEMORIAL ACCLAMATION A

We pro-claim your Death, O Lord, and pro-fess your Res - ur - rec-tion un-til you come, un-til you come a - gain.

Text: ICEL, © 2010
Music: *Mass of Light,* David Haas, © 1988, 2010, GIA Publications, Inc.

326 MEMORIAL ACCLAMATION B

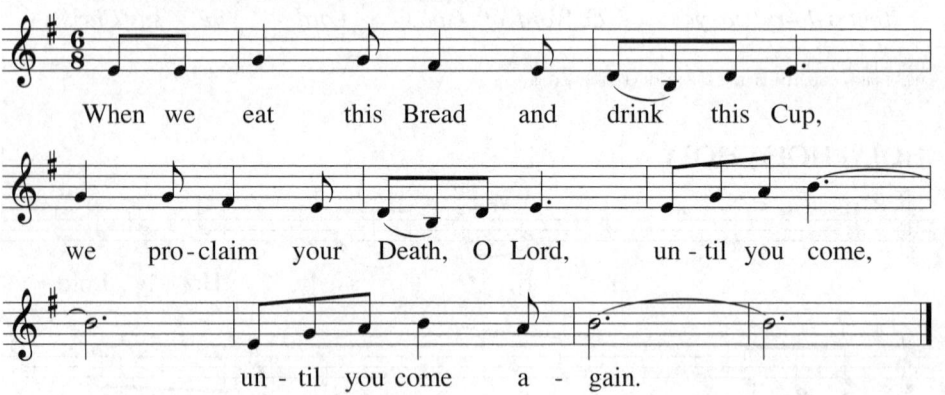

When we eat this Bread and drink this Cup, we pro-claim your Death, O Lord, un - til you come, un - til you come a - gain.

Text: ICEL, © 2010
Music: *Mass of Light,* David Haas, © 1988, 2010, GIA Publications, Inc.

327 MEMORIAL ACCLAMATION C

Save us, Sav-ior of the world, for by your Cross and Res - ur - rec-tion you have set us free, you have set us free.

Text: ICEL, © 2010
Music: *Mass of Light,* David Haas, © 1988, 2010, GIA Publications, Inc.

AMEN

328

A - men, a - men, a - men, a - men.

Music: *Mass of Light,* David Haas, © 1988, GIA Publications, Inc.

LAMB OF GOD

329

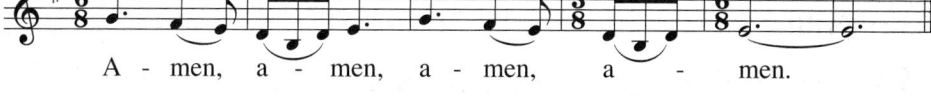

Cantor: All:

Lamb of God, you take a - way the sins of the

To repeat

world, have mer - cy on us.

Last time

world, grant us peace.

Music: *Mass of Light,* David Haas, © 1988, GIA Publications, Inc.

Setting Seven: Mass in Honor of St. Ignatius

330 KYRIE

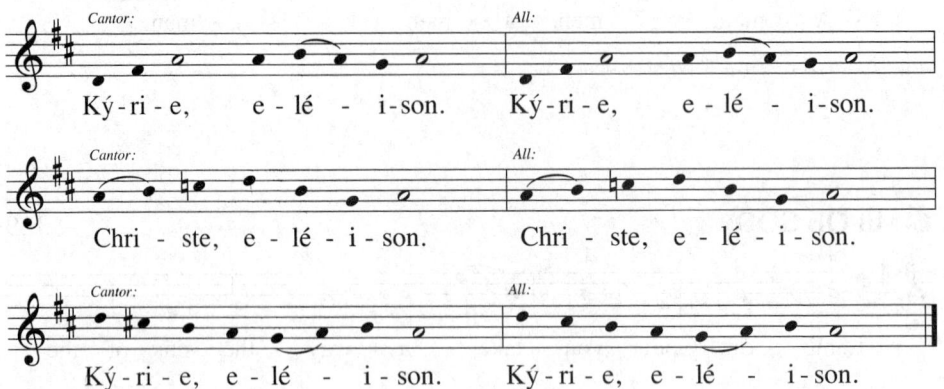

Cantor: Ký - ri - e, e - lé - i - son. *All:* Ký - ri - e, e - lé - i - son.

Cantor: Chri - ste, e - lé - i - son. *All:* Chri - ste, e - lé - i - son.

Cantor: Ký - ri - e, e - lé - i - son. *All:* Ký - ri - e, e - lé - i - son.

Music: *Mass in Honor of St. Ignatius,* Russell Weismann, © 2012, GIA Publications, Inc.

331 GLORIA

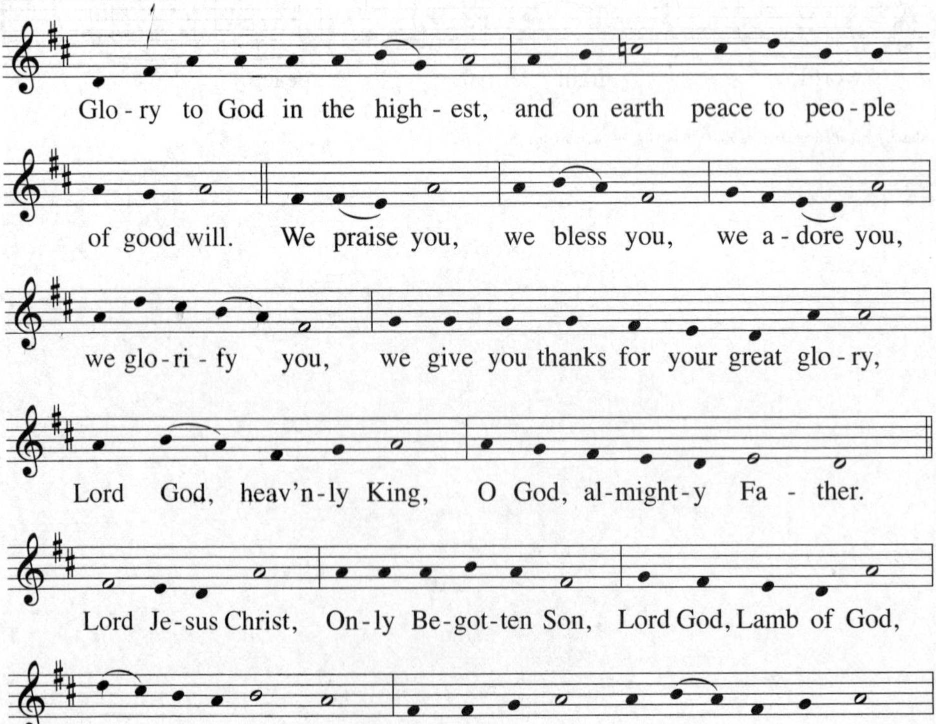

Glo - ry to God in the high - est, and on earth peace to peo - ple

of good will. We praise you, we bless you, we a - dore you,

we glo - ri - fy you, we give you thanks for your great glo - ry,

Lord God, heav'n - ly King, O God, al - might - y Fa - ther.

Lord Je - sus Christ, On - ly Be - got - ten Son, Lord God, Lamb of God,

Son of the Fa - ther, you take a - way the sins of the world, have mer-cy on us; you take a-way the sins of the world,

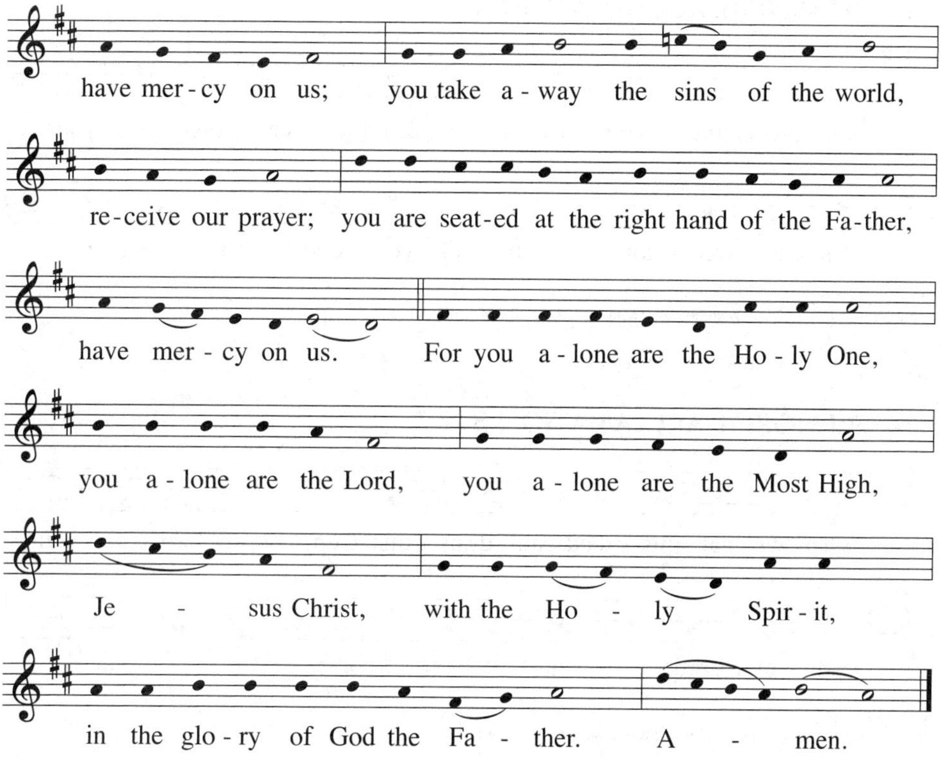

re-ceive our prayer; you are seat-ed at the right hand of the Fa-ther,

have mer-cy on us. For you a-lone are the Ho-ly One,

you a-lone are the Lord, you a-lone are the Most High,

Je - sus Christ, with the Ho - ly Spir-it,

in the glo-ry of God the Fa - ther. A - men.

Text: ICEL, © 2010
Music: *Mass in Honor of St. Ignatius*, Russell Weismann, © 2012, GIA Publications, Inc.

HOLY, HOLY, HOLY

332

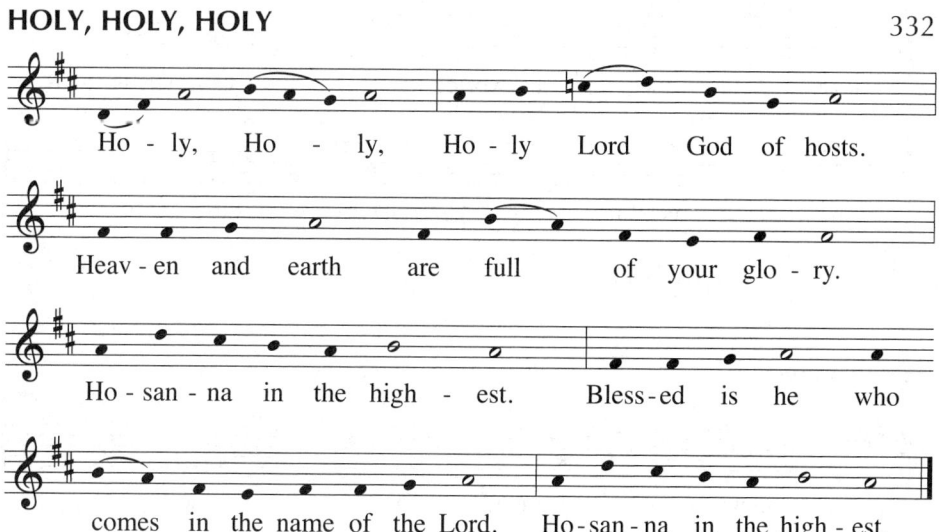

Ho - ly, Ho - ly, Ho - ly Lord God of hosts.

Heav - en and earth are full of your glo - ry.

Ho - san - na in the high - est. Bless-ed is he who

comes in the name of the Lord. Ho-san - na in the high - est.

Text: ICEL, © 2010
Music: *Mass in Honor of St. Ignatius*, Russell Weismann, © 2012, GIA Publications, Inc.

333 MEMORIAL ACCLAMATION A

We pro-claim your Death, O Lord, and pro-fess your Res - ur - rec - tion un - til you come a - gain.

Text: ICEL, © 2010
Music: *Mass in Honor of St. Ignatius,* Russell Weismann, © 2012, GIA Publications, Inc.

334 MEMORIAL ACCLAMATION B

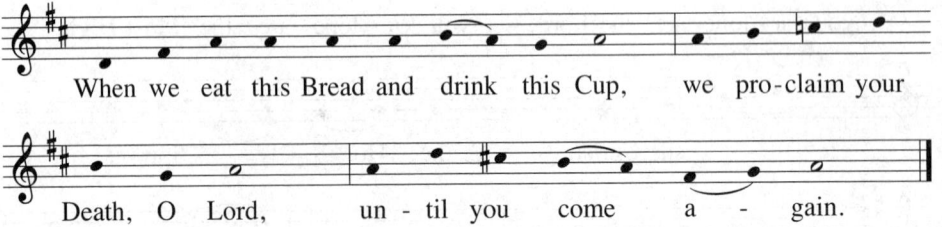

When we eat this Bread and drink this Cup, we pro-claim your Death, O Lord, un - til you come a - gain.

Text: ICEL, © 2010
Music: *Mass in Honor of St. Ignatius,* Russell Weismann, © 2012, GIA Publications, Inc.

335 MEMORIAL ACCLAMATION C

Save us, Sav - ior of the world, for by your Cross and Res - ur - rec - tion you have set us free.

Text: ICEL, © 2010
Music: *Mass in Honor of St. Ignatius,* Russell Weismann, © 2012, GIA Publications, Inc.

336 AMEN

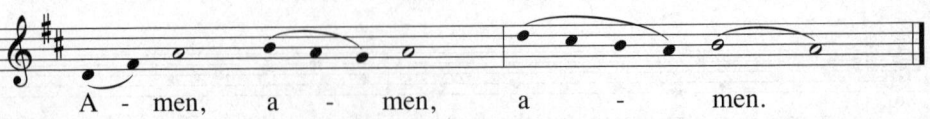

A - men, a - men, a - men.

Music: *Mass in Honor of St. Ignatius,* Russell Weismann, © 2012, GIA Publications, Inc.

LAMB OF GOD

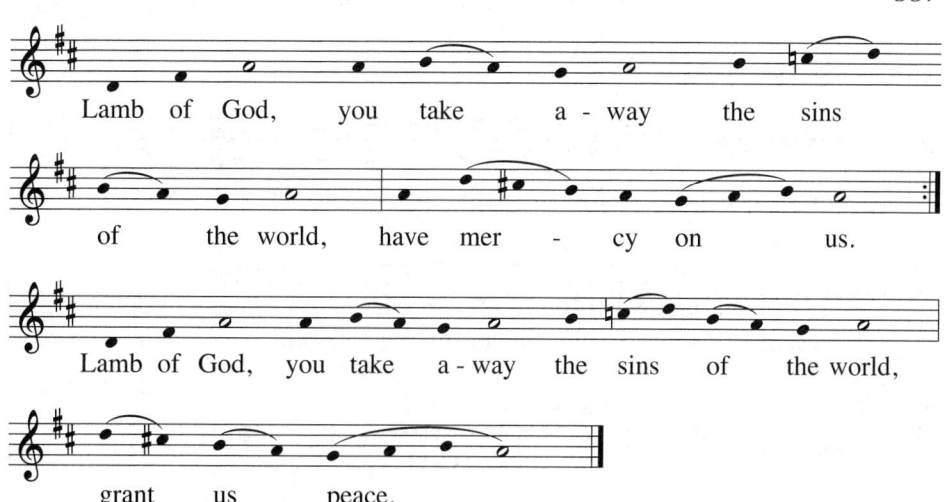

Lamb of God, you take a - way the sins of the world, have mer - cy on us. Lamb of God, you take a - way the sins of the world, grant us peace.

Music: *Mass in Honor of St. Ignatius,* Russell Weismann, © 2012, GIA Publications, Inc.

Setting Eight: Storrington Mass

338   **PENITENTIAL ACT**

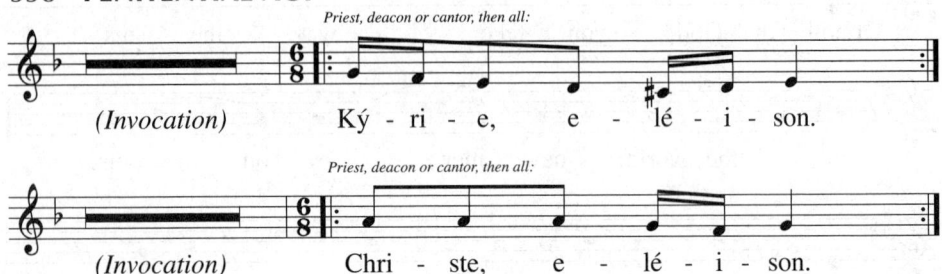

Priest, deacon or cantor, then all:

(Invocation)   Ký - ri - e,   e - lé - i - son.

Priest, deacon or cantor, then all:

(Invocation)   Chri - ste,   e - lé - i - son.

Priest, deacon or cantor, then all:

(Invocation)   Ký - ri - e,   e - lé - i - son.

Priest: May almighty God...everlasting life.

Assembly:

A - men.

Music: *Storrington Mass,* Marty Haugen, © 2010, GIA Publications, Inc.

339   **GLORIA**

Refrain

Glo - ry to God in the high - est,   and on earth peace to peo - ple

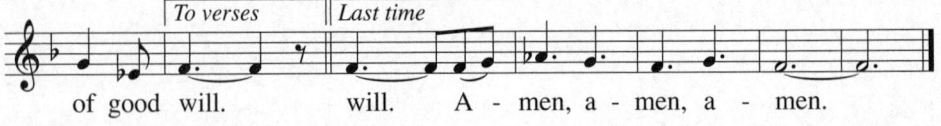

| To verses | Last time |

of good will.   will.   A - men, a - men, a - men.

Verses

1. We praise you,
   we bless you,
   we adore you,
   we glorify you,
   we give you thanks for your great glory,
   Lord God, heavenly King,
   O God, almighty Father.

2. Lord Jesus Christ, Only Begotten Son,
   Lord God, Lamb of God, Son of the Father,
   you take away the sins of the world,
   have mercy on us;
   you take away the sins of the world,
   receive our prayer;
   you are seated at the right hand of the Father,
   have mercy on us.

3. For you alone are the Holy One,
   you alone are the Lord,
   you alone are the Most High,
   Jesus Christ,
   with the Holy Spirit,
   in the glory of God the Father.
   Amen.

Text: ICEL, © 2010
Music: *Storrington Mass*, Marty Haugen, © 2010, GIA Publications, Inc.

GOSPEL ACCLAMATION 340

Al - le-lu-ia, al - le-lu-ia, al - le-lu - ia.

Al - le-lu-ia, al - le-lu-ia, al - le-lu - ia.

Music: *Storrington Mass*, Marty Haugen, © 2010, GIA Publications, Inc.

LENTEN GOSPEL ACCLAMATION 341

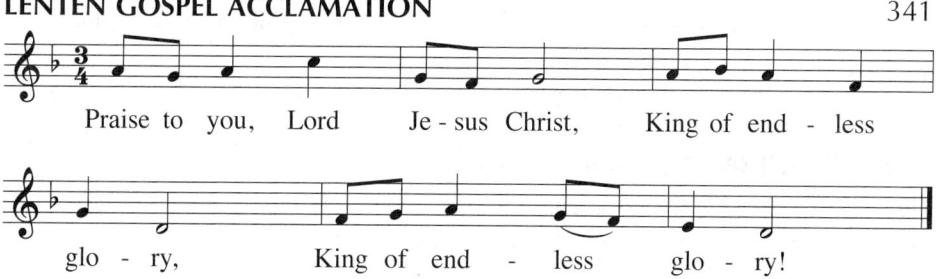

Praise to you, Lord Je - sus Christ, King of end - less

glo - ry, King of end - less glo - ry!

Text: ICEL, © 1969
Music: *Storrington Mass*, Marty Haugen, © 2010, GIA Publications, Inc.

342 HOLY, HOLY, HOLY

Ho - ly, Ho - ly, Ho - ly

Lord God of hosts. Heav-en and earth are full of your

glo-ry. Ho - san-na in the high - est. Bless-ed is he who

comes in the name of the Lord. Ho - san-na, ho -

san - na, ho - san - na in the high - est.

Text: ICEL, © 2010
Music: *Storrington Mass*, Marty Haugen, © 2010, GIA Publications, Inc.

343 MEMORIAL ACCLAMATION A

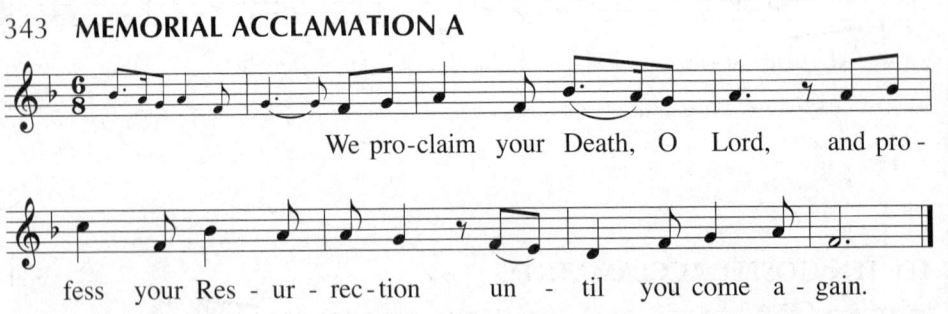

We pro-claim your Death, O Lord, and pro-

fess your Res - ur - rec-tion un - til you come a - gain.

Text: ICEL, © 2010
Music: *Storrington Mass*, Marty Haugen, © 2010, GIA Publications, Inc.

344 MEMORIAL ACCLAMATION B

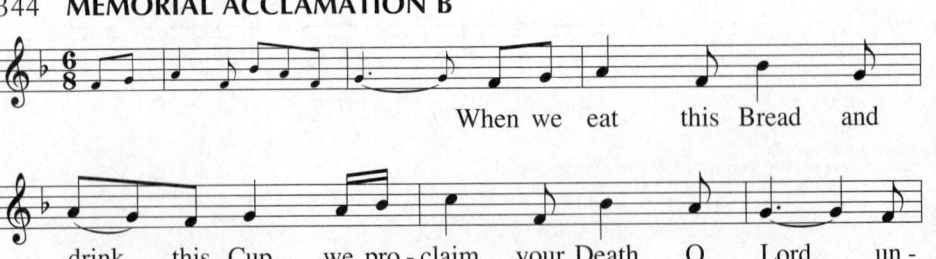

When we eat this Bread and

drink this Cup, we pro - claim your Death, O Lord, un -

til you come a - gain, un - til you come a - gain.

Text: ICEL, © 2010
Music: *Storrington Mass,* Marty Haugen, © 2010, GIA Publications, Inc.

MEMORIAL ACCLAMATION C   345

Save us, Sav-ior of the world, for by your

Cross and Res - ur - rec - tion you have set us free.

Text: ICEL, © 2010
Music: *Storrington Mass,* Marty Haugen, © 2010, GIA Publications, Inc.

AMEN   346

A - men, a - men, a - men.

A - men, a - men, a - men.

Music: *Storrington Mass,* Marty Haugen, © 2010, GIA Publications, Inc.

LAMB OF GOD   347

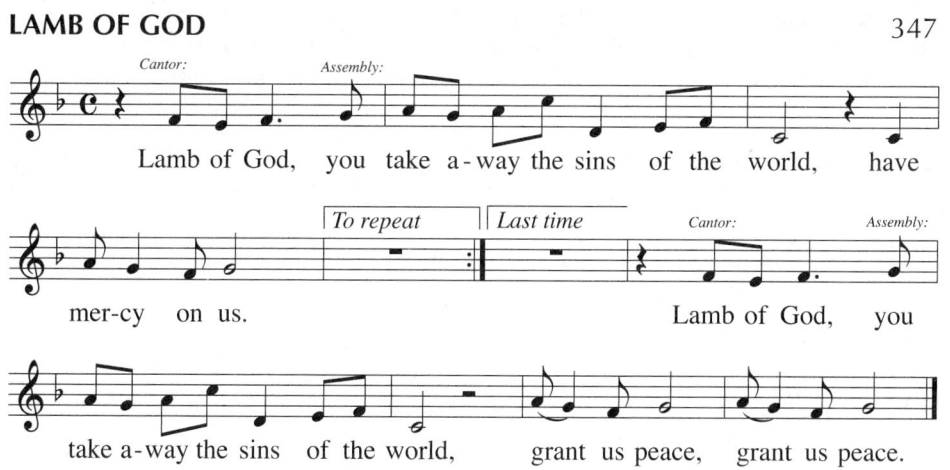

Cantor: *Assembly:*

Lamb of God, you take a-way the sins of the world, have

To repeat *Last time* *Cantor:* *Assembly:*

mer-cy on us. Lamb of God, you

take a-way the sins of the world, grant us peace, grant us peace.

Music: *Storrington Mass,* Marty Haugen, © 2010, GIA Publications, Inc.

Setting Nine: Mass of Christ, Light of the Nations

348 PENITENTIAL ACT 1

Have mer-cy on us, O Lord. For we have sinned a-gainst you.

Show us, O Lord, your mer - cy. And grant us your sal - va-tion.

Priest: May almighty God...everlasting life.

A - men.

Text: ICEL, © 2010
Music: *Mass of Christ, Light of the Nations*, Tony E. Alonso, © 2016, GIA Publications, Inc.

349 PENITENTIAL ACT 2

(Invocation) Ký-ri-e, e - lé-i-son. Ký-ri-e, e - lé-i - son.

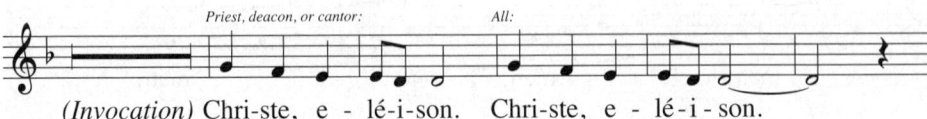

(Invocation) Chri-ste, e - lé-i-son. Chri-ste, e - lé-i - son.

(Invocation) Ký-ri-e, e - lé-i-son. Ký-ri-e, e - lé-i - son.

Priest: May almighty God...everlasting life.

A - men.

Music: *Mass of Christ, Light of the Nations*, Tony E. Alonso, © 2016, GIA Publications, Inc.

350 GLORIA*

𝄋 Refrain

Glo-ry to God in the high - est, and on

A through-composed version of this Gloria may found at no. 351.

earth peace to peo - ple, peo - ple of good will.

Last time

A - men. A - men.

Verses

1. We praise you,
   we bless you,
   we adore you,
   we glorify you,
   we give you thanks for your great glory,
   Lord God, heavenly King,
   O God, almighty Father.

2. Lord Jesus Christ, Only Begotten Son,
   Lord God, Lamb of God, Son of the Father,

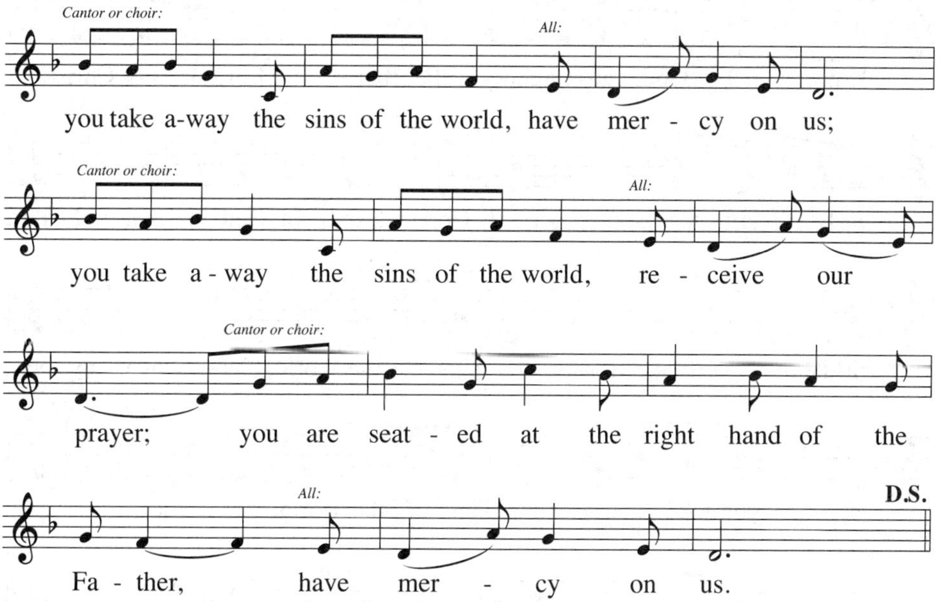

Cantor or choir: *All:*

you take a-way the sins of the world, have mer - cy on us;

Cantor or choir: *All:*

you take a - way the sins of the world, re - ceive our

Cantor or choir:

prayer; you are seat - ed at the right hand of the

All: **D.S.**

Fa - ther, have mer - cy on us.

3. For you alone are the Holy One,
   you alone are the Lord,
   you alone are the Most High,
   Jesus Christ,
   with the Holy Spirit,
   in the glory of God the Father.

Text: ICEL, © 2010
Music: *Mass of Christ, Light of the Nations*, Tony E. Alonso, © 2016, GIA Publications, Inc.

351 GLORIA*

Glo-ry to God in the high-est, and on earth peace to peo-ple, peo-ple of good will. We praise you, we bless you, we a-dore you, we glo-ri-fy you, we give you thanks for your great glo-ry, Lord God, heav-en-ly King, O God, al-might-y Fa-ther. Lord Je-sus Christ, On-ly Be-got-ten Son, Lord God, Lamb of God, Son of the Fa-ther, you take a-way the sins of the world, have mer-cy on us; you take a-way the sins of the world, re-ceive our prayer; you are seat-ed at the right hand of the Fa-ther, have

*A Refrain/Verses version of this Gloria may be found at no. 350.

mer - cy on us. For you a - lone are the Ho-ly One,

you a - lone are the Lord, you a - lone are the Most High, Je - sus

Christ, with the Ho - ly Spir-it, in the glo-ry of God the

Fa - ther. A - men. A - men.

Text: ICEL, © 2010
Music: *Mass of Christ, Light of the Nations*, Tony E. Alonso, © 2016, GIA Publications, Inc.

GOSPEL ACCLAMATION 352

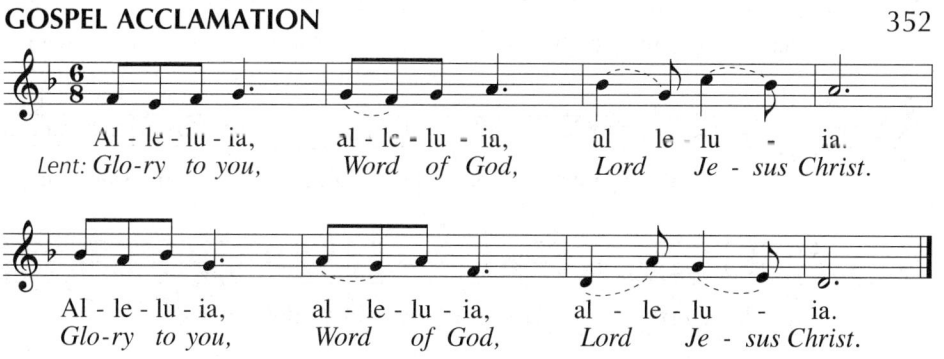

Al - le - lu - ia, al - le - lu - ia, al le - lu - ia.
Lent: Glo-ry to you, *Word of God,* *Lord Je - sus Christ.*

Al - le - lu - ia, al - le - lu - ia, al - le - lu - ia.
Glo-ry to you, *Word of God,* *Lord Je - sus Christ.*

Text: ICEL, © 1969
Music: *Mass of Christ, Light of the Nations*, Tony E. Alonso, © 2016, GIA Publications, Inc.

353 PRAYER OF THE FAITHFUL

Cantor, then all:

Lord, hear our prayer. *(Intercessions)*

Response

Cantor:

We pray to the Lord:

All:

Lord, hear our prayer.

Music: *Mass of Christ, Light of the Nations*, Tony E. Alonso, © 2016, GIA Publications, Inc.

354 HOLY, HOLY, HOLY

Ho-ly, Ho-ly, Ho-ly Lord God of hosts.

Heav-en and earth are full of your glo-ry. Ho-

san-na in the high-est. Bless-ed is he who

comes in the name of the Lord. Ho-san-na

in the high-est. Ho-san-na in the high-est.

Text: ICEL, © 2010
Music: *Mass of Christ, Light of the Nations*, Tony E. Alonso, © 2016, GIA Publications, Inc.

MEMORIAL ACCLAMATION A 355

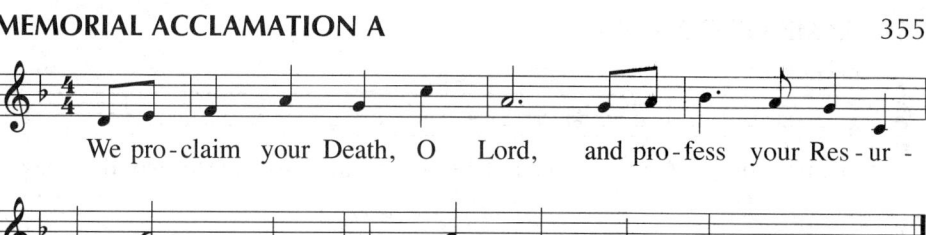

We pro-claim your Death, O Lord, and pro-fess your Res-ur-rec-tion un-til you come a-gain.

Text: ICEL, © 2010
Music: *Mass of Christ, Light of the Nations*, Tony E. Alonso, © 2016, GIA Publications, Inc.

MEMORIAL ACCLAMATION B 356

When we eat this Bread and drink this Cup, we pro-claim your Death, O Lord, un-til you come a-gain.

Text: ICEL, © 2010
Music: *Mass of Christ, Light of the Nations*, Tony E. Alonso, © 2016, GIA Publications, Inc.

MEMORIAL ACCLAMATION C 357

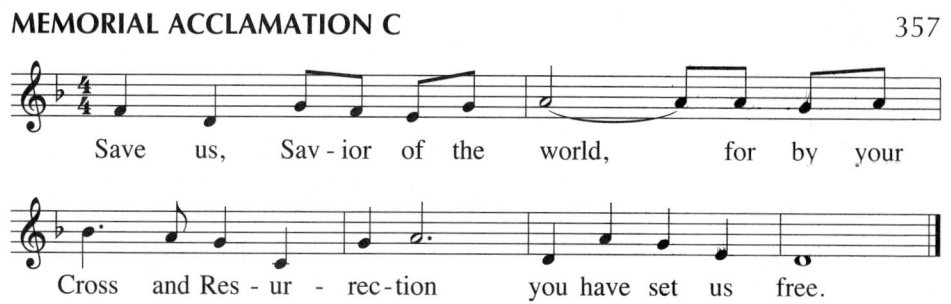

Save us, Sav-ior of the world, for by your Cross and Res-ur-rec-tion you have set us free.

Text: ICEL, © 2010
Music: *Mass of Christ, Light of the Nations*, Tony E. Alonso, © 2016, GIA Publications, Inc.

AMEN 358

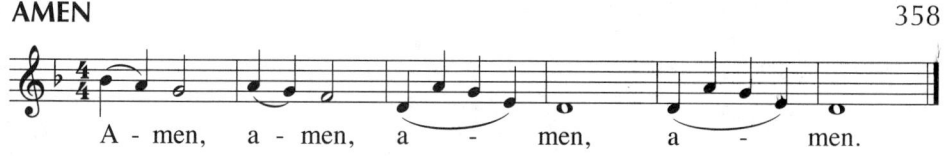

A-men, a-men, a-men, a-men.

Music: *Mass of Christ, Light of the Nations*, Tony E. Alonso, © 2016, GIA Publications, Inc.

359   LAMB OF GOD

Lamb of God, you take a-way the sins of the world, have mer - cy on us. Lamb of God, you take a-way the sins of the world, grant us peace.

Music: *Mass of Christ, Light of the Nations*, Tony E. Alonso, © 2016, GIA Publications, Inc.

Setting Ten: Holy Name of Jesus Mass

PENITENTIAL ACT

PENITENTIAL ACT

Priest, deacon, or cantor, then all:

(Invocation) Ký - ri - e, e - lé - i - son.

(Invocation) Chri - ste, e - lé - i - son.

(Invocation) Ký - ri - e, e - lé - i - son.

Priest: May almighty God...everlasting life.

Assembly: A - men.

Text: ICEL, © 2010
Music: *Holy Name of Jesus Mass*, Norah Duncan IV, © 2015, GIA Publications, Inc.

GLORIA

Glo - ry to God in the high - est, and on earth peace to peo - ple of good will. We praise you, we bless you, we a - dore you, we glo-ri-fy you, we give you thanks for your great glo - ry, Lord God, heav - en-ly King, O God, al - might-y Fa-ther.

Choir (Cong. ad lib.):

Lord Je-sus Christ, On - ly Be-got-ten Son, Lord God, Lamb of God, Son of the Fa-ther, you take a-way the sins of the world, have mer - cy on us; you take a-way the sins of the world, re - ceive our prayer; you are seat-ed at the right hand of the Fa - ther, have mer - cy on us.

All:

For you a-lone are the Ho-ly One, you a-lone are the Lord, you a-lone are the Most High, Je - sus Christ, with the Ho - ly Spir-it, in the glo-ry of God the Fa - ther. A - men.

Text: ICEL, © 2010
Music: *Holy Name of Jesus Mass*, Norah Duncan IV, © 2011, GIA Publications, Inc.

GOSPEL ACCLAMATION 362

Al - le - lu - ia, al - le -
Lent: Praise and hon - or to you, hon - or to

lu - ia, al - le - lu - ia. Al - le - lu -
you, O Lord Je - sus Christ. Praise and hon - or to

ia, al - le - lu - ia, al - le - lu - ia.
you, hon - or to you, O Lord Je - sus Christ.

Text: ICEL, © 1969
Music: *Holy Name of Jesus Mass*, Norah Duncan IV, © 2015, GIA Publications, Inc.

HOLY, HOLY, HOLY 363

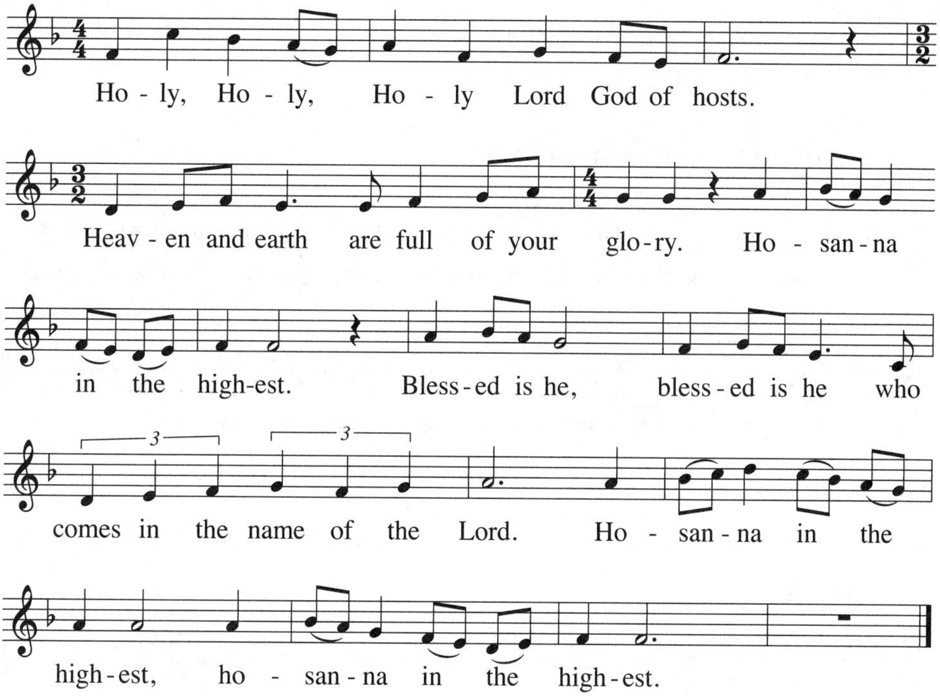

Ho - ly, Ho - ly, Ho - ly Lord God of hosts.

Heav - en and earth are full of your glo - ry. Ho - san - na

in the high - est. Bless - ed is he, bless - ed is he who

comes in the name of the Lord. Ho - san - na in the

high - est, ho - san - na in the high - est.

Text: ICEL, © 2010
Music: *Holy Name of Jesus Mass*, Norah Duncan IV, © 2015, GIA Publications, Inc.

364 MEMORIAL ACCLAMATION A

We pro-claim your Death, O Lord, and pro-fess your Res-ur-rec-tion un-til you come a-gain.

Text: ICEL, © 2010
Music: *Holy Name of Jesus Mass,* Norah Duncan IV, © 2015, GIA Publications, Inc.

365 MEMORIAL ACCLAMATION B

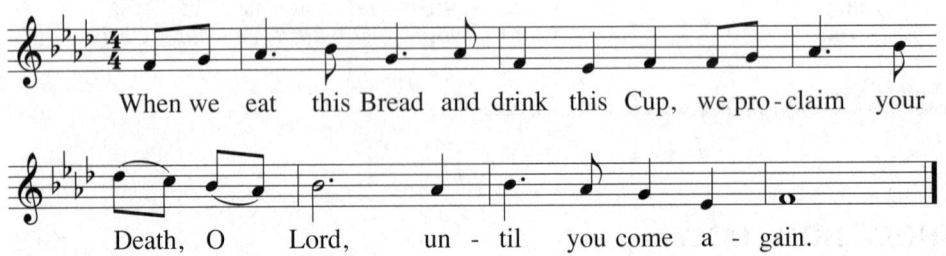

When we eat this Bread and drink this Cup, we pro-claim your Death, O Lord, un-til you come a-gain.

Text: ICEL, © 2010
Music: *Holy Name of Jesus Mass,* Norah Duncan IV, © 2015, GIA Publications, Inc.

366 MEMORIAL ACCLAMATION C

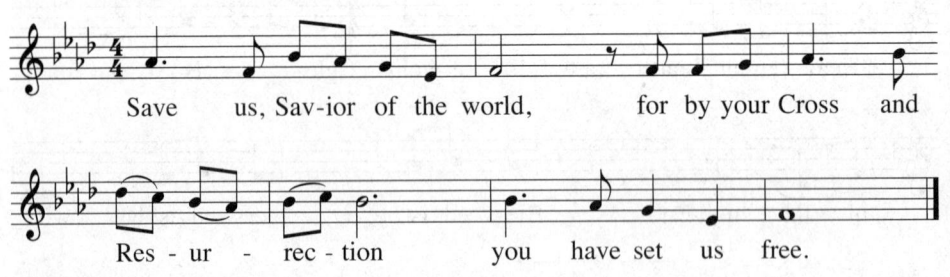

Save us, Sav-ior of the world, for by your Cross and Res-ur-rec-tion you have set us free.

Text: ICEL, © 2010
Music: *Holy Name of Jesus Mass,* Norah Duncan IV, © 2015, GIA Publications, Inc.

367 AMEN

A-men, a-men, a-men.

Music: *Holy Name of Jesus Mass,* Norah Duncan IV, © 2015, GIA Publications, Inc.

LAMB OF GOD

Lamb of God, you take a - way the sins of the world, have mer - cy on us. Lamb of God, you take a - way the sins of the world, grant us peace, grant us peace.

Music: *Holy Name of Jesus Mass,* Norah Duncan IV, © 2015, GIA Publications, Inc.

Setting Eleven: Cantus Missae

369 **KYRIE**

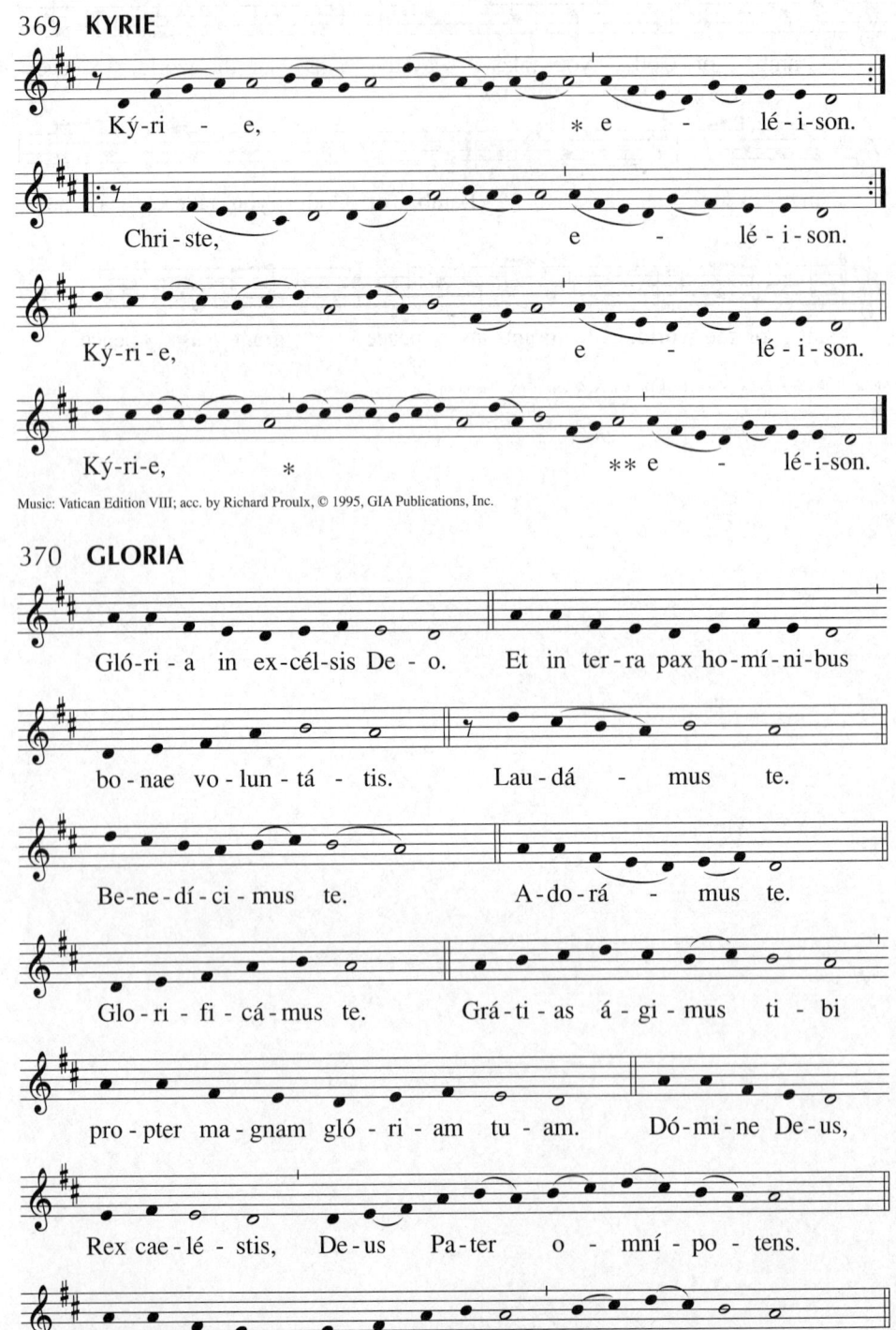

Ký-ri - e, * e - lé - i - son.

Chri - ste, e - lé - i - son.

Ký-ri - e, e - lé - i - son.

Ký-ri-e, * ** e - lé-i-son.

Music: Vatican Edition VIII; acc. by Richard Proulx, © 1995, GIA Publications, Inc.

370 **GLORIA**

Gló-ri - a in ex-cél-sis De - o. Et in ter-ra pax ho-mí-ni-bus

bo - nae vo-lun-tá - tis. Lau-dá - mus te.

Be-ne-dí-ci - mus te. A-do-rá - mus te.

Glo-ri - fi - cá-mus te. Grá-ti - as á - gi-mus ti - bi

pro-pter ma-gnam gló - ri - am tu - am. Dó-mi-ne De-us,

Rex cae-lé - stis, De-us Pa-ter o - mní-po - tens.

Dó-mi-ne Fi - li u - ni-gé-ni-te, Je - su Chri-ste.

Dó - mi - ne De - us, A - gnus De - i, Fí - li - us Pa - tris.

Qui tol - lis pec - cá - ta mun - di, mi - se - ré - re no - bis.

Qui tol - lis pec - cá - ta mun - di, sú - sci - pe de - pre - ca - ti - ó -

nem no - stram. Qui se - des ad déx - te - ram Pa - tris,

mi - se - ré - re no - bis. Quó - ni - am tu so - lus San - ctus.

Tu so - lus Dó - mi - nus. Tu so - lus Al - tís - si - mus,

Je - su Chri - ste. Cum San - cto Spí - ri - tu:

in gló - ri - a De - i Pa - tris. A - men.

Music: Vatican Edition VIII, acc. by Richard Proulx, © 1995, GIA Publications, Inc.

LITURGY OF THE WORD

FIRST READINGS

371

After the first reading:

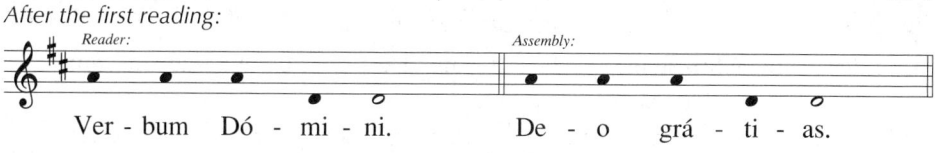

Reader: Ver - bum Dó - mi - ni. Assembly: De - o grá - ti - as.

After the second reading or if there is only one reading before the gospel:

Reader: Ver - bum Dó - mi - ni. Assembly: De - o grá - ti - as.

372 GOSPEL

Before the gospel reading:

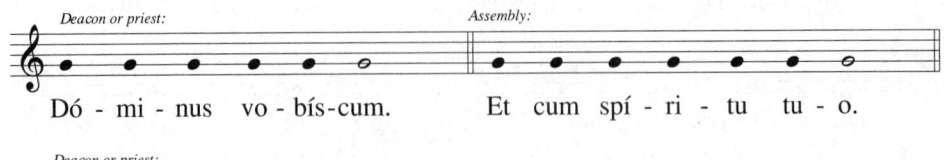

Dó - mi - nus vo - bís-cum. Et cum spí - ri - tu tu - o.

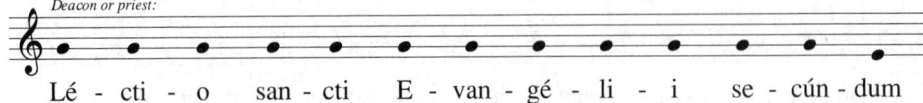

Lé - cti - o san - cti E - van - gé - li - i se - cún - dum

N... Gló - ri - a ti - bi, Dó - mi - ne.

After the reading:

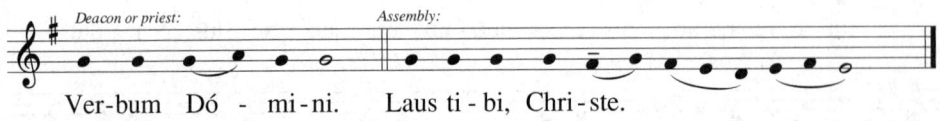

Ver-bum Dó - mi-ni. Laus ti - bi, Chri - ste.

373 CREDO

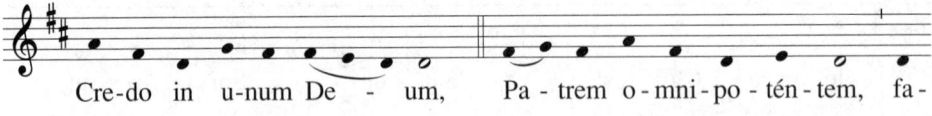

Cre-do in u-num De - um, Pa - trem o-mni-po-tén-tem, fa-

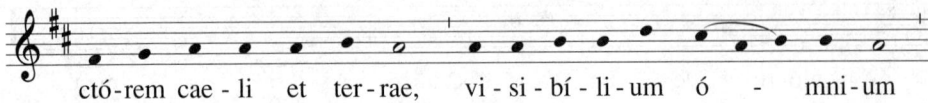

ctó-rem cae - li et ter - rae, vi - si - bí - li - um ó - mni-um

et in - vi - si - bí - li-um. Et in u-num Dó - mi-num

Je - sum Chri-stum, Fí - li - um De - i U - ni - gé - ni-tum.

Et ex Pa-tre na - tum an-te ó-mni-a saé - cu-la.

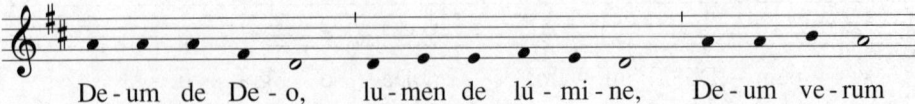

De-um de De - o, lu-men de lú - mi-ne, De-um ve-rum

de De-o ve-ro. Gé-ni-tum, non fa - ctum, con-sub-stan - ti -

á - lem Pa - tri: per quem ó - mni - a fa - cta sunt.

Qui pro-pter nos hó-mi-nes et pro-pter no-stram sa - lú-tem de -

scén-dit de cae-lis. Et in-car-ná-tus est de Spí-ri - tu

San - cto ex Ma-rí - a Vír-gi - ne, et ho-mo fa-ctus est.

Cru - ci - fí - xus é - ti - am pro no - bis sub

Pón - ti - o Pi - lá - to; pas - sus et se - púl - tus est.

Et re-sur-ré-xit tér-ti - a di - e, se - cún-dum Scri-ptú - ras.

Et a - scén - dit in cae - lum, se-det ad déx-te-ram Pa - tris.

Et í - te-rum ven-tú - rus est cum gló - ri - a, ju-di-cá-re

vi - vos et mór-tu - os, cu - ius re-gni non e - rit fi - nis.

Et in Spí - ri-tum San-ctum, Dó - mi-num et vi - vi - fi - cán-tem:

qui ex Pa - tre Fi - li - ó - que pro - cé - dit.

Qui cum Pa - tre et Fí - li - o si - mul a - do - rá - tur et con - glo -

ri - fi - cá - tur: qui lo - cú - tus est per pro - phé - tas. Et u - nam,

san - ctam, ca - thó - li - cam et a - po - stó - li - cam Ec - clé - si - am.

Con - fí - te - or u - num ba - ptís - ma in re - mis - si - ó - nem pec - ca -

tó - rum. Et ex - spé - cto re - sur - re - cti - ó - nem

mor - tu - ó - rum. Et vi - tam ven - tú - ri saé - cu - li.

A - men.

Music: Vatican Edition III; acc. by Richard Proulx, © 1995, GIA Publications, Inc.

374 PRAYER OF THE FAITHFUL

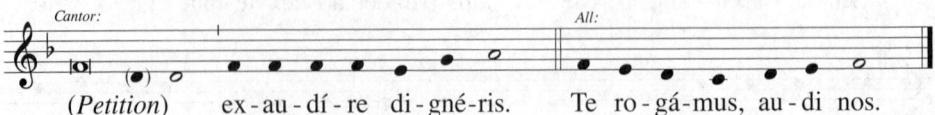

Cantor: (*Petition*) ex - au - dí - re di - gné - ris. *All:* Te ro - gá - mus, au - di nos.

LITURGY OF THE EUCHARIST

375 PREFACE DIALOGUE

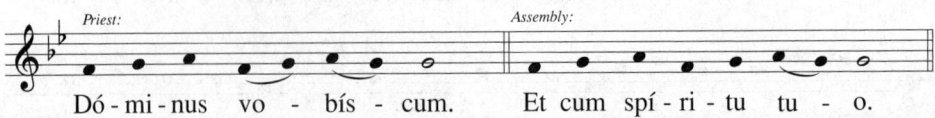

Priest: Dó - mi - nus vo - bís - cum. *Assembly:* Et cum spí - ri - tu tu - o.

SANCTUS

A

Sanc - ctus, * San - ctus, San - ctus Dó - mi - nus De - us Sá - ba - oth. Ple-ni sunt cae - li et ter - ra gló - ri - a tu - a. Ho-sán - na in ex - cél - sis. Be - ne - dí - ctus qui ve - nit in nó-mi-ne Dó - mi-ni. Ho-sán - na in ex - cél - sis.

Music: Vatican Edition VIII; acc. by Richard Proulx, © 1995, GIA Publications, Inc.

377 SANCTUS

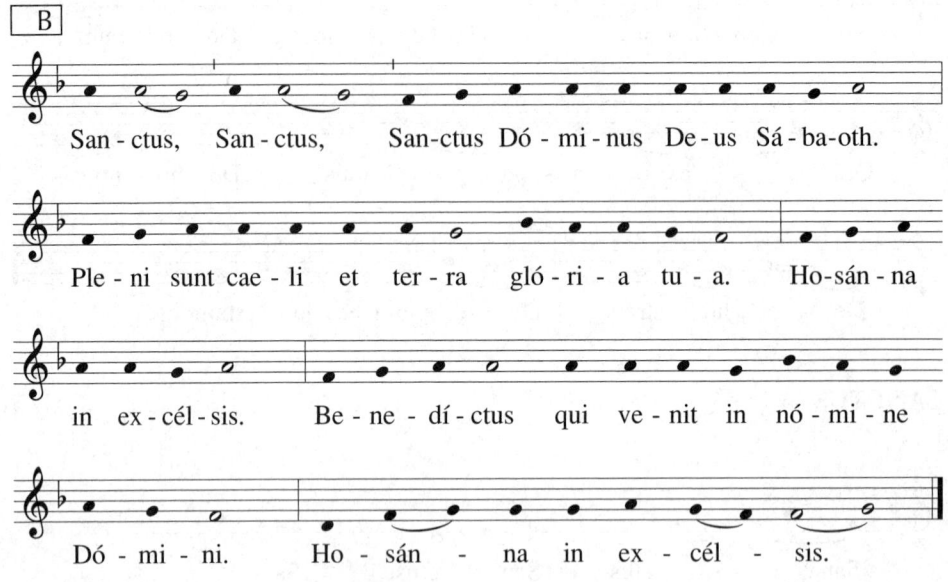

San - ctus, San - ctus, San-ctus Dó - mi - nus De - us Sá - ba-oth.

Ple - ni sunt cae - li et ter - ra gló - ri - a tu - a. Ho-sán - na

in ex - cél - sis. Be - ne - dí - ctus qui ve - nit in nó - mi - ne

Dó - mi - ni. Ho - sán - na in ex - cél - sis.

Music: Vatican Edition XVIII; acc. by Richard Proulx, © 1995, GIA Publications, Inc.

378 MEMORIAL ACCLAMATION

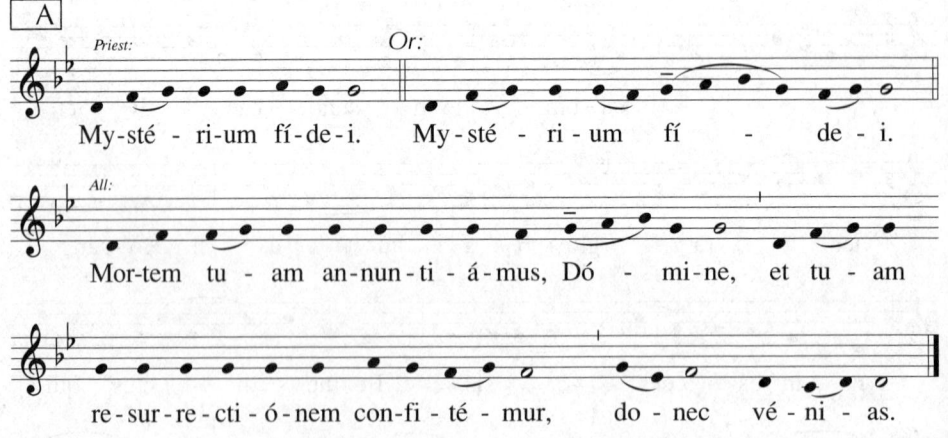

Priest: *Or:*

My-sté - ri-um fí - de - i.   My-sté - ri - um fí - de - i.

All:

Mor-tem tu - am an-nun-ti - á-mus, Dó - mi-ne, et tu - am

re-sur-re-cti - ó - nem con-fi - té - mur, do - nec vé - ni - as.

Music: Vatican Edition; acc. by Richard Proulx, © 1995, GIA Publications, Inc.

379 MEMORIAL ACCLAMATION

Priest:

My - sté - ri - um fí - de - i.

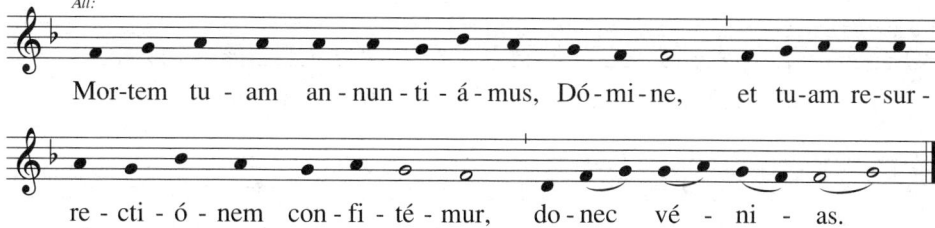

All:
Mor-tem tu - am an - nun - ti - á - mus, Dó - mi - ne, et tu-am re-sur -
re - cti - ó - nem con - fi - té - mur, do - nec vé - ni - as.

Music: Vatican Edition; acc. by Richard Proulx, © 1995, GIA Publications, Inc.

AMEN 380

After the doxology:

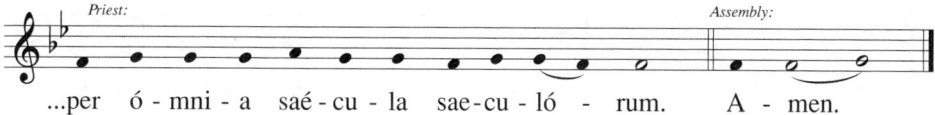

Priest:
...per ó - mni - a saé - cu - la sae - cu - ló - rum.
Assembly:
A - men.

COMMUNION RITE

THE LORD'S PRAYER 381

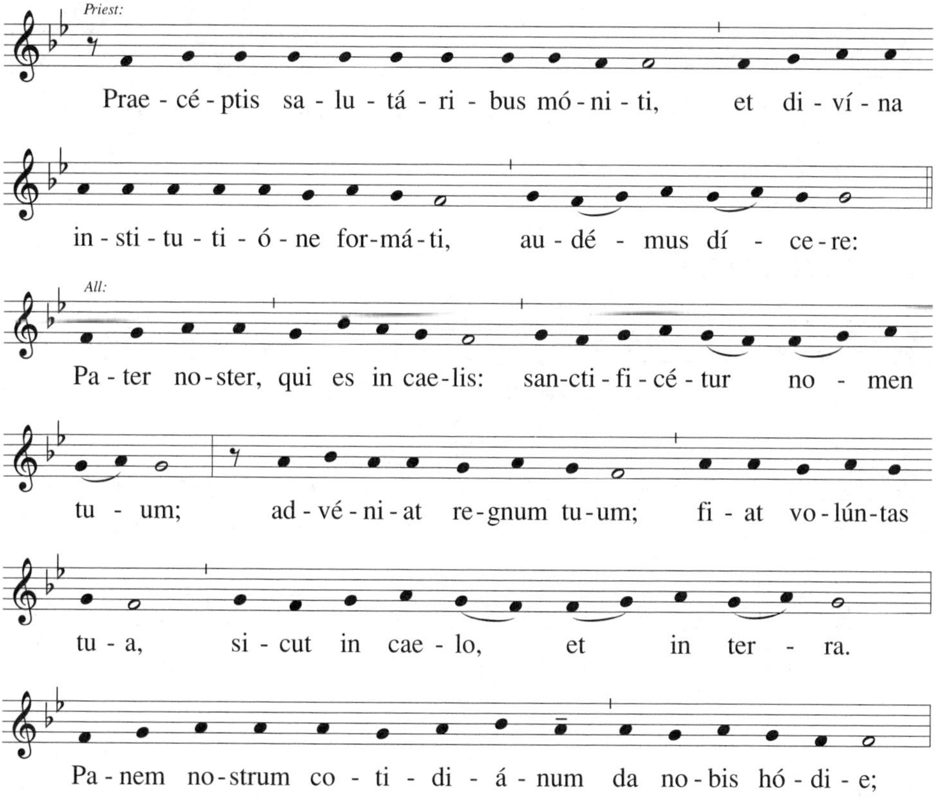

Priest:
Prae - cé - ptis sa - lu - tá - ri - bus mó - ni - ti, et di - ví - na
in - sti - tu - ti - ó - ne for - má - ti, au - dé - mus dí - ce - re:
All:
Pa - ter no - ster, qui es in cae - lis: san - cti - fi - cé - tur no - men
tu - um; ad - vé - ni - at re - gnum tu - um; fi - at vo - lún - tas
tu - a, si - cut in cae - lo, et in ter - ra.
Pa - nem no - strum co - ti - di - á - num da no - bis hó - di - e;

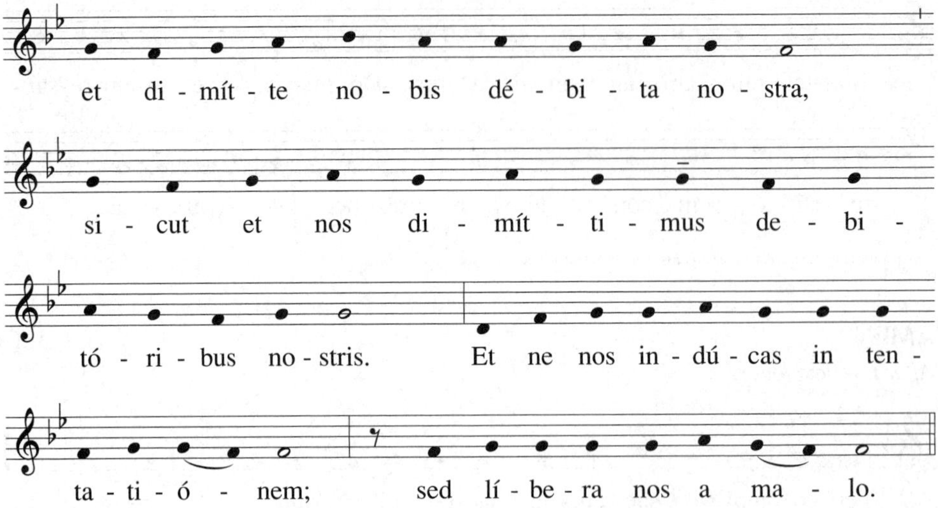

et di - mít - te no - bis dé - bi - ta no - stra,

si - cut et nos di - mít - ti - mus de - bi -

tó - ri - bus no - stris. Et ne nos in - dú - cas in ten -

ta - ti - ó - nem; sed lí - be - ra nos a ma - lo.

Priest: Líbera nos...Jesu Christi.

All:

Qui - a tu - um est re - gnum, et po - té - stas,

et gló - ri - a in saé - cu - la.

382 SIGN OF PEACE

Priest:

Qui vivis et regnas in saécula sae - cu - ló - rum.

Assembly: Priest:

A - men. Pax Dó - mi - ni sit sem - per

Assembly:

vo - bís - cum. Et cum spí - ri - tu tu - o.

AGNUS DEI

383

A

A - gnus De - i, * qui tol - lis pec-cá -

ta mun - di: mi - se - ré - re no - bis.

A - gnus De - i, * qui tol - lis pec - cá -

ta mun - di: mi - se - ré - re no - bis.

A - gnus De - i, * qui tol - lis pec-cá -

ta mun - di: do - na no - bis pa - cem.

Music: Vatican Edition VIII; acc. by Richard Proulx, © 1995, GIA Publications, Inc.

AGNUS DEI

384

B

Cantor: All:

A-gnus De - i, qui tol-lis pec-cá-ta mun-di: mi-se-ré-re no - bis.

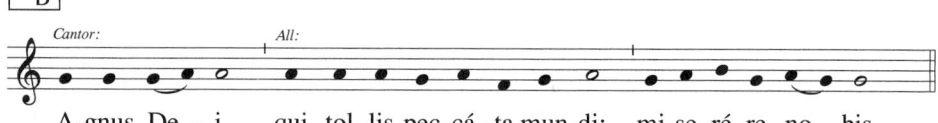
A-gnus De - i, qui tol - lis pec-cá-ta mun-di: mi-se-ré-re no - bis.

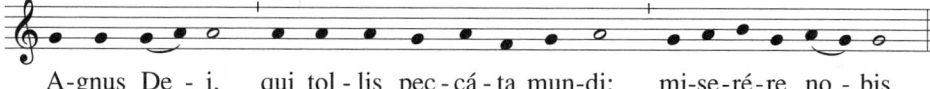
A - gnus De - i, qui tol-lis pec-cá-ta mun-di: do-na no-bis pa-cem.

Music: Vatican Edition XVIII; acc. by Robert J. Batastini, © 1993, GIA Publications, Inc.

CONCLUDING RITES

385 DISMISSAL

Deacon or priest, then all:

I - te,   mis - sa est.
De - o   grá - ti - as.

Music: Vatican Edition VIII; acc. by Richard Proulx, © 1995, GIA Publications, Inc.

Or:

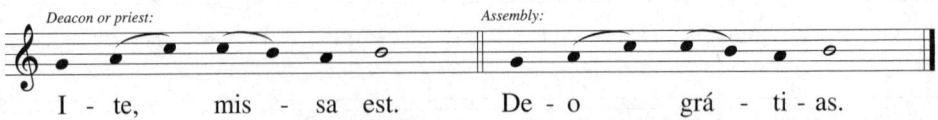

Deacon or priest: *Assembly:*

I - te,   mis - sa est.   De - o   grá - ti - as.

For Easter Sunday and the octave of Easter:

Deacon or priest, then all:

I - te, mis-sa est,   al-le-lú - ia,   al-le - lú - ia.
De-o grá-ti - as,   al-le-lú - ia,   al-le - lú - ia.

Service Music

SPRINKLING SONG 386

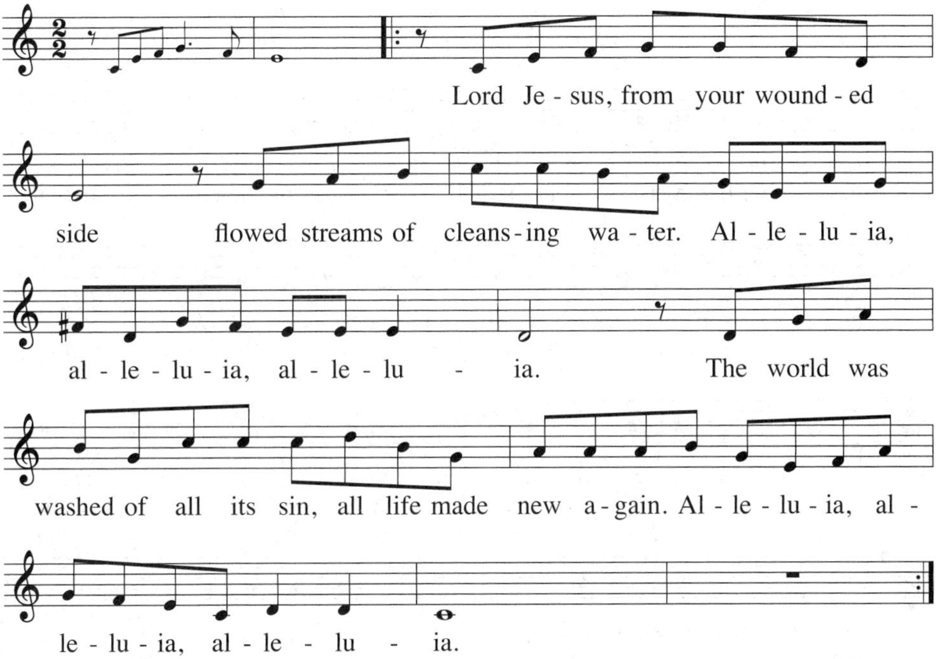

Lord Je-sus, from your wound-ed side flowed streams of cleans-ing wa-ter. Al-le-lu-ia, al-le-lu-ia, al-le-lu - ia. The world was washed of all its sin, all life made new a-gain. Al-le-lu-ia, al - le-lu-ia, al-le-lu - ia.

Text: ICEL, © 1973
Music: *Festival Liturgy,* Richard Hillert, © 1983, GIA Publications, Inc.

SPRINKLING SONG 387

Cleanse us, Lord, from all our sins; wash us and we shall be
Lim - pia nues-tros pe - ca-dos, Se-ñor; cre-a_en no - so-tros un

clean as new snow. Cleanse us, Lord, from all our sins;
co - ra-zón pu - ro. Lim - pia nues-tros pe - ca-dos, Se - ñor;

wash us and we shall be clean as new snow.
cre - a_en no - so - tros un co - ra - zón pu - ro.

Text: Psalm 51:9; Daniel 3:64–68, 78; Ezekiel 36:25, 26, 28 and 47:1–2, 9; 1 Peter 2:9; Michael Joncas; tr. by Ronald F. Krisman
Music: Michael Joncas
© 1988, tr. 2012, GIA Publications, Inc.

388 SPRINKLING SONG

A - spér - ges me, Dó - mi - ne hys -
Cleanse me from sin, O Lord God, wash

só - po, et mun-dá - bor: la - vá - bis me,
me with hys - sop branch - es: cleanse me from guilt,

et su - per ni - vem de - al - bá - bor.
and I shall be clean as the new snow.

Mi - se - ré - re me - i, De - us, se - cún -
Have mer - cy on me, O my God, ac - cord -

D.C. (ad lib.)

dum magnam miseri - cór - di - am tu - am.
ing to your great com - pas - sion.

Gló - ri - a Patri, et Fílio, et Spi - rí - tu-i San - cto:
Glo - ry be to the Father
and to the Son, and to the Ho - ly Spir - it:

Si - cut erat in princípio, et nunc, et sem - per,
As it was in the beginning, is now and ev - er shall be,

D.C.

et in saécula sae - cu - ló - rum. A - men.
world with - out end. A - men.

Text: *Roman Missal*; Psalm 51:9, 1; trans. by Richard Proulx, © 1975, GIA Publications, Inc.
Music: Vatican Edition, Mode VII; adapt. by Richard Proulx, © 1975, GIA Publications, Inc.

SPRINKLING SONG 389

Refrain

Springs of wa-ter, bless the Lord! Give him glo-ry and praise for ev-er!

Verses

Cantor:

1. O - ceans of earth, sing glo-ry to God! Praise to the one who
2. Riv - ers and lakes, sing glo-ry to God! Praise, all you ponds and
3. Brooks of the hills, sing glo-ry to God! Praise to the source of
4. Show - ers and springs, sing glo-ry to God! Praise, all you liv - ing

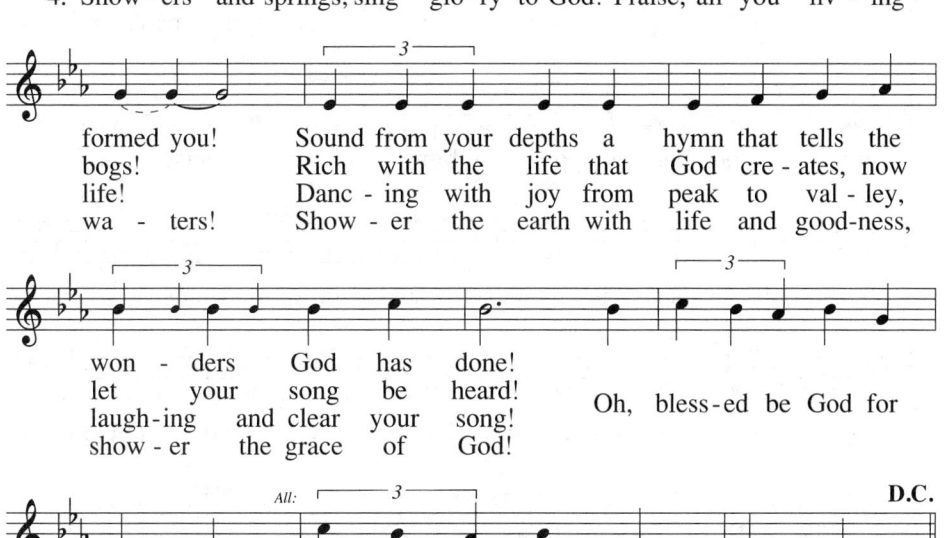

formed you! Sound from your depths a hymn that tells the
bogs! Rich with the life that God cre - ates, now
life! Danc - ing with joy from peak to val - ley,
wa - ters! Show - er the earth with life and good-ness,

won - ders God has done!
let your song be heard!
laugh-ing and clear your song!
show - er the grace of God!

Oh, bless-ed be God for

All: D.C.

ev - er! Bless - ed be God for ev - er!

Text: Refrain trans. © 1973, ICEL; additional text by Marty Haugen, © 1994, GIA Publications, Inc.
Music: Marty Haugen, © 1994, GIA Publications, Inc.

SPRINKLING SONG 390

Refrain*

Springs of wa - ter, bless the Lord, Sing your glo-ry and praise for-

ev - er. Al - le - lu - ia! Sing your glo - ry and praise!

Refrain may be sung continuously under verses.

Music: *Beneath the Tree of Life*; Marty Haugen, © 2000, 2001, GIA Publications, Inc.

391 SPRINKLING SONG

Refrain

Al-le - lu - ia, al-le - lu - ia, al-le - lu - ia.

Music: SURGIT IN HAEC DIES, 12th C., adapt. by Leo Nestor, © 2011, GIA Publications, Inc.

392 CONFITEOR

I con-fess to al-

might-y God and to you, my broth-ers and sis - ters, that I have

great - ly sinned, in my thoughts and in my words, in

what I have done and in what I have failed to do, through my

fault, through my fault, through my most griev-ous fault;

there-fore I ask bless-ed Mar - y, ev - er - Vir - gin,

all the An - gels and Saints, and you, my broth - ers and

sis - ters, to pray for me to the Lord our God.

Text: ICEL, © 2010
Music: Tony E. Alonso, © 2016, GIA Publications, Inc.

KYRIE

Ký - ri - e, e - léi - son. Ký - ri - e, e - léi - son.
Chri - ste, e - léi - son. Chri - ste, e - léi - son.
Ký - ri - e, e - léi - son. Ký - ri - e, e - léi - son.

Ký - ri - e, e - léi - son.
Chri - ste, e - léi - son.
Ký - ri - e, e - léi - son.

Music: Russian Orthodox; arr. by John L. Bell, © 1990, Iona Community, GIA Publications, Inc., agent

PENITENTIAL ACT

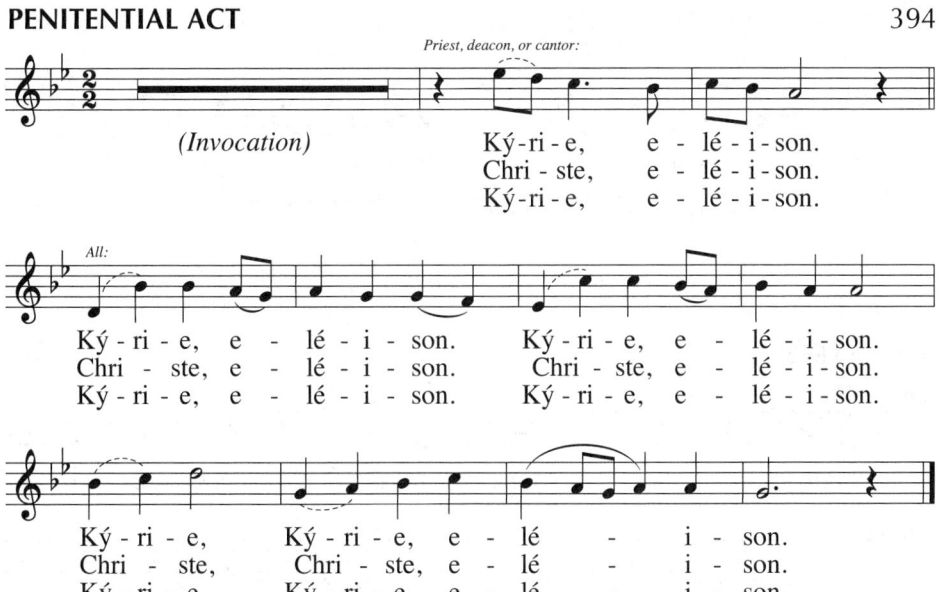

Priest, deacon, or cantor:

(Invocation)

Ký - ri - e, e - lé - i - son.
Chri - ste, e - lé - i - son.
Ký - ri - e, e - lé - i - son.

All:

Ký - ri - e, e - lé - i - son. Ký - ri - e, e - lé - i - son.
Chri - ste, e - lé - i - son. Chri - ste, e - lé - i - son.
Ký - ri - e, e - lé - i - son. Ký - ri - e, e - lé - i - son.

Ký - ri - e, Ký - ri - e, e - lé - i - son.
Chri - ste, Chri - ste, e - lé - i - son.
Ký - ri - e, Ký - ri - e, e - lé - i - son.

Music: *No Greater Love Mass,* Michael Joncas, © 1988, 2015, GIA Publications, Inc.

395 KYRIE

Priest, deacon, or cantor, then all:

Ký-ri-e, e - lé - i-son,

Ký-ri-e, e - lé - i-son, Ký-ri - e, e - lé - i - son.

[1.] [2.] *Cantor or choir:*

Chri - ste, e - lé - i - son,

Chri - ste, e - lé - i - son, Chri - ste, e -

lé - i - son, e - lé - i - son.

All:

Ký-ri-e, e - lé - i-son, Ký-ri-e, e - lé - i-son, Ký-ri -

e, e - lé - i - son, e - lé - i - son.

Music: *Music for Celebration*, David Hurd, © 1979, GIA Publications, Inc.

396 KYRIE

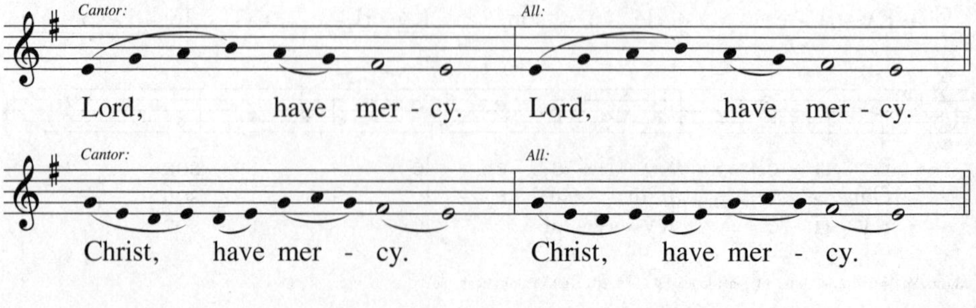

Cantor: *All:*

Lord, have mer - cy. Lord, have mer - cy.

Cantor: *All:*

Christ, have mer - cy. Christ, have mer - cy.

Music: *Kyrie cum jubilo,* Vatican edition; acc. by Gerard Farrell, OSB, © 1986, GIA Publications, Inc.

KYRIE 397

Music: *The Psallite Mass,* Michael Joncas, © 1988, GIA Publications, Inc.

KYRIE 398

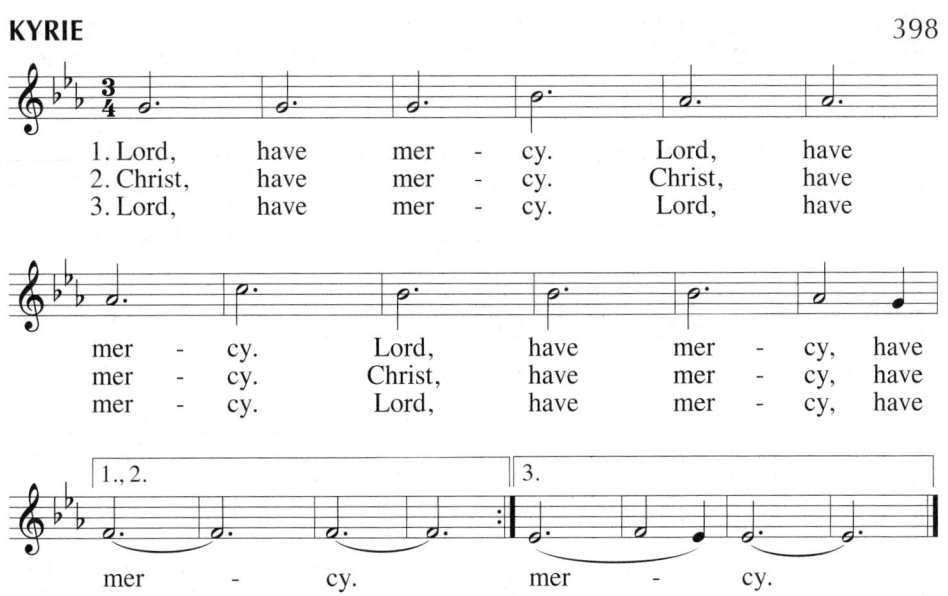

Music: *Mass of St. Augustine,* Leon C. Roberts, © 1981, GIA Publications, Inc.

399 GLORIA

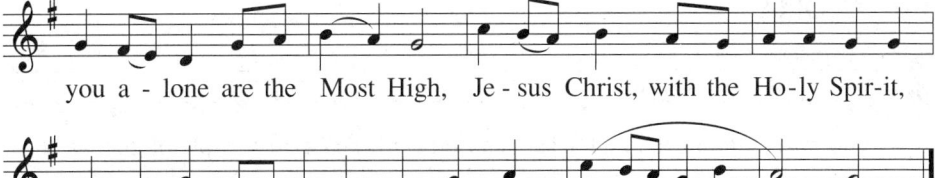

you a - lone are the Most High, Je - sus Christ, with the Ho-ly Spir-it,

in the glo - ry of God the Fa - ther. A - men.

Text: ICEL, © 2010
Music: *A New Mass for Congregations,* Carroll T. Andrews, revised by Ronald F. Krisman, © 1970, 2011, GIA Publications, Inc.

GLORIA   400

Refrain

Gló - ri - a! Gló - ri - a! Glo - ry to God in the high - est,

and on earth peace to peo - ple of good will.

Verses

1. We praise you,
   we bless you,
   we adore you,
   we glorify you,
   we give you thanks for your great glory,
   Lord God, heavenly King,
   O God, almighty Father.

2. Lord Jesus Christ, Only Begotten Son,
   Lord God, Lamb of God, Son of the Father,
   you take away the sins of the world,
   have mercy on us;
   you take away the sins of the world,
   receive our prayer;
   you are seated at the right hand of the Father,
   have mercy on us.

3. For you alone are the Holy One,
   you alone are the Lord,
   you alone are the Most High,
   Jesus Christ,
   with the Holy Spirit,
   in the glory of God the Father.
   Amen.

Text: ICEL, © 2010
Music: *Missa Pacem,* L. Randolph Babin, © 2004, 2010, GIA Publications, Inc.

401 **GLORIA**

Text: ICEL, © 2010
Music: *Congregational Mass;* John Lee, revised by Ronald F. Krisman, © 1970, 2011, GIA Publications, Inc.

GLORIA

Refrain

Glo - ry, glo - ry, glo - ry to God in the high - est, and on earth peace to peo - ple of good will.

Verses

1. We praise you,
   we bless you,
   we adore you,
   we glorify you,
   we give you thanks for your great glory,
   Lord God, heavenly King,
   O God, almighty Father.

2. Lord Jesus Christ, Only Begotten Son,
   Lord God, Lamb of God, Son of the Father,
   you take away the sins of the world,
   have mercy on us;
   you take away the sins of the world,
   receive our prayer;
   you are seated at the right hand of the Father,
   have mercy on us.

3. For you alone are the Holy One,
   you alone are the Lord,
   you alone are the Most High,
   Jesus Christ,
   with the Holy Spirit,
   in the glory of God the Father.
   Amen.

Text: ICEL, © 2010
Music: *Mass of Christ, Our Hope*, David Haas, © 2014, GIA Publications, Inc.

403 **GLORIA**

Glo-ry! Glo-ry to God in the

high-est. Glo-ry! Glo-ry to God in the high-est, and on

earth peace to peo - ple of good will. We

praise you, we bless you, we a - dore you, we glo - ri-fy you,

we give you thanks for your great glo - ry,

Lord God, heav - en - ly King, O God, al - might - y

Fa-ther. Lord Je - sus Christ, On-ly Be - got-ten Son,

Lord God, Lamb of God, Son of the Fa-ther, you take a -

way the sins of the world, have mer-cy on us; you take a -

way the sins of the world, re - ceive our prayer; you are

seat-ed at the right hand of the Fa-ther, have mer-cy on us.

For you a-lone are the Ho-ly One, you a-lone are the

Lord, you a-lone are the Most High, Je - sus Christ,

with the Ho - ly Spir-it, in the glo-ry of God the Fa-ther.

Glo-ry! Glo-ry to God in the high-est. Glo-ry!

Glo - ry to God in the high-est, and on earth peace to

peo - ple of good will. A - men.

Text: ICEL, © 2010
Music: *Mass of Saint Ann,* Ed Bolduc, © 2011, World Library Publications

404 CHILDREN'S DISMISSAL FOR LITURGY OF THE WORD

Refrain

Go forth now and lis-ten to God's Word. Hold it close

to your heart, and fol-low the Lord. Lord. Lord.

1. 2.–4.

Verses

1. O - pen our ears to hear your voice.
2. O - pen our minds to know your Word.

D.C.

O - pen our hearts!
O - pen our lives!

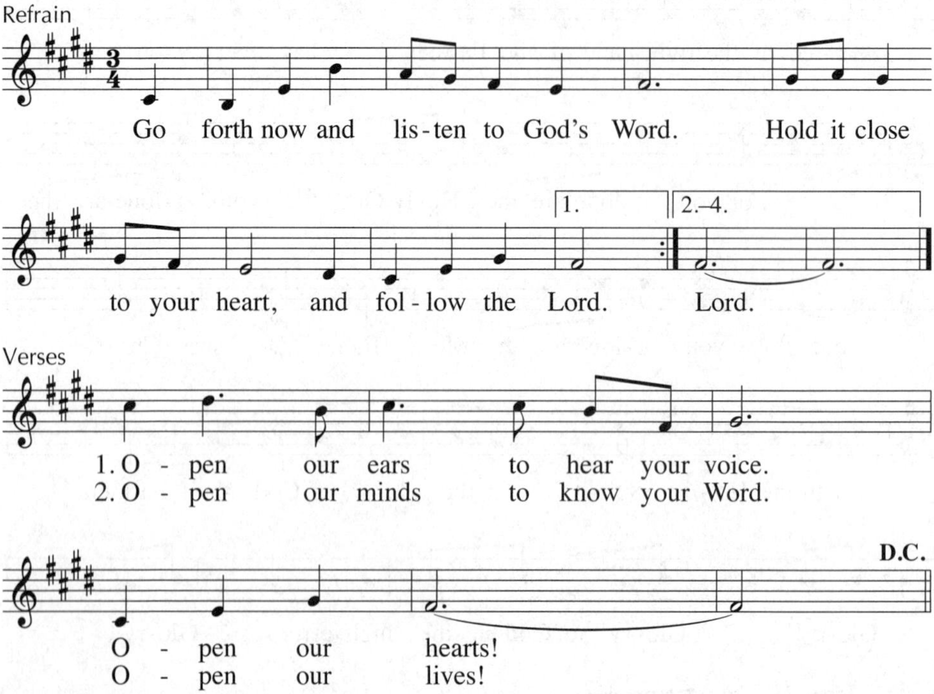

Text: David Haas
Music: David Haas
© 1999, GIA Publications, Inc.

405 CHILDREN'S DISMISSAL FOR LITURGY OF THE WORD

Cantor: All:

Go and lis-ten to the Word of God. Go and lis-ten to the

Cantor:

Word of God. God has the words of ev-er-last-ing life.

All:

God has the words of ev-er-last-ing life.

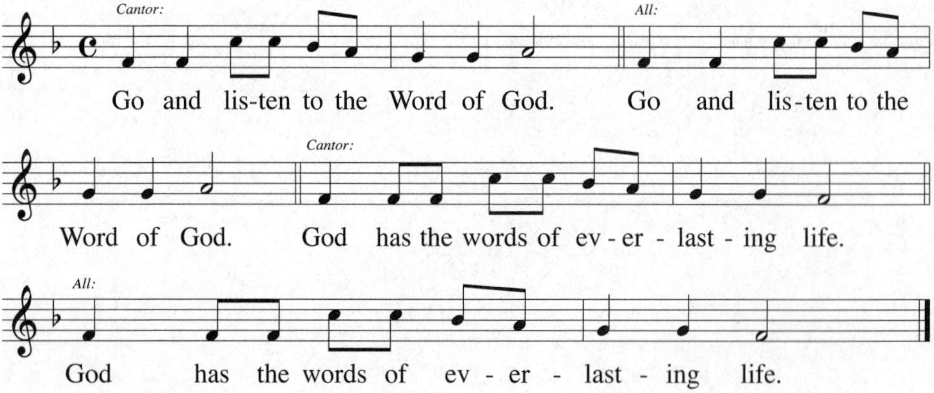

Text: Robert J. Batastini
Music: Robert J. Batastini
© 2003, GIA Publications, Inc.

CHILDREN'S DISMISSAL FOR LITURGY OF THE WORD 406

O - pen our hearts, o - pen our ears. Your words, O Lord, bring

life for - ev - er. O - pen our hearts, o - pen our ears.

1. Christ here a - mong us, speak to us now.

2. speak to us now.

Christ here a - mong us, speak to us now.

Text: Thomas Stehle
Music: Thomas Stehle
© 2016, GIA Publications, Inc.

GOSPEL ACCLAMATION 407

Al - le - lu - ia, al - le - lu - ia, al - le - lu - ia.

Music: Chant Mode VI; acc. by Richard Proulx, © 1985, GIA Publications, Inc.

GOSPEL ACCLAMATION 408

Al - le - lu - ia, al - le - lu - ia, al - le - lu - ia.

Music: A. Gregory Murray, OSB, © 1958, The Grail, GIA Publications, Inc., agent

GOSPEL ACCLAMATION 409

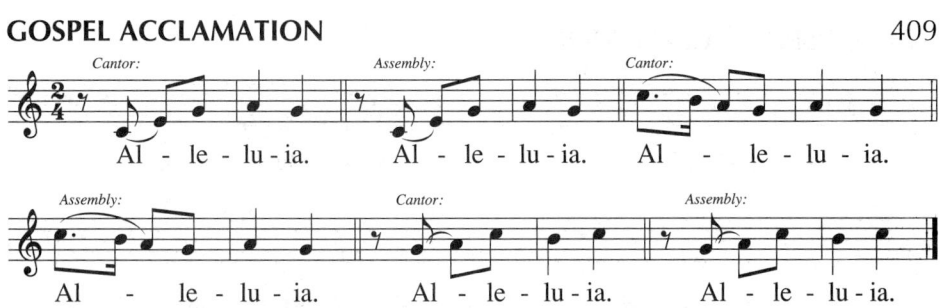

Cantor: Al - le - lu - ia. *Assembly:* Al - le - lu - ia. *Cantor:* Al - le - lu - ia.

Assembly: Al - le - lu - ia. *Cantor:* Al - le - lu - ia. *Assembly:* Al - le - lu - ia.

Music: *Alleluia in C*, Howard Hughes, SM, © 1973, 1982, GIA Publications, Inc.

410 GOSPEL ACCLAMATION

Al - le - lu – ia, al - le - lu - ia, al - le - lu - ia.

Music: O FILII ET FILIAE, Mode II; acc. by Richard Proulx, © 1975, GIA Publications, Inc.

411 GOSPEL ACCLAMATION

Al - le - lu – ia, al - le - lu - ia, al - le - lu – ia.

Music: Robert F. Twynham, © 1958, World Library Publications

412 GOSPEL ACCLAMATION

Al - le - lu – ia, al - le - lu - ia, al - le - lu - ia, al - le - lu - ia, al - le - lu – ia.

Music: Richard Proulx, © 1980, ICEL

413 GOSPEL ACCLAMATION

Al - le - lu – ia, al - le - lu - ia! Al - le - lu – ia, al - le - lu - ia!

Text: Fintan O'Carroll and Christopher Walker
Music: Fintan O'Carroll and Christopher Walker
© 1985, Fintan O'Carroll and Christopher Walker. Published by OCP.

414 GOSPEL ACCLAMATION

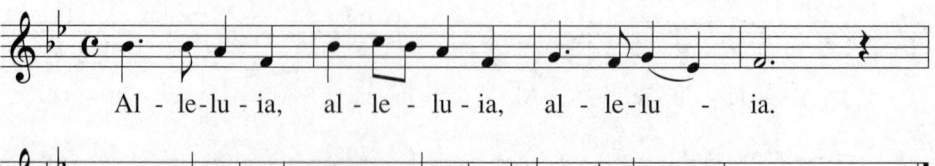

Al - le - lu - ia, al - le - lu - ia, al - le - lu – ia.

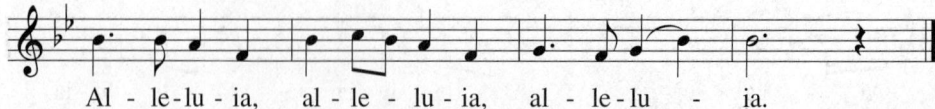

Al - le - lu - ia, al - le - lu - ia, al - le - lu – ia.

Music: *Festival Alleluia*, James J. Chepponis, © 1999, *Morningstar Music Publishers*

GOSPEL ACCLAMATION 415

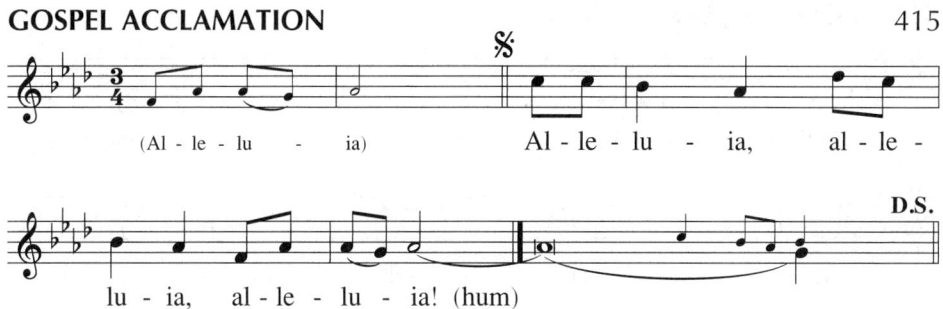

(Al - le - lu - ia) Al - le - lu - ia, al - le - lu - ia, al - le - lu - ia! (hum)

Music: Alleluia 11, Jacques Berthier, © 1984, Les Presses de Taizé, GIA Publications, Inc., agent

GOSPEL ACCLAMATION 416

Cantor, then all:

¡A - le - lu - ya, a - le - lu - ya! ¡A - le - lu - ya, a - le - lu - ya! ¡A - le - lu - ya, a - le - lu - ya! ¡El Se - ñor re - su - ci - tó! ¡A - le -

Last time

Music: The Honduras Alleluia, Rob Glover, © 1997, GIA Publications, Inc.

GOSPEL ACCLAMATION 417

Refrain

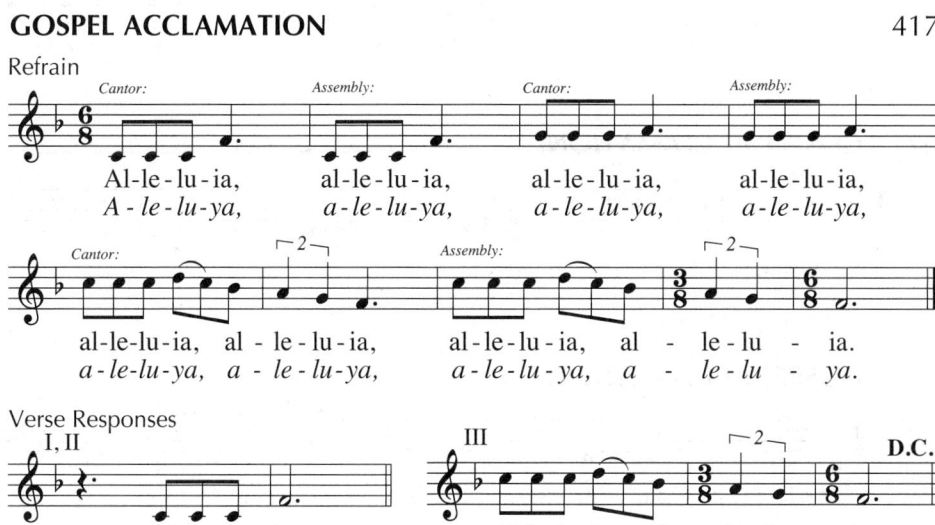

Cantor: Assembly: Cantor: Assembly:

Al - le - lu - ia, al - le - lu - ia, al - le - lu - ia, al - le - lu - ia,
A - le - lu - ya, a - le - lu - ya, a - le - lu - ya, a - le - lu - ya,

Cantor: Assembly:

al - le - lu - ia, al - le - lu - ia, al - le - lu - ia, al - le - lu - ia.
a - le - lu - ya, a - le - lu - ya, a - le - lu - ya, a - le - lu - ya.

Verse Responses

I, II

Al - le - lu - ia.
A - le - lu - ya.

III D.C.

Al - le - lu - ia, al - le - lu - ia.
A - le - lu - ya, a - le - lu - ya.

Text: Tony E. Alonso
Music: Based on LAMBILLOTTE, Louis Lambillotte, SJ, 1796–1855; adapt. by Tony E. Alonso
© 2007, GIA Publications, Inc.

418 GOSPEL ACCLAMATION

Hal-le, hal-le, hal-le - lu - jah! Hal-le, hal-le, hal-

le - lu - jah! Hal - le, hal - le, hal - le -

lu - jah! Hal-le - lu-jah! Hal-le - lu - jah!

Music: Traditional Caribbean, arr. by John L. Bell, © 1990, Iona Community, GIA Publications, Inc., agent; verses and acc. by Marty Haugen, © 1993, GIA Publications, Inc.

419 GOSPEL ACCLAMATION

Al-le-lu-ia, al-le-lu-ia, al-le-lu-ia, al-le-lu-ia!

Music: Alleluia 17; Jacques Berthier, © 1998, Les Presses de Taizé, GIA Publications, Inc., agent

420 GOSPEL ACCLAMATION

Al - le - lu - ia, al - le - lu - ia, al - le - lu - ia!

Music: *Mass of Remembrance*, Marty Haugen, © 1987, GIA Publications, Inc.

421 GOSPEL ACCLAMATION

Al-le-lu - ia, al-le-lu - ia, al-le-lu - ia.

Music: GELOBT SEI GOTT, Melchior Vulpius

422 GOSPEL ACCLAMATION

Al - le - lu - ia, al - le - lu - ia, al - le - lu - ia.

Al - le - lu - ia, al-le-lu - ia, al-le-lu - ia!

Music: Alleluia 7; Jacques Berthier, © 1984, Les Presses de Taizé, GIA Publications, Inc., agent

GOSPEL ACCLAMATION 423

Al - le - lu - ia, al - le - lu - ia!

Al - le-lu - ia, al - le - lu - ia! Al - le - lu - ia, al - le - lu - ia!

Al - le-lu - ia, al - le - lu - ia! Al - le - lu - ia, al - le - lu - ia!

Al - le - lu - ia, al - le-lu - ia! Al - le - lu - ia, al - le-lu - ia!

Al - le-lu - ia, al - le-lu - ia!

Music: *Joyful Alleluia;* Howard Hughes, SM, © 1973, 1979, GIA Publications, Inc.

GOSPEL ACCLAMATION 424

Al - le - lu - ia! Al - le - lu - ia!
Lent: Praise to you, Lord Je - sus Christ,

Al - le - lu - ia, al - le - lu - ia!
King of end - less glo - ry!

Text: ICEL, © 1969
Music: *Mass for John Carroll,* Michael Joncas, © 1990, GIA Publications, Inc.

LENTEN GOSPEL ACCLAMATION 425

Glo-ry to you, O Word of God, Lord Je-sus Christ!

Text: ICEL, © 1969
Music: Richard Proulx, © 1975, GIA Publications, Inc.

426 LENTEN GOSPEL ACCLAMATION

Praise and hon - or to you, O Lord Je - sus Christ.

Text: ICEL, © 1969
Music: *Kyrie Orbis Factor*, acc. by David Hurd, © 1979, GIA Publications, Inc.

427 LENTEN GOSPEL ACCLAMATION

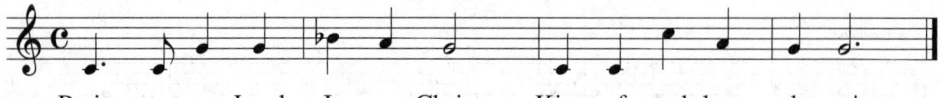

Praise to you, Lord Je - sus Christ, King of end - less glo - ry!

Text: ICEL, © 1969
Music: Frank Schoen, © 1970, GIA Publications, Inc.

428 LENTEN GOSPEL ACCLAMATION

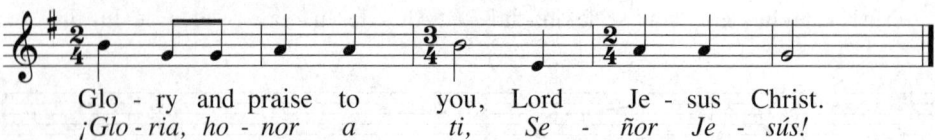

Glo - ry and praise to you, Lord Je - sus Christ.
¡Glo - ria, ho - nor a ti, Se - ñor Je - sús!

Text: English, ICEL, © 1969
Music: Lucien Deiss, © 1965, 1966, 1968, 1973, World Library Publications

429 LENTEN GOSPEL ACCLAMATION

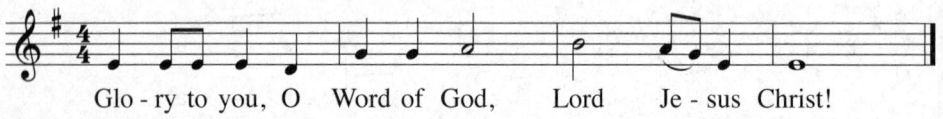

Glo - ry to you, O Word of God, Lord Je - sus Christ!

Text: ICEL, © 1969
Music: Based on KINGSFOLD, David Haas, © 2013, GIA Publications, Inc.

430 LENTEN GOSPEL ACCLAMATION

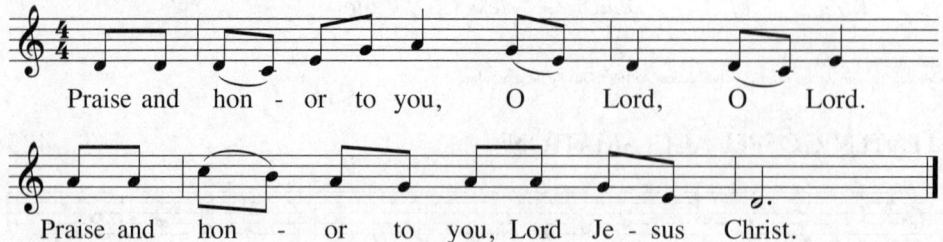

Praise and hon - or to you, O Lord, O Lord.

Praise and hon - or to you, Lord Je - sus Christ.

Text: ICEL, © 1969
Music: Based on WONDROUS LOVE, Stephen Pishner, © 1998, GIA Publications, Inc.

NICENE CREED

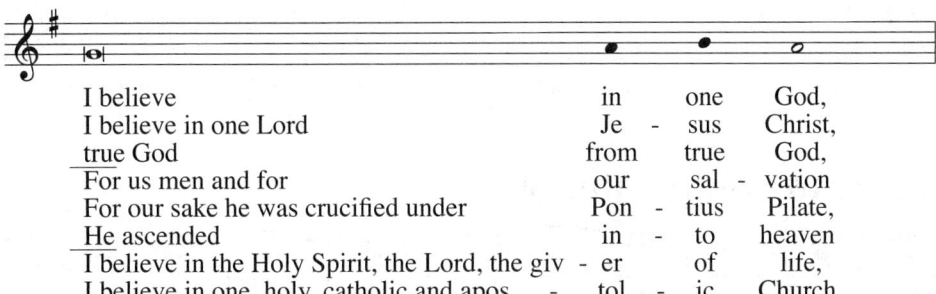

I believe	in	one	God,
I believe in one Lord	Je -	sus	Christ,
true God	from	true	God,
For us men and for	our	sal -	vation
For our sake he was crucified under	Pon -	tius	Pilate,
He ascended	in -	to	heaven
I believe in the Holy Spirit, the Lord, the giv - er		of	life,
I believe in one, holy, catholic and apos - tol -		ic	Church.

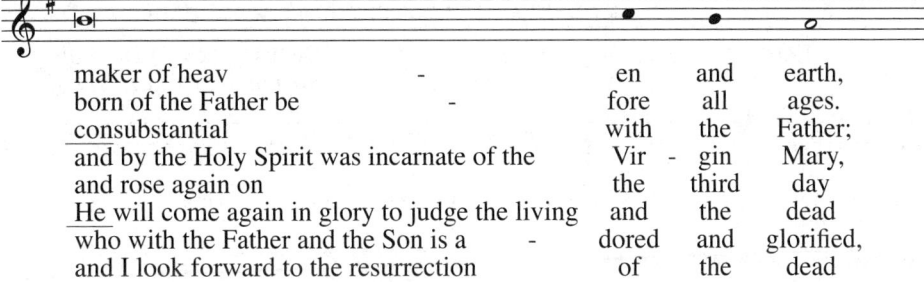

the Fa - ther		al -	mighty,
the Only Begotten	Son	of	God,
begot - ten,		not	made,
he came	down	from	heaven,
he suffered death	and	was	buried,
and is seated at the right hand	of	the	Father.
who proceeds from the Father	and	the	Son,
I confess one Baptism for the forgive - ness		of	sins

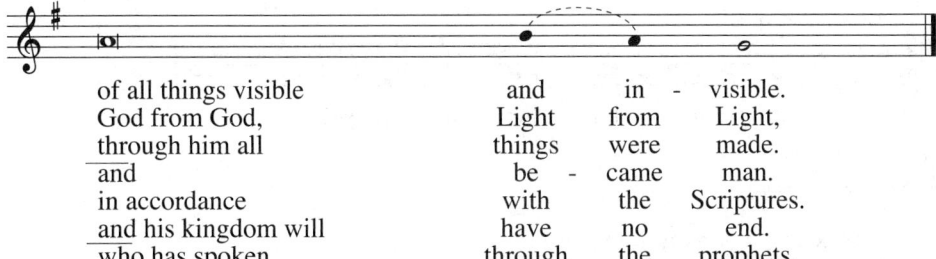

maker of heav - en		and	earth,
born of the Father be - fore		all	ages.
consubstantial	with	the	Father;
and by the Holy Spirit was incarnate of the	Vir -	gin	Mary,
and rose again on	the	third	day
He will come again in glory to judge the living	and	the	dead
who with the Father and the Son is a - dored		and	glorified,
and I look forward to the resurrection	of	the	dead

of all things visible	and	in -	visible.
God from God,	Light	from	Light,
through him all	things	were	made.
and	be -	came	man.
in accordance	with	the	Scriptures.
and his kingdom will	have	no	end.
who has spoken	through	the	prophets.
and the life of the world to come.	A -		men.

Text: ICEL, © 2010
Music: *Jubilation Mass,* James J. Chepponis, © 1999, 2010, GIA Publications, Inc.

432 PRAYER OF THE FAITHFUL

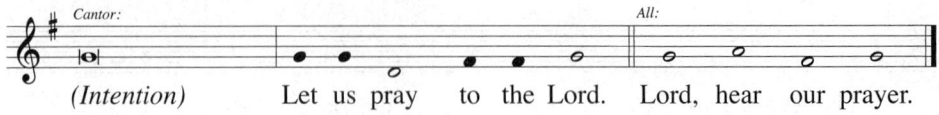

(Intention) Let us pray to the Lord. Lord, hear our prayer.

Music: Byzantine chant

433 PRAYER OF THE FAITHFUL

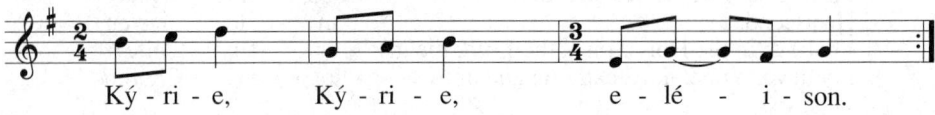

Ký - ri - e, Ký - ri - e, e - lé - i - son.

Music: Jacques Berthier, © 1980, Les Presses de Taizé, GIA Publications, Inc., agent

434 PRAYER OF THE FAITHFUL

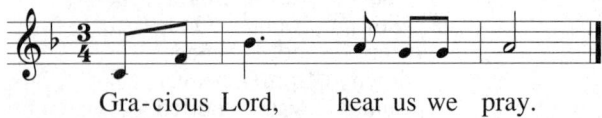

Gra - cious Lord, hear us we pray.

Music: Ronald F. Krisman, © 1977, GIA Publications, Inc.

435 PRAYER OF THE FAITHFUL

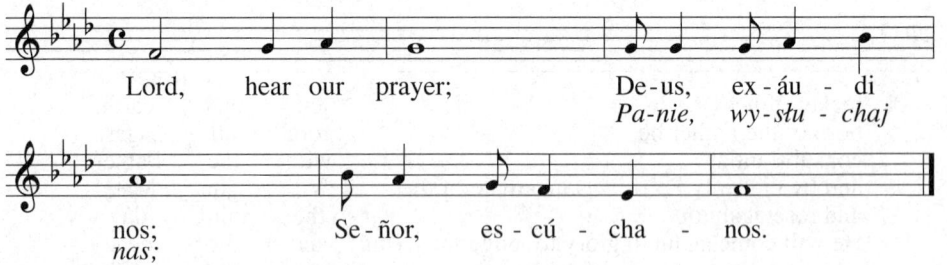

Lord, hear our prayer; De - us, ex - áu - di
Pa - nie, wy - słu - chaj

nos; Se - ñor, es - cú - cha - nos.
nas;

Music: Michael Hay, © 1994, World Library Publications

436 PRAYER OF THE FAITHFUL

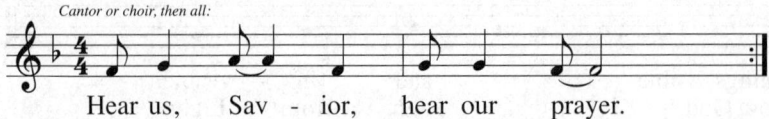

Hear us, Sav - ior, hear our prayer.

Text: Gabe Huck
Music: Tony E. Alonso
© 2004, GIA Publications, Inc.

437 PRAYER OF THE FAITHFUL

O Lord, hear our prayer.

Text: Ray East
Music: Ray East
© 1987, GIA Publications, Inc.

PRAYER OF THE FAITHFUL 438

Te ro - ga - mos, ó - ye - nos.   Lord, hear our prayer.

Music: Peter M. Kolar, © 2001, World Library Publications

PRAYER OF THE FAITHFUL 439

Ký - ri - e,   Ký - ri - e,   e - lé - i - son;   Ký - ri - e,

Ký - ri - e,   e - lé - i - son.   *(hum)*

Music: Jacques Berthier, © 1980, Les Presses de Taizé, GIA Publications, Inc., agent

PRAYER OF THE FAITHFUL 440

Cantor, then all:

Hear, O Lord, en - fold us in your mer - cy.

After each Intercession

Cantor: *All:*

Cry out for God's mer - cy: Hear, O Lord, en-fold us in your mer - cy.

Text: Gabe Huck
Music: Based on PARCE DOMINE; adapt. and arr. by Tony E. Alonso
© 2004, GIA Publications, Inc.

PRAYER OF THE FAITHFUL 441

Response

Cantor, then all (first time only):

O Lord, hear our prayer. Lord, hear us.   O Lord, hear our prayer.

Petitions

All:

O Lord, hear our prayer.

All: **D.C.**

O Lord, hear our prayer.

Music: *Mass of the Nations*, Donna Peña, © 2000, GIA Publications, Inc.

442 HOLY, HOLY, HOLY–MASS OF REMEMBRANCE

Ho - ly, Ho - ly, Ho - ly Lord God of hosts.

Heav'n and earth are full of your glo - ry.

Ho - san - na in the high - est. Bless - ed is

he who comes in the name of the Lord. Ho - san - na

in the high - est. Ho - san - na in the high - est.

Text: ICEL, © 2010
Music: *Mass of Remembrance*, Marty Haugen, © 1987, 2010, GIA Publications, Inc.

443 MEMORIAL ACCLAMATION B

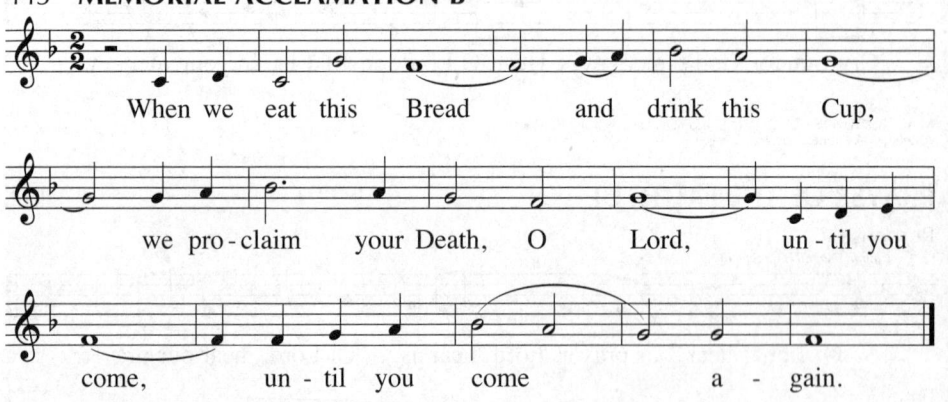

When we eat this Bread and drink this Cup,

we pro - claim your Death, O Lord, un - til you

come, un - til you come a - gain.

Text: ICEL, © 2010
Music: *Mass of Remembrance*, Marty Haugen, © 1987, 2010, GIA Publications, Inc.

444 AMEN

A - men, a - men, a - men, a - men.

Music: *Mass of Remembrance*, Marty Haugen, © 1987, 2010, GIA Publications, Inc.

HOLY, HOLY, HOLY–UNITY MASS 445

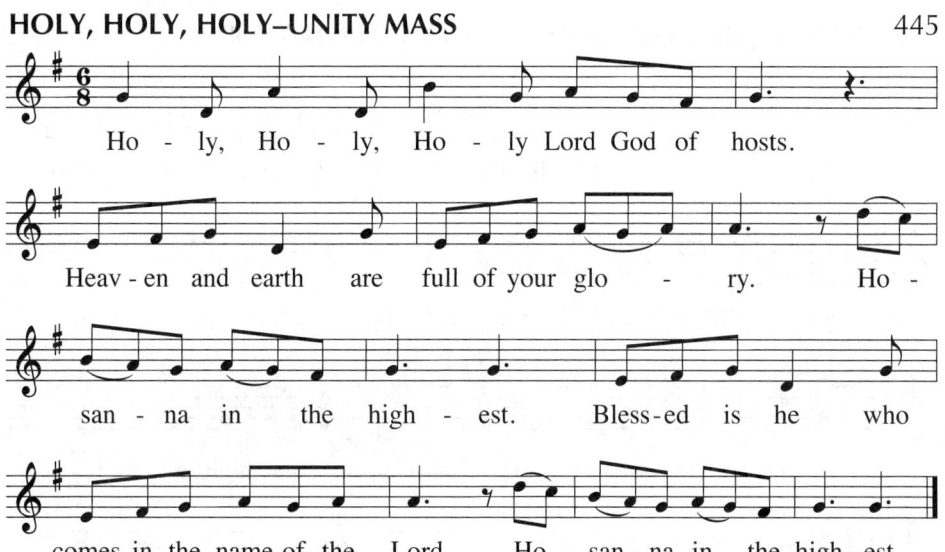

Ho - ly, Ho - ly, Ho - ly Lord God of hosts. Heav - en and earth are full of your glo - ry. Ho - san - na in the high - est. Bless-ed is he who comes in the name of the Lord. Ho - san - na in the high - est.

Text: ICEL, © 2010
Music: *Unity Mass,* Norah Duncan IV, © 2010, GIA Publications, Inc.

MEMORIAL ACCLAMATION C 446

Save us, Sav - ior of the world, for by your Cross and Res - ur - rec - tion you have set us free.

Text: ICEL, © 2010
Music: *Unity Mass,* Norah Duncan IV, © 2010, GIA Publications, Inc.

AMEN 447

A - men, a - men, a - men, a - men, a - men.

Music: *Unity Mass,* Norah Duncan IV, © 2010, GIA Publications, Inc.

448 HOLY, HOLY, HOLY–THE GLENDALOUGH MASS

Ho - ly, Ho - ly, Ho - ly Lord, Lord God of

Or: Ho - ly,

hosts. Heav - en and earth are full of your glo-ry. Ho -

san - na, ho-san-na, ho - san - na in the high - est. Ho -

san - na, ho - san - na, ho - san - na in the

high-est. Bless - ed is he who comes in the name of the

Lord. Ho - san - na, ho - san - na, ho -

san - na in the high - est. Ho - san - na, ho -

san - na, ho - san - na in the high - est.

Text: ICEL, © 2010
Music: *The Glendalough Mass*, Liam Lawton; arr. by Paul A. Tate, © 2010, GIA Publications, Inc.

449 MEMORIAL ACCLAMATION A

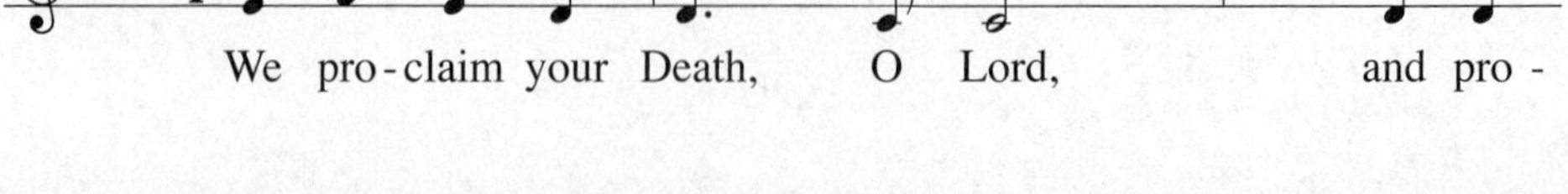

We pro-claim your Death, O Lord, and pro-

fess your Res - ur - rec - tion un - til you come a - gain.

Text: ICEL, © 2010
Music: *The Glendalough Mass,* Liam Lawton; arr. by Paul A. Tate, © 2010, GIA Publications, Inc.

AMEN   450

A - men, a - men, a - men, a - men.

Music: *The Glendalough Mass,* Liam Lawton; arr. by Paul A. Tate, © 2010, GIA Publications, Inc.

HOLY, HOLY, HOLY–LAND OF REST   451

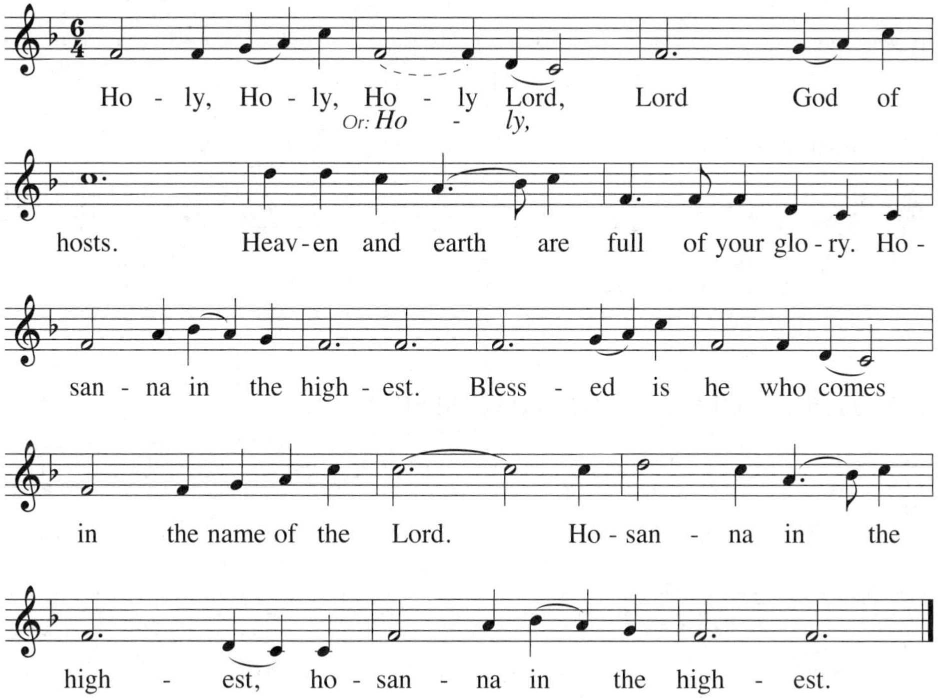

Ho - ly, Ho - ly, Ho - ly Lord, Lord God of
Or: Ho - ly,

hosts. Heav-en and earth are full of your glo - ry. Ho -

san - na in the high - est. Bless - ed is he who comes

in the name of the Lord. Ho - san - na in the

high - est, ho - san - na in the high - est.

Text: ICEL, © 2010
Music: *Land of Rest*; acc. by Richard Proulx, © 1986, 2011, GIA Publications, Inc.; choral arr. by Kelly Dobbs-Mickus, © 2004, GIA Publications, Inc.

452 MEMORIAL ACCLAMATION C

Save us, save us, Sav - ior of the world, for

by your Cross and Res - ur-rec-tion you have set us free.

Text: ICEL, © 2010
Music: *Land of Rest,* acc. by Richard Proulx, © 1986, GIA Publications, Inc.; choral arr. and adapt. by Kelly Dobbs-Mickus, © 2004, 2011, GIA Publications, Inc.

453 AMEN 1

A - men, a - men, a - men.

Music: *Land of Rest,* adapt. by Richard Proulx, © 1986, GIA Publications, Inc.; choral arr. by Kelly Dobbs-Mickus, © 2004, GIA Publications, Inc.

454 AMEN 2

A - men, a - men, a - men.

Music: *Land of Rest,* acc. by Richard Proulx, © 1986, GIA Publications, Inc.; choral arr. and adapt. by Kelly Dobbs-Mickus, © 2004, 2011, GIA Publications, Inc.

455 HOLY, HOLY, HOLY–DEUTSCHE MESSE

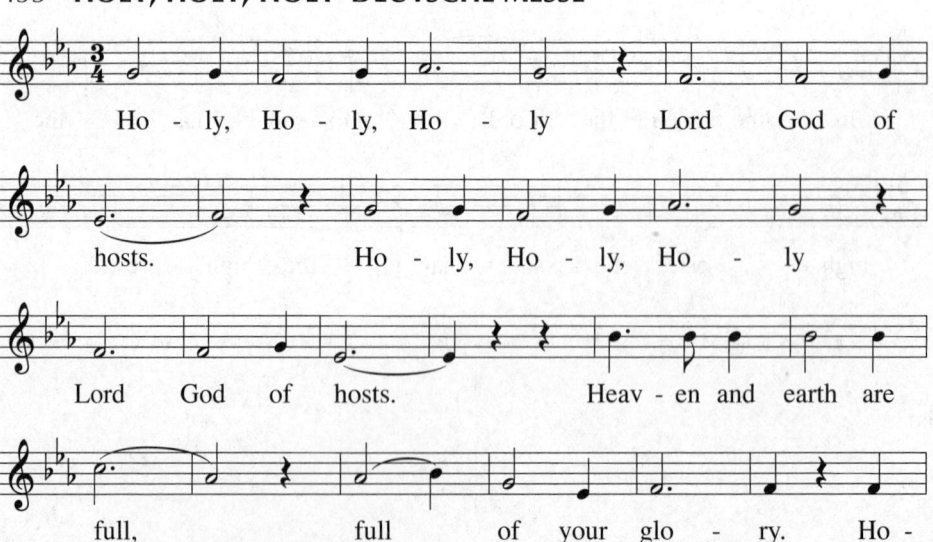

Ho - ly, Ho - ly, Ho - ly Lord God of

hosts. Ho - ly, Ho - ly, Ho - ly

Lord God of hosts. Heav - en and earth are

full, full of your glo - ry. Ho -

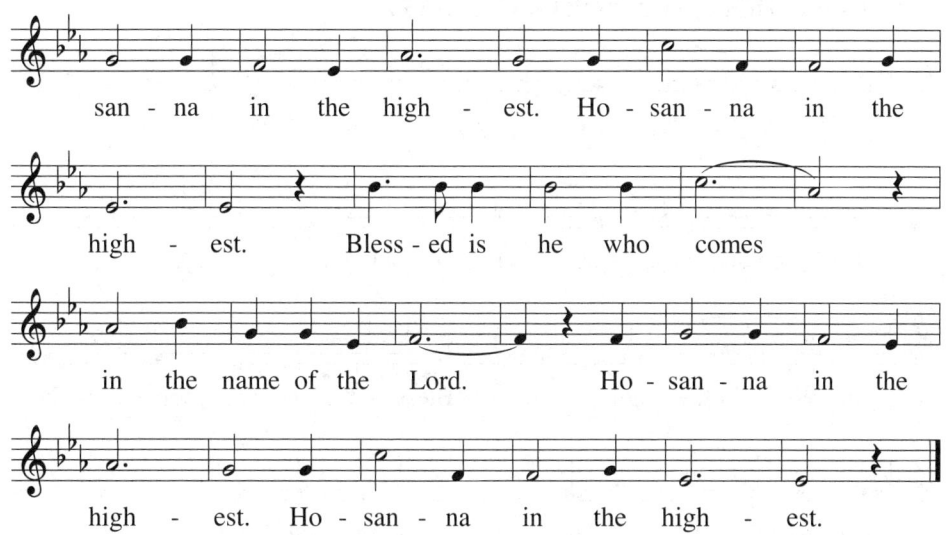

Text: ICEL, © 2010
Music: *Deutsche Messe,* Franz Schubert, 1797–1828, adapt. by Richard Proulx, © 1985, 1989, 2010, GIA Publications, Inc.

MEMORIAL ACCLAMATION A 456

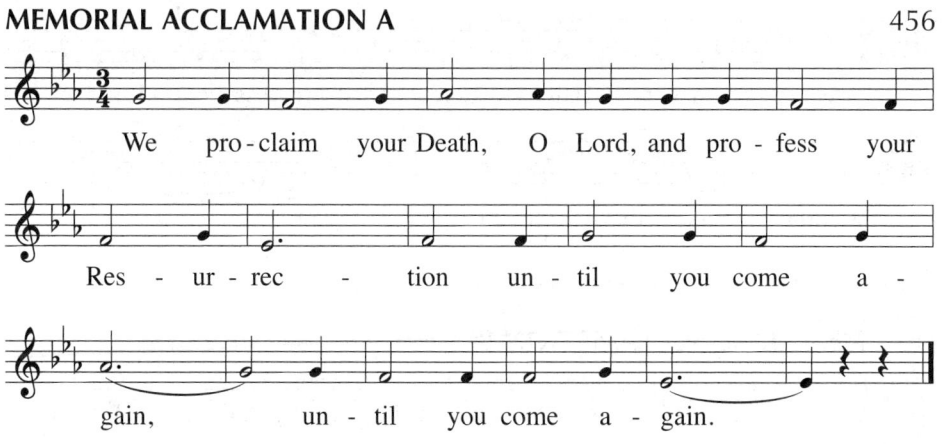

Text: ICEL, © 2010
Music: *Deutsche Messe,* Franz Schubert, 1797–1828; adapt. by Ronald F. Krisman, © 2012, GIA Publications, Inc.

AMEN 457

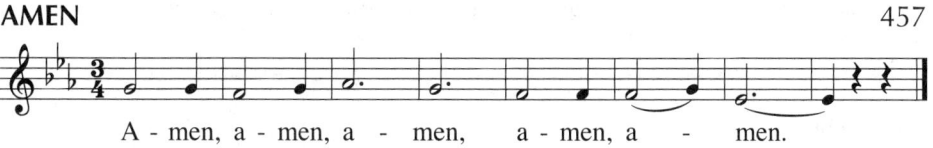

Music: *Deutsche Messe,* Franz Schubert, 1797–1828, adapt. by Richard Proulx, © 1985, 1989, GIA Publications, Inc.

458 HOLY, HOLY, HOLY–PEOPLE'S MASS

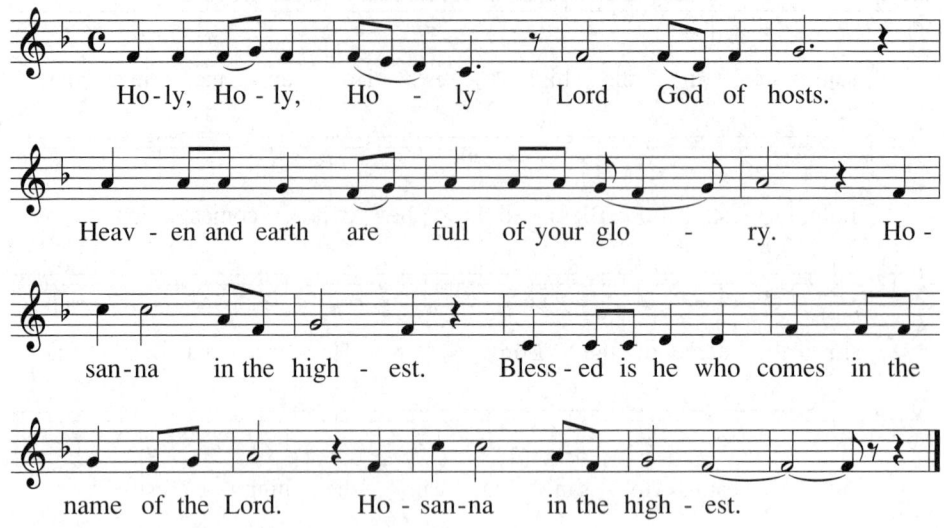

Ho-ly, Ho-ly, Ho-ly Lord God of hosts.

Heav - en and earth are full of your glo - ry. Ho -

san-na in the high - est. Bless - ed is he who comes in the

name of the Lord. Ho - san-na in the high - est.

Text: ICEL, © 2010
Music: *People's Mass*, Jan M. Vermulst; arr. and adapt. by Richard Proulx, © 1970, 1987, 2010, World Library Publications

459 MEMORIAL ACCLAMATION A

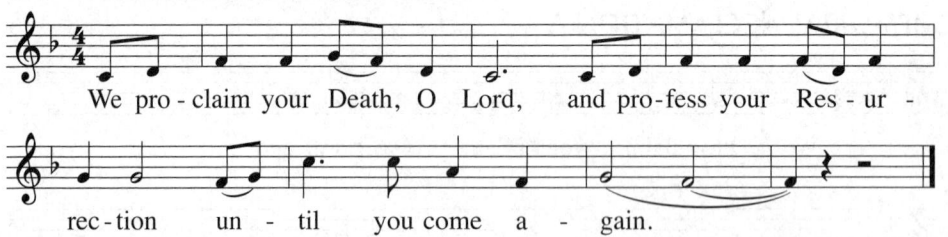

We pro - claim your Death, O Lord, and pro-fess your Res - ur -

rec - tion un - til you come a - gain.

Text: ICEL, © 2010
Music: *People's Mass*, Richard Proulx, © 2010, World Library Publications

460 MEMORIAL ACCLAMATION B

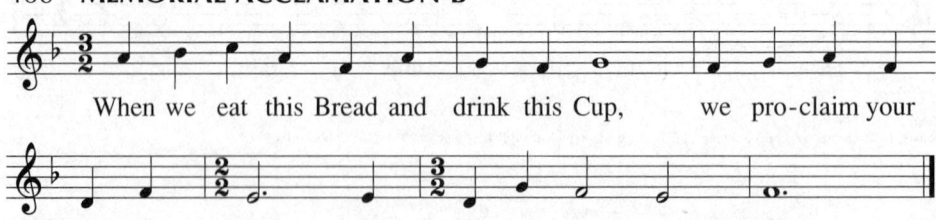

When we eat this Bread and drink this Cup, we pro-claim your

Death, O Lord, un - til you come a - gain.

Text: ICEL, © 2010
Music: *Danish Amen Mass*, David Kraehenbuehl; acc. by Charles G. Frischmann, © 1970, 1973, 2011, World Library Publications

461 AMEN

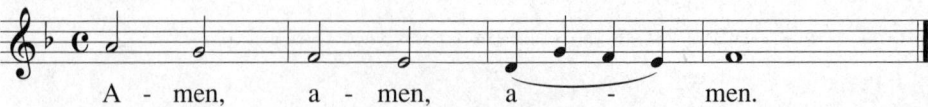

A - men, a - men, a - men.

Music: Danish Amen

HOLY, HOLY, HOLY–MASS OF WISDOM 462

Ho - ly, Ho - ly, Ho - ly Lord God of hosts. Heav-en and earth are full of your glo-ry. Ho - san - na, ho - san - na, ho - san - na in the high-est. Bless-ed is he who comes in the name of the Lord. Ho - san - na, ho - san - na, ho - san - na in the high-est.

Text: ICEL, © 2010
Music: *Mass of Wisdom,* Steven R. Janco, © 2010, World Library Publications

MEMORIAL ACCLAMATION C 463

Save us, Sav - ior of the world, for by your Cross and Res - ur - rec - tion you have set us free.

Text: ICEL, © 2010
Music: *Mass of Wisdom,* Steven R. Janco, © 2010, World Library Publications

AMEN 464

A - men, a - men, a - men. A - men, a - men, a - men.

Music: *Mass of Wisdom,* Steven R. Janco, © 2010, World Library Publications

465 HOLY, HOLY, HOLY–NO GREATER LOVE MASS

Ho - ly, Ho - ly,

Ho - ly Lord God of hosts. Heav - en and earth are

full of your glo - ry. Ho - san-na in the high - est.

Bless-ed is he, bless - ed is he who comes, who

comes in the name of the Lord. Ho - san-na in the high - est,

in the high - est. Ho - san-na in the high - est.

Text: ICEL, © 2010
Music: *No Greater Love Mass,* Michael Joncas, © 1988, 2015, GIA Publications, Inc.

466 MEMORIAL ACCLAMATION A

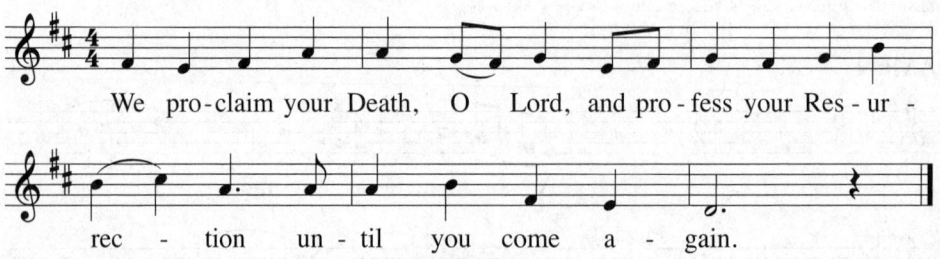

We pro-claim your Death, O Lord, and pro - fess your Res - ur -

rec - tion un - til you come a - gain.

Text: ICEL, © 2010
Music: *No Greater Love Mass,* Michael Joncas, © 1988, 2015, GIA Publications, Inc.

MEMORIAL ACCLAMATION B 467

When we eat this Bread and drink this Cup, we pro-claim your Death, O Lord, un - til you come a - gain.

Text: ICEL, © 2010
Music: *No Greater Love Mass,* Michael Joncas, © 1988, 2015, GIA Publications, Inc.

AMEN 468

A - men, a - men, a - men, a - men.

Music: *No Greater Love Mass*, Michael Joncas, © 1988, 2015, GIA Publications, Inc.

HOLY, HOLY, HOLY–MASS OF CHRIST THE SAVIOR 469

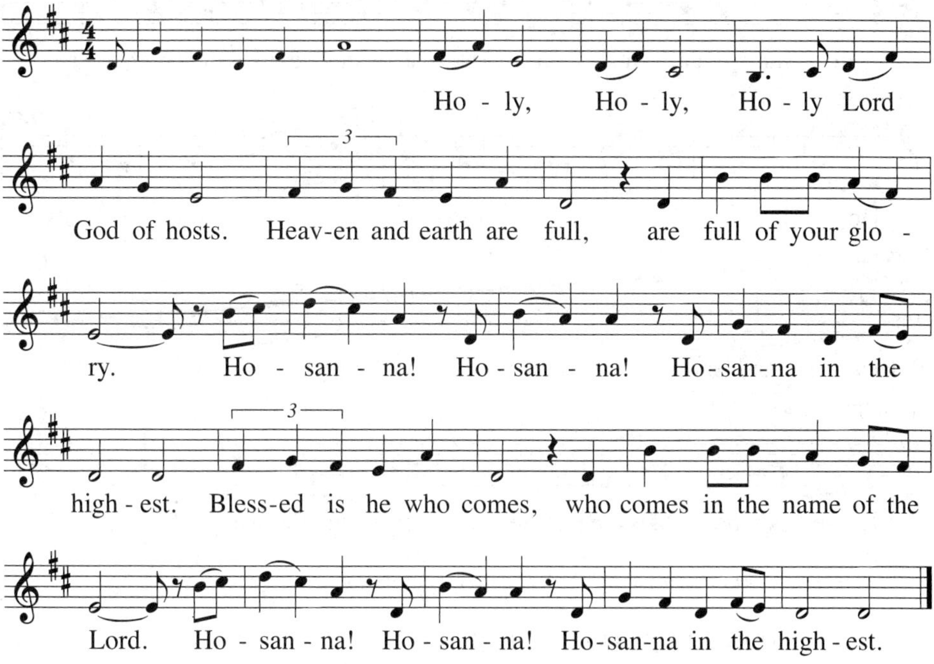

Ho - ly, Ho - ly, Ho - ly Lord God of hosts. Heav-en and earth are full, are full of your glo - ry. Ho - san - na! Ho - san - na! Ho-san-na in the high - est. Bless-ed is he who comes, who comes in the name of the Lord. Ho - san - na! Ho - san - na! Ho-san-na in the high-est.

Text: ICEL, © 2010
Music: *Mass of Christ the Savior,* Dan Schutte, © 2007, 2009, Daniel L. Schutte. Published by OCP.

470 MEMORIAL ACCLAMATION A

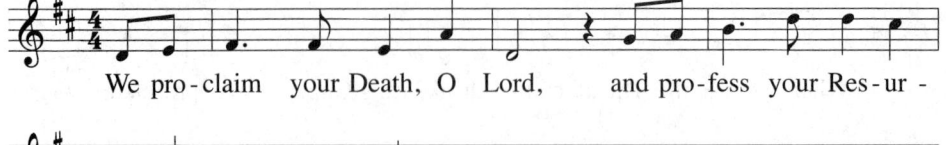

We pro-claim your Death, O Lord, and pro-fess your Res-ur-

rec-tion un-til you come a-gain.

Text: ICEL, © 2010
Music: *Mass of Christ the Savior*, Dan Schutte, © 2007, 2009, Daniel L. Schutte. Published by OCP.

471 AMEN

A-men, a-men, a-men.

Text: ICEL, © 2010
Music: *Mass of Christ the Savior*, Dan Schutte, © 2007, 2009, 2010, Daniel L. Schutte. Published by OCP.

472 HOLY, HOLY, HOLY–MASS OF THE DIVINE WORD

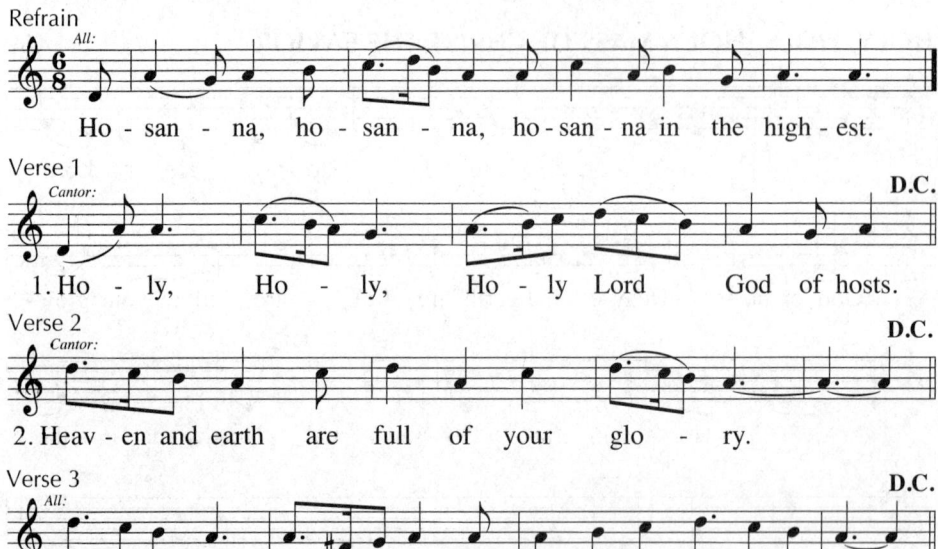

Refrain
All:

Ho-san-na, ho-san-na, ho-san-na in the high-est.

Verse 1
Cantor:
D.C.

1. Ho-ly, Ho-ly, Ho-ly Lord God of hosts.

Verse 2
Cantor:
D.C.

2. Heav-en and earth are full of your glo-ry.

Verse 3
All:
D.C.

3. Bless-ed is he, bless-ed is he who comes in the name of the Lord.

Text: ICEL, © 2010
Music: *Mass of the Divine Word*, Howard Hughes, SM, © 1981, 2001, 2012, GIA Publications, Inc.

473 MEMORIAL ACCLAMATION B

When we eat this Bread and drink this Cup, we pro-

claim your Death, O Lord, un - til you come a - gain.

Text: ICEL, © 2010
Music: *Mass of the Divine Word*, Howard Hughes, SM, © 1981, 2001, 2012, GIA Publications, Inc.

AMEN

474

A - men, a - men, a - men.

Music: *Mass of the Divine Word*, Howard Hughes, SM, © 1981, 2001, 2012, GIA Publications, Inc.

HOLY, HOLY, HOLY–MASS FOR THE CITY

475

Ho - ly, Ho - ly, Ho - ly

Lord God of hosts. Heav - en and earth are

full of your glo - ry. Ho - san - na, ho - san - na, ho -

san - na in the high - est. Bless - ed is he who

comes in the name of the Lord. Ho - san - na, ho -

san - na, ho - san - na in the high - est. Ho - san - na, ho -

san - na, ho - san - na in the high - est.

Text: ICEL, © 2010
Music: *Mass for the City*, Richard Proulx, © 1991, 2010, GIA Publications, Inc.

476 MEMORIAL ACCLAMATION B

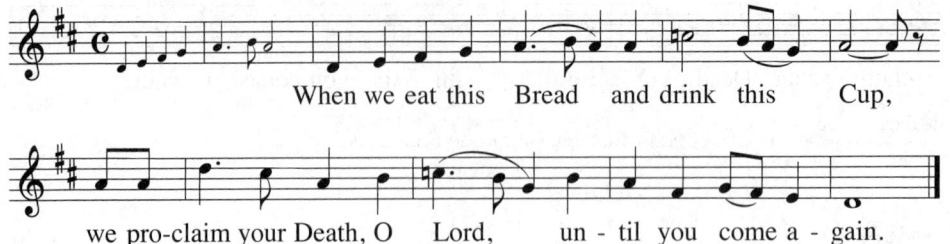

When we eat this Bread and drink this Cup,

we pro-claim your Death, O Lord, un - til you come a - gain.

Text: ICEL, © 2010
Music: *Mass for the City*, Richard Proulx, © 1991, 2010, GIA Publications, Inc.

477 AMEN

A - men, a - men, a - men.

Music: *Mass for the City*, Richard Proulx, © 1995, GIA Publications, Inc.

478 HOLY, HOLY, HOLY–CORPUS CHRISTI MASS

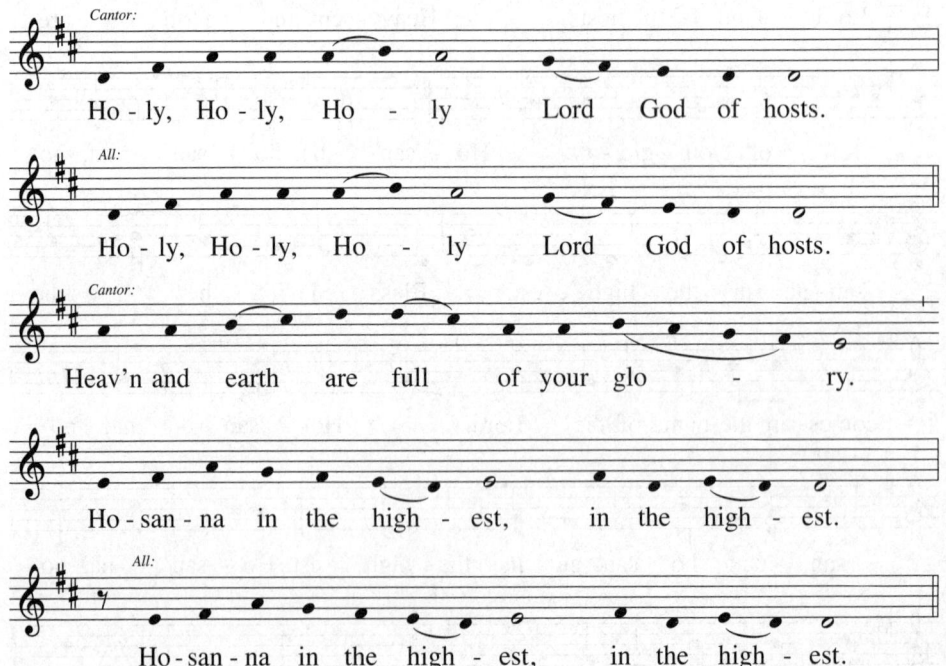

Cantor:
Ho - ly, Ho - ly, Ho - ly Lord God of hosts.

All:
Ho - ly, Ho - ly, Ho - ly Lord God of hosts.

Cantor:
Heav'n and earth are full of your glo - ry.

Ho - san - na in the high - est, in the high - est.

All:
Ho - san - na in the high - est, in the high - est.

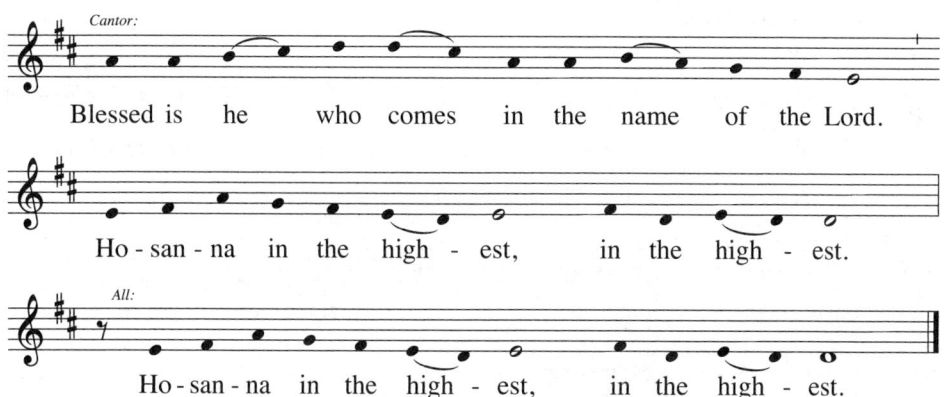

Blessed is he who comes in the name of the Lord.

Ho - san - na in the high - est, in the high - est.

Ho - san - na in the high - est, in the high - est.

Text: ICEL, © 2010
Music: *Corpus Christi Mass, Adoro te devote*, setting by Richard Proulx, © 1992, 2002, GIA Publications, Inc.

MEMORIAL ACCLAMATION B 479

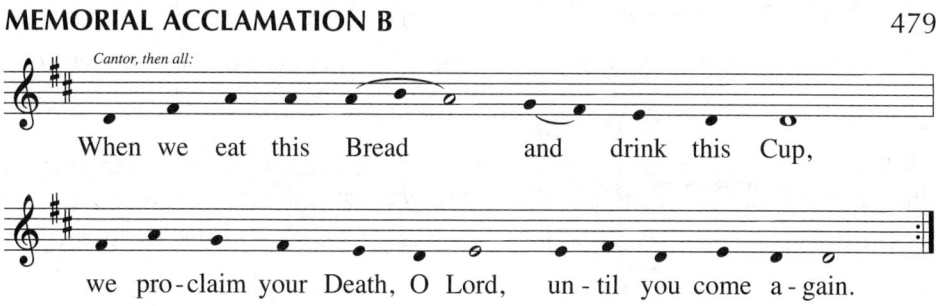

When we eat this Bread and drink this Cup,

we pro-claim your Death, O Lord, un - til you come a - gain.

Text: ICEL, © 2010
Music: *Corpus Christi Mass, Adoro te devote*, setting by Richard Proulx, © 1992, 2002, GIA Publications, Inc.

AMEN 480

A - men, a - men, a - men.

Music: *Corpus Christi Mass, Adoro te devote*, setting by Richard Proulx, © 1992, 2002, GIA Publications, Inc.

481 LAMB OF GOD

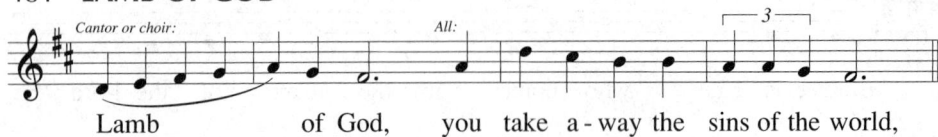

Cantor or choir: / *All:* / 3

Lamb of God, you take a-way the sins of the world,

To repeat / *Last time*

have mer-cy on us. grant us peace.

Music: *Holy Cross Mass,* David Clark Isele, © 1979, GIA Publications, Inc.

482 LAMB OF GOD

Cantors: / *All:* / *To repeat*

Lamb of God, you take a-way the sins of the world, have mer-cy on

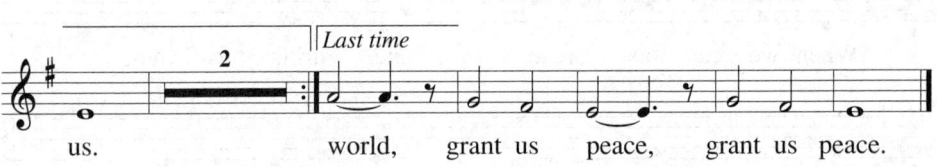

Last time

us. world, grant us peace, grant us peace.

Music: *Mass of Remembrance,* Marty Haugen, © 1987, GIA Publications, Inc.

483 LAMB OF GOD

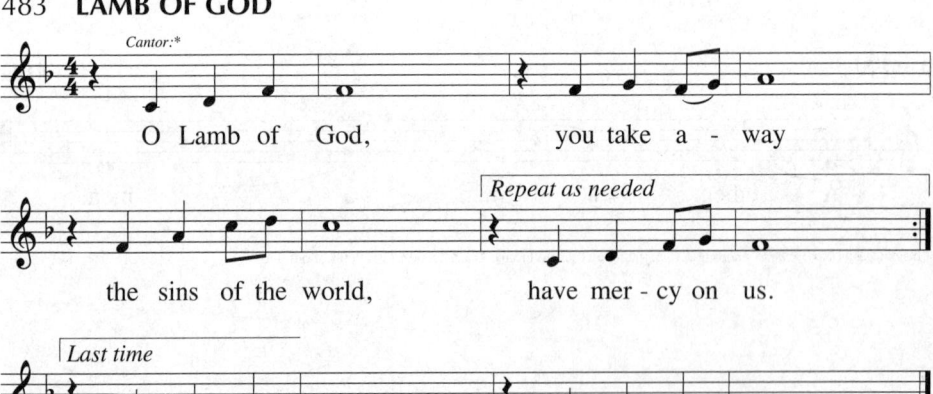

Cantor:*

O Lamb of God, you take a - way

Repeat as needed

the sins of the world, have mer - cy on us.

Last time

Grant us peace, grant us peace.

*The assembly echoes each phrase of the cantor at the interval of one measure.

Music: Ralph R. Stewart, © 1999, GIA Publications, Inc.; acc. by Robert J. Batastini, © 2003, GIA Publications, Inc.

LAMB OF GOD 484

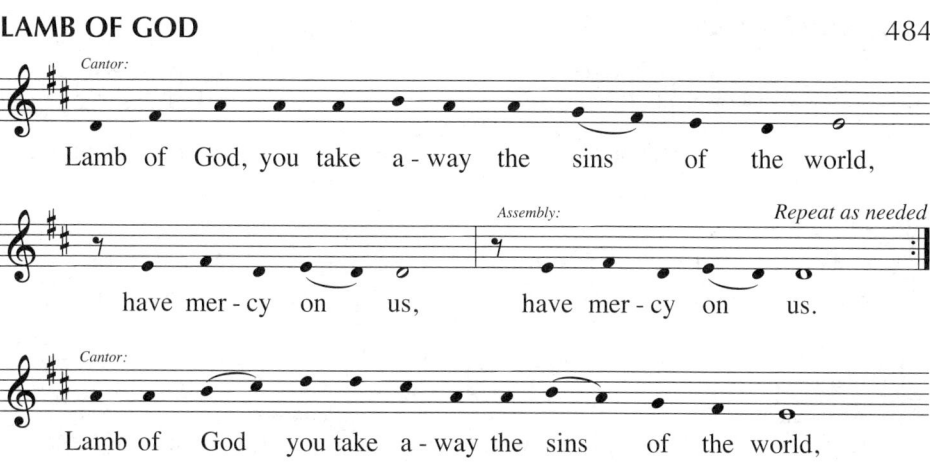

Lamb of God, you take a-way the sins of the world,

have mer-cy on us, have mer-cy on us.

Lamb of God you take a-way the sins of the world,

grant us peace, grant us peace.

Grant us peace, grant us peace.

Music: *Corpus Christi Mass, Adoro te devote*, setting by Richard Proulx, © 1992, 2002, GIA Publications, Inc.

LAMB OF GOD 485

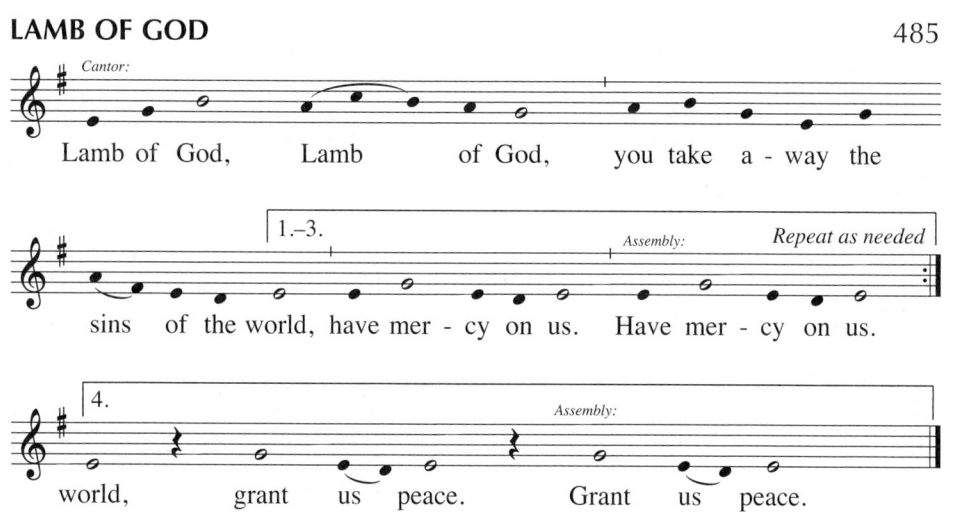

Lamb of God, Lamb of God, you take a-way the

1.–3.

sins of the world, have mer-cy on us. Have mer-cy on us.

4.

world, grant us peace. Grant us peace.

Music: *Missa Emmanuel*, Richard Proulx, © 1991, 2002, GIA Publications, Inc.

486 LAMB OF GOD

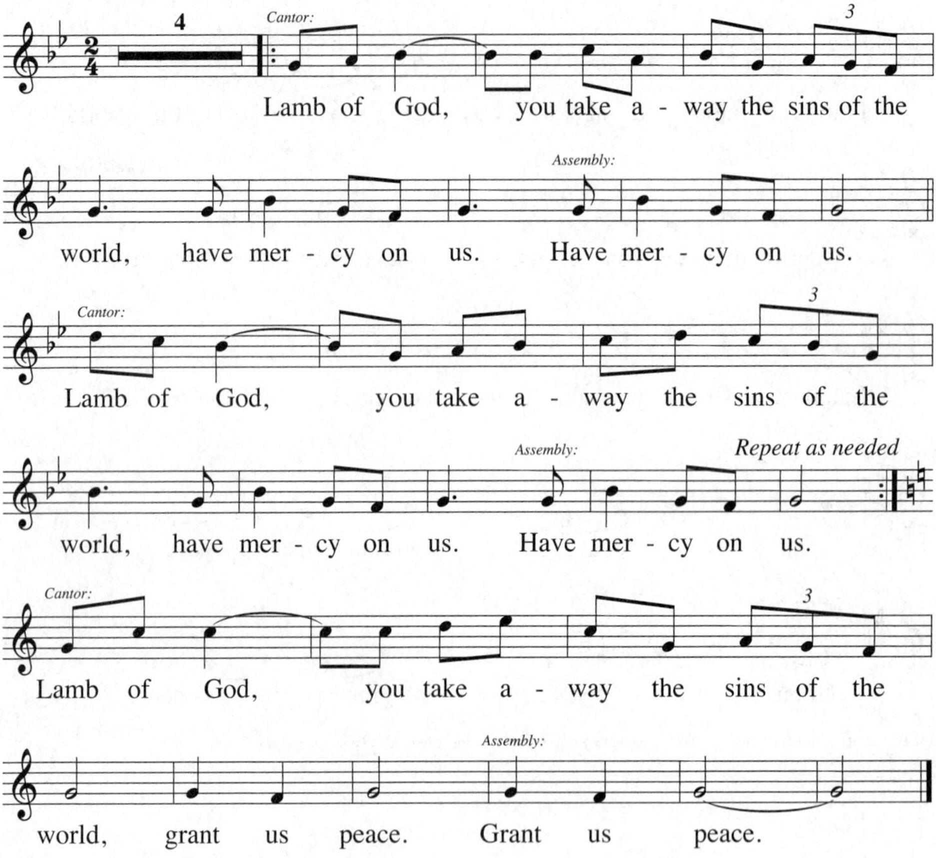

4
Cantor:
Lamb of God, you take a - way the sins of the
world, have mer - cy on us.
Assembly:
Have mer - cy on us.
Cantor:
Lamb of God, you take a - way the sins of the
world, have mer - cy on us.
Assembly:
Have mer - cy on us.
Repeat as needed
Cantor:
Lamb of God, you take a - way the sins of the
world, grant us peace.
Assembly:
Grant us peace.

Music: Howard Hughes, SM, © 1981, GIA Publications, Inc.

487 LAMB OF GOD

Cantor or choir:
Lamb of God, you take away the sins of the world,
All:
have mer-cy on us.
Last time
Cantor or choir:
Lamb of God, you take away the sins of the world,
All:
grant us peace.

Music: Orthodox chant; arr. by Michael Silhavy, © 2006, World Library Publications

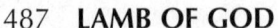

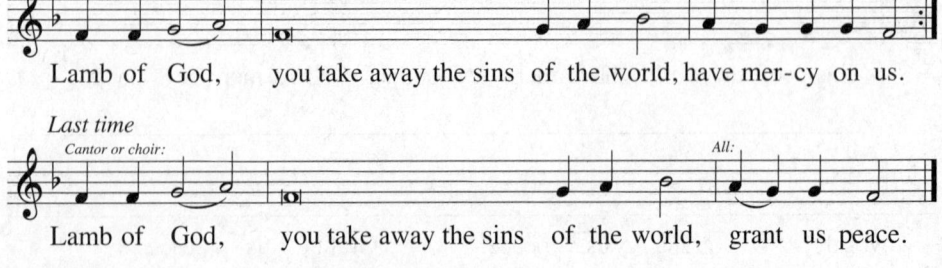

LAMB OF GOD   488

A - gnus De - i, qui tol - lis pec-cá - ta mun-di:

mi - se - ré - re no - bis.

A - gnus De - i, qui tol - lis pec-cá - ta mun-di:

do - na no - bis pa - cem,

do - na no - bis pa - cem.

Music: *No Greater Love Mass,* Michael Joncas, © 1988, 2015, GIA Publications, Inc.

LAMB OF GOD   489

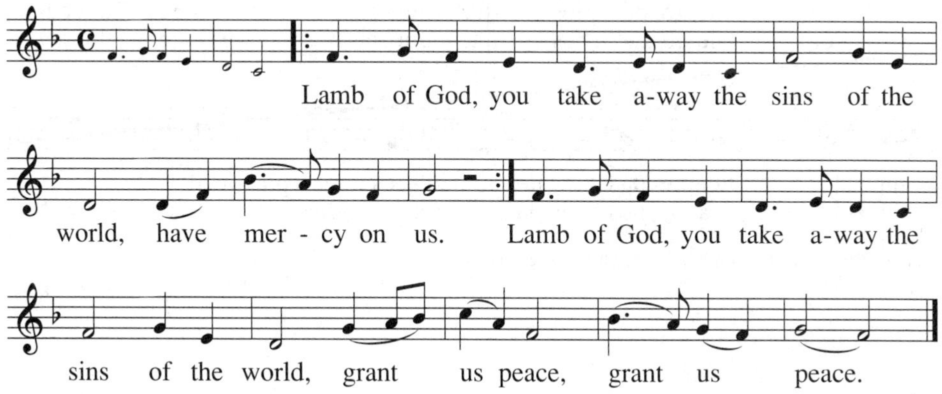

Lamb of God, you take a-way the sins of the

world, have mer - cy on us. Lamb of God, you take a-way the

sins of the world, grant us peace, grant us peace.

Music: Richard Proulx, © 1975, GIA Publications, Inc.

490 CORDERO DE DIOS

Cantor: 1., 2. Cor - de - ro de Dios, *All/Todos:* Cor - de - ro de Dios, *Cantor:* que
3. Cor - de - ro de Dios, Cor - de - ro de Dios, que

qui - tas el pe - ca - do del mun - do, ten pie - dad de no -
qui - tas el pe - ca - do del mun - do, da - nos la

All/Todos: so - tros. Ten pie - dad de no - so - tros.
paz. Da - nos la paz.

Music: *Misa Mariachi*; acc. by Paul A. Tate, © 2012, GIA Publications, Inc.

491 CORDERO DE DIOS

1., 2. Cor - de - ro de Dios, que qui - tas el pe - ca - do del
3. Cor - de - ro de Dios, que qui - tas el pe - ca - do del

mun - do, ten pie - dad de no - so - tros, ten pie - dad.
mun - do, da - nos la paz, dá - nos - la.

Music: *Misa Popular*; acc. by Paul A. Tate, © 2012, GIA Publications, Inc.

O Come, O Come, Emmanuel 492

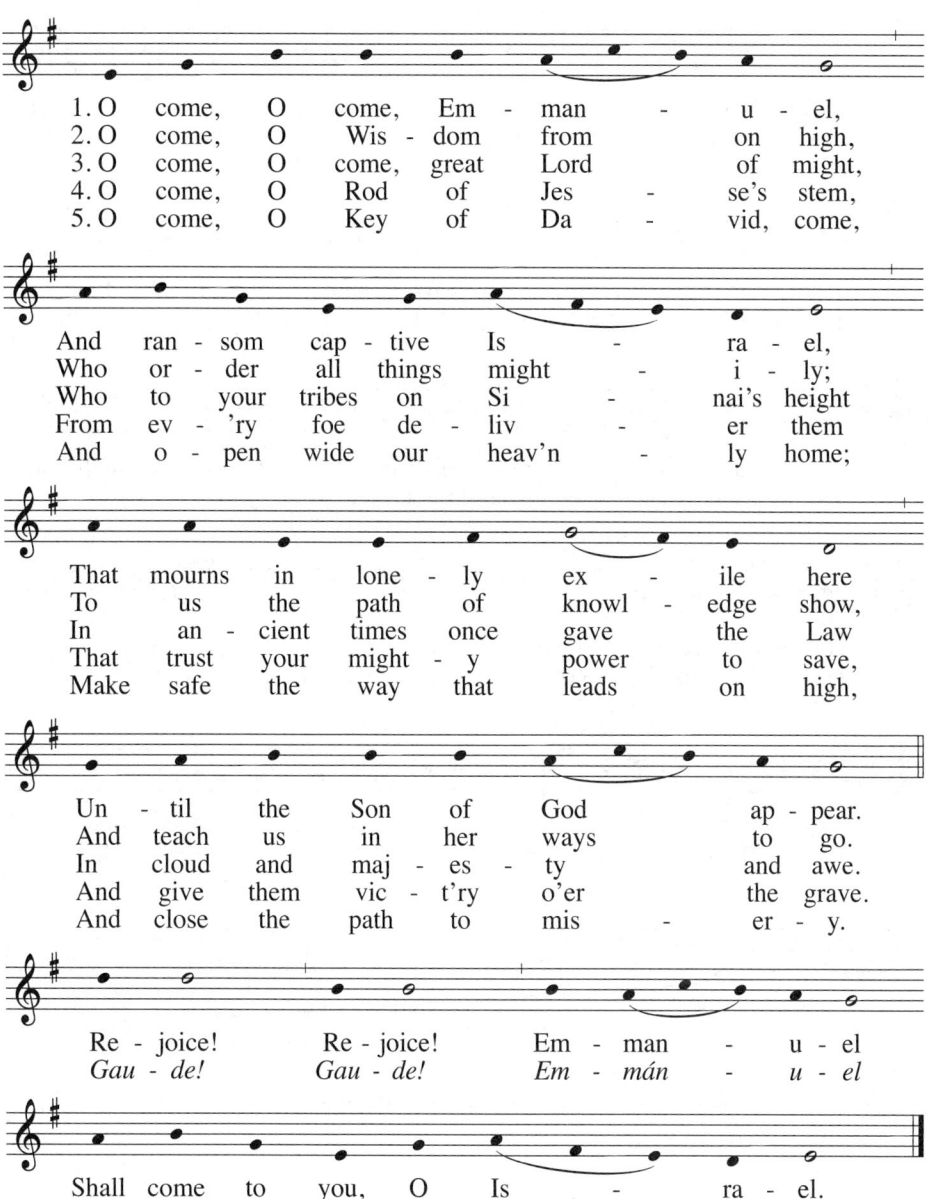

1. O come, O come, Em - man - u - el,
2. O come, O Wis - dom from on high,
3. O come, O come, great Lord of might,
4. O come, O Rod of Jes - se's stem,
5. O come, O Key of Da - vid, come,

And ran - som cap - tive Is - ra - el,
Who or - der all things might - i - ly;
Who to your tribes on Si - nai's height
From ev - 'ry foe de - liv - er them
And o - pen wide our heav'n - ly home;

That mourns in lone - ly ex - ile here
To us the path of knowl - edge show,
In an - cient times once gave the Law
That trust your might - y power to save,
Make safe the way that leads on high,

Un - til the Son of God ap - pear.
And teach us in her ways to go.
In cloud and maj - es - ty and awe.
And give them vic - t'ry o'er the grave.
And close the path to mis - er - y.

Re - joice! Re - joice! Em - man - u - el
Gau - de! Gau - de! Em - mán - u - el

Shall come to you, O Is - ra - el.
Na - scé - tur pro te Ís - ra - el.

6. O come, O Dayspring from on high,
And cheer us by your drawing nigh;
Disperse the gloomy clouds of night,
And death's dark shadow put to flight.

7. O come, Desire of nations, bind
In one the hearts of humankind;
O bid our sad divisions cease,
And be for us our King of Peace.

Text: *Veni, veni Emmanuel*; Latin 9th C.; tr. by John M. Neale, 1818–1866, alt.
Tune: VENI EMMANUEL, LM with refrain; Mode I, 15th C. French; adapt. by Thomas Helmore, 1811–1890; acc. by Richard Proulx, 1937–2010,
© 1975, GIA Publications, Inc.

493 Come, O Long-Expected Jesus

1. Come, O long-ex-pect-ed Je-sus, Born to set your
2. Born your peo-ple to de-liv-er, Born a child, and

peo-ple free; From our fears and sins re-lease us:
yet a king; Born to reign in us for-ev-er,

Christ, in you our rest shall be. Is-rael's strength and
Now your grac-ious king-dom bring. By your own e-

con-so-la-tion, Hope to all the earth im-part;
ter-nal Spir-it Rule in all our hearts a-lone;

Dear de-sire of ev-'ry na-tion,
By your all-suf-fi-cient mer-it

En-ter ev-'ry long-ing heart.
Raise us to your glo-rious throne.

Text: Haggai 2:7; Charles Wesley, 1707–1788, alt.
Tune: JEFFERSON, 8 7 8 7 D; William Walker's *Southern Harmony*, 1855; acc. by Theophane Hytrek, OSF, 1915–1992, © 1981, ICEL

Alternate tune: STUTTGART, 4 stanzas

Prepare! Prepare! 494

Ostinato Refrain

Pre-pare! Pre-pare the way of the Lord.

Pre-pare! Pre-pare the way of the Lord, oh,

Pre-pare! Pre-pare the way of the Lord. The Lord our God is

To repeat   *To verses*   *Last time*

com - ing soon. Oh, com - ing soon.

Verses   *Cantor:*

1. Pre - pare the way,   the
2. Make straight the path,
3. Jus - tice and peace,
4. Sing and re - joice!   The
5. A vir - gin will bear a son,   Em -

way of the Lord.   Read - y your hearts.
lev - el the hills,   lift up the gates.
kind - ness and truth shall come to the earth.
Lord is near,   I say re - joice!
man - u - el: God with us!

D.C.

Oh, the Lord our God is com-ing soon!

Text: Stephen Pishner
Tune: Stephen Pishner
© 2007, GIA Publications, Inc.

495 Creator of the Stars of Night

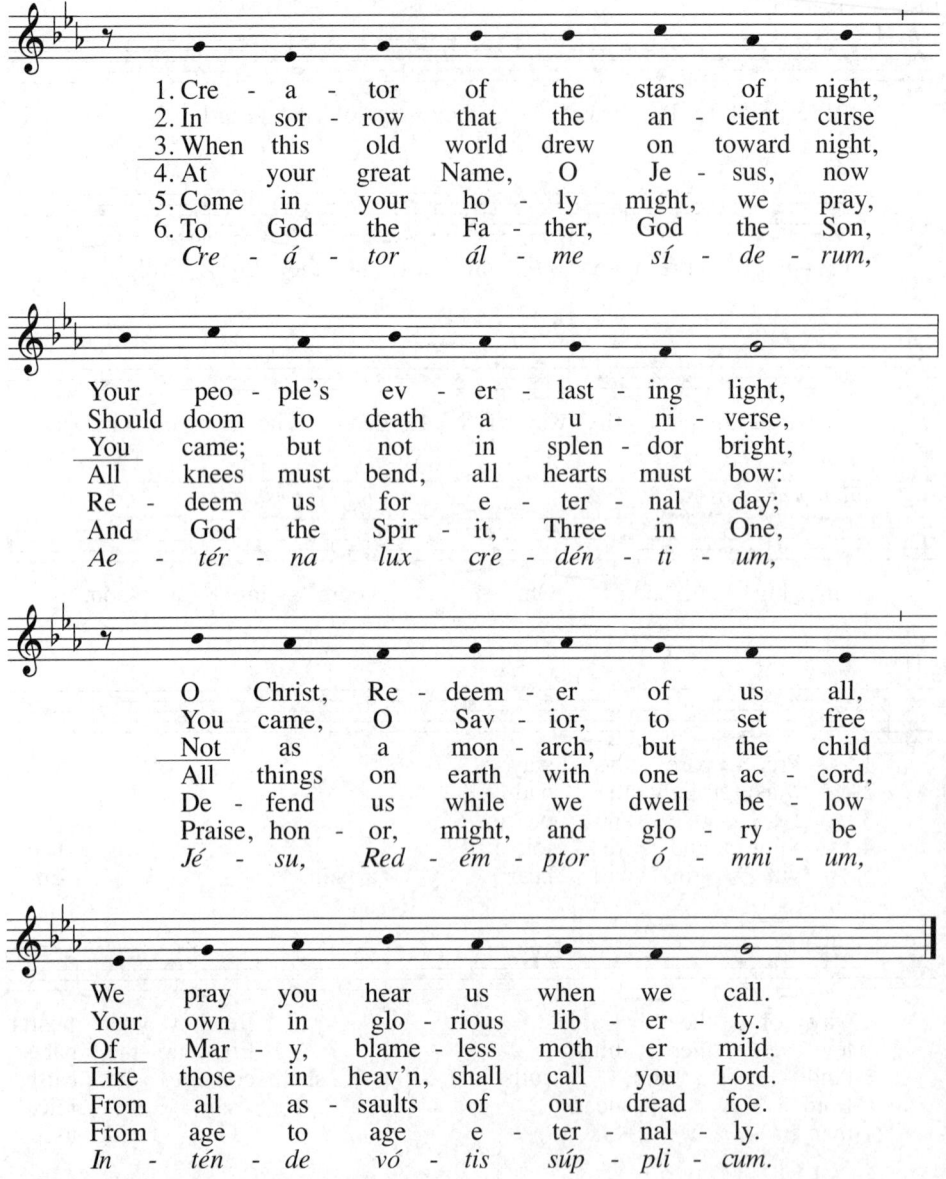

1. Cre - a - tor of the stars of night,
2. In sor - row that the an - cient curse
3. When this old world drew on toward night,
4. At your great Name, O Je - sus, now
5. Come in your ho - ly might, we pray,
6. To God the Fa - ther, God the Son,
   Cre - á - tor ál - me sí - de - rum,

Your peo - ple's ev - er - last - ing light,
Should doom to death a u - ni - verse,
You came; but not in splen - dor bright,
All knees must bend, all hearts must bow:
Re - deem us for e - ter - nal day;
And God the Spir - it, Three in One,
Ae - tér - na lux cre - dén - ti - um,

O Christ, Re - deem - er of us all,
You came, O Sav - ior, to set free
Not as a mon - arch, but the child
All things on earth with one ac - cord,
De - fend us while we dwell be - low
Praise, hon - or, might, and glo - ry be
Jé - su, Red - ém - ptor ó - mni - um,

We pray you hear us when we call.
Your own in glo - rious lib - er - ty.
Of Mar - y, blame - less moth - er mild.
Like those in heav'n, shall call you Lord.
From all as - saults of our dread foe.
From age to age e - ter - nal - ly.
In - tén - de vó - tis súp - pli - cum.

Text: *Creator alme siderum*, Latin 9th. C., revised 1632; tr. *The Hymnal 1982*, alt., © 1985, The Church Pension Fund
Tune: CONDITOR ALME SIDERUM, LM; Mode IV, Sarum, 9th C.; acc. by Gerard Farrell, OSB, 1919–2000, © 1986, GIA Publications, Inc.

When the King Shall Come Again   496

1. When the King shall come a-gain, All his pow'r re-
2. In the des-ert trees take root Fresh from his cre-
3. Strength-en fee-ble hands and knees, Faint-ing hearts, be
4. There God's high-way shall be seen Where no roar-ing

veal-ing, Splen-dor shall an-nounce his reign,
a-tion; Plants and flow'rs and sweet-est fruit
cheer-ful! God, who comes for such as these,
li-on, Noth-ing e-vil or un-clean,

Life and joy and heal-ing: Earth no
Join the cel-e-bra-tion; Riv-ers
Seeks and saves the fear-ful. Deaf ears
Walks the road to Zi-on. Ran-somed

long-er in de-cay, Hope no more frus-trat-ed;
spring up from the earth, Bar-ren lands a-dorn-ing;
hear the si-lent tongues Sing a-way their weep-ing;
peo-ple home-ward bound, All your prais-es voic-ing,

This is God's re-demp-tion day
Val-leys, this is your new birth,
Blind eyes see the life-less ones
See your Lord with glo-ry crowned,

Long-ing-ly a-wait-ed.
Moun-tains, greet the morn-ing!
Walk-ing, run-ning, leap-ing.
Share in his re-joic-ing!

Text: Isaiah 35; Christopher M. Idle, b.1938, alt., © 1982, The Jubilee Group (admin. by Hope Publishing Company)
Tune: GAUDEAMUS PARITER, 7 6 7 6 D; Johann Horn, c. 1495–1547

497   Comfort, Comfort, O My People

1. Com - fort, com - fort, O my peo - ple,
2. Hark, the voice of one who's cry - ing
3. O make straight what long was crook - ed,

Speak of peace, now says our God.
In the des - ert far and near,
Make the rough - er plac - es plain.

Com - fort those who sit in dark - ness,
Bid - ding all to full re - pent - ance
Let your hearts be true and hum - ble,

Mourn - ing un - der sor - rows' load.
Since the king - dom now is here.
As be - fits his ho - ly reign.

Speak un - to Je - ru - sa - lem
Oh, that warn - ing cry o - bey!
For the glo - ry of the Lord

Of the peace that waits for them.
Now pre - pare for God a way!
Now o'er earth is shed a - broad.

Tell of all the sins I cov - er,
Let the val - leys rise to meet him
And all flesh shall see the to - ken

And   that   war - fare   now   is   o - ver.
And   the   hills   bow   down to   greet   him.
That   his   word   is   nev - er   bro - ken.

Text: Isaiah 40:1–8; *Tröstet, tröstet, meine Lieben;* Johann Olearius, 1611–1684; tr. by Catherine Winkworth, 1827–1878, alt.
Tune: GENEVA 42, 8 7 8 7 77 88; *Genevan Psalter,* 1551; harm. adapt. from Claude Goudimel, 1505–1572

Savior of the Nations, Come   498

1. Sav - ior   of   the   na - tions, come;   Vir - gin's Son, make
2. Not   by   hu - man   flesh and blood, But   the   Spir - it
3. Won - drous birth! O   won - drous child   Of   the   Vir - gin
4. From God's heart the   Sav - ior speeds,   Back to   God   his
5. Bright - ly does Christ's man - ger shine, Glo - rious is   its

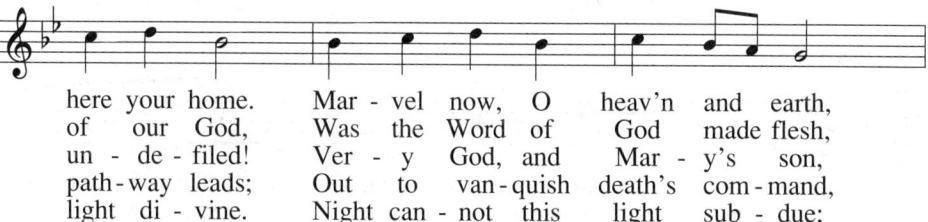

here your home.   Mar - vel   now, O   heav'n and earth,
of   our God,   Was   the   Word of   God   made flesh,
un - de - filed! Ver - y   God, and   Mar - y's son,
path - way leads; Out   to van - quish death's com - mand,
light di - vine.   Night can - not this   light   sub - due;

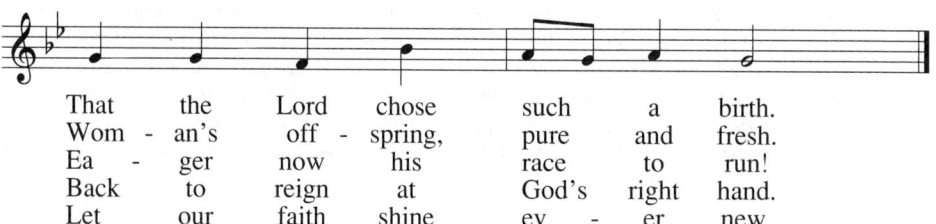

That   the   Lord   chose   such   a   birth.
Wom - an's off - spring, pure and fresh.
Ea - ger   now   his   race   to   run!
Back to   reign   at   God's right hand.
Let   our   faith shine   ev - er new.

Text: *Veni Redemptor gentium;* ascr. to St. Ambrose of Milan, 340–397; German tr. by Martin Luther, 1483–1546; English tr. sts. 1–3, 5 by
William M. Reynolds, 1812–1876, alt.; st. 4 by Martin L. Seltz, 1909–1967, alt., © 2006, Augsburg Fortress
Tune: NUN KOMM DER HEIDEN HEILAND, 77 77; *Geistliche Gesangbüchlein,* Wittenberg, 1524

499 My Soul in Stillness Waits / En el Silencio Te Aguardo

Refrain / Estribillo

For you, O Lord, my soul in still-ness waits;
En el si - len - cio te a-guar-do a ti, Se - ñor.

To verses | Last time

tru - ly my hope is in you. | you.
Tú e - res mi luz y mi a - mor. | *mor.*

Verses / Estrofas

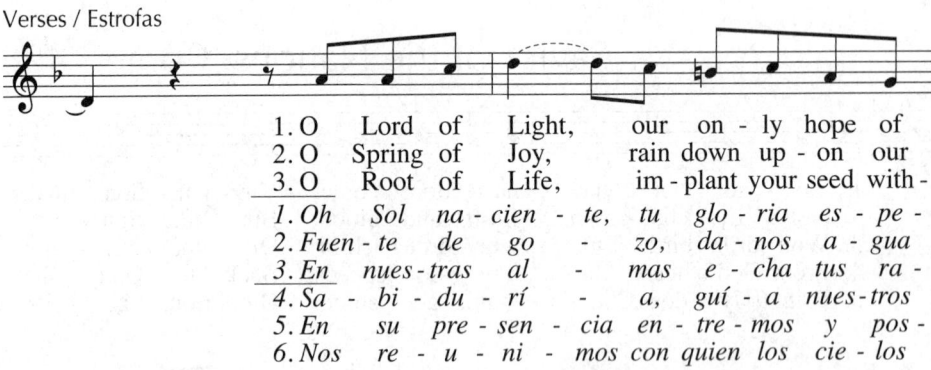

1. O Lord of Light, our on - ly hope of
2. O Spring of Joy, rain down up - on our
3. O Root of Life, im - plant your seed with -
1. *Oh Sol na - cien - te, tu glo - ria es - pe -*
2. *Fuen - te de go - zo, da - nos a - gua*
3. *En nues - tras al - mas e - cha tus ra -*
4. *Sa - bi - du - rí - a, guí - a nues - tros*
5. *En su pre - sen - cia en - tre - mos y pos -*
6. *Nos re - u - ni - mos con quien los cie - los*

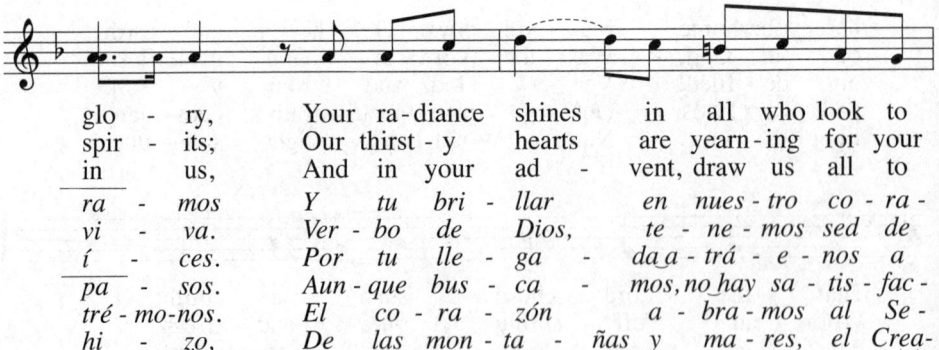

glo - ry, Your ra - diance shines in all who look to
spir - its; Our thirst - y hearts are yearn-ing for your
in us, And in your ad - vent, draw us all to
ra - mos Y tu bri - llar en nues - tro co - ra -
vi - va. Ver - bo de Dios, te - ne - mos sed de
í - ces. Por tu lle - ga - da a - trá - e - nos a
pa - sos. Aun - que bus - ca - mos, no hay sa - tis - fac -
tré - mo - nos. El co - ra - zón a - bra - mos al Se -
hi - zo, De las mon - ta - ñas y ma - res, el Crea-

you;   Come, light the hearts   of all in dark and
Word;   Come, make us whole,   be com - fort to our
you,   Our hope re - born   in dy - ing and in
zón.   Ven, con tu luz,   a los que_es-tán en
ti.   Ven y res - táu - ra - nos, sé nues - tro con -
ti.   Y por tu pas -   cua da - nos la_es - pe -
ción.   Dios de la paz,   en - sé - ña - nos tus
ñor.   So - mos el pue -   blo que Dios es - co -
dor.   Es - tás a - quí,   Se - ñor de las es -

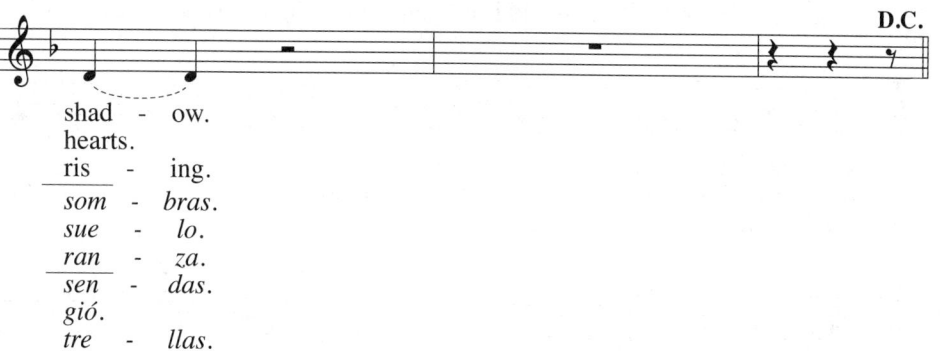

shad - ow.
hearts.
ris - ing.
som - bras.
sue - lo.
ran - za.
sen - das.
gió.
tre - llas.

Verses 4–6

4. O Key of Knowledge, guide us in our pilgrimage;
   we ever seek, yet unfulfilled remain;
   open to us the pathway of your peace.

5. Come, let us bow before the God who made us;
   let ev'ry heart be opened to the Lord,
   for we are all the people of his hand.

6. Here we shall meet the Maker of the heavens,
   Creator of the mountains and the seas,
   Lord of the stars, and present to us now.

Text: Psalm 95 and "O" Antiphons; Marty Haugen, b.1950; tr. by Ronald F. Krisman, b.1946
Tune: Marty Haugen, b.1950
© 1982, tr. © 2005, GIA Publications, Inc.

500 O Come, Divine Messiah!

1. O come, Di-vine Mes-si - ah! The world in si - lence
2. O come, De-sired of na - tions, Whom priest and proph - et
3. O come in peace and meek - ness, For low - ly will your

waits the day When hope shall sing its tri - umph, And
long fore-told. Come break the cap - tive fet - ters, Re -
cra - dle be: Though clothed in hu - man weak - ness We

sad - ness flee a - way.
deem the long - lost fold. Dear Sav-ior, haste! Come, come to
shall your God-head see.

earth. Dis-pel the night and show your face, And bid us

hail the dawn of grace. O come, Di - vine Mes -

si - ah! The world in si - lence waits the day When

hope shall sing its tri - umph, And sad - ness flee a - way.

Text: *Venez, divin Messie;* Abbé Simon-Joseph Pellegrin, 1663–1745; tr. by Mary of St. Philip, SND, 1825–1904, alt.
Tune: VENEZ, DIVIN MESSIE, 7 8 7 6 with refrain; French carol, 16th C.

People, Look East 501

1. Peo - ple, look East. The time is near
2. Fur - rows, be glad. Though earth is bare,
3. Birds, though you long have ceased to build,
4. Stars, keep the watch. When night is dim,
5. An - gels an - nounce with shouts of mirth

Of the crown - ing of the year.
One more seed is plant - ed there.
Guard the nest that must be filled.
One more light the bowl shall brim,
Him who brings new life to earth.

Make your house fair as you are a - ble,
Give up your strength the seed to nour - ish,
E - ven the hour when wings are fro - zen
Shin - ing be - yond the frost - y weath - er,
Set ev - 'ry peak and val - ley hum - ming

Trim the hearth and set the ta - ble.
That in course the flow'r may flour - ish.
God for fledg - ing - time has cho - sen.
Bright as sun and moon to - geth - er.
With the word, the Lord is com - ing.

Peo - ple, look East and sing to - day—

Love, the Guest, is on the way.
Love, the Rose, is on the way.
Love, the Bird, is on the way.
Love, the Star, is on the way.
Love, the Lord, is on the way.

Text: Eleanor Farjeon, 1881–1965, © David Higham Assoc. Ltd.
Tune: BESANÇON, 87 98 87; French carol; harm. by Martin Shaw, 1875–1958, © 1928, Oxford University Press

502   Wait for the Lord

Ostinato Refrain

	Wait	for	the Lord,	whose day	is	near.
Spanish:	Con -	tem - pla - ré		tu vi -	da en	mí.
Polish:	Pan	blis - ko jest,		o - cze -	kuj	Go.
Italian:	Cri -	sto Ge - sù		io spe -	ro in	Te.
Vietnamese:	Hãy	biết đợi Chúa		Đây ngày	gần	rồi

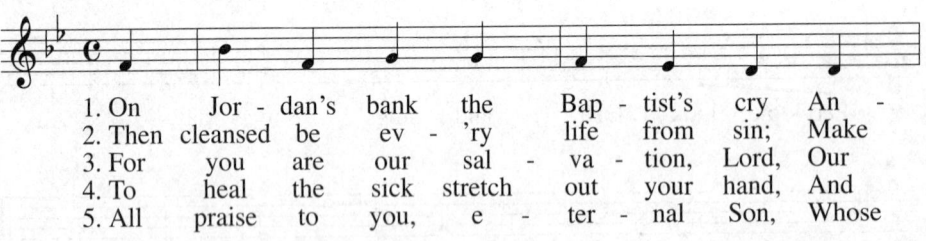

Wait	for	the Lord:	be strong,	take	heart!
Con -	tem - pla - ré,		Se - ñor,	tu a -	mor.
Pan	blis - ko jest,		w Nim ser -	ca	moc!
Sei	tu Si - gnor		la pa -	ce del	cuor.
Chờ	mong Thiên Chúa:		tâm trí	kiên	cường.

Text: Isaiah 40, Philippians 4, Matthew 6–7; Taizé Community, 1984
Tune: Jacques Berthier, 1923–1994
© 1984, Les Presses de Taizé, GIA Publications, Inc., agent

503   On Jordan's Bank

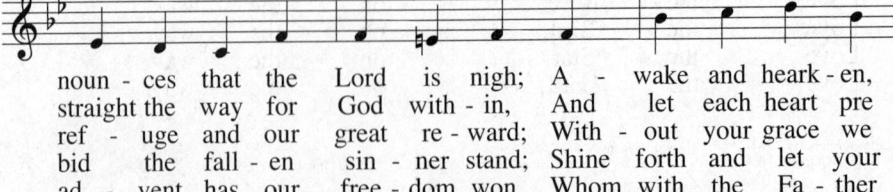

1. On	Jor - dan's	bank	the	Bap - tist's	cry	An -
2. Then	cleansed be	ev -	'ry	life	from	sin;	Make
3. For	you	are	our	sal - va -	tion,	Lord,	Our
4. To	heal	the	sick	stretch	out	your	hand, And
5. All	praise	to	you,	e - ter -	nal	Son,	Whose

noun - ces	that	the	Lord	is	nigh;	A - wake and	heark - en,
straight the	way	for	God	with - in,	And	let each heart	pre -
ref - uge	and	our	great	re - ward;	With -	out your grace	we
bid	the	fall - en	sin -	ner stand;	Shine	forth and let	your
ad - vent	has	our	free -	dom won,	Whom	with the	Fa - ther

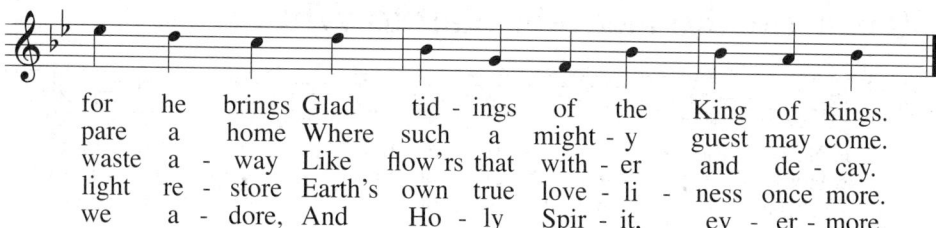

for   he   brings Glad   tid - ings   of   the   King   of   kings.
pare   a   home Where   such   a   might - y   guest may come.
waste   a - way   Like   flow'rs that with - er   and   de - cay.
light   re - store Earth's own   true   love - li -   ness once more.
we   a - dore,   And   Ho - ly   Spir - it,   ev - er - more.

Text: *Jordanis oras praevia*; Charles Coffin, 1676–1749; tr. by John Chandler, 1806–1876, alt.
Tune: WINCHESTER NEW, LM; adapt. from *Musikalisches Handbuch*, Hamburg, 1690

Alternate tune: PUER NOBIS

The King Shall Come When Morning Dawns   504

1. The   King   shall   come   when   morn - ing   dawns   And
2. Not,   as   of   old,   a   lit - tle   child,   To
3. The   King   shall   come   when   morn - ing   dawns   And
4. And   let   the   end - less   bliss   be - gin,   By
5. The   King   shall   come   when   morn - ing   dawns   And

light   tri - um - phant   breaks,   When beau - ty   gilds   the
suf - fer   and   to   die,   But   crowned with   glo - ry
earth's dark   night   is   past;   O   haste   the   ris - ing
wea - ry   saints fore - told,   When right   shall   tri - umph
light   and   beau - ty   brings.   Hail,   Christ,   the   Lord! Your

east - ern   hills   And   life   to   joy   a - wakes.
like   the   sun   That   lights   the   morn - ing   sky.
of   that   morn   Whose   day   shall   ev - er   last.
o - ver   wrong,   And   truth   shall   be   ex - tolled.
peo - ple   pray: Come   quick - ly,   King   of   kings.

Text: John Brownlie, 1857–1925, alt.
Tune: MORNING SONG, CM; Wyeth's *Repository of Sacred Music*, 1813; arr. by Robert J. Batastini, b.1942, © 1994, GIA Publications, Inc.

505 Now the Heavens Start to Whisper

1. Now the heav - ens start to whis - per As the veil is
2. Heav - y clouds that block the moon-light Now be - gin to
3. Christ, e - ter - nal sun of jus - tice, Christ, the rose of

grow - ing thin. Earth from slum - ber wakes to lis - ten
drift a - way. Dia - mond bril - liance through the dark - ness
wis - dom's seed, Come to bless with fire and fra - grance

To the stir - ring, faint with - in: Seed of prom - ise,
Shines the hope of com - ing day. Christ, the morn - ing
Hours of yearn - ing, hurt, and need. In the lone - ly,

deep - ly plant - ed, Child to spring from Jes - se's stem!
star of splen-dor, Gleams with - in a world grown dim.
in the stran-ger, In the out - cast hid from view:

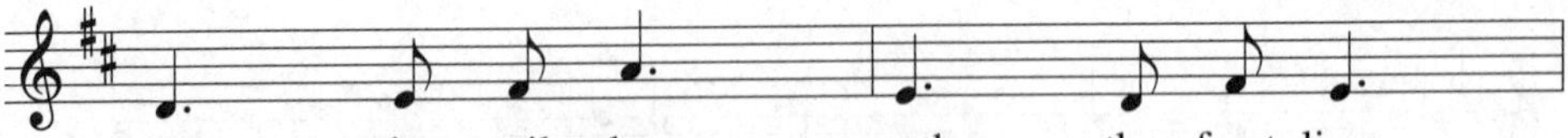

Like the soil be - neath the frost - line,
Heav - en's em - ber fans to full - ness;
Child who comes to grace the man - ger,

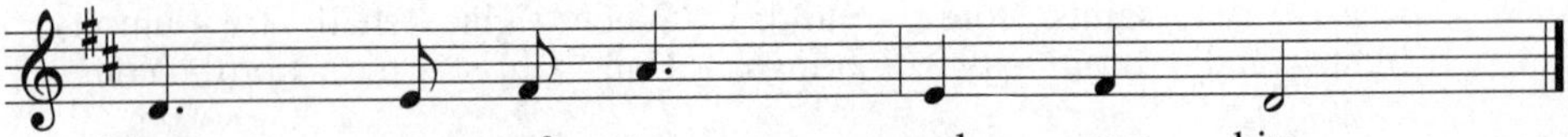

Hearts grow soft to wel - come him.
Hearts grow warm to wel - come him.
Teach our hearts to wel - come you.

Text: Mary Louise Bringle, b.1953, © 2006, GIA Publications, Inc.
Tune: SUO GAN, 8 7 8 7 D; Welsh melody; arr. by Nicholas Palmer, b.1963, © 2008, GIA Publications, Inc.

506 Like a Bird

1. Like a bird that spreads her wings to gath - er in her
2. From the ends of earth you call your sons and daugh-ters
3. For the na - tions you pre - pare and spread a splen - did

young,   So you o-pen wide your   arms   to
home,   Say-ing, "Gath-er now from far   and
feast,   Gath-er ev-'ry tribe and   race,   the

gath   -   er in your own.   For our free re-sponse you
near,   my peo-ple, come."   For our sim-ple trust you
great -   est to the least.   For one fam-'ly, how   you

wait,   Ear - ly morn-ing, noon,   and   late.
yearn   Till,   at   last in love, we   turn.
long;   'Round your ta - ble, vast the   throng.

Come and   wake us, come and   wake us, come and wake us to your

wel-come.   Ma-ra-na - tha,   come.

Text: Delores Dufner, OSB, b.1939
Tune: WAKE US, 13 13 77 with refrain; Michael Joncas, b.1951
© 2011, GIA Publications, Inc.

Prepare the Way of the Lord   507

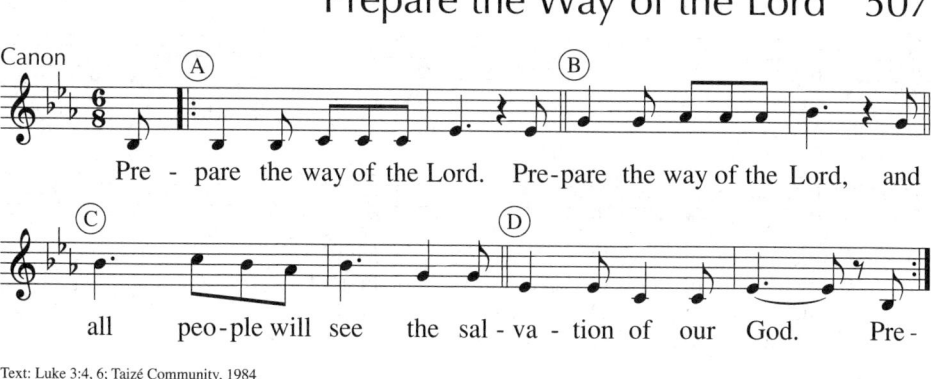

Canon   (A)   (B)

Pre - pare the way of the Lord.   Pre-pare the way of the Lord,   and

(C)   (D)

all   peo-ple will see   the sal - va - tion of   our God.   Pre-

Text: Luke 3:4, 6; Taizé Community, 1984
Tune: Jacques Berthier, 1923–1994
© 1984, Les Presses de Taizé, GIA Publications, Inc., agent

508 Jesus, Hope of the World

Refrain

Je-sus, hope of the world, Je-sus, light in our

dark - ness, here we a - wait you, O Mas-ter Di - vine.

Here we re-ceive you in Bread and in Wine:

Je - sus, hope of the world.

Verses

All:

Come, Lord Je - sus!

Cantor(s):

1. Come to us, O Son of God!
2. Come to us, O Prom - ised King!
3. Come to us, O Ris - ing Sun!
4. Come to us, O Heart's De - sire!

Come, Lord Je - sus!

Come to us, O Son of Man!
Come to us, O Prom - ised Peace!
Come to us, O End - less Light!
Come to us, O Sav - ing Love!

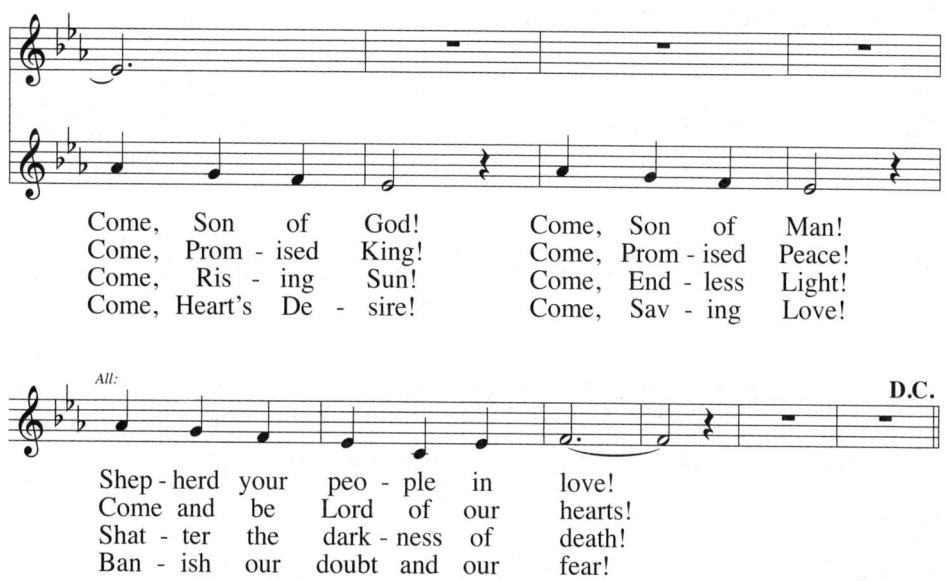

Come, Son of God!   Come, Son of Man!
Come, Prom - ised King!   Come, Prom - ised Peace!
Come, Ris - ing Sun!   Come, End - less Light!
Come, Heart's De - sire!   Come, Sav - ing Love!

All: **D.C.**

Shep - herd your peo - ple in love!
Come and be Lord of our hearts!
Shat - ter the dark - ness of death!
Ban - ish our doubt and our fear!

Text: Deanna Light, b.1967, and Paul A. Tate, b.1968
Tune: Deanna Light, b.1967, and Paul A. Tate, b.1968
© 2001, World Library Publications

Come, Emmanuel   509

Verse Response

Come, O come, Em - man - u - el.

Refrain

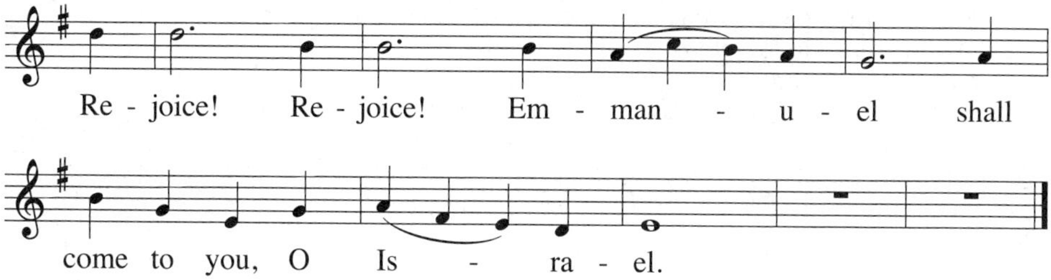

Re - joice! Re - joice! Em - man - u - el shall

come to you, O Is - ra - el.

Text: Gabe Huck, b.1941
Tune: VENI EMMANUEL, adapt. and arr. by Tony E. Alonso, b.1980
© 2005, GIA Publications, Inc.

510 Come, Lord Jesus

Refrain

Ma - ra - na - tha! Come, Lord Je - sus. Ma - ra - na - tha!

God with us. Ma - ra - na - tha! Come, Lord Je - sus.

Come, Em - man - u - el, come, Em - man - u - el.

Verses

Cantor:

1. You are light with - in our dark - ness:
2. Son of God, show us your mer - cy:
3. Send your Spir - it to those wait - ing:
4. Give your hope to all the na - tions:
5. As we gath - er at your ta - ble:

All: *Cantor:*

Ma - ra - na - tha! God with us.

You are light through -
Son of Mar - y,
Send your peace to
Give your joy to
Bless the ones who

All:

out your king - dom:
hold us close - ly:
all here, gath - ered: Come, Em - man - u - el,
all who love you:
call up - on you:

D.C.

come, Em - man - u - el.

Text: Chris de Silva, b.1967
Tune: Chris de Silva, b.1967
© 2012, GIA Publications, Inc.

Lift Up Your Heads 511

1. Lift up your heads, e - ter - nal gates, Al - le - lu -
2. But not in arms or bat - tle dress, Al - le - lu -
3. God brings a new face to the brave, Al - le - lu -
4. God's match - less and ma - jes - tic strength, Al - le - lu -

ia! See how the King of glo - ry waits,
ia! God comes, a child a - midst dis - tress,
ia! God re - de - fines who best can save:
ia! In all its height, depth, breadth, and length,

Al - le - lu - ia! The Lord of Hosts is draw - ing
Al - le - lu - ia! No might - y ar - mies shield the
Al - le - lu - ia! Not those whose pow'r re - lies on
Al - le - lu - ia! Now is re - vealed, its pow'r to

near, The Sav - ior of the world is here.
way, On - ly coarse lin - en, wool, and hay.
threat, Ter - ror or tor - ture, de - struc - tion or debt.
prove, By Christ pro - test - ing "God is love!"

Al-le-lu - ia! Al-le-lu - ia! Al - le - lu - ia!

Text: George Weissel, 1590–1635; tr. by Catherine Winkworth, 1827–1878; adapt. by John L. Bell, b.1949, © 2001, Iona Community,
GIA Publications, Inc., agent
Tune: CH THREE, 8 8 8 8 with alleluias; John L. Bell, b.1949, © 2001, Iona Community, GIA Publications, Inc., agent

512 Wake, O Wake, and Sleep No Longer

1. Wake, O wake, and sleep no long - er, For he who calls you is no stran - ger: A - wake, God's own Je - ru - sa - lem! Hear, the mid - night bells are chim - ing The sig - nal for his roy - al com - ing: Let voice to voice an - nounce his name! We feel his foot - steps near, The Bride - groom at the

2. Zi - on hears the sound of sing - ing; Our hearts are thrilled with sud - den long - ing: She stirs, and wakes, and stands pre - pared. Christ, her friend, and lord, and lov - er, Her star and sun and strong re - deem - er— At last his might - y voice is heard. The Son of God has come To make with us his

3. Glo - ry, glo - ry, sing the an - gels, While mu - sic sounds from strings and cym - bals; All hu - man - kind, with songs a - rise! Twelve the gates in - to the cit - y, Each one a pearl of shin - ing beau - ty; The streets of gold ring out with praise. All crea - tures round the throne A - dore the ho - ly

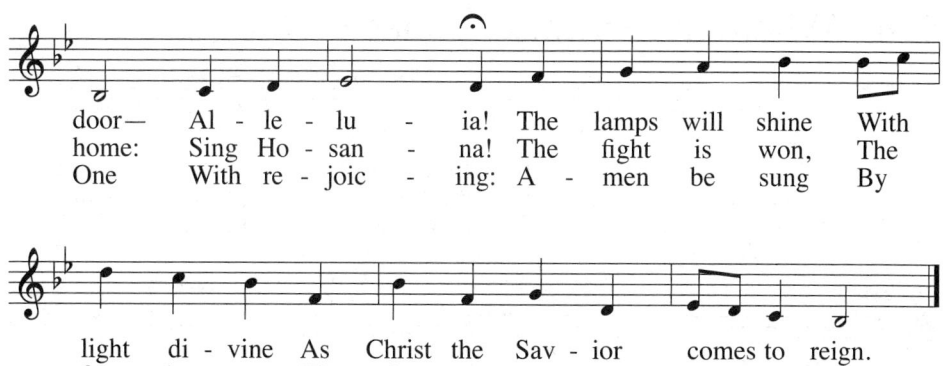

door—	Al - le - lu - ia!	The	lamps	will	shine	With
home:	Sing Ho - san - na!	The	fight	is	won,	The
One	With re - joic - ing:	A - men	be	sung	By

light	di - vine	As	Christ the Sav - ior	comes to	reign.
feast	be - gun;	We	fix our eyes on	Christ a - lone.
ev -	'ry tongue	To	crown their wel - come	to the King.

Text: Matthew 25:1–13; *Wachet auf, ruft uns die Stimme*, Philipp Nicolai, 1556–1608; tr. and adapt. by Christopher M. Idle, b.1938, © 1982,
    The Jubilate Group (admin. by Hope Publishing Company)
Tune: WACHET AUF, 89 8 89 8 66 4 44 8; Philipp Nicolai, 1556–1608; harm. by J. S. Bach, 1685–1750

Drop Down Dew / Rorate Caeli 513

Antiphon

Drop down dew, heav-ens from a - bove, let skies rain down the Just One.
Ro - rá - te cae - li de su-per, et nu - bes plu - ant ju - stum.

Verses

1. Do not be angry with us, Lord; do not remember our iniquities.
   Behold, your holy city has become a wasteland.
   Zion has become a desert, Jerusalem has become desolate,
   your holy house and your glory where our ancestors praised you.

2. We have all sinned and have become like those unclean.
   We have fallen, like a leaf that is decayed.
   Our sins have swept us away like the wind.
   You have hidden your face from us; you have consumed us because of our sins.

3. Lord, see the affliction of your people; send the One who is to come.
   Send forth the Lamb who rules all earthly kingdoms,
   who rules from the desert to the height of Mount Zion.
   Let him take off the yoke that keeps us captive.

4. Be consoled and comforted, my people! Your salvation will quickly come.
   Why are you filled with sorrow, with grief that overwhelms you?
   Do not be afraid, I will save you.
   I am the Lord God, your Savior, the Holy One of Israel.

Text: *Rorate caeli*; Latin hymn; tr. composite sources
Music: Antiphon, Mode I chant; verses, Gregory J. Polan, OSB, © 2010, Conception Abbey, admin. by GIA Publications, Inc.

514 Where the Promise Shines

1. When a star is shin - ing o - ver east - ern
2. Where the world is wait - ing for an un - known
3. Lead us on, O Day - star, in the qui - et

hills, When the air is si - lent,
day, Where a voice for - got - ten
night; Guide us through the shad - ow

and the clam - or stills, When the night is
cries, "Pre - pare the way!" Where an earth - ly
with your gen - tle light; Show us in a

wait - ing, and the old hopes rise,
pow - er makes the heart turn cold,
man - ger our re - demp - tion's sign;

Then the time has rip - ened and the heart grows
There the gifts are of - fered— in - cense, myrrh, and
Bring us to a morn - ing where the prom - ise

wise. Lead us on, lead us on,
gold.
shines.

to a morn - ing where the prom - ise shines.

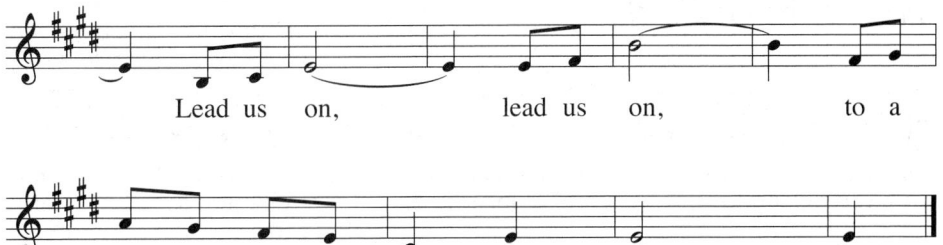

Lead us on, lead us on, to a

morn - ing where the prom - ise shines.

Text: Sylvia G. Dunstan, 1955–1993, © 1995, GIA Publications, Inc.
Tune: Bob Moore, b.1962, © 2003, GIA Publications, Inc.

Lo, How a Rose E'er Blooming 515

1. Lo, how a Rose e'er bloom-ing From ten - der stem hath
2. I - sa - iah 'twas for - told it, The Rose I have in
3. O Flow'r, whose fra - grance ten - der With sweet-ness fills the

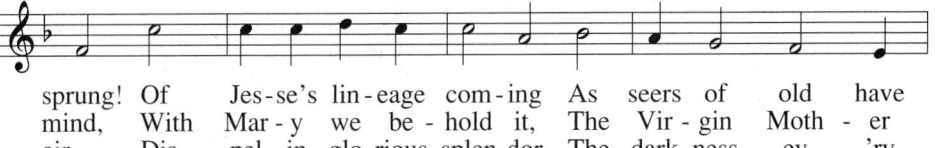

sprung! Of Jes-se's lin-eage com-ing As seers of old have
mind, With Mar-y we be - hold it, The Vir - gin Moth - er
air, Dis - pel in glo-rious splen-dor The dark-ness ev - 'ry -

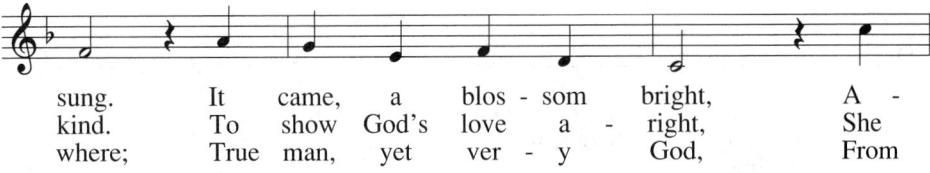

sung. It came, a blos - som bright, A -
kind. To show God's love a - right, She
where; True man, yet ver - y God, From

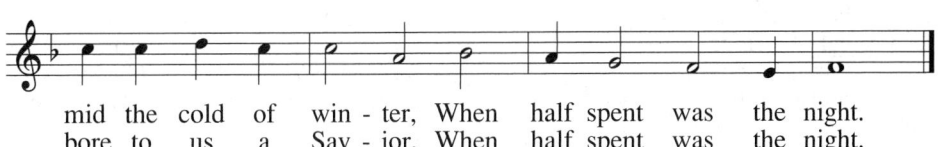

mid the cold of win - ter, When half spent was the night.
bore to us a Sav - ior, When half spent was the night.
sin and death now save us, And share our ev - 'ry load.

Text: Isaiah 11:1; *Es ist ein' Ros' entsprungen; Speyer Gesangbuch*, 1599; tr. sts. 1, 2 by Theodore Baker, 1851–1934; st. 3, *The Hymnal, 1940*
Tune: ES IST EIN' ROS' ENSTSPRUNGEN, 7 6 7 6 6 7 6; *Geistliche Kirchengesänge*, Cologne, 1599; harm. by Michael Praetorius, 1571–1621

516 Gift of God

Refrain

Christmas: Gift of God, O Em-man-u-el. Gift of God, O Em-
Advent: Come to us, O Em-man-u-el. Come to us, O Em-

Last time **Christmas Verses**
Cantor:

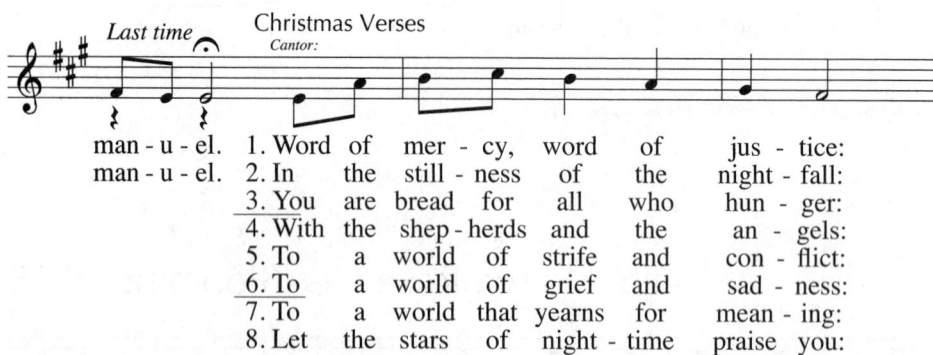

man-u-el.
man-u-el.
1. Word of mer-cy, word of jus-tice:
2. In the still-ness of the night-fall:
3. You are bread for all who hun-ger:
4. With the shep-herds and the an-gels:
5. To a world of strife and con-flict:
6. To a world of grief and sad-ness:
7. To a world that yearns for mean-ing:
8. Let the stars of night-time praise you:

All: *Cantor:*

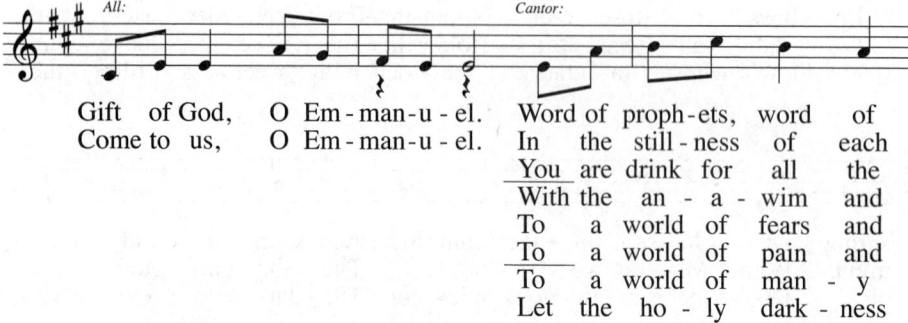

Gift of God, O Em-man-u-el. Word of proph-ets, word of
Come to us, O Em-man-u-el. In the still-ness of each
You are drink for all the
With the an-a-wim and
To a world of fears and
To a world of pain and
To a world of man-y
Let the ho-ly dark-ness

All: *Cantor:*

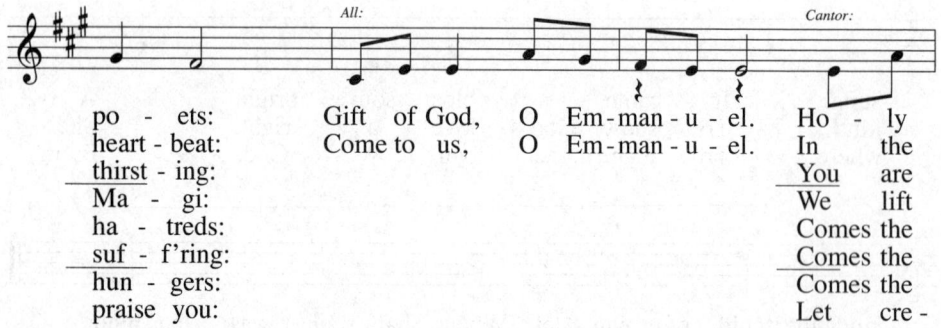

po-ets: Gift of God, O Em-man-u-el. Ho-ly
heart-beat: Come to us, O Em-man-u-el. In the
thirst-ing: You are
Ma-gi: We lift
ha-treds: Comes the
suf-f'ring: Comes the
hun-gers: Comes the
praise you: Let cre-

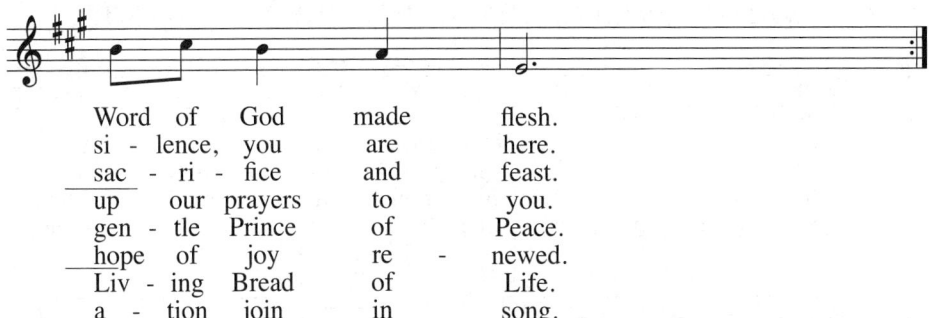

Word	of	God	made	flesh.
si - lence,	you		are	here.
sac - ri - fice		and		feast.
up	our	prayers	to	you.
gen - tle	Prince		of	Peace.
hope	of	joy	re -	newed.
Liv - ing	Bread		of	Life.
a - tion	join		in	song.

Advent Verses

1. Come, O Wisdom, breathe within us:
   Come, O mighty, tender Teacher:
   Come, and show us how to live.

2. Come, O Lord, of ancient Israel:
   You who lead us through the desert:
   Come, and set your people free.

3. Come, O Root of Jesse's lineage:
   Come, O ruler of all nations:
   Come, and be our Savior sure.

4. Come, O Holy Key of David:
   Come, and open hearts to knowledge:
   Come, and break the chains of death.

5. Come, O Radiant Sun of Justice:
   Come, and shine on those in darkness:
   All who dwell in shades of death.

6. Come, O Light of all the nations:
   Come, bright Morning Star of new hope:
   Come, and shine among us here.

7. Come, O Living Flame of Freedom:
   Living hope of our redemption:
   Come, and lead us to new life.

Text: Advent verses based on "O" Antiphons; Marty Haugen, b.1950
Tune: Marty Haugen, b.1950

517 Awake! Awake, and Greet the New Morn

1. A - wake! A - wake, and greet the new morn, For
2. To us, to all in sor - row and fear, Em -
3. In dark - est night his com - ing shall be, When
4. Re - joice, re - joice, take heart in the night, Though

an - gels her - ald its dawn - ing. Sing out your joy, for
man - u - el comes a - sing - ing; His hum - ble song is
all the world is de - spair - ing, As morn - ing light so
dark the win - ter and cheer - less, The ris - ing sun shall

soon* he is born, Be - hold the Child of our long - ing!
qui - et and near, Yet fills the earth with its ring - ing.
qui - et and free, So warm and gen - tle and car - ing.
crown you with light; Be strong and lov - ing and fear - less.

Come as a ba - by weak and poor, To bring all hearts to -
Mu - sic to heal the bro - ken soul And hymns of lov - ing -
Then shall the mute break forth in song, The lame shall leap in
Love be our song and love our prayer And love our end - less

geth - er, He o - pens wide the heav'n - ly door And
kind - ness, The thun - der of his an - thems roll To
won - der, The weak be raised a - bove the strong, And
sto - ry. May God fill ev - 'ry day we share And

lives now in - side us for ev - er.
shat - ter all ha - tred and blind - ness.
weap - ons be bro - ken a - sun - der.
bring us at last in - to glo - ry.

*During the Christmas season: "now"

Text: Marty Haugen, b.1950
Tune: REJOICE, REJOICE, 9 8 9 8 8 7 8 9; Marty Haugen, b.1950
© 1983, GIA Publications, Inc.

Joy to the World 518

1. Joy to the world, the Lord is come! Let earth re-ceive her king; Let ev-'ry heart pre-pare him room And heav'n and na-ture sing, And heav'n and na-ture sing, And heav'n, and heav'n and na-ture sing.

2. Joy to the earth, the Sav-ior reigns! Let us our songs em-ploy; While fields and floods, rocks, hills and plains Re-peat the sound-ing joy, Re-peat the sound-ing joy, Re-peat, re-peat the sound-ing joy.

3. No more let sin and sor-row grow, Nor thorns in-fest the ground; He comes to make his bless-ings flow Far as the curse is found, Far as the curse is found, Far as, far as the curse is found.

4. He rules the world with truth and grace, And makes the na-tions prove The glo-ries of his right-eous-ness, And won-ders of his love, And won-ders of his love, And won-ders, won-ders of his love.

Text: Psalm 98; Isaac Watts, 1674–1748
Tune: ANTIOCH, CM; arr. from George F. Handel, 1685–1759, in T. Hawkes' *Collection of Tunes*, 1833

519 A Child Is Born in Bethlehem / Puer Natus in Bethlehem

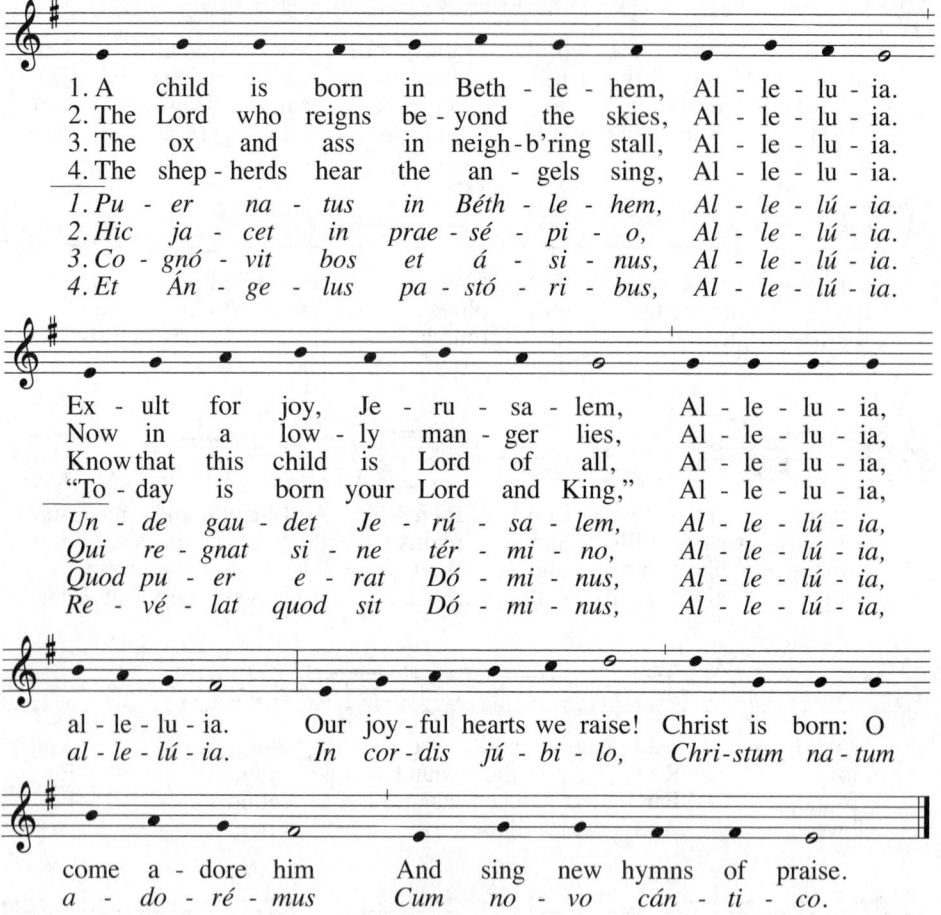

1. A child is born in Beth - le - hem, Al - le - lu - ia.
2. The Lord who reigns be - yond the skies, Al - le - lu - ia.
3. The ox and ass in neigh - b'ring stall, Al - le - lu - ia.
4. The shep - herds hear the an - gels sing, Al - le - lu - ia.

1. *Pu - er na - tus in Béth - le - hem, Al - le - lú - ia.*
2. *Hic ja - cet in prae - sé - pi - o, Al - le - lú - ia.*
3. *Co - gnó - vit bos et á - si - nus, Al - le - lú - ia.*
4. *Et Án - ge - lus pa - stó - ri - bus, Al - le - lú - ia.*

Ex - ult for joy, Je - ru - sa - lem, Al - le - lu - ia,
Now in a low - ly man - ger lies, Al - le - lu - ia,
Know that this child is Lord of all, Al - le - lu - ia,
"To - day is born your Lord and King," Al - le - lu - ia,

Un - de gau - det Je - rú - sa - lem, Al - le - lú - ia,
Qui re - gnat si - ne tér - mi - no, Al - le - lú - ia,
Quod pu - er e - rat Dó - mi - nus, Al - le - lú - ia,
Re - vé - lat quod sit Dó - mi - nus, Al - le - lú - ia,

al - le - lu - ia. Our joy - ful hearts we raise! Christ is born: O
al - le - lú - ia. In cor - dis jú - bi - lo, Chri - stum na - tum

come a - dore him And sing new hymns of praise.
a - do - ré - mus Cum no - vo cán - ti - co.

5. Of virgin-mother born this night, Alleluia.
   He is our God, the Light from Light, Alleluia, alleluia.

6. Our human race he enters in, Alleluia.
   But bears no single taint of sin, Alleluia, alleluia.

7. That we, from sin's allure set free, Alleluia.
   Like him, and so like God, may be, Alleluia, alleluia.

5. *De Matre natus Vírgine, Allelúia.*
   Qui lumen est de lúmine, Allelúia, allelúia.

6. *In carne nobis símilis, Allelúia.*
   Peccáto sed dissímilis, Allelúia, allelúia.

7. *Ut rédderet nos hómines, Allelúia.*
   Deo et sibi símiles, Allelúia, allelúia.

Text: *Puer natus in Bethlehem;* Latin 14th C.; tr. by Ronald F. Krisman, b.1946, © 2011, GIA Publications, Inc.
Tune: PUER NATUS, 88 with alleluias and refrain; Mode I; acc. by Richard Proulx, 1937–2010, © 1986, GIA Publications, Inc.

Hark! The Herald Angels Sing 520

1. Hark! The her - ald an - gels sing, "Glo - ry to the
2. Christ, by high - est heav'n a - dored; Christ, the ev - er -
3. Hail the heav'n - born Prince of Peace! Hail the Sun of

new - born King! Peace on earth and mer - cy mild,
last - ing Lord! Late in time be - hold him come,
Right-eous-ness! Light and life to all he brings,

God and sin - ners rec - on - ciled!" Joy - ful, all you
Off - spring of the Vir - gin's womb. Veiled in flesh the
Ris'n with heal - ing in his wings. Mild he lays his

na - tions, rise; Join the tri - umph of the skies;
God-head see; Hail the in - car - nate De - i - ty,
glo - ry by, Born that we no more may die,

With the an-gel - ic host pro-claim, "Christ is born in Beth-le - hem!"
Pleased as man with us to dwell, Je - sus, our Em-man - u - el.
Born to raise us from the earth, Born to give us sec-ond birth.

Hark! The her-ald an-gels sing, "Glo-ry to the new-born King!"

Text: Charles Wesley, 1707–1788, alt.
Tune: MENDELSSOHN, 77 77 D with refrain; Felix Mendelssohn, 1809–1847

521 O Come, All Ye Faithful / Venid, Fieles Todos / Adeste Fideles

Stanzas 1, 2

1. O come, all ye faith-ful, joy-ful and tri-um-phant, O
2. God of God, Light of Light,
1. Ve - nid, fie - les to - dos, a Be - lén mar-che - mos De
2. El que_es Hi - jo_e - ter - no del e - ter - no Pa - dre, Y
1. Ad - é - ste fi - dé - les, laé - ti, tri - um-phán - tes, Ve-
2. De - um de De - o, Lu - men de Lú - mi-ne

come ye, O come ye to Beth - le - hem;
Lo! He comes forth from the Vir - gin's womb.
go - zo triun - fan - tes, y lle - nos de_a - mor; Y_al
Dios ver - da - de - ro que_al mun - do cre - ó, Al
ní - te, ve - ní - te in Béth - le - hem.
Ge - stant pu - él - lae ví - sce - ra.

Come and be - hold him, born the King of an - gels;
Our ver - y God, be - got - ten not cre - a - ted,
Rey de los cie - los con - tem - plar po - dre - mos;
se - no vir - gí - neo vi - no de_u - na ma - dre;
Na - tum vi - dé - te, Re - gem an - ge - ló - rum.
De - um ve - rum, gé - ni - tum, non fa - ctum.

𝄋 Refrain

O come, let us a - dore him, O come, let us a - dore
Ve - nid, a - do - re - mos, ve - nid, a - do - re -
Ve - ní - te a - do - ré - mus, ve - ní - te a - do - ré -

him, O come, let us a - dore him, Christ, the Lord!
mos, ve - nid, a - do - re - mos a Cris - to_el Se - ñor.
mus, ve - ní - te a - do - ré - mus Dó - mi - num.

Stanzas 3, 4

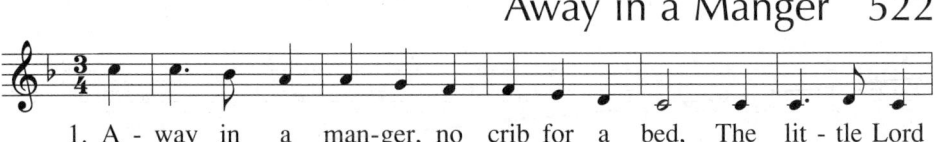

3. Sing, choirs of an - gels, sing in ex - ul - ta - tion,
4. Yea, Lord, we greet thee, born this hap - py morn - ing,
3. *Can - tad ju - bi - lo - sas, cé - li - cas cria - tu - ras: Re -*
4. *Je - sús, ce - le - bra - mos tu ben - di - to nom - bre Con*
3. Can - tet nunc i - o, cho - rus an - ge - ló - rum,
4. Er - go qui na - tus Di - e ho - di - ér - na,

Sing, all ye cit - i - zens of heav'n a - bove!
Je - sus, to thee be all glo - ry giv'n;
suen - en los cie - los con vues - tra can - ción; ¡Al
him - nos so - lem - nes de gra - to lo - or; Por
Can - tet nunc au - la cae - lé - sti - um.
Je - su ti - bi sit gló - ri - a.

D.S.

Glo - ry to God, all glo - ry in the high - est;
Word of the Fa - ther, now in flesh ap - pear - ing;
Dios bon - da - do - so, glo - ria en las al - tu - ras;
si - glos e - ter - nos to - do ser te a - do - re;
Gló - ri - a, gló - ria in ex - cél - sis De - o.
Pa - tris ae - ter - nae ver - bum ca - ro fa - ctum.

Text: *Adeste fideles;* John F. Wade, c.1711–1786; English tr. by Frederick Oakeley, 1802–1880, alt.; Spanish tr. by Juan Bautista Cabrera, 1837–1916
Tune: ADESTE FIDELES, Irregular with refrain; John F. Wade, c.1711–1786

Away in a Manger 522

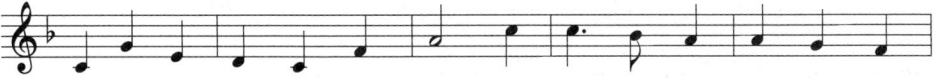

1. A - way in a man-ger, no crib for a bed, The lit - tle Lord
2. The cat - tle are low-ing; the ba - by a - wakes, But lit - tle Lord
3. Be near me, Lord Je - sus; I ask you to stay Close by me for -

Je - sus laid down his sweet head. The stars in the bright sky looked
Je - sus, no cry - ing he makes. I love you, Lord Je - sus! Look
ev - er, and love me, I pray. Bless all the dear chil - dren in

down where he lay, The lit - tle Lord Je - sus, a - sleep on the hay.
down from the sky And stay by my cra - dle till morn - ing is nigh.
your ten - der care, And fit us for heav - en, to live with you there.

Text: St. 1, 2, anonymous, st. 3, John T. McFarland, 1851–1913
Tune: MUELLER, 11 11 11 11; James R. Murray, 1841–1905; harm. by Robert J. Batastini, b.1942, © 1994, GIA Publications, Inc.

523 O Little Town of Bethlehem

1. O lit - tle town of Beth - le - hem, How
2. For Christ is born of Mar - y And,
3. How si - lent - ly, how si - lent - ly The
4. O ho - ly Child of Beth - le - hem, De -

still we see thee lie! A - bove thy deep and
gath - ered all a - bove While mor - tals sleep, the
won - drous gift is giv'n! So God im - parts to
scend to us, we pray; Cast out our sin and

dream - less sleep The si - lent stars go by;
an - gels keep Their watch of won - d'ring love.
hu - man hearts The bless - ings of his heav'n.
en - ter in, Be born in us to - day.

Yet in the dark streets shin - eth The
O morn - ing stars, to - geth - er Pro -
No ear may hear his com - ing, But
We hear the Christ - mas an - gels The

ev - er - last - ing Light. The hopes and fears of
claim the ho - ly birth, And prais - es sing to
in this world of sin, Where meek souls will re -
great glad tid - ings tell; O come to us, a -

all the years Are met in thee to - night.
God the King, And peace to all on earth!
ceive him, still The dear Christ en - ters in.
bide with us, Our Lord Em - man - u - el!

Text: Phillips Brooks, 1835–1893
Tune: ST. LOUIS, 8 6 8 6 7 6 8 6; Lewis H. Redner, 1831–1908

Angels We Have Heard on High 524

1. An - gels we have heard on high Sweet - ly sing - ing
2. Shep - herds, why this ju - bi - lee? Why your joy - ous
3. Come to Beth - le - hem and see Him whose birth the
4. See him in a man - ger laid Whom the choirs of

o'er the plains, And the moun - tains in re - ply
strains pro - long? Say what may the tid - ings be
an - gels sing; Come, a - dore on bend - ed knee
an - gels praise; Mar - y, Jo - seph, lend your aid,

Ech - o back their joy - ous strains.
Which in - spire your heav'n - ly song.
Christ the Lord, the new - born King.
While our hearts in love we raise.

Gló - - - ri - a
in ex - cél - sis De - o. Gló - -
- - ri - a in ex - cél - sis De - o.

Text: *Les anges dans nos campagnes;* French carol, c. 18th C.; tr. from *Crown of Jesus Music,* London, 1862
Tune: GLORIA, 7 7 7 7 with refrain; French carol

525 God Rest You Merry, Gentlemen

1. God rest you mer - ry, gen - tle - men, Let noth - ing you dis -
2. In Beth - le - hem in Ju - dah This bless - ed babe was
3. From God our heav'n - ly Fa - ther A bless - ed an - gel
4. The shep - herds at those tid - ings Re - joic - ed much in
5. Now to the Lord sing prais - es, All you with - in this

may; Re - mem - ber Christ our Sav - ior Was
born, And laid with - in a man - ger Up -
came, And un - to cer - tain shep - herds Brought
mind, And left their flocks a - feed - ing In
place, And with true love and char - i - ty Each

born on Christ - mas day To save us all from
on this bless - ed morn, For which his moth - er
tid - ings of the same, How that in Beth - le -
tem - pest, storm, and wind, And went to Beth - le -
oth - er now em - brace; This ho - ly tide of

Sa - tan's pow'r When we were gone a - stray.
Mar - y Did noth - ing take in scorn.
hem was born The Son of God by name.
hem straight - way, This bless - ed babe to find.
Christ - mas All oth - ers shall re - place.

O tid - ings of com - fort and joy, com-fort and

joy; O tid - ings of com - fort and joy!

Text: English carol, 18th C.
Tune: GOD REST YOU MERRY, 8 6 8 6 8 6 with refrain; English carol, 18th C.; harm. by John Stainer, 1840–1901

Good Christian Friends, Rejoice   526

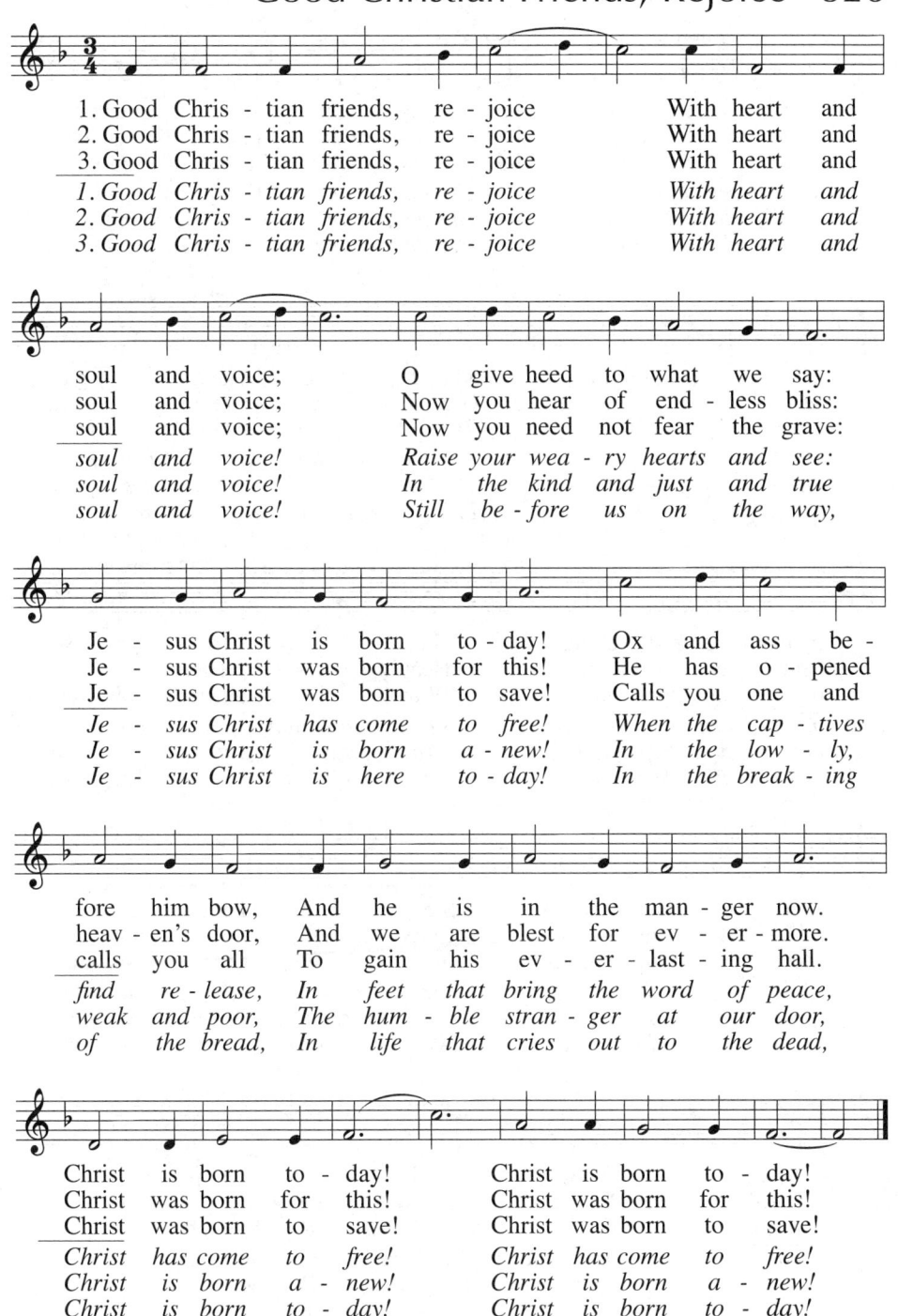

1. Good Chris - tian friends, re - joice   With heart and
2. Good Chris - tian friends, re - joice   With heart and
3. Good Chris - tian friends, re - joice   With heart and
1. Good Chris - tian friends, re - joice   With heart and
2. Good Chris - tian friends, re - joice   With heart and
3. Good Chris - tian friends, re - joice   With heart and

soul and voice;   O   give heed to what we   say:
soul and voice;   Now you hear of end - less bliss:
soul and voice;   Now you need not fear the grave:
soul and voice!   Raise your wea - ry hearts and see:
soul and voice!   In   the kind and just and true
soul and voice!   Still be - fore us on the way,

Je - sus Christ is born to - day!   Ox and ass be -
Je - sus Christ was born for this!   He has o - pened
Je - sus Christ was born to save!   Calls you one and
Je - sus Christ has come to free!   When the cap - tives
Je - sus Christ is born a - new!   In the low - ly,
Je - sus Christ is here to - day!   In the break - ing

fore him bow,   And he is in the man - ger now.
heav - en's door, And we are blest for ev - er - more.
calls you all To gain his ev - er - last - ing hall.
find re - lease, In feet that bring the word of peace,
weak and poor, The hum - ble stran - ger at our door,
of the bread, In life that cries out to the dead,

Christ is born to - day!   Christ is born to - day!
Christ was born for this!   Christ was born for this!
Christ was born to save!   Christ was born to save!
Christ has come to free!   Christ has come to free!
Christ is born a - new!   Christ is born a - new!
Christ is born to - day!   Christ is born to - day!

Text: *In dulci jubilo;* Latin and German, 14th C.; tr. by John M. Neale, 1818–1866; alt. verses, Marty Haugen, b.1950, © 1992, GIA Publications, Inc.
Tune: IN DULCI JUBILO, 66 77 78 55; 14th C. German melody; harm. by Robert L. Pearsall, 1795–1856

527 Silent Night / Noche de Paz

1. Si - lent night, ho - ly night! All is calm,
2. Si - lent night, ho - ly night! Shep - herds quake
3. Si - lent night, ho - ly night! Son of God,

1. ¡No-che de paz, no - che de a - mor! To - do duer - me_en
2. ¡No-che de paz, no - che de a - mor! O - ye_hu -mil - de_el
3. ¡No-che de paz, no - che de a - mor! Mi - ra qué gran

all is bright Round yon vir - gin
at the sight; Glo - ries stream from
love's pure light Ra - diant beams from

de - rre - dor, En - tre los as - tros que_es -
fiel pas - tor Co - ros ce - les - tes que_a -
res - plan - dor Lu - ce_en el ros - tro del

moth - er and child. Ho - ly In - fant so
heav - en a - far; Heav'n - ly hosts sing
thy ho - ly face, With the dawn of re -

par - cen su luz, Be - lla,_a-nun - cian - do_al ni -
nun - cian sa - lud, Gra - cias y glo - rias en
ni - ño Je - sús, En el pe - se - bre, del

ten - der and mild, Sleep in heav - en - ly
al - le - lu - ia! Christ, the Sav - ior, is
deem - ing grace, Je - sus, Lord, at thy

ñi - to Je - sús, Bri - lla la_es - tre - lla de
gran ple - ni - tud, Por nues - tro buen Re - den -
mun - do la luz, As - tro de_e - ter - no ful -

peace, Sleep in heav - en - ly peace.
born! Christ, the Sav - ior, is born!
birth, Je - sus, Lord, at thy birth.

paz, Bri - lla la_es - tre - lla de paz.
tor, Por nues - tro buen Re - den - tor.
gor, As - tro de_e - ter - no ful - gor.

Text: *Stille Nacht, heilige Nacht;* Joseph Mohr, 1792–1848; English tr. by John F. Young, 1820–1885; Spanish tr. by Federico Fliedner, 1845–1901
Tune: STILLE NACHT, 66 89 66; Franz X. Gruber, 1787–1863

Night of Silence 528

1. Cold are the peo - ple, win - ter of life, We
2. Voice in the dis - tance, call in the night, On
3. Spir - it a - mong us, shine like the star, Your

trem - ble in shad - ows this cold end - less night.
wind you en - fold us, you speak of the light.
light that guides shep - herds and kings from a - far.

Fro - zen in the snow lie ros - es sleep - ing,
Gen - tle on the ear you whis - per, soft - ly,
Shim - mer in the sky so emp - ty, lone - ly,

Flow - ers that will ech - o the sun - rise.
Ru - mors of a dawn so em - brac - ing.
Ris - ing in the warmth of the Son's love.

Fire of hope is our on - ly warmth;
Breath-less love a - waits dark - ened souls.
Star un - know - ing of night and day,

Wea - ry, its flame will be dy - ing soon.
Soon will we know of the morn - ing.
Spir - it, we wait for the lov - ing Son.

Text: Daniel Kantor, b.1960
Tune: Daniel Kantor, b.1960
© 1984, GIA Publications, Inc.

529 Of the Father's Love Begotten

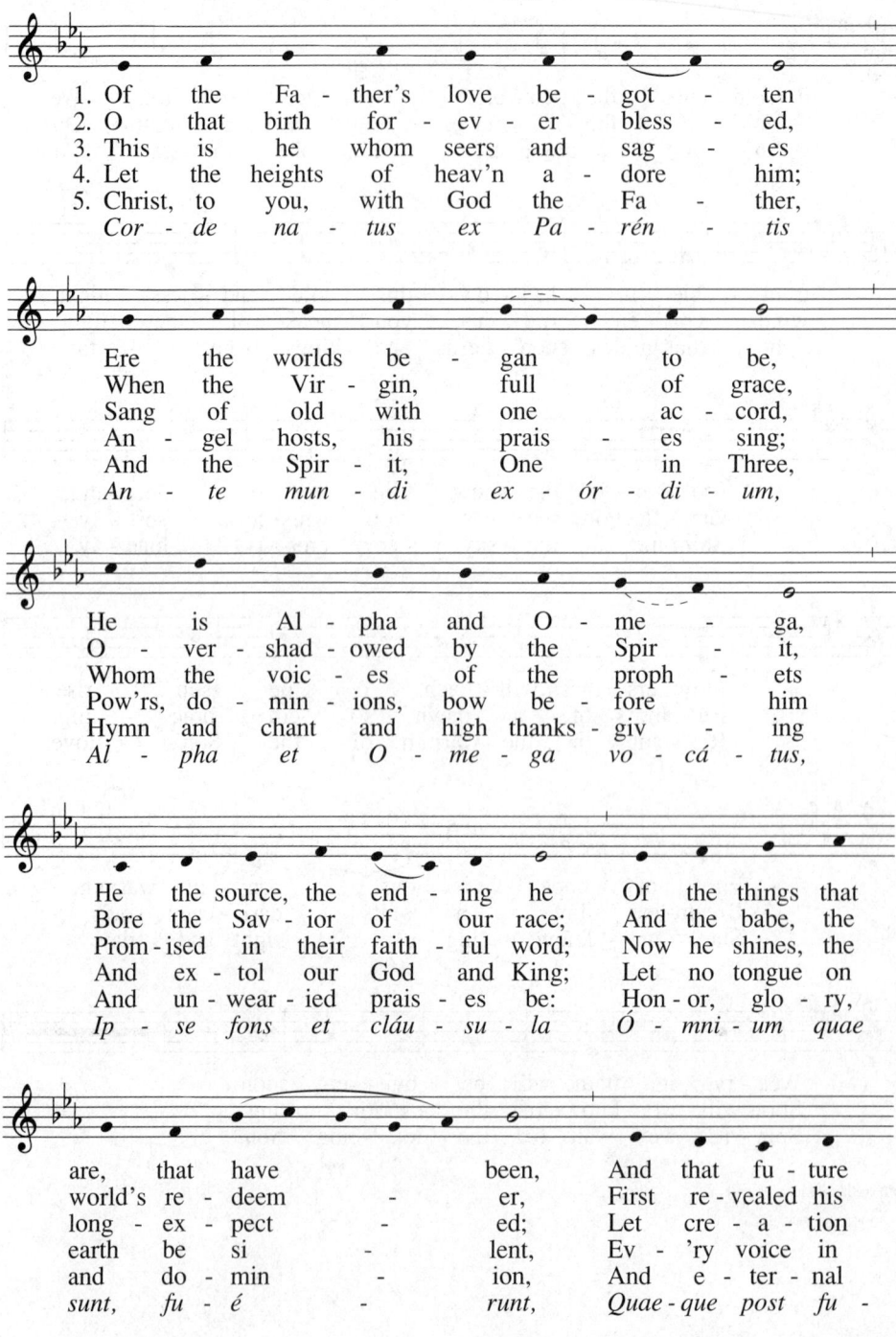

1. Of the Fa - ther's love be - got - ten
2. O that birth for - ev - er bless - ed,
3. This is he whom seers and sag - es
4. Let the heights of heav'n a - dore him;
5. Christ, to you, with God the Fa - ther,
   Cor - de na - tus ex Pa - rén - tis

Ere the worlds be - gan to be,
When the Vir - gin, full of grace,
Sang of old with one ac - cord,
An - gel hosts, his prais - es sing;
And the Spir - it, One in Three,
An - te mun - di ex - ór - di - um,

He is Al - pha and O - me - ga,
O - ver - shad - owed by the Spir - it,
Whom the voic - es of the proph - ets
Pow'rs, do - min - ions, bow be - fore him
Hymn and chant and high thanks - giv - ing
Al - pha et O - me - ga vo - cá - tus,

He the source, the end - ing he
Bore the Sav - ior of our race;
Prom - ised in their faith - ful word;
And ex - tol our God and King;
And un - wear - ied prais - es be:
Ip - se fons et cláu - su - la

Of the things that
And the babe, the
Now he shines, the
Let no tongue on
Hon - or, glo - ry,
Ó - mni - um quae

are, that have been,
world's re - deem - er,
long - ex - pect - ed;
earth be si - lent,
and do - min - ion,
sunt, fu - é - runt,

And that fu - ture
First re - vealed his
Let cre - a - tion
Ev - 'ry voice in
And e - ter - nal
Quae - que post fu -

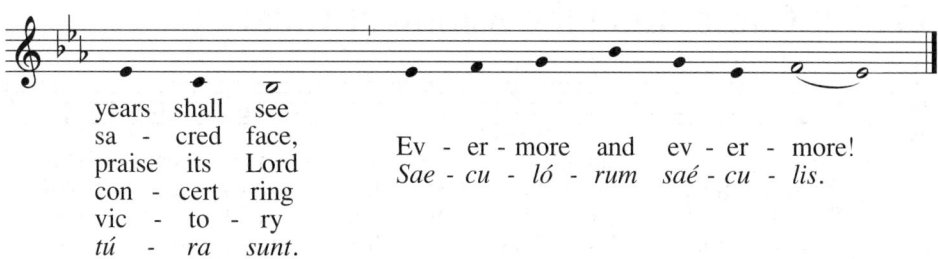

years   shall   see
sa - cred   face,
praise   its   Lord
con - cert   ring
vic - to - ry
tú - ra   sunt.

Ev - er - more   and   ev - er - more!
Sae - cu - ló - rum   saé - cu - lis.

Text: *Corde natus ex Parentis;* Aurelius Prudentius, 348–413; tr. by John M. Neale, 1818–1866 and Henry W. Baker, 1821–1877, alt.
Tune: DIVINUM MYSTERIUM, 8 7 8 7 8 7 7; 12th C.; Mode V; acc. by Richard Proulx, 1937–2010, © 1985, GIA Publications, Inc.

Go Tell It on the Mountain   530

Refrain

Go tell it on the moun - tain,   O - ver the hills and   ev - 'ry - where;

Go   tell   it on the moun - tain That   Je - sus   Christ is   born!

Verses

1. While   shep - herds   kept   their   watch - ing   O'er
2. The   shep - herds   feared   and   trem - bled   When
3. Down   in   a   low - ly   man - ger   The

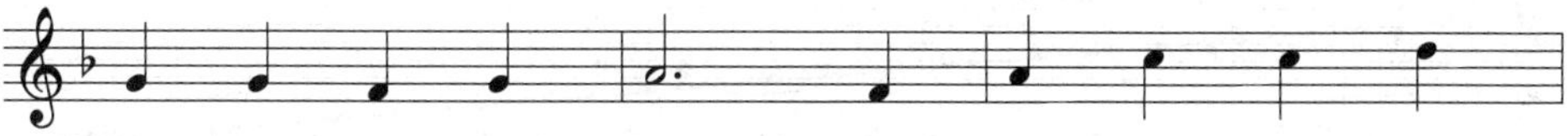

si - lent   flocks   by   night,   Be - hold, through - out   the
lo!   a - bove   the   earth   Rang   out   the   an - gel
hum - ble   Christ   was   born,   And   God   sent   us   sal -

D.C.

heav - ens   There   shone   a   ho - ly   light.
cho - rus   That   hailed   our   Sav - ior's   birth.
va - tion   That   bless - ed   Christ - mas   morn.

Text: African American spiritual; adapt. by John W. Work, Jr. 1871–1925
Tune: GO TELL IT ON THE MOUNTAIN, 7 6 7 6 with refrain; African American spiritual; harm. by Paul Sjolund, b.1935, © Walton Music Corp.,
    a division of GIA Publications, Inc.

531 It Came upon the Midnight Clear

1. It came up-on the mid-night clear, That glo-rious song of old, From an-gels bend-ing near the earth To touch their harps of gold: "Peace on the earth, good will to all, From heav'n's all-gra-cious King." The world in sol-emn still-ness lay, To hear the an-gels sing.

2. Still through the clo-ven skies they come With peace-ful wings un-furled, And still their heav'n-ly mu-sic floats O'er all the wea-ry world. A-bove its sad and low-ly plains They bend on hov-'ring wing, And ev-er o'er its Ba-bel sounds The bless-ed an-gels sing.

3. Yet with the woes of sin and strife The world has suf-fered long; Be-neath the heav'n-ly hymn have rolled Two thou-sand years of wrong; And war-ring hu-man-kind hears not The tid-ings which they bring; O hush the noise and cease your strife And hear the an-gels sing.

4. For lo! The days are has-t'ning on, By proph-ets seen of old, When with the ev-er-cir-cling years Shall come the time fore-told, When peace shall o-ver all the earth Its an-cient splen-dors fling, And all the world give back the song Which now the an-gels sing.

Text: Edmund H. Sears, 1810–1876, alt.
Tune: CAROL, CMD; Richard S. Willis, 1819–1900

Wood of the Cradle 532

Verses

1. Wood of the cra - dle, wood of the cross,
2. Shep - herds lie sleep - ing, deep in their dreams;
3. Star in the heav - ens bear - ing new light,
4. Come, all who hun - ger, come, all who thirst;

Bear - ing a life - time of joy and of loss,
An - gels a - wak - en them. "What could this mean?
Guid - ing the sag - es and a - ges this night:
Come, all who seek him, God's joy on the earth.

Who is your loved one? Who could he be,
Whom do you her - ald? Whom must we find? A
Where will you lead us? Where can he be, The
Find him a shel - ter, bright, safe, and warm;

Born in a man-ger to die on a tree?"
child in a man-ger? Our God born in time?"
child born of mys-t'ry who died on a tree?
See in all peo - ple his love be - ing born.

Refrain

This, this is Je - sus the Lord, Here in the bod - y and

blood out-poured. Come, come, walk in his ways. Kneel at the

man - ger and rise from the grave.

Text: Francis Patrick O'Brien, b.1958
Tune: ABINGTON, 9 10 9 10 with refrain; Francis Patrick O'Brien, b.1958
© 2002, GIA Publications, Inc.

533 Gaudete

Refrain

Cantor or choir:

Gau-de-te, gau-de-te, Chri-stus est na-tus ex Ma-ri-a

All:

Vir-gi-ne, gau-de-te. Gau-de-te, gau-de-te,

Last time

Chri-stus est na-tus ex Ma-ri-a Vir-gi-ne, gau-de-te.

Verses

1. Gen - tle Mar - y laid her child Low - ly in a man - ger;
2. Such a babe in such a place, Can he be the Sav - ior?
3. An - gels sang a - bout his birth, Wise men sought and found him.
4. Shep-herds saw the won - drous sight, Heard the an - gels sing - ing.
5. Gen - tle Mar - y laid her child Low - ly in a man - ger;
6. Son of God of hum - ble birth, Beau - ti - ful the sto - ry!

D.C.

There he lay, the un - de - filed, To the world a stran - ger.
Ask the saved of all the race Who have found his fa - vor.
Heav - en's star shone bright - ly forth, Glo - ry all a - round him!
All the plains were lit that night; All the hills were ring - ing.
He is still the un - de - filed, But no more a stran - ger.
Praise his name in all the earth, Hail the King of glo - ry!

Text: Refrain, Latin, 16th C.; verses, Joseph S. Cook, 1859–1933
Tune: *Piae Cantiones*, 1582; arr. by Robert J. Batastini, b.1942, © 1987, GIA Publications, Inc.

534 Love Has Come

1. Love has come, a light in the dark - ness! Love shines
2. Love is born! Come, share in the won - der. Love is
3. Love has come and nev - er will leave us! Love is

forth in the Beth - le - hem skies. See, all heav - en has
God now a - sleep in the hay. See the glow in the
life ev - er - last - ing and free. Love is Je - sus with -

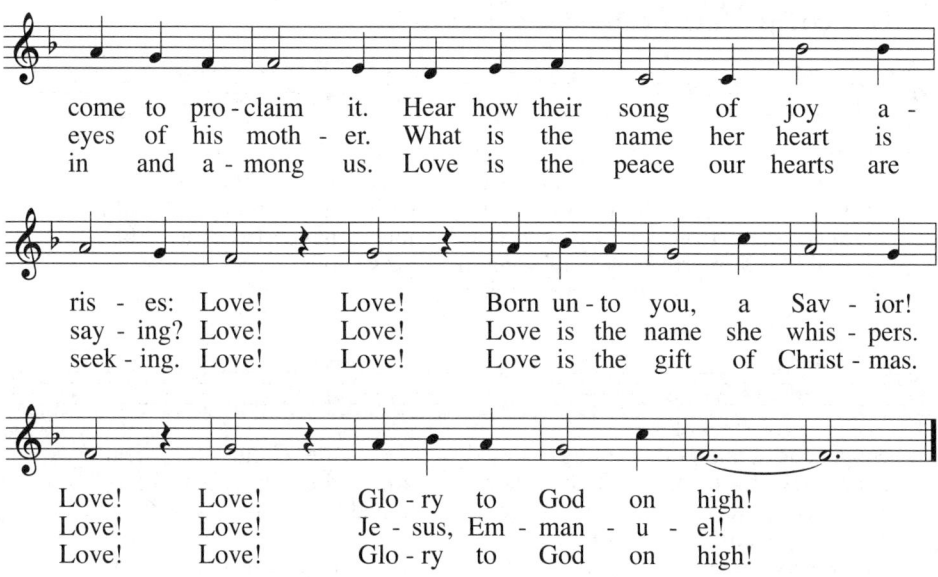

come to pro-claim it. Hear how their song of joy a-
eyes of his moth-er. What is the name her heart is
in and a-mong us. Love is the peace our hearts are

ris - es: Love! Love! Born un-to you, a Sav - ior!
say - ing? Love! Love! Love is the name she whis - pers.
seek - ing. Love! Love! Love is the gift of Christ - mas.

Love! Love! Glo - ry to God on high!
Love! Love! Je - sus, Em - man - u - el!
Love! Love! Glo - ry to God on high!

Text: Ken Bible, b.1950, © 1996, LNWhymns.com. Admin. by Music Services
Tune: UN FLAMBEAU, 9 9 10 9 9 8; French carol; harm. by Ronald F. Krisman, b.1946, © 2011, GIA Publications, Inc.

He Came Down   535

He came down that we may have *love; He

came down that we may have love; He came down that we may

Cantor: Why did he come?

have love, Hal - le - lu - jah for ev - er - more.

Substitute peace, joy, hope, life, *etc.*

Text: Cameroon traditional
Tune: Cameroon traditional; transcribed and arr. by John L. Bell, b.1949, © 1990, Iona Community, GIA Publications, Inc., agent

536 Sing We Now of Christmas

1. Sing we now of Christ - mas, No - ël sing we here.
2. An - gels called to shep - herds, "Leave your flocks at rest.
3. In a stall they found him with his moth - er mild.
4. Wise men from the O - rient jour - neyed from a - far
5. Gold and myrrh they of - fered, gifts of great-est price.
6. Praise we now our Sav - ior on this ho - ly night.

Sing our grate - ful prais - es to the Child so dear.
Jour - ney forth to Beth - l'hem; find the In - fant blest."
Jo - seph, at the man - ger, watched the ho - ly Child.
Bear - ing cost - ly treas - ure, guid - ed by a star.
There was ne'er a sta - ble so like par - a - dise.
Let us gath - er 'round him, Christ, the Lord of light.

Sing we No - ël, the King is born, No - ël!

Sing we now of Christ - mas, sing we here No - ël!

Text: French carol; tr. anonymous; adaptation, hymnal version, © 2011, GIA Publications, Inc.
Tune: NOËL NOUVELET, 11 11 with refrain; French carol; harm. by Martin Shaw, 1875–1958, © Oxford University Press

537 Gloria, Gloria

Canon

1. 2.
Gló - ri - a, gló - ri - a, in ex - cél - sis De - o!

3. 4.
Gló - ri - a, gló - ri - a, al - le - lú - ia, al - le - lú - ia!

Tune: Jacques Berthier, 1923–1994, © 1979, 1988, Les Presses de Taizé, GIA Publications, Inc., agent

The People Who Walked in Darkness 538

Verses

1. The peo-ple who walked in dark-ness A - wak - en to
2. For God has en-larged the na - tion, And pros-pered the
3. The yoke of de - spair and bond-age, The chains and the
4. For us now a child is giv-en, For all the de -
5. How vast is our God's do - min-ion! How far truth and

see a great light. The peo-ple who dwelt in the land of the
fruit of its land. God's peo-ple are blest with the har - vest of
slave - mas - ter's rod Are shat-tered and scat-tered like dust in a
spised and for - lorn. The rule of com - pas - sion shall rest on his
mer - cy ex - tend. The zeal of the Lord will ac - com-plish its

Refrain

shad - ow Rise to a Star shin - ing bright.
vic - t'ry, Gift from a boun - ti - ful hand.
wind-storm Loosed by the jus - tice of God. His name is
shoul - der. God's own Mes - si - ah is born!
pur - pose: Jus - tice shall reign with - out end.

Won - der-ful, Coun-sel-or, Al-might-y God, Fa - ther for - ev - er,

Prince of Peace. Won - der-ful, Coun-sel-or, Al-might-y God,

To verses   D.C.   Last time

Fa-ther for-ev-er, Prince of Peace. Peace.

Text: Isaiah 9:1–6; Mary Louise Bringle, b.1953
Tune: ISAIAH 9, 8 8 12 7 with refrain; Sally Ann Morris, b.1952

539 Sing Alleluia

Verses

1. Dark is the night and deep are the shad - ows;
2. Who would be - lieve that here in a man - ger
3. Great is the joy of Mar - y, his moth - er.
4. Hope for the poor, re - lease for the cap - tive,

Qui - et the ba - by bathed in lan - tern light.
God comes a - mong us as a ti - ny child?
Great is the joy of Jo - seph by her side.
Love for the out - cast, light for wea - ry eyes;

Hushed are the sounds of cat - tle and shep - herds;
See in his eyes the glo - ry of heav - en;
Great is the joy of all those in dark - ness.
Word that brings life, em - brac - ing hu - man - i - ty,

Sweet is the mu - sic the an - gels bring this night.
Hear in his laugh-ter the joy of God on high.
Here lies the Sav - ior so soon to die and rise.
Je - sus, com-pan - ion, be born in - to our lives.

Refrain

Sing al - le - lu - ia, sing al - le - lu - ia.

Wel - come the Sav - ior, the prom-ise of new life.

Sing al - le - lu - ia, sing al - le - lu - ia.

All of cre - a - tion, sing this night.

Text: Francis Patrick O'Brien, b.1958
Tune: BRAINTREE, 10 10 10 11 with refrain; Francis Patrick O'Brien, b.1958
© 1996, GIA Publications, Inc.

The Table of Emmanuel 540

Refrain

As we taste the bread of heav-en and the cup of love out-poured, we pro-claim your birth, Em-man-u-el, Child of Mar-y, Christ the Lord.

Verses

Cantor:

1. The House of Bread re-joic-es, Sing-ing
2. On those who walk in dark-ness, Those who
3. Be-hold the Vir-gin Moth-er, As she
4. This ban-quet of God's good-ness Now re-
5. So let us join our voic-es With the

heav-en's great re-frain. Let us join them in their
dwell in lands of gloom, Shines the light of love's e-
casts her lov-ing gaze On the love she bears in-
veals the love of Christ: Child of heav-en, child of
an-gels high a-bove In their hymn of praise through

D.C.

"Glo-ri-a," And give glo-ry to God's name.
ter-nal flame, Je-sus, fruit of Mar-y's womb.
to the world, Sing-ing lull-a-bies of praise.
Beth-le-hem, Who has died to bear new life.
all the earth, Tell-ing won-ders of God's love.

Text: Tony E. Alonso, b.1980, © 2014, GIA Publications, Inc.
Tune: THE HOLLY AND THE IVY, 7 7 9 7 with refrain; English melody, arr. by Tony E. Alonso, b.1980, © 2014, GIA Publications, Inc.

541 Hacia Belén / Mary Journeyed with Her Husband

Text: Anonymous; tr. by Mary Louise Bringle, b.1953, © 2005, GIA Publications, Inc.
Tune: HACIA BELÉN, 8 8 8 8 with refrain; Puerto Rican traditional; harm. by Ronald F. Krisman, b.1946, © 2005, GIA Publications, Inc.

Tomorrow Shall Be My Dancing Day 542

1. To - mor-row shall be my danc - ing day: I
2. Then was I born of a vir - gin pure, Of
3. In a man - ger laid and wrapped I was, So
4. Then af - ter - wards bap - tized I was; The

would my true love did so chance To see the
her I took flesh - ly sub - stance; Thus was I
ver - y poor, this was my chance, Be - twixt an
Ho - ly Ghost on me did glance, My Fa - ther's

leg - end of my play,
knit to hu - man na - ture,
ox and a sil - ly poor ass,   To call my true love
voice heard from a - bove,

to my dance: Sing, O my love, O my love, my

love, my love; This have I done for my true love.

Optional

5. Then down to hell I took my way
   For my true love's deliverance,
   And rose again on the third day,
   Up to my true love and the dance:
   Sing, O my love...

6. Then up to heaven I did ascend,
   Where now I dwell in sure substance
   On the right hand of God, that man
   May come unto the general dance:
   Sing, O my love...

Text: English traditional
Tune: English traditional; Sandys' *Christmas Carols Ancient and Modern*, 1833

543 Once in Royal David's City

1. Once in roy - al Da - vid's cit - y Stood a
2. He came down to earth from heav - en Who is
3. And, through all his won - drous child - hood, He would
4. For he is our child - hood's pat - tern, Day by
5. And our eyes at last shall see him, Through his

low - ly cat - tle shed, Where a moth - er laid her
God and Lord of all, And his shel - ter was a
hon - or and o - bey, Love and watch the low - ly
day like us he grew; He was lit - tle, weak, and
own re - deem - ing love; For that child so dear and

ba - by In a man - ger for his bed.
sta - ble, And his cra - dle was a stall.
maid - en In whose gen - tle arms he lay.
help - less, Tears and smiles like us he knew.
gen - tle Is our Lord in heav'n a - bove.

Mar - y was that moth - er mild;
With the poor and meek and low - ly
Chris - tian chil - dren all should be
And he feels for all our sad - ness,
And he leads his chil - dren on

Je - sus Christ, her lit - tle child.
Lived on earth our Sav - ior ho - ly.
Kind, o - be - dient, good as he.
And he shares in all our glad - ness,
To the place where he is gone.

Text: Cecil F. Alexander, 1818–1895, alt.
Tune: IRBY, 8 7 8 7 7 77; Henry J. Gauntlett, 1805–1876

Come, Sing a Home and Family 544

1. Come, sing a home and fam - i - ly In Naz - a - reth of old, Whose hum - ble grace a no - ble place In Chris - tian life now holds: A maid - en's ho - ly, vi - brant faith, Which said, "Let it be done!" A dream - er who risked life and limb Pro - tect - ing God's own Son.

2. At Mar - y's ta - ble Je - sus learned To bless, give thanks, and eat, To wel - come all as hon - ored guests By wash - ing wea - ry feet. Her sweep - ing floors and light - ing lamps, Her knead - ing bread with leav'n, Her jour - neys to the well fore - told To Christ the reign of heav'n.

3. By Jo - seph's side young Je - sus learned To work and read and pray, The law and love of God a - bove Placed in his heart to stay. While cra - dled by the car - pen - ter, The boy came to dis - cern That prod - i - gal, for - giv - ing arms A - wait a child's re - turn.

4. What - ev - er form our fam - 'ly takes, The gos - pel way we seek: To feed the hun - gry, heal the sick, Lift up the poor and weak. In dai - ly life and sim - ple tasks Our song must nev - er cease Of dream - ing work - er, maid - en bold, And child of last - ing peace.

Text: Alan J. Hommerding, b.1956, © 1994, World Library Publications
Tune: FOREST GREEN, CMD; English melody; harm. by Ralph Vaughan Williams, 1872–1958, alt.

545 Sing of Mary, Pure and Lowly

1. Sing of Mar - y, pure and low - ly, Vir - gin Moth - er
2. Sing of Je - sus, son of Mar - y, In the home at
3. Glo - ry be to God the Fa - ther; Glo - ry be to

un - de - filed. Sing of God's own Son most ho - ly,
Naz - a - reth. Toil and la - bor can - not wea - ry
God the Son; Glo - ry be to God the Spir - it;

Who be - came her lit - tle child. Fair - est Child of
Love en - dur - ing un - to death. Con - stant was the
Glo - ry to the Three in One. From the heart of

fair - est Moth - er, God the Lord who came to earth,
love he gave her, Though he went forth from her side,
bless - ed Mar - y, From all saints the song as - cends,

Word - made - flesh, our ver - y broth - er,
Forth to preach, and heal, and suf - fer,
And the Church the strain re - ech - oes

Takes our na - ture by his birth.
Till on Cal - va - ry he died.
Un - to earth's re - mot - est ends.

Text: Roland F. Palmer, 1891–1985, © Parish of Saint John the Evangelist, Victoria, BC
Tune: PLEADING SAVIOR, 8 7 8 7 D; *Christian Lyre*, 1830; harm. by Richard Proulx, 1937–2010, © 1986, GIA Publications, Inc.

Gentle Mary Laid Her Child 546

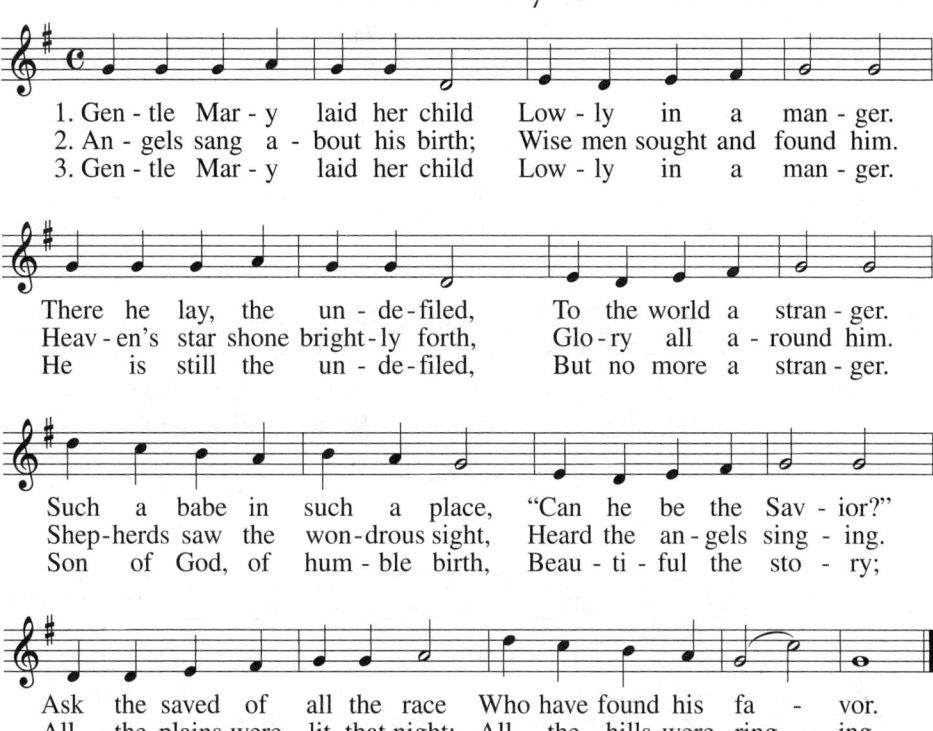

1. Gen - tle Mar - y   laid her child   Low - ly   in   a   man - ger.
2. An - gels sang a - bout his birth;   Wise men sought and found him.
3. Gen - tle Mar - y   laid her child   Low - ly   in   a   man - ger.

There he   lay, the   un - de - filed,   To the world a   stran - ger.
Heav - en's   star shone bright-ly forth,   Glo - ry   all   a - round him.
He   is   still the   un - de - filed,   But no more a   stran - ger.

Such   a   babe in   such   a   place,   "Can   he   be   the   Sav - ior?"
Shep-herds saw the   won-drous sight,   Heard the   an - gels sing - ing.
Son   of   God, of   hum - ble birth,   Beau - ti - ful the   sto - ry;

Ask   the saved of   all the race   Who have found his   fa - vor.
All   the plains were   lit that night;   All   the   hills were   ring - ing.
Praise his name in   all the earth,   Hail   the   King of   glo - ry!

Text: Joseph S. Cook, 1859–1933
Tune: TEMPUS ADEST FLORIDUM, 7 6 7 6 D; *Piae Cantiones*, 1582; arr. by Ernest C. MacMillan, 1893–1973

547   We Three Kings of Orient Are

1. We three kings of O - ri - ent are; Bear - ing
2. Born a King on Beth - le - hem's plain, Gold I
3. Frank - in - cense to of - fer have I; In - cense
4. Myrrh is mine: its bit - ter per - fume Breathes a
5. Glo - rious now be - hold him a - rise, King and

gifts, we trav - erse a - far Field and foun - tain,
bring to crown him a - gain; King for - ev - er,
owns a De - i - ty nigh; Prayer and prais - ing,
life of gath - er - ing gloom; Sor - rowing, sigh - ing,
God and Sac - ri - fice; "Al - le - lu - ia,

Moor and moun - tain, Fol - low - ing yon - der star.
Ceas - ing nev - er, O - ver us all to reign.
Glad - ly rais - ing, Wor - ship - ing God on high.
Bleed - ing, dy - ing, Sealed in the stone - cold tomb.
Al - le - lu - ia!" Sounds through the earth and skies.

O star of won - der, star of night, Star with

roy - al beau - ty bright, West - ward lead - ing,

still pro - ceed - ing, Guide us to the per - fect Light.

Text: Matthew 2:1–11; John H. Hopkins, Jr., 1820–1891, alt.
Tune: KINGS OF ORIENT, 88 44 6 with refrain; John H. Hopkins, Jr., 1820–1891

Songs of Thankfulness and Praise   548

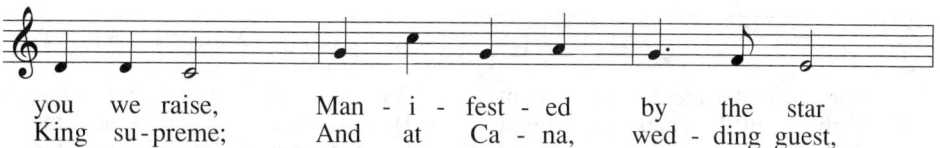

1. Songs of thank - ful - ness and praise,   Je - sus, Lord, to
2. Man - i - fest at Jor - dan's stream,   Proph - et, Priest, and
3. Man - i - fest in mak - ing whole   Weak - ened bo - dy,
4. Grant us grace to see you, Lord,   Mir - rored in your

you we raise,   Man - i - fest - ed by the star
King su - preme;   And at Ca - na, wed - ding guest,
faint - ing soul;   Man - i - fest in val - iant fight,
ho - ly word;   May we im - i - tate you now,

To the sag - es from a - far;   Branch of roy - al
In your God - head man - i - fest;   Man - i - fest in
Quell - ing all the dev - il's might;   Man - i - fest in
And on us your grace en - dow;   That we like to

Da - vid's stem   In your birth at Beth - le - hem;
pow'r di - vine,   Chang - ing wa - ter in - to wine;
gra - cious will,   Ev - er bring - ing good from ill;
you may be   At your great e - piph - a - ny;

An - thems be to you ad - drest,   God in flesh made man - i - fest.
An - thems be to you ad - drest,   God in flesh made man - i - fest.
An - thems be to you ad - drest,   God in flesh made man - i - fest.
And may praise you ev - er blest,   God in flesh made man - i - fest.

Text: Christopher Wordsworth, 1807–1885
Tune: SALZBURG, 77 77 D; Jakob Hintze, 1622–1702, alt; harm. by J. S. Bach, 1685–1750

549 Epiphany Carol

1. Ev - 'ry na - tion sees the glo - ry Of a
2. Ev - 'ry tongue shall sing the prais - es Of his
3. Once a - gain may we dis - cov - er Word made
4. Gath - er, God, the world to - geth - er In the

star that pierced the night. As we tell the won-drous
birth in deep - est night. He is heal - ing for the
flesh sent from a - bove. In our neigh - bor, sis - ter,
bright - ness of your day. Fill our hearts with joy for -

sto - ry We are bathed in ra - diant light.
a - ges; He is Christ, our God's de - light.
broth - er, In the lone - ly and un - loved.
ev - er; Help us walk the ho - ly way.

Star sent forth from high-est heav - en, Danc-ing
He pro - claims with - in his be - ing All our
May we touch him, may we hold him, May we
May your jus - tice rule the na - tions; May all

light of God's de - sign, Shine up - on the gift that's
hopes, our great de - sires. He shall die to rise, re -
cra - dle him with care As we learn to love each
peo - ple live as one. Now we see our true sal -

giv - en: Word made flesh now born in time.
deem - ing All who fol - low with their lives.
oth - er, Bring-ing hope from out de - spair.
va - tion In the glo - ry of your Son.

Text: Francis Patrick O'Brien, b.1958, © 2002, GIA Publications, Inc.
Tune: BEACH SPRING, 8 7 8 7 D; *The Sacred Harp*, 1844; harm. by Ronald A. Nelson, 1927–2014, © 1978, *Lutheran Book of Worship*, admin. Augsburg Fortress

Jesus, the Light of the World 550

1. Hark! The her - ald an - gels sing.
2. Joy - ful, all you na - tions, rise.
3. Christ, by high - est heav'n a - dored.
4. Hail the heav'n - born Prince of Peace.

Je - sus, the light of the world.

Glo - ry to the new - born King,
Join the tri - umph of the skies.
Christ, the ev - er - last - ing Lord,
Hail the Sun of Right - eous - ness!

Je - sus, the light of the world. We'll walk in the

light, beau - ti - ful light. Come where the

dew - drops of mer - cy shine bright. Oh, shine all a -

round us by day and by night. Je - sus, the light of the world.

Text: George D. Elderkin; verses by Charles Wesley, 1707–1788
Tune: WE'LL WALK IN THE LIGHT, 7 7 7 7 with refrain; George D. Elderkin; arr. by Evelyn Simpson-Curenton, b.1953, © 2000,
   GIA Publications, Inc.

551 As with Gladness Men of Old

1. As with glad - ness men of old Did the guid - ing
2. As with joy - ful steps they sped To that low - ly
3. As they of - fered gifts most rare At that man - ger
4. Christ Re - deem - er, with us stay, Help us live your
5. In the heav'n - ly cit - y bright None shall need cre -

star be - hold; As with joy they hailed its light,
man - ger - bed, There to bend the knee be - fore
crude and bare; So may we this ho - ly day,
ho - ly way; And when earth - ly things are past,
a - ted light; You, its light, its joy, its crown,

Lead - ing on - ward, beam - ing bright; So, most gra - cious
Christ whom heav'n and earth a - dore; So may we with
Drawn to you with - out de - lay, All our cost - liest
Bring our ran - somed souls at last Where they need no
You, its sun which goes not down; There for - ev - er

Lord, may we Ev - er - more your splen - dor see.
hur - ried pace Run to seek your throne of grace.
treas - ures bring, Christ, to you, our heav'n - ly King.
star to guide, Where no clouds your glo - ry hide.
may we sing Al - le - lu - ias to our King.

Text: William C. Dix, 1837–1898, alt.
Tune: DIX, 77 77 77; arr. from Conrad Kocher, 1786–1872, by William H. Monk, 1823–1889

552 What Child Is This

1. What child is this, who, laid to rest, On
2. Why lies he in such mean es - tate Where
3. So bring him in - cense, gold, and myrrh; Come,

Mar - y's lap is sleep - ing, Whom an - gels greet with
ox and ass are feed - ing? Good Chris - tian, fear; for
peas - ant, king, to own him. The King of kings sal -

an - thems sweet While shep - herds watch are keep - ing?
sin - ners here The si - lent Word is plead - ing.
va - tion brings; Let lov - ing hearts en - throne him.

This, this is Christ the King, Whom shep - herds guard and an-gels sing;

Haste, haste to bring him laud, The babe, the son of Mar - y.

Text: William C. Dix, 1837–1898, alt.
Tune: GREENSLEEVES, 8 7 8 7 with refrain; English melody, 16th C.; harm. by John Stainer, 1840–1901

What Star Is This 553

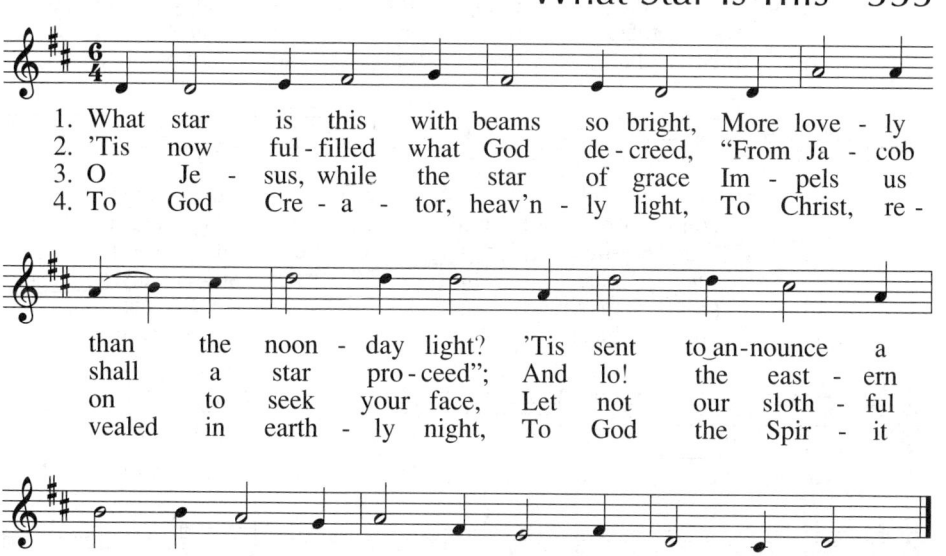

1. What star is this with beams so bright, More love - ly
2. 'Tis now ful - filled what God de - creed, "From Ja - cob
3. O Je - sus, while the star of grace Im - pels us
4. To God Cre - a - tor, heav'n - ly light, To Christ, re -

than the noon - day light? 'Tis sent to an-nounce a
shall a star pro - ceed"; And lo! the east - ern
on to seek your face, Let not our sloth - ful
vealed in earth - ly night, To God the Spir - it

new - born king, Glad tid - ings of our God to bring.
sag - es stand, To read in heav'n the Lord's com-mand.
hearts re - fuse The guid - ance of your light to use.
blest we raise An end - less song of thank - ful praise!

Text: *Quem stella sole pulchrior,* Charles Coffin, 1676–1749; tr. by John Chandler, 1806–1876, alt.
Tune: PUER NOBIS, LM; adapt. by Michael Praetorius, 1571–1621

554 The First Nowell

1. The first No - well the an - gel did say Was to
2. They look - ed up and saw a star Shin - ing
3. And by the light of that same star Three
4. This star drew nigh to the north - west, O'er
5. Then en - tered in those wise men three, Full
6. Then let us all with one ac - cord Sing

cer - tain poor shep - herds in fields as they lay; In
in the east be - yond them far; And
wise men came from coun - try far; To
Beth - le - hem it took its rest; And
rev - 'rent - ly up - on their knee, And
prais - es to our heav - 'nly Lord; Who

fields where they lay keep - ing their sheep, On a
to the earth it gave great light, And
seek for a king was their in - tent, And to
there it did both stop and stay Right
of - fered there in his pres - ence Their
with the Fa - ther we a - dore And

cold win - ter's night that was so deep.
so it con - tin - ued both day and night.
fol - low the star wher - ev - er it went.
o - ver the place where Je - sus lay.
gold and myrrh and frank - in - cense.
Spir - it blest for - ev - er - more.

No - well, No - well, No - well, No - well!

Born is the King of Is - ra - el.

Text: English carol, 17th C.
Tune: THE FIRST NOWELL, Irregular with refrain; English carol; harm. from *Christmas Carols New and Old*, 1871

When John Baptized by Jordan's River   555

1. When John bap - tized by Jor - dan's riv - er
2. There as the Lord, bap - tized and pray - ing,
3. O Son of Man, our na - ture shar - ing,

In faith and hope the peo - ple came, That John and
Rose from the stream, the sin - less one, A voice was
In whose o - be - dience all are blest, Sav - ior, our

Jor - dan might de - liv - er Their trou - bled
heard from heav - en say - ing, "This is my
sins and sor - rows bear - ing, Hear us and

souls from sin and shame. They came to seek a
own be - lov - ed Son." There as the Fa - ther's
grant us this re - quest: Dai - ly to grow, by

new be - gin - ning, The hu - man spir - it's age - less
word was spo - ken, Not in the pow'r of wind and
grace de - fend - ed, Filled with the Spir - it from a -

quest, Re - pen - tance, and an end of
flame, But of his love and peace the
bove; In Christ bap - tized, be - loved, be -

sin - ning, Re - nounc - ing ev - 'ry wrong con - fessed.
to - ken, Seen as a dove, the Spir - it came.
friend - ed, Chil - dren of God in peace and love.

Text: Timothy Dudley-Smith, b.1926, © 1984, Hope Publishing Company
Tune: RENDEZ À DIEU, 9 8 9 8 D; *Genevan Psalter*, 1551; attr. to Louis Bourgeois, c.1510–1561

556 To Jordan Jesus Humbly Came

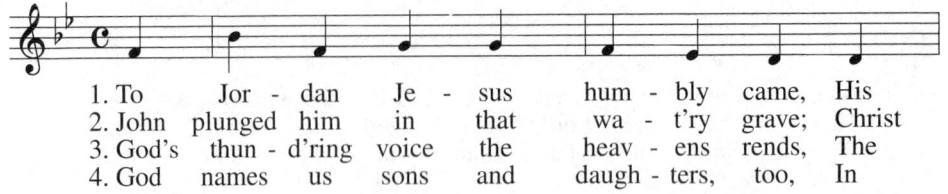

1. To Jor - dan Je - sus hum - bly came, His
2. John plunged him in that wa - t'ry grave; Christ
3. God's thun - d'ring voice the heav - ens rends, The
4. God names us sons and daugh - ters, too, In

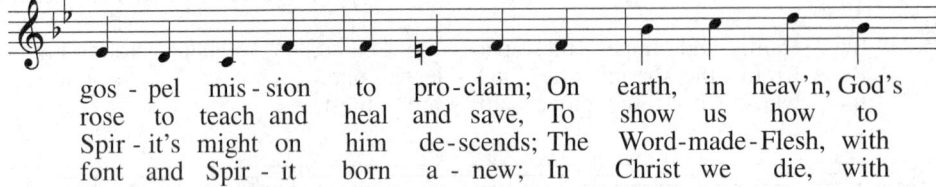

gos - pel mis - sion to pro-claim; On earth, in heav'n, God's
rose to teach and heal and save, To show us how to
Spir - it's might on him de-scends; The Word-made-Flesh, with
font and Spir - it born a - new; In Christ we die, with

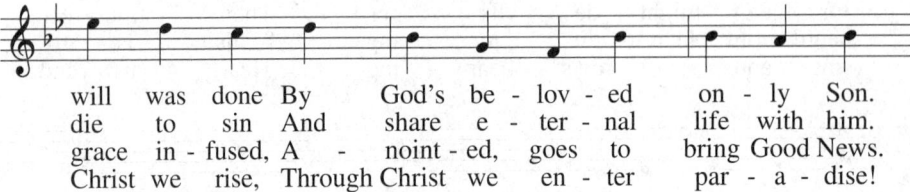

will was done By God's be - lov - ed on - ly Son.
die to sin And share e - ter - nal life with him.
grace in - fused, A - noint - ed, goes to bring Good News.
Christ we rise, Through Christ we en - ter par - a - dise!

Text: Alan J. Hommerding, b.1956, © 2004, World Library Publications
Tune: WINCHESTER NEW, LM; adapt. from *Musikalisches Handbuch*, Hamburg, 1690

557 Remember You Are Dust / Del Polvo Eres Tú

Refrain / Estribillo

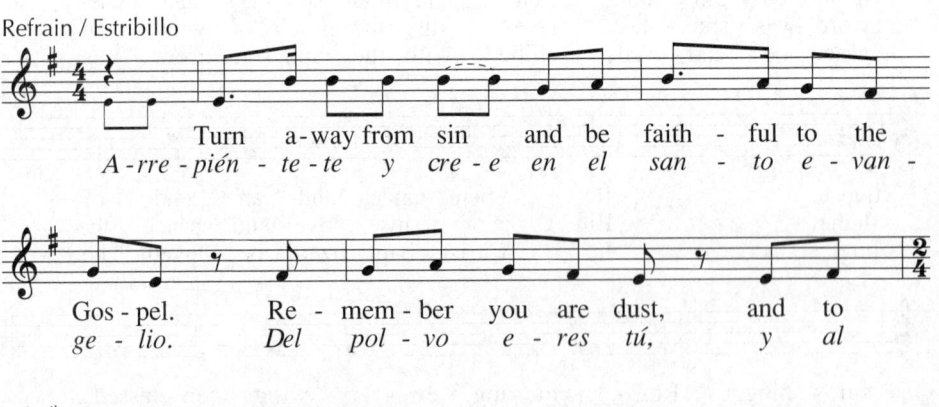

Turn a-way from sin and be faith - ful to the
A - rre - pién - te - te y cre - e en el san - to e - van -

Gos - pel. Re - mem - ber you are dust, and to
ge - lio. Del pol - vo e - res tú, y al

dust you will re - turn.
pol - vo_has de vol - ver.

Verses / Estrofas

1.–4. Re - pent, the king - dom is at hand.
1.–4. El rei - no de Dios es - tá muy cer - ca.

Re - pent, the king - dom is at hand.
El rei - no de Dios es - tá muy cer - ca.

1. Rend your hearts, not your gar - ments.
2. Blow the trum - pet in Zi - on.
3. For - give one an - oth - er.
4. Now, the day of sal - va - tion.

1. Ras - ga hoy tu co - ra - zón.
2. En Sión to - ca la trom - pe - ta.
3. Per - do - na_a tus her - ma - nos.
4. Dí - a de la sal - va - ción.

Now, the ac - cept - a - ble time.
Es a - ho - ra_el tiem - po fa - vo - ra - ble.

All/Todos: D.C.

Now, the ac - cept - a - ble time.
Es a - ho - ra_el tiem - po fa - vo - ra - ble.

*The following are verse tropes
for the season of Lent:*

*Los siguientes son tropos adicionales
para el uso durante la Cuaresma:*

Seek the God of compassion…
Live in kindness and mercy…
Trust in God and be faithful…
Praise the God of salvation…
Let us bow down in worship…

Busca_al Dios de compasión…
Sé amable, sé clemente…
En tu Redentor confía…
A tu Salvador alaba…
Rinde culto_a tu Señor…

Text: Joel 2:12–18, 2 Corinthians 5:20—6:2; Paul A. Tate, b.1968, © 2003, GIA Publications, Inc.; refrain from the *Sacramentary*, © 1973, ICEL;
tr. by Ronald F. Krisman, b.1946, © 2008, GIA Publications, Inc.
Tune: Paul A. Tate, b.1968, © 2003, GIA Publications, Inc.

558 Merciful God

Refrain

Ash Wednesday: Sign us with ash-es, mer-ci-ful God,
Lent Gathering: Gath-er your peo-ple, mer-ci-ful God,
Lent Communion: Feed us and guide us, mer-ci-ful God:

Chil-dren of dust, as to dust we re-turn. Sign us with
Gath-er the long-ing, the lost, and un-sure. Gath-er your
Light, when the shad-ows of life cloud our view. Feed us and

ash-es, mer-ci-ful God; Mark us and make us your
peo-ple, mer-ci-ful God, Name us and claim us as
guide us, mer-ci-ful God, Peo-ple who hun-ger for

To verses / Last time

own. own, mark us and make us your own.
yours. yours, name us and claim us as yours.
you. you, peo-ple who hun-ger for you.

Verses

1. Sure-ly, you a-lone can save us. You pay our price with
2. Sure-ly, you a-lone up-hold us. You give us strength for
3. Sure-ly, you a-lone can heal us. Yours is the will to
4. Sure-ly, you a-lone can free us. You break the bonds of
5. Sure-ly, you a-lone re-fine us. You give us grace for
6. Sure-ly, you a-lone re-deem us. You fill our dust with

pre-cious blood. Reach-ing through your great com-
all our needs. Shield-ing with a fa-ther's
make us whole. Sooth-ing with a moth-er's
guilt and sin. Brac-ing, till we walk up-
lives made new, Forg-ing, through your fire and
ho-ly breath. Burst-ing from the grave in

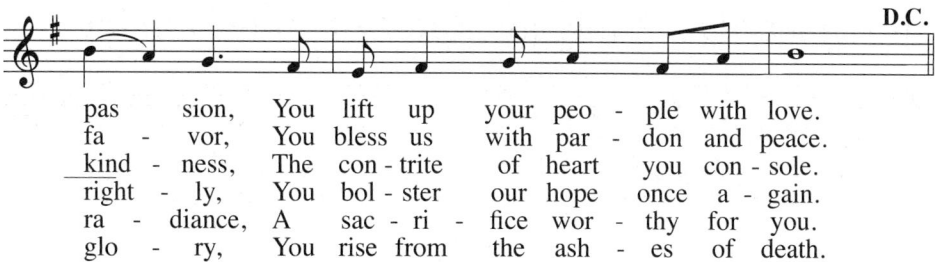

D.C.

pas - sion, You lift up your peo - ple with love.
fa - vor, You bless us with par - don and peace.
kind - ness, The con - trite of heart you con - sole.
right - ly, You bol - ster our hope once a - gain.
ra - diance, A sac - ri - fice wor - thy for you.
glo - ry, You rise from the ash - es of death.

Text: Mary Louise Bringle, b.1953, © 2006, 2009, GIA Publications, Inc.
Tune: INDIGO, LM with refrain; Tony E. Alonso, b.1980, © 2009, GIA Publications, Inc.

O Sun of Justice 559

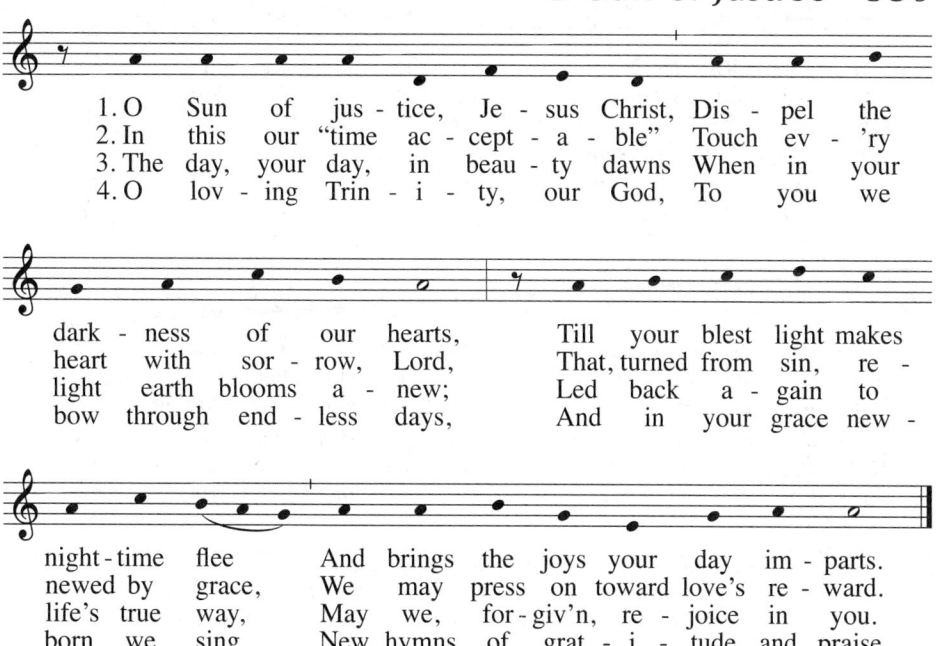

1. O Sun of jus - tice, Je - sus Christ, Dis - pel the
2. In this our "time ac - cept - a - ble" Touch ev - 'ry
3. The day, your day, in beau - ty dawns When in your
4. O lov - ing Trin - i - ty, our God, To you we

dark - ness of our hearts, Till your blest light makes
heart with sor - row, Lord, That, turned from sin, re -
light earth blooms a - new; Led back a - gain to
bow through end - less days, And in your grace new -

night - time flee And brings the joys your day im - parts.
newed by grace, We may press on toward love's re - ward.
life's true way, May we, for - giv'n, re - joice in you.
born we sing New hymns of grat - i - tude and praise.

Text: *Jam Christe sol justitiae;* Latin, 6th C.; tr. by Peter J. Scagnelli, b.1949, © 1982, Peter J. Scagnelli, published by World Library Publications
Tune: JESU DULCIS MEMORIA, LM; Mode I; acc. by Richard Proulx, 1937–2010, © 1975, GIA Publications, Inc.

560 Hear Us, Almighty Lord / Attende Domine

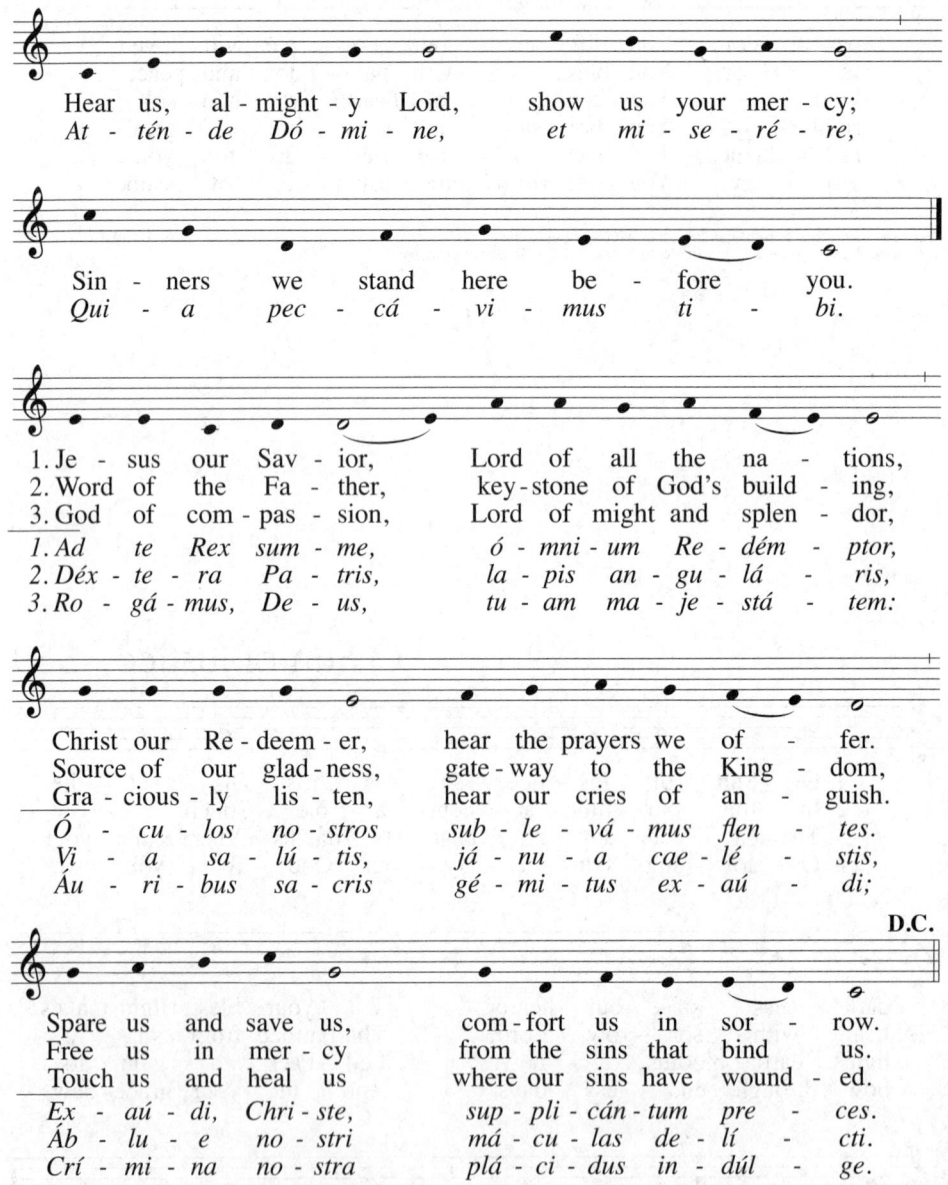

Hear us, al - might - y Lord, show us your mer - cy;
At - tén - de Dó - mi - ne, et mi - se - ré - re,

Sin - ners we stand here be - fore you.
Qui - a pec - cá - vi - mus ti - bi.

1. Je - sus our Sav - ior, Lord of all the na - tions,
2. Word of the Fa - ther, key - stone of God's build - ing,
3. God of com - pas - sion, Lord of might and splen - dor,
1. *Ad te Rex sum - me, ó - mni - um Re - dém - ptor,*
2. *Déx - te - ra Pa - tris, la - pis an - gu - lá - ris,*
3. *Ro - gá - mus, De - us, tu - am ma - je - stá - tem:*

Christ our Re - deem - er, hear the prayers we of - fer.
Source of our glad - ness, gate - way to the King - dom,
Gra - cious - ly lis - ten, hear our cries of an - guish.
Ó - cu - los no - stros sub - le - vá - mus flen - tes.
Vi - a sa - lú - tis, já - nu - a cae - lé - stis,
Áu - ri - bus sa - cris gé - mi - tus ex - aú - di;

D.C.

Spare us and save us, com - fort us in sor - row.
Free us in mer - cy from the sins that bind us.
Touch us and heal us where our sins have wound - ed.
Ex - aú - di, Chri - ste, sup - pli - cán - tum pre - ces.
Áb - lu - e no - stri má - cu - las de - lí - cti.
Crí - mi - na no - stra plá - ci - dus in - dúl - ge.

4. Humbly confessing that we have offended,
   Stripped of illusions, naked in our sorrow,
   Pardon, Lord Jesus, those your blood has ransomed.

5. Innocent captive, you were led to slaughter,
   Sentenced by sinners when they brought false witness.
   Keep from damnation those your death has rescued.

4. *Tibi fatémur, crímina admíssa,*
   Contríto corde pándimus occúlta;
   Tua, Redémptor, píetas ignóscat.

5. *Ínnocens captus, nec repúgnans ductus,*
   Téstibus falsis, pro ímpiis damnátus:
   Quos redemísti, tu consérva, Christe.

Text: *Attende Domine*, Latin, 10th C.; tr. by Ralph Wright, OSB, b.1938, © 1980, ICEL
Tune: ATTENDE DOMINE, 11 11 11 with refrain; Mode V; acc. by Richard Proulx, 1937–2010, © 1975, GIA Publications, Inc.

Turn to the Living God   561

Refrain

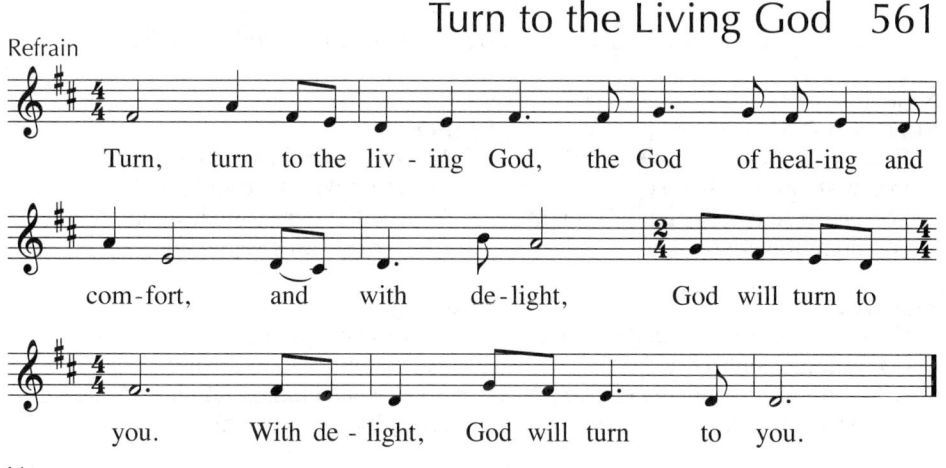

Turn, turn to the liv-ing God, the God of heal-ing and com-fort, and with de-light, God will turn to you. With de-light, God will turn to you.

Verses

1. For now is the time of fulfillment. The reign of our God is at hand.
   Reform your life, turn from sin and believe this glorious news.

2. Come, and return to the Lord. All you weary, bring your grieving hearts.
   With kindness and mercy God's compassion will fill your hearts with love.

3. Have mercy, O Lord, on your people. In your goodness wipe away our guilt.
   Wash us clean, free us to become your living song of praise.

4. Come, sing with joy to the Lord. Listen with an open heart.
   Hear God's voice and follow; our good shepherd is guiding the way.

Text: Lori True, b.1961
Tune: Lori True, b.1961
© 2003, GIA Publications, Inc.

562 From Ashes to the Living Font

1. From ash - es to the liv - ing font Your
2. Through fast - ing, prayer, and char - i - ty Your
3. *Insert appropriate stanza*
4. From ash - es to the liv - ing font Your

Church must jour - ney, Lord, Bap - tized in grace, in
voice speaks deep with - in, Re - turn - ing us to

Church must jour - ney still, Through cross and tomb to

grace re - newed By your most ho - ly word.
ways of truth And turn - ing us from sin.

East - er joy, In Spir - it - fire ful - filled.

Year A

Sundays I & II
3. From desert to the mountaintop
   In Christ our way we see,
   So, tempered by temptation's might
   We might transfigured be.

Sunday III
3. For thirsting hearts let waters flow,
   Our fainting souls revive;
   And at the well your waters give
   Our everlasting life.

Sunday IV
3. We sit beside the road and plead,
   "Come, save us, David's son!"
   Now with your vision heal our eyes,
   The world's true Light alone.

Sunday V
3. Our graves split open, bring us back,
   Your promise to proclaim;
   To darkened tombs call out, "Arise!"
   And glorify your name.

Year B

Sundays I & II
3. From desert to the mountaintop
   In Christ our way we see,
   So, tempered by temptation's might
   We might transfigured be.

Sunday III
3. Come, purify our hearts and lives,
   Cast out our sinful ways;
   As temples of the Spirit, cleansed,
   Restore us for your praise.

Sunday IV
3. The Son of Man is lifted up,
   Our eyes behold the sign:
   You are God's own beloved Son,
   The source of life divine.

Sunday V
3. Unless, like grains of wheat, we fall
   Upon the ground to die,
   We cannot share the gift of life,
   Raised up, like you, on high.

Year C
Sundays I & II
3. From desert to the mountaintop
   In Christ our way we see,
   So, tempered by temptation's might
   We might transfigured be.

Sunday III
3. You call us to be penitent,
   You tend us patiently,
   Preserving us from perishing,
   So fruitful we might be.

Sunday IV
3. When we repent, you run to us,
   Forgiving arms spread wide;
   You celebrate when we return,
   And come home to your side.

Sunday V
3. When we self-righteously condemn,
   You ask: "Who has no sin?"
   We hear you say "Go, sin no more."
   New life in you begins.

Text: Alan J. Hommerding, b.1956, © 1994, 2011, World Library Publications
Tune: ST. FLAVIAN, CM; John Day's *Psalter*, 1562

Return to God / Volvamos Hoy a Nuestro Dios   563

Refrain / Estribillo

Re - turn to God with all your heart, the source of grace and
Vol - va - mos hoy a nues - tro Dios, Se - ñor de to - da

mer - cy; come seek the ten - der faith - ful - ness of God.
gra - cia, bus - can - do su per - dón y le - al - tad.

Verses / Estrofas

1. Now the time of grace has come,
   the day of salvation;
   come and learn now the way of our God.

2. I will take your heart of stone
   and place a heart within you,
   a heart of compassion and love.

3. If you break the chains of oppression,
   if you set the pris'ner free;
   if you share your bread with the hungry,
   give protection to the lost;
   give a shelter to the homeless,
   clothe the naked in your midst,
   then your light shall break forth
     like the dawn.

1. *Día de la salvación,*
   y tiempo favorable;
   caminemos por las sendas de Dios.

2. *Quitaré tu corazón de piedra;*
   te daré un corazón
   de amor y compasión.

3. *Si tú rompes vínculos injustos,*
   y a los presos das libertad;
   ofreciendo pan al hambriento,
   protección al extraviado;
   dando abrigo a quien está
     sin techo,
   y vestido al desnudo;
   surgirá tu luz como la aurora.

Text: Marty Haugen, b.1950; tr. by Ronald F. Krisman, b.1946
Tune: Marty Haugen, b.1950
© 1990, 1991, tr. © 2005, GIA Publications, Inc.

564 Lord, Who throughout These Forty Days

1. Lord, who through-out these for - ty days For
2. As you with Sa - tan did con - tend And
3. As you did hun - ger and did thirst, So
4. And through these days of pen - i - tence, And
5. A - bide with us that, when this life Of

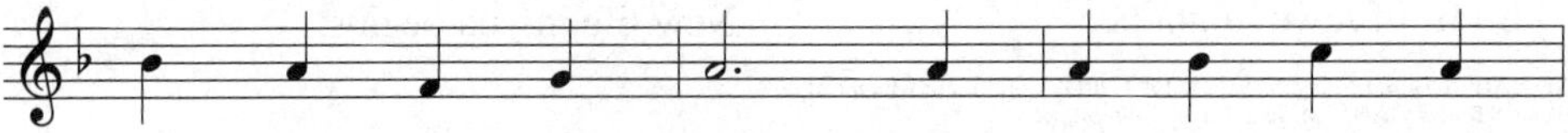

us did fast and pray, Teach us to o - ver -
did the vic - t'ry win, O give us strength in
teach us, gra - cious Lord, To die to self, and
through your Pas - sion - tide, For ev - er - more, in
suf - fer - ing is past, An East - er of un -

come our sins, And close by you to stay.
you to fight, In you to con - quer sin.
on - ly live By your most ho - ly word.
life and death, O Lord, with us a - bide.
end - ing joy We may at - tain at last!

Text: Claudia F. Hernaman, 1838–1898, alt.
Tune: ST. FLAVIAN, CM; John Day's *Psalter,* 1562; harm. based on the original *faux-bourdon* setting

565 Forty Days and Forty Nights

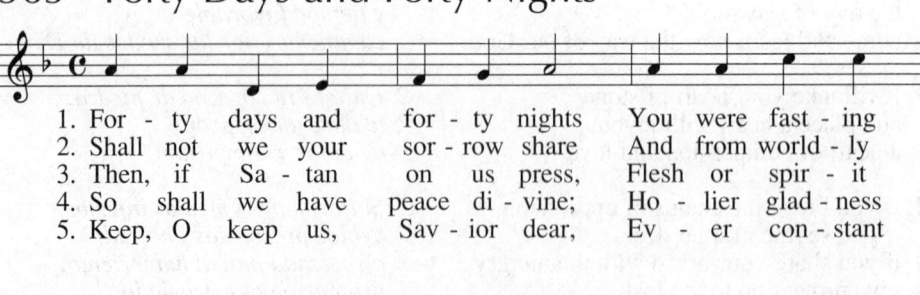

1. For - ty days and for - ty nights You were fast - ing
2. Shall not we your sor - row share And from world - ly
3. Then, if Sa - tan on us press, Flesh or spir - it
4. So shall we have peace di - vine; Ho - lier glad - ness
5. Keep, O keep us, Sav - ior dear, Ev - er con - stant

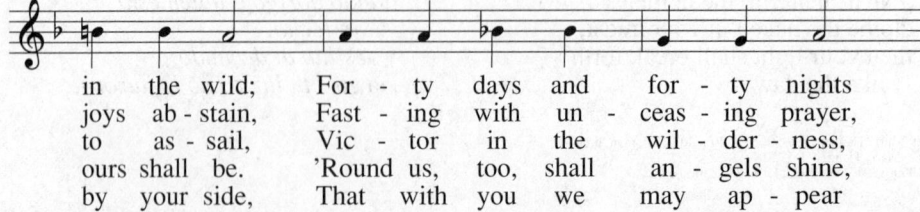

in the wild; For - ty days and for - ty nights
joys ab - stain, Fast - ing with un - ceas - ing prayer,
to as - sail, Vic - tor in the wil - der - ness,
ours shall be. 'Round us, too, shall an - gels shine,
by your side, That with you we may ap - pear

Tempt - ed, and yet un - de - filed.
Strong with you to suf - fer pain?
Grant we may not faint nor fail!
Such as served you faith - ful - ly.
At the e - ter - nal East - er - tide.

Text: George H. Smyttan, 1822–1870, alt.
Tune: HEINLEIN, 7 7 7 7; attr. to Martin Herbst, 1654–1681, *Nürnbergisches Gesangbuch*, 1676

Again We Keep This Solemn Fast 566

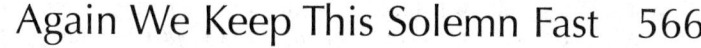

1. A - gain we keep this sol - emn fast,
2. The law and proph - ets from of old
3. More spar - ing, there - fore, let us make
4. Let us a - void each harm - ful way
5. We pray, O bless - ed Three in One,

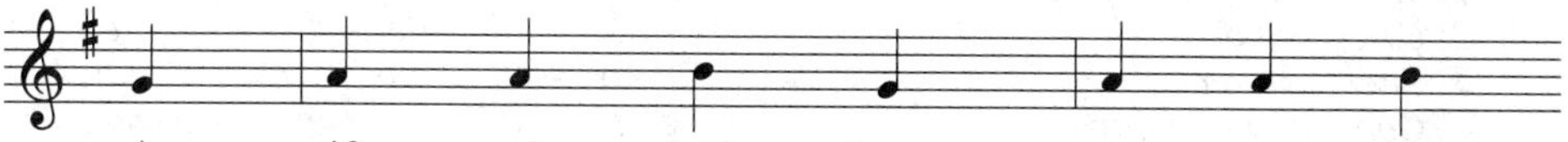

A gift of faith from a - ges past,
In fig - ured ways this Lent fore - told,
The words we speak, the food we take,
That lures the care - less mind a - stray;
Our God while end - less a - ges run,

These for - ty days that, year by year,
Which Christ, all a - ges' Lord and Guide,
Our sleep, our laugh - ter, ev - 'ry sense;
By watch - ful prayer our spir - its free
That this, our Lent of for - ty days,

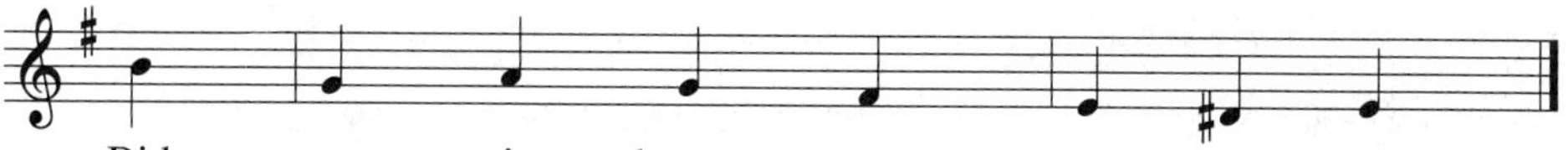

Bid con - trite hearts to Christ draw near.
In these last days has sanc - ti - fied.
Learn peace through ho - ly pen - i - tence.
From schem - ing of the En - e - my.
May bring us growth and give you praise.

Text: *Ex more docti mystico*; ascr. to St. Gregory the Great, c.540–604; tr. by Peter J. Scagnelli, b.1949, after John M. Neale, 1818–1866,
© 1975, Peter J. Scagnelli, published by World Library Publications
Tune: ERHALT UNS HERR, LM; Klug's *Geistliche Lieder*, 1543; harm. by J. S. Bach, 1685–1750

Alternate tune: OLD HUNDREDTH

567 Parce Domine / Spare Us, Gracious Lord /
Ten Piedad, Señor

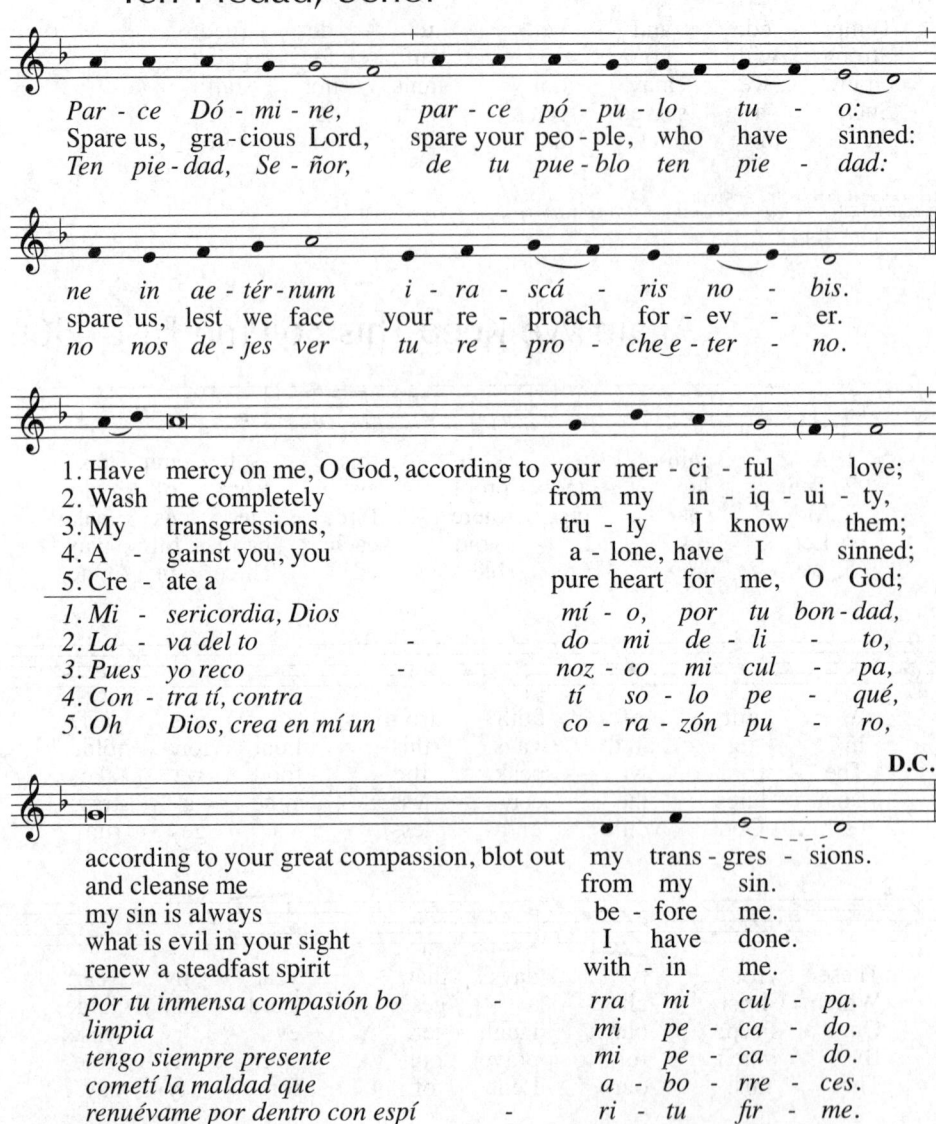

Par - ce Dó - mi - ne, par - ce pó - pu - lo tu - o:
Spare us, gra - cious Lord, spare your peo - ple, who have sinned:
Ten pie - dad, Se - ñor, de tu pue - blo ten pie - dad:

ne in ae - tér - num i - ra - scá - ris no - bis.
spare us, lest we face your re - proach for - ev - er.
no nos de - jes ver tu re - pro - che̱e - ter - no.

1. Have mercy on me, O God, according to your mer - ci - ful love;
2. Wash me completely from my in - iq - ui - ty,
3. My transgressions, tru - ly I know them;
4. A - gainst you, you a - lone, have I sinned;
5. Cre - ate a pure heart for me, O God;

1. Mi - sericordia, Dios mí - o, por tu bon - dad,
2. La - va del to - do mi de - li - to,
3. Pues yo reco - noz - co mi cul - pa,
4. Con - tra tí, contra tí so - lo pe - qué,
5. Oh Dios, crea en mí un co - ra - zón pu - ro,

D.C.

according to your great compassion, blot out my trans - gres - sions.
and cleanse me from my sin.
my sin is always be - fore me.
what is evil in your sight I have done.
renew a steadfast spirit with - in me.

por tu inmensa compasión bo - rra mi cul - pa.
limpia mi pe - ca - do.
tengo siempre presente mi pe - ca - do.
cometí la maldad que a - bo - rre - ces.
renuévame por dentro con espí - ri - tu fir - me.

Text: *Parce Domine*; Joel 2:17; refrain, English and Spanish, tr. by Ronald F. Krisman, b.1946, © 2011, GIA Publications, Inc.; verses, Psalm 51:3–6, 12,
The Revised Grail Psalms, © 2010, Conception Abbey and The Grail, admin. by GIA Publications, Inc.; Spanish verses, © 1970,
Conferencia Episcopal Española
Tune: PARCE DOMINE; Mode I with Tonus Peregrinus; acc. by Robert LeBlanc, b.1948, © 1986, GIA Publications, Inc.

Jerusalem, My Destiny 568

Refrain

I have fixed my eyes on your hills, Je-ru-sa-lem, my des-ti-ny! Though I can-not see the end for me, I can-not turn a-way. We have set our hearts for the way; this jour-ney is our des-ti-ny. Let no one walk a-lone. The jour-ney makes us one.

Verses

1. Oth-er spir-its, less-er gods, have court-ed me with lies.
2. See, I leave the past be-hind; a new land calls to me.
3. In my thirst, you let me drink the wa-ters of your life.
4. All the worlds I have not seen you o-pen to my view.
5. To the tombs I went to mourn the hope I thought was gone.

D.C.

Here a-mong you I have found a truth which bids me rise.
Here a-mong you now I find a glimpse of what might be.
Here a-mong you I have met the sa-viour, Je-sus Christ.
Here a-mong you I have found a vi-sion, bright and new.
Here a-mong you I a-woke to un-ex-pect-ed dawn.

Text: Rory Cooney, b.1952
Tune: Rory Cooney, b.1952
© 1990, GIA Publications, Inc.

569 The Cross of Jesus

1. Come, O God, re - new your peo - ple,
2. Deep with - in cre - ate a new heart;
3. In the dark - ness that sur - rounds us
4. Call us forth to walk in jus - tice;

We who long to see your face.
Melt a - way the win - ter chill.
We have lost you from our sight.
Res - cue us from sin and grave.

Strength - en hearts that have grown fee - ble;
Help us now to make a new start;
E - ven though your love has found us,
Through the pow - er of your Spir - it,

Fill our lives with truth and grace.
Help us now to know your will.
We em - brace the powers of night.
Breathe in us the breath that saves.

On - ly you can win our free - dom;
Washed in wa - ters of for - give - ness,
Scat - ter now our deep - est dark - ness;
Strength - en us in our com - mun - ion,

On - ly you can bring us peace.
Cleansed in wa - ters of new birth,
Guide our hearts in - to the light.
One in Word and cup and bread.

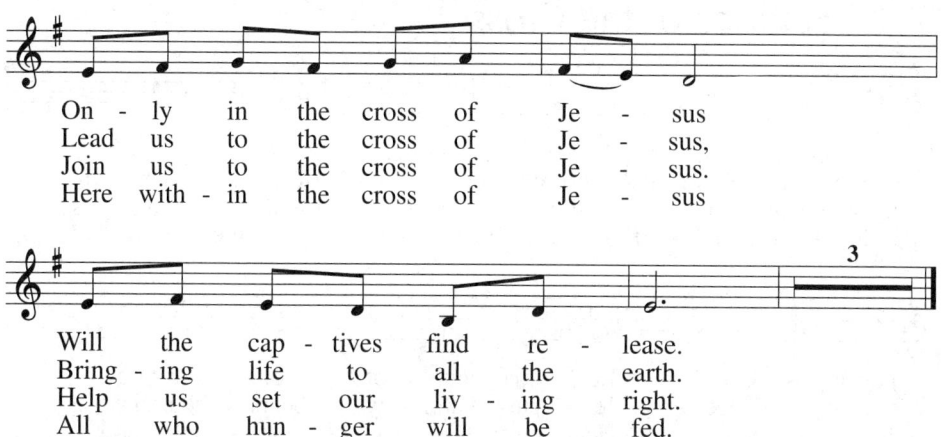

On - ly in the cross of Je - sus
Lead us to the cross of Je - sus,
Join us to the cross of Je - sus.
Here with - in the cross of Je - sus

Will the cap - tives find re - lease.
Bring - ing life to all the earth.
Help us set our liv - ing right.
All who hun - ger will be fed.

Text: Francis Patrick O'Brien, b.1958
Tune: TREMONT, 8 7 8 7 D; Francis Patrick O'Brien, b.1958
© 1996, GIA Publications, Inc.

The Glory of These Forty Days   570

1. The glo - ry of these for - ty days We
2. A - lone and fast - ing Mo - ses saw The
3. So Dan - iel trained his mys - tic sight, De -
4. Then grant, O God, that we may, too, Re -

cel - e - brate with songs of praise; For Christ, through whom all
lov - ing God who gave the law; And to E - li - jah,
liv - ered from the li - ons' might; And John, the Bride-groom's
turn in fast and prayer to you. Our spir - its strength - en

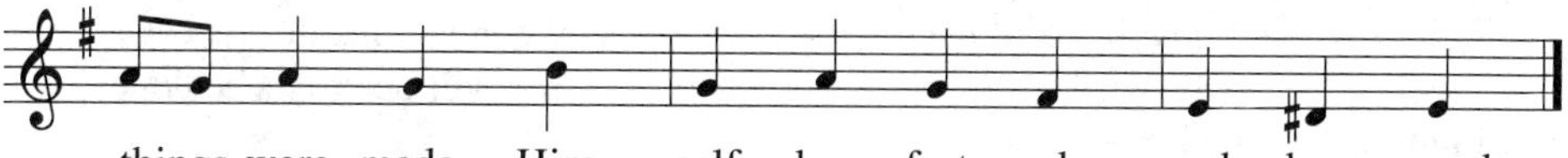

things were made, Him - self has fast - ed and has prayed.
fast - ing, came The steeds and char - i - ots of flame.
friend, be - came The her - ald of Mes - si - ah's name.
with your grace, And give us joy to see your face.

Text: *Clarum decus jejunii*; ascr. to St. Gregory the Great, c.540–604; tr. by Maurice F. Bell, 1862–1947, alt.
Tune: ERHALT UNS HERR, LM; Klug's *Geistliche Lieder*, 1543; harm. by Ronald F. Krisman, b.1946, © 2011, GIA Publications, Inc.

Alternate tune: OLD HUNDREDTH

571 Stations of the Cross

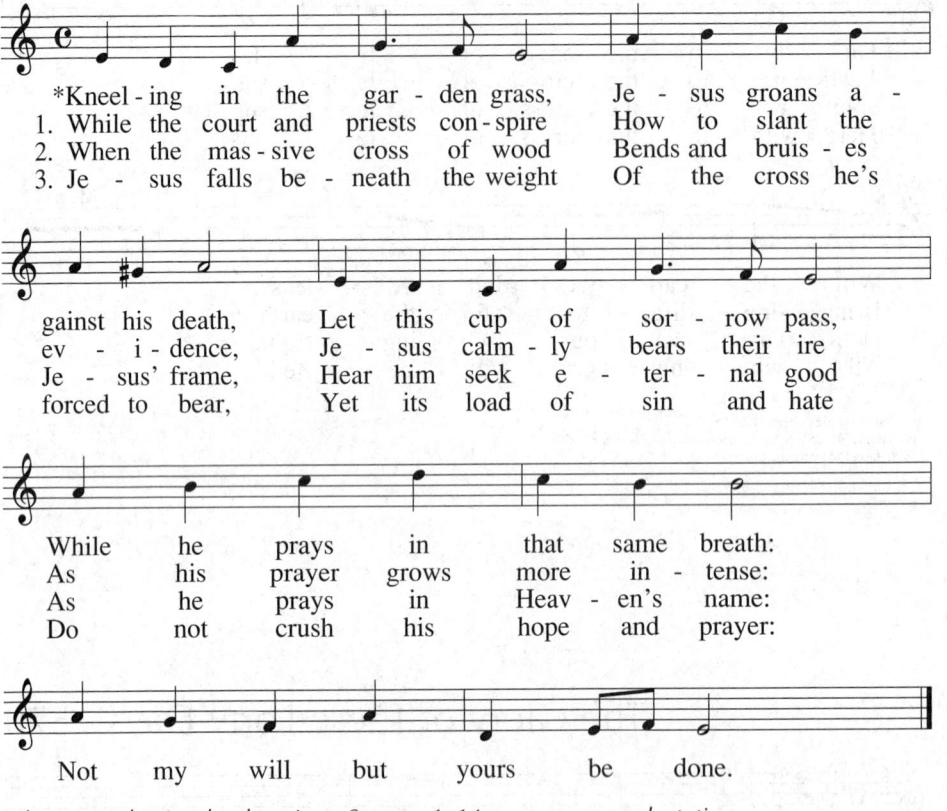

*Kneel - ing in the gar - den grass, Je - sus groans a -
1. While the court and priests con - spire How to slant the
2. When the mas - sive cross of wood Bends and bruis - es
3. Je - sus falls be - neath the weight Of the cross he's

gainst his death, Let this cup of sor - row pass,
ev - i - dence, Je - sus calm - ly bears their ire
Je - sus' frame, Hear him seek e - ter - nal good
forced to bear, Yet its load of sin and hate

While he prays in that same breath:
As his prayer grows more in - tense:
As he prays in Heav - en's name:
Do not crush his hope and prayer:

Not my will but yours be done.

This stanza begins the devotions. Stanzas 1–14 accompany each station.

1. Jesus is condemned to death

2. Jesus carries his Cross

3. Jesus falls the first time

4. Jesus meets his afflicted mother
Jesus reads in Mary's eyes
all the sorrow mothers bear,
and he prays his friend supplies
grace to strengthen her own prayer:
    Not my will but yours be done.

**5. Simon of Cyrene helps Jesus to
    carry his Cross**
We with Simon of Cyrene
help the Savior bear the cross.
Step by step we slowly glean
what true faith and prayer will cost:
    Not my will but yours be done.

6. Veronica wipes the face of Jesus
Seek the courage and the grace
that Veronica displays
when she wipes the bleeding face
of the one who bravely prays:
    Not my will but yours be done.

7. Jesus falls the second time
Jesus trips and falls again
as he struggles through the street
where the mob's unceasing din
mocks the prayer his lips repeat:
    Not my will but yours be done.

8. Jesus meets the women of Jerusalem
Christ directs the women's tears
toward the coming judgment day
when God weighs our faithless years
with our willingness to pray:
    Not my will but yours be done.

9. Jesus falls a third time
Jesus stumbles one last time,
nearly broken by the load,
yet by prayer finds strength to climb
Calvary's final stretch of road:
    Not my will but yours be done.

10. Jesus is stripped of his clothes
Naked to the sun and clouds
and the jeers and gawking stare
of the soldiers and the crowds,
Christ continues with his prayer:
    Not my will but yours be done.

11. Jesus is nailed to the Cross
While the soldiers throw their dice,
they ignore their victim's groans,
lost to them the sacrifice
and the prayer that Jesus moans:
    Not my will but yours be done.

12. Jesus dies on the Cross
Jesus gives one loud last cry
at the moment of his death
while his prayer moves heaven's sky
with his final, parting breath:
    Not my will but yours be done.

**13. The body of Jesus is taken
    down from the Cross**
As they take the body down
and they wrap it in a sheet,
in their hearts they hear the sound
that his lips no more repeat:
    Not my will but yours be done.

14. Jesus is laid in the tomb
Quiet is the hollowed cave.
Peace and tears and grief descend.
Mourners offer at the grave
what they learned from Christ their
    friend:
    Not my will but yours be done.

Text: Thomas H. Troeger, b.1945, © 1994, Oxford University Press
Tune: VIA CRUCIS, 7 7 7 7 with refrain; William P. Rowan, b.1951, © 1995, GIA Publications, Inc.

Salvator Mundi 572

Sal-va-tor mun-di sal-va nos. Sal-va-tor mun-di sal-va nos.

Sal-va nos, sal-va nos. Sal-va-tor mun-di sal-va nos.

Text: *Savior of the world, save us;* Taizé Community, 1980
Tune: Jacques Berthier, 1923–1994
© 1980, Les Presses de Taizé, GIA Publications, Inc., agent

573 Somebody's Knockin' at Your Door

Text: African American spiritual
Tune: SOMEBODY'S KNOCKIN', Irregular; African American spiritual; harm. by Richard Proulx, 1937–2010, © 1986, GIA Publications, Inc.

Deep Within 574

Refrain

Deep with-in I will plant my law, not on stone, but in your heart. Fol-low me, I will bring you back, you will be my own, and I will be your God.

Verses

1. I will give you a new heart, a new spir-it with-
2. Seek my face, and see your
3. Re-turn to me, with all your

D.C.

1. in you, for I will be your strength.
2. God, for I will be your hope.
3. heart, and I will bring you back.

Text: Jeremiah 31:33, Ezekiel 36:26, Joel 2:12; David Haas, b.1957
Tune: David Haas, b.1957; acc. by Jeanne Cotter, b.1964
© 1987, GIA Publications, Inc.

575 Mercy, O God

Refrain

Mer-cy, O God, have mer-cy on us. Send down your mer-cy to set us free. Mer-cy, O God, have mer-cy on us. Send down your mer-cy to set us free.

Verses

1. Gath-er the peo-ple, the chil-dren, the eld-ers; come now and gath-er be-fore the Lord. O-pen your hearts to com-pas-sion and mer-cy; O-pen your hearts to the Lord.
2. Now is the hour, the day of sal-va-tion; now is the time to re-turn to God. O-pen your lives to for-give-ness and mer-cy; O-pen your lives to the Lord.
3. Long is the jour-ney and steep are the moun-tains, come now and guide us, O gra-cious God. Show us your face, give us hope for the jour-ney; Lead us to walk in your love.
4. Wash us a-new in your life-giv-ing wa-ter; come quench the thirst of our yearn-ing hearts. Break through the si-lence, the fear and the long-ing; em-brace us with un-end-ing love.
5. Once lost in dark-ness you did not for-sake us, but called us your chil-dren and gave us light. O-pen our eyes, come re-move all our blind-ness. O-pen our eyes to your love.
6. Wake, O sleep-er, a-wake from your slum-ber; rise from the chains of the dark, cold tomb. Walk in the light of com-pas-sion and mer-cy; walk in the light of the Lord.

D.C.

Communion Verses

1. Now, at this ta - ble, you call us to - geth - er,
2. Out - cast and sin - ner be - long at this ta - ble; you
3. Bread come from heav - en, in Christ's bod - y bro - ken, will
4. Here is sal - va - tion, a - bun - dant and flow-ing, poured
5. Lord, in your jus - tice you raise up the low - ly; the
6. Heav - en and earth come to praise at this ta - ble;

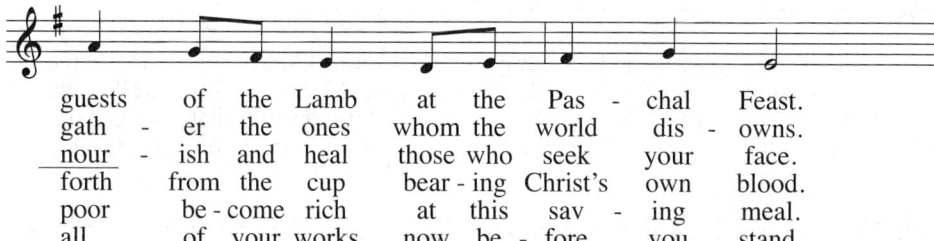

guests of the Lamb at the Pas - chal Feast.
gath - er the ones whom the world dis - owns.
nour - ish and heal those who seek your face.
forth from the cup bear - ing Christ's own blood.
poor be - come rich at this sav - ing meal.
all of your works now be - fore you stand.

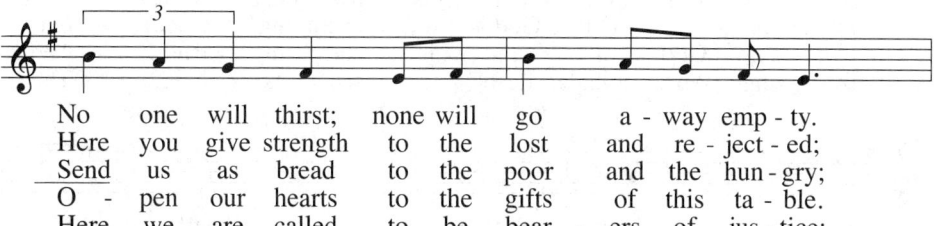

No one will thirst; none will go a - way emp - ty.
Here you give strength to the lost and re - ject - ed;
Send us as bread to the poor and the hun - gry;
O - pen our hearts to the gifts of this ta - ble.
Here we are called to be bear - ers of jus - tice;
Teach us to nour - ish and care for cre - a - tion,

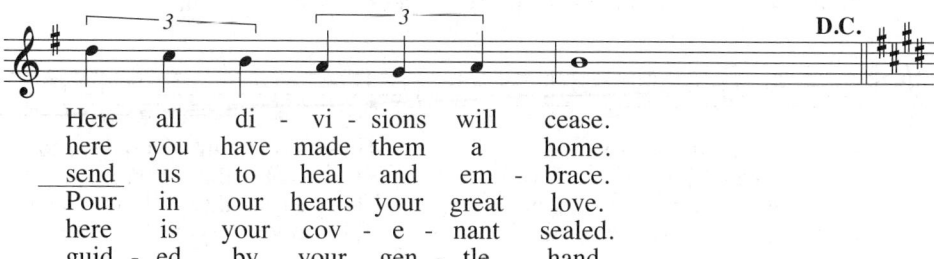

D.C.

Here all di - vi - sions will cease.
here you have made them a home.
send us to heal and em - brace.
Pour in our hearts your great love.
here is your cov - e - nant sealed.
guid - ed by your gen - tle hand.

7. Christ, the Good Shepherd, has led us to freedom;
   all are released from the bonds of sin.
   Call us to love with the heart of the Shepherd;
   here let our new life begin.

8. Love beyond measure has brought us together.
   Love calls us forth as one family.
   Send us to bear this great love to all people:
   Love born of death on a tree.

Text: Francis Patrick O'Brien, b.1958
Tune: Francis Patrick O'Brien, b.1958

576 Led by the Spirit

1. Led by the Spir - it of our God, We go to fast and pray With Christ in - to the wil - der - ness; We join his pas - chal way. "Rend not your gar - ments, rend your hearts. Turn back your lives to me." Thus says our kind and gra - cious God, Whose reign is lib - er - ty.

2. Led by the Spir - it, we con - front Temp - ta - tion face to face, And know full well we must re - ly On God's re - deem - ing grace. On bread a - lone we can - not live, But nour - ished by the Word We seek the will of God to do: This is our drink and food.

3. Led by the Spir - it, now draw near The wa - ters of re - birth With hearts that long to wor - ship God In spir - it and in truth. "Who - ev - er drinks the drink I give Shall nev - er thirst a - gain." Thus says the Lord who died for us, Our Sav - ior, kin, and friend.

4. Led by the Spir - it, now sing praise To God the Trin - i - ty: The Source of Life, the liv - ing Word Made flesh to set us free, The Spir - it blow - ing where it will To make us friends of God: This mys - t'ry far be - yond our reach, Yet near in heal - ing love.

Text: Bob Hurd, b.1950, © 1996, Bob Hurd. Published by OCP.
Tune: KINGSFOLD, CMD; English traditional; harm. by Ralph Vaughan Williams, 1872–1958

Gather Us in Mercy, Lord 577

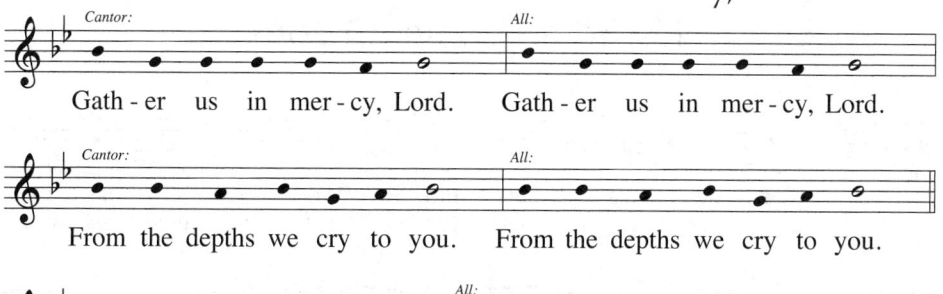

Gath-er us in mer-cy, Lord. Gath-er us in mer-cy, Lord.

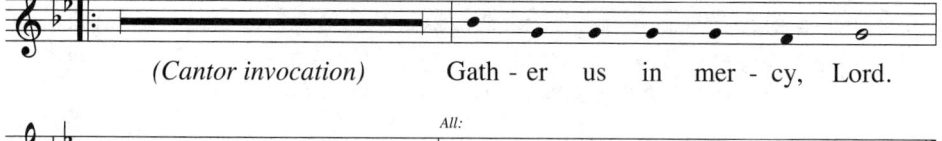

From the depths we cry to you. From the depths we cry to you.

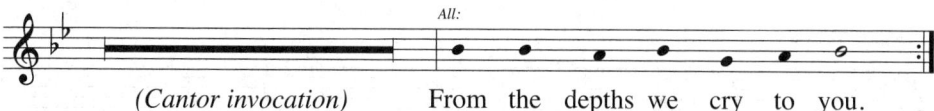

(Cantor invocation) Gath-er us in mer-cy, Lord.

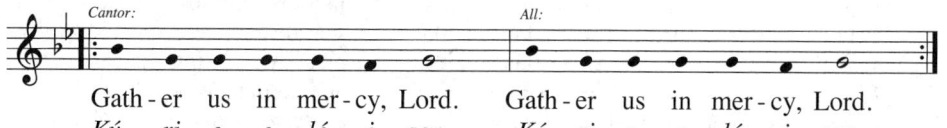

(Cantor invocation) From the depths we cry to you.

Gath-er us in mer-cy, Lord. Gath-er us in mer-cy, Lord.
Ký - ri - e, e - lé - i - son. Ký - ri - e, e - lé - i - son.

Text: Gabe Huck, b.1941
Tune: Traditional chant, adapt. and arr. by Tony E. Alonso, b.1980
© 2005, GIA Publications, Inc.

Grant to Us, O Lord 578

Refrain

Grant to us, O Lord, a heart re - newed;

re - cre-ate in us your own Spir - it, Lord!

Verses

1. Behold, the days are coming, says the Lord our God,
   when I will make a new covenant with the house of Israel.

2. Deep within their being I will implant my law;
   I will write it in their hearts.

3. I will be their God, and they shall be my people.

4. And for all their faults I will grant forgiveness;
   nevermore will I remember their sins.

Text: Jeremiah 31:31–34; Lucien Deiss, CSSp, 1921–2007
Tune: Lucien Deiss, CSSp, 1921–2007
© 1965, 1966, 1968, 1973, World Library Publications

579 Perdona a Tu Pueblo, Señor / Forgive Us, Your People, O Lord

Estribillo / Refrain

Per - do - na‿a tu pue - blo, Se - ñor. Per - do - na‿a tu
For - give us, your peo - ple, O Lord. For - give us, your

pue - blo, per - dó - na - le, Se - ñor.
peo - ple, for - give us, ho - ly Lord.

Estrofas / Verses

1. No‿es - tés e - ter - na - men - te‿e - no - ja -
2. Por las pro - fun - das lla - gas cru - e -
3. Por las he - ri - das de pies y ma -

1. Look not up - on your peo - ple with wrath, O
2. You stretch your arms to love and to heal, O
3. For wounds that we in - flict on your hands, O

do. No‿es - tés e - ter - na - men - te‿e - no -
les, Por las sa - li - vas y por las
nos, Por los a - zo - tes tan in - hu -

Christ; Look not up - on your peo - ple with
Christ; We an - swer love with hate; now we
Christ; For hurt and vio - lence spread through our

D.C.

ja - do: Per - dó - na - le, Se - ñor.
hie - les: Per - dó - na - le, Se - ñor.
ma - nos: Per - dó - na - le, Se - ñor.

wrath, O Christ: For - give us, ho - ly Lord.
kneel, O Christ: For - give us, ho - ly Lord.
lands, O Christ: For - give us, ho - ly Lord.

4. Por los tres clavos que te clavaron,
   Y las espinas que te punzaron:
   Perdónale, Señor.

5. Por las tres horas de tu agonía,
   En que por Madre diste a María:
   Perdónale, Señor.

6. Por la abertura de tu costado,
   No estés eternamente enojado:
   Perdónale, Señor.

7. Por ese amor que nos redimía
   Y es nuestra fuerza de cada día:
   Perdónale, Señor.

4. *For dignity we mock with our thorns,*
   O Christ;
   For outcast ones we jeer at and scorn,
   O Christ: Forgive us, holy Lord.

5. *For hours you spent in pain on the cross,*
   O Christ;
   With Mary, comfort all stunned by loss,
   O Christ: Forgive us, holy Lord.

6. *For all the sorrows borne on your path,*
   O Christ;
   Look not upon your people with wrath,
   O Christ: Forgive us, holy Lord.

7. *With love that draws us back when*
   we stray, O Christ;
   Redeeming us afresh every day,
   O Christ: Forgive us, holy Lord.

Test: Anonymous; tr. by Mary Louise Bringle, b.1953, © 2005, GIA Publications, Inc.
Tune: Anonymous; harm. by Ronald F. Krisman, b.1946, © 2005, GIA Publications, Inc.

Kyrie 580

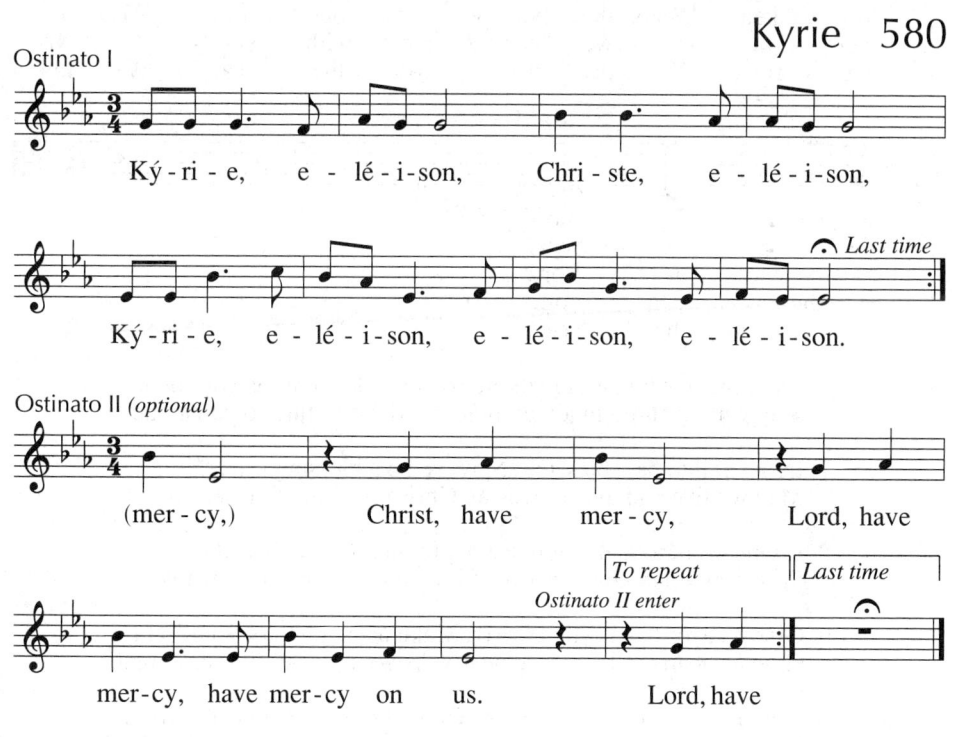

Text: Marty Haugen, b.1950
Tune: Marty Haugen, b.1950
© 2001, GIA Publications, Inc.

581 Tree of Life

1. Tree of Life and awe-some mys-t'ry, In your
2. Seed that dies to rise in glo-ry, May we
3. We re-mem - ber truth once spo-ken, Love passed
4. Gen-tle Je - sus, might-y Spir-it, Come in-
5. Christ, you lead and we shall fol-low, Stum-bling

death we are re - born, Though you die in all of
see our-selves in you, If we learn to live your
on through act and word, Ev-'ry per - son lost and
flame our hearts a - new, We may all your joy in-
though our steps may be, One with you in joy and

his - t'ry, Still you rise with ev-'ry morn, Still you
sto - ry We may die to rise a - new, We may
bro - ken Wears the bod-y of our Lord, Wears the
her - it If we bear the cross with you, If we
sor - row, We the riv-er, you the sea, We the

rise with ev - 'ry morn.
die to rise a - new.
bod-y of our Lord.
bear the cross with you.
riv-er, you the sea.

6. From the dawning of creation, You have loved us as your own;
Stay with us through all temptation, Make us turn to you alone.

7. In our call to be a blessing, May we be a blessing true;
May we live and die confessing Christ as Lord of all we do.

8. Living Water of salvation, Be the fountain of each soul;
Springing up in new creation, Flow in us and make us whole.

9. Give us eyes to see you clearly, Make us children of your light;
Give us hearts to live more nearly As your gospel shining bright.

10. God of all our fear and sorrow, God who lives beyond our death;
Hold us close through each tomorrow, Love as near as every breath.

Text: Marty Haugen, b.1950
Tune: THOMAS, 8 7 8 77; Marty Haugen, b.1950
© 1984, GIA Publications, Inc.

Adoramus Te Christe 582

Canon Refrain

A - do - rá - mus te Chri - ste, a - do - rá - mus te Chri - ste,

a - do - rá - mus te Chri - ste, a - do - rá - mus Chri - ste.

Text: Antiphon from Good Friday Liturgy; *We adore you, O Christ, and we bless you, because by your holy cross you have redeemed the world.*
Tune: Marty Haugen, b.1950, © 1984, GIA Publications, Inc.

Hold Us in Your Mercy: Penitential Litany 583

Cantor: Hold us in your mer - cy. All: Hold us in your mer - cy.

Cantor: Hold us in your mer - cy. All: Hold us in your mer - cy.

Cantor: (Invocation) All: Hold us in your mer - cy.

Cantor: (Invocation) All: Hold us in your mer - cy.

Text: Rory Cooney, b.1952
Tune: Based on PARCE DOMINE; Gary Daigle, b.1957
© 1993, GIA Publications, Inc.

584 This Is the Time of Fulfillment

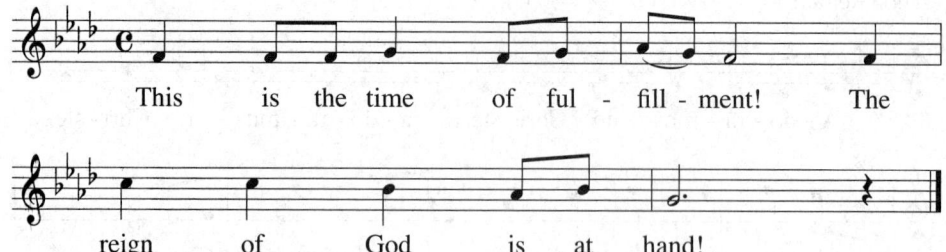

This is the time of ful - fill - ment! The

reign of God is at hand!

Text: Mark 1:15, James J. Chepponis, b.1956
Tune: James J. Chepponis, b.1956
© 1994, GIA Publications, Inc.

585 All Glory, Laud, and Honor

Refrain

All glo - ry, laud, and hon - or To you, Re - deem - er, King!

To whom the lips of chil - dren Made sweet ho - san - nas ring.

Verses

1. You are the King of Is - ra - el And Da - vid's roy - al Son,
2. The com - pa - ny of an - gels Are prais - ing you on high;
3. The peo - ple of the He - brews With palms be - fore you went;
4. To you, be - fore your pas - sion, They sang their hymns of praise.
5. Their prais - es you ac - cept - ed; Ac - cept the prayers we bring,

D.C.

Now in the Lord's Name com - ing, Our King and Bless - ed One.
And we, with all cre - a - tion, In cho - rus make re - ply.
Our praise and prayers and an - thems Be - fore you we pre - sent.
To you, now high ex - alt - ed, Our mel - o - dy we raise.
Great source of love and good - ness, Our Sav - ior and our King.

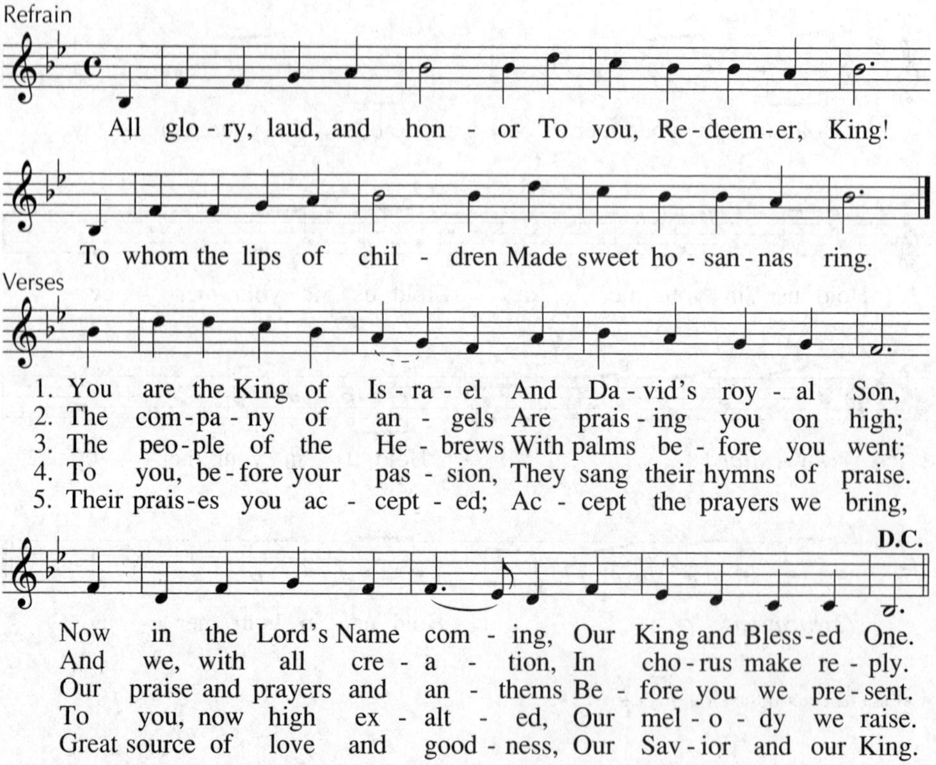

Text: *Gloria, laus et honor;* Theodulph of Orléans, c.760–821; tr. by John M. Neale, 1818–1866, alt.
Tune: ST. THEODULPH, 7 6 7 6 with refrain; Melchior Teschner, 1584–1635

Palm Sunday Processional   586

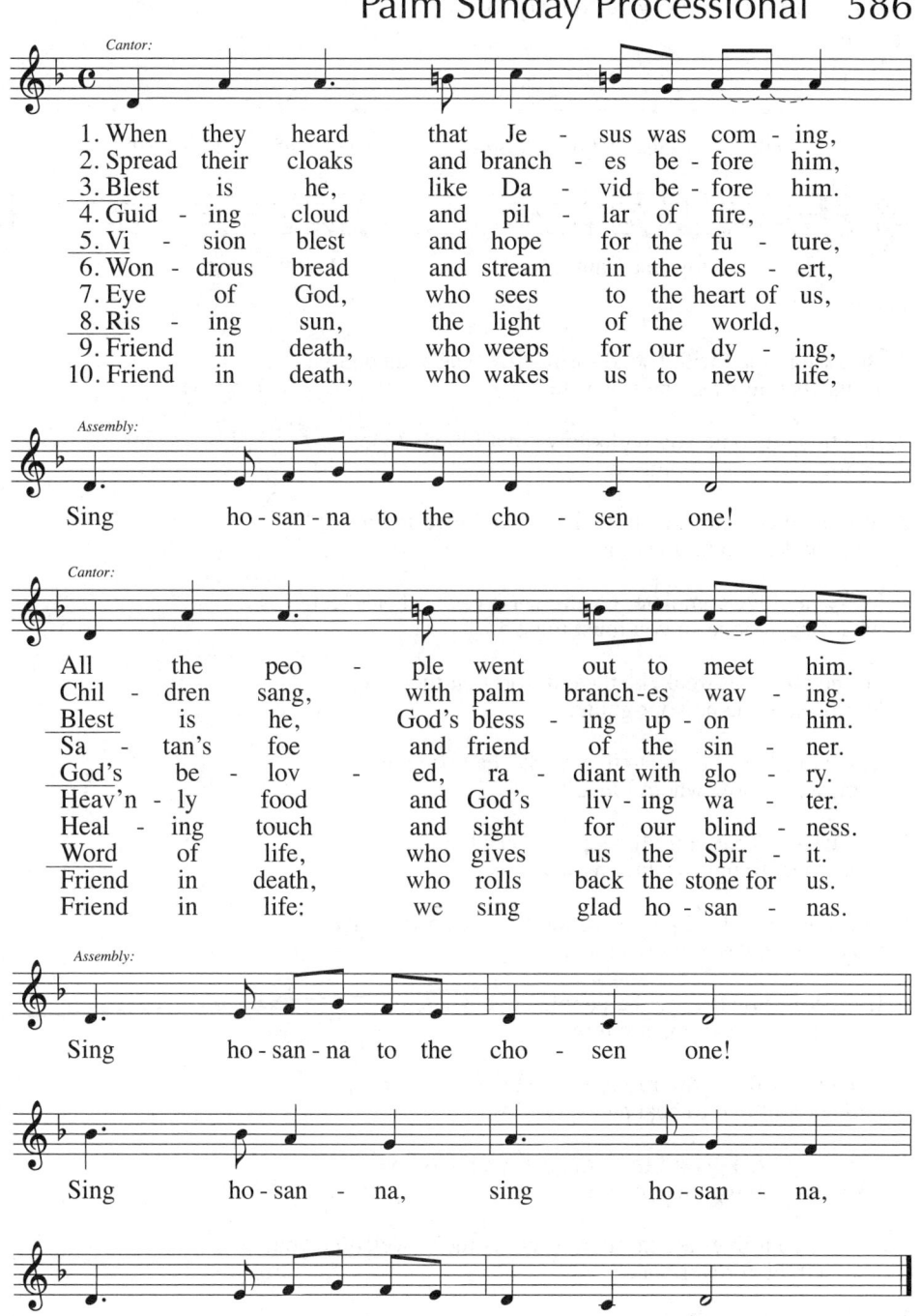

Cantor:

1. When they heard that Je - sus was com - ing,
2. Spread their cloaks and branch - es be - fore him,
3. Blest is he, like Da - vid be - fore him.
4. Guid - ing cloud and pil - lar of fire,
5. Vi - sion blest and hope for the fu - ture,
6. Won - drous bread and stream in the des - ert,
7. Eye of God, who sees to the heart of us,
8. Ris - ing sun, the light of the world,
9. Friend in death, who weeps for our dy - ing,
10. Friend in death, who wakes us to new life,

Assembly:

Sing ho - san - na to the cho - sen one!

Cantor:

All the peo - ple went out to meet him.
Chil - dren sang, with palm branch - es wav - ing.
Blest is he, God's bless - ing up - on him.
Sa - tan's foe and friend of the sin - ner.
God's be - lov - ed, ra - diant with glo - ry.
Heav'n - ly food and God's liv - ing wa - ter.
Heal - ing touch and sight for our blind - ness.
Word of life, who gives us the Spir - it.
Friend in death, who rolls back the stone for us.
Friend in life: we sing glad ho - san - nas.

Assembly:

Sing ho - san - na to the cho - sen one!

Sing ho - san - na, sing ho - san - na,

sing ho - san - na to the cho - sen one!

Text: Rory Cooney, b.1952
Tune: Rory Cooney, b.1952
© 1999, GIA Publications, Inc.

587 This Is My Example

Refrain

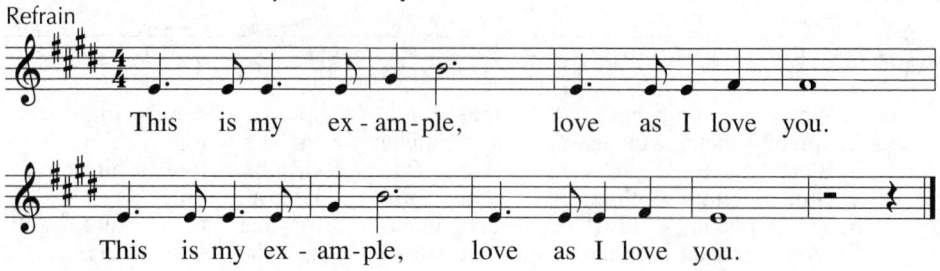

This is my ex-am-ple, love as I love you.

This is my ex-am-ple, love as I love you.

Verses

1. Breaking bread with friends as his life was at an end,
   Jesus knelt to wash their their feet.

2. In a time to come you will know what I have done;
   let me wash you, let me serve.

3. Simon Peter said, "Wash my hands, my feet, my head!"
   Jesus looked on him with love.

4. Make my love complete, go and wash each other's feet;
   what I have done so you must must do.

5. To the poor and weak, be the comfort that they seek;
   let my example be your guide.

6. May your lives be one in this work I have begun;
   come and follow where I lead.

7. Go forth and care for all people ev'rywhere.
   Find your strength within my love.

8. Speak my words of peace. To the captives bring release.
   Go embrace them in my name.

9. If my love you bear to the people ev'rywhere,
   all will know that you are mine.

10. In your faith is pow'r to embrace the darkest hour;
    go without fear to heal and serve.

11. This my life I give; I must die that you may live.
    All this I do for love of you.

12. When your lives are through, I will come to welcome you.
    We will be forever one.

Text: Francis Patrick O'Brien, b.1958
Tune: Francis Patrick O'Brien, b.1958
© 2001, GIA Publications, Inc.

So You Must Do   588

Refrain

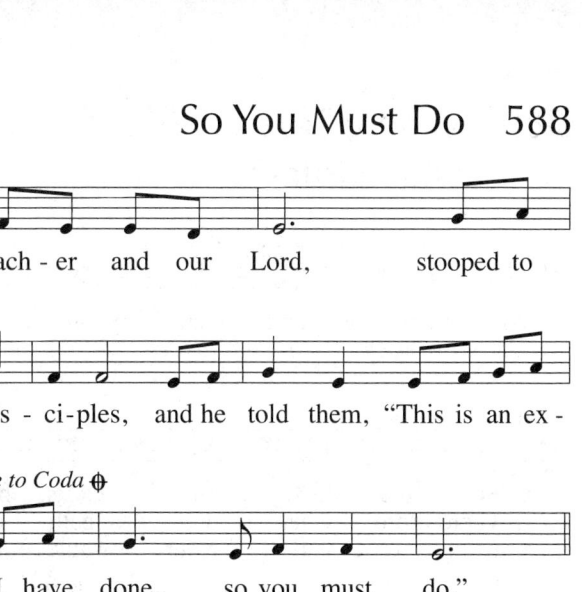

Je - sus, our teach - er and our Lord, stooped to

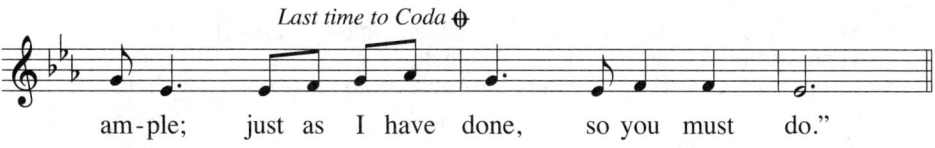

wash the feet of his dis - ci - ples, and he told them, "This is an ex -

Last time to Coda ⊕

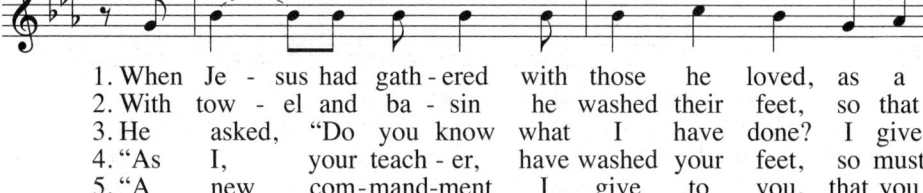

am - ple; just as I have done, so you must do."

Verses

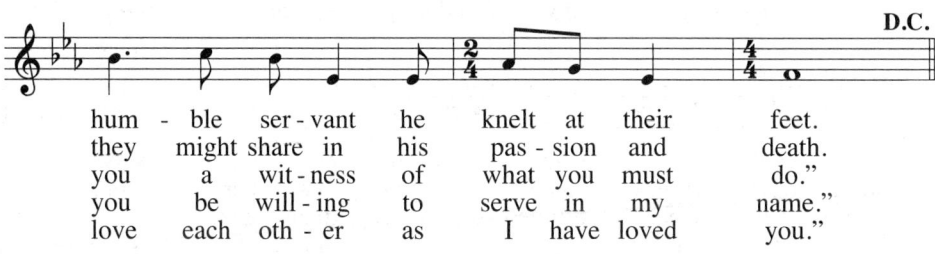

1. When Je - sus had gath - ered with those he loved, as a
2. With tow - el and ba - sin he washed their feet, so that
3. He asked, "Do you know what I have done? I give
4. "As I, your teach - er, have washed your feet, so must
5. "A new com - mand - ment I give to you, that you

D.C.

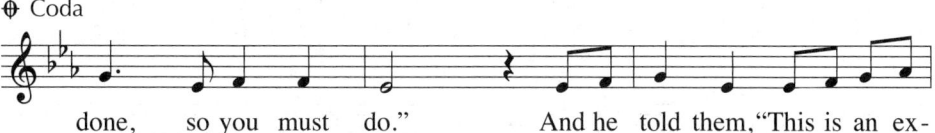

hum - ble ser - vant he knelt at their feet.
they might share in his pas - sion and death.
you a wit - ness of what you must do."
you be will - ing to serve in my name."
love each oth - er as I have loved you."

⊕ Coda

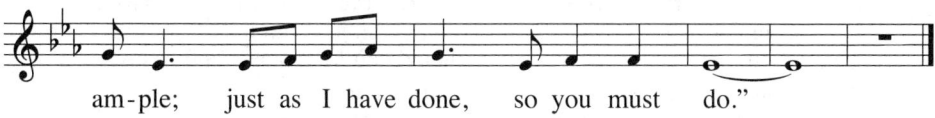

done, so you must do." And he told them, "This is an ex -

am - ple; just as I have done, so you must do."

Text: John 13:1–15, adapt. by Marty Haugen, b.1950
Tune: Marty Haugen, b.1950
© 1998, GIA Publications, Inc.

589 Where True Love and Charity Are Found / Ubi Caritas

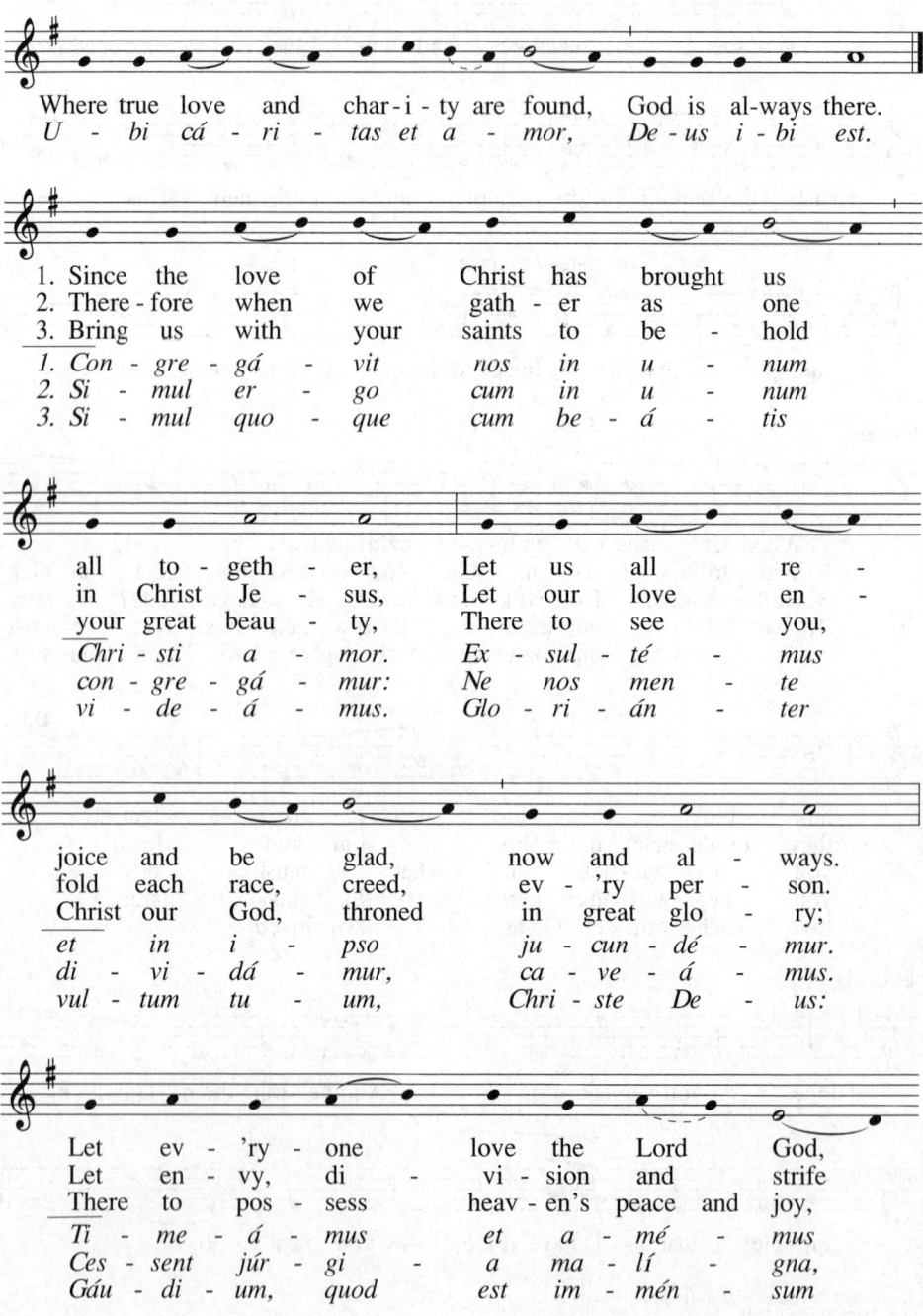

Where true love and char-i-ty are found, God is al-ways there.
U - bi cá - ri - tas et a - mor, De - us i - bi est.

1. Since the love of Christ has brought us
2. There-fore when we gath - er as one
3. Bring us with your saints to be - hold

1. *Con - gre - gá - vit nos in u - num*
2. *Si - mul er - go cum in u - num*
3. *Si - mul quo - que cum be - á - tis*

all to-geth - er, Let us all re -
in Christ Je - sus, Let our love en -
your great beau - ty, There to see you,

Chri - sti a - mor. Ex - sul - té - mus
con - gre - gá - mur: Ne nos men - te
vi - de - á - mus. Glo - ri - án - ter

joice and be glad, now and al - ways.
fold each race, creed, ev - 'ry per - son.
Christ our God, throned in great glo - ry;

et in i - pso ju - cun - dé - mur.
di - vi - dá - mur, ca - ve - á - mus.
vul - tum tu - um, Chri - ste De - us:

Let ev - 'ry - one love the Lord God,
Let en - vy, di - vi - sion and strife
There to pos - sess heav - en's peace and joy,

Ti - me - á - mus et a - mé - mus
Ces - sent júr - gi - a ma - lí - gna,
Gáu - di - um, quod est im - mén - sum

the liv - ing God; And with sin - cere
cease a - mong us; May Christ our Lord
your truth and love, For end - less a -
De - um vi - vum. Et ex cor - de
ces - sent li - tes. Et in mé - di -
at - que pro - bum. Saé - cu - la per

D.C.

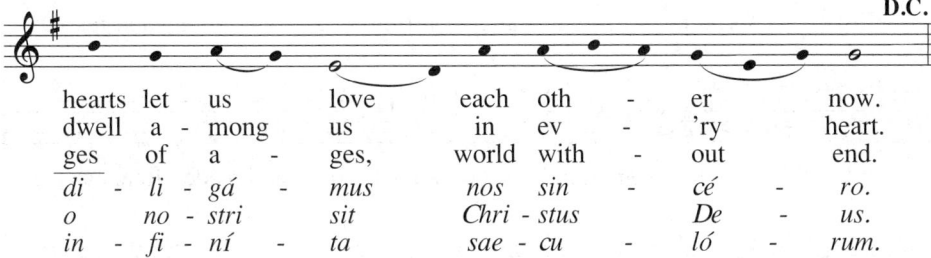

hearts let us love each oth - er now.
dwell a - mong us in ev - 'ry heart.
ges of a - ges, world with - out end.
di - li - gá - mus nos sin - cé - ro.
o no - stri sit Chri - stus De - us.
in - fi - ní - ta sae - cu - ló - rum.

Text: *Ubi caritas et amor*, Latin, 9th C.; tr. by Richard Proulx, 1937–2010, © 1975, 1986, GIA Publications, Inc.
Tune: UBI CARITAS, 12 12 12 12 with refrain; Mode VI; acc. by Richard Proulx, 1937–2010, © 1986, GIA Publications, Inc.

Stay with Me   590

Ostinato Refrain

Stay with me, re - main here with me, watch and
Spanish: Ve - la - ré con - ti - go, Se - ñor, mien - tras yo
German: Blei - bet hier und wa - chet mit mir, wa - chet und

pray, watch and pray.
vi - va, mien - tras yo vi - va.
be - tet, wa - chet und be - tet.

Text: Matthew 26:36–42; Taizé Community
Tune: Jacques Berthier, 1923–1994
© 1984, Les Presses de Taizé, GIA Publications, Inc., agent

591 Glory in the Cross

Refrain

We should glo - ry in the cross of our Lord Je - sus Christ, for he is our sal - va - tion, our life and res - ur - rec - tion; through him we are saved and made free.

Verses

1. Sing, my tongue, the hymn of glo - ry;
2. Tell how, when at length the full - ness
3. With the thir - ty years now end - ed,
4. Faith - ful Cross, true sign of tri - umph,

Of the fi - nal con - flict sing. Shout the tri - umph
Of the ho - ly time had come, Christ was sent, the
Which on earth he willed to see, Will - ing - ly he
Be for all the no - blest tree; None in fol - iage,

of the vic - tim; Far and wide the
world's Cre - a - tor, From the Fa - ther's
meets his pas - sion, Born to set his
none in blos - som, None in fruit your

ech - oes ring: Je - sus Christ, the world's sal - va - tion,
heav'n - ly home, And was found a - mong us dwell - ing,
peo - ple free; On the cross the Lamb is lift - ed,
peer may be; Sym - bol of the world's re - demp - tion,

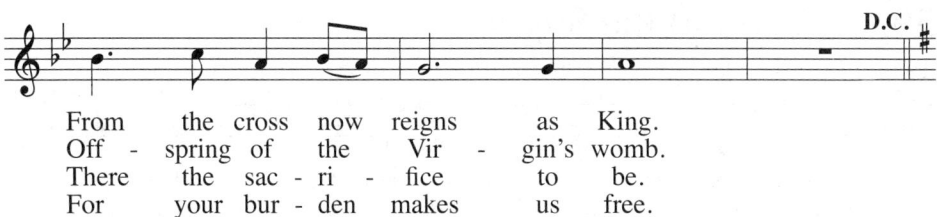

D.C.

From the cross now reigns as King.
Off - spring of the Vir - gin's womb.
There the sac - ri - fice to be.
For your bur - den makes us free.

Text: Refrain from *Rite of Holy Week*, © 1972, ICEL; verses by Venantius Fortunatus, c.530–609; verses 1–3 tr. by Steven R. Janco, b.1961, alt.,
© 1997, GIA Publications, Inc.; verse 4 tr. by John M. Neale, 1818–1866, alt.
Tune: GLORY IN THE CROSS, 8 7 8 7 8 7 with refrain; Steven R. Janco, b.1961, © 1997, GIA Publications, Inc.

Stay Here and Keep Watch 592

Ostinato Refrain

Stay here and keep watch with me. The hour has come.
Es - tén des -pier -tos, qué - den - se a - quí con - mi -go.

Stay here and keep watch with me. Watch and pray.
Es - tén des -pier -tos, qué - den - se. O - ren y ve -len.

Text: Matthew 26:38–40; Taizé Community
Tune: Jacques Berthier, 1923–1994
© 1984, 2011, Les Presses de Taizé, GIA Publications, Inc., agent

593 Called to the Supper

Refrain

Blessed are we, blessed to be called, called to the
Cuer - po_y San - gre, Cris - to Je - sús: ¡*Ven al ban -*

sup - per of the Lamb! His sac - ri - fice re - newed, here
que - te del Se - ñor! *La Víc - ti - ma Pas - cual es*

Christ is our feast, Our prom - ise of the glo - ry to
nues - tra sal - va - ción, Pro - me - sa de la glo - ria que ven -

come.
drá.

Verses

1. Pan - ge lin - gua glo - ri - ó - si,
2. No - bis da - tus, no - bis na - tus,
3. In su - pré - mae no - cte coe - nae,
4. Ver - bum ca - ro, pa - nem ve - rum,
5. Tan - tum er - go Sa - cra - mén - tum,
6. Ge - ni - tó - ri, Ge - ni - tó - que,

Sing, my tongue, in glo - ry, sing
Gift of heav - en, born to save,
At the meal that fi - nal night
Christ the Word speaks his com - mand:
Won - drous sac - ra - ment di - vine!
To the Fa - ther and the Son,

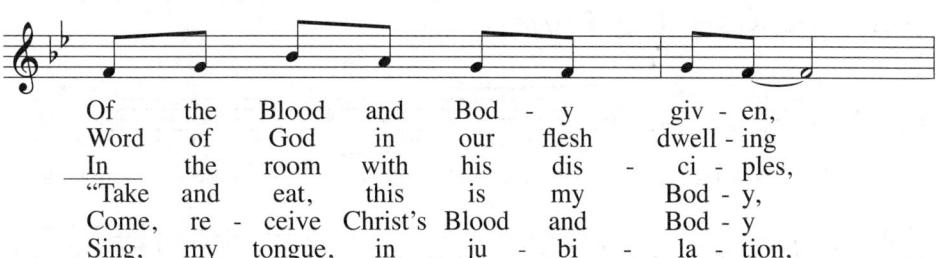

Of	the	Blood	and	Bod	-	y		giv	-	en,
Word	of	God	in	our	flesh		dwell	-	ing
In	the	room	with	his	dis	-	ci	-	ples,
"Take	and	eat,	this	is	my		Bod	-	y,
Come,	re	-	ceive	Christ's	Blood	and		Bod	-	y
Sing,	my	tongue,	in	ju	-	bi	-	la	-	tion,

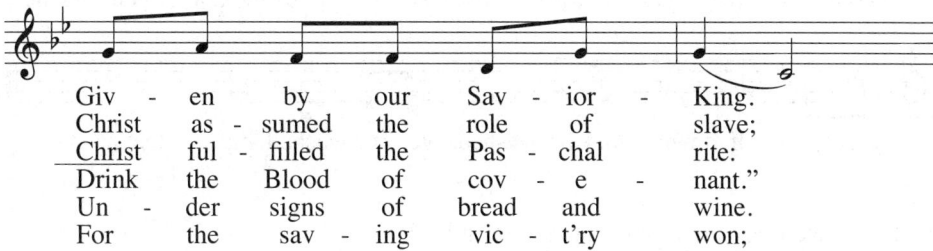

Giv	-	en	by	our	Sav	-	ior	-	King.
Christ	as	-	sumed	the	role	of		slave;
Christ	ful	-	filled	the	Pas	-	chal		rite:
Drink	the	Blood	of	cov	-	e	-	nant."
Un	-	der	signs	of	bread	and		wine.
For	the	sav	-	ing	vic	-	t'ry		won;

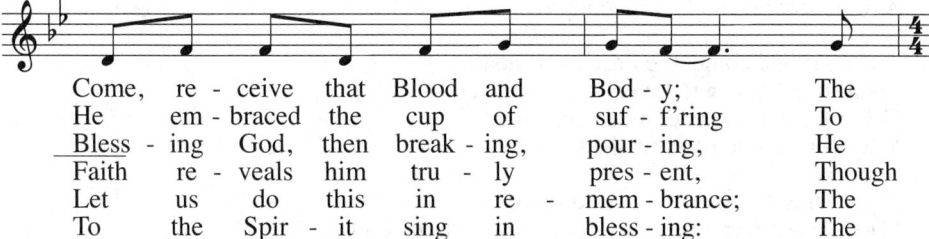

Come,	re	-	ceive	that	Blood	and	Bod	-	y;		The
He	em	-	braced	the	cup	of	suf	-	f'ring		To
Bless	-	ing	God,	then	break	-	ing,	pour	-	ing,	He
Faith	re	-	veals	him	tru	-	ly	pres	-	ent,	Though
Let	us	do	this	in	re	-	mem	-	brance;		The
To	the	Spir	-	it	sing	in	bless	-	ing:		The

D.C.

price	of	our	ran	-	som	-	ing.
face	his	own	death	and	grave.
gave	us	his	sac	-	ri	-	fice.
sens	-	es	don't	un	-	der	-	stand.
Lord	in	our	hearts	en	-	shrined.
Trin	-	i	-	ty,	ev	-	er	one!

Text: Alan J. Hommerding, b.1956; refrain tr. by Peter M. Kolar, b.1973
Tune: Based on PANGE LINGUA GLORIOSI, 8 7 8 7 8 7 with refrain; Tony E. Alonso, b.1980
© 2004, 2012, tune © 2012, World Library Publications

594 Jesus Took a Towel

Refrain

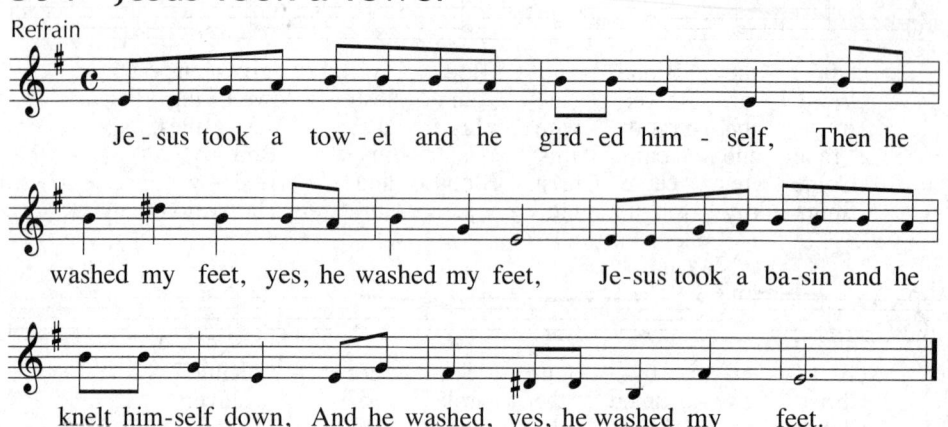

Je-sus took a tow-el and he gird-ed him-self, Then he washed my feet, yes, he washed my feet, Je-sus took a ba-sin and he knelt him-self down, And he washed, yes, he washed my feet.

Verses

1. The heavens are the Lord's, and the earth is his,
   The clouds are his chariot, glory his cloak;
   He made the mountains, set the limits of the sea;
   And he stooped and washed my feet.

2. The hour had come, the Pasch was near;
   Jesus loved his own, loved them to the end.
   O Lord, let me see, let me understand
   Why you stooped and washed my feet.

3. Jesus came to Peter; Peter said to him,
   "Do you wash my feet? Lord, do you wash my feet?"
   Jesus knelt down, but Peter cried out,
   "Lord, you'll never wash my feet!"

4. Jesus said to Peter, "Don't you understand?
   If you want to be mine, I must wash your feet."
   "Then not just my feet, but my head and my hands!
   O Lord, I want to be yours."

5. He is King of kings and Lord of lords,
   Who dwells in light inaccessible;
   No one has seen him where he sits on high,
   Yet he stooped to wash my feet.

6. "Do you know, little children, what I've done for you?
   You call me Master, and you call me Lord.
   If I am your Master, and if I am your Lord,
   Then, what I've done, you must do."

7. Now friends, let's be glad, let our joy be full.
   For God is love, and he abides in us.
   He washed our feet, he washes them still
   When we do what he once did.

8. Who is like you, Lord, now enthroned on high,
   Where you look upon the heavens and the earth below?
   Before your face the earth trembles and quakes,
   Yet you stoop to wash my feet!

9. O the path is rugged, and the going is rough,
   The journey is long to our heav'nly home,
   Our feet are weary and covered with mud,
   So the Lord still washes our feet.

Text: John 13; Chrysogonus Waddell, OCSO, 1930–2008
Tune: JESUS TOOK A TOWEL, Irregular; Chrysogonus Waddell, OCSO, 1930–2008
© 1986, GIA Publications, Inc.

Jesu, Jesu / Jesús, Jesús 595

Refrain / Estribillo

Je - su, Je - su, fill us with your love, show
Je - sús, Je - sús, en - sé - ña - nos tú a_a -

us how to serve the neigh-bors we have from you.
mar y ser-vir al pró - ji - mo ya a - quí.

Verses / Estrofas

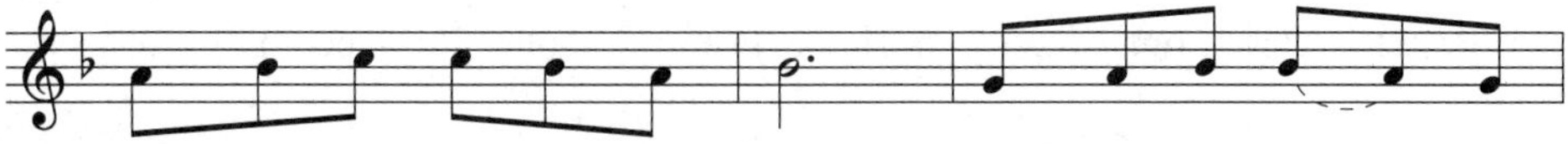

1. Kneels at the feet of his friends, Si - lent-ly wash-es their
2. Neigh-bors are wealth-y and poor, Var - ied in col - or and
3. These are the ones we should serve, These are the ones we should
4. Kneel at the feet of our friends, Si - lent-ly wash-ing their

1. *Te_a - rro - di - llas-te_a los pies De tus a - mi - gos, Se -*
2. *Po - bres y ri - cos se - rán, De to - da ra - za_y co -*
3. *Hoy les que - re - mos ser - vir, Hoy les que - re - mos a -*
4. *Nues - tra ro - di - lla do - blar Y_a - sí sus pies la -*

D.C.

feet, Mas - ter who pours out him - self for them.
race, Neigh-bors are near - by and far a - way.
love: All these are neigh-bors to us and you.
feet: This is the way we should live with you.

ñor; Se los la - vas-te_en se - ñal de_a - mor.
lor, De to - do pue - blo_y na - ción tam - bién.
mar; So - mos i - gua - les, Je - sús, en ti.
var, Es el man - da - to que Dios nos da.

Text: Tom Colvin, 1925–2000; tr. by Felicia Fina, alt.
Tune: CHEREPONI, 7 7 9 with refrain; Ghanian folk song; adapt. by Tom Colvin, 1925–2000; acc. by Jane M. Marshall, b.1924
© 1969, arr. and trans. © 1982, Hope Publishing Company

596 We Glory in the Cross

1. We glo - ry in the cross of Christ, For
2. Bap - tized in - to the death of Christ, We
3. We cel - e - brate the life of Christ, Are
4. Pro - claim to all the love of Christ, Who

he is our sal - va - tion. His res - ur - rec - tion
rise through liv - ing wa - ters. A - noint - ed with the
nour - ished with his pres - ence. He gives his bod - y,
died and rose to save us. By serv - ing oth - ers

from the dead Gives life to all cre - a - tion.
sa - cred oil, God names us sons and daugh - ters.
shares his blood: A cov - e - nant re - mem - brance.
we o - bey The man - date that he gave us.

Praise Christ, our Sav - ior! Praise our Re - deem - er!

Praise and a - dore him for - ev - er!

Text: James J. Chepponis, b.1956, © 2015, GIA Publications, Inc.
Tune: ICH GLAUB AN GOTT, 8 7 8 7 with refrain; Mainz *Gesangbuch*, 1870; harm. by Richard Proulx, 1937–2010, © 1986, GIA Publications, Inc.

597 All You Who Pass This Way

Refrain

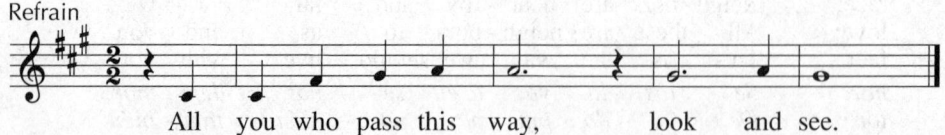

All you who pass this way, look and see.

Text: From the Passion Gospels; Taizé Community, 1984
Tune: Jacques Berthier, 1923–1994
© 1984, Les Presses de Taizé, GIA Publications, Inc., agent

O Sacred Head Surrounded 598

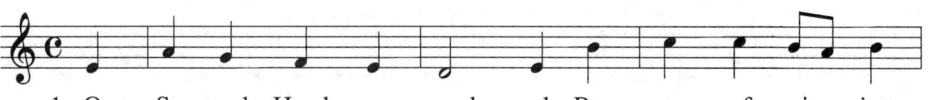

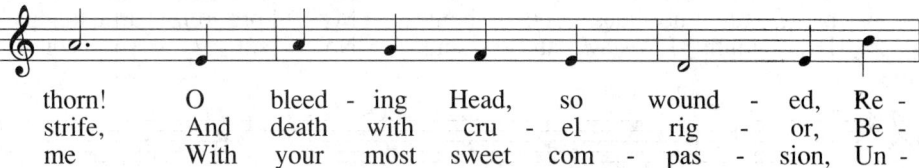

1. O Sa - cred Head sur - round - ed By crown of pierc - ing
2. I see your strength and vig - or All fad - ing in the
3. In this, your bit - ter pas - sion, Good Shep - herd, think of

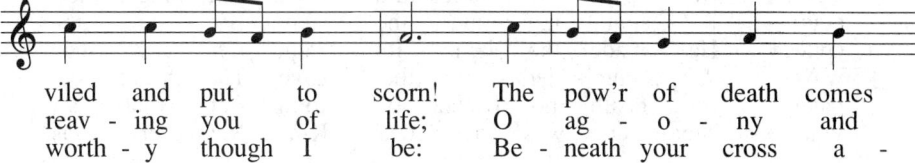

thorn! O bleed - ing Head, so wound - ed, Re -
strife, And death with cru - el rig - or, Be -
me With your most sweet com - pas - sion, Un -

viled and put to scorn! The pow'r of death comes
reav - ing you of life; O ag - o - ny and
worth - y though I be: Be - neath your cross a -

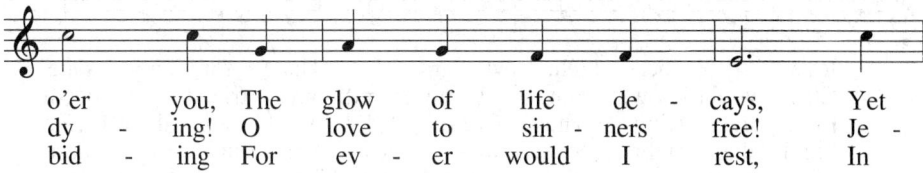

o'er you, The glow of life de - cays, Yet
dy - ing! O love to sin - ners free! Je -
bid - ing For ev - er would I rest, In

an - gel hosts a - dore you, And trem - ble as they gaze.
sus, all grace sup - ply - ing, O turn your face on me.
your dear love con - fid - ing, And with your pres - ence blest.

Text: *Salve caput cruentatum;* ascr. to Bernard of Clairvaux, 1091–1153; tr. by Henry Baker, 1821–1877
Tune: PASSION CHORALE, 7 6 7 6 D; Hans Leo Hassler, 1564–1612; harm. by J. S. Bach, 1685–1750

599 My Song Is Love Unknown

1. My song is love un-known, My Sav-ior's love to
2. He came from his blest throne Sal - va - tion to be -
3. Some-times they strew his way And his sweet prais - es
4. Why, what has my Lord done? What makes this rage and
5. They rise, and needs will have My dear Lord made a -
6. In life no house, no home My Lord on earth might
7. Here might I stay and sing No sto - ry so di -

me, Love to the love - less shown That they might
stow; But peo - ple scorned him; none The longed - for
sing, Re - sound - ing all the day Ho - san - nas
spite? He made the lame to run, He gave the
way; A mur - der - er they save, The Prince of
have; In death no friend - ly tomb But what a
vine! Nev - er was love, dear King, Nev - er was

love - ly be. Oh, who am I, That for my sake
Christ would know. But, O my friend, My friend in - deed,
to their King. Then "Cru - ci - fy!" Is all their breath,
blind their sight. Sweet in - jur - ies! Yet they at these
life they slay. Yet cheer - ful he To suf - f'ring goes
stran - ger gave. What may I say? Heav'n was his home;
grief like thine. This is my friend, In whose sweet praise

My Lord should take Frail flesh and die?
Who at my need His life did spend!
And for his death They thirst and cry.
Them - selves dis - please And 'gainst him rise.
That he his foes From thence might free.
But mine the tomb Where - in he lay.
I all my days Could glad - ly spend!

Text: Samuel Crossman, c.1624–1683, alt.
Tune: LOVE UNKNOWN, 6 6 6 6 4 44 4; John Ireland, 1879–1962, © John Ireland Trust

Were You There   600

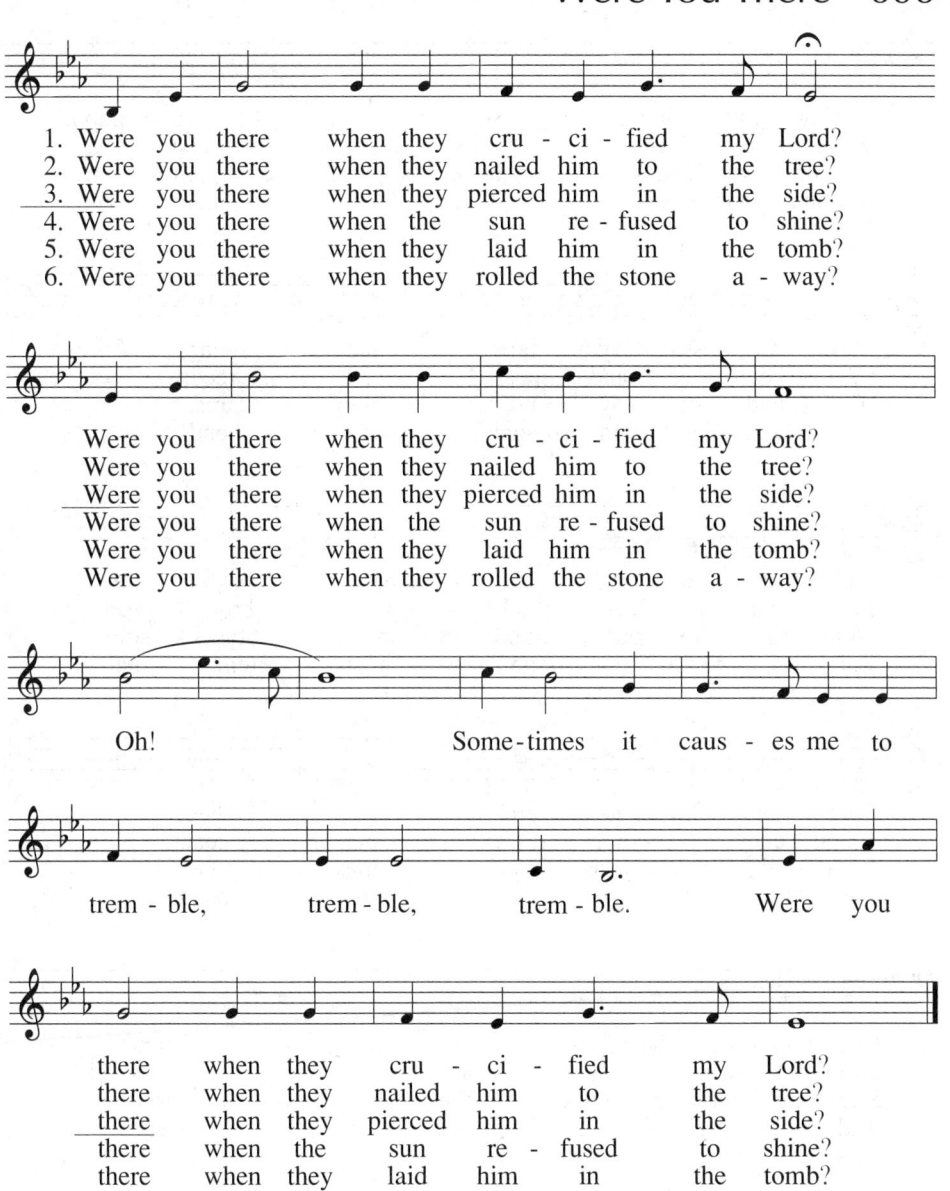

1. Were you there when they cru - ci - fied my Lord?
2. Were you there when they nailed him to the tree?
3. Were you there when they pierced him in the side?
4. Were you there when the sun re - fused to shine?
5. Were you there when they laid him in the tomb?
6. Were you there when they rolled the stone a - way?

Were you there when they cru - ci - fied my Lord?
Were you there when they nailed him to the tree?
Were you there when they pierced him in the side?
Were you there when the sun re - fused to shine?
Were you there when they laid him in the tomb?
Were you there when they rolled the stone a - way?

Oh!   Some-times it caus - es me to

trem - ble,   trem - ble,   trem - ble.   Were you

there when they cru - ci - fied my Lord?
there when they nailed him to the tree?
there when they pierced him in the side?
there when the sun re - fused to shine?
there when they laid him in the tomb?
there when they rolled the stone a - way?

Text: African American spiritual
Tune: WERE YOU THERE, 10 10 with refrain; African American spiritual; harm. by C. Winfred Douglas, 1867–1944, © 1940, 1943, 1961,
   The Church Pension Fund

601 Sing, My Tongue, the Song of Triumph

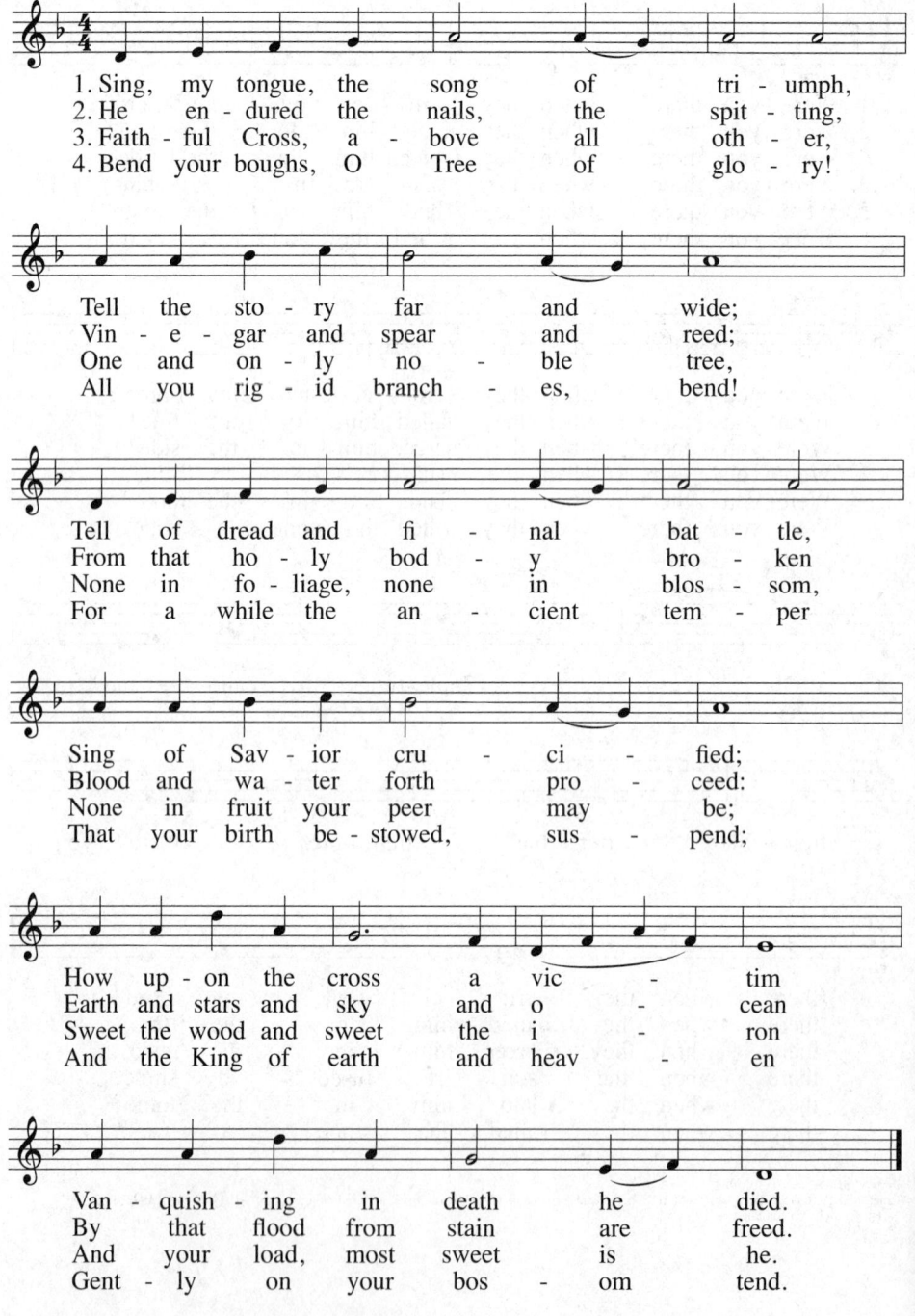

1. Sing, my tongue, the song of tri - umph,
2. He en - dured the nails, the spit - ting,
3. Faith - ful Cross, a - bove all oth - er,
4. Bend your boughs, O Tree of glo - ry!

Tell the sto - ry far and wide;
Vin - e - gar and spear and reed;
One and on - ly no - ble tree,
All you rig - id branch - es, bend!

Tell of dread and fi - nal bat - tle,
From that ho - ly bod - y bro - ken
None in fo - liage, none in blos - som,
For a while the an - cient tem - per

Sing of Sav - ior cru - ci - fied;
Blood and wa - ter forth pro - ceed:
None in fruit your peer may be;
That your birth be - stowed, sus - pend;

How up - on the cross a vic - tim
Earth and stars and sky and o - cean
Sweet the wood and sweet the i - ron
And the King of earth and heav - en

Van - quish - ing in death he died.
By that flood from stain are freed.
And your load, most sweet is he.
Gent - ly on your bos - om tend.

Text: *Pange, lingua, gloriosi lauream certaminis*; Venantius Fortunatus, c.530–609; tr. from *The Three Days*, 1981
Tune: PICARDY, 8 7 8 7 8 7; French carol; harm. by Richard Proulx, 1937–2010, © 1986, GIA Publications, Inc.

Crucem Tuam / O Lord, Your Cross   602

Ostinato Refrain

Cru - cem tu - am a - do - rá - mus Dó - mi -
O Lord, your cross we a - dore and glo - ri -

ne, re - sur - re - cti - ó - nem tu - am lau - dá - mus Dó - mi -
fy; for your ho - ly res - ur - rec - tion we praise you, Lord of

ne. Lau - dá - mus et glo - ri - fi - cá - mus.
life. We praise you and we glo - ri - fy you.

Re - sur - re - cti - ó - nem tu - am lau - dá - mus Dó - mi - ne.
For your ho - ly res - ur - rec - tion we praise you, Lord of life.

Text: Taizé Community, 1991
Tune: Jacques Berthier, 1923–1994
© 1991, Les Presses de Taizé, GIA Publications, Inc., agent

603 Way of the Cross

Refrain

We car - ry the sav-ing cross through the roads of the
world, through the al - leys of pov-er-ty and mis - er -
y, march-ing to a dawn-ing day, to free - dom and
vic - to-ry, to God's life and end - less glo - ry.

English Verses

Cantor:

1. Christ, sent by God, o - be - dient to the
2. Christ, Re - deem - er, crowned with
3. Christ, Son of Da - vid, stripped of his
4. Christ, Son of Mar - y, im-mo - lat - ed for
5. Christ, Lamb of God, for us sin - ners
6. Christ, our Sav - ior, in the tomb

D.C.

Fa - ther's will:
pierc-ing thorns:
glo - ry:
all of us: He leads the way of the cross.
cru - ci - fied:
laid to rest:

Filipino Verses

```
Cantor:
1. Si Krist - o,       su - go   ng   Diyos,      su -
2. Si Krist - o,   Ta - ga - pag - ad - ya,       na -
3. Si Krist - o,        a - nak ni Da - vid,       ti -
4. Si Krist - o,   si - na - kri - pi - syo
5. Si Krist - o, Kor - de - ro   ng   Diyos,       sa
6. Si Krist - o, Ta - ga - pag - lig - tas,        sa
```

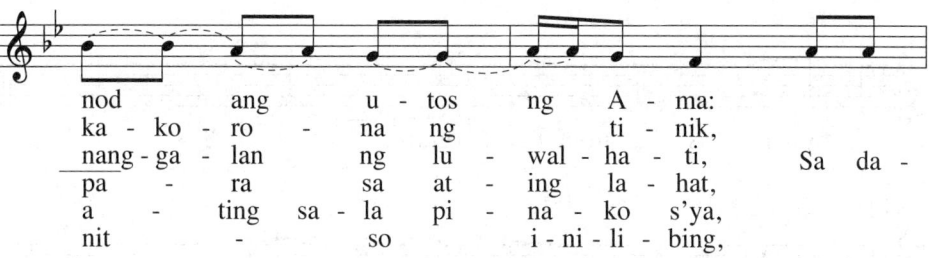

```
nod       ang      u - tos   ng   A - ma:
ka - ko - ro       na - ng          ti - nik,
nang - ga - lan    ng   lu - wal - ha - ti,      Sa da -
pa -  ra       sa   at - ing   la - hat,
a -   ting sa - la  pi - na - ko  s'ya,
nit -          so    i - ni - li - bing,
```

D.C.

```
an         ng krus Siya'y na - ngun - gu  na.
```

Spanish Verses

```
Cantor:
1. Cris - to, por Dios man - da - do,  o - be - dien - te  al
2. Cris - to,          Re - den - tor, co - ro - na - do  de es -
3. Cris - to,      Hi - jo   de Da - vid, des - nu - da - do  de su
4. Cris - to, Hi - jo de Ma - rí - a,  in - mo - la - do  por no -
5. Cris - to, cru - ci - fi - ca - do  por no - so - tros  pe - ca -
6. Cris - to,      nues - tro Sal - va - dor, co - lo - ca - do en el se -
```

D.C.

```
Pa - dre,
pi - nas,
glo - ria,       nos lle - va por la ví - a  de la  cruz.
so - tros,
do - res,
pul - cro,
```

Text: Manoling Francisco, SJ; Filipino verses tr. by Anita Mendoza and Ricky Manalo, CSP; Spanish verses tr. by Pedro Rubalcava, Mary Straub, and Katy Haerling
Tune: Manoling Francisco, SJ; acc. by Kerey Quaid
© 1995, 2003, 2009 Jesuit Communications Foundation, Inc. Published by OCP.

604 Tree of Life and Glory

Refrain

Tree of life and glo - ry, tree that heals and
saves, tree that tells the an - cient sto - ry:
dy - ing, ris - ing from the grave.

Verses

1. The roy - al ban - ners for - ward go, the
2. Where deep for us the spear was dyed, life's
3. Ful - filled is all that Da - vid told in
4. O tree of beau - ty, tree most fair, or -
5. Blest tree, whose cho - sen branch - es bore the
6. O cross, our one re - li - ance hail! Still

cross shines forth in mys - tic glow where
tor - rent rush - ing from his side, to
true pro - phet - ic song of old, that
dained those ho - ly limbs to bear; gone
wealth that did the world re - store, the
may your pow'r with us a - vail more

he, by whom our flesh was made, in
wash us in the pre - cious flood where
he the na - tions' king should be and
is your shame, each crim - soned bough pro -
price of hu - man - kind to pay and
good for right - eous souls to win; and

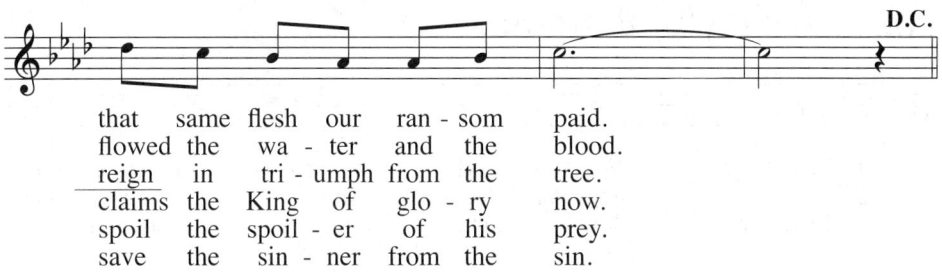

that same flesh our ran - som paid.
flowed the wa - ter and the blood.
reign in tri - umph from the tree.
claims the King of glo - ry now.
spoil the spoil - er of his prey.
save the sin - ner from the sin.

Text: Refrain, Francis Patrick O'Brien, b.1958; verses, Venantius Fortunatus, c.530–609; tr. *The Hymnal 1982*, alt.
Tune: Francis Patrick O'Brien, b.1958

In Manus Tuas, Pater 605

Ostinato Refrain

(spí - ri-tum)

In ma - nus tu - as, Pa - ter, com - mén - do spí - ri-tum
In - to your hands, O Fa - ther, I now com - mend my
Oh Pa-dre, en - tre tus ma - nos mi_es-pí - ri - tu en -

me - um. In ma - nus tu - as, Pa - ter, com -
spir - it. In - to your hands, O Fa - ther, I
tre - go. Oh Pa-dre, en - tre tus ma - nos mi_es-

Last time

mén - do spí - ri - tum me - um. In
now com - mend my spir - it. In -
pí - ri - tu en - tre - go. Oh

Last time

Text: Psalm 31:6, Luke 23:46; Taizé Community
Tune: Taizé Community

606 This Joyful Eastertide

1. This joy-ful East-er-tide A - way with sin and
2. My flesh in hope shall rest And for a sea - son
3. Death's flood has lost its chill Since Je - sus crossed the

sor - row! My love, the Cru - ci - fied
slum - ber Till trump from east to west
riv - er; Lov - er of souls, from ill

Has sprung to life this mor - row:
Shall wake the dead in num - ber:
My pass - ing soul de - liv - er:

Had Christ, who once was slain, Not burst his

three-day pris - on, Our faith had been in vain: But

now has Christ a - ris - en, a - ris - en, a -

ris - en, a - ris - en!

Text: George R. Woodward, 1848–1934
Tune: VRUECHTEN, 6 7 6 7 with refrain; Melody in Oudaen's *David's Psalmen*, 1685; harm. by Charles Wood, 1866–1926

Now the Green Blade Rises 607

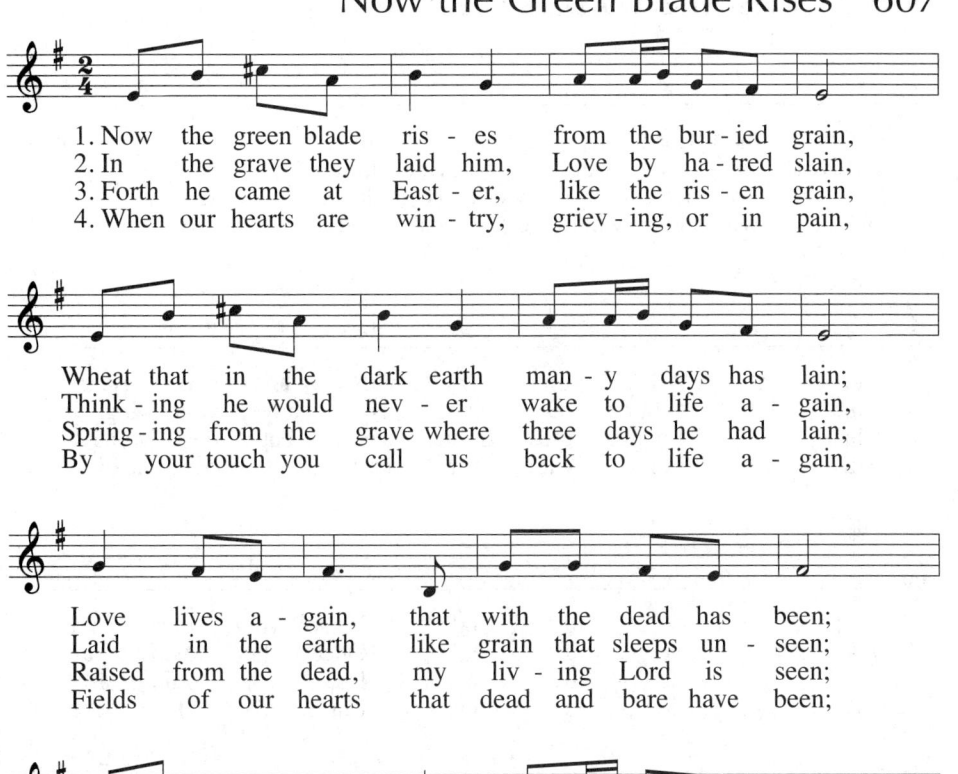

1. Now the green blade ris - es from the bur - ied grain,
2. In the grave they laid him, Love by ha - tred slain,
3. Forth he came at East - er, like the ris - en grain,
4. When our hearts are win - try, griev - ing, or in pain,

Wheat that in the dark earth man - y days has lain;
Think - ing he would nev - er wake to life a - gain,
Spring - ing from the grave where three days he had lain;
By your touch you call us back to life a - gain,

Love lives a - gain, that with the dead has been;
Laid in the earth like grain that sleeps un - seen;
Raised from the dead, my liv - ing Lord is seen;
Fields of our hearts that dead and bare have been;

Love is come a - gain, like wheat a - ris - ing green.

Text: John M. C. Crum, 1872–1958, *Oxford Book of Carols,* alt., © Oxford University Press
Tune: NOËL NOUVELET, 11 11 with refrain; French carol; harm. by Martin Shaw, 1875–1958, © Oxford University Press

608 Christ the Lord Is Risen Today

1. Christ the Lord is ris'n to - day, Al - le - lu - ia! All on earth with an - gels say: Al - le - lu - ia! Raise your joys and tri - umphs high, Al - le - lu - ia! Sing, O heav'ns; and, earth, re - ply: Al - le - lu - ia!

2. Lives a - gain our glo - rious king, Al - le - lu - ia! Where, O death, is now your sting? Al - le - lu - ia! Once he died our souls to save, Al - le - lu - ia! Where your vic - to - ry, O grave?

3. Love's re - deem - ing work is done, Al - le - lu - ia! Fought the fight, the bat - tle won, Al - le - lu - ia! Death in vain for - bids him rise, Al - le - lu - ia! Christ has o - pened par - a - dise.

4. Soar we now where Christ has led, Al - le - lu - ia! Fol - l'wing our ex - alt - ed Head, Al - le - lu - ia! Made like him, like him we rise, Al - le - lu - ia! Ours the cross, the grave, the skies.

Text: Charles Wesley, 1707–1788, alt.
Tune: LLANFAIR, 77 77 with alleluias; Robert Williams, 1781–1821

Sing with All the Saints in Glory 609

1. Sing with all the saints in glo - ry, Sing the res - ur -
rec - tion song! Death and sor - row, earth's dark sto - ry,
To the for - mer days be - long. All a - round the
clouds are break-ing, Soon the storms of time shall cease; In God's
like - ness we a - wak-en, Know-ing ev - er - last - ing peace.

2. O what glo - ry, far ex - ceed - ing All that eye has
yet per-ceived! Ho - liest hearts, for a - ges plead - ing,
Nev - er that full joy con-ceived. God has prom-ised,
Christ pre - pares it, There on high our wel-come waits. Ev - 'ry
hum - ble spir - it shares it; Christ has passed the e - ter - nal gates.

3. Life e - ter - nal! heav'n re - joic - es: Je - sus lives who
once was dead. Shout with joy, O death - less voic - es!
Child of God, lift up your head! Pa - tri - archs from
dis - tant a - ges, Saints all long - ing for their heav'n, Proph - ets,
psalm-ists, seers, and sag - es, All a - wait the glo - ry giv'n.

4. Life e - ter - nal! O what won - ders Crowd on faith; what
joy un-known, When, a - mid earth's clos - ing thun - ders,
Saints shall stand be - fore the throne! Oh, to en - ter
that bright por - tal, See that glow-ing fir - ma - ment, Know, with
you, O God im - mor-tal, Je - sus Christ whom you have sent!

Text: 1 Corinthians 15:20; William J. Irons, 1812–1883, alt.
Tune: HYMN TO JOY, 8 7 8 7 D; arr. from Ludwig van Beethoven, 1770–1827, by Edward Hodges, 1796–1867

610 Come, You Faithful, Raise the Strain

1. Come, you faith-ful, raise the strain Of tri - um-phant
2. 'Tis the spring of souls to - day: Christ has burst his
3. Now the queen of sea - sons, bright With the day of
4. Nei - ther could the gates of death, Nor the tomb's dark
5. "Al - le - lu - ia!" now we cry To our King im-

glad - ness! God has brought his Is - ra - el
pris - on, And from three days' sleep in death
splen - dor, With the roy - al feast of feasts,
por - tal, Nor the watch - ers, nor the seal
mor - tal, Who tri - um-phant burst the bars

In - to joy from sad - ness; Loosed from
As a sun has ris - en. All the
Comes its joy to ren - der; Comes to
Hold him as a mor - tal: For to -
Of the tomb's dark por - tal; "Al - le -

Phar - aoh's bit - ter yoke Ja - cob's sons and
win - ter of our sins, Long and dark, is
glad Je - ru - sa - lem, Who with true af -
day a - mong his own Christ ap - pears, be -
lu - ia!" with the Son, God the Fa - ther

daugh - ters; Led them with un - moist-ened foot
fly - ing From the Light, to whom we give
fec - tion Wel - comes in un - wea - ried strains
stow - ing Last - ing peace which ev - er - more
prais - ing; "Al - le - lu - ia!" yet a - gain

Through   the   Red   Sea   wa - ters.
Laud   and   praise un - dy - ing.
Je -   sus'   res - ur - rec - tion.
Pass - es   hu - man know - ing.
To   the   Spir - it   rais - ing.

Text: Ασωμεν παντεξ λαοι; St. John of Damascus, c.675–c.749; tr. by John M. Neale, 1818–1886, alt.
Tune: GAUDEAMUS PARITER, 7 6 7 6 D; Johann Horn, c.1495–1547

I Know That My Redeemer Lives! 611

1. I   know that my   Re - deem - er   lives!
2. He   lives to   bless   me   with   his   love;
3. He   lives and grants me   dai - ly   breath;
4. He   lives, all glo - ry   to   his   name;

What   joy   this blest   as - sur - ance gives!
He   lives to   plead   for   me   a - bove;
He   lives, and I   shall con - quer death;
He   lives, my Sav - ior,   still   the   same;

He   lives, he   lives   who   once was   dead;
He   lives my hun - gry soul   to   feed;
He   lives my man - sion   to   pre - pare;
What   joy   this blest   as - sur - ance gives:

He   lives, my ev - er - last - ing Head!
He   lives to   help   in   time   of   need.
He   lives to   bring me   safe - ly   there.
I   know that my   Re - deem - er   lives!

Text: Samuel Medley, 1738–1799
Tune: DUKE STREET, LM; John Hatton, c.1710–1793

612   O Sons and Daughters

Al - le - lu - ia,   al - le - lu - ia,   al - le - lu - ia.

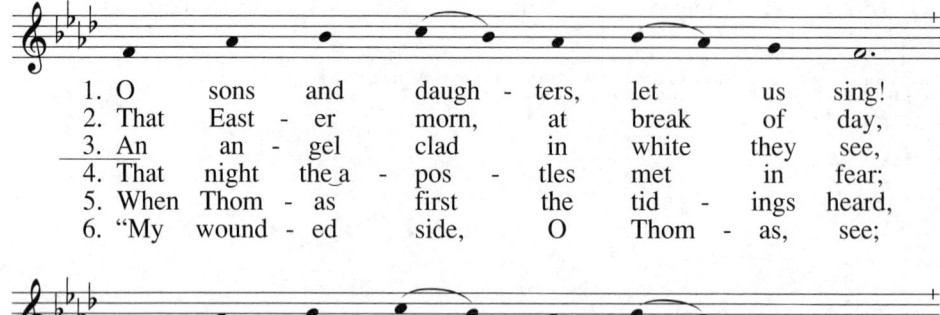

1. O   sons   and   daugh - ters,   let   us   sing!
2. That   East - er   morn,   at   break   of   day,
3. An   an - gel   clad   in   white   they   see,
4. That   night   the a - pos - tles   met   in   fear;
5. When   Thom - as   first   the   tid - ings   heard,
6. "My   wound - ed   side,   O   Thom - as,   see;

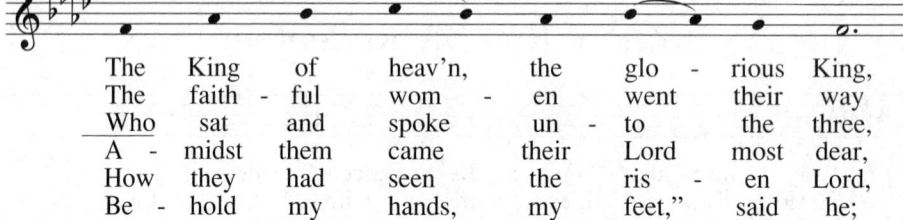

The   King   of   heav'n,   the   glo - rious   King,
The   faith - ful   wom - en   went   their   way
Who   sat   and   spoke   un - to   the   three,
A - midst them   came   their   Lord   most   dear,
How   they   had   seen   the   ris - en   Lord,
Be - hold my   hands,   my   feet,"   said   he;

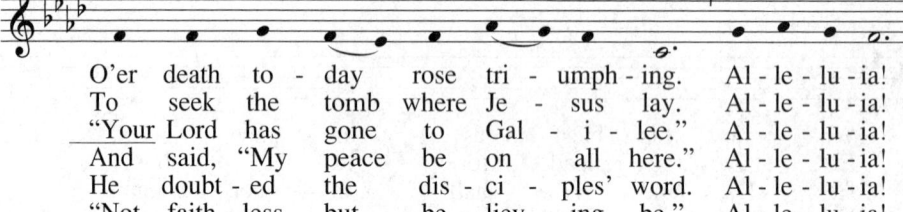

D.C.

O'er   death   to - day   rose   tri - umph - ing.   Al - le - lu - ia!
To   seek   the   tomb   where   Je - sus   lay.   Al - le - lu - ia!
"Your   Lord   has   gone   to   Gal - i - lee."   Al - le - lu - ia!
And   said,   "My   peace   be   on   all   here."   Al - le - lu - ia!
He   doubt - ed   the   dis - ci - ples'   word.   Al - le - lu - ia!
"Not   faith - less   but   be - liev - ing   be."   Al - le - lu - ia!

7. No longer Thomas then denied;
   He saw the feet, the hands, the side;
   "You are my Lord and God," he cried. Alleluia!

8. How blest are they who have not seen,
   And yet whose faith has constant been,
   For they eternal life shall win. Alleluia!

9. On this most holy day of days,
   To God your hearts and voices raise,
   In laud and jubilee and praise. Alleluia!

Text: *O filii et filiae;* Jean Tisserand, d.1494; tr. by John M. Neale, 1818–1866, alt.
Tune: O FILII ET FILIAE, 888 with alleluia and refrain; Mode II, French carol, 15th C.; acc. by Richard Proulx, 1937–2010,
  © 1975, GIA Publications, Inc.

At the Lamb's High Feast We Sing 613

1. At the Lamb's high feast we sing Praise to our vic-
to-rious King, Who has washed us in the tide
Flow-ing from his pierc-ed side. Praise we him, whose
love di-vine Gives his sa-cred Blood for wine,
Gives his Bod-y for the feast:
Christ the vic-tim, Christ the priest.

2. Where the Pas-chal blood is poured, Death's dark an-gel
sheathes his sword; Is-rael's hosts tri-umph-ant go
Through the wave that drowns the foe. Praise we Christ, whose
blood was shed, Pas-chal vic-tim, Pas-chal bread;
With sin-cer-i-ty and love
Eat we man-na from a-bove.

3. Might-y vic-tim from on high, Hell's fierce pow'rs be-
neath you lie; You have con-quered in the fight,
You have brought us life and light. Now no more can
death ap-pall, Now no more the grave en-thrall;
You have o-pened par-a-dise,
And in you your saints shall rise.

4. East-er tri-umph, East-er joy, This a-lone can
sin de-stroy; From sin's pow'r, Lord, set us free,
New-born souls in you to be. Fa-ther, who the
crown shall give, Sav-ior, by whose death we live,
Spir-it, guide through all our days:
Three in One, your name we praise.

Text: *Ad regias agni dapes;* Latin, 4th C.; tr. by Robert Campbell, 1814–1868, alt.
Tune: SALZBURG, 77 77 D; Jakob Hintze, 1622–1702; harm. by J. S. Bach, 1685–1750

614 Jesus Christ Is Risen Today

1. Je - sus Christ is ris'n to - day, Al - le - lu - ia!
2. Hymns of praise then let us sing, Al - le - lu - ia!
3. But the pains which he en - dured, Al - le - lu - ia!
4. Sing we to our God a - bove, Al - le - lu - ia!

Our tri - um - phant ho - ly day, Al - le - lu - ia!
Un - to Christ, our heav'n - ly King, Al - le - lu - ia!
Our sal - va - tion have pro - cured; Al - le - lu - ia!
Praise e - ter - nal, as his love; Al - le - lu - ia!

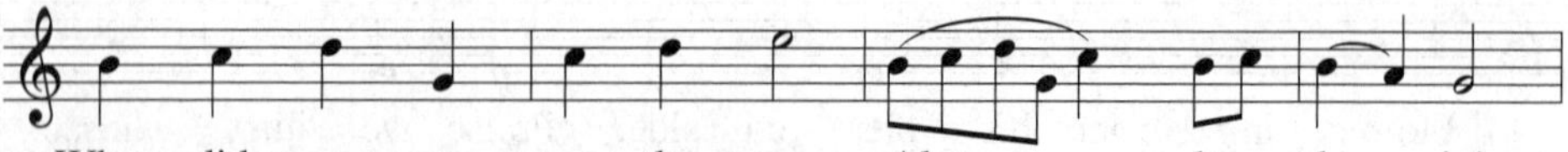

Who did once up - on the cross, Al - le - lu - ia!
Who en - dured the cross and grave, Al - le - lu - ia!
Now a - bove the sky he's King, Al - le - lu - ia!
Praise him, now his might con - fess, Al - le - lu - ia!

Suf - fer to re - deem our loss. Al - le - lu - ia!
Sin - ners to re - deem and save. Al - le - lu - ia!
Where the an - gels ev - er sing. Al - le - lu - ia!
Fa - ther, Son, and Spir - it blest. Al - le - lu - ia!

Text: St. 1, *Surrexit Christus hodie*, Latin, 14th C.; para. in *Lyra Davidica*, 1708, alt.; st. 2, 3, *The Compleat Psalmodist*, c.1750, alt.; st. 4, Charles Wesley, 1707–1788, alt.
Tune: EASTER HYMN, 77 77 with alleluias; *Lyra Davidica*, 1708

615 Regina Caeli / O Queen of Heaven

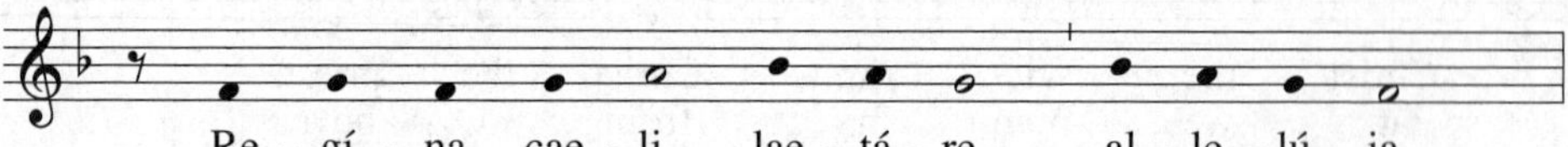

Re - gí - na cae - li, lae - tá - re, al - le - lú - ia,
O Queen of heav - en, be joy - ful, al - le - lu - ia,

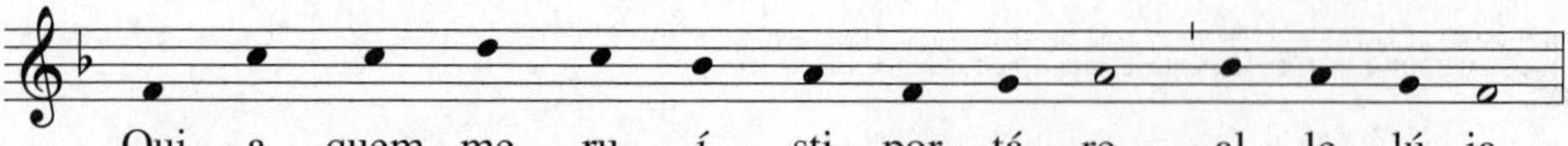

Qui - a quem me - ru - í - sti por - tá - re, al - le - lú - ia,
For he whom you have hum - bly borne for us, al - le - lu - ia,

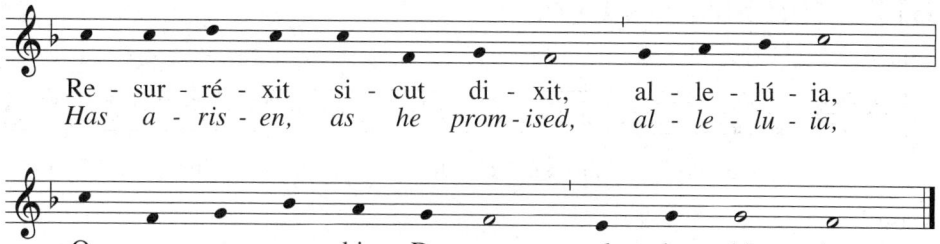

Re - sur - ré - xit si - cut di - xit, al - le - lú - ia,
Has a - ris - en, as he prom - ised, al - le - lu - ia,

O - ra pro no - bis De - um, al - le - lú - ia.
Of - fer now our prayer to God, al - le - lu - ia.

Text: Latin, 12th C.; tr. by C. Winfred Douglas, 1867–1944, alt.
Tune: REGINA CAELI, Irregular; Mode VI; acc. by Robert LeBlanc, OSB, b.1948, © 1986, GIA Publications, Inc.

Be Joyful, Mary   616

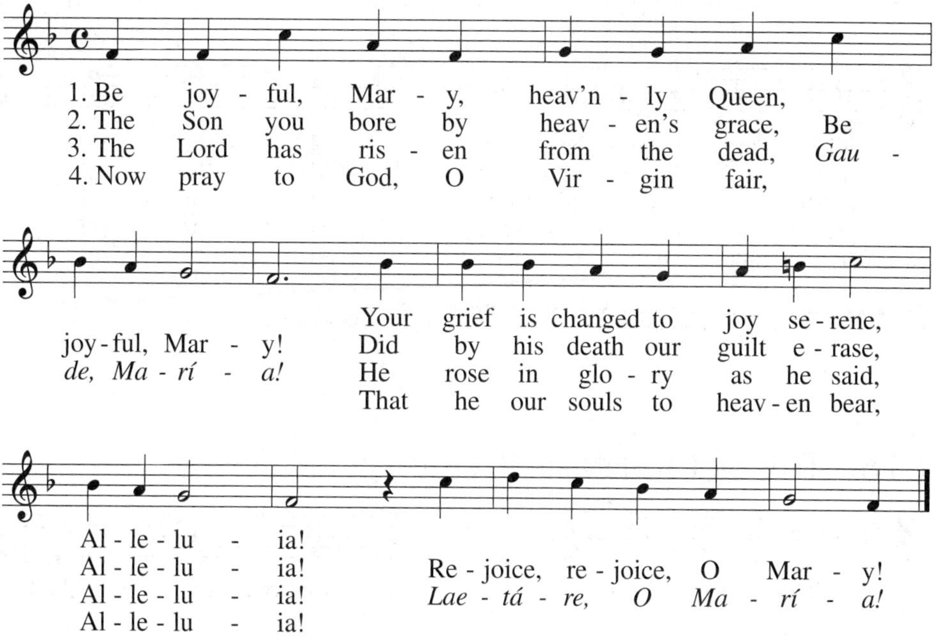

1. Be joy - ful, Mar - y, heav'n - ly Queen,
2. The Son you bore by heav - en's grace, Be
3. The Lord has ris - en from the dead, *Gau -*
4. Now pray to God, O Vir - gin fair,

joy - ful, Mar - y! Your grief is changed to joy se - rene,
de, Ma - rí - a! Did by his death our guilt e - rase,
He rose in glo - ry as he said,
That he our souls to heav - en bear,

Al - le - lu - ia!
Al - le - lu - ia!
Al - le - lu - ia! Re - joice, re - joice, O Mar - y!
Al - le - lu - ia! *Lae - tá - re, O Ma - rí - a!*

Text: *Regina caeli jubila*; Latin, 17th C.; tr. anon. in *Psallite,* 1901
Tune: REGINA CAELI, 8 5 8 4 7; Leisentritt's *Gesangbuch,* 1584, alt.

617 The Strife Is O'er

Refrain

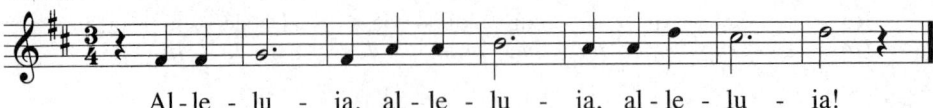

Al - le - lu - ia, al - le - lu - ia, al - le - lu - ia!

Verses

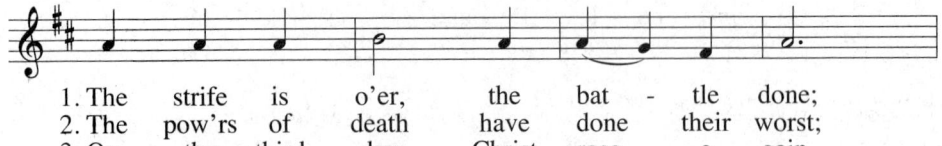

1. The strife is o'er, the bat - tle done;
2. The pow'rs of death have done their worst;
3. On the third day Christ rose a - gain,
4. He closed the yawn - ing gates of hell;
5. Lord, by the stripes which wound - ed you,

Now is the Vic - tor's tri - umph won! Songs of re -
But Christ their le - gions has dis - persed. Let shouts of
Glo - rious in maj - es - ty to reign. O let us
The bars from heav'n's high por - tals fell. Let hymns of
Free from death's sting your ser - vants too, That we may

D.C.

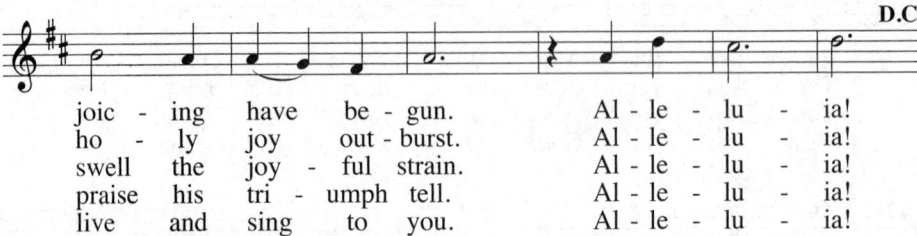

joic - ing have be - gun. Al - le - lu - ia!
ho - ly joy out - burst. Al - le - lu - ia!
swell the joy - ful strain. Al - le - lu - ia!
praise his tri - umph tell. Al - le - lu - ia!
live and sing to you. Al - le - lu - ia!

Text: *Finita jam sunt praelia;* Latin, 12th C.; tr. by Francis Pott, 1832–1909, alt.
Tune: VICTORY, 888 with alleluia and refrain; Giovanni da Palestrina, 1525–1594; adapt. by William H. Monk, 1823–1889

618 This Is the Feast of Victory

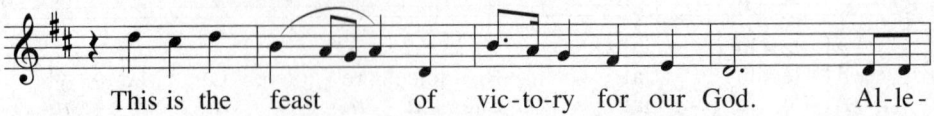

This is the feast of vic-to-ry for our God. Al-le-

To verses | Last time

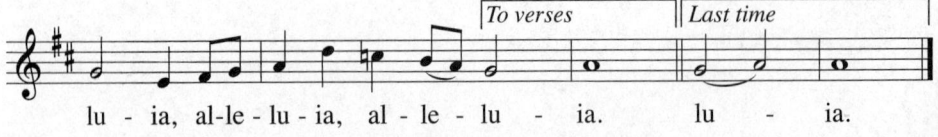

lu - ia, al-le-lu-ia, al - le - lu - ia. lu - ia.

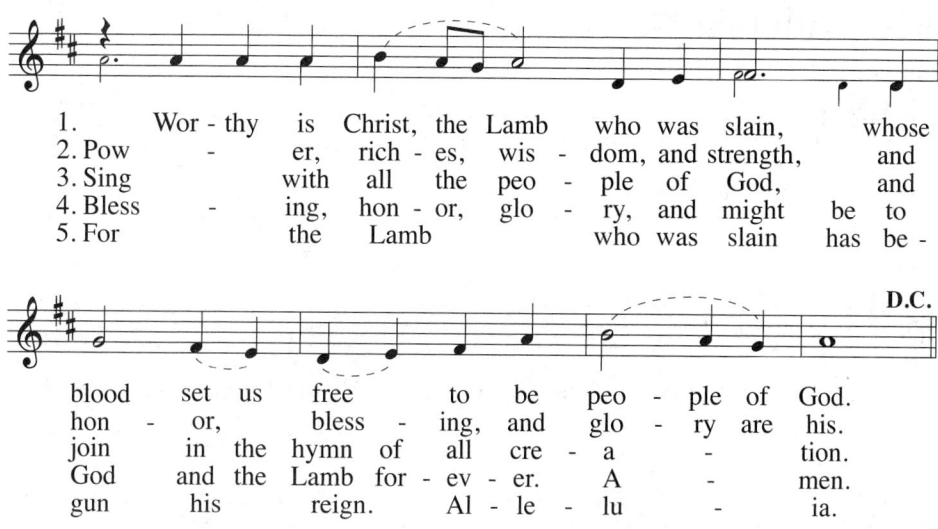

1. Wor - thy is Christ, the Lamb who was slain, whose
2. Pow - er, rich - es, wis - dom, and strength, and
3. Sing with all the peo - ple of God, and
4. Bless - ing, hon - or, glo - ry, and might be to
5. For the Lamb who was slain has be -

D.C.

blood set us free to be peo - ple of God.
hon - or, bless - ing, and glo - ry are his.
join in the hymn of all cre - a - tion.
God and the Lamb for - ev - er. A - men.
gun his reign. Al - le - lu - ia.

Text: Based on Revelation 5, © 1978, *Lutheran Book of Worship*, admin. by Augsburg Fortress
Tune: FESTIVAL CANTICLE, Irregular with refrain; Richard Hillert, 1923–2010, © 1975, 1988, 1993, Richard Hillert, OCP, agent

That Easter Day with Joy Was Bright 619

1. That East - er day with joy was bright; The sun shone
2. His ris - en flesh with ra - diance glowed; His wound - ed
3. O Je - sus, King of gen - tle - ness, With con - stant
4. O Lord of all, with us a - bide In this our
5. All praise to you, O ris - en Lord, Now both by

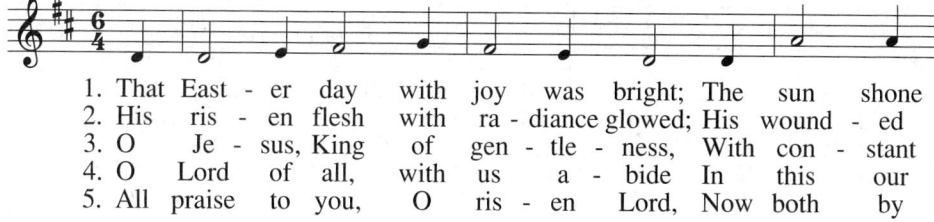

out with fair - er light When, to their long - ing
hands and feet he showed. Those scars their sol - emn
love our hearts pos - sess That we may give you
joy - ful East - er - tide; From ev - 'ry weap - on
heav'n and earth a - dored; To God the Fa - ther

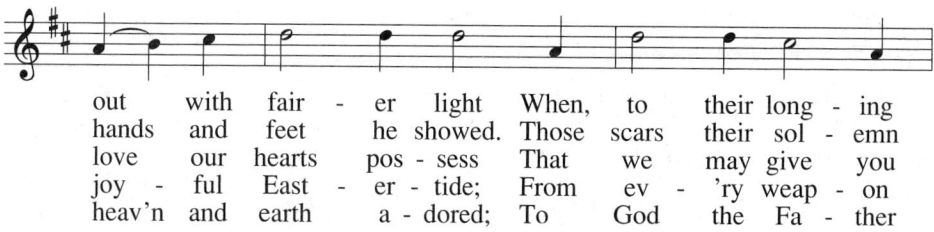

eyes re - stored, The a - pos - tles saw their ris - en Lord!
wit - ness gave That Christ was ris - en from the grave.
all our days The trib - ute of our grate - ful praise.
death can wield Your own re - deemed for - ev - er shield.
e - qual praise, And God the Spir - it, now we raise!

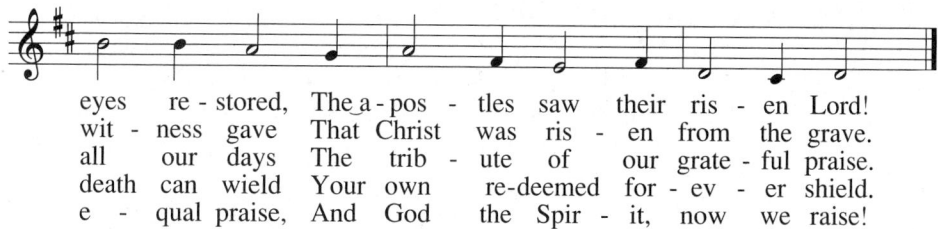

Text: *Claro paschali gaudio*; Latin 5th C.; tr. by John M. Neale, 1818–1866, alt.
Tune: PUER NOBIS, LM; adapt. by Michael Praetorius, 1571–1621

620　Alleluia No. 1

Refrain

Al - le - lu - ia, al - le - lu - ia, give thanks to the ris - en Lord. Al - le - lu - ia, al - le - lu - ia, give praise to his Name.

Verses

1. Je - sus is Lord of all the earth.
2. Spread the good news o'er all the earth:
3. We have been cru - ci - fied with Christ.
4. God has pro - claimed his gra - cious gift:
5. Come, let us praise the liv - ing God,

D.C.

He is the King of cre - a - tion.
Je - sus has died and has ris - en.
Now we shall live for ev - er.
Life e - ter - nal for all who be - lieve.
Joy - ful - ly sing to our Sav - ior.

Text: Donald Fishel, b.1950
Tune: ALLELUIA NO. 1, 8 8 with refrain; Donald Fishel, b.1950; descant harm. by Betty Pulkingham, b.1928, Charles Mallory, b.1953, and
  George Mims, b.1938
© 1973, and descant © 1979, International Liturgy Publications

Christ the Lord Is Risen!   621

1. Christ the Lord is ris'n! Christ the Lord is ris'n!
2. He has con - quered death. He has con - quered death.
3. Sin has done its worst. Sin has done its worst.
4. He is King of kings. He is King of kings.
5. He is Lord of lords. He is Lord of lords.
6. All the world is his. All the world is his.
7. Come and wor - ship him. Come and wor - ship him.
8. Christ our Lord is ris'n! Christ our Lord is ris'n!
9. Hal - le - lu - jah! Hal - le - lu - jah!

Je - su. Christ the Lord is ris'n!
Je - su. He has con - quered death.
Je - su. Sin has done its worst.
Je - su. He is King of kings.
Je - su. He is Lord of lords.
Je - su. All the world is his.
Je - su. Come and wor - ship him.
Je - su. Christ our Lord is ris'n!
Je - su. Hal - le - lu - jah!

Christ the Lord is ris'n! Je - su.
He has con - quered death. Je - su.
Sin has done its worst. Je - su.
He is King of kings. Je - su.
He is Lord of lords. Je - su.
All the world is his. Je - su.
Come and wor - ship him. Je - su.
Christ our Lord is ris'n! Je - su.
Hal - le - lu - jah! Je - su.

Text: Tom Colvin, 1925–2000
Tune: GARU, 55 2 55 2, Ghanian folk song, adapt. by Tom Colvin, 1925–2000, arr. by Kevin R. Hackett, b.1956
© 1969, Hope Publishing Company

622 Alleluia! Jesus Is Risen!

1. Al - le - lu - ia! Je - sus is ris - en!
2. Walk - ing the way, Christ in the cen - ter
3. Je - sus the vine, We are the branch - es;
4. Weep - ing, be gone; Sor - row, be si - lent:
5. Cit - y of God, East - er for - ev - er,

Trum - pets re - sound - ing in glo - ri - ous light!
Tell - ing the sto - ry to o - pen our eyes;
Life in the Spir - it the fruit of the tree;
Death put a - sun - der, and East - er is bright.
Gold - en Je - ru - sa - lem, Je - sus the Lamb,

Splen - dor, the Lamb, Heav - en for - ev - er!
Break - ing our bread, Giv - ing us glo - ry:
Heav - en to earth, Christ to the peo - ple,
Cher - u - bim sing: O grave, be o - pen!
Riv - er of life, Saints and arch - an - gels,

Oh, what a mir - a - cle God has in sight!
Je - sus our bless - ing, our con - stant sur - prise.
Gift of the fu - ture now flow - ing to me.
Clothe us in won - der, a - dorn us in light.
Sing with cre - a - tion to God the I AM!

Je - sus is ris - en and we shall a - rise.

Give God the glo - ry! Al-le-lu - ia!

Text: Herbert F. Brokering, 1926–2009, © 1995, Augsburg Fortress
Tune: EARTH AND ALL STARS, 4 5 10 D with refrain; David N. Johnson, 1922–1987, © 1969, *Contemporary Worship 1*, admin. by Augsburg Fortress

Goodness Is Stronger than Evil 623

Good-ness is strong-er than e - vil; love is strong-er than

hate; light is strong-er than dark - ness;

life is strong-er than death. Vic-t'ry is ours, vic-t'ry is

ours through him who loved us. Vic-t'ry is

ours, vic-t'ry is ours through him who loved us.

Text: Desmond Tutu, b.1931, ©; adapt. by John L. Bell, b.1949
Tune: GOODNESS IS STRONGER, Irregular; John L. Bell, b.1949, © 1996, Iona Community, GIA Publications, Inc., agent

Surrexit Christus 624

Ostinato Refrain

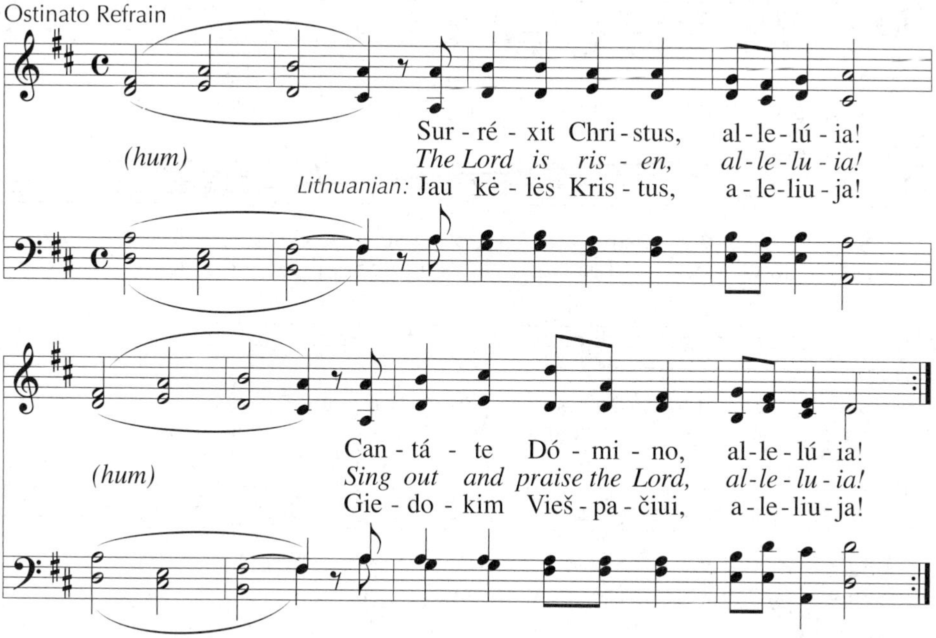

(hum)

Sur - ré - xit Chri - stus, al - le - lú - ia!
The Lord is ris - en, al - le - lu - ia!
Lithuanian: Jau kė - lės Kris - tus, a - le - liu - ja!

(hum)

Can - tá - te Dó - mi - no, al - le - lú - ia!
Sing out and praise the Lord, al - le - lu - ia!
Gie - do - kim Vieš - pa - čiui, a - le - liu - ja!

Text: Daniel 3; Taizé Community, 1984
Tune: Jacques Berthier, 1923–1994
© 1984, Les Presses de Taizé, GIA Publications, Inc., agent

625 Day of Delight

Refrain

Day of de-light and beau-ty un-bound-ed, Tell the
news, the gos-pel spread! Day of all won-der,
day of all splen-dor, Praise Christ ris - en from the dead!

Verses

1. Sing of the sun, from dark-ness ap-pear-ing;
2. Sing now of mourn-ing turned in-to danc-ing;

Sing of the seed, from bar-ren earth green-ing;
Sing now the mys-t'ry, hope of our glo-ry;

Sing of cre-a-tion, al-le-lu-ia!
Sing with thanks-giv-ing, al-le-lu-ia!

Sing of the stream, from Je-sus' side flow-ing;
Sing now of fast-ing turned in-to feast-ing;

Sing of the saints, in wa-ter made ho-ly;
Sing the Lord's fa-vor last-ing for-ev-er;

D.C.

Sing of sal-va-tion, al-le-lu-ia!
Sing, all things liv-ing, al-le-lu-ia!

Text: Delores Dufner, OSB, b.1939, © 2010, GIA Publications, Inc.
Tune: IN DIR IST FREUDE, 10 10 9 D with refrain; Giovanni Giacomo Gastoldi, c.1554–1609

Let Christians All Their Voices Raise 626

Refrain

Al - le - lu - ia, al - le - lu - ia, al - le - lu - ia.

Verses

1. Let Chris - tians all their voic - es raise
2. Christ, sin - less Lamb from heav'n a - bove,
3. When death to life in fear - some strains
4. What saw you, Mar - y, on the way?
5. "I saw the an - gels and did hear
6. "Christ now ap - pears be - fore his own
7. We know that Christ now lives in - deed;

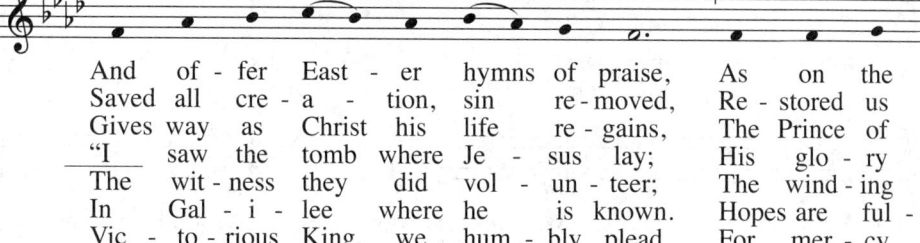

And of - fer East - er hymns of praise, As on the
Saved all cre - a - tion, sin re - moved, Re - stored us
Gives way as Christ his life re - gains, The Prince of
"I saw the tomb where Je - sus lay; His glo - ry
The wit - ness they did vol - un - teer; The wind - ing
In Gal - i - lee where he is known. Hopes are ful -
Vic - to - rious King, we hum - bly plead For mer - cy

D.C.

Pas - chal Lamb they gaze.
to the Fa - ther's love.
Life im - mor - tal reigns.
bright - ens us this day."   O praise the Lamb!
cloths were al - so near."
filled; his wounds are shown."
in our ev - 'ry need.

Text: Easter Sequence; attr. to Wipo of Burgundy, c.1000–c.1050; tr. by Jerome Siwek, 1930–2004, © 1980, World Library Publications
Tune: O FILII ET FILIAE, 888 4 with refrain; Mode II, French carol, 15th C.; acc. by Richard Proulx, 1937–2010,
    © 1975, GIA Publications, Inc.

627 We Walk His Way / Ewe, Thina

Refrain

We walk his way. We walk
E - we, thi - na. E - we,

We walk his way. We walk his way.
E - we, thi - na. E - we, thi - na.

his way. We walk
thi - na. E - we,

We walk his way. We walk his way. We walk his way.
E - we, thi - na. E - we, thi - na. E - we, thi - na.

Verses

1. Unarmed, he faces forces of demons and death.

2. He breaks the bonds of hell, dying on the cross.

3. The tree of freedom blooms by his empty grave.

1. Sizowa nyathela amadimoni.

Text: South African; tr. by Anders Nyberg, b.1955, and Sven-Bernhard Fast
Tune: South African; arr. by Anders Nyberg, b.1955
© 1984, Peace of Music Publishing AB, admin. by Walton Music Corp., a division of GIA Publications, Inc.

Be Not Afraid   628

Ostinato Refrain

Be not a-fraid, sing out for joy! Christ is ris-en, al - le -
Czech: *Ne - boj - te se,* *ra - duj - te se!* *Kris - tus slav-ný ví - těz*
Polish: Nie bój - cie się, ra - duj-cie się! Chry - stus rze-czy-wi-ście
Croatian: *O - dag - naj strah i ra - duj se!* *Krist je do - is - ta us -*

lu - ia! Be not a-fraid, sing out for joy!
z hro-bu vstal. *Ne - boj - te se,* *ra - duj - te se!*
z gro-bu wstał. Nie bój - cie się, ra - duj - cie się!
krs - nu - o! *O - dag - naj strah i ra - duj se!*

Christ is ris - en, al - le - lu - ia!
Kris - tus slav - ný ví - těz z hro - bu vstal.
Chry - stus rze - czy - wi - ście z gro - bu wstał.
Krist je do - is - ta us - krs - nu - o!

Text: Taizé Community
Tune: Taizé Community
© 2007, Les Presses de Taizé, GIA Publications, Inc., agent

629 Easter Alleluia

Refrain

Al-le-lu-ia, al - le - lu-ia, al - le - lu - ia!

Verses

1. Glo - ry to God who does won - drous things, Let all the
2. See how sal - va - tion for all has been won, Up from the
3. Now in our pres - ence the Lord will ap - pear, Shine in the
4. Call us, Good Shep - herd, we lis - ten for you, Want-ing to
5. Lord, we are o - pen to all that you say, Read - y to
6. If we have love, then we dwell in the Lord, God will pro -

peo - ple God's prais - es now sing, All of cre - a - tion in
grave our new life has be - gun, Life now per - fect - ed in
fac - es of all of us here, Fill us with joy and cast
see you in all that we do, We would the gate of sal -
lis - ten and fol - low your way, You are the pot - ter and
tect us from fire and sword, Fill us with love and the

D.C.

splen - dor shall ring:
Je - sus, the Son:
out all our fear:
va - tion pass through:
we are the clay:
peace of his word:

Al - le - lu - ia!

Text: Marty Haugen, b.1950
Tune: O FILII ET FILIAE, 10 10 10 with alleluias; adapt. by Marty Haugen, b.1950
© 1986, GIA Publications, Inc.

Resucitó 630

Refrain

Re - su - ci - tó,   re - su - ci - tó,   re - su - ci -
A - le - lu - ya,   a - le - lu - ya,   a - le - lu -

To verses | *Final ending*

tó,   a - le - lu - ya.   A - le - lu - ya.
ya,   re - su - ci - tó.

Verses

1. La muer - te   ¿dón - de es - tá la
2. Gra - cias se - an   da - das al
3. A - le - grí - a,   a - le - grí - a her -
4. Si con Él mo - ri - mos,   y con Él vi -
1. And death now,   van - ished is the
2. The king - dom,   praise to God, the
3. Our glad - ness,   bliss - ful in our
4. With him then,   die and live with

muer - te?   ¿Dón - de es - tá mi
Pa - dre   que nos pa - só a su
ma - nos,   que si hoy nos que -
vi - mos,   y con Él can -
fear now,   *ban - ished are my*
king - dom!   *Raised up to the*
glad - ness,   *this will be our*
him then,   *rise and sing our*

D.C.

muer - te?   ¿Dón - de su vic - to - ria?
rei - no   dón - de se vi - ve de a - mor.
re - mos   es que re - su - ci - tó.
ta - mos.   y ¡A - le - lu - ya!
tears now,   *death has passed a - way.*
king - dom,   *we shall live in love.*
glad - ness,   *that he is a - live.*
hymn then,   *sing al - le - lu - ia.*

Text: Spanish, Kiko Argüello, © 1973, Kiko Argüello; tr. by Robert C. Trupia, © 1988, OCP
Tune: Kiko Argüello, © 1973, Kiko Argüello; acc. by Diana Kodner, b.1957
Published by OCP.

631 Joyous Cup

Verses

Cantor: *All:*

1. Slaves and chil - dren, take a stand:
2. Sea, stand straight! And riv - ers, flee:
3. Trem - ble, earth, to see God's face:
4. Heav - ens, sing! O earth, in - tone:
5. Eve and A - dam, tell it plain: Al - le - lu -
6. God, our lov - er, long be - trayed
7. O hap - py fault, O need - ful sin:
8. Go pro - claim a ju - bi - lee:
9. Go pro - claim a ju - bi - lee:

Cantor: *All:*

Come to milk and hon - ey land:
Moun-tains, skip like lambs to see:
Flint shall flow with wa - ter's grace:
Death and hell now wail and groan:
ia!   All was lost but more's the gain: Al - le - lu -
O Christ our sav - ior, Christ our kin:
Nei - ther rich nor poor shall be:
Now from ev - 'ry debt set free:

Refrain

ia!   Christ has died and death is dead: earth and heav - en

bold - ly wed.   Joy - ous cup and *ho - ly bread.

Al - le - lu - ia.

Or: hearty

Text: Based on Psalm 114 and the Exsultet; Gabe Huck, b.1941
Tune: Tony E. Alonso, b.1980
© 2004, GIA Publications, Inc.

Earth, Earth, Awake! 632

1. Earth, earth, a - wake! Your prais - es sing! Greet
2. All na - ture sings of hope re - born! Christ
3. Win - ter is past; the night is gone! Christ's
4. Praise we the Fa - ther, Spir - it, Son! Praise

with the dawn your ris - en King! Al - le - lu - ia! Al - le -
lives to com - fort those who mourn! Al - le - lu - ia! Al - le -
light, tri - um - phant, brings the dawn! Al - le - lu - ia! Al - le -
we the vic - t'ry God has won! Al - le - lu - ia! Al - le -

lu - ia! Bright suns and stars, your hom - age pay! Life
lu - ia! First fruit of all the dead who sleep! Prom -
lu - ia! Cre - a - tion spreads its spring-time bloom! Life
lu - ia! Praise we the Lamb who reigns a - bove! Praise

reigns a - gain this East - er day!
ise of joy for all who weep!
bursts like flame from death's cold tomb! Al - le - lu - ia! Al - le -
we the King whose rule is love!

lu - ia! Al - le - lu - ia! Al - le - lu - ia! Al - le - lu - ia!

Text: Herman G. Stuempfle, Jr., 1923–2007, © 1996, GIA Publications, Inc.
Tune: LASST UNS ERFREUEN, LM with alleluias; *Geistliche Kirchengesänge*, Cologne, 1623; harm. by Ralph Vaughan Williams, 1872–1958

633 Christ Has Arisen, Alleluia / Mfurahini, Haleluya

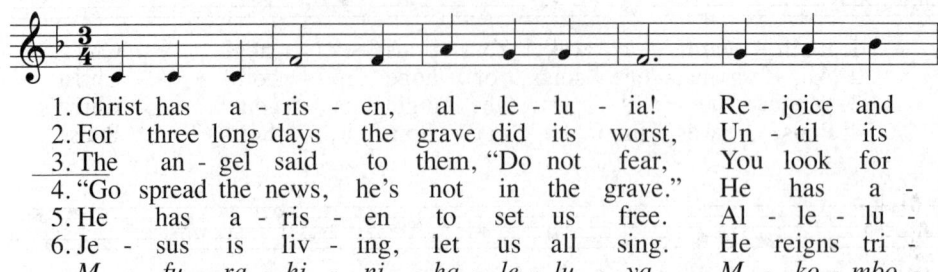

1. Christ has a - ris - en, al - le - lu - ia! Re - joice and
2. For three long days the grave did its worst, Un - til its
3. The an - gel said to them, "Do not fear, You look for
4. "Go spread the news, he's not in the grave." He has a -
5. He has a - ris - en to set us free. Al - le - lu -
6. Je - sus is liv - ing, let us all sing. He reigns tri -
   M - fu - ra - hi - ni, ha - le - lu - ya, M - ko - mbo -

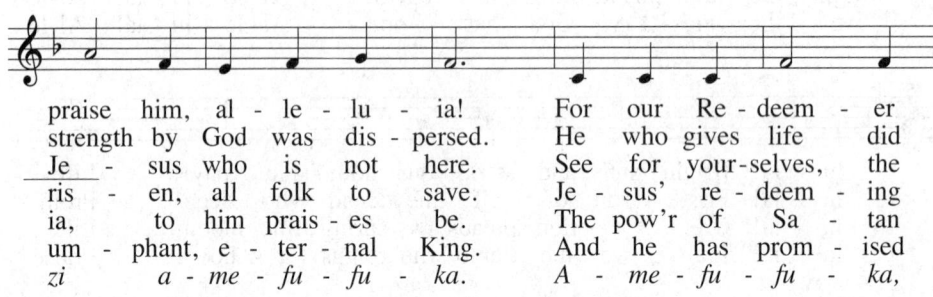

praise him, al - le - lu - ia! For our Re - deem - er
strength by God was dis - persed. He who gives life did
Je - sus who is not here. See for your-selves, the
ris - en, all folk to save. Je - sus' re - deem - ing
ia, to him prais - es be. The pow'r of Sa - tan
um - phant, e - ter - nal King. And he has prom - ised
zi a - me - fu - fu - ka. A - me - fu - fu - ka,

burst from the tomb, E - ven from death dis - pel - ling its gloom.
death un - der - go, And in its con - quest his might did show.
tomb is all bare. On - ly the grave cloths are ly - ing there."
la - bors are done. E - ven the bat - tle with sin is won.
no long - er binds, Nor can en - slave the thoughts of our minds.
those who be - lieve In - to his king - dom he will re - ceive.
Ha - le - lu - ya, M - si - fu - ni sa - sa yu ha - i.

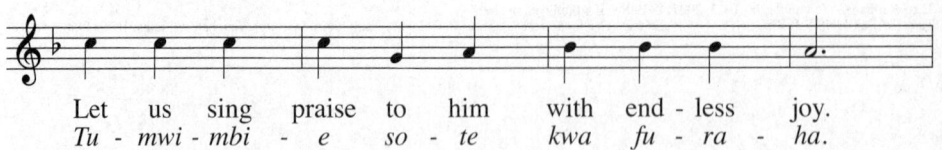

Let us sing praise to him with end - less joy.
Tu - mwi - mbi - e so - te kwa fu - ra - ha.

Swahili phonetics:
Mm-foo-rah-hee-nee, hah-lay-loo-yah, Mm-koh-mboh-zee ah-may-foo-foo-kah.
Ah-may-foo-foo-kah, hah-lay-loo-yah, Mm-see-foo-nee sah-sah yoo hah-ee.

Too-mwee-mbee-ay soh-tay kwah foo-rah-hah.
Yay-soo ah-may-toh-kah kah-boo-ree-nee.
Kah-shee-ndah kee-foh, hah-lay-loo-yah, hah-lay-loo-yah, Yay-soo yoo hah-ee.

Death's fear - ful sting he has come to de - stroy.
Ye - su a - me-to-ka ka-bu - ri - ni.

Our sins for - giv - ing, al - le - lu - ia!
Ka - shi - nda ki - fo, ha - le - lu - ya,

Je - sus is liv - ing, al - le - lu - ia!
ha - le - lu - ya, Ye - su yu ha - i.

Text: Swahili; Bernard Kyamanywa, b.1938; tr. by Howard S. Olson, 1922–2010, © 1977, Augsburg Fortress
Tune: MFURAHINI, HALELUYA, 99 99 with refrain; Haya tune

Good Christians All 634

1. Good Chris - tians all, re - joice and sing!
2. The Lord of life is ris'n to - day!
3. Praise we in songs of vic - to - ry
4. Your Name we bless, O ris - en Lord,
5. To God the Fa - ther, God the Son,

Now is the tri - umph of our King!
Sing songs of praise a - long his way;
That love, that life which can - not die,
And sing to - day with one ac - cord
To God the Spir - it, al - ways One,

To all the world glad news we bring:
Let all the earth re - joice and say:
And sing with hearts up - lift - ed high:
The life laid down, the life re - stored:
We sing for life in us be - gun:

Al - le - lu - ia, al - le - lu - ia, al - le - lu - ia!

Text: Cyril A. Alington, 1872–1955, alt., © 1956, ren. 1986, Hymns Ancient and Modern, Ltd.; st. 5, Norman Mealy, 1923–1987,
© 1971, Walton Music Corp., a div. of GIA Publications, Inc.
Tune: GELOBT SEI GOTT, 888 with alleluias; Melchior Vulpius, c.1560–1616; acc. Robert J. Batastini, b.1942, © 1987, GIA Publications, Inc.

635 Be My Hands and Feet

Verses

1. Touch that soothes and heals the hurt - ing, Hands that
2. Feed the hun - gry, clothe the na - ked, Vis - it
3. Love and serve with - out dis-tinc - tion All earth's
4. Hands that beck - on lit - tle chil - dren, Bind a

break a loaf of bread; Steps that walk be -
ones in need of care, Give the home - less
peo - ple, first and least. Know with - in each
wound, pre - pare a meal, Feet that rush to

side the wea - ry, Bear - ing bur - dens in their stead:
warmth and shel - ter: Christ will find a wel-come there.
act of kind - ness Hope and whole-ness are in - creased.
share good tid - ings, Christ a - ris - en, still re - veal.

Refrain

See my hands and feet, said Je-sus, love a - ris-en from the

grave. Be my hands and feet, said Je - sus,

live as ones I died to save.

Text: Mary Louise Bringle, b.1953, © 2002, GIA Publications, Inc.
Tune: ANDERSON, 8 7 8 7 with refrain; Tony E. Alonso, b.1980, © 2015, GIA Publications, Inc.

On the Journey to Emmaus 636

1. On the jour - ney to Em - ma - us with our
2. And our hearts burned with - in us as we
3. And that eve - ning at the ta - ble as he
4. On our jour - ney to Em - ma - us, in our

hearts cold as stone— The One who would
talked on the way, How all that was
blessed and broke bread, We saw it was
stor - ies and feast, With Je - sus we

save us had left us a - lone. Then a
prom - ised was ours on that day. So we
Je - sus a - ris'n from the dead; Though he
claim that the great - est is least: And his

stran - ger walks with us and, to our sur - prise, He
begged him, "Stay with us and grant us your word." We
van - ished be - fore us we knew he was near— The
words burn with - in us— let none be ig - nored— Who

o - pens our stor - ies and he o - pens our eyes.
wel - comed the stran - ger and we wel - comed the Lord.
life in our dy - ing and the hope in our fear.
wel - comes the stran - ger shall wel - come the Lord.

Text: Luke 24:13–35; Marty Haugen, b.1950
Tune: COLUMCILLE, Irregular; Gaelic, arr. by Marty Haugen, b.1950
© 1995, GIA Publications, Inc.

637 Hail Thee, Festival Day!

Refrain

Easter: Hail thee, fes - ti - val day! Blest day to be
Ascension: Hail thee, fes - ti - val day! Blest day to be
Pentecost: Hail thee, fes - ti - val day! Blest day to be

hal - lowed for - ev - er; Day when our Lord was
hal - lowed for - ev - er; Day when our Lord as -
hal - lowed for - ev - er; Day God re - news the

First time only / *All other times*

raised, break - ing the king - dom of death. death.
cends, high in the heav - ens to reign. reign.
earth, send - ing the Spir - it of Life. Life.

Verses 1, 3, 5

Easter: 1. All the fair beau - ty of earth From the
Ascension: 1. He who was nailed to the cross Is
Pentecost: 1. Bright, in the like - ness of fire, On
3. God the Al - might - y, the Lord, The
5. Spir - it of life and of pow'r, Now

death of the win - ter a - ris - ing! Ev - 'ry good
rul - er and Lord of all peo - ple. All things cre -
those who a - wait your ap - pear - ing You, whom the
rul - er of earth and the heav - ens, Guard us from
flow in us, fount of our be - ing, Light that en -

D.C.

gift of the year Now with its Mas - ter re - turns.
at - ed on earth Sing to the glo - ry of God.
Lord had fore - told, Sud - den - ly, swift - ly de - scend.
harm with - out; Cleanse us from e - vil with - in.
light - ens us all, Life that in all may a - bide.

Verses 2, 4, 6

Easter: 2. Rise from the grave now, O Lord, The au - thor of
Ascension: 2. Show us your face, Je - sus Christ, That we may re -
Pentecost: 2. Forth from the Fa - ther you come With sev - en-fold
4. Je - sus, the health of the world, En - light - en our
6. Praise to the Giv - er of good! O Lov - er and

life and cre - a - tion. Tread - ing the path - way of
joice in your bright - ness. Give us the light of your
mys - ti - cal of - f'ring, Pour - ing on all hu - man
minds, great Re - deem - er, Son of the Fa - ther su -
Au - thor of con - cord, Pour out your balm on our

D.C.

death, New life you give to us all.
day, Dark - ened on earth at your death.
souls In - fi - nite rich - es of God.
preme, On - ly - be - got - ten of God.
days; Or - der our ways in your peace.

Text: *Salve festa dies*; Venantius Fortunatus, c.530–609; tr. composite
Tune: SALVE FESTA DIES, Irregular with refrain; Ralph Vaughan Williams, 1872–1958

638 Lord, You Give the Great Commission

1. Lord, you give the great com - mis-sion: "Heal the
2. Lord, you call us to your serv - ice: "In my
3. Lord, you make the com - mon ho - ly: "This my
4. Lord, you show us love's true meas-ure: "Fa - ther,
5. Lord, you bless with words as - sur-ing: "I am

sick and preach the word." Lest the Church ne -
name bap - tize and teach." That the world may
bod - y, this my blood." Let us all, for
what they do, for - give." Yet we hoard as
with you to the end." Faith and hope and

glect its mis - sion And the Gos - pel go un-heard,
trust your prom-ise, Life a - bun - dant meant for each,
earth's true glo - ry, Dai - ly lift life heav - en-ward,
pri - vate treas-ure All that you so free - ly give.
love re - stor-ing, May we serve as you in - tend,

Help us wit - ness to your pur-pose With re -
Give us all new fer - vor, draw us Clos - er
Ask - ing that the world a - round us Share your
May your care and mer - cy lead us To a
And, a - mid the cares that claim us, Hold in

newed in - teg - ri - ty;
in com - mun - i - ty;
chil - dren's lib - er - ty;
just so - ci - e - ty;
mind e - ter - ni - ty;

With the Spir - it's gifts em -

pow'r us For the work of min - is - try.

Text: Jeffery Rowthorn, b.1934, © 1978, Hope Publishing Company
Tune: ABBOT'S LEIGH, 8 7 8 7 D; Cyril V. Taylor, 1907–1991, © 1942, ren. 1970, Hope Publishing Company

Alternate tune: HYFRYDOL

A Hymn of Glory Let Us Sing! 639

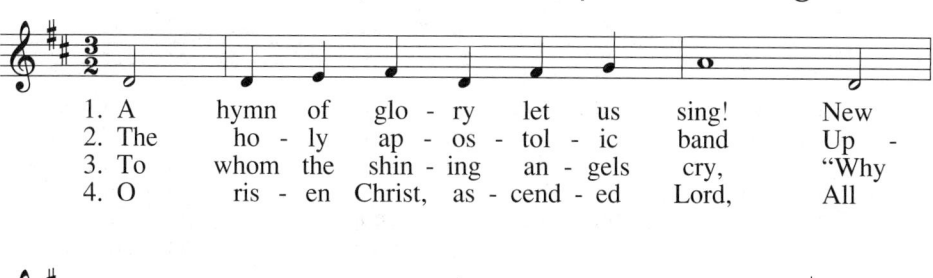

1. A hymn of glo - ry let us sing! New
2. The ho - ly ap - os - tol - ic band Up -
3. To whom the shin - ing an - gels cry, "Why
4. O ris - en Christ, as - cend - ed Lord, All

hymns through-out the world shall ring: Al - le - lu - ia! Al - leon the Mount of Ol - ives stand. Al - le - lu - ia! Al - le-
stand and gaze up - on the sky?" Al - le - lu - ia! Al - le-
praise to you let earth ac - cord: Al - le - lu - ia! Al - le-

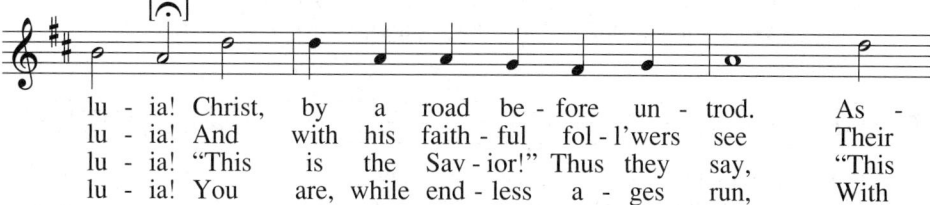

lu - ia! Christ, by a road be - fore un - trod. As -
lu - ia! And with his faith - ful fol - l'wers see Their
lu - ia! "This is the Sav - ior!" Thus they say, "This
lu - ia! You are, while end - less a - ges run, With

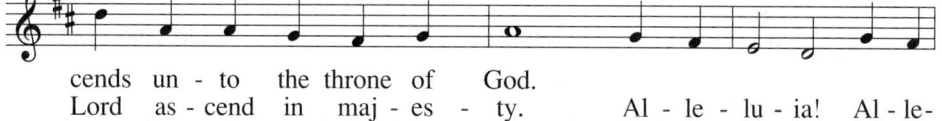

cends un - to the throne of God.
Lord as - cend in maj - es - ty. Al - le - lu - ia! Al - le-
is his glo - rious tri - umph day!"
Fa - ther and with Spir - it one.

lu - ia! Al - le - lu - ia! Al - le - lu - ia! Al - le - lu - ia!

Text: *Hymnum canamus gloriae;* Venerable Bede, 673–735; tr. by Benjamin Webb, 1819–1885, *The Hymnal Noted,* 1854, alt.
Tune: LASST UNS ERFREUEN, LM with alleluias; *Geistliche Kirchengesänge,* Cologne, 1623; harm. by Ralph Vaughan Williams, 1872–1958

640 Hail the Day That Sees Him Rise

1. Hail the day that sees him rise, Al - le - lu - ia!
2. There the glo - rious tri - umph waits; Al - le - lu - ia!
3. High - est heav'n its Lord re - ceives, Al - le - lu - ia!
4. See, he lifts his hands a - bove; Al - le - lu - ia!
5. Christ, for us still in - ter - cede, Al - le - lu - ia!
6. There we shall with you re - main, Al - le - lu - ia!

To his throne a - bove the skies; Al - le - lu - ia!
Lift your heads, e - ter - nal gates; Al - le - lu - ia!
Yet he loves the earth he leaves; Al - le - lu - ia!
See, he shows the wounds of love; Al - le - lu - ia!
By your suf - f'ring for us plead; Al - le - lu - ia!
Part - ners of your end - less reign; Al - le - lu - ia!

Christ, the Lamb for sin - ners giv'n, Al - le - lu - ia!
Christ has con - quered death and sin; Al - le - lu - ia!
Though re - turn - ing to his throne, Al - le - lu - ia!
Hark, his gra - cious lips be - stow, Al - le - lu - ia!
Make us wor - thy of the place, Al - le - lu - ia!
There your face un - cloud-ed see, Al - le - lu - ia!

Now as - cends the high - est heav'n. Al - le - lu - ia!
Take the King of glo - ry in! Al - le - lu - ia!
Still he calls the world his own. Al - le - lu - ia!
Bless - ings on his Church be - low. Al - le - lu - ia!
Which you of - fer us by grace. Al - le - lu - ia!
Live with you e - ter - nal - ly. Al - le - lu - ia!

Text: Charles Wesley, 1707–1788, alt.; st. 5 from *The New Century Hymnal*, © 1992, The Pilgrim Press
Tune: LLANFAIR, 77 77 with alleluias; Robert Williams, 1781–1821

641 Go to the World!

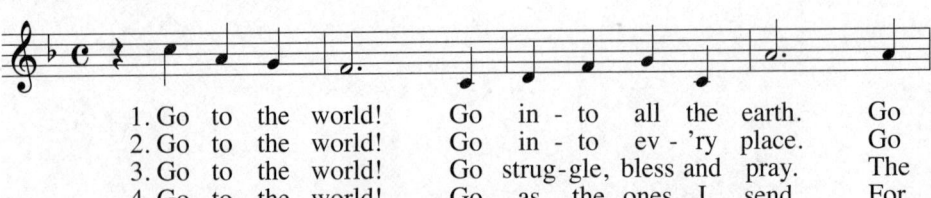

1. Go to the world! Go in - to all the earth. Go
2. Go to the world! Go in - to ev - 'ry place. Go
3. Go to the world! Go strug-gle, bless and pray. The
4. Go to the world! Go as the ones I send, For

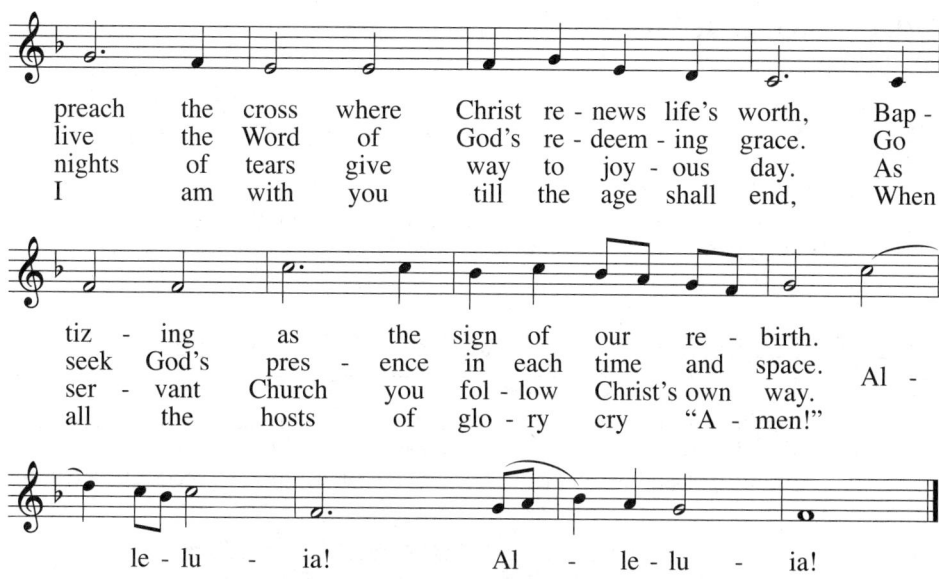

preach   the   cross   where   Christ re - news life's worth,   Bap -
live   the   Word   of   God's re - deem - ing grace.   Go
nights   of   tears   give   way   to   joy - ous   day.   As
I   am   with   you   till   the age   shall end,   When

tiz - ing   as   the   sign of   our   re - birth.
seek God's   pres - ence in   each time and   space.   Al -
ser - vant   Church you   fol - low Christ's own way.
all   the   hosts   of   glo - ry   cry   "A - men!"

le - lu - ia!   Al - le - lu - ia!

Text: Sylvia G. Dunstan, 1955–1993, © 1991, GIA Publications, Inc.
Tune: SINE NOMINE, 10 10 10 with alleluias; Ralph Vaughan Williams, 1872–1958

Song to Jesus Christ   642

1. You   have passed by, you came   like fire that lights the skies,
2. You   have passed by, as brief   as foot - prints on the sea;
3. You   have passed by, a strange   and yet fa - mil - iar face,

Sparks fall - ing from your name   glow in   our hearts like eyes.
Why   did you go   so   far? You went too   far   for me.
A   frag - ment of our being,   a flick - 'ring light, a trace.

In   tat - ters hangs your word, draped   round our world and torn;
You are for - ev - er now   as   deep in God as breath;
Your light is in my blood, my   bod - y is your day;

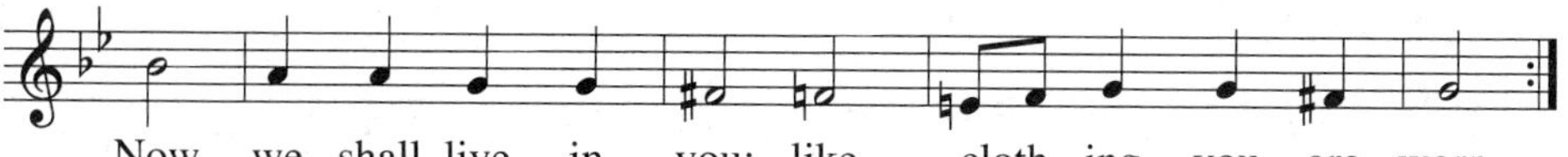

Now we shall live in   you; like   cloth - ing you are worn.
No   still - ness cap - tures you, un - think - a - ble your death.
I   hope my whole life long to   meet you on the way.

Text: Huub Oosterhuis, b.1933; tr. by Redmond McGoldrick, © 1971, Gooi En Sticht, OCP, agent
Tune: BELLE QUI TIENS MA VIE, 12 12 12 12; Jehan Tabourot, 1519–1595, alt.; harm. by Bernard Huijbers, 1922–2003

643 Go Out to the World

Verses

1. With hands of jus - tice and faith, we go to
(2. With lives of) cour - age and strength, we spread the
(3. With gen - tle) spir - its, we go to share the

serve the world, to bring good news to the poor and op - pressed.
mes-sage of love to all the weak, the lone - ly, the hurt.
mes-sage of peace with all the trou - bled, lost, and dis - tressed.

With hearts of love and of hope, we go to
With lives that an - swer the call, we spread the
With hum - ble spir - its, we go to share the

live the word that em - pow-ers us to new life.
word of God that em - pow-ers us to new life.
love of God that em - pow-ers us to new life.

𝄋 Refrain

Go out to the world and tell all the good news,

tell all the good news of God's end - less love.

Go out to the world and tell all the good news,

tell all the good news of God's end-less love.

To verses

To bridge and Last time

Last time Solo:

2. With lives of God's end-less love. With
3. With gen-tle

Bridge

warmth in our hearts, we of-fer peace and con-so-la-tion. We reach

D.S.

out to the world, reach out to the world!

Text: Chris de Silva, b.1967
Tune: Chris de Silva, b.1967
© 2007, GIA Publications, Inc.

Holy Spirit, Come to Us 644

Ostinato Refrain

Ho-ly Spir-it, come to us, kin-dle in us the fire of your love.
Ven, Es-pí-ri-tu de Dios, y de tu a-mor en-cien-de la lla-ma.
Ve-ni San-cte Spí-ri-tus, tu-i a-mó-ris i-gnem ac-cén-de.

Ho-ly Spir-it, come to us, Ho-ly Spir-it, come to us.
Ven, Es-pí-ri-tu de a-mor, ven, Es-pí-ri-tu de a-mor.
Ve-ni San-cte Spí-ri-tus, ve-ni San-cte Spí-ri-tus.

Text: John 13:35, 15:12–13, 1 John 3:16, 4:10, 16
Tune: Jacques Berthier, 1923–1994
© 1998, Les Presses de Taizé, GIA Publications, Inc., agent

645 Praise the Spirit in Creation

1. Praise the
2. Praise the
3. Praise the
4. Tell of
5. Pray we

Spir - it in cre - a - tion, Breath of God, life's or - i -
Spir - it, close com - pan - ion Of our in - most thoughts and
Spir - it, who en - light - ened Priests and proph - ets with the
how the as - cend - ed Je - sus Armed a peo - ple for his
then, O Lord the Spir - it, On our lives de - scend in

gin: Spir - it mov - ing on the wa - ters Quick-'ning
ways; Who, in show - ing us God's won - ders, Is him -
word; His the truth be - hind the wis - doms Which as
own; How a hun - dred men and wom - en Turned the
might; Let your flame break out with - in us, Fire our

worlds to life with - in, Source of breath to all things
self the pow'r to gaze; And God's will, to those who
yet know not our Lord; By whose love and pow'r, in
known world up - side down, To its dark and fur - thest
hearts and clear our sight, Till, white - hot in your pos -

breath - ing, Life in whom all lives be - gin.
lis - ten, By a still, small voice con - veys.
Je - sus, God him - self was seen and heard.
cor - ners By the wind of heav - en blown.
ses - sion, We, too, set the world a - light.

Text: Michael Hewlett, 1916–2010, alt., © 1975, Michael Hewlett/Oxford University Press
Tune: JULION, 8 7 8 7 8 7; David Hurd, b.1950, © 1983, GIA Publications, Inc.

Come Down, O Love Divine 646

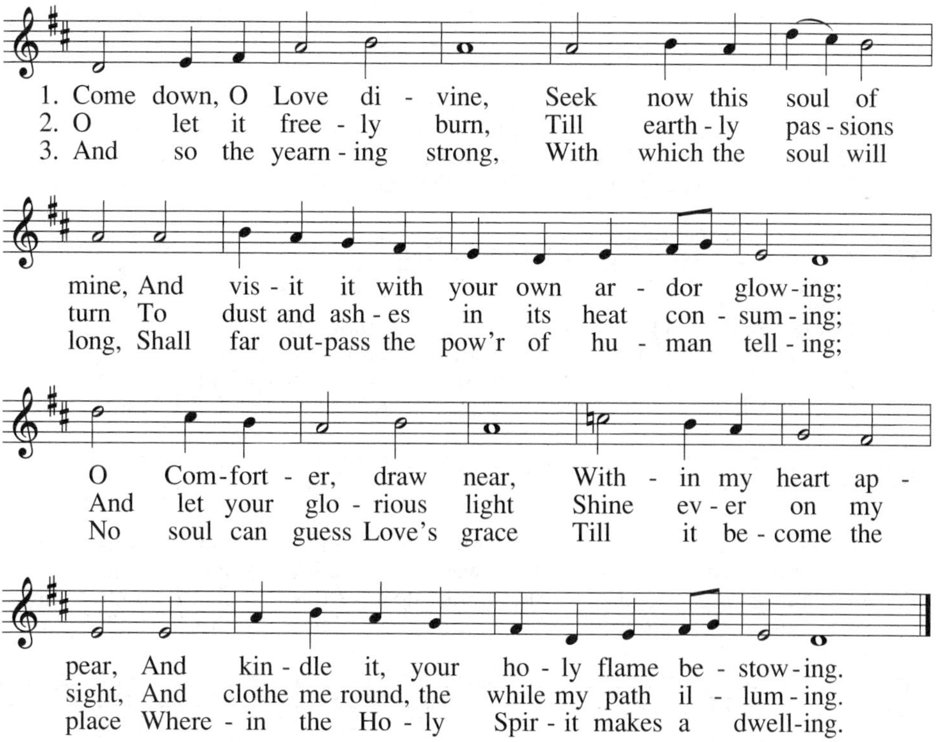

1. Come down, O Love di - vine, Seek now this soul of
2. O let it free - ly burn, Till earth - ly pas - sions
3. And so the yearn - ing strong, With which the soul will

mine, And vis - it it with your own ar - dor glow-ing;
turn To dust and ash - es in its heat con - sum - ing;
long, Shall far out-pass the pow'r of hu - man tell - ing;

O Com-fort - er, draw near, With - in my heart ap -
And let your glo - rious light Shine ev - er on my
No soul can guess Love's grace Till it be - come the

pear, And kin - dle it, your ho - ly flame be - stow-ing.
sight, And clothe me round, the while my path il - lum - ing.
place Where - in the Ho - ly Spir - it makes a dwell-ing.

Text: *Discendi, Amor Santo*; Bianco da Siena, d.1434; tr. by Richard F. Littledale, 1833–1890, alt.
Tune: DOWN AMPNEY, 66 11 D; Ralph Vaughan Williams, 1872–1958

Veni Sancte Spiritus 647

Ostinato Refrain

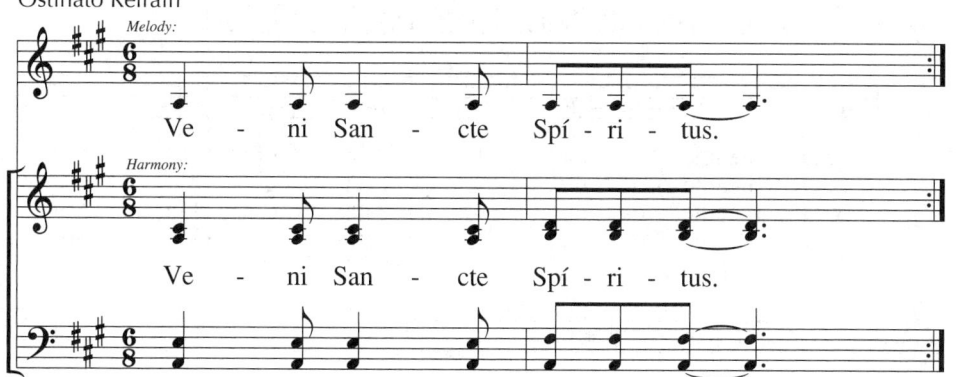

Melody:
Ve - ni San - cte Spí - ri - tus.

Harmony:
Ve - ni San - cte Spí - ri - tus.

Text: *Come Holy Spirit*; Verses drawn from the Pentecost Sequence; Taizé Community, 1978
Tune: Jacques Berthier, 1923–1994
© 1979, Les Presses de Taizé, GIA Publications, Inc., agent

648 Come, Holy Ghost

1. Come, Ho - ly Ghost, Cre - a - tor blest, And in our
2. O Com - fort - er, to thee we cry, Thou heav'n - ly
3. O Ho - ly Ghost, through thee a - lone Know we the
4. Praise we the Lord, Fa - ther and Son, And Ho - ly

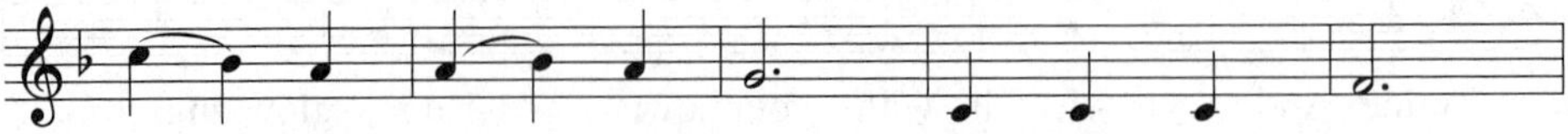

hearts take up thy rest; Come with thy grace
gift of God most high, Thou fount of life,
Fa - ther and the Son; Be this our firm
Spir - it with them one; And may the Son

and heav'n - ly aid To fill the hearts which thou hast
and fire of love, And sweet a - noint - ing from a -
un - chang - ing creed, That thou dost from them both pro -
on us be - stow All gifts that from the Spir - it

made, To fill the hearts which thou hast made.
bove, And sweet a - noint - ing from a - bove.
ceed, That thou dost from them both pro - ceed.
flow, All gifts that from the Spir - it flow.

Text: *Veni Creator Spiritus;* attr. to Rabanus Maurus, 776–856; tr. by Edward Caswall, 1814–1878, alt.
Tune: LAMBILLOTTE, LM with repeat; Louis Lambillotte, SJ, 1796–1855; harm. by Richard Proulx, 1937–2010, © 1986, GIA Publications, Inc.

649 O Breathe on Me, O Breath of God

1. O breathe on me, O Breath of God, Fill
2. O breathe on me, O Breath of God, Un -
3. O breathe on me, O Breath of God, My
4. O breathe on me, O Breath of God, So

me with life a - new, That I may love the
til my heart is pure; Un - til my will is
will to yours in - cline, Un - til this self - ish
shall I nev - er die, But live with you the

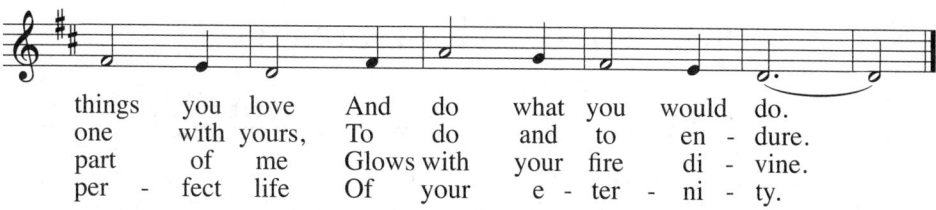

things	you	love	And	do	what	you	would	do.
one	with	yours,	To	do	and	to	en -	dure.
part	of	me	Glows with	your	fire	di -	vine.
per -	fect	life	Of	your	e -	ter -	ni -	ty.

Text: Edwin Hatch, 1835–1889
Tune: ST. COLUMBA, CM; Irish melody; harm. by A. Gregory Murray, OSB, 1905–1992, © Downside Abbey

Veni Creator Spiritus 650

1. Ve - ni Cre - á - tor Spí - ri - tus,
2. Qui dí - ce - ris Pa - rá - cli - tus,
3. Tu se - pti - fór - mis mú - ne - re,
4. Ac - cén - de lu - men sén - si - bus,
5. Ho - stem re - pél - las lón - gi - us,
6. Per te sci - á - mus da Pa - trem,
7. De - o Pa - tri sit gló - ri - a,

Men - tes tu - ó - rum ví - si - ta:
Al - tís - si - mi do - num De - i,
Dí - gi - tus pa - tér - nae déx - te - rae,
In - fún - de a - mó - rem cór - di - bus,
Pa - cém - que do - nes pró - ti - nus:
No - scá - mus at - que Fí - li - um
Et Fí - li - o, qui a mór - tu - is

Im - ple su - pér - na grá - ti - a
Fons vi - vus, i - gnis, cá - ri - tas,
Tu ri - te pro - mís - sum Pa - tris,
In - fír - ma no - stri cór - po - ris
Du - ctó - re sic te práe - vi - o,
Te - que u - tri - ús - que Spí - ri - tum
Sur - ré - xit, ac Pa - rá - cli - to,

Quae tu cre - á - sti pé - cto - ra.
Et spi - ri - tá - lis ún - cti - o.
Ser - mó - ne di - tans gút - tu - ra.
Vir - tú - te fir - mans pér - pe - ti.
Vi - té - mus o - mne nó - xi - um.
Cre - dá - mus o - mni tém - po - re.
In sae - cu - ló - rum saé - cu - la. A - men.

Text: *Veni Creator Spiritus*, attr. to Rabanus Maurus, 776–856
Tune: VENI CREATOR SPIRITUS, LM; Mode VIII; acc. by Richard Proulx, 1937–2010, © 1975, GIA Publications, Inc.

English paraphrases are found at nos. 648 and 651.

651 O Holy Spirit, by Whose Breath

1. O Holy Spirit, by whose breath
   Life rises vibrant out of death:
   Come to create, renew, inspire;
   Come, kindle in our hearts your fire.

2. You are the seeker's sure resource,
   Of burning love the living source,
   Protector in the midst of strife,
   The giver and the Lord of life.

3. In you God's energy is shown,
   To us your varied gifts make known.
   Teach us to speak, teach us to hear;
   Yours is the tongue and yours the ear.

4. Flood our dull senses with your light;
   In mutual love our hearts unite.
   Your pow'r the whole creation fills;
   Confirm our weak, uncertain wills.

5. From inner strife grant us release;
   Turn nations to the ways of peace.
   To fuller life your people bring
   That as one body we may sing:

6. Praise to the Father, Christ the Word,
   And to the Spirit: God the Lord,
   To whom all honor, glory be
   Both now and for eternity.

Text: *Veni Creator Spiritus;* attr. to Rabanus Maurus, 776–856; tr. by John W. Grant, 1919–2006, © 1971
Tune: VENI CREATOR SPIRITUS, LM; Mode VIII; setting by Richard J. Wojcik, 1923–2013, © 1975, GIA Publications, Inc.

O Spirit All-Embracing 652

1. O Spir-it all-em-brac-ing and coun-sel-or all-wise,
2. O Beau-ty ev-er blaz-ing in flow-er, field, and face,
3. Come, pas-sion's pow-er ho-ly, your in-sight here im-part,

Un-bound-ed splen-dor grac-ing a shore-less sea of skies:
You show your-self a-maz-ing in un-ex-pect-ed place.
And give your ser-vants low-ly an un-der-stand-ing heart

Un-fail-ing is your treas-ure, un-fad-ing your re-ward;
We see you and re-mem-ber what once our dreams had been;
To know your care more clear-ly when faith and love are tried,

Sur-pass-ing world-ly pleas-ure, the rich-es you af-ford.
You fan the glow-ing em-ber and kin-dle hope with-in.
To seek you more sin-cere-ly when false i-deals have died:

Come, stream of end-less flow-ing, and res-cue us from death;
Come, fire of glo-ry gra-cious, bless all who trust in you;
For vi-sion we im-plore you, for wis-dom's pure de-light;

Come, wind of spring-time blow-ing, and warm us by your breath.
Un-dy-ing flame te-na-cious, burn in your Church a-new.
In prayer we come be-fore you to wait up-on your light.

Text: Delores Dufner, OSB, b.1939, © 1995, 2003, GIA Publications, Inc.
Tune: THAXTED, 13 13 13 13 13 13; Gustav Holst, 1874–1934

653　Send Down the Fire

Refrain

Send down the fire of your jus-tice,

Send down the rains of your love; Come,

send down the Spir-it, breathe life in your peo-ple, and

we shall be peo-ple of God.

Verses

1. Call us to be your com - pas - sion,
2. Call us to learn of your mer - cy,
3. Call us to an - swer op - pres - sion,
4. Call us to wit - ness your King - dom,

Teach us the song of your love; Give us
Teach us the way of your peace; Give us
Teach us the fire of your truth; Give us
Give us the pres - ence of Christ; May your

hearts that sing, Give us deeds that ring, Make us
hearts that feel, Give us hands that heal, Make us
right - eous souls, 'Til your jus - tice rolls, Make us
ho - ly light Keep us shin - ing bright, Ev - er

D.C.

ring with the song of your love.
walk in the way of your peace.
burn with the fire of your truth.
shine with the pres - ence of Christ.

Text: Marty Haugen, b.1950
Tune: Marty Haugen, b.1950
© 1989, GIA Publications, Inc.

Send Us Your Spirit   654

Refrain

*1.
2.

Come Lord Je-sus, send us your Spir-it, re-

new the face of the earth. Come Lord

Je-sus, send us your Spir-it, re-new the face of the

earth.

Verses

1. Come to us, Spir-it of God, breathe in us
2. Fill us with the fire of your love, burn in us
3. Send us the wings of new birth, fill all the

now, we sing to-geth-er. Spir-it of
now, bring us to-geth-er. Come to us,
earth with the love you have taught us. Let all cre-

hope and of light, fill our lives,
dwell in us, change our lives, O Lord,
a - tion now be shak-en with love,

D.C.

come to us, Spir-it of God.
come to us, Spir-it of God.
come to us, Spir-it of God.

May be sung in canon.

Text: David Haas, b.1957
Tune: David Haas, b.1957; acc. by Jeanne Cotter, b.1964
© 1981, 1982, 1987, GIA Publications, Inc.

655　By the Waking of Our Hearts

Refrain

By the wak - ing of our hearts,

by the stir-ring of our souls, may the Spir-it of

God a-bide and bring us to-geth-er in Christ.

Verses

1. Come, O Spir - it, from a - bove, come from
2. Come, O Sav - ior of the poor, come, O
3. In our la - bor, rest most sweet; grate - ful
4. Bend the stub-born heart and will, melt the
5. Grant us vir - tue's sure re - ward, may your

your ce - les - tial heights. Come with your
source of gifts en - sured. Come with your
cool - ness in the heat. Con - sole our
fro - zen, warm the chill. Come guide our
gra - cious love be sent. Come with your

D.C.

bless - ed light so ra - diant, bright.
gen - tle hope, so won - drous and pure.
rest - less lives, by your com - fort, we seek.
search - ing minds toward your prom - ise ful - filled.
peace and joy that shall nev - er end.

Text: Verses based on the Pentecost Sequence; Ricky Manalo, CSP, b.1965
Tune: Ricky Manalo, CSP, b.1965
© 1998, Ricky Manalo, CSP. Published by OCP.

Come, Holy Spirit, on Us Shine 656

Refrain

Al - le - lu - ia, al - le - lu - ia, al - le - lu - ia.

Verses

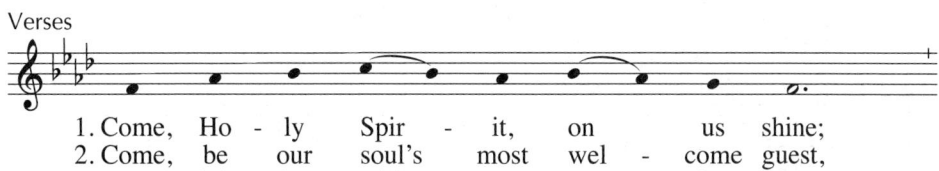

1. Come, Ho - ly Spir - it, on us shine;
2. Come, be our soul's most wel - come guest,
3. Come, Light, be with us ev - 'ry day:
4. Come, heal sin's wounds and give us grace.
5. Come, Par - a - clete, with gifts de - scend.

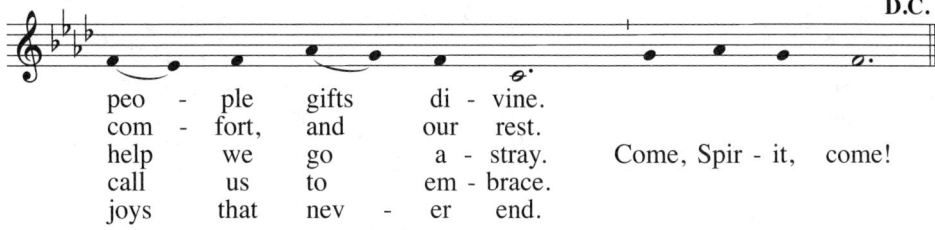

Look on the poor with love be - nign, And give your
En - dow - ing us with all the best; Be sol - ace,
In prayer, in rest, at work, at play; With - out your
All wrong you wish us to e - rase; All good you
Through all our life you are our friend; Come, bring us

D.C.

peo - ple gifts di - vine.
com - fort, and our rest.
help we go a - stray. Come, Spir - it, come!
call us to em - brace.
joys that nev - er end.

Text: *Veni Sancte Spiritus*; attr. to Stephen Langton, c.1150–1228; tr. by Jerome Siwek, 1930–2004, © 1980, World Library Publications
Tune: O FILII ET FILIAE, 888 4 with refrain; Mode II, French carol, 15th C.; acc. by Richard Proulx, 1937–2010, © 1975, GIA Publications, Inc.

Jesus, Your Spirit in Us 657

Ostinato Refrain

Je - sus, your Spir-it in us is a well-spring of life ev - er-last-ing.
Swedish: Kris-tus, din An-de i oss är en käl - la med por-lan-de vat-ten.
Spanish: Cris-to, tu Es-pí - ri-tu en mí es la fuen - te con a - gua de vi-da.

Text: Psalm 63:1–4, 7–8, John 7:37–39; Taizé Community
Tune: Taizé Community
© 2003, 2011, Les Presses de Taizé, GIA Publications, Inc., agent

658 Be Present, Spirit of the Lord

1. Be pres - ent, Spir - it of the Lord, Let
2. In pow'r un - seen up - on us rest, Your
3. Love's sov - 'reign work of grace ful - fill, Our
4. O Spir - it, come, and with us stay; Make

sounds of earth be dumb; The Fa - ther's love be
gra - cious gifts im - part: A mind re - newed, a
souls to Christ in - cline, In - tent to do the
ev - 'ry heart your home. So work in us that

shed a - broad, The dew of bless - ing
spir - it blessed, A life where Christ is
Fa - ther's will And stand by faith be -
we who pray May walk with Christ in

on us poured: O si - lent Spir - it,
man - i - fest, An un - der - stand - ing
fore him still In right - eous - ness di -
wis - dom's way: O Ho - ly Spir - it,

come! O si - lent Spir - it, come!
heart, An un - der - stand - ing heart.
vine, In right - eous - ness di - vine.
come! O Ho - ly Spir - it, come!

Text: Timothy Dudley-Smith, b.1926, © 1988, Hope Publishing Company
Tune: REPTON, 8 6 88 66; Charles H. H. Parry, 1848–1918

659 Holy, Holy, Holy! Lord God Almighty!

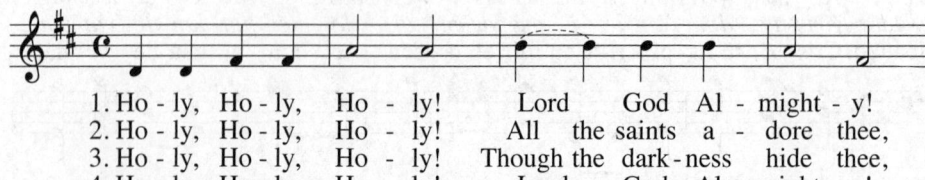

1. Ho - ly, Ho - ly, Ho - ly! Lord God Al - might - y!
2. Ho - ly, Ho - ly, Ho - ly! All the saints a - dore thee,
3. Ho - ly, Ho - ly, Ho - ly! Though the dark-ness hide thee,
4. Ho - ly, Ho - ly, Ho - ly! Lord God Al - might - y!

Ear - ly in the morn - ing our song shall rise to thee.
Cast - ing down their gold - en crowns a - round the glass - y sea;
Though the eye made blind by sin thy glo - ry may not see,
All thy works shall praise thy Name in earth and sky and sea.

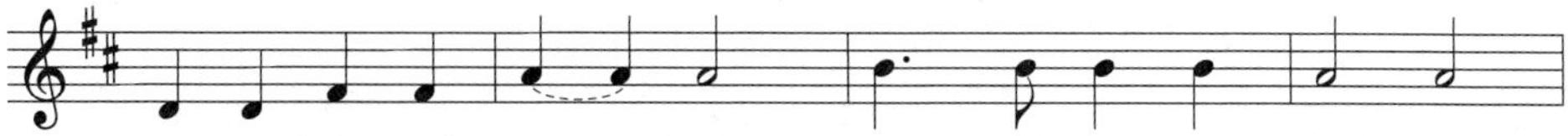

Ho - ly, Ho - ly, Ho - ly, mer - ci - ful and might - y!
Cher - u - bim and ser - a - phim fall - ing down be - fore thee,
On - ly thou art ho - ly; there is none be - side thee,
Ho - ly, Ho - ly, Ho - ly, mer - ci - ful and might - y!

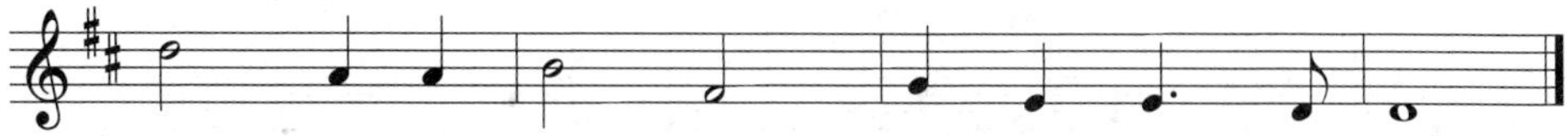

God in three Per - sons, bless - ed Trin - i - ty.
God ev - er - last - ing through e - ter - ni - ty.
Per - fect in pow'r, in love, and pu - ri - ty.
God in three Per - sons, bless - ed Trin - i - ty.

Text: Reginald Heber, 1783–1826, alt.
Tune: NICAEA, 11 12 12 10; John B. Dykes, 1823–1876

O God, Almighty Father 660

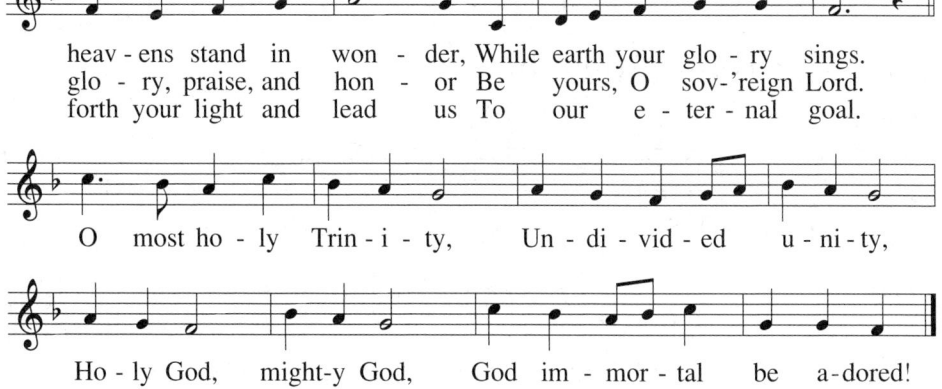

1. O God, al - might - y Fa - ther, Cre - a - tor of all things, The
2. O Je - sus, Word in - car - nate, Re - deem - er most a - dored, All
3. O God, the Ho - ly Spir - it, Who lives with - in our soul, Send

heav - ens stand in won - der, While earth your glo - ry sings.
glo - ry, praise, and hon - or Be yours, O sov - 'reign Lord.
forth your light and lead us To our e - ter - nal goal.

O most ho - ly Trin - i - ty, Un - di - vid - ed u - ni - ty,

Ho - ly God, might - y God, God im - mor - tal be a - dored!

Text: *Gott Vater sei gepriesen*; anon; tr. by Irvin Udulutsch, OFM Cap., 1920–2010, alt. © 1959, 1977, Order of Saint Benedict, admin. Liturgical Press
Tune: GOTT VATER SEI GEPRIESEN, 7 6 7 6 with refrain; Limburg *Gesangbuch*, 1838; harm. by Robert J. Batastini, b.1942, © 1975,
  GIA Publications, Inc.

661 God, Whose Almighty Word

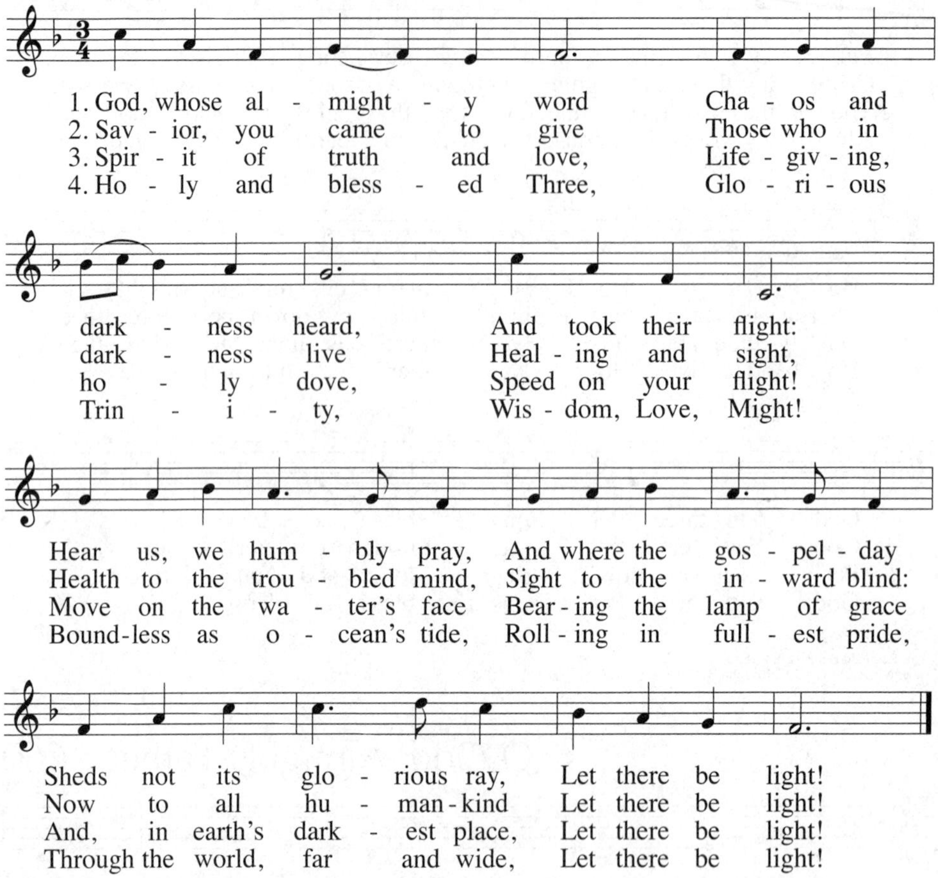
1. God, whose al - might - y word Cha - os and
2. Sav - ior, you came to give Those who in
3. Spir - it of truth and love, Life - giv - ing,
4. Ho - ly and bless - ed Three, Glo - ri - ous
dark - ness heard, And took their flight:
dark - ness live Heal - ing and sight,
ho - ly dove, Speed on your flight!
Trin - i - ty, Wis - dom, Love, Might!
Hear us, we hum - bly pray, And where the gos - pel - day
Health to the trou - bled mind, Sight to the in - ward blind:
Move on the wa - ter's face Bear - ing the lamp of grace
Bound-less as o - cean's tide, Roll - ing in full - est pride,
Sheds not its glo - rious ray, Let there be light!
Now to all hu - man - kind Let there be light!
And, in earth's dark - est place, Let there be light!
Through the world, far and wide, Let there be light!

Text: John Marriott, 1780–1825, alt.
Tune: ITALIAN HYMN, 66 4 666 4; Felice de Giardini, 1716–1796

662 Let There Be Light

Refrain

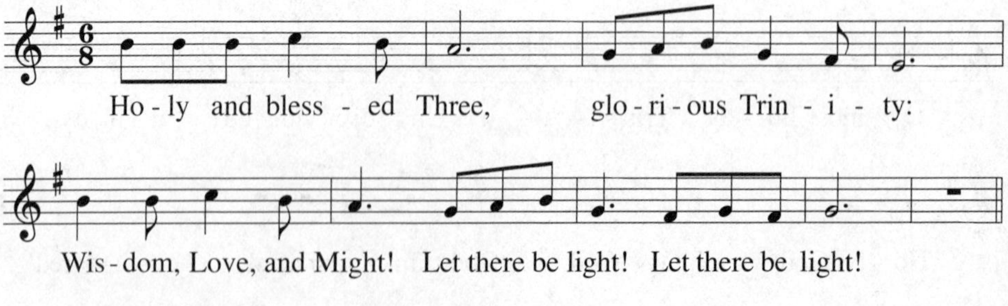
Ho - ly and bless - ed Three, glo - ri - ous Trin - i - ty:
Wis - dom, Love, and Might! Let there be light! Let there be light!

Verses 1, 2

1. You, whose al - might - y word cha - os and dark - ness heard.
2. Hope for all you bring, on your re - deem - ing wing.

Let there be light! Vic - tor of sin and death,
Let there be light! Dawn out of sin - ful night,

D.C.

giv - er of ho - ly breath. Let there be light!
mak - ing the dark - ness bright. Let there be light!

Verse 3

3. Spir - it of truth and love, life - giv - ing Ho - ly Dove.

Let there be light! Bring - er of ho - ly fire,

aim of our heart's de - sire. Let there be light!

Final Refrain

Ho - ly and bless - ed Three, glo - ri - ous Trin - i -

ty: Wis - dom, Love, and Might! Let there be light! Let there be

light! Oh, let there be light!

Text: John Marriott, 1780–1825; adapt. by Paul Melley, b.1973
Tune: Paul Melley, b.1973
© 2008, GIA Publications, Inc.

663 O Dawn of All Creation

1. O Dawn of all cre - a - tion And Mys - ter - y un -
2. O Light of in - car - na - tion, The face of Love here
3. O Flame of trans - for - ma - tion And Pow - er yet un -
4. O Dawn of all the liv - ing, What is and what shall

known, Whose ways are not as our ways, Whose
known, Whose ways were not as our ways, Whose
known, Whose ways are not as our ways, Whose
be, O Light and Flame of lov - ing, Tran -

thoughts are not our own: In grace you made and
thoughts were not our own: In fol - ly was your
thoughts are not our own: In per - il you are
scen - dent Mys - ter - y: You dwell where none can

blessed us; In mer - cy you for - gave; In ten - der - ness and
wis - dom; Your wealth, in pov - er - ty; A cross, your ex - al -
fear - less; In hu - man weak - ness, strong; In bond - age you are
fol - low, In worlds be - yond our own, Yet all who seek may

long - ing, In faith - ful - ness you save.
ta - tion; De - feat, your vic - to - ry.
free - dom; In griev - ing hearts, a song.
find you In flesh and blood and bone.

Text: Delores Dufner, OSB, b.1939, © 1999, 2003, GIA Publications, Inc.
Tune: ANDÚJAR, 7 6 7 6 D; David Hurd, b.1950, © 1984, GIA Publications, Inc.

Alternate tune: AURELIA

I Bind unto Myself Today 664

1. I bind un-to my-self to-day The strong Name
2. I bind un-to my-self to-day The pow'r of
3. The wis-dom of my God shall teach, With hand to
4. I bind un-to my-self to-day E-ter-nal

of the Trin-i-ty, By in-vo-ca-tion
God to hold and lead, God's eye to watch, God's
guide, and shield to ward; The word of God shall
Fa-ther, Spir-it, Son, The strong name of the

of the same, The Three in One, and One in Three.
might to stay, God's ear to heark-en to my need.
give me speech, God's heav'n-ly host shall be my guard.
Trin-i-ty, The One in Three, and Three in One.

O Christ, be with me, Christ be-hind, be-fore, be-side, be-

low, a-bove. In com-fort and dan-ger, in friend and

stran-ger, may Christ be in all hearts that love.

Text: Ascribed to St. Patrick; tr. by Cecil F. Alexander, 1818–1895; adapt. by Jennifer Kerr Budziak, © 2016, GIA Publications, Inc.
Tune: YE BANKS AND BRAES, 8 8 8 8 with refrain; Scottish traditional; arr. by Jennifer Kerr Budziak, © 2016, GIA Publications, Inc.

665   Creating God

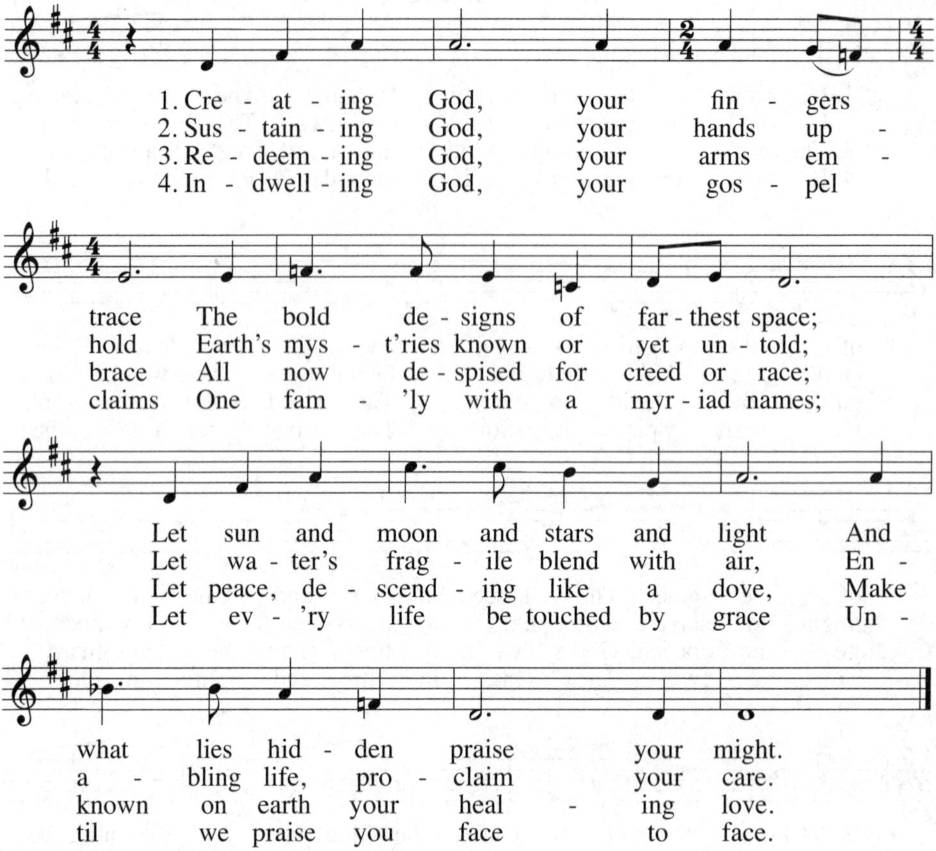

```
1. Cre - at - ing     God,     your     fin - gers
2. Sus - tain - ing   God,     your     hands   up -
3. Re - deem - ing    God,     your     arms    em -
4. In - dwell - ing   God,     your     gos - pel
```

```
trace  The bold      de - signs   of   far - thest space;
hold   Earth's mys - t'ries known or   yet un - told;
brace  All now       de - spised  for  creed or race;
claims One fam -  'ly with    a    myr - iad names;
```

```
Let sun  and  moon  and  stars  and  light  And
Let wa - ter's frag - ile blend with  air,   En -
Let peace, de - scend - ing like  a   dove, Make
Let ev - 'ry life  be touched by  grace Un -
```

```
what  lies hid - den  praise  your  might.
a -   bling life, pro - claim  your  care.
known on  earth your  heal -  ing  love.
til   we praise you  face    to   face.
```

Text: Jeffery Rowthorn, b.1934, © 1979, Hymn Society, alt. (Admin. by Hope Publishing Company)
Tune: PRESENCE, LM; David Haas, b.1957, © 1989, GIA Publications, Inc.

Alternate tune: PROSPECT

666   Hidden Here before Me / Adoro Te Devote

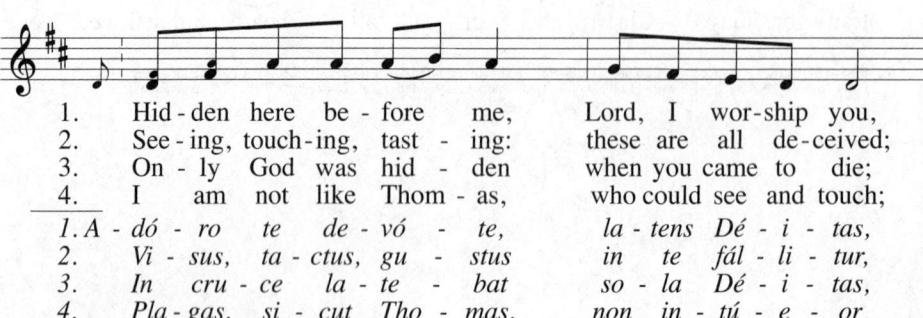

```
1.  Hid - den here be - fore   me,    Lord, I  wor-ship you,
2.  See - ing, touch-ing, tast - ing:  these are  all de-ceived;
3.  On - ly God was hid - den  when you came to  die;
4.  I  am  not like Thom - as,  who could see and touch;
```

```
1. A - dó - ro    te    de - vó - te,   la - tens Dé - i - tas,
2. Ví - sus, ta - ctus, gu - stus     in  te fál - li - tur,
3. In cru - ce la - te - bat      so - la Dé - i - tas,
4. Pla - gas, si - cut Tho - mas,   non in - tú - e - or
```

Hid - den in these sym - bols, yet com - plete - ly true.
On - ly through the hear - ing can it be be - lieved.
Hu - man na - ture al - so here es - capes the eye.
Though your wounds are hid - den, I be - lieve as much.
Quae sub his fi - gú - ris ve - re lá - ti - tas:
Sed au - dí - tu so - lo tu - to cré - di - tur:
At hic la - tet si - mul et hu - má - ni - tas:
De - um ta - men me - um te con - fí - te - or:

Lord, my soul sur - ren - ders, long - ing to o - bey,
Noth - ing is more cer - tain: Christ has told me so;
Both are my pro - fes - sion, both are my be - lief;
Let me say so bold - ly, mean - ing what I say,
Ti - bi se cor me - um to - tum súb - ji - cit,
Cre - do quid-quid di - xit De - i Fí - li - us:
Am - bo ta - men cre - dens at - que cón - fi - tens
Fac me ti - bi sem - per ma - gis cré - de - re,

And in con - tem - pla - tion whol - ly faints a - way.
What the Truth has ut - tered, I be - lieve and know.
Bring me to your King - dom, like the dy - ing thief.
Lov - ing you and trust - ing, now and ev - 'ry day.
Qui - a te con - tém - plans to - tum dé - fi - cit.
Nil hoc ver - bo ve - ri - tá - tis vé - ri - us.
Pe - to quod pe - tí - vit la - tro paé - ni - tens.
In te spem ha - bé - re, te di - lí - ge - re.

5. Record of the Passion when the
   Lamb was slain,
   Living bread that brings us back to
   life again:
   Feed me with your presence, make me
   live on you;
   Let that lovely fragrance fill me through
   and through.

6. Once a nesting pelican gashed herself
   to blood
   For the preservation of her starving brood.
   Now heal me with your blood, take away
   my guilt:
   All the world is ransomed if one drop is spilt.

7. Jesus, for the present seen as through a mask,
   Give me what I thirst for, give me what I ask:
   Let me see your glory in a blaze of light,
   And instead of blindness give me, Lord,
   my sight.

5. *O memoriále mortis Dómini,*
   Panis vivus vitam praestans hómini,
   Praesta meae menti de te vívere,
   Et ti illi semper dulce sápere.

6. *Pie pellicáne, Jesu Dómine,*
   Me immúndum munda tuo sánguine,
   Cuius una stilla salvum fácere,
   Totum mundum quit ab omni scélere.

7. *Jesu, quem velátum nunc aspício,*
   Oro fiat illud quod tam sítio:
   Ut te reveláta cernens fácie,
   Visu sim beátus tuae glóriae.

Text: *Adoro te devote*, attr. to St. Thomas Aquinas, c.1225–1274; English tr. from *A Book of Prayers*, © 1982, ICEL
Tune: ADORO TE DEVOTE, 11 11 11 11; Mode V, *Processionale*, Paris, 1697; acc. by Richard Proulx, 1937–2010, © 1986, GIA Publications, Inc.

667 Praise, O Zion, Voices Raising

1. Praise, O Zi - on, voic - es rais - ing, Glo - ri - fy your
2. Here re - call - ing Christ's own Pas - sion, Come, dis - ci - ples,
3. Christ, the Pas - chal lamb o - be - dient, Gave him - self as
4. As we keep this won - drous mys - t'ry, Heart and mind in
5. Though a mul - ti - tude re - ceives him, Christ, in man - y
6. Though the bread has now been bro - ken, Though the wine has

Shep - herd - King; Let un - wor - thy yet im - pas - sioned
as his friends; Bless - ing, break - ing, pour - ing, shar - ing—
God had planned; Now re - plac - ing for - mer of - f'rings,
faith com - bine. Here we eat the bread, his Bod - y,
parts, is one; Shared a - like by saints and sin - ners,
now been poured, Christ, here pres - ent on the al - tar,

Thank - ful hymns of hom - age ring! Join your hum - ble
By these ac - tions, Christ still sends To the world his
In self - giv - ing, here he stands, Prays a - gain in
Drink his pre - cious Blood in wine; This, the death - less
He re - mains God's on - ly Son. This, the choice and
Still is whole, and tru - ly Lord. Through one meal one

ac - cla - ma - tions To the psalm which an - gels sing.
Blood and Bod - y, Cov - e - nant which nev - er ends.
con - se - cra - tion; "Eat and drink!" his great com - mand.
Vic - tim's ta - ble Set in sac - ra - men - tal sign.
gift of heav - en: Sav - ing grace with - held from none.
Church is nour - ished, Lead - ing to one life re - stored.

7. Bread of Angels! for God's children
Pilgrims' strength along the way;
God provides in love, as always,
Holy manna ev'ry day.
Christ, as Isaac on the altar,
Still our debt to God will pay.

8. Living bread, Good Shepherd, feed us,
Endless mercy offering;
With your hallowed saints unite us,
To your heav'nly banquet bring;
There will we, forever feasting,
"Amen! Alleluia!" sing!

Text: Corpus Christi Sequence, Thomas Aquinas, c.1225–1274; tr. by Alan J. Hommerding, b.1956, © 2000, World Library Publications
Tune: ST. THOMAS, 8 7 8 7 8 7; John Wade, 1711–1786

O Christ, Your Heart Compassionate 668

1. O Christ, your heart com - pas - sion - ate, Bore
2. As once you wel - comed those cast down And
3. O Christ, cre - ate new hearts in us That
4. O Love that made the dis - tant stars Yet

ev - 'ry hu - man pain. Its beat - ing was the
healed the sick, the blind, So may all bruised and
beat in time with yours, That, joined by faith with
marks the spar - row's fall, Whose arms, stretched wide up -

pulse of God; Its breadth, God's vast do - main.
bro - ken lives Through us your help still find.
your great heart, Be - come Love's o - pen doors.
on a cross, Em - brace and bear us all:

The heart of God, the heart of Christ, Com -
Lord, join our hearts with those who weep That
We are your bod - y, ris - en Christ; Our
Come, make your Church a ser - vant Church That

bined in per - fect rhyme To write God's love in
none may weep a - lone, And help us bear an -
hearts, our hands, we yield That through our life and
walks your ser - vant ways, Whose deeds of love rise

hu - man deeds, E - ter - ni - ty in time.
oth - er's pain As though it were our own.
min - is - try Your love may be re - vealed.
up to you, A sac - ri - fice of praise!

Text: Herman G. Stuempfle, Jr., 1923–2007, © 2006, GIA Publications, Inc.
Tune: RESIGNATION, CMD; Funk's *Compilation of Genuine Church Music*, 1832; harm. by Richard Proulx, 1937–2010, © 1975, GIA Publications, Inc.

669 Crown Him with Many Crowns

1. Crown him with man - y crowns, The Lamb up - on his throne. Hark! How the heav'n - ly an - them drowns All mu - sic but its own. A - wake, my soul, and sing Of him who set us free, And hail him as your heav'n - ly King Through all e - ter - ni - ty.

2. Crown him the Lord of life, Who tri - umphed o'er the grave, And rose vic - to - rious in the strife For those he came to save. His glo - ries now we sing, Who died and rose on high, Who died, e - ter - nal life to bring, And lives that death may die.

3. Crown him the Lord of love— Be - hold his hands and side, Rich wounds, yet vis - i - ble a - bove, In beau - ty glo - ri - fied. No an - gel in the sky Can ful - ly bear that sight, But down - ward bends his burn - ing eye At mys - ter - ies so bright.

4. Crown him the Lord of peace, Whose pow'r a scep - ter sways From pole to pole, that wars may cease, Ab - sorbed by prayer and praise. His reign shall know no end, And round his pierc - ed feet Fair flow'rs of par - a - dise ex - tend Their fra - grance ev - er sweet.

5. Crown him the Lord of years, The mas - ter of all time, Cre - a - tor of the roll - ing spheres, And ris - en Lord sub - lime. All hail, Re - deem - er, hail! For you have died for me; Your praise and glo - ry shall not fail Through - out e - ter - ni - ty.

Text: Revelation 19:12; sts. 1, 3–5, Matthew Bridges, 1800–1894; st. 2, Godfrey Thring, 1823–1903
Tune: DIADEMATA, SMD; George J. Elvey, 1816–1893

Christ Is the King! 670

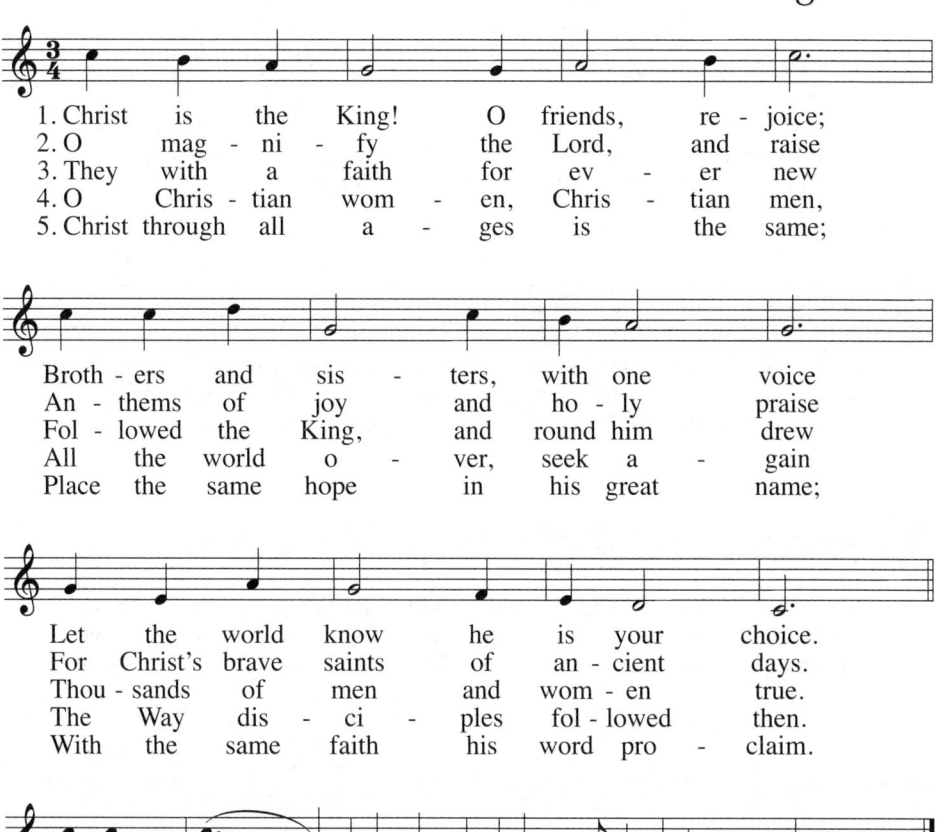

1. Christ is the King! O friends, re - joice;
2. O mag - ni - fy the Lord, and raise
3. They with a faith for ev - er new
4. O Chris - tian wom - en, Chris - tian men,
5. Christ through all a - ges is the same;

Broth - ers and sis - ters, with one voice
An - thems of joy and ho - ly praise
Fol - lowed the King, and round him drew
All the world o - ver, seek a - gain
Place the same hope in his great name;

Let the world know he is your choice.
For Christ's brave saints of an - cient days.
Thou - sands of men and wom - en true.
The Way dis - ci - ples fol - lowed then.
With the same faith his word pro - claim.

Al - le - lu - ia, al - le - lu - ia, al - le - lu - ia.

6. Let Love's all reconciling might
   Your scattered companies unite
   In service to the Lord of light.
   Alleluia, alleluia, alleluia.

7. So shall the Church at last be one;
   So shall God's will on earth be done,
   New lamps be lit, new tasks begun.
   Alleluia, alleluia, alleluia.

Text: George K. A. Bell, 1883–1958, alt., © Oxford University Press
Tune: GELOBT SEI GOTT, 888 with alleluias; Melchior Vulpius, c.1560–1615

671 To Jesus Christ, Our Sovereign King

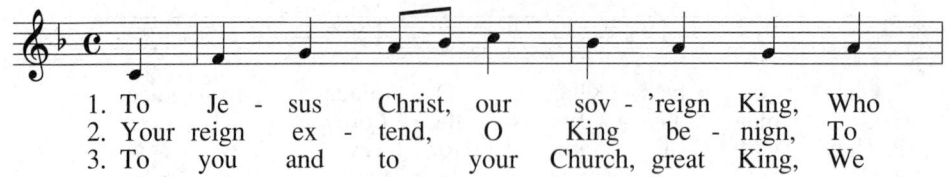

1. To Je - sus Christ, our sov - 'reign King, Who
2. Your reign ex - tend, O King be - nign, To
3. To you and to your Church, great King, We

is the world's sal - va - tion, All praise and hom - age
ev - 'ry land and na - tion; For in your king - dom,
pledge our hearts' ob - la - tion Un - til be - fore your

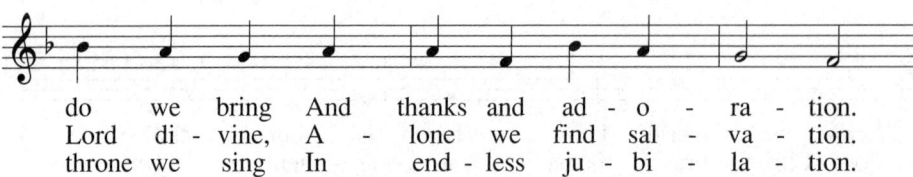

do we bring And thanks and ad - o - ra - tion.
Lord di - vine, A - lone we find sal - va - tion.
throne we sing In end - less ju - bi - la - tion.

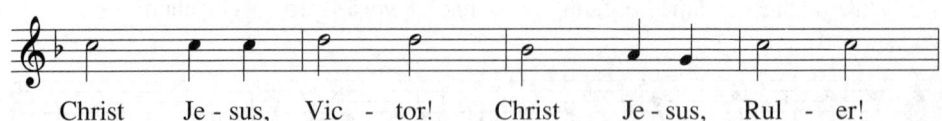

Christ Je - sus, Vic - tor! Christ Je - sus, Rul - er!

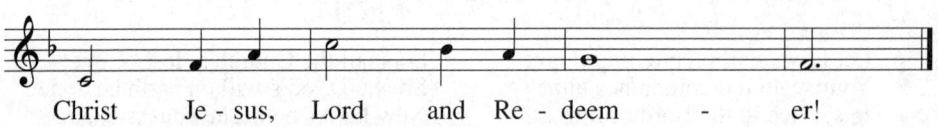

Christ Je - sus, Lord and Re - deem - er!

Text: Martin B. Hellriegel, 1890–1981, alt., © 1941, Irene C. Mueller
Tune: ICH GLAUB AN GOTT, 8 7 8 7 with refrain; Mainz *Gesangbuch*, 1870; harm. by Richard Proulx, 1937–2010, © 1986, GIA Publications, Inc.

672 All Hail the Power of Jesus' Name!

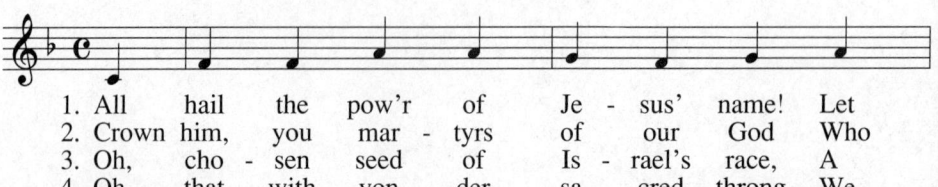

1. All hail the pow'r of Je - sus' name! Let
2. Crown him, you mar - tyrs of our God Who
3. Oh, cho - sen seed of Is - rael's race, A
4. Oh, that with yon - der sa - cred throng We

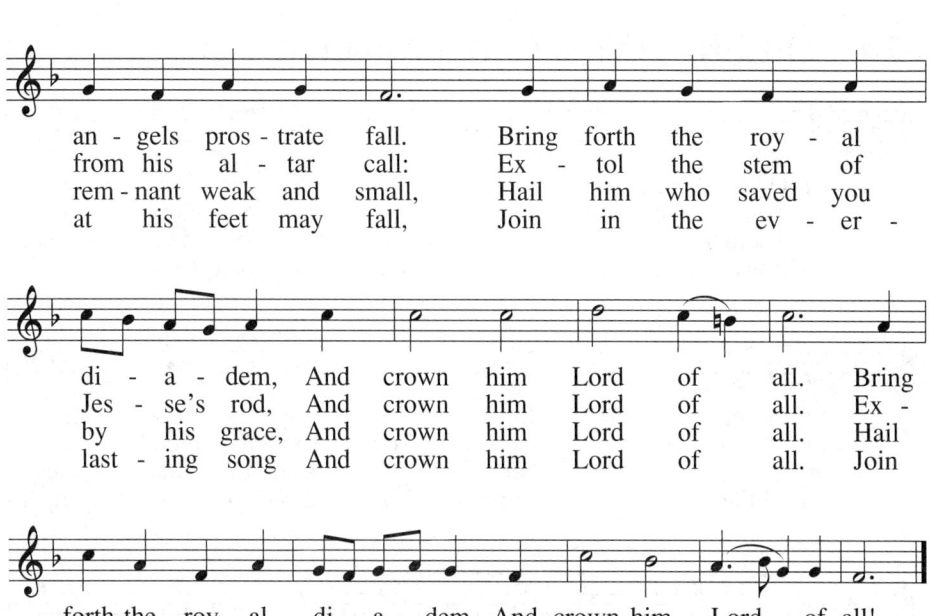

an - gels pros - trate fall. Bring forth the roy - al
from his al - tar call: Ex - tol the stem of
rem - nant weak and small, Hail him who saved you
at his feet may fall, Join in the ev - er -

di - a - dem, And crown him Lord of all. Bring
Jes - se's rod, And crown him Lord of all. Ex -
by his grace, And crown him Lord of all. Hail
last - ing song And crown him Lord of all. Join

forth the roy - al di - a - dem, And crown him Lord of all!
tol the stem of Jes - se's rod, And crown him Lord of all!
him who saved you by his grace, And crown him Lord of all!
in the ev - er - last - ing song And crown him Lord of all!

Text: Edward Perronet, 1726–1792; alt. by John Rippon, 1751–1836, alt.
Tune: CORONATION, 8 6 8 6 8 6; Oliver Holden, 1765–1844

At the Name of Jesus 673

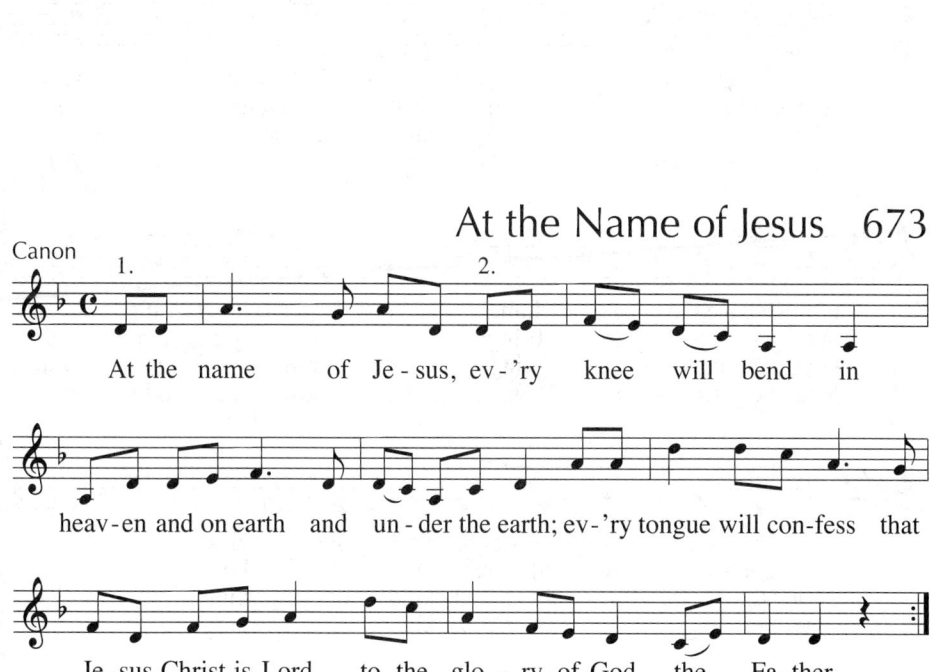

Canon

At the name of Je - sus, ev - 'ry knee will bend in

heav-en and on earth and un - der the earth; ev-'ry tongue will con-fess that

Je - sus Christ is Lord, to the glo - ry of God the Fa - ther.

Text: Philippians 2:10–11
Tune: James E. Clemens, © 2008, James E. Clemens

674 O Christ, What Can It Mean for Us

1. O Christ, what can it mean for us To claim you as our king? What roy-al face have you re-vealed Whose praise the Church would sing? As-pir-ing not to glo-ry's height, To pow-er, wealth, and fame, You walked a dif-f'rent, low-ly way, An-oth-er's will your aim.

2. You came, the im-age of our God, To heal and to for-give, To shed your blood for sin-ners' sake That we might rise and live. To break the law of death you came, A dif-f'rent rule of law of love to bring: A dif-f'rent kind of king.

3. Though some would make their great-ness felt And lord it o-ver all, You said the first must be the last And serv-ice be our call. O Christ, in work-place, church, and home Let none to pow-er cling; For still, through us, you come to serve, A dif-f'rent kind of king.

4. You chose a hum-ble hu-man form And shunned the world's re-nown; You died for us up-on a cross With thorns your on-ly crown. But still, be-yond the span of years, Our glad ho-san-nas ring, For now at God's right hand you reign, A dif-f'rent kind of king!

Text: Delores Dufner, OSB, b.1939, © 2001, 2003, GIA Publications, Inc.
Tune: IN NOMINE DEI, CMD; Sally Ann Morris, b.1952, © 2009, GIA Publications, Inc.

Alternate tune: KINGSFOLD

To You Who Bow   675

1. To you who bow, to you who bend, to you who
2. To you who teach, to you who heal, to you, the
3. To you who weep, to you who bleed, who dreamed the
4. To you who starve, to you who thirst, to you con -
5. To you who rise, to you, our peace, to you who

do not cling to heav-en, but un - to us de - scend; you who
lep - er's res - to - ra - tion, the vic - tim's last ap - peal; you whose
bound - 'ries of O - ri - on, but will not break the reed; you who
demned to death by mal-ice, a - ban-doned and ac - cursed; you who
lead the way be-fore us, whose spir - it binds and frees; at once the

sum - mon us as ser - vants and call your ser - vants friends:
life is sown and gath - ered and of - fered as a meal:
sow the end of em - pire with ti - ny, peace-ful seed:
prom-ised to the wretch - ed the last will be made first:
Al - pha and O - me - ga, whose love shall nev - er cease:

To you we lift our song, love ev - er new, O

1.–4.   **D.C.**

God who bows, we sing our song to you.

5.

you.   O God who bows, we sing our song to you.

Text: Rory Cooney, b.1952
Tune: Rory Cooney, b.1952
© 2014, GIA Publications, Inc.

676 I Sing the Mighty Power of God

1. I sing the might-y pow'r of God That
2. I sing the good-ness of the Lord That
3. There's not a plant or flow'r be-low But

made the moun-tains rise, That spread the flow-ing
filled the earth with food. God formed the crea-tures
makes your glo-ries known; And clouds a-rise and

seas a-broad, And built the loft-y skies. I
with a word And then pro-nounced them good. Lord,
tem-pests blow By or-der from your throne. Your

sing the wis-dom that or-dained The
how your won-ders are dis-played Wher-
crea-tures, count-less though they be, Are

sun to rule by day; The moon shines full at
e'er I turn my eye, If I sur-vey the
sub-ject to your care. There's not a place where

God's com-mand, And all the seas o-bey.
ground I tread, Or gaze up-on the sky!
we can flee, But you are pres-ent there.

Text: Isaac Watts, 1674–1748, alt.
Tune: ELLACOMBE, CMD; *Gesangbuch der Herzogl*, Wirtemberg, 1784

Canticle of the Sun 677

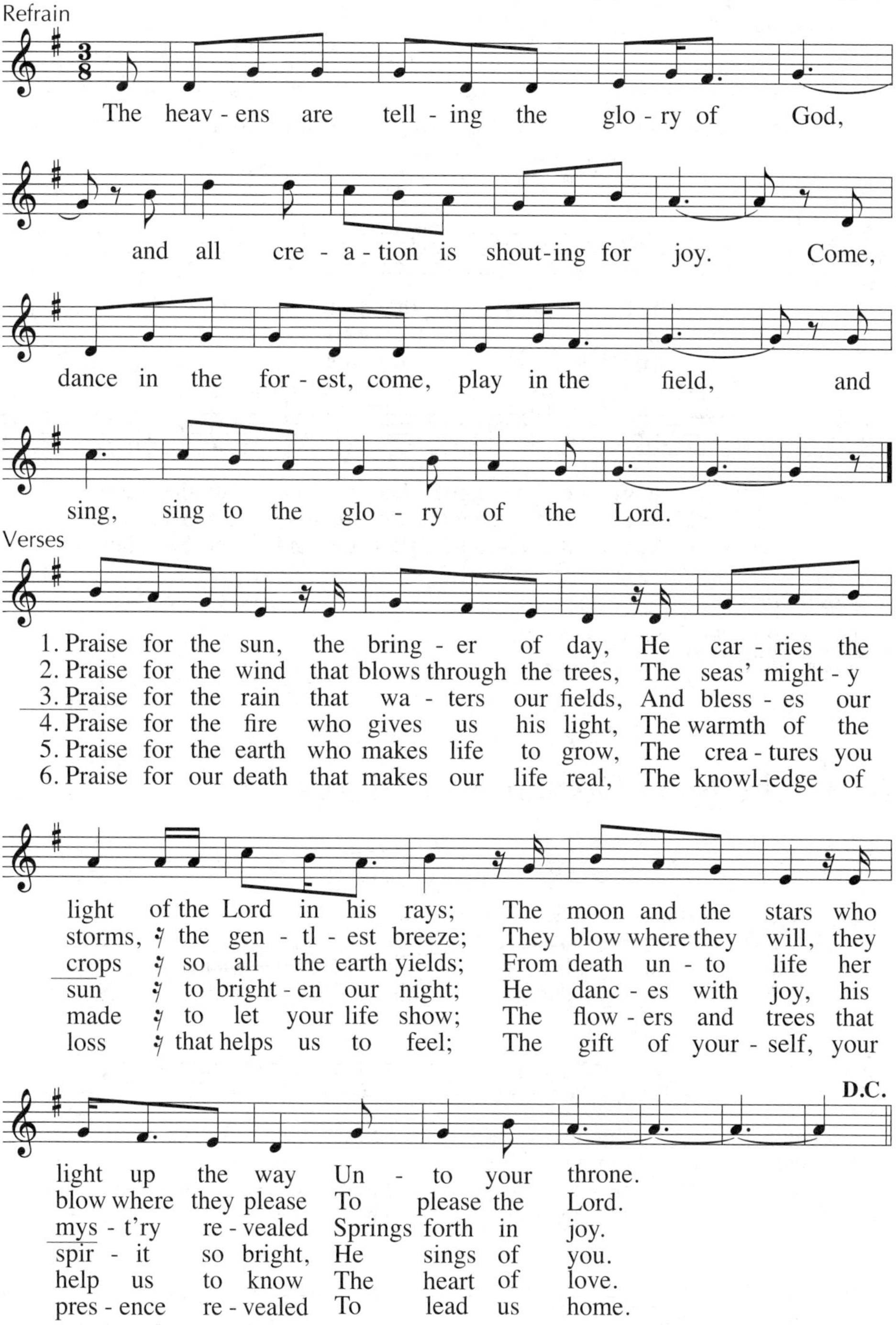

Refrain

The heav - ens are tell - ing the glo - ry of God,

and all cre - a - tion is shout-ing for joy. Come,

dance in the for - est, come, play in the field, and

sing, sing to the glo - ry of the Lord.

Verses

1. Praise for the sun, the bring - er of day, He car - ries the
2. Praise for the wind that blows through the trees, The seas' might - y
3. Praise for the rain that wa - ters our fields, And bless - es our
4. Praise for the fire who gives us his light, The warmth of the
5. Praise for the earth who makes life to grow, The crea - tures you
6. Praise for our death that makes our life real, The knowl-edge of

light of the Lord in his rays; The moon and the stars who
storms, ⁊ the gen - tl - est breeze; They blow where they will, they
crops ⁊ so all the earth yields; From death un - to life her
sun ⁊ to bright - en our night; He danc - es with joy, his
made ⁊ to let your life show; The flow - ers and trees that
loss ⁊ that helps us to feel; The gift of your - self, your

D.C.

light up the way Un - to your throne.
blow where they please To please the Lord.
mys - t'ry re - vealed Springs forth in joy.
spir - it so bright, He sings of you.
help us to know The heart of love.
pres - ence re - vealed To lead us home.

Text: *Altissimu, onnipotente bon Signore*; St. Francis of Assisi, 1181–1226; adapt. by Marty Haugen, b.1950
Tune: Marty Haugen, b.1950
© 1980, GIA Publications, Inc.

678 Let Us Sing to the Lord

Ostinato Refrain

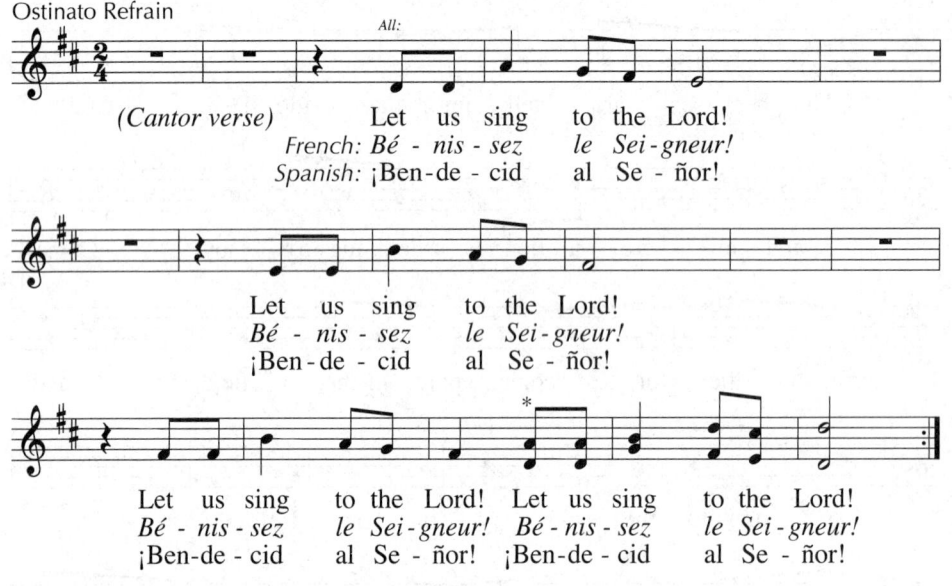

(Cantor verse) Let us sing to the Lord!
French: *Bé - nis - sez le Sei - gneur!*
Spanish: ¡Ben-de - cid al Se - ñor!

Let us sing to the Lord!
Bé - nis - sez le Sei - gneur!
¡Ben-de - cid al Se - ñor!

Let us sing to the Lord! Let us sing to the Lord!
Bé - nis - sez le Sei - gneur! Bé - nis - sez le Sei - gneur!
¡Ben-de - cid al Se - ñor! ¡Ben-de - cid al Se - ñor!

*Choose either part

Text: Daniel 3:57–75, Luke 1:46–47, 49, Psalm 5:1–2; Taizé Community
Tune: Jacques Berthier, 1923–1994
© 1998, Les Presses de Taizé, GIA Publications, Inc., agent

679 The Stars Declare His Glory

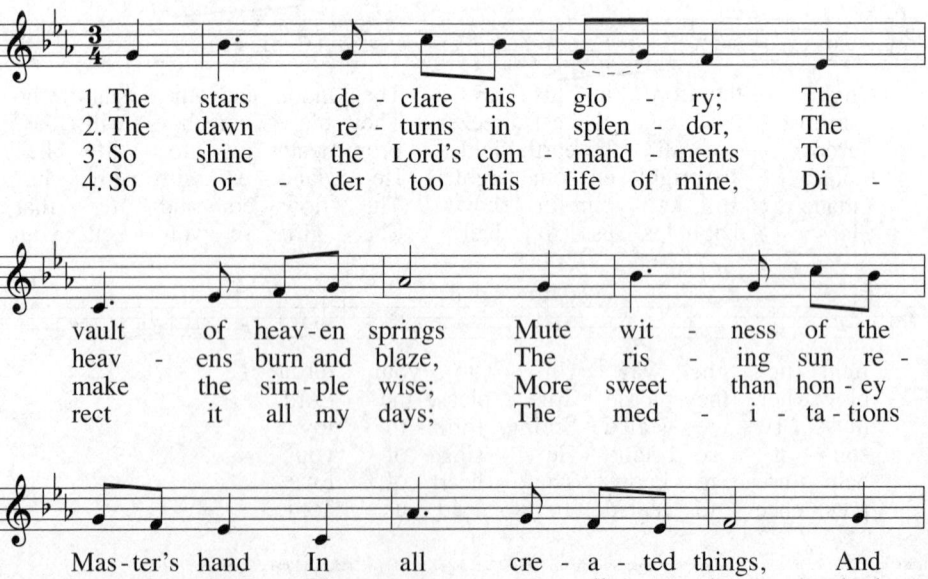

1. The stars de - clare his glo - ry; The
2. The dawn re - turns in splen - dor, The
3. So shine the Lord's com - mand - ments To
4. So or - der too this life of mine, Di -

vault of heav-en springs Mute wit - ness of the
heav - ens burn and blaze, The ris - ing sun re -
make the sim - ple wise; More sweet than hon - ey
rect it all my days; The med - i - ta - tions

Mas-ter's hand In all cre - a - ted things, And
news the race That meas - ures all our days, And
to the taste, More rich than an - y prize, A
of my heart Be in - no - cence and praise, My

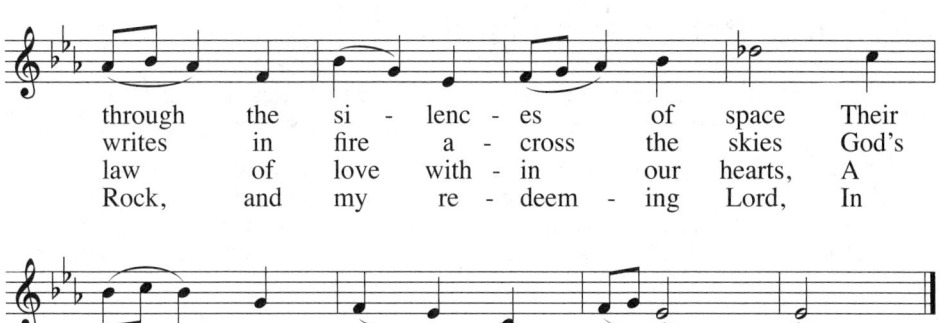

through the si - lenc - es of space Their
writes in fire a - cross the skies God's
law of love with - in our hearts, A
Rock, and my re - deem - ing Lord, In

sound - less mu - sic sings.
maj - es - ty and praise.
light be - fore our eyes.
all my words and ways.

Text: Psalm 19; Timothy Dudley-Smith, b.1926, © 1981, Hope Publishing Company
Tune: ALDINE, 7 6 8 6 8 6; Richard Proulx, 1937–2010, © 1986, 1992, GIA Publications, Inc.

For Every Child   680

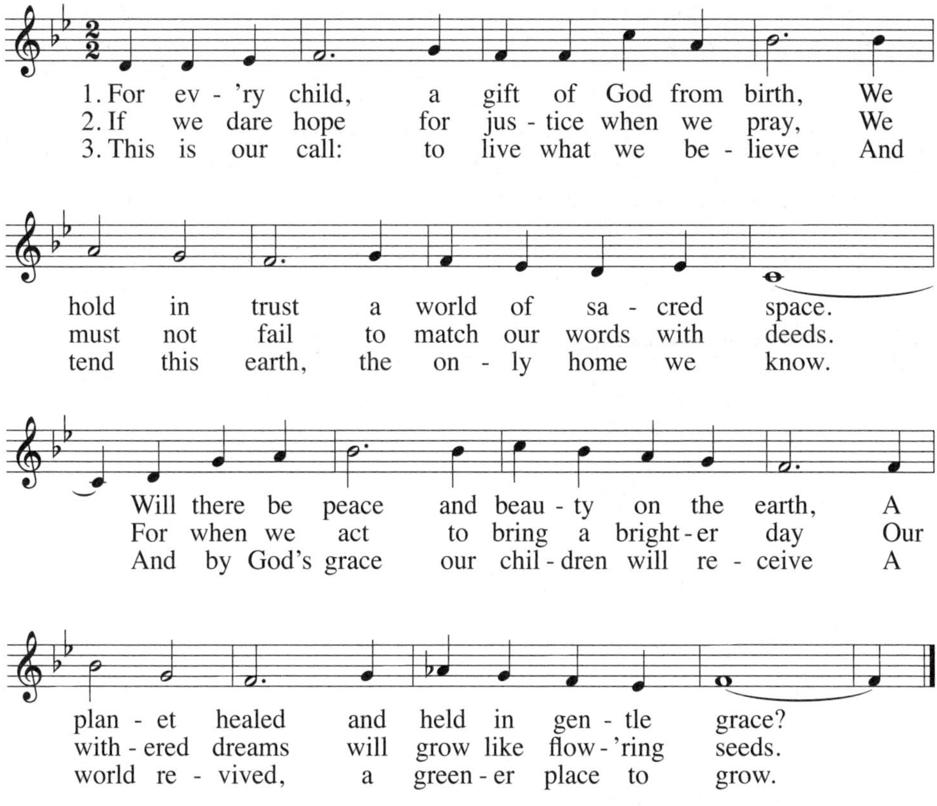

1. For ev - 'ry child, a gift of God from birth, We
2. If we dare hope for jus - tice when we pray, We
3. This is our call: to live what we be - lieve And

hold in trust a world of sa - cred space.
must not fail to match our words with deeds.
tend this earth, the on - ly home we know.

Will there be peace and beau - ty on the earth, A
For when we act to bring a bright - er day Our
And by God's grace our chil - dren will re - ceive A

plan - et healed and held in gen - tle grace?
with - ered dreams will grow like flow - 'ring seeds.
world re - vived, a green - er place to grow.

Text: Adam M. L. Tice, b.1979, © 2011, GIA Publications, Inc.
Tune: EVERETT, 10 10 10 10; Marty Haugen, b.1950, © 2014, GIA Publications, Inc.

681   Touch the Earth Lightly

1. Touch the earth light-ly, Use the earth gen-tly,
2. We who en - dan-ger, Who cre - ate hun-ger,
3. Let there be green-ing, Birth from the burn-ing,
4. God of all liv-ing, God of all lov-ing,

Nour-ish the life of the world in our care:
A - gents of death for all crea-tures that live,
Wa-ter that bless-es, and air that is sweet,
God of the seed-ling, the snow, and the sun,

Gift of great won-der, Ours to sur-ren-der,
We who would fos-ter Clouds of dis-as-ter—
Health in God's gar-den, Hope in God's chil-dren,
Teach us, de-flect us, Christ re-con-nect us,

Trust for the chil-dren to - mor-row will bear.
God of our plan-et, fore-stall and for-give!
Re - gen-er - a - tion that peace will com-plete.
Us - ing us gen-tly, and mak-ing us one.

Text: Shirley Erena Murray, b.1931, © 1992, Hope Publishing Company
Tune: ELLA ROSE, 55 10 55 10; Tony E. Alonso, b.1980, © 2007, GIA Publications, Inc.

Light Dawns on a Weary World   682

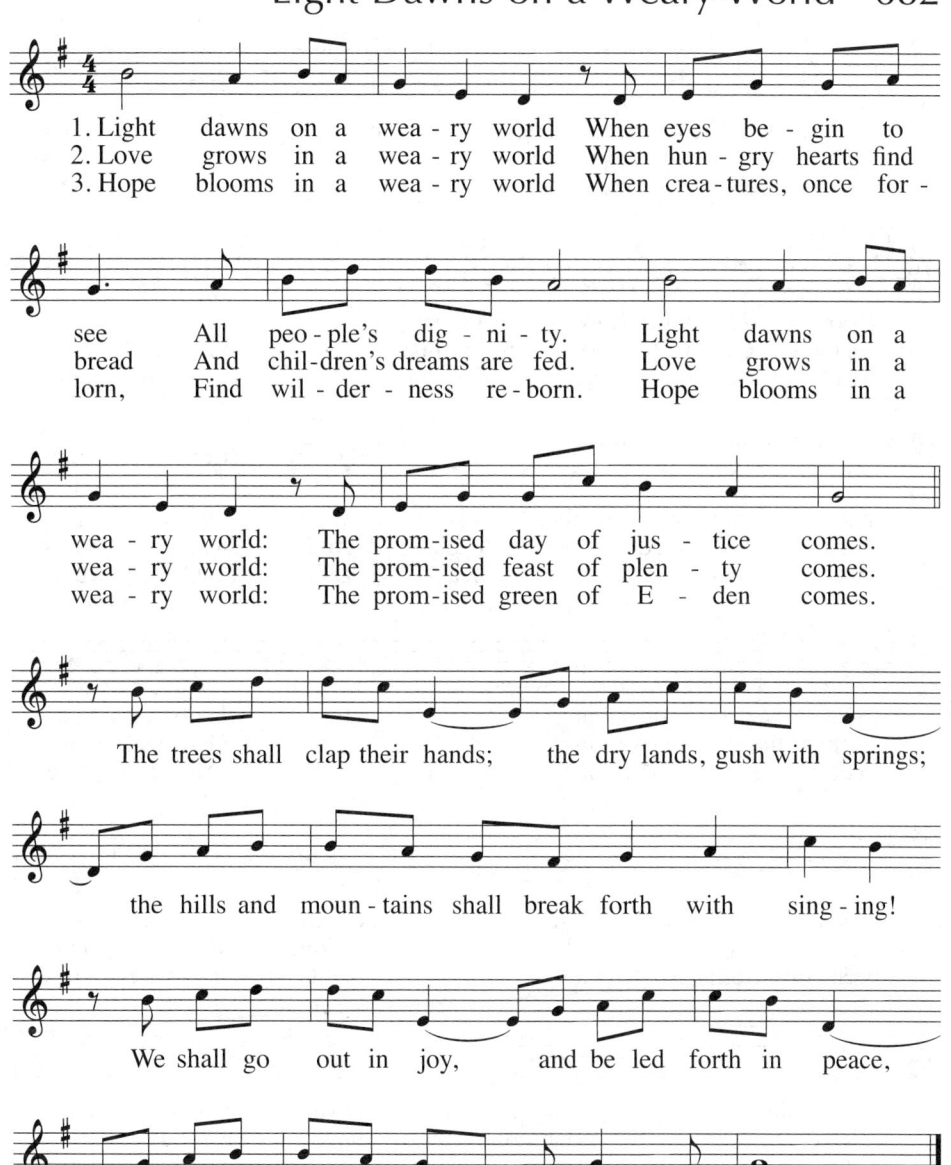

1. Light dawns on a wea-ry world When eyes be-gin to
2. Love grows in a wea-ry world When hun-gry hearts find
3. Hope blooms in a wea-ry world When crea-tures, once for-

see All peo-ple's dig-ni-ty. Light dawns on a
bread And chil-dren's dreams are fed. Love grows in a
lorn, Find wil-der-ness re-born. Hope blooms in a

wea-ry world: The prom-ised day of jus-tice comes.
wea-ry world: The prom-ised feast of plen-ty comes.
wea-ry world: The prom-ised green of E-den comes.

The trees shall clap their hands; the dry lands, gush with springs;

the hills and moun-tains shall break forth with sing-ing!

We shall go out in joy, and be led forth in peace,

as all the world in won-der ech-oes sha-lom.

Text: Mary Louise Bringle, b.1953, © 2002, GIA Publications, Inc.
Tune: TEMPLE OF PEACE, 7 6 6 7 8 with refrain; William P. Rowan, b.1951, © 2000, William P. Rowan, admin. GIA Publications, Inc.

683 Abundant Life

1. We can-not own the sun-lit sky,
2. When bod-ies shiv-er in the night
3. God calls hu-man-i-ty to join

The
And,
As

moon, the wild-flow'rs grow-ing,
wea-ry, wait for morn-ing,
part-ners in cre-at-ing

For we are
When chil-dren
A fu-ture

part of all that is
have no bread but tears,
free from want or fear,

With-in life's
And war-horns
Life's good-ness

riv-er flow-ing.
sound their warn-ing,
cel-e-brat-ing.

With o-pen
God calls hu-
That new world

hands re-ceive and share
man-i-ty to wake,
beck-ons from a-far,

The gifts of God's cre-
To join in com-mon
In-vites our shared en-

a-tion,
la-bor,
deav-or,

That all may have a-bun-dant
That all may have a-bun-dant
That all may have a-bun-dant

life In ev-'ry earth-ly na-tion.
life In one-ness with their neigh-bor.
life And peace en-dure for-ev-er.

Text: Ruth Duck, b.1947, © 1992, GIA Publications, Inc.
Tune: LA GRANGE, 8 7 8 7 D; Marty Haugen, b.1950, © 1994, GIA Publications, Inc.

Alternate tune: HOW CAN I KEEP FROM SINGING

Immortal, Invisible, God Only Wise 684

1. Im - mor - tal, in - vis - i - ble, God on - ly wise,
2. Un - rest - ing, un - hast - ing, and si - lent as light,
3. Life - giv - ing Cre - a - tor of both great and small,
4. Great Fa - ther of glo - ry, pure Fa - ther of light,

In light in - ac - ces - si - ble hid from our eyes,
Not want - ing or wast - ing, you rule day and night;
Of all life the mak - er, the true life of all;
Your an - gels a - dore you, all veil - ing their sight;

Most bless - ed, most glo - rious, the An - cient of Days,
Your jus - tice, like moun-tains, high soar - ing a - bove
We blos - som, then with - er as leaves on a tree,
We too, God in - vis - i - ble, of - fer our praise,

Al - might - y, vic - to - rious, your great name we praise.
Your clouds, which are foun-tains of good - ness and love.
But you live for - ev - er, who are and will be.
O light in - ac - ces - si - ble, An - cient of Days!

Text: 1 Timothy 1:17; Walter C. Smith, 1824–1908, alt.
Tune: ST. DENIO, 11 11 11 11; adapt. from a Welsh ballad in John Roberts' *Hymns of the Sanctuary*, 1839

685 Who Can Measure Heaven and Earth

1. Who can meas - ure heav'n and earth? God was pres - ent
2. Who can tell what wis - dom brings, First of all cre -
3. Wis - dom in his plans he laid, Plant - ed her in
4. Wis - dom gives the sur - est wealth, Brings her chil - dren

at their birth; Who can num - ber seeds or sands?
at - ed things? One a - lone is tru - ly wise,
all he made; Grant - ed her to hu - man - kind,
life and health; Teach - es us to fear the Lord,

Ev - 'ry grain is in his hands: Through cre - a - tion's
Hid - den from our earth-bound eyes: Knowl - edge lies in
Sowed her truth in ev - 'ry mind: But with rich - est
Marks a u - ni - verse re - stored: Heav'n and earth she

count - less days Ev - 'ry dawn sings out his praise.
him a - lone— God, the Lord up - on his throne!
wis - dom blessed Those who love him first and best.
will out - last— Hap - py those who hold her fast!

Text: Ecclesiastes 1; Christopher M. Idle, b.1938, © 1982, The Jubilate Group, (admin. by Hope Publishing Company)
Tune: DIX, 77 77 77; arr. from Conrad Kocher, 1786–1872, by William H. Monk, 1823–1889

686 Give Me Jesus

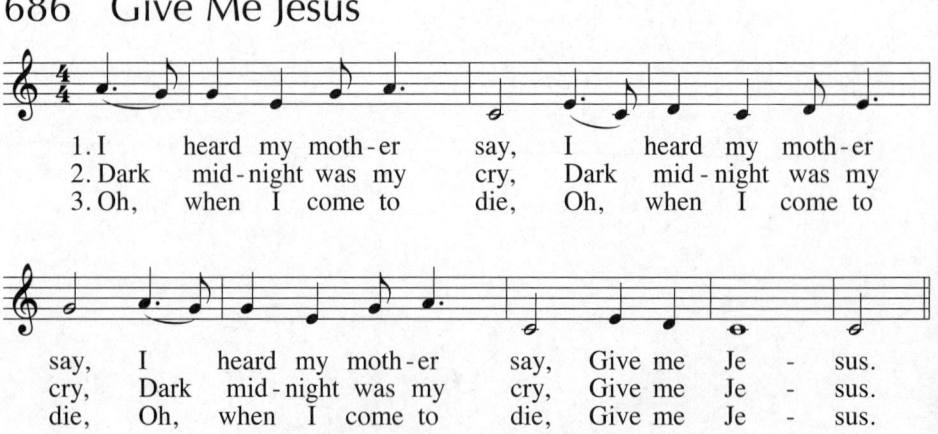

1. I heard my moth - er say, I heard my moth - er
2. Dark mid - night was my cry, Dark mid - night was my
3. Oh, when I come to die, Oh, when I come to

say, I heard my moth - er say, Give me Je - sus.
cry, Dark mid - night was my cry, Give me Je - sus.
die, Oh, when I come to die, Give me Je - sus.

Give me Je - sus. Give me Je - sus,

You may have all this world, Give me Je - sus.

Text: African American spiritual
Tune: GIVE ME JESUS, 666 4 with refrain; African American spiritual; arr. by Nolan Williams, Jr., b.1969, © 2000, GIA Publications, Inc.

You Are All We Have 687

Refrain

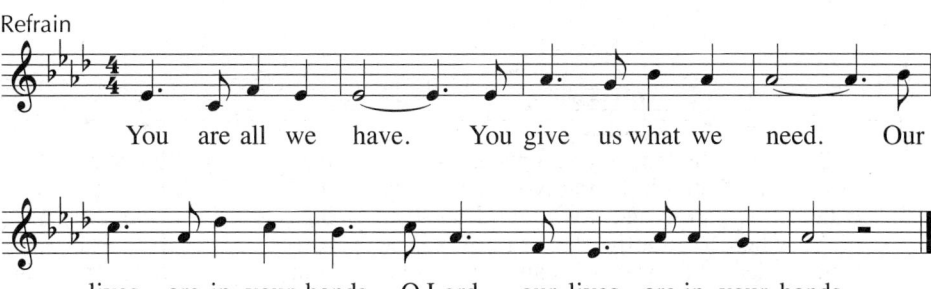

You are all we have. You give us what we need. Our

lives are in your hands, O Lord, our lives are in your hands.

Verses

1. Protect me, Lord; I come to you for safety.
   I say, "You are my God."
   All good things, Lord, all good things
   that I have come from you,
   the God of my salvation.

2. How wonderful are your gifts to me,
   how good they are!
   I praise the Lord who guides me
   and teaches me the way of truth and life.

3. You are near, the God I seek.
   Nothing can take me from your side.
   All my days I rest secure;
   you will show me the path that leads to life.

Text: Francis Patrick O'Brien, b.1958
Tune: Francis Patrick O'Brien, b.1958
© 1992, GIA Publications, Inc.

688 O God, You Search Me

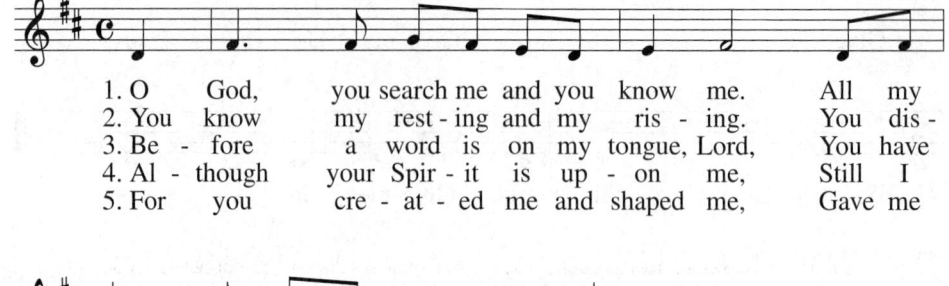

1. O God, you search me and you know me. All my
2. You know my rest-ing and my ris-ing. You dis-
3. Be-fore a word is on my tongue, Lord, You have
4. Al-though your Spir-it is up-on me, Still I
5. For you cre-at-ed me and shaped me, Gave me

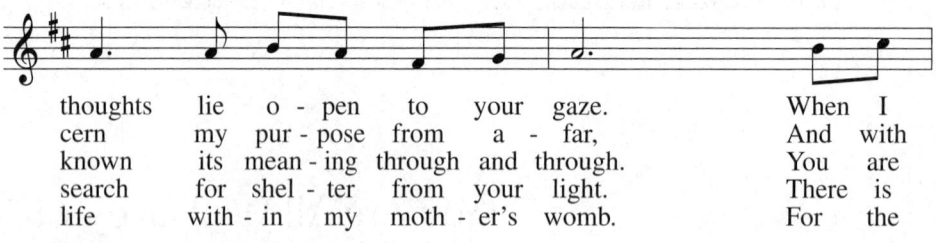

thoughts lie o-pen to your gaze. When I
cern my pur-pose from a-far, And with
known its mean-ing through and through. You are
search for shel-ter from your light. There is
life with-in my moth-er's womb. For the

walk or lie down you are be-fore me: Ev-er the
love ev-er-last-ing you be-siege me: In ev-'ry
with me be-yond my un-der-stand-ing: God of my
no-where on earth I can es-cape you: E-ven the
won-der of who I am, I praise you: Safe in your

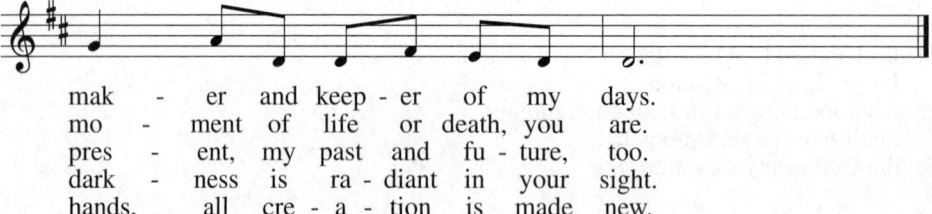

mak-er and keep-er of my days.
mo-ment of life or death, you are.
pres-ent, my past and fu-ture, too.
dark-ness is ra-diant in your sight.
hands, all cre-a-tion is made new.

Text: Based on Psalm 139; Bernadette Farrell, b.1957
Tune: Bernadette Farrell, b.1957
© 1992, Bernadette Farrell. Published by OCP.

Over My Head 689

Refrain

O - ver my head, I hear mu - sic in the air; o - ver my head,

I hear mu - sic in the air; o - ver my head, I hear

mu - sic in the air; there must be a God some - where.

Verses

Solo: *Assembly:*   *Solo:*

1. Oh, when the world is si - lent,   oh,
2. And when I'm feel - ing lone - ly, I hear mu - sic in the air;   and
3. Now when I think on Je - sus,   now

Assembly: *Solo:*

when the world is si - lent,   oh,
when I'm feel - ing lone - ly, I hear mu - sic in the air;   and
when I think on Je - sus,   now

Assembly:

when the world is si - lent,
when I'm feel - ing lone - ly, I hear mu - sic in the air;
when I think on Je - sus,

All: **D.C.**

there must be a God some - where.

Text: African American spiritual
Tune: African American spiritual; arr. by John L. Bell, b.1949, © 1997, Iona Community, GIA Publications, Inc., agent

690　Come to the Water

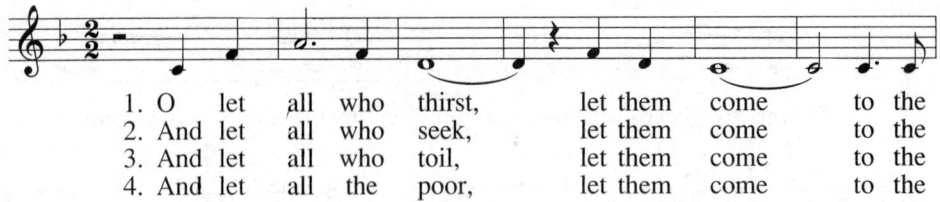

1. O let all who thirst, let them come to the
2. And let all who seek, let them come to the
3. And let all who toil, let them come to the
4. And let all the poor, let them come to the

wa - ter. And let all who have noth - ing,
wa - ter. And let all who have noth - ing,
wa - ter. And let all who are wea - ry,
wa - ter. Bring the ones who are lad - en,

let them come to the Lord: With-out mon-ey,
let them come to the Lord: With-out mon-ey,
let them come to the Lord: All who la - bor,
bring them all to the Lord: Bring the chil-dren

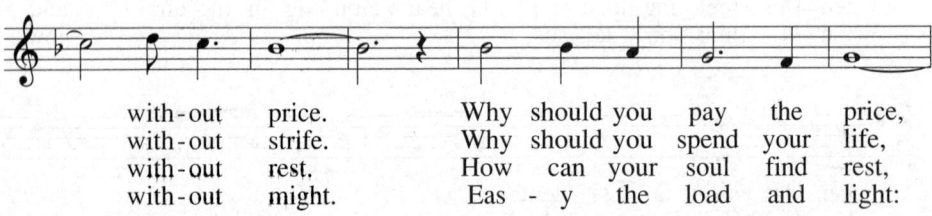

with-out price. Why should you pay the price,
with-out strife. Why should you spend your life,
with-out rest. How can your soul find rest,
with-out might. Eas - y the load and light:

ex - cept for the Lord?
ex - cept for the Lord?
ex - cept for the Lord?
come to the Lord.

Text: Isaiah 55:1, 2, Matthew 11:28–30; John Foley, SJ, b.1939
Tune: John Foley, SJ, b.1939
© 1978, John B. Foley, SJ, and OCP

Fresh as the Morning 691

1. God of the Bi - ble, God in the Gos - pel,
2. God in our strug-gles, God in our hun - ger,
3. Those with - out sta - tus, those who are noth - ing,
4. Not by your fin - ger, not by your an - ger
5. Hope we must car - ry, shin - ing and cer - tain

Hope seen in Je - sus, hope yet to come,
Suf - fer - ing with us, tak - ing our part,
You have made roy - al, gift - ed with rights,
Will our world or - der change in a day,
Through all our tur - moil, ter - ror and loss,

You are our cen - ter, day - light or dark - ness,
Still you em - pow'r us, moth - er - ing Spir - it,
Cho - sen as part - ners, mid - wives of jus - tice,
But by your peo - ple, fear - less and faith - ful,
Bond - ing us glad - ly one to the oth - er,

Free - dom or pris - on, you are our home.
Feed - ing, sus - tain - ing, from your own heart.
Birth - ing new sys - tems, light - ing new lights.
Small pa - per lan - terns, light - ing the way.
Till our world chang - es fac - ing the Cross.

Fresh as the morn - ing, sure as the sun - rise,

God al - ways faith - ful, you do not change.

Fresh as the morn - ing, sure as the sun - rise,

God al - ways faith - ful, you do not change.

Text: Shirley Erena Murray, b.1931, © 1996, Hope Publishing Company
Tune: SUNRISE SONG, 10 9 10 9 with refrain; Tony E. Alonso, b.1980, © 2001, GIA Publications, Inc.

692 Christ, Be Our Light!

Verses

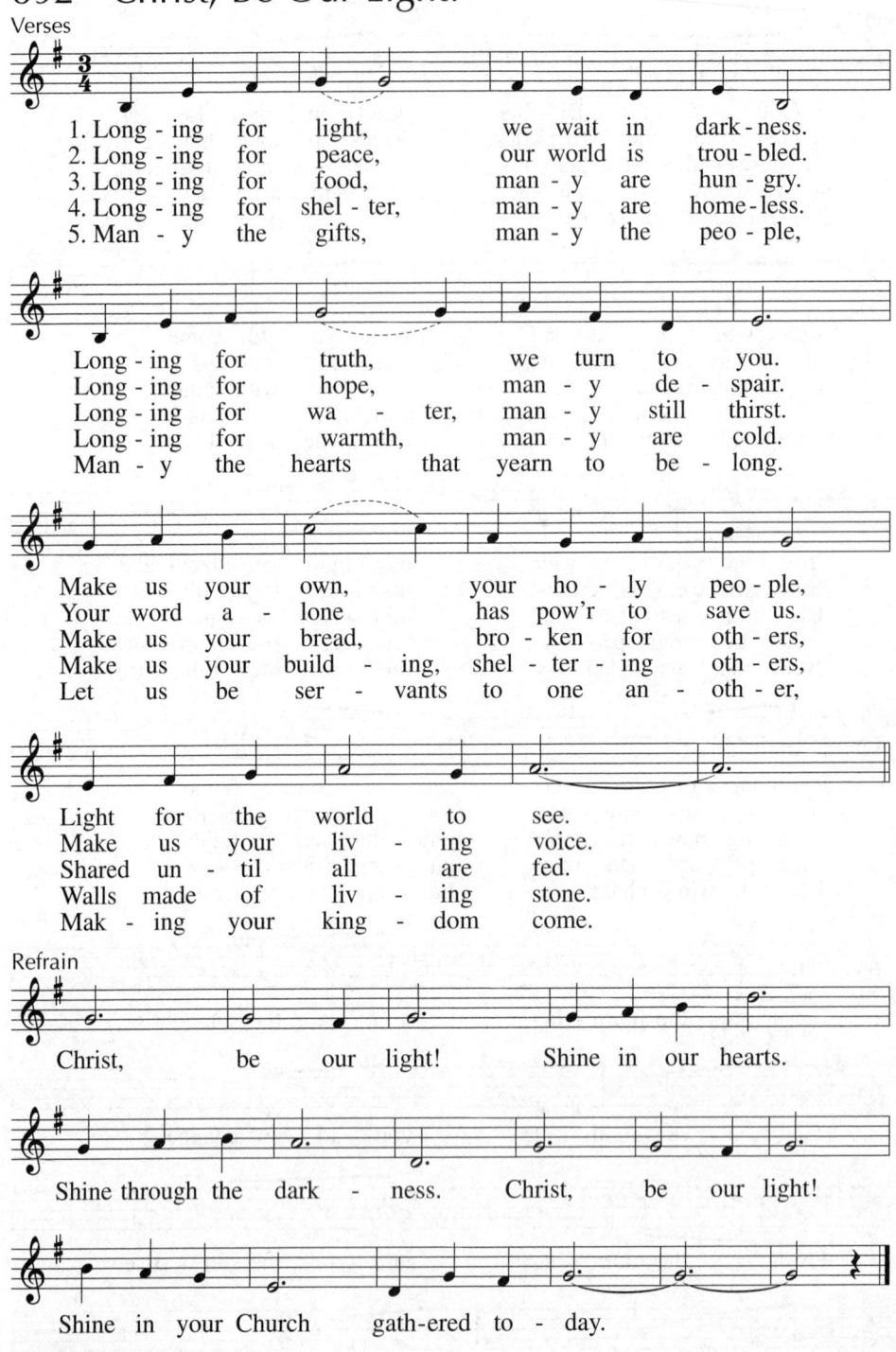

1. Long - ing for light, we wait in dark - ness.
2. Long - ing for peace, our world is trou - bled.
3. Long - ing for food, man - y are hun - gry.
4. Long - ing for shel - ter, man - y are home - less.
5. Man - y the gifts, man - y the peo - ple,

Long - ing for truth, we turn to you.
Long - ing for hope, man - y de - spair.
Long - ing for wa - ter, man - y still thirst.
Long - ing for warmth, man - y are cold.
Man - y the hearts that yearn to be - long.

Make us your own, your ho - ly peo - ple,
Your word a - lone has pow'r to save us.
Make us your bread, bro - ken for oth - ers,
Make us your build - ing, shel - ter - ing oth - ers,
Let us be ser - vants to one an - oth - er,

Light for the world to see.
Make us your liv - ing voice.
Shared un - til all are fed.
Walls made of liv - ing stone.
Mak - ing your king - dom come.

Refrain

Christ, be our light! Shine in our hearts.

Shine through the dark - ness. Christ, be our light!

Shine in your Church gath-ered to - day.

Text: Bernadette Farrell, b.1957
Tune: CHRIST, BE OUR LIGHT, 9 8 9 6 with refrain; Bernadette Farrell, b.1957
© 1993, 2000, Bernadette Farrell. Published by OCP.

I Want to Walk as a Child of the Light   693

1. I want to walk as a child of the light.
2. I want to see the bright-ness of God.
3. I'm look-ing for the com-ing of Christ.

I want to fol - low Je - sus.
I want to look at Je - sus.
I want to be with Je - sus.

God set the stars to give light to the world. The
Clear sun of right-eous-ness shine on my path And
When we have run with pa-tience the race, We

star of my life is Je - sus.
show me the way to the Fa - ther.
shall know the joy of Je - sus.

In him there is no dark-ness at all. The

night and the day are both a - like. The

Lamb is the light of the cit - y of God.

Shine in my heart, Lord Je - sus.

Text: Ephesians 5:8–10, Revelation 21:23, John 12:46, 1 John 1:5, Hebrews 12:1; Kathleen Thomerson, b.1934
Tune: HOUSTON, 10 7 10 8 with refrain; Kathleen Thomerson, b.1934
© 1970, 1975, Celebration

694 We Are Marching / Siyahamba

Alternate text: dancing, singing, praying

Zulu phonetics: See-yah-hahmb eh-koo-kah-nyen kwen-kose. See-yah-hahm-bah.

Text: South African
Tune: South African
© 1984, Peace of Music Publishing AB, admin. by Walton Music Corp., a division of GIA Publications, Inc.

Lord Jesus Christ 695

Ostinato Refrain

Lord Je - sus Christ, your light shines with - in us.
French: Jé - sus le Christ, lu - mière in - té - rieu - re,
Spanish: Cris - to Je - sús, oh fue - go que a-bra - sa,
Polish: Je - zu, Tyś jest świat - łoś - cią mej du - szy.

Let not my doubts nor my dark - ness speak to me.
ne lais - se pas mes té - nè - bres me par - ler.
que las ti - nie - blas en mí no ten - gan voz.
Niech ciem-ność ma nie prze - ma - wia do mnie już.

Lord Je - sus Christ, your light shines with - in us.
Jé - sus le Christ, lu - mière in - té - rieu - re,
Cris - to Je - sús, di - si - pa mis som - bras.
Je - zu, Tyś jest świat - łoś - cią mej du - szy.

Let my heart al - ways wel - come your love.
don - ne - moi d'ac-cueil - lir ton a - mour.
Y que en mí só - lo ha - ble tu A-mor.
Daj mi moc przy - jąć dziś mi - łość Twą.

Text: Psalm 139
Tune: Jacques Berthier, 1923–1994
© 1998, Les Presses de Taizé, GIA Publications, Inc., agent

696 Love, Burn Bright

Refrain

Christ our Light, il - lu - mi - nate ev - 'ry path that leads to you.

Give us grace, Lord, guide our way: Love, burn bright.

In your light, Lord, ev - 'ry day,

ev - 'ry way we fol - low you. Grant us peace to

jour - ney through: Love, burn bright.

Verses

Cantor:

1. From the shad - ows of the night, to your
2. In our words that tear a - part, place a
3. Where there's doubt, un - cer - tain - ty, let us

All:

ho - li - ness and light:
rec - on - cil - ing heart: May your love burn
wit - ness faith - ful - ly:

Cantor:

bright with - in our heart.
                   From the ha - tred born of
                   In our wounds of war and
                   Where there's sad - ness, pov - er -

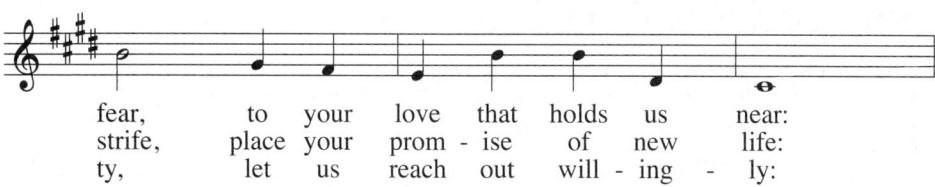

fear, to your love that holds us near:
strife, place your prom - ise of new life:
ty, let us reach out will - ing - ly:

All: ... D.C.

May your love burn bright with - in our heart.

Text: Chris de Silva, b.1967
Tune: Chris de Silva, b.1967
© 2014, GIA Publications, Inc.

This Little Light of Mine   697

1. This lit - tle light of mine I'm gon-na let it shine,
2. Ev - 'ry - where I go, I'm gon-na let it shine,
3. Je - sus gave it to me, I'm gon-na let it shine,

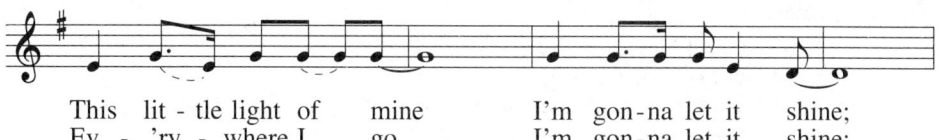

This lit - tle light of mine I'm gonna let it shine;
Ev - 'ry - where I go, I'm gon na let it shine;
Je - sus gave it to me, I'm gon na let it shine;

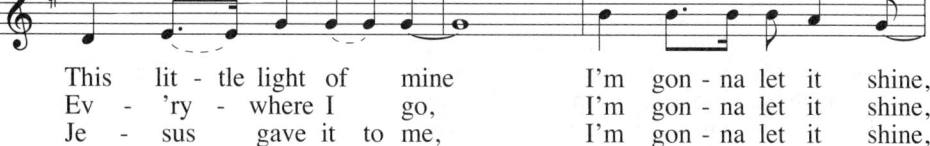

This lit - tle light of mine I'm gon - na let it shine,
Ev - 'ry - where I go, I'm gon na let it shine,
Je - sus gave it to me, I'm gon na let it shine,

Let it shine, let it shine, let it shine.
Let it shine, let it shine, let it shine.
Let it shine, let it shine, let it shine.

Text: Harry Dixon Loes, 1895–1965
Tune: Harry Dixon Loes, 1895–1965; harm. by Horace Clarence Boyer, 1935–2009, © 1992

698 God Is Still Speaking

Refrain

God is still speak-ing: bless-ed in - vi - ta - tion. God is still speak-ing: lis-ten and draw near. God is still speak-ing: see a new cre-a-tion. God is still speak-ing: stand and do not fear.

Verses

Cantor:
1. O - pen up your ears to hear:
2. In the bleak and mid-night hour:
3. Though the na - tions rage and fight: God is still speak - ing.
4. All cre - a - tion groans and yearns:
5. Hear the sound of jus - tice ring:

Cantor:
Liv - ing Good News, strong and clear:
Sing the word of truth to pow'r:
Hear God's voice of grace and light: lis-ten and draw near.
"Seek the way that life re-turns":
Hear the song of mer - cy sing:

Cantor:
Through the strug - gle, grief and pain:
To our frag - ile, wound-ed earth:
Choose the way that leads to peace: God is still speak - ing.
Through our bro - ken, wound-ed earth:
To the ones in deep de - spair:

Cantor: D.C.
God can raise us up a - gain:
God can bring new hope to birth:
True com-pas - sion, sweet re - lease: stand and do not fear.
God can bring new seeds to birth:
Be the sign of hope and care:

Text: Marty Haugen, b.1950
Tune: Marty Haugen, b.1950
© 2009, GIA Publications, Inc.

God Has Spoken by the Prophets 699

1. God has spo - ken by the proph - ets, Spo - ken
2. God has spo - ken by Christ Je - sus, Christ, the
3. God is speak - ing by the Spir - it, Speak - ing

his un - chang - ing word, Each from age to age pro -
ev - er - last - ing Son, Bright - ness of the Fa - ther's
to our hearts a - gain, In the age - less Word de -

claim - ing God, the one, the right - eous Lord.
glo - ry, With the Fa - ther ev - er one;
clar - ing God's own mes - sage, now as then.

In the world's de - spair and tur - moil, One firm
Spo - ken by the Word in - car - nate, God from
Through the rise and fall of na - tions One sure

an - chor holds us fast: God e - ter - nal reigns for -
God, be - fore time was; Light from Light, to earth de -
faith is hold - ing fast: God a - bides, his word un -

ev - er, God the first and God the last.
scend - ing, Christ re - veals our God to us.
chang - ing, God the first and God the last.

Text: George W. Briggs, 1875–1959, alt., © 1953, ren. 1981, The Hymn Society (admin. by Hope Publishing Company)
Tune: RUSTINGTON, 8 7 8 7 D; Charles H. H. Parry, 1848–1918

Alternate tune: HYMN TO JOY

700 Love Has Come

Verses

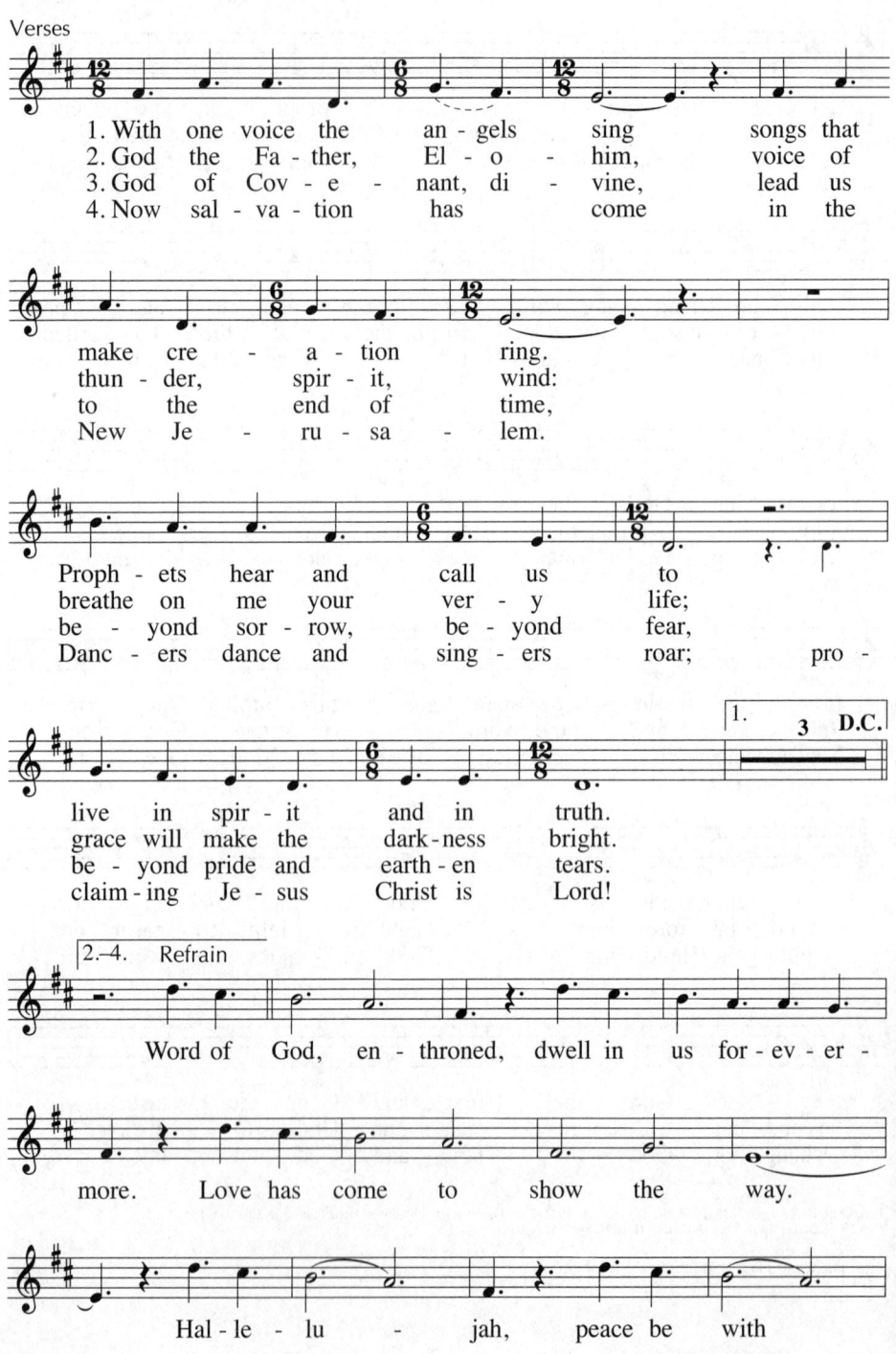

1. With one voice the an - gels sing songs that
2. God the Fa - ther, El - o - him, voice of
3. God of Cov - e - nant, di - vine, lead us
4. Now sal - va - tion has come in the

make cre - a - tion ring.
thun - der, spir - it, wind:
to the end of time,
New Je - ru - sa - lem.

Proph - ets hear and call us to
breathe on me your ver - y life;
be - yond sor - row, be - yond fear,
Danc - ers dance and sing - ers roar; pro -

live in spir - it and in truth.
grace will make the dark - ness bright.
be - yond pride and earth - en tears.
claim - ing Je - sus Christ is Lord!

2.–4. Refrain

Word of God, en - throned, dwell in us for - ev - er -

more. Love has come to show the way.

Hal - le - lu - jah, peace be with

To verses 3 D.C.

us. Love has come to show the way.

Final ending

way, the way.

Text: Matt Maher
Tune: Matt Maher; acc. by Ed Bolduc, b.1969
© 2001, Matt Maher. Published by Spirit & Song, a division of OCP.

Word of God, Come Down on Earth 701

1. Word of God, come down on earth, Liv - ing rain from
2. Word e - ter - nal, throned on high, Word that brought to
3. Word that caused blind eyes to see, Speak and heal our
4. Word that speaks God's ten - der love, One with God be -

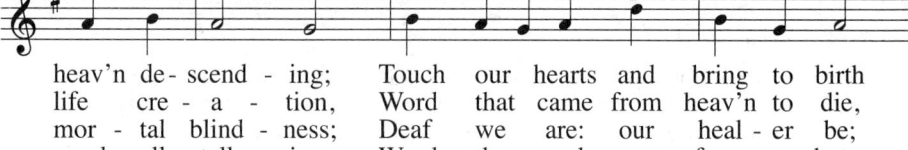

heav'n de - scend - ing; Touch our hearts and bring to birth
life cre - a - tion, Word that came from heav'n to die,
mor - tal blind - ness; Deaf we are: our heal - er be;
yond all tell - ing, Word that sends us from a - bove

Faith and hope and love un - end - ing. Word al - might - y,
Cru - ci - fied for our sal - va - tion, Sav - ing Word, the
Loose our tongues to tell your kind - ness. Be our Word in
God the Spir - it, with us dwell - ing, Word of truth, to

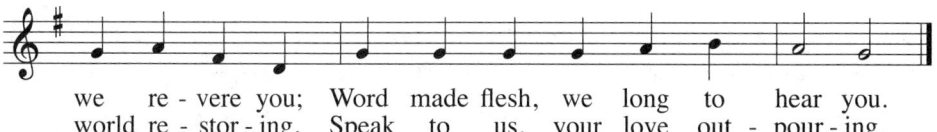

we re - vere you; Word made flesh, we long to hear you.
world re - stor - ing, Speak to us, your love out - pour - ing.
pit - y spo - ken, Heal the world, by our sin bro - ken.
all truth lead us; Word of life, with one Bread feed us.

Text: James Quinn, SJ, 1919–2010, © 1969, James Quinn, SJ. Published by OCP.
Tune: LIEBSTER JESU, 7 8 7 8 88; Johann R. Ahle, 1625–1673; harm. by George H. Palmer, 1846–1926

702 Praise to You, O Christ, Our Savior

Refrain

Praise to you, O Christ, our Sav - ior, Word of the Fa - ther, call - ing us to life; Son of God who leads us to free - dom: glo - ry to you, Lord Je - sus Christ!

Verses

1. You are the Word who calls us out of dark - ness;
2. You are the one whom proph - ets hoped and longed for;
3. You are the Word who calls us to be ser - vants;
4. You are the Word who binds us and u - nites us;

You are the Word who leads us in - to light;
You are the one who speaks to us to - day;
You are the Word whose on - ly law is love;
You are the Word who calls us to be one;

You are the Word who brings us through the des - ert:
You are the one who leads us to our fu - ture:
You are the Word - made - flesh who lives a - mong us:
You are the Word who teach - es us for - give - ness:

D.C.

Glo - ry to you, Lord Je - sus Christ!
Glo - ry to you, Lord Je - sus Christ!
Glo - ry to you, Lord Je - sus Christ!
Glo - ry to you, Lord Je - sus Christ!

Text: Bernadette Farrell, b.1957
Tune: Bernadette Farrell, b.1957
© 1986, Bernadette Farrell. Published by OCP.

God, We Praise You! 703

1. God, we praise you! God, we bless you! God, we name you sov-'reign Lord! Might-y King whom an-gels wor-ship, Fa-ther, by your Church a-dored: All cre-a-tion shows your glo-ry, Heav'n and earth draw near your throne, Sing-ing "Ho-ly, ho-ly, ho-ly, Lord of hosts, and God a-lone!"

2. True a-pos-tles, faith-ful proph-ets, Saints who set their world a-blaze, Mar-tyrs, once un-known, un-heed-ed, Join one grow-ing song of praise, While your Church on earth con-fess-es One ma-jes-tic Trin-i-ty: Fa-ther, Son, and Ho-ly Spir-it, God, our hope e-ter-nal-ly.

3. Je-sus Christ, the King of glo-ry, Ev-er-last-ing Son of God, Hum-ble was your vir-gin moth-er, Hard the lone-ly path you trod: By your cross is sin de-feat-ed, Hell con-front-ed face to face, Heav-en o-pened to be-liev-ers, Sin-ners jus-ti-fied by grace.

4. Christ, at God's right hand vic-to-rious, You will judge the world you made; Lord, in mer-cy help your ser-vants For whose free-dom you have paid: Raise us up from dust to glo-ry, Guard us from all sin to-day; King en-throned a-bove all prais-es, Save your peo-ple, God, we pray.

Text: Based on the *Te Deum*; Christopher M. Idle, b.1938, © 1982, The Jubilate Group (admin. by Hope Publishing Company)
Tune: NETTLETON, 8 7 8 7 D; Wyeth's *Repository of Sacred Music*, 1813

704 Sing Praise to God Who Reigns Above

1. Sing praise to God who reigns a-bove, The God of all cre - a - tion, The God of pow'r, the God of love, The God of our sal - va - tion. With heal-ing balm our souls are filled; All our la-ments with peace are stilled. To God all praise and glo - ry!

2. O God, what your great pow'r has made, In mer - cy you are keep - ing; By morn-ing glow or eve - ning shade, Your eye is nev - er sleep-ing; In the do - min - ion of your might All things are just and good and right. To God all praise and glo - ry!

3. We seek you, Lord, in our dis - tress; O God, in mer - cy hear us. O Sav - ior, see our help - less - ness And come with peace to cheer us. For this we thank and praise you, Lord, Who are by one and all a - dored. To God all praise and glo - ry!

4. All who con - fess Christ's ho - ly name, Give God the praise and glo - ry! And all who know God's pow'r, pro - claim: Give God the praise and glo - ry! Cast ev - 'ry i - dol from its throne; God is the Lord, and God a - lone: To God all praise and glo - ry!

Text: *Sei Lob und Ehr' dem höchsten Gut*; Johann J. Schütz, 1640–1690; tr. by Frances E. Cox, 1812–1897, alt.
Tune: MIT FREUDEN ZART, 8 7 8 7 88 7; Bohemian Brethren's *Kirchengesänge*, 1566

Holy God, We Praise Thy Name   705

1. Ho - ly God, we praise thy name;
2. Hark! the loud ce - les - tial hymn
3. Lo, the ap - os - tol - ic train
4. Ho - ly Fa - ther, Ho - ly Son,

Lord of all, we bow be - fore thee!
An - gel choirs a - bove are rais - ing;
Joins, the sa - cred name to hal - low;
Ho - ly Spir - it, Three we name thee;

All on earth thy scep - ter claim,
Cher - u - bim and Ser - a - phim,
Proph - ets swell the loud re - frain,
While in es - sence on - ly One,

All in heav'n a - bove a - dore thee;
In un - ceas - ing cho - rus prais - ing,
And the white - robed mar - tyrs fol - low;
Un - di - vid - ed God we claim thee;

In - fi - nite thy vast do - main,
Fill the heav'ns with sweet ac - cord:
And from morn to set - ting sun,
And a - dor - ing bend the knee,

Repeat ad lib.

Ev - er - last - ing is thy reign.
"Ho - ly, ho - ly, ho - ly Lord!"
Through the Church the song goes on.
While we own the mys - ter - y.

Text: *Grosser Gott, wir loben dich;* ascr. to Ignaz Franz, 1719–1790; tr. by Clarence Walworth, 1820–1900, alt.
Tune: GROSSER GOTT, 7 8 7 8 77; *Katholisches Gesangbuch*, Vienna, c.1774

706 All Creatures of Our God and King

6. And you, most kind and gentle death,
   Waiting to hush our final breath,
      Alleluia! Alleluia!
   You lead to heav'n the child of God,
   Where Christ our Lord the way has trod.
      Alleluia! Alleluia!
      Alleluia, alleluia, alleluia!

7. Let all things their Creator bless,
   And worship God in humbleness,
      Alleluia! Alleluia!
   Oh praise the Father, praise the Son,
   And praise the Spirit, Three in One!
      Alleluia! Alleluia!
      Alleluia, alleluia, alleluia!

Text: *Laudato si, mi Signor;* Francis of Assisi, 1182–1226; tr. by William H. Draper, 1855–1933, alt.
Tune: LASST UNS ERFREUEN, LM with alleluias; *Geistliche Kirchengesänge,* 1623; harm. by Ralph Vaughan Williams, 1872–1958

Joyful, Joyful, We Adore You   707

1. Joy - ful, joy - ful, we a - dore you, God of glo - ry,
   Lord of love; Hearts un - fold like flow'rs be - fore you,
   O - p'ning to the sun a - bove. Melt the clouds of
   sin and sad - ness; Drive the dark of doubt a - way;
   Giv - er of im - mor - tal glad - ness, Fill us with the light of day!

2. All your works with joy sur - round you, Earth and heav'n re -
   flect your rays, Stars and an - gels sing a - round you,
   Cen - ter of un - bro - ken praise. Field and for - est,
   vale and moun - tain, Flow - 'ry mead - ow, flash - ing sea,
   Chant - ing bird, and flow - ing foun - tain Sound their praise e - ter - nal - ly!

3. You are giv - ing and for - giv - ing, Ev - er bless - ing,
   ev - er blest, Well - spring of the joy of liv - ing,
   O - cean - depth of hap - py rest! God our Fa - ther,
   Christ our broth - er, Let your light up - on us shine;
   Teach us how to love each oth - er, Lift us to the joy di - vine.

4. Mor - tals, join the might - y cho - rus, Which the morn - ing
   stars be - gan; God's own love is reign - ing o'er us,
   Join - ing peo - ple hand in hand. Ev - er sing - ing,
   march we on - ward, Vic - tors in the midst of strife;
   Joy - ful mu - sic leads us sun - ward In the tri - umph - song of life.

Text: Henry van Dyke, 1852–1933, alt.
Tune: HYMN TO JOY, 8 7 8 7 D; arr. from Ludwig van Beethoven, 1770–1827, by Edward Hodges, 1796–1867

708 You, Lord, Are Both Lamb and Shepherd

1. You, Lord, are both Lamb and Shep - herd.
2. Clothed in light up - on the moun - tain,
3. You, who walk each day be - side us,
4. Wor - thy is our earth - ly Je - sus!

You, Lord, are both prince and slave.
Stripped of might up - on the cross,
Sit in pow - er at God's side.
Wor - thy is our cos - mic Christ!

You, peace - mak - er and sword - bring - er
Shin - ing in e - ter - nal glo - ry,
You, who preach a way that's nar - row,
Wor - thy your de - feat and vic - t'ry.

Of the way you took and gave.
Beg - gar'd by a sol - dier's toss.
Have a love that reach - es wide.
Wor - thy still your peace and strife.

You, the ev - er - last - ing in - stant;
You, the ev - er - last - ing in - stant;
You, the ev - er - last - ing in - stant;
You, the ev - er - last - ing in - stant;

You, whom we both scorn and crave.
You, who are both gift and cost.
You, who are our pil - grim guide.
You, who are our death and life.

Text: *Christus Paradox*, Sylvia G. Dunstan, 1955–1993, © 1991, GIA Publications, Inc.
Tune: PICARDY, 8 7 8 7 8 7; French carol; harm. by Richard Proulx, 1937–2010, © 1986, GIA Publications, Inc.

Laudate Dominum 709

Ostinato Refrain

Lau - dá - te Dó - mi - num, lau - dá - te Dó - mi - num, o - mnes

gen - tes, al - le - lú - ia. al - le - lú - ia.

Text: Psalm 117, *Praise the Lord, all you peoples;* Taizé Community, 1980
Tune: Jacques Berthier, 1923–1994
© 1980, Les Presses de Taizé, GIA Publications, Inc., agent

Sing a New Song to the Lord 710

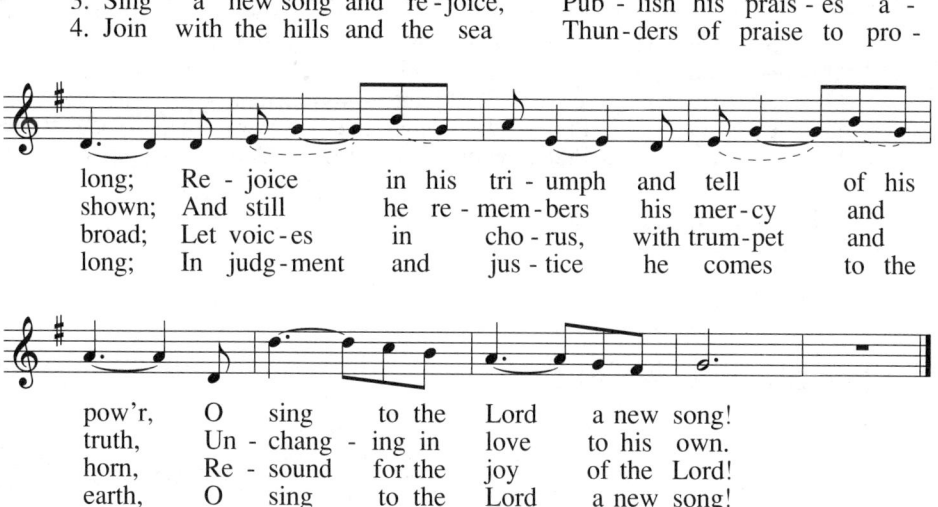

1. Sing a new song to the Lord, He to whom won - ders be -
2. Now to the ends of the earth See his sal - va - tion is
3. Sing a new song and re - joice, Pub - lish his prais - es a -
4. Join with the hills and the sea Thun - ders of praise to pro -

long; Re - joice in his tri - umph and tell of his
shown; And still he re - mem - bers his mer - cy and
broad; Let voic - es in cho - rus, with trum - pet and
long; In judg - ment and jus - tice he comes to the

pow'r, O sing to the Lord a new song!
truth, Un - chang - ing in love to his own.
horn, Re - sound for the joy of the Lord!
earth, O sing to the Lord a new song!

Text: Psalm 98; Timothy Dudley-Smith, b.1926, © 1973, Hope Publishing Company
Tune: CANTATE DOMINO (ONSLOW SQUARE), Irregular; David G. Wilson, b.1940, © 1973, The Jubilate Group
   (admin. by Hope Publishing Company)

711 Praise, My Soul, the King of Heaven

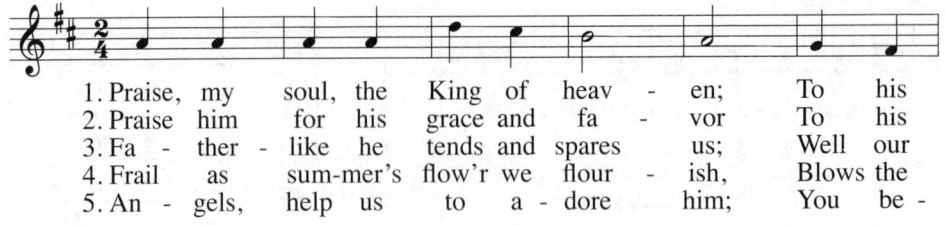

1. Praise, my soul, the King of heav - en; To his
2. Praise him for his grace and fa - vor To his
3. Fa - ther - like he tends and spares us; Well our
4. Frail as sum-mer's flow'r we flour - ish, Blows the
5. An - gels, help us to a - dore him; You be -

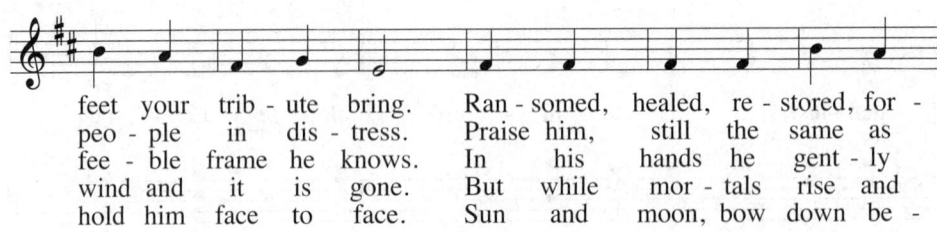

feet your trib - ute bring. Ran - somed, healed, re - stored, for -
peo - ple in dis - tress. Praise him, still the same as
fee - ble frame he knows. In his hands he gent - ly
wind and it is gone. But while mor - tals rise and
hold him face to face. Sun and moon, bow down be -

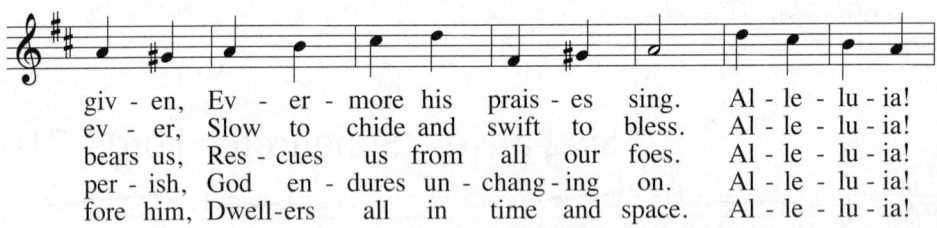

giv - en, Ev - er - more his prais - es sing. Al - le - lu - ia!
ev - er, Slow to chide and swift to bless. Al - le - lu - ia!
bears us, Res - cues us from all our foes. Al - le - lu - ia!
per - ish, God en - dures un - chang - ing on. Al - le - lu - ia!
fore him, Dwell-ers all in time and space. Al - le - lu - ia!

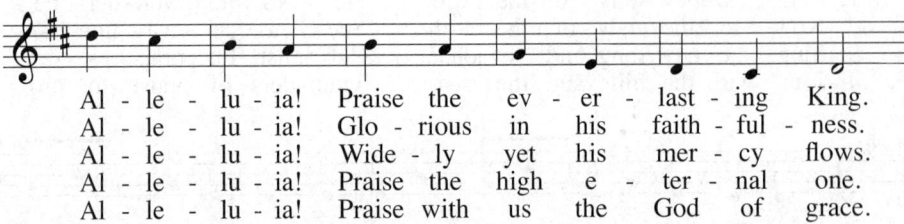

Al - le - lu - ia! Praise the ev - er - last - ing King.
Al - le - lu - ia! Glo - rious in his faith - ful - ness.
Al - le - lu - ia! Wide - ly yet his mer - cy flows.
Al - le - lu - ia! Praise the high e - ter - nal one.
Al - le - lu - ia! Praise with us the God of grace.

Text: Psalm 103; Henry F. Lyte, 1793–1847, alt.
Tune: LAUDA ANIMA, 8 7 8 7 8 7; John Goss, 1800–1880

712 Jubilate, Servite

Canon

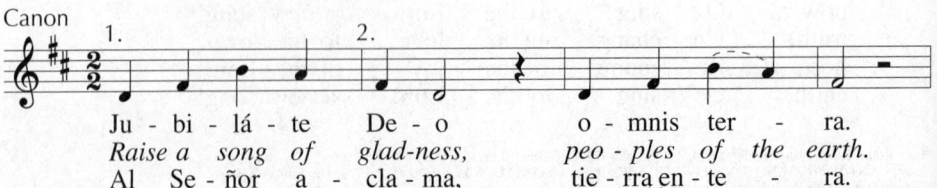

Ju - bi - lá - te De - o o - mnis ter - ra.
Raise a song of glad-ness, peo - ples of the earth.
Al Se - ñor a - cla - ma, tie - rra en - te - ra.

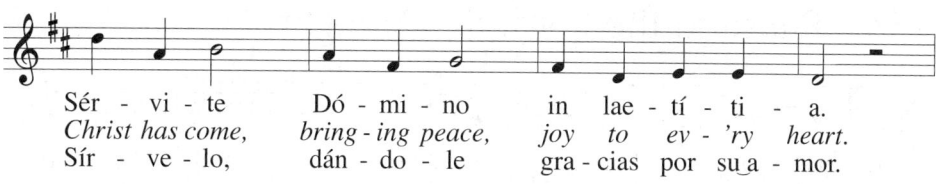

Sér - vi - te   Dó - mi - no   in lae - tí - ti - a.
Christ has come,   bring - ing peace,   joy to ev - 'ry heart.
Sír - ve - lo,   dán - do - le   gra - cias por su a - mor.

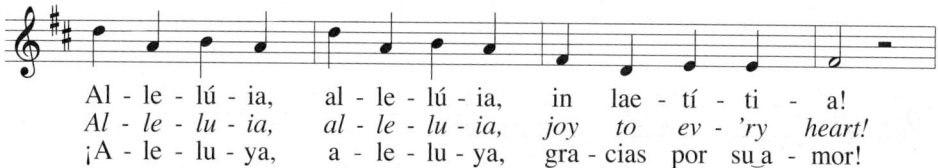

Al - le - lú - ia,   al - le - lú - ia,   in lae - tí - ti - a!
Al - le - lu - ia,   al - le - lu - ia,   joy to ev - 'ry heart!
¡A - le - lu - ya,   a - le - lu - ya,   gra - cias por su a - mor!

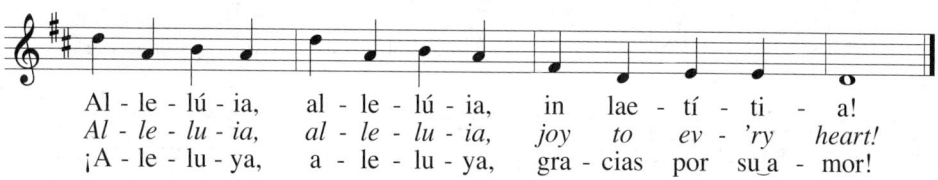

Al - le - lú - ia,   al - le - lú - ia,   in lae - tí - ti - a!
Al - le - lu - ia,   al - le - lu - ia,   joy to ev - 'ry heart!
¡A - le - lu - ya,   a - le - lu - ya,   gra - cias por su a - mor!

Text: Psalm 100, *Rejoice in God, all the earth, Serve the Lord with gladness*; Taizé Community, 1978
Tune: Jacques Berthier, 1923–1994
© 1979, 2011, Les Presses de Taizé, GIA Publications, Inc., agent

Magnificat 713

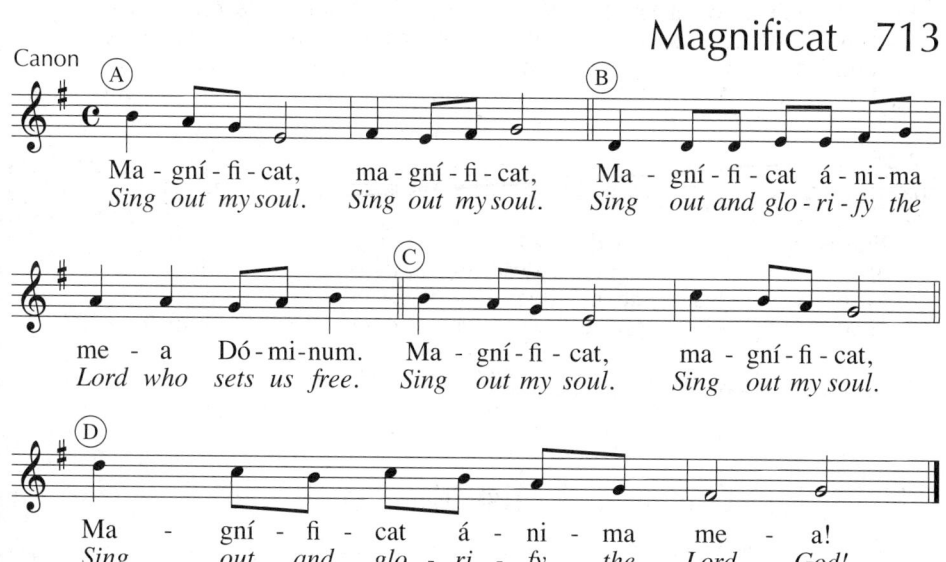

Canon

Ma - gní - fi - cat,   ma - gní - fi - cat,   Ma - gní - fi - cat á - ni - ma
Sing out my soul.   Sing out my soul.   Sing out and glo - ri - fy the

me - a Dó - mi - num.   Ma - gní - fi - cat,   ma - gní - fi - cat,
Lord who sets us free.   Sing out my soul.   Sing out my soul.

Ma - gní - fi - cat á - ni - ma   me - a!
Sing out and glo - ri - fy the Lord God!

Text: Luke 1:46, *My soul magnifies the Lord;* Taizé Community, 1978
Tune: Jacques Berthier, 1923–1994
© 1979, Les Presses de Taizé, GIA Publications, Inc., agent

714 Praise to the Lord, the Almighty

1. Praise to the Lord, the Al - might - y, the King of cre -
2. Praise to the Lord, who o'er all things is won - drous - ly
3. Praise to the Lord, who will pros - per your work and de -
4. Praise to the Lord! O let all that is in me a -

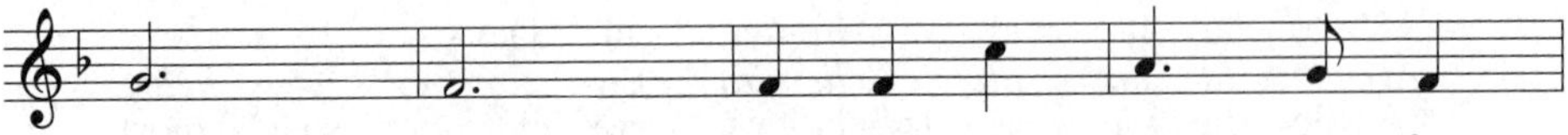

a - tion! O my soul, praise him, for
reign - ing And, as on wings of an
fend you; Sure - ly his good - ness and
dore him! All that has life and breath,

he is your health and sal - va - tion!
ea - gle, up - lift - ing, sus - tain - ing.
mer - cy shall dai - ly at - tend you.
come now with prais - es be - fore him!

All you who hear, Now to his tem - ple draw near.
Have you not seen All you have need - ed has been
Pon - der a - new What the Al - might - y can do,
Let the "A - men" Sound from his peo - ple a - gain!

Praise him in glad ad - o - ra - tion!
Met by his gra - cious or - dain - ing?
Who with his love does be - friend you.
Glad - ly with praise we a - dore him!

Text: *Lobe den Herren, den mächtigen König*; Joachim Neander, 1650–1680; tr. by Catherine Winkworth, 1827–1878, alt.
Tune: LOBE DEN HERREN, 14 14 47 8; *Stralsund Gesangbuch*, 1665

715 I Just Came to Praise the Lord

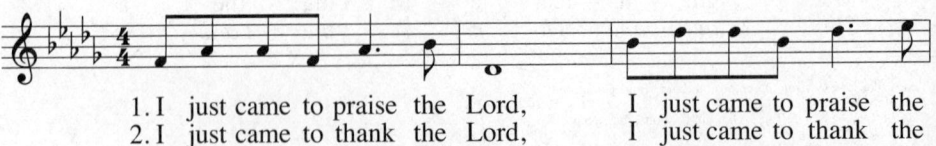

1. I just came to praise the Lord,   I just came to praise the
2. I just came to thank the Lord,   I just came to thank the
3. I just came to love the Lord,   I just came to love the

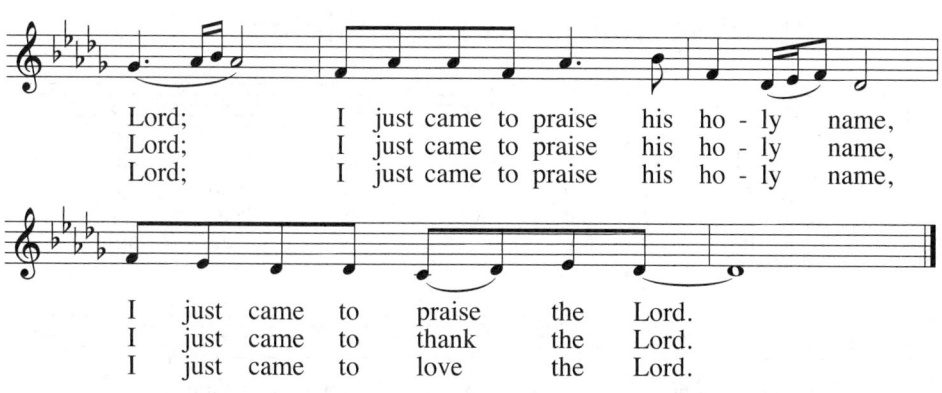

Lord; I just came to praise his ho - ly name,
Lord; I just came to praise his ho - ly name,
Lord; I just came to praise his ho - ly name,

I just came to praise the Lord.
I just came to thank the Lord.
I just came to love the Lord.

Text: Wayne Romero, b.1950
Tune: Wayne Romero, b.1950
© 1975, New Spring Publishing, Inc. (admin. CapitolCMGPublishing.com)

When in Our Music God Is Glorified 716

1. When in our mu - sic God is glo - ri - fied,
2. How of - ten, mak - ing mu - sic, we have found
3. So has the Church, in lit - ur - gy and song,
4. And did not Je - sus sing a psalm that night
5. Let ev - 'ry in - stru-ment be tuned for praise!

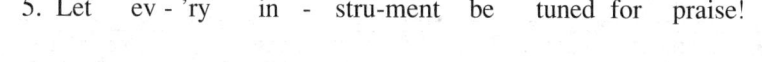

And ad - o - ra - tion leaves no room for pride,
A new di - men - sion in the world of sound,
In faith and love, through cen - tu - ries of wrong,
When ut - most e - vil strove a - gainst the light?
Let all re - joice who have a voice to raise!

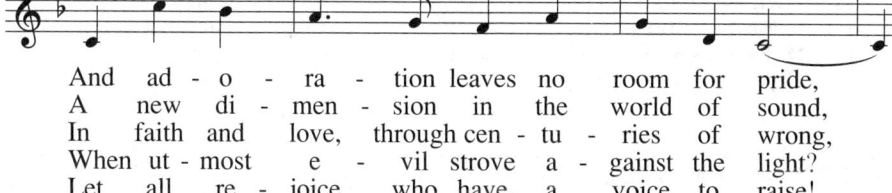

It is as though the whole cre - a - tion cried:
As wor - ship moved us to a more pro - found
Borne wit - ness to the truth in ev - 'ry tongue:
Then let us sing, for whom he won the fight:
And may God give us faith to sing al - ways:

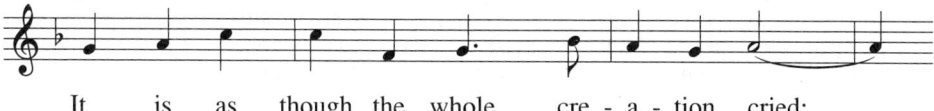

Al - le - lu - ia!

Text: Fred Pratt Green, 1903–2000, © 1972, Hope Publishing Company
Tune: ENGELBERG, 10 10 10 with alleluia; Charles V. Stanford, 1852–1924

717 Let All Mortal Flesh Keep Silence

1. Let all mor - tal flesh keep si - lence,
2. King of kings, yet born of Mar - y,
3. Rank on rank the host of heav - en
4. At his feet the six - winged ser - aph;

And with fear and trem - bling stand;
As of old on earth he stood,
Spreads its van - guard on the way;
Cher - u - bim with sleep - less eye

Pon - der noth - ing earth - ly - mind - ed,
Lord of lords in hu - man ves - ture,
As the Light of Light, de - scend - ing
Veil their fac - es to the Pres - ence,

For with bless - ing in his hand
In the Bod - y and the Blood
From the realms of end - less day,
As with cease - less voice they cry:

Christ our God, to earth de - scend -
He will give to all the faith -
Comes, the pow'rs of hell to van -
"Al - le - lu - ia, al - le - lu -

ing, Comes, our hom - age to de - mand.
ful His own self for heav'n - ly food.
quish, As the dark - ness clears a - way.
ia! Al - le - lu - ia, Lord Most High!"

Text: Liturgy of St. James, 5th C.; para. by Gerard Moultrie, 1829–1885, alt.
Tune: PICARDY, 8 7 8 7 8 7; French carol; harm. by Richard Proulx, 1937–2010, © 1986, GIA Publications, Inc.

Sing a New Song 718

Refrain

Sing a new song un-to the Lord; let your song be
sung from moun - tains high. Sing a new song
un - to the Lord, sing-ing al - le - lu - ia.

Verses

1. Shout with glad - ness! Dance for joy! O come be -
2. Rise, O chil - dren, from your sleep; your Sav - ior
3. Glad my soul for I have seen the glo - ry

fore the Lord. And play for God on
now has come. He has turned your
of the Lord. The trum - pet sounds; the

D.C.

glad tam - bou - rines, and let your trum - pet sound.
sor - row to joy, and filled your soul with song.
dead shall be raised. I know my Sav - ior lives.

Text: Based on Psalm 98:1, 4–6; Dan Schutte, b.1947
Tune: Dan Schutte, b.1947
© 1972, Daniel L. Schutte. Published by OCP.

Adoramus Te Domine 719

Ostinato Refrain

(hum)
A - do - rá - mus te Dó - mi - ne.
We a - dore you, Lord Je - sus Christ.
Korean: 오
주 를 찬 미 하 나 이 다.

Korean transliteration: O ju-leul chan-mi-ha-na-i-da.

Text: Taizé Community
Tune: Jacques Berthier, 1923–1994
© 1979, Les Presses de Taizé, GIA Publications, Inc., agent

720 Alabaré

Estribillo / Refrain

A - la - ba - ré,   a - la - ba - ré,   a -
A - la - ba - ré,   *a - la - ba - ré,*   *we*

la - ba - ré a mi Se - ñor.   A - la - ba - ré,   a - la - ba -
sing the prais - es of our God.   *A - la - ba - ré,*   *a - la - ba -*

ré,   a - la - ba - ré a mi Se - ñor.
ré,   *we sing the prais - es of our God.*

Estrofas / Verses

1. Juan vio el nú - me - ro de los re - di - mi - dos, Y
2. To - dos u - ni - dos, a - le - gres can - ta - mos
3. So - mos tus hi - jos, Dios Pa - dre e - ter - no,

1. *John had a vis - ion of those re - deemed by Je - sus, And*
2. *One in our prais - ing, with joy - ful hearts and voic - es, We*
3. *We are your chil - dren, O God, e - ter - nal Fa - ther. You*

to - dos a - la - ba - ban al Se - ñor.
Glo - ria y a - la - ban - zas al Se - ñor.
Tú nos has cre - a - do por a - mor.

all were prais - ing God with one ac - cord.
glo - ri - fy the Lord who reigns a - bove:
guide us and pro - tect us all our days.

U - nos o - ra - ban, o - tros can - ta - ban, Y
¡Glo - ria al Pa - dre! ¡Glo - ria al Hi - jo! Y
Te a - do - ra - mos, te ben - de - ci - mos, Y

Thou - sands were pray - ing, thou - sands were sing - ing, But
Praise to the Fa - ther, praise to Christ Je - sus, And
With all cre - a - tion, in ju - bi - la - tion, We

D.S.

to - dos	a - la - ba - ban	al	Se - ñor.
¡Glo - ria al	Es - pí - ri - tu	de a - mor!	A - la - ba -
to - dos	can - ta - mos	en tu ho - nor.	
all were joined	*in prais - es*	*to the Lord.*	
praise to God	*the Spir - it,*	*bond of love.*	A - la - ba -
hon - or you	*with songs*	*of end - less praise.*	

Text: Manuel José Alonso, José Pagán; tr. by Ronald F. Krisman, b.1946
Tune: Manuel José Alonso, José Pagán; acc. by Ronald F. Krisman, b.1946
© 1979, 2011, Manuel José Alonso and José Pagán, OCP, agent

Shout for Joy, Loud and Long   721

1. Shout for joy,   loud and long;   God be praised
2. By God's word   all was made,   Heav'n and earth,
3. Yet our pride   made us fall!   So Christ came
4. Now has Christ   tru - ly ris'n,   And his Spir -

with a song!   To the Lord   we be - long,
light and shade,   Na - ture's won - ders dis - played,
for us all,   Not the right - eous to call,
it is giv'n   To all those   un - der heav'n

Chil - dren of the Fa - ther, God the great life - giv - er!
We to rule cre - a - tion From its first foun - da - tion.
By his cross and pas - sion Bring - ing us sal - va - tion!
Who will walk be - side him, Though they once de - nied him!

Shout for joy,   joy, joy!   Shout for joy,   joy, joy!

God is love,   God is light,   God is ev - er - last - ing!

Text: David Mowbray, b.1938, alt., © 1982, The Jubilate Group (admin. by Hope Publishing Company)
Tune: PERSONENT HODIE, 666 66 with refrain; *Piae Cantiones*, 1582; harm. by Richard Proulx, 1937–2010, © 1978, GIA Publications, Inc.

722 Christians, Lift Up Your Hearts

Refrain

Chris - tians, lift up your hearts, and make this a

day of re - joic - ing; God is our strength and

song; glo - ry and praise to his name!

Verses 1, 3, 5

1. This is the house of the Lord, where
3. Praise that his love o - ver - flowed in the
5. Come, Ho - ly Spir - it, to us, who

seek - ers and find - ers are wel - come; En - ter its
hearts of all who re - ceived him, Join - ing to -
live by your pres - ence with - in us, Come to di -

D.C.

gates with your praise, fill all its courts with your song:
geth - er in peace those once di - vid - ed by sin:
rect our course, give us your life and your pow'r:

Verses 2, 4, 6

2. Strong and a - lert in his grace, God's peo - ple are
4. Those who are bur - dened with sin find here the
6. Al - might - y God, send us out to live to your

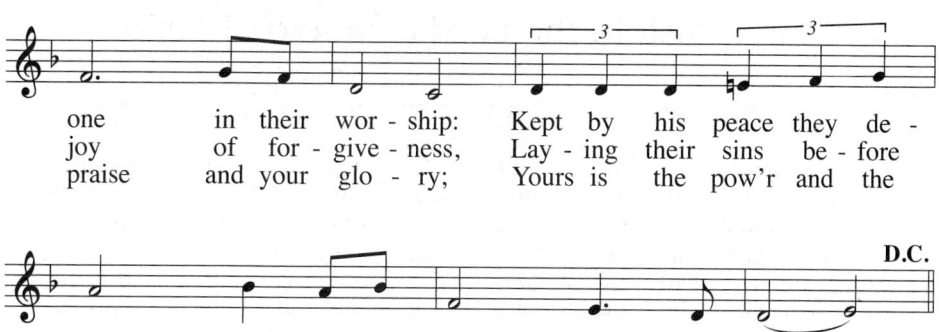

one   in their wor - ship: Kept by his peace they de -
joy   of for - give - ness,   Lay - ing their sins be - fore
praise   and your glo - ry;   Yours is the pow'r and the

part,   read - y for serv - ing their Lord:
Christ,   par - don and peace their re - ward:
might,   ours be the cour - age and faith:

Text: John E. Bowers, b.1923, alt., © Canon John E. Bowers
Tune: SALVE FESTA DIES, Irregular with refrain; Ralph Vaughan Williams, 1872–1958

Jesus Christ, Yesterday, Today, and Forever / 723
Jesucristo Ayer

Ostinato Refrain

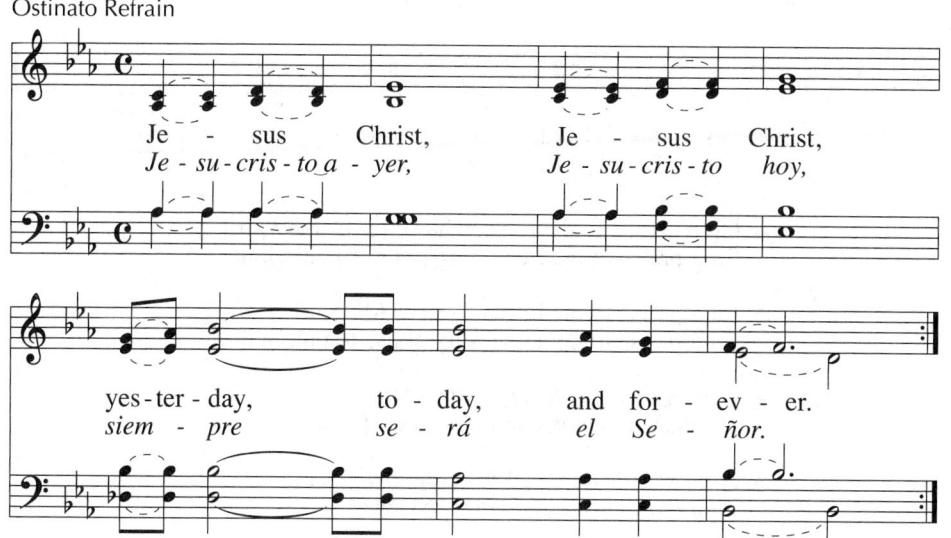

Je - sus Christ, Je - sus Christ,
Je - su - cris - to_a - yer, Je - su - cris - to hoy,

yes - ter - day, to - day, and for - ev - er.
siem - pre se - rá el Se - ñor.

Text: Suzanne Toolan, RSM, b.1927; Spanish tr. by Ronald F. Krisman, b.1946
Tune: Suzanne Toolan, RSM, b.1927
© 1988, tr. © 2004, GIA Publications, Inc.

724   Sing Praise to the Lord / Cantad al Señor

1. Sing praise to the Lord, O sing out a new song.
2. Cre - a - tor of all, God rules with com - pas - sion.
3. Ac - claim Je - sus Christ as wor - thy of hon - or.

1. Can - tad al Se - ñor un cán - ti - co nue - vo.
2. Él es Cre - a - dor y due - ño de to - do.
3. Can - tad a Je - sús, por - que él es dig - no.

Sing praise to the Lord, O sing out a new song.
Cre - a - tor of all, God rules with com - pas - sion.
Ac - claim Je - sus Christ as wor - thy of hon - or.
Can - tad al Se - ñor un cán - ti - co nue - vo.
Él es Cre - a - dor y due - ño de to - do.
Can - tad a Je - sús, por - que él es dig - no.

Sing praise to the Lord, O sing out a new song.
Cre - a - tor of all, God rules with com - pas - sion.
Ac - claim Je - sus Christ as wor - thy of hon - or.
Can - tad al Se - ñor un cán - ti - co nue - vo.
Él es Cre - a - dor y due - ño de to - do.
Can - tad a Je - sús, por - que él es dig - no.

Sing praise to the Lord, sing praise to our God.
¡Can - tad al Se - ñor, can - tad al Se - ñor!

4. Give thanks to the Lord, who sends us the Spirit. . .
   Sing praise to the Lord, sing praise to our God.

5. Sing praise to the Lord, "Amen, Alleluia!". . .
   Sing praise to the Lord, sing praise to our God.

4. Es él quien nos da su Espíritu Santo. . .
   ¡Cantad al Señor, cantad al Señor!

5. Cantad al Señor: "¡Amén, aleluya!". . .
   ¡Cantad al Señor, cantad al Señor!

Text: Traditional Brazilian; Spanish tr. anonymous; English tr. by Ronald F. Krisman, b.1946, © 2005, GIA Publications, Inc.
Tune: CANTAI AO SENHOR, 11 11 11 10; traditional Brazilian; harm. by Ronald F. Krisman, b.1946, © 2005, GIA Publications, Inc.

O God beyond All Praising 725

1. O God be-yond all prais-ing, we wor-ship you to-day
*2. The flow'r of earth-ly splen-dor in time must sure-ly die,
3. Then hear, O gra-cious Sav-ior, ac-cept the love we bring,

And sing the love a-maz-ing that songs can-not re-pay;
Its frag-ile bloom sur-ren-der to you, the Lord most high;
That we who know your fa-vor may serve you as our King;

For we can on-ly won-der at ev-'ry gift you send,
But hid-den from all na-ture the e-ter-nal seed is sown,
And wheth-er our to-mor-rows be filled with good or ill,

At bless-ings with-out num-ber and mer-cies with-out end.
Though small in mor-tal stat-ure to heav-en's gar-den grown.
We'll tri-umph through our sor-rows and rise to bless you still,

We lift our hearts be-fore you and wait up-on your word;
For Christ, the man from heav-en, from death has set us free,
To mar-vel at your beau-ty and glo-ry in your ways,

We hon-or and a-dore you, our great and might-y Lord.
And we through him are giv-en the fin-al vic-to-ry!
And make a joy-ful du-ty our sac-ri-fice of praise.

May be omitted.

Text: Michael Perry, 1942–1996, © 1982, The Jubilate Group (admin. by Hope Publishing Company)
Tune: THAXTED, 13 13 13 13 13 13; Gustav Holst, 1874–1934

726 Lift Every Voice and Sing

1. Lift ev - 'ry voice and sing, Till earth and heav - en
2. Ston - y the road we trod, Bit - ter the chas - t'ning
3. God of our wea - ry years, God of our si - lent

ring, Ring with the har - mo - nies of lib - er -
rod, Felt in the days when hope un - born had
tears, Thou who hast brought us thus far on the

ty; Let our re - joic - ing rise High as the lis - t'ning
died; Yet with a stead - y beat, Have not our wea - ry
way; Thou who hast by thy might Led us in - to the

skies, Let it re-sound loud as the roll - ing sea.
feet Come to the place for which our peo - ple sighed?
light, Keep us for - ev - er in the path, we pray.

Sing a song full of the faith that the dark past has
We have come o - ver a way that with tears has been
Lest our feet stray from the plac - es, our God, where we

taught us; Sing a song full of the
wa - tered; We have come, tread - ing our
met thee; Lest our hearts, drunk with the

hope that the pres - ent has brought us; Fac - ing the
path through the blood of the slaugh - tered; Out from the
wine of the world, we for - get thee; Shad - owed be -

ris - ing sun Of our new day be - gun,
gloom - y past, Till now we stand at last
neath thy hand, May we for - ev - er stand,

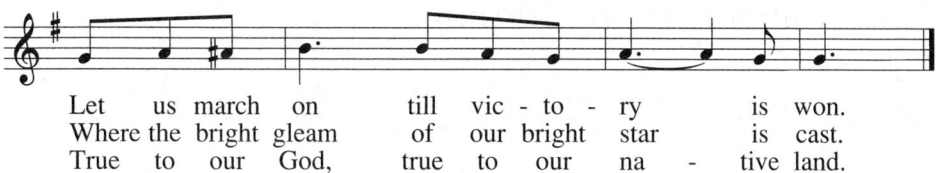

Let us march on till vic - to - ry is won.
Where the bright gleam of our bright star is cast.
True to our God, true to our na - tive land.

Text: James W. Johnson, 1871–1938
Tune: ANTHEM, 66 10 66 10 14 14 66 10; J. Rosamund Johnson, 1873–1954

Praise, I Will Praise You, Lord   727

1. Praise, I will praise you, Lord, with all my
2. Love, I will love you, Lord, with all my
3. Serve, I will serve you, Lord, with all my
French: Je loue - rai l'E - ter - nel de tout mon

heart. O God, I will tell the won-ders of your ways, And
heart. O God, I will tell the won-ders of your ways, And
heart. O God, I will tell the won-ders of your ways, And
coeur, Je ra - con - te - rai tou - tes tes mer - veilles, Je

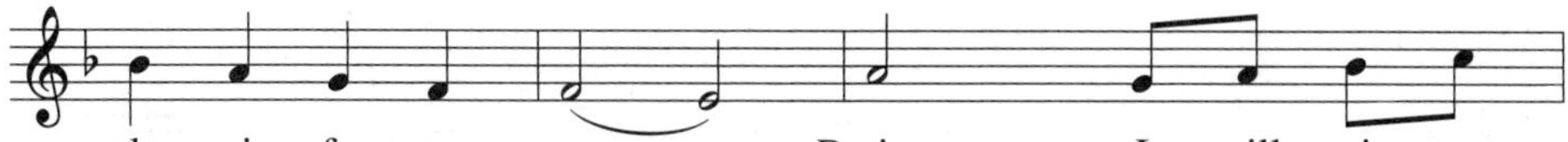

glo - ri - fy your name. Praise, I will praise you,
glo - ri - fy your name. Love, I will love you,
glo - ri - fy your name. Serve, I will serve you,
chan - te - rai ton nom. Je loue - rai l'E - ter -

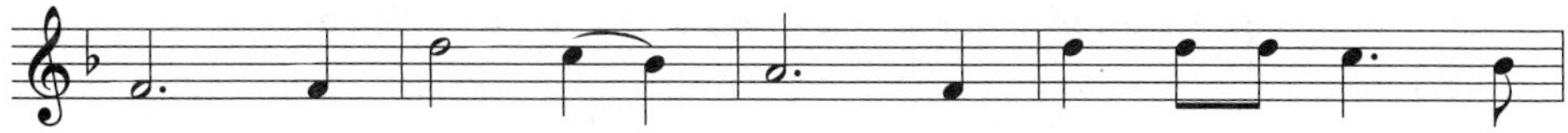

Lord, with all my heart. In you I will find the
Lord, with all my heart. In you I will find the
Lord, with all my heart. In you I will find the
nel de tout mon coeur, Je fe - rai de toi le

source of all my joy. Al - le - lu - ia!
source of all my joy. Al - le - lu - ia!
source of all my joy. Al - le - lu - ia!
su - jet de ma joie. Al - le - lu - ia!

Text: Claude Fraysse, 1941–2002, © 1975, Claude Fraysse; tr. by Kenneth I. Morse, © 1989, The Hymnal Project, admin. by Brethren Press
Tune: JE LOUERAI L'ÉTERNEL, 10 11 6 10 11 4; Claude Fraysse, 1941–2002; harm. by Alain Bergèse, © 1975, Claude Fraysse

728 Canticle of the Turning

Verses

1. My soul cries out with a joy - ful shout that the
2. Though I am small, my God, my all, you
3. From the halls of power to the for - tress tower, not a
4. Though the na - tions rage from age to age, we re -

God of my heart is great, And my spir - it sings of the
work great things in me, And your mer - cy will last from the
stone will be left on stone. Let the king be - ware for your
mem - ber who holds us fast: God's mer - cy must de -

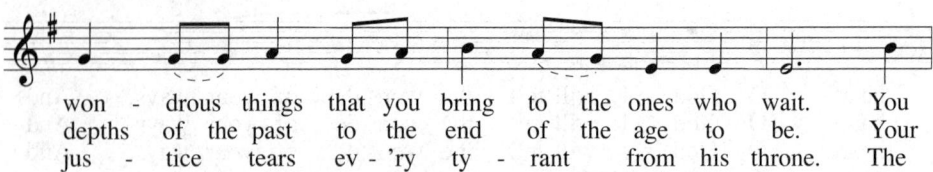

won - drous things that you bring to the ones who wait. You
depths of the past to the end of the age to be. Your
jus - tice tears ev - 'ry ty - rant from his throne. The
liv - er us from the con - quer - or's crush - ing grasp. This

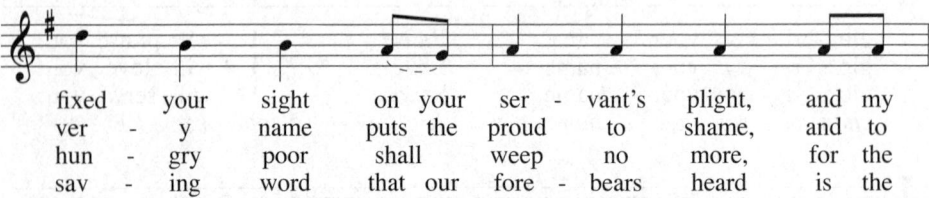

fixed your sight on your ser - vant's plight, and my
ver - y name puts the proud to shame, and to
hun - gry poor shall weep no more, for the
sav - ing word that our fore - bears heard is the

weak - ness you did not spurn, So from east to west shall my
those who would for you yearn, You will show your might, put the
food they can nev - er earn; There are ta - bles spread, ev - 'ry
prom - ise which holds us bound, 'Til the spear and rod can be

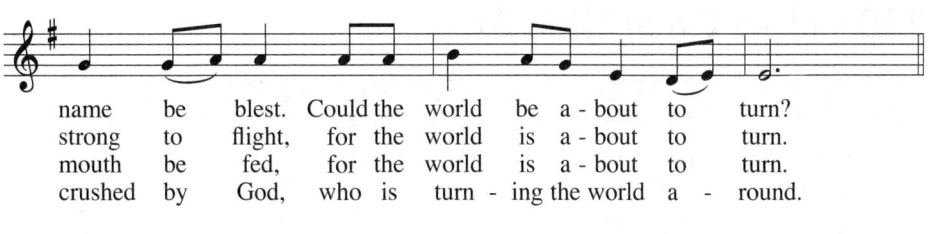

name   be   blest. Could the world be a - bout to   turn?
strong to   flight,   for the   world is a - bout to   turn.
mouth   be   fed,   for the   world is a - bout to   turn.
crushed by   God,   who is   turn - ing the world a -   round.

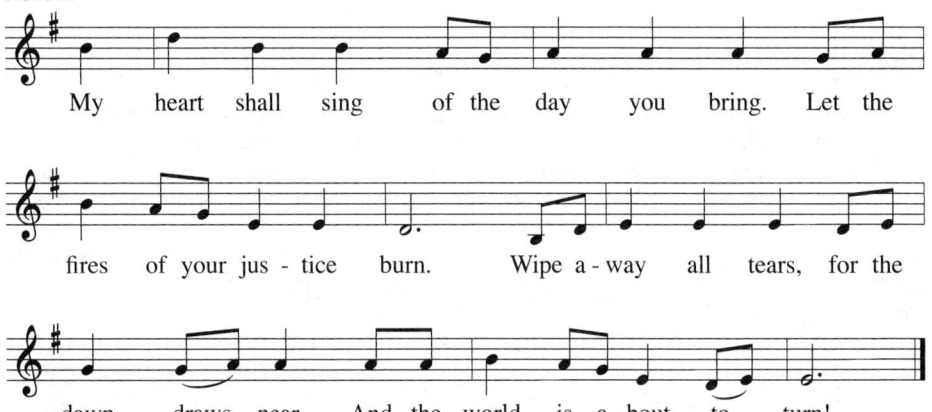

Refrain

My   heart shall sing   of the   day   you   bring. Let the

fires of your jus - tice burn.   Wipe a - way all   tears, for the

dawn draws near, And the world is a - bout to   turn!

Text: Luke 1:46–58; Rory Cooney, b.1952
Tune: STAR OF THE COUNTY DOWN, Irregular with refrain; Irish melody; arr. by Rory Cooney, b.1952
© 1990, GIA Publications, Inc.

Jubilate Deo 729

Canon

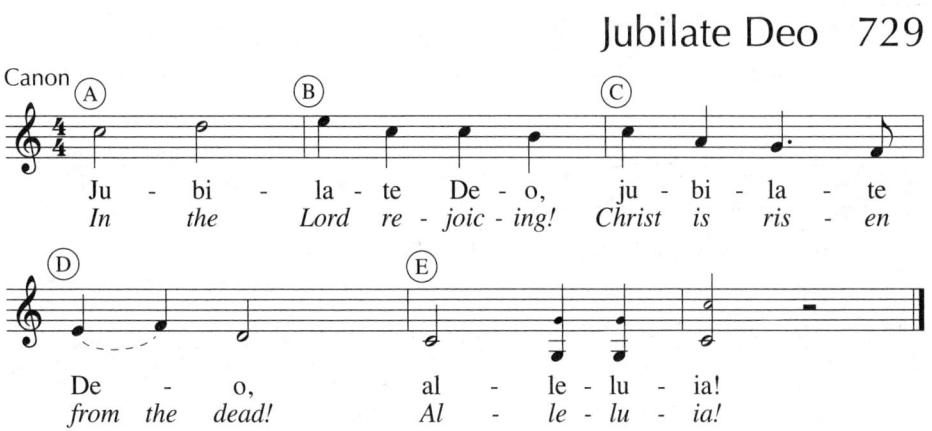

Ju - bi - la - te De - o,   ju - bi - la - te   te
In   the   Lord re - joic - ing! Christ is   ris - en

De -   o,   al - le - lu - ia!
from the   dead!   Al - le - lu - ia!

Text: Psalm 100:1; tr. Taizé Community, 1990, © 1978, 1990, Les Presses de Taizé, GIA Publications, Inc., agent
Tune: Michael Praetorius, 1571–1621; acc. by Jacques Berthier, 1923–1994, © 1978, 1990, Les Presses de Taizé, GIA Publications, Inc., agent

730 How Great Thou Art

1. O Lord my God, when I in awe-some
2. When through the woods and for - est glades I
3. And when I think that God, his Son not
4. When Christ shall come with shout of ac - cla -

won - der Con - sid - er all the works thy hands have
wan - der And hear the birds sing sweet - ly in the
spar - ing, Sent him to die, I scarce can take it
ma - tion And take me home, what joy shall fill my

made, I see the stars, I hear the roll - ing
trees, When I look down from loft - y moun-tain
in That on the cross, my bur - den glad - ly
heart! Then I shall bow in hum - ble ad - o -

thun - der, Thy pow'r through-out the u - ni-verse dis - played!
gran - deur And hear the brook and feel the gen - tle breeze,
bear - ing, He bled and died to take a - way my sin!
ra - tion And there pro - claim, "My God, how great thou art!"

Then sings my soul, my Sav-ior God, to thee: How great thou

art, how great thou art! Then sings my soul, my Sav-ior God, to

thee: How great thou art, how great thou art!

Text: Stuart K. Hine, 1899–1989
Tune: HOW GREAT THOU ART, 11 10 11 10 with refrain; Swedish folk melody; adapt. and arr. by Stuart K. Hine, 1899–1989
© 1949, 1953, The Stuart Hine Trust. Print rights administered by Hope Publishing Company in North, Central and South America.

Heaven Is Singing for Joy / 731
El Cielo Canta Alegría

Verses / Estrofas

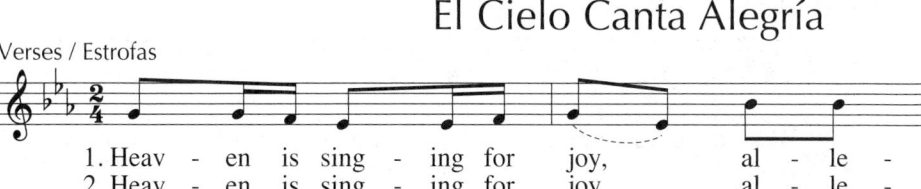

1. Heav - en is sing - ing for joy, al - le -
2. Heav - en is sing - ing for joy, al - le -
3. Heav - en is sing - ing for joy, al - le -

1. El cie - lo can - ta_a - le - grí - a, ¡a - le -
2. El cie - lo can - ta_a - le - grí - a, ¡a - le -
3. El cie - lo can - ta_a - le - grí - a, ¡a - le -

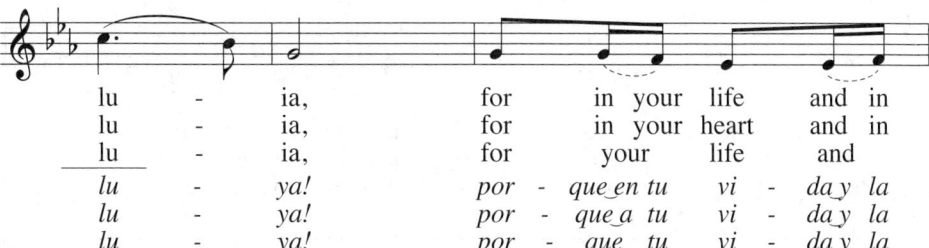

lu - ia, for in your life and in
lu - ia, for in your heart and in
lu - ia, for your life and

lu - ya! por - que_en tu vi - da_y la
lu - ya! por - que_a tu vi - da_y la
lu - ya! por - que tu vi - da_y la

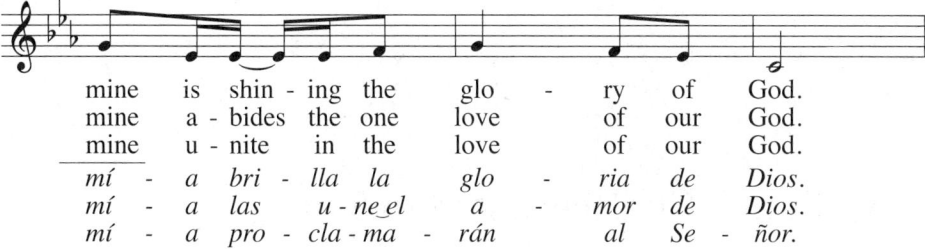

mine is shin - ing the glo - ry of God.
mine a - bides the one love of our God.
mine u - nite in the love of our God.

mí - a bri - lla la glo - ria de Dios.
mí - a las u - ne_el a - mor de Dios.
mí - a pro - cla - ma - rán al Se - ñor.

Refrain / Estribillo

Al - le - lu - ia, al - le - lu - ia!
¡A - le - lu - ya, a - le - lu - ya!

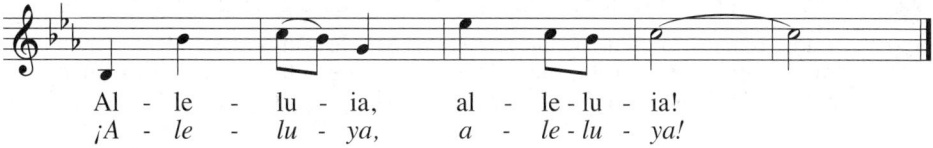

Al - le - lu - ia, al - le - lu - ia!
¡A - le - lu - ya, a - le - lu - ya!

Text: Pablo Sosa, b.1933
Tune: ALEGRÍA, Irregular with alleluias; Pablo Sosa, b.1933
© 1958, GIA Publications, Inc.

732 Bless the Lord

Ostinato Refrain

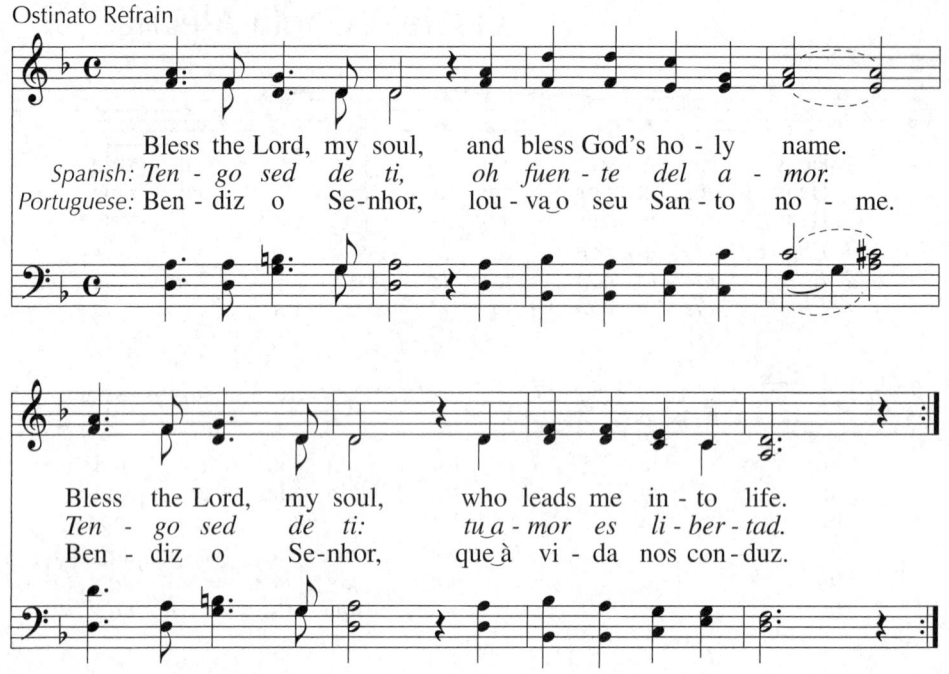

Bless the Lord, my soul, and bless God's ho - ly name.
Spanish: Ten - go sed de ti, oh fuen - te del a - mor.
Portuguese: Ben - diz o Se-nhor, lou - va_o seu San - to no - me.

Bless the Lord, my soul, who leads me in - to life.
Ten - go sed de ti: tu_a - mor es li - ber - tad.
Ben - diz o Se-nhor, que_à vi - da nos con - duz.

Text: Psalm 103
Tune: Jacques Berthier, 1923–1994
© 1998, Les Presses de Taizé, GIA Publications, Inc., agent

733 Come, Christians, Join to Sing

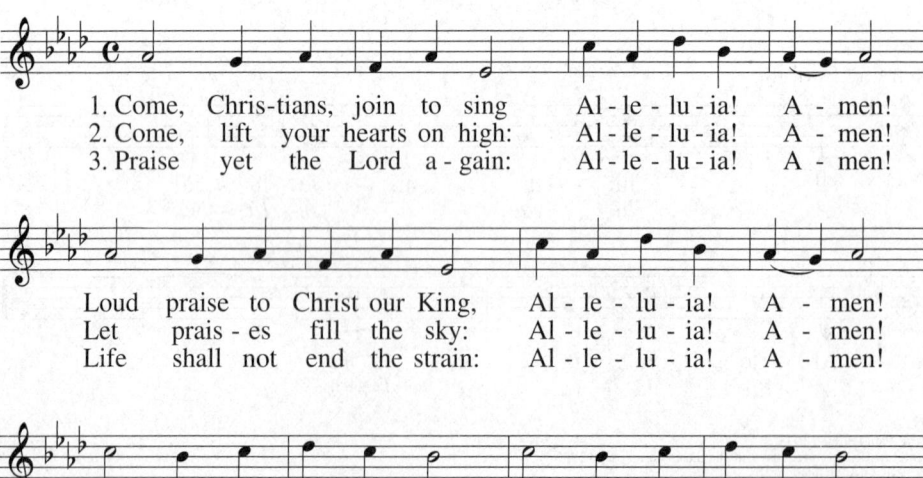

1. Come, Chris-tians, join to sing   Al - le - lu - ia!   A - men!
2. Come, lift your hearts on high: Al - le - lu - ia!   A - men!
3. Praise yet the Lord a - gain: Al - le - lu - ia!   A - men!

Loud praise to Christ our King,   Al - le - lu - ia!   A - men!
Let prais - es fill the sky: Al - le - lu - ia!   A - men!
Life shall not end the strain: Al - le - lu - ia!   A - men!

Let all, with heart and voice,   Be - fore his throne re-joice;
He is our guide and friend;   Our needs he will at-tend;
On heav-en's bliss - ful shore   His good-ness we'll a - dore,

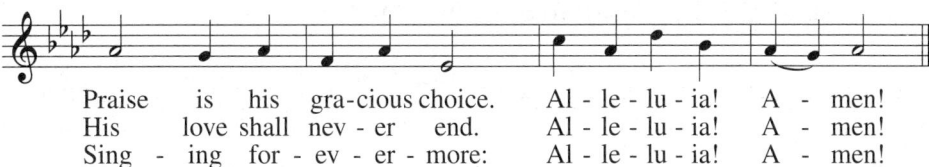

Praise   is   his   gra-cious choice.   Al - le - lu - ia!   A - men!
His   love shall nev - er   end.   Al - le - lu - ia!   A - men!
Sing - ing   for - ev - er - more: Al - le - lu - ia!   A - men!

Text: Christian H. Bateman, 1813–1889
Tune: MADRID, 6 6 6 6 66 6 6; Spanish melody; arr. by Benjamin Carr, 1768–1831; harm. by David Evans, 1874–1948

For the Beauty of the Earth   734

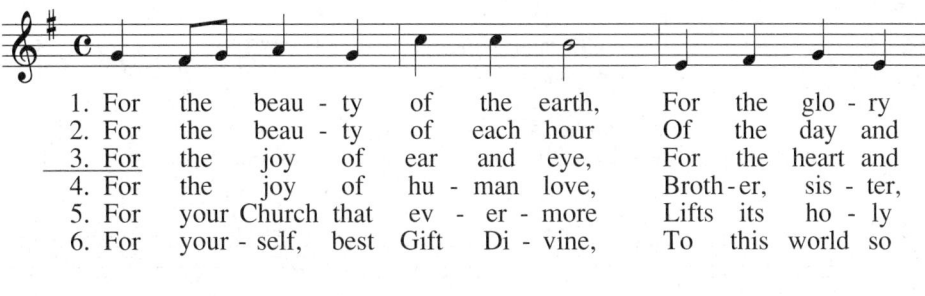

1. For   the   beau - ty   of   the   earth,   For   the   glo - ry
2. For   the   beau - ty   of   each   hour   Of   the   day and
3. For   the   joy   of   ear   and   eye,   For   the   heart and
4. For   the   joy   of   hu - man   love,   Broth-er,   sis - ter,
5. For   your Church that   ev - er - more   Lifts   its   ho - ly
6. For   your - self,   best   Gift   Di - vine,   To   this   world so

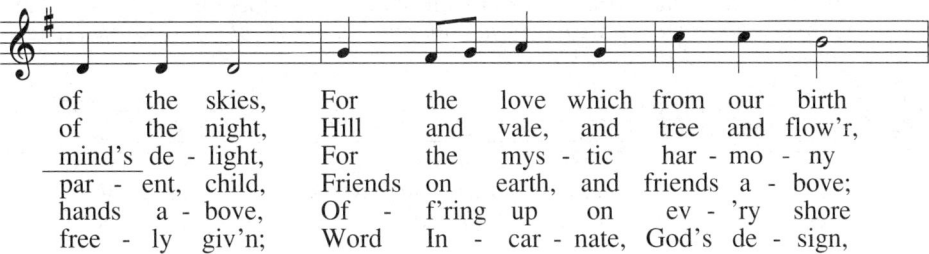

of   the   skies,   For   the   love which from our   birth
of   the   night,   Hill   and   vale,   and   tree   and flow'r,
mind's de - light,   For   the   mys - tic   har - mo - ny
par - ent,   child,   Friends   on   earth,   and   friends a - bove;
hands   a - bove,   Of - f'ring   up   on   ev - 'ry   shore
free - ly   giv'n;   Word   In - car - nate,   God's de - sign,

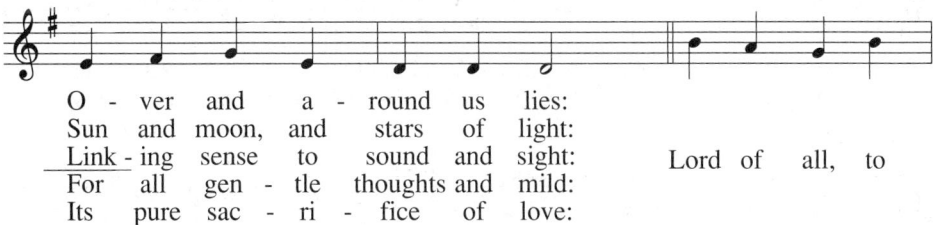

O - ver   and   a - round   us   lies:
Sun   and   moon,   and   stars   of   light:
Link - ing   sense   to   sound and   sight: Lord of   all,   to
For   all   gen - tle   thoughts and   mild:
Its   pure   sac - ri - fice   of   love:
Peace on   earth   and   joy   in   heav'n:

you   we raise   This   our   hymn   of   grate - ful praise.

Text: Folliott S. Pierpoint, 1835–1917, alt.
Tune: DIX, 7 7 7 7 with refrain; arr. from Conrad Kocher, 1786–1872, by William H. Monk, 1823–1889

735 Laudate, Laudate Dominum

Refrain

Lau - dá - te, lau - dá - te Dó - mi - num, o - mnes
We praise you, we praise your ho - ly name, God of

gen - tes, lau - dá - te Dó - mi - num. Ex - sul - tá - te, ju - bi -
jus - tice, e - ter-nal - ly the same. May our liv - ing be thanks-

lá - te per an - nos Dó - mi - ni, o - mnes gen - tes. Lau -
giv - ing, re - joic-ing in your name now and al - ways. We

dá - te, lau - dá - te Dó - mi - num, o - mnes gen - tes, lau -
praise you, we praise your ho - ly name, God of jus - tice, e -

dá - te Dó - mi - num. Ex - sul - tá - te, ju - bi -
ter - nal - ly the same. May our liv - ing be thanks-

Last time

lá - te per an - nos Dó - mi - ni, o - mnes gen - tes.
giv - ing, re - joic-ing in your name now and al - ways.

Verses 1–3

1. In the faith of Christ we walk hand in hand,
2. In the name of Christ we will spread the seed;
3. In the pow'r of Christ we pro - claim one Lord.

1. *Ca - mi - na - mos jun - tos en la fe de Cris - to.*
2. *Con los po - bres com-par - ti - mos luz de Cris - to,*
3. *Los bau - ti - za - dos en un so - lo Se - ñor,*

light   be - fore   our   path   as   the   Lord   has   planned;
share   the   Word   of   God   with   all   those   in   need,
All   who   put   on   Christ   are   by   faith   re - stored;
Luz   en   nues - tra   sen - da   es   el   don   de   Dios,   an -
y   sem - bra - mos   la   pa - la - bra   del   Se - ñor,
res - tau - ra - dos   to - dos   por   la   fe   en   Cris - to,

shin - ing   the   torch   of   faith   in   our   land:
faith - ful   in   thought   and   word   and   deed:
shar - ing   new   life,   sal - va - tion's   re - ward:
tor - cha   de   fe   que i - lu - mi - na al   mun - do,
fie - les   en   o - bra   y   nues - tro   pen - sar,
al - can - za - mos   la   nue - va   vi - da,

D.C.

in   the   name   of   Christ   Je - sus.
en   el   nom - bre   de   Cris - to.

Verses 4–6

4. In the life of Christ, through the blood
    he shed,
  we are justified, and by him are fed,
  nourished by word and living bread:
  in the name of Christ Jesus.

5. In the Church of God we are unified,
  by the Spirit's pow'r we are sanctified,
  temples of grace, where God may abide:
  by the pow'r of the Spirit.

6. Praise to God the Father while ages run.
  Praise to Christ the Savior, God's only Son,
  praise to the Holy Spirit be sung:
  omnes gentes, laudáte.

4. *Oigan al Señor y síganle,*
  vengan a alabar y comer de Él,
  alimentados con pan de vida,
  en el nombre de Cristo.

5. *En la Iglesia estamos unidos,*
  santificados por el Espíritu,
  morada de la gracia de Dios,
  por el poder del Espíritu.

6. *Siempre bendito sea el Padre,*
  siempre bendito sea el Hijo de Dios,
  siempre bendito el Espíritu Santo,
  omnes gentes, laudáte.

Text: Christopher Walker, b.1947
Tune: Christopher Walker, b.1947
© 1997, Christopher Walker. Published by OCP.

736 Soli Deo Gloria

1. O God of bless-ings, all praise to you!
2. All praise for proph-ets, through grace in-spired
3. All praise for mu-sic, deep gift pro-found,
4. All praise for Je-sus, best gift di-vine

Your love sur-rounds us our whole life through.
To preach and wit-ness with hearts on fire.
Through hands and voic-es in ho-ly sound:
Through word and wit-ness, in bread and wine;

You are the free-dom of those op-pressed;
Your Spir-it choos-es the weak and small
The psalms of Da-vid, and Mar-y's praise,
In-car-nate Love Song of bound-less grace,

You are the com-fort of all dis-tressed:
To sing the new reign where might-y fall;
In word-less splen-dor and lyr-ic phrase.
Priest, teach-er, proph-et in time and space,

Come now, O ho-ly and wel-come Guest:
With them may we live your Gos-pel call:
With all cre-a-tion one song we raise:
Your stead-fast kind-ness with hu-man face:

*So-li De-o gló-ri-a, So-li De-o gló-ri-a!

*Glory be to God alone.

Text: Marty Haugen, b.1950
Tune: SOLI DEO GLORIA, 99 999 77; Marty Haugen, b.1950
© 1999, GIA Publications, Inc.

Praise the One Who Breaks the Darkness   737

1. Praise the One who breaks the dark - ness With a
   lib - er - at - ing light. Praise the One who frees the
   pris - 'ners, Turn - ing blind - ness in - to sight.
   Praise the One who preached the gos - pel, Heal - ing
   ev - 'ry dread dis - ease, Calm - ing storms and feed - ing
   thou - sands With the ver - y bread of peace.

2. Praise the One who blessed the chil - dren With a
   strong yet gen - tle word. Praise the One who drove out
   de - mons With a pierc - ing, two - edged sword.
   Praise the One who brings cool wa - ter To the
   des - ert's burn - ing sand. From this well comes liv - ing
   wa - ter Quench-ing thirst in ev - 'ry land.

3. Praise the one true love in - car - nate: Christ, who
   suf - fered in our place. Je - sus died and rose for
   man - y That we may know God by grace.
   Let us sing for joy and glad - ness, See - ing
   what our God has done. Praise the one re - deem - ing
   glo - ry; Praise the One who makes us one.

Text: Rusty Edwards, b.1955, © 1987, Hope Publishing Company
Tune: NETTLETON, 8 7 8 7 D, from Wyeth's *Repository of Sacred Music, Pt. II*, 1813

738 Halleluya! We Sing Your Praises / Haleluya! Pelo Tsa Rona

Refrain

Hal - le - lu - ya! We sing your prais-es, all our
Ha - le - lu - ya! Pe - lo tsa ro - na, di tha -

hearts are filled with glad - ness. Hal - le - lu - ya! We sing your
bi - le ka - o - fe - la. Ha - le - lu - ya! Pe - lo tsa

prais-es, all our hearts are filled with glad - ness.
ro - na, di tha - bi - le ka - o - fe - la.

Verses

1. Christ the Lord to us said: I am
2. Now he sends us all out, strong in

wine, I am bread, I am wine, I am
faith, free of doubt, strong in faith, free of

bread, give to all who thirst and hun - ger.
doubt, to pro - claim the joy - ful Gos - pel.

Sotho phonetics:

Hah-lay-loo-yah! Pay-loh tsah roh-nah, dee tah-bil-lay kah-oh-fay-lah.

Text: South African
Tune: South African
© 1984, Peace of Music Publishing AB, admin. by Walton Music Corp., a division of GIA Publications, Inc.

Laudate Omnes Gentes   739

Ostinato Refrain

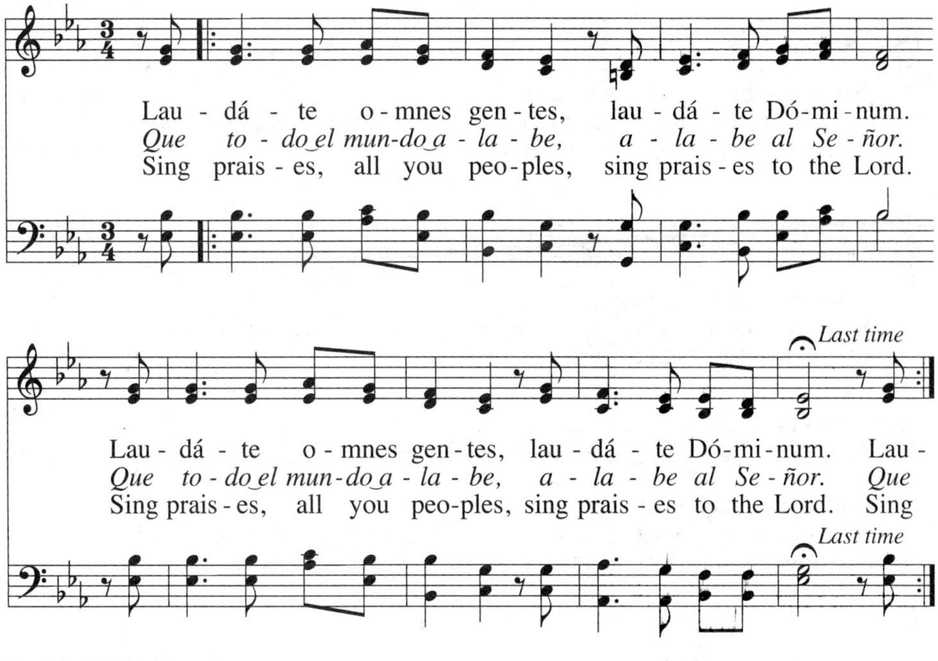

Lau - dá - te o - mnes gen - tes, lau - dá - te Dó - mi - num.
Que to - do el mun-do a - la - be, a - la - be al Se - ñor.
Sing prais - es, all you peo - ples, sing prais - es to the Lord.

Last time

Lau - dá - te o - mnes gen - tes, lau - dá - te Dó - mi - num. Lau -
Que to - do el mun-do a - la - be, a - la - be al Se - ñor. Que
Sing prais - es, all you peo - ples, sing prais - es to the Lord. Sing

Last time

Text: Psalm 117:1; Taizé Community
Tune: Jacques Berthier, 1923–1994
© 1979, Les Presses de Taizé, GIA Publications, Inc., agent

740   Te Deum

Refrain*

You are God: we praise you. You are Lord: we ac - claim you. To
you, Cre-a-tor ho - ly, all cre - a-tion of-fers praise. praise.

1.
2. To verses

Last time

praise, all cre - a-tion of-fers praise, all cre - a-tion of-fers praise.

Verses

Cantor: All: Cantor:
1. With the an - gels in heav - en: With the
2. Cre - a - tor of all things: We praise you, we praise you! O
3. O Christ, King of glo - ry: You be-

All: Cantor:
cher - u - bim and ser - a-phim: With a-
Je - sus Christ, Re - deem - er: We praise you, we praise you! O
came like us to set us free: You have

All: Cantor:
pos - tles and proph-ets: With the
Spir - it, most Ho - ly: We praise you, we praise you! To the
ris - en to free us: You have

All: D.C.
mar - tyrs and your ho - ly Church:
Trin - i - ty most bless - ed. We sing in end-less praise!
hal - lowed our hu - man-i - ty:

*The refrain may be sung as a two- or three-part canon.

Text: Based on the *Te Deum*; Marty Haugen, b.1950
Tune: Marty Haugen, b.1950
© 1995, GIA Publications, Inc.

Sing of the Lord's Goodness 741

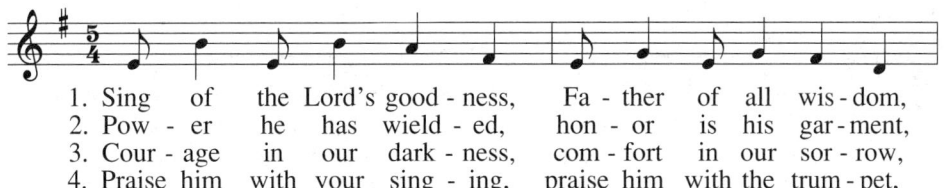

1. Sing of the Lord's good - ness, Fa - ther of all wis - dom,
2. Pow - er he has wield - ed, hon - or is his gar - ment,
3. Cour - age in our dark - ness, com - fort in our sor - row,
4. Praise him with your sing - ing, praise him with the trum - pet,

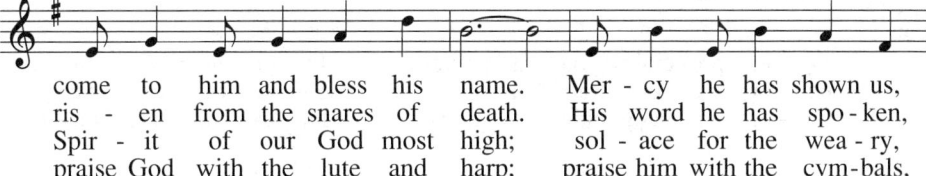

come to him and bless his name. Mer - cy he has shown us,
ris - en from the snares of death. His word he has spo - ken,
Spir - it of our God most high; sol - ace for the wea - ry,
praise God with the lute and harp; praise him with the cym - bals,

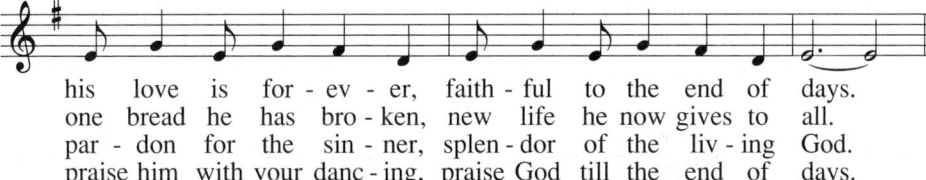

his love is for - ev - er, faith - ful to the end of days.
one bread he has bro - ken, new life he now gives to all.
par - don for the sin - ner, splen - dor of the liv - ing God.
praise him with your danc - ing, praise God till the end of days.

Come, then, all you na - tions, sing of your Lord's good - ness,

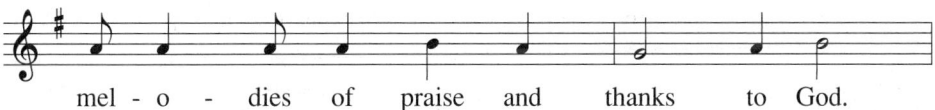

mel - o - dies of praise and thanks to God.

Ring out the Lord's glo - ry, praise him with your mu - sic,

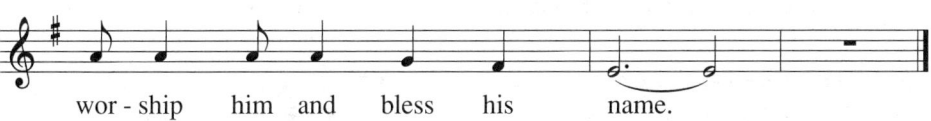

wor - ship him and bless his name.

Text: Ernest Sands, 1949–2016, © 1981, Ernest Sands
Tune: Ernest Sands, 1949–2016, © 1981, Ernest Sands; acc. by Paul Inwood, b.1947, © 1986, Paul Inwood
Published by OCP.

742 Ever We Praise You

Verses

Cantor:

1. Ev - er we praise you, O God of all mys - t'ry,
2. Ev - er we call you when our hearts are bro - ken,
3. Ev - er we see you in eyes of an - oth - er,

ev - er pro - claim you in prayer, Ev - er we praise you in
nev - er we cry out in vain. Ev - er we hear you in
nev - er in judg - ment or shame. Ev - er we share you in

time and in his - t'ry, our light in dark - ness each
words you have spo - ken, for you have called us by
bread that is bro - ken, ev - er sing praise to your

day.
name. You are there, you are there. And
name.

Refrain

all the earth shall sing of your jus - tice and truth. And

all the earth shall pray for your peo - ple re - newed. We will

praise you in won - der and awe: Al - le - lu - ia. We will

praise you in won - der and awe: Al - le - lu - ia.

Text: Liam Lawton, b.1959
Tune: Liam Lawton, b.1959; arr. by Chris de Silva, b.1967
© 2012, GIA Publications, Inc.

Now Thank We All Our God 743

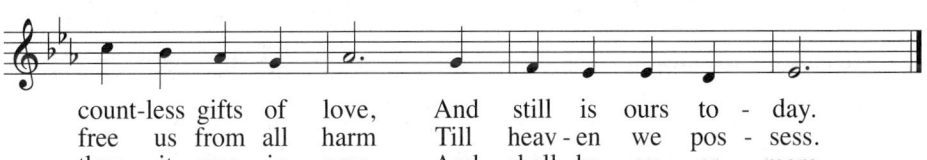

1. Now thank we all our God With hearts and hands and
2. O may this boun-teous God Through all our life be
3. All praise and thanks to God The Fa - ther now be

voic - es, Who won - drous things has done, In
near us, With ev - er joy - ful hearts And
giv - en, The Son, and him who reigns With

whom his world re - joic - es; Who from our moth-ers'
bless - ed peace to cheer us; Pre - serve us in his
them in high - est heav - en— The one e - ter - nal

arms Has blessed us on our way With
grace, And guide us in dis - tress, And
God, Whom earth and heav'n a - dore— For

count-less gifts of love, And still is ours to - day.
free us from all harm Till heav - en we pos - sess.
thus it was, is now, And shall be ev - er - more.

Text: *Nun danket alle Gott;* Martin Rinkhart, 1586–1649; tr. by Catherine Winkworth, 1827–1878, alt.
Tune: NUN DANKET, 6 7 6 7 6 6 6 6; Johann Crüger, 1598–1662; harm. by A. Gregory Murray, OSB, 1905–1992, © Downside Abbey

744 In the Lord I'll Be Ever Thankful

Ostinato Refrain

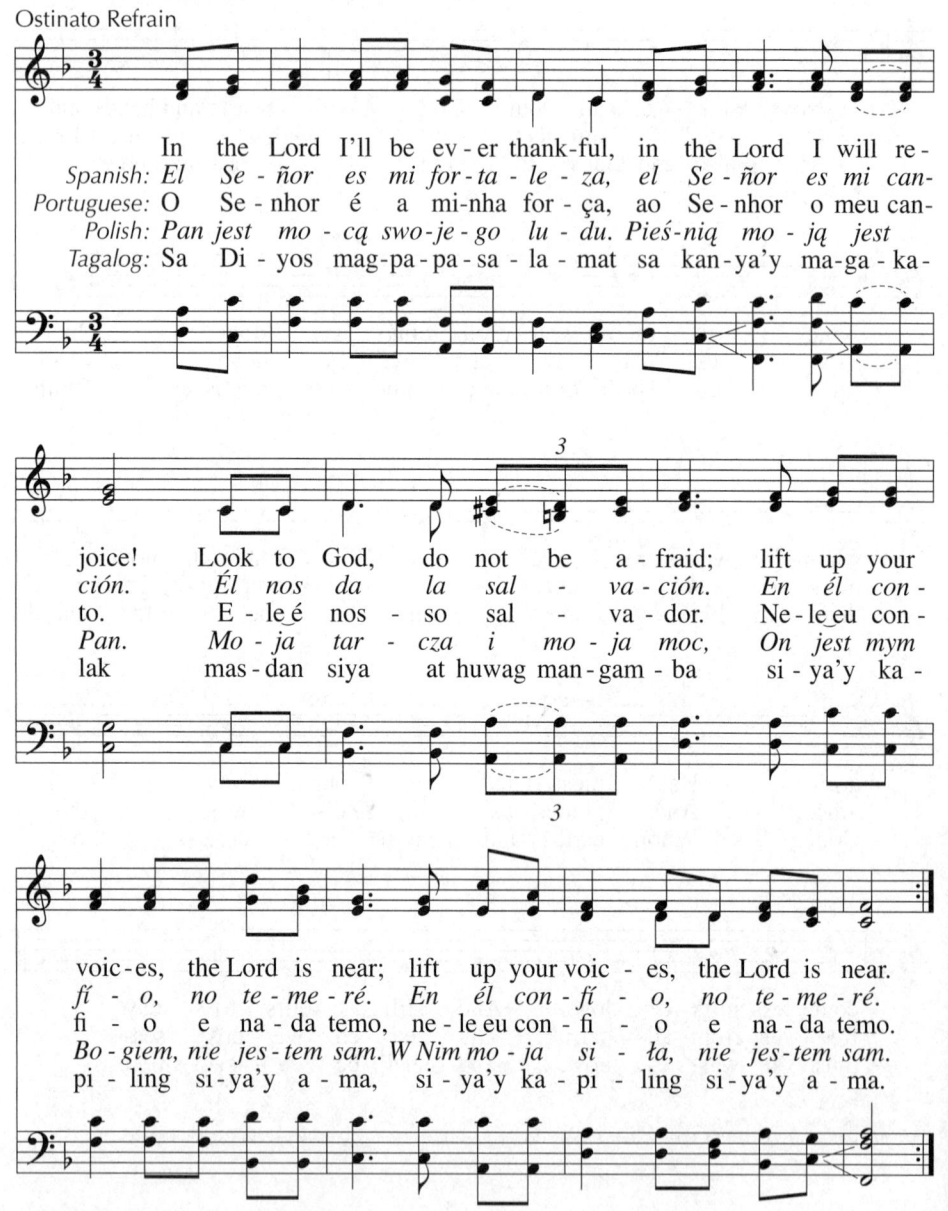

In the Lord I'll be ev-er thank-ful, in the Lord I will re-
Spanish: El Se-ñor es mi for-ta-le-za, el Se-ñor es mi can-
Portuguese: O Se-nhor é a mi-nha for-ça, ao Se-nhor o meu can-
Polish: Pan jest mo-cą swo-je-go lu-du. Pieś-nią mo-ją jest
Tagalog: Sa Di-yos mag-pa-pa-sa-la-mat sa kan-ya'y ma-ga-ka-

joice! Look to God, do not be a-fraid; lift up your
ción. Él nos da la sal - va-ción. En él con-
to. E-le é nos - so sal - va-dor. Ne-le eu con-
Pan. Mo-ja tar-cza i mo-ja moc, On jest mym
lak mas-dan siya at huwag man-gam-ba si-ya'y ka-

voic-es, the Lord is near; lift up your voic-es, the Lord is near.
fí - o, no te-me-ré. En él con-fí - o, no te-me-ré.
fi - o e na-da temo, ne-le eu con-fi - o e na-da temo.
Bo-giem, nie jes-tem sam. W Nim mo-ja si - ła, nie jes-tem sam.
pi-ling si-ya'y a-ma, si-ya'y ka-pi-ling si-ya'y a-ma.

Text: Taizé Community
Tune: Jacques Berthier, 1923–1994
© 1986, 1991, 2011, Les Presses de Taizé, GIA Publications, Inc., agent

Father, We Thank You, Who Have Planted   745

1. Fa - ther, we thank you, who have plant - ed
2. Watch o'er your Church, O Lord, in mer - cy,

Your ho - ly name with - in our hearts.
Save it from e - vil, guard it still;

Knowl - edge and faith and life im - mor - tal
Per - fect it in your love, u - nite it,

Je - sus your Son to us im - parts.
Cleansed and con - formed un - to your will.

Lord, you have made all for your pleas - ure,
As grain, once scat - tered on the hill - sides,

And giv'n us food for all our days,
Was in this bro - ken bread made one,

Giv - ing in Christ the bread e - ter - nal;
So from all lands your Church be gath - ered

Yours is the pow'r, yours be the praise.
In - to your king - dom by your Son.

Text: From the *Didache*, c.110; tr. by F. Bland Tucker, 1895–1984, alt., © 1940, The Church Pension Fund
Tune: RENDEZ À DIEU, 9 8 9 8 D; *Genevan Psalter,* 1551; attr. to Louis Bourgeois, c.1510–1561

746 We Gather Together

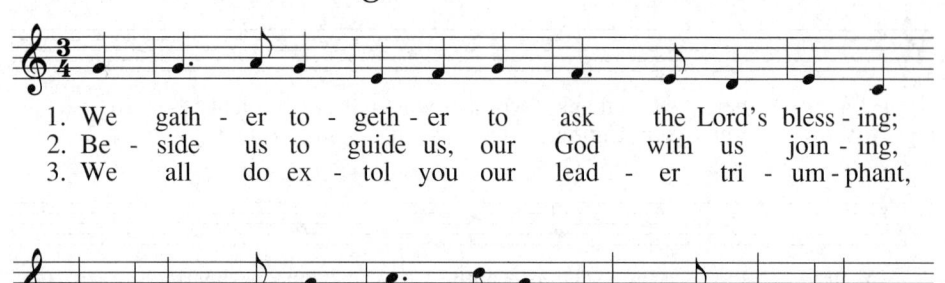

1. We gath - er to - geth - er to ask the Lord's bless - ing;
2. Be - side us to guide us, our God with us join - ing,
3. We all do ex - tol you our lead - er tri - um - phant,

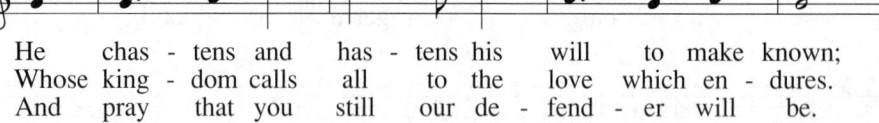

He chas - tens and has - tens his will to make known;
Whose king - dom calls all to the love which en - dures.
And pray that you still our de - fend - er will be.

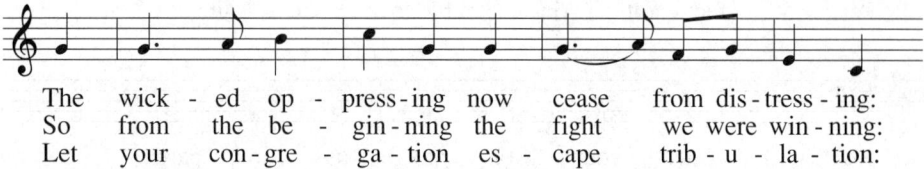

The wick - ed op - press - ing now cease from dis - tress - ing:
So from the be - gin - ning the fight we were win - ning:
Let your con - gre - ga - tion es - cape trib - u - la - tion:

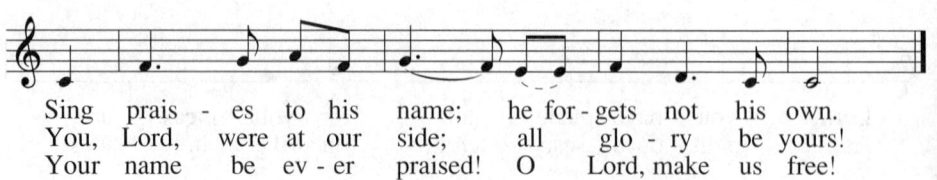

Sing prais - es to his name; he for - gets not his own.
You, Lord, were at our side; all glo - ry be yours!
Your name be ev - er praised! O Lord, make us free!

Text: *Wilt heden nu treden,* Netherlands folk hymn; tr. by Theodore Baker, 1851–1934, alt.
Tune: KREMSER, 12 11 12 11; *Nederlandtsch Gedenck-clanck,* 1626; harm. by Edward Kremser, 1838–1914

Let All Things Now Living 747

1. Let all things now liv-ing A song of thanks-giv-ing
2. The Law God en - forc-es, The stars in their cours-es,

To God the Cre - a - tor tri - um - phant - ly raise,
The sun in its or - bit o - be - dient - ly shine;

Who fash - ioned and made us, Pro - tect - ed and stayed us,
The hills and the moun-tains, The riv - ers and foun-tains,

By guid - ing us on to the end of our days.
The depths of the o - cean pro - claim God di - vine.

God's ban - ners are o'er us, Pure light goes be - fore us,
We too should be voic - ing Our love and re - joic-ing;

A pil - lar of fire shin - ing forth in the night,
With glad ad - o - ra - tion a song let us raise

Till shad - ows have van-ished And dark - ness is ban-ished,
Till all things now liv - ing U - nite in thanks-giv - ing:

As for - ward we trav - el from light in - to light.
"To God in the high - est, ho - san - na and praise!"

Text: Katherine K. Davis, 1892–1980, alt., © 1939, 1966, E. C. Schirmer Music Co.
Tune: ASH GROVE, 66 11 66 11 D; Welsh melody; harm. by Gerald H. Knight, 1908–1979, © The Royal School of Church Music

748 Confitemini Domino

Ostinato Refrain

Text: Psalm 136, *Give thanks to the Lord for he is good;* Taizé Community, 1982
Tune: Jacques Berthier, 1923–1994
© 1982, 1991, 2011, Les Presses de Taizé, GIA Publications, Inc., agent

749 Thank You, Lord

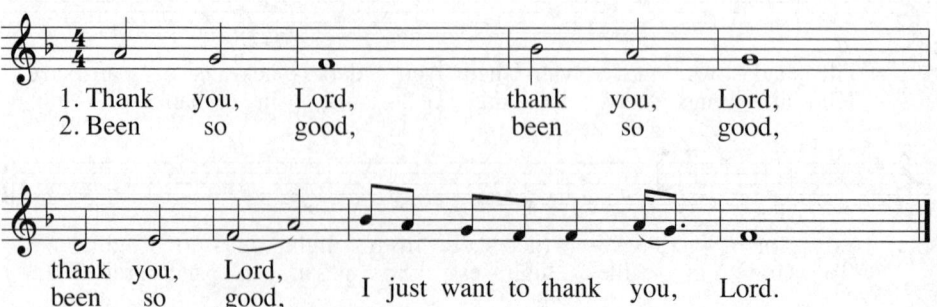

Text: Traditional
Tune: African American spiritual; arr. by Stephen Key, © 2000, GIA Publications, Inc.

For the Fruits of All Creation   750

1. For the fruits of all cre - a - tion, Thanks be to
2. In the just re - ward of la - bor, God's will is
3. For the har - vests of the Spir - it, Thanks be to

God. For the gifts to ev - 'ry na - tion,
done. In the help we give our neigh - bor,
God. For the good we all in - her - it,

Thanks be to God. For the plow - ing, sow - ing, reap - ing,
God's will is done. In our world-wide task of car - ing
Thanks be to God. For the won - ders that a - stound us,

Si - lent growth while we are sleep - ing, Fu - ture needs in
For the hun - gry and de - spair - ing, In the har - vests
For the truths that still con-found us, Most of all, that

earth's safe keep - ing, Thanks be to God.
we are shar - ing, God's will is done.
love has found us, Thanks be to God.

Text: Fred Pratt Green, 1903–2000, © 1970, Hope Publishing Company
Tune: AR HYD Y NOS, 8 4 8 4 888 4; Welsh melody

751 We Give You Thanks

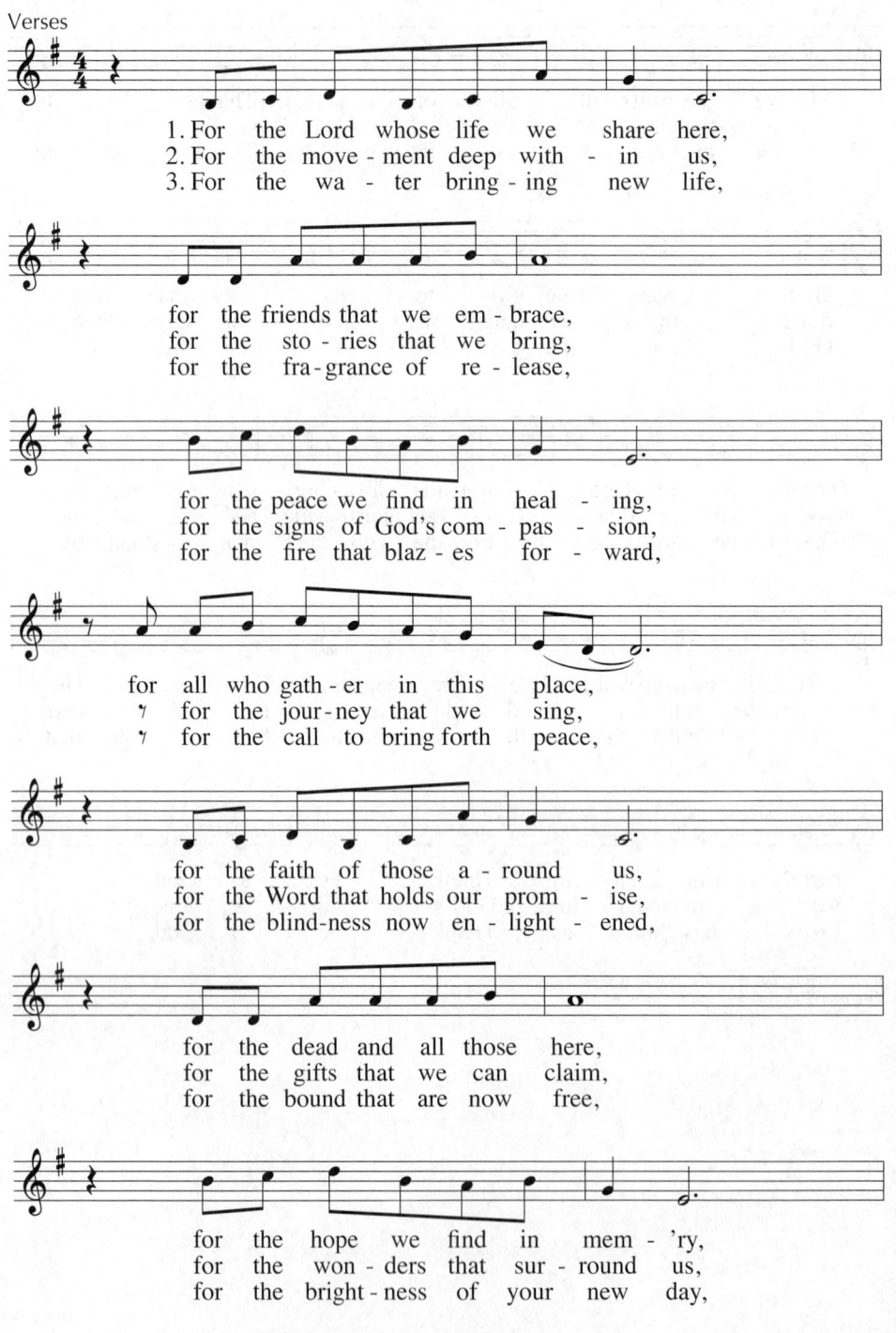

Verses

1. For the Lord whose life we share here,
2. For the move-ment deep with - in us,
3. For the wa - ter bring - ing new life,

for the friends that we em - brace,
for the sto - ries that we bring,
for the fra-grance of re - lease,

for the peace we find in heal - ing,
for the signs of God's com - pas - sion,
for the fire that blaz - es for - ward,

for all who gath - er in this place,
for the jour - ney that we sing,
for the call to bring forth peace,

for the faith of those a - round us,
for the Word that holds our prom - ise,
for the blind-ness now en - light - ened,

for the dead and all those here,
for the gifts that we can claim,
for the bound that are now free,

for the hope we find in mem - 'ry,
for the won - ders that sur - round us,
for the bright - ness of your new day,

for the love that draws us near:
for the song that sings our name:
for the king-dom we will be:

Refrain

We give you thanks, we give you thanks

for the grace to re-ceive, in you we be-lieve. We

give you thanks, we give you thanks. With

faith and hope and love, we give you thanks.

Text: David Haas, b.1957
Tune: WE GIVE YOU THANKS, 8 7 8 7 D with refrain; David Haas, b.1957
© 1998, GIA Publications, Inc.

752 Come, You Thankful People, Come

1. Come, you thank - ful peo - ple, come; Raise the song of
2. All the world is God's own field, Fruit un - to his
3. For the Lord our God shall come And shall take his
4. E - ven so, Lord, quick - ly come To your fi - nal

har - vest home. All is safe - ly gath - ered in
praise to yield; Wheat and tares to - geth - er sown,
har - vest home; From his field shall in that day
har - vest home. Gath - er all your peo - ple in,

Ere the win - ter storms be - gin. God, our Mak - er,
Un - to joy or sor - row grown. First the blade, and
All of - fens - es purge a - way, Giv - ing an - gels
Free from sor - row, free from sin, There, for ev - er

does pro - vide For our wants to be sup - plied.
then the ear, Then the full corn shall ap - pear.
charge at last In the fire the tares to cast,
pu - ri - fied, In your pres - ence to a - bide.

Come to God's own tem - ple, come.
Lord of har - vest, grant that we
But the fruit - ful ears to store
Come with all your an - gels, come!

Raise the song of har - vest home.
Whole - some grain and pure may be.
In God's gar - ner ev - er - more.
Raise the glo - rious har - vest home.

Text: Henry Alford, 1810–1871, alt.
Tune: ST. GEORGE'S WINDSOR, 77 77 D; George J. Elvey, 1816–1893

Praise and Thanksgiving 753

1. Praise and thanks - giv - ing, Fa - ther, we of - fer,
2. Lord, bless the la - bor We bring to serve you,
3. Fa - ther, pro - vid - ing Food for your chil - dren,
4. Then will your bless - ing Reach ev - 'ry peo - ple,

For all things liv - ing You have made good:
That with our neigh - bor We may be fed.
By your wise guid - ing Teach us to share
Free - ly con - fess - ing Your gra - cious hand.

Har - vest of sown fields, Fruits of the or - chard,
Sow - ing or till - ing, We would work with you,
One with an - oth - er, So that, re - joic - ing
Where you are reign - ing No one will hun - ger,

Hay from the mown fields, Blos - som and wood.
Har - vest - ing, mill - ing, For dai - ly bread.
With us, all oth - ers May know your care.
Your love sus - tain - ing Fruit - ful the land.

Text: Albert F. Bayly, 1901–1984, © 1988, Oxford University Press
Tune: BUNESSAN, 5 5 5 4 D; Gaelic; harm. by Robert J. Batastini, b.1942, © 1999, GIA Publications, Inc.

754 A Generous Heart

Refrain

Show us your way, give us on-ly what we need; teach us to serve as you de-serve. As you emp-tied your-self, let us give as we re-ceive. Cre-ate in us a gen-er-ous heart. Cre-ate in us a gen-er-ous heart.

Verses

Cantor:

1. That we may give our all with-out count-ing the cost:
2. To toil for what is right, nev-er look-ing for rest:
Lent: 3. Show us your mer-cy, Lord, as we thirst for your peace:

All:

Cre-ate a gen-er-ous heart.

Cantor:

That we may fight for jus-tice, not heed-ing the wounds:
To la-bor on for peace, not to ask for re-ward:
For-give our sins, O Lord, as we yearn for your love:

Change our

D.C.

All:

heart, Lord. Cre-ate a gen-er-ous heart.

Text: Based on *Prayer for Generosity*, St. Ignatius, 1491–1556; Chris de Silva, b.1967
Tune: Chris de Silva, b.1967
© 2014, GIA Publications, Inc.

There's a Wideness in God's Mercy 755

1. There's a wide-ness in God's mer-cy Like the wide-ness
2. For the love of God is broad-er Than the meas-ures
3. Trou-bled souls, why will you scat-ter Like a crowd of

of the sea; There's a kind-ness in God's jus-tice
of the mind; And the heart of the E-ter-nal
fright-ened sheep? Fool-ish hearts, why will you wan-der

Which is more than lib-er-ty. There is plen-ti-
Is most won-der-ful-ly kind. If our love were
From a love so true and deep? There is wel-come

ful re-demp-tion In the blood that has been shed;
but more faith-ful, We should rest up-on God's word;
for the sin-ner, And more grac-es for the good;

There is joy for all the mem-bers
And our lives would be thanks-giv-ing
There is mer-cy with the Sav-ior,

In the sor-rows of the Head.
For the good-ness of our Lord.
There is heal-ing in his blood.

Text: Frederick W. Faber, 1814–1863, alt.
Tune: IN BABILONE, 8 7 8 7 D; *Oude en Nieuwe Hollantse Boerenlieties en Contredansen*, c.1710

756 Si Fui Motivo de Dolor / If I Have Been the Source of Pain

1. Si fui mo - ti - vo de do - lor, oh Dios, Si por mi
2. Si va - na y fú - til mi pa - la - bra fue, Si al que su -
3. Si por la vi - da qui - se an - dar en paz, Tran - qui - lo,
4. Es - cu - cha, oh Dios, mi po - bre con - fe - sión Y lí - bra -

1. If I have been the source of pain, O God, If to the
2. If I have spo - ken words of cru - el - ty, If I have
3. If I've in - sist - ed on a peace - ful life, Far from the
4. Re - ceive, O God, this ar - dent word of prayer, And free me

cau - sa el dé - bil tro - pe - zó, Si en tus ca -
frí - a en su do - lor de - jé, No me con -
li - bre y sin lu - char por ti, Cuan - do an - he -
me de ten - ta - ción su - til; Pre - ser - va

weak I have re - fused my strength, If, in re -
left some suf - f'ring un - re - lieved, Con - demn not
strug - gles that the gos - pel brings, When you pre -
from temp - ta - tion's sub - tle snare; With ten - der

mi - nos yo no qui - se an - dar, ¡Per - dón, oh Dios!
de - nes, tú, por mi mal - dad. ¡Per - dón, oh Dios!
la - bas ver - me en la lid, ¡Per - dón, oh Dios!
siem - pre mi al - ma en tu re - dil. A - mén, a - mén.

bel - lion, I have strayed a - way, For - give me, God.
my in - sen - si - tiv - i - ty. For - give me, God.
fer to guide me to the strife, For - give me, God.
pa - tience, lead me to your care. A - men, a - men.

Text: Based on a text by C. Maude Battersby, Sara Menéndez de Hall, alt., © 1988, GIA Publications, Inc.; tr. by Janet W. May, © 1992, The Pilgrim Press
Tune: CAMACUÁ, 10 10 10 4; Pablo D. Sosa, b.1933, © 1988, GIA Publications, Inc.

757 Amazing Grace!

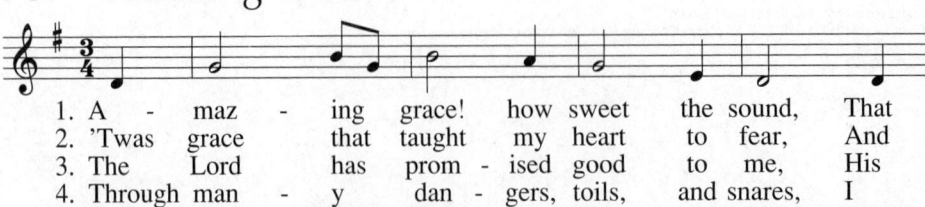

1. A - maz - ing grace! how sweet the sound, That
2. 'Twas grace that taught my heart to fear, And
3. The Lord has prom - ised good to me, His
4. Through man - y dan - gers, toils, and snares, I
5. When we've been there ten thou - sand years, Bright

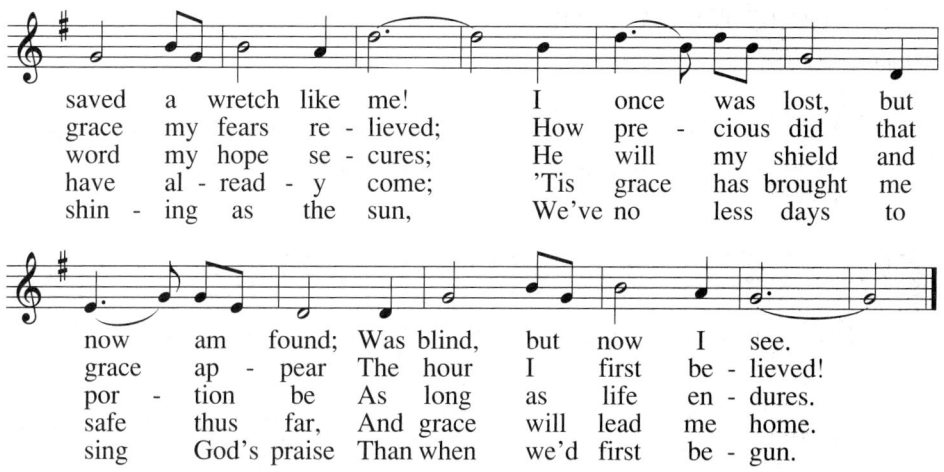

saved a wretch like me!   I   once was lost, but
grace my fears re - lieved; How pre - cious did that
word my hope se - cures; He will my shield and
have al - read - y come; 'Tis grace has brought me
shin - ing as the sun, We've no less days to

now am found; Was blind, but now I see.
grace ap - pear The hour I first be - lieved!
por - tion be As long as life en - dures.
safe thus far, And grace will lead me home.
sing God's praise Than when we'd first be - gun.

Text: Sts. 1–4, John Newton, 1725–1807; st. 5, attr. to John Rees, fl.1859
Tune: NEW BRITAIN, CM; *Virginia Harmony,* 1831; harm. by Edwin O. Excell, 1851–1921

Lord of All Hopefulness 758

1. Lord of all hope - ful - ness, Lord of all joy,
2. Lord of all ea - ger - ness, Lord of all faith,
3. Lord of all kind - li - ness, Lord of all grace,
4. Lord of all gen - tle - ness, Lord of all calm,

Whose trust, ev - er child - like, no cares could de - stroy,
Whose strong hands were skilled at the plane and the lathe,
Your hands swift to wel - come, your arms to em - brace,
Whose voice is con - tent - ment, whose pres - ence is balm,

Be there at our wak - ing, and give us, we pray,
Be there at our la - bors, and give us, we pray,
Be there at our hom - ing, and give us, we pray,
Be there at our sleep - ing, and give us, we pray,

Your bliss in our hearts, Lord, at the break of the day.
Your strength in our hearts, Lord, at the noon of the day.
Your love in our hearts, Lord, at the eve of the day.
Your peace in our hearts, Lord, at the end of the day.

Text: Jan Struther, 1901–1953, © 1931, Oxford University Press
Tune: SLANE, 10 11 11 12; Irish melody; harm. by Erik Routley, 1917–1982, © 1975, Hope Publishing Company

759 Lead Me, Guide Me

Refrain

Lead me, guide me, a - long the way, For if you lead me, I can - not stray. Lord, let me walk each day with thee. Lead me, O Lord, lead me.

Verses

1. I am weak and I need thy strength and pow'r To help me o - ver my weak - est hour. Help me through the dark-ness thy face to see. Lead me, O Lord, lead me.
2. Help me tread in the paths of right - eous - ness. Be my aid when Sa - tan and sin op - press. I am put - ting all my trust in thee. Lead me, O Lord, lead me.
3. I am lost if you take your hand from me, I am blind with - out thy Light to see. Lord, just al - ways let me thy ser - vant be. Lead me, O Lord, lead me.

D.C.

Text: Doris M. Akers, 1922–1995
Tune: LEAD ME, GUIDE ME, Irregular with refrain; Doris M. Akers, 1922–1995; harm. by Richard Smallwood, b.1948
© 1953, (renewed), arr. © 2011, Doris M. Akers, admin. by Chappell & Co., Inc.

O Lord, Hear My Prayer   760

Ostinato Chorale

O   Lord,   hear my prayer,   O   Lord, hear my prayer:
*The   Lord   is my song,   the Lord   is my praise:
Se - ñor,   ten pie - dad,   Se - ñor,   ten pie - dad:

when   I   call   an - swer me.   O   Lord, hear my prayer,   O
all   my   hope   comes from God.   The Lord   is my song,   the
si   te in - vo - co,   ó - ye - me.   Se - ñor,   ten pie - dad,   Se -

Lord, hear my prayer.   Come   and lis - ten   to me.   O
Lord is my praise: God,   the well-spring of life.   The
ñor, ten pie - dad: Ven,   y es - cu - cha   mi voz.   Se -

Last time

Last time

*Alternate text

Text: Psalm 102; Taizé Community, 1982
Tune: Jacques Berthier, 1923–1994

761 Come, My Way, My Truth, My Life

1. Come, my Way, my Truth, my Life: Such a
2. Come, my Light, my Feast, my Strength: Such a
3. Come, my Joy, my Love, my Heart: Such a

way as gives us breath; Such a truth as ends all
light as shows a feast; Such a feast as mends in
joy as none can move; Such a love as none can

strife; Such a life as kill - eth death.
length; Such a strength as makes his guest.
part; Such a heart as joys in love.

Text: George Herbert, 1593–1632
Tune: THE CALL, 7 7 7 7; Ralph Vaughan Williams, 1872–1958

762 Come to Us, Creative Spirit

1. Come to us, cre - a - tive Spir - it; In our Fa - ther's
2. Po - et, paint - er, mu - sic - mak - er, All your treas - ures
3. Word from God, e - ter - nal spring - ing, Fill our minds, we
4. In all plac - es and for ev - er Glo - ry be ex -

house Ev - 'ry hu - man tal - ent hal - low,
bring; Crafts-man, ac - tor, grace - ful danc - er,
pray; And in all ar - tis - tic vi - sion
pressed To the Son, with God the Fa - ther

Hid - den skills a - rouse That, with - in your earth - ly
Make your of - fer - ing. Join your hands in cel - e -
Give in - teg - ri - ty. May the flame with - in us
And the Spir - it blessed. In our wor - ship and our

tem - ple,   Wise and sim - ple   May   re - joice.
bra - tion;   Let cre - a - tion   Shout   and   sing!
burn - ing   Kin - dle yearn - ing   Day   by   day.
liv - ing   Keep us striv - ing   For   the   best.

Text: David Mowbray, b.1938, © Stainer & Bell, Ltd. (admin. by Hope Publishing Company)
Tune: CASTLEWOOD, 8 5 8 5 84 3; Richard Proulx, 1937–2010, © 1986, GIA Publications, Inc.

Open My Eyes   763

Verses

1. O - pen my   eyes,   Lord.   Help me to   see   your   face.
2. O - pen my   ears,   Lord.   Help me to   hear   your   voice.
3. O - pen my   heart, Lord.   Help me to   love   like   you.
4. I   live with - in   you.   Deep in your heart, O   Love.

O - pen my   eyes,   Lord.   Help me to   see. *(To verse 2)*
O - pen my   ears,   Lord.   Help me to   hear. *(To verse 3)*
O - pen my   heart, Lord.   Help me to   love. *(To bridge)*
I   live with - in   you.   Rest now in   me.

Bridge

And   the first   shall be last,   and our eyes are   o - pened,

and we'll hear like nev - er be - fore. And we'll speak in   new ways,

D.C.

and we'll see God's face   in   plac - es we've nev - er   known.

Text: Based on Mark 8:22–25; Jesse Manibusan, b.1958
Tune: Jesse Manibusan, b.1958; acc. by Ed Bolduc, b.1969, choral arr. by Ken Canedo, b.1953
© 1988, 1998, 1999, Jesse Manibusan. Published by Spirit & Song, a division of OCP.

764 Take, O Take Me As I Am

Ostinato Refrain

Take, O take me as I am; sum - mon out what I shall be; set your seal up-on my heart and live in me.

Text: John L. Bell, b.1949
Tune: John L. Bell, b.1949
© 1995, Iona Community, GIA Publications, Inc., agent

765 Healing River of the Spirit

1. Heal - ing riv - er of the Spir - it, Bathe the wounds that liv - ing brings. Plunge our pain, our sin, our sad - ness Deep be - neath your sa - cred springs.
2. Well-spring of the heal - ing Spir - it, Stream that flows to bring re - lease, As we gain our selves, our sens - es, May our lives re - flect your peace.
3. Liv - ing stream that heals the na - tions, Make us chan - nels of your pow'r. All the world is torn by con - flict; Wars are rag - ing at this hour.

Wea - ry from the rest - less search - ing That has
Grate - ful for the flood that heals us, May your
Sav - ing Spir - it, move a - mong us, Guide our

lured us from your side, We dis - cov - er in your
Church en - act your grace. As we meet both friend and
wind - ing hu - man course, Till we find our way to -

pres - ence Peace the world can - not pro - vide.
stran - ger, May we see our Sav - ior's face.
geth - er, Flow - ing home - ward to our Source.

Text: Ruth Duck, © 1996, The Pilgrim Press
Tune: BEACH SPRING, 8 7 8 7 D; *The Sacred Harp*, 1844; harm. by Ronald A. Nelson, 1927–2014, © 1978, *Lutheran Book of Worship*,
  admin. Augsburg Fortress

These Alone Are Enough   766

1. Take my heart, O Lord, take my hopes and dreams.
2. Take my thoughts, O Lord, and my mem - o - ry.
3. I sur - ren - der, Lord, all I have and hold.
4. When the dark - ness falls on my fi - nal days,

Take my mind with all its plans and schemes.
Take my tears, my joys, my lib - er - ty.
I re - turn to you your gifts un - told.
take the ver - y breath that sang your praise.

Give me noth - ing more than your love and grace.

These a - lone, O God, are e - nough for me.

Text: Based on *"Suscipe"* Prayer of Ignatius of Loyola; Dan Schutte, b.1947
Tune: Dan Schutte, b.1947
© 2004, Daniel L. Schutte. Published by OCP.

767 Turn My Heart, O God

Refrain

Turn my heart, O God. Turn my heart, O God. Take my pain and bro - ken - ness; shape my life for you. Come and turn my heart, O God.

To verses | *To repeat refrain and last time*

Verses

turn my heart, O God.

Cantor:

1. From all that leads to death, to
2. From bit - ter - ness and hate, to
3. O let your Spir - it come and
4. O bring me home to you, Most

All:

Come and turn my heart, O

seek the way of life: From
ten - der - ness and care: From
cleanse my in - most heart: Give
Ho - ly, Bless - ed One: And

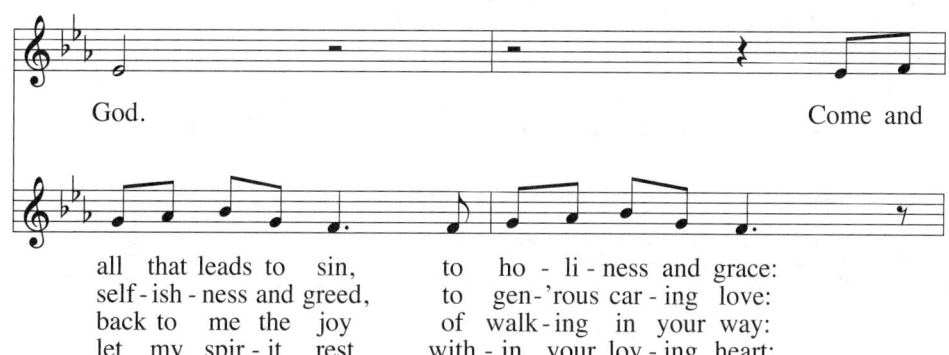

God.   Come and

all   that leads to   sin,   to   ho - li - ness and grace:
self - ish - ness and greed,   to   gen-'rous car - ing love:
back to   me the   joy   of walk - ing in your way:
let   my spir - it   rest   with - in your lov - ing heart:

turn   my   heart,   O   God.

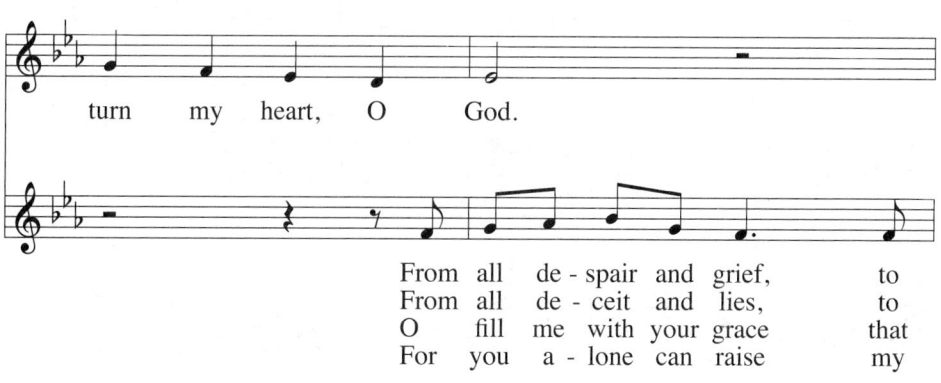

From all   de - spair and grief,   to
From all   de - ceit   and lies,   to
O   fill   me with your grace   that
For   you   a - lone can raise   my

D.C.

Come and turn my heart, O   God.

hope of   life re - newed:
faith - ful - ness and   truth:
I   might sing your praise:
wea - ry   soul to   life:

Text: Marty Haugen, b.1950
Tune: Marty Haugen, b.1950
© 2002, GIA Publications, Inc.

768 Let All Who Are Thirsty, Come

Ostinato Refrain

Let all who are thirst-y, come. Let all who wish, re-

ceive the wa-ter of life free-ly. A-

men, come, Lord Je-sus. A-men, come, Lord Je-sus.

Text: Taizé Community
Tune: Taizé Community
© 2011, Les Presses de Taizé, GIA Publications, Inc., agent

769 A Prayer Canticle

Antiphon

We do not know how to pray as we ought, but the Spir-it

in-ter-cedes for us with sighs too deep for words.

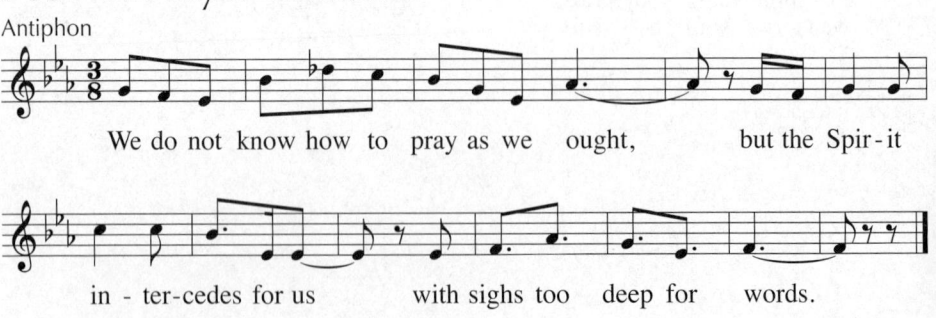

Verses

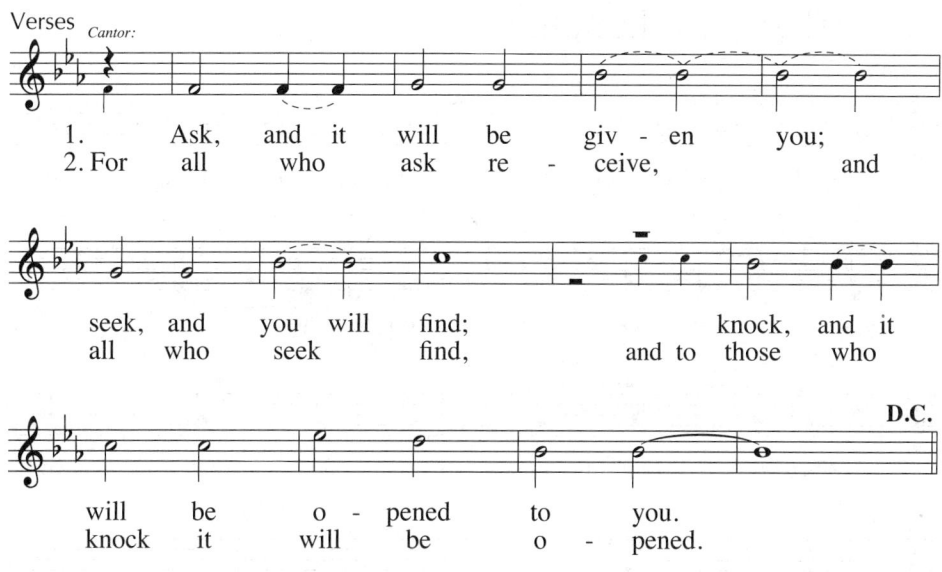

1. Ask, and it will be giv-en you;
2. For all who ask re-ceive, and

seek, and you will find; knock, and it
all who seek find, and to those who

D.C.

will be o-pened to you.
knock it will be o-pened.

Text: Romans 8:26, Luke 11:9–10; adapt. by Alan Luff, alt.
Tune: PRAYER CANTICLE, Irregular with refrain; Erik Routley, 1917–1982
© 1969, Stainer & Bell, Ltd. (admin. by Hope Publishing Company)

Christ Be beside Me 770

1. Christ be be-side me, Christ be be-fore me,
2. Christ on my right hand, Christ on my left hand,
3. Christ be in all hearts Think-ing a-bout me;

Christ be be-hind me, King of my heart.
Christ all a-round me, Shield in the strife.
Christ be on all tongues Tell-ing of me.

Christ be with-in me, Christ be be-low me,
Christ in my sleep-ing, Christ in my sit-ting,
Christ be the vis-ion In eyes that see me;

Christ be a-bove me, Nev-er to part.
Christ in my ris-ing, Light of my life.
In ears that hear me, Christ ev-er be.

Text: Ascribed to St. Patrick; James Quinn, SJ, 1919–2010, © 1969, James Quinn, SJ. Published by OCP.
Tune: BUNESSAN, 5 5 5 4 D; Gaelic melody; acc. by Robert J. Batastini, b.1942, © 1999, GIA Publications, Inc.

771 There Is a Longing

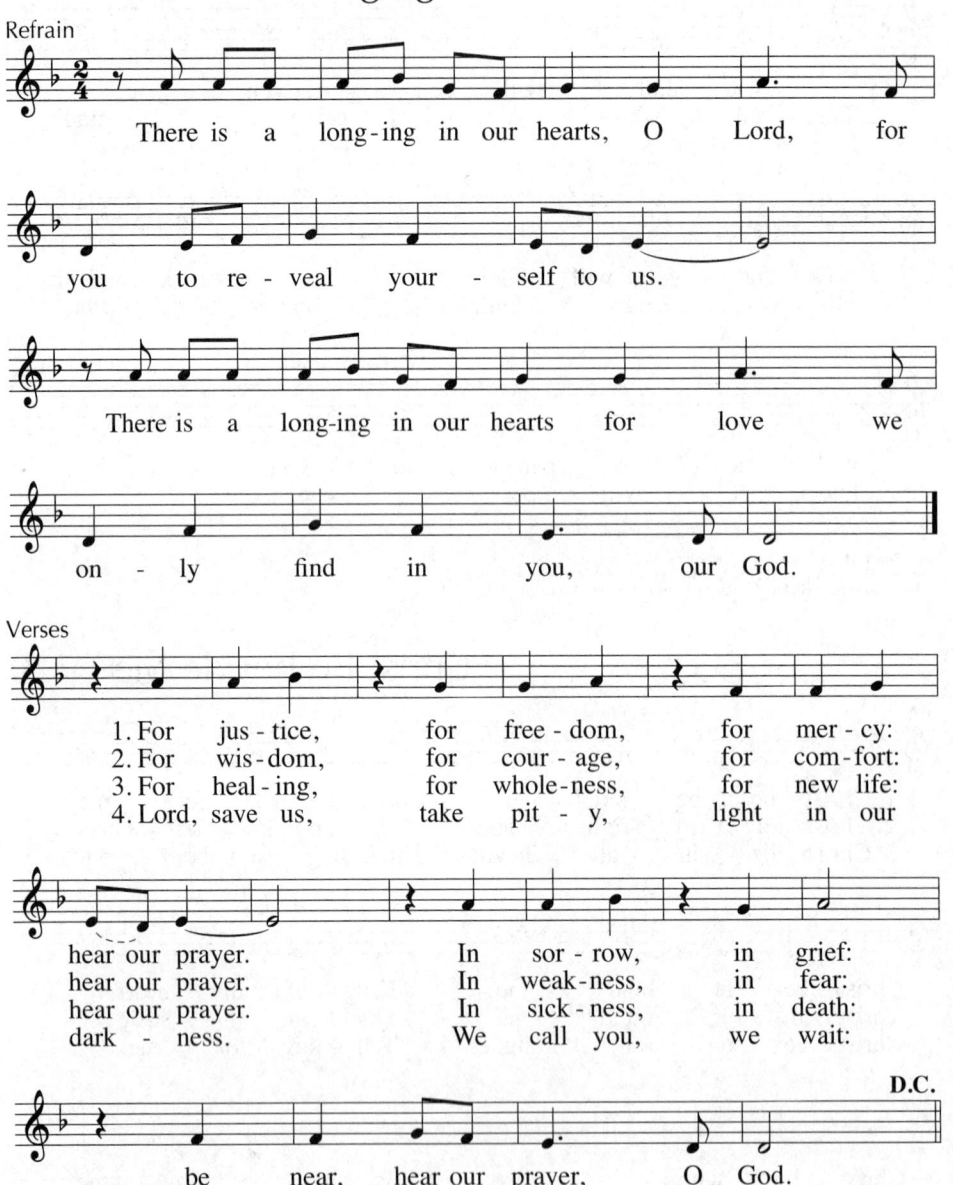

Refrain

There is a long-ing in our hearts, O Lord, for
you to re-veal your-self to us.
There is a long-ing in our hearts for love we
on-ly find in you, our God.

Verses

1. For jus-tice, for free-dom, for mer-cy:
2. For wis-dom, for cour-age, for com-fort:
3. For heal-ing, for whole-ness, for new life:
4. Lord, save us, take pit-y, light in our

hear our prayer. In sor-row, in grief:
hear our prayer. In weak-ness, in fear:
hear our prayer. In sick-ness, in death:
dark-ness. We call you, we wait:

D.C.

be near, hear our prayer, O God.

Text: Anne Quigley
Tune: Anne Quigley
© 1992, Anne Quigley. Published by OCP.

God Weeps with Us Who Weep and Mourn 772

1. God weeps with us who weep and mourn, God's
2. Through tears and sor - row, God, we share A
3. And yet, be - cause, like us, you weep, We

tears flow down with ours, And God's own heart is
sense of your vast grief; The weight of bear - ing
trust you will re - ceive And in your ten - der

bruised and worn From all the heav - y hours Of
ev - 'ry prayer For heal - ing and re - lief, The
heart will keep The ones for whom we grieve, While

watch - ing while the soul's bright fire Burned
bur - den of our ques - tions why, The
with your tears our hearts will taste The

low - er day by day, And pulse and breath and
doubts that they en - gage, And as our friends and
deep, dear core of things From which both life and

love's de - sire Dimmed down to ash and clay.
loved ones die, Our hope - less - ness and rage.
death are graced By love's re - new - ing springs.

Text: Thomas H. Troeger, b.1945, © 2002, Oxford University Press
Tune: KINGSFOLD, CMD; English melody; harm. by Ralph Vaughan Williams, 1872–1958

773 Once We Sang and Danced with Gladness

1. Once we sang and danced with glad - ness, Once de -
2. All the wil - lows bow in weep - ing, All the
3. God, who came to dwell a - mong us, God, who
4. Come, O Christ, a - mong these ash - es, Come to

light filled ev - 'ry breath; Now we sit a - mong the
riv - ers rage and moan, As cre - a - tion joins our
suf - fered our dis - grace, From your own heart, grieved and
wipe our tears a - way, Death de - stroy and sor - row

ash - es, All our dreams de - stroyed by death.
plead - ing: "God, do not leave us a - lone."
wound - ed, Come the rich - es of your grace.
ban - ish; Now and al - ways, come and stay.

Text: Susan Briehl, b.1952, © 2003, GIA Publications, Inc.
Tune: KAS DZIEDAJA, 8 7 8 7; Latvian melody; acc. by Robert J. Batastini, b.1942, © 1995, GIA Publications, Inc.

774 By the Waters of Babylon

Canon

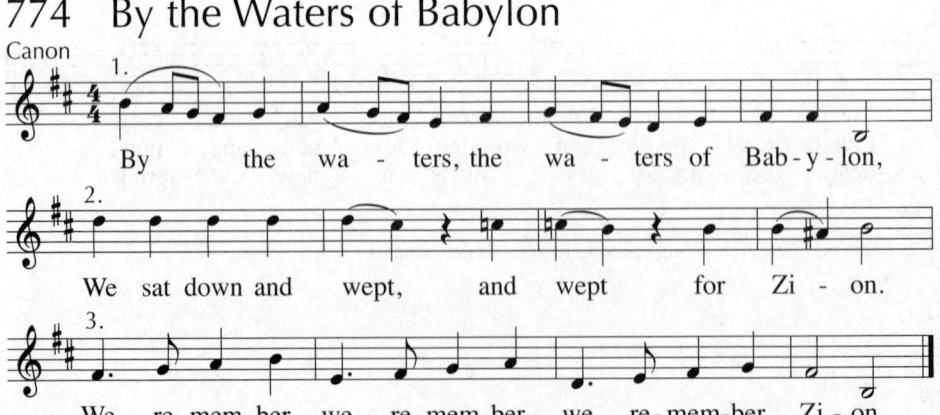

By the wa - ters, the wa - ters of Bab - y - lon,

We sat down and wept, and wept for Zi - on.

We re - mem - ber, we re - mem - ber, we re - mem - ber Zi - on.

Text: Psalm 137:1
Tune: BY THE WATERS OF BABYLON, Irregular; *The Muses Delight*, Philip Hayes, 1786

The Steadfast Love of the Lord 775

Verses

1. O God of all the bro - ken, Look and see: your chil - dren die; They are griev - ing, lost, for - sak - en. Do you hear them when they cry? Yet, e - ven now, we re - mem - ber, and we hope, still we hope:

2. O God, do not keep si - lent While the strong op - press the weak. While your chil - dren groan and suf - fer, Have you no kind word to speak? Yet, e - ven now, they re - mem - ber, and they hope, still they hope:

3. O God, fill us with cour - age. Rise and turn, and hear our prayer: That our lives might bring your pres - ence, Bring your mer - cy, bring your care. We gath - er here to re - mem - ber, and we hope, still we hope:

Refrain

For the stead - fast love of the Lord nev - er ceas - es, God's mer - cies nev - er come to an end. They are new ev - 'ry morn - ing, new ev - 'ry morn - ing. How great is your faith - ful - ness, great is your faith - ful - ness, O God!

Text: Marty Haugen, b.1950
Tune: Marty Haugen, b.1950
© 2015, GIA Publications, Inc.

776 O God, Why Are You Silent?

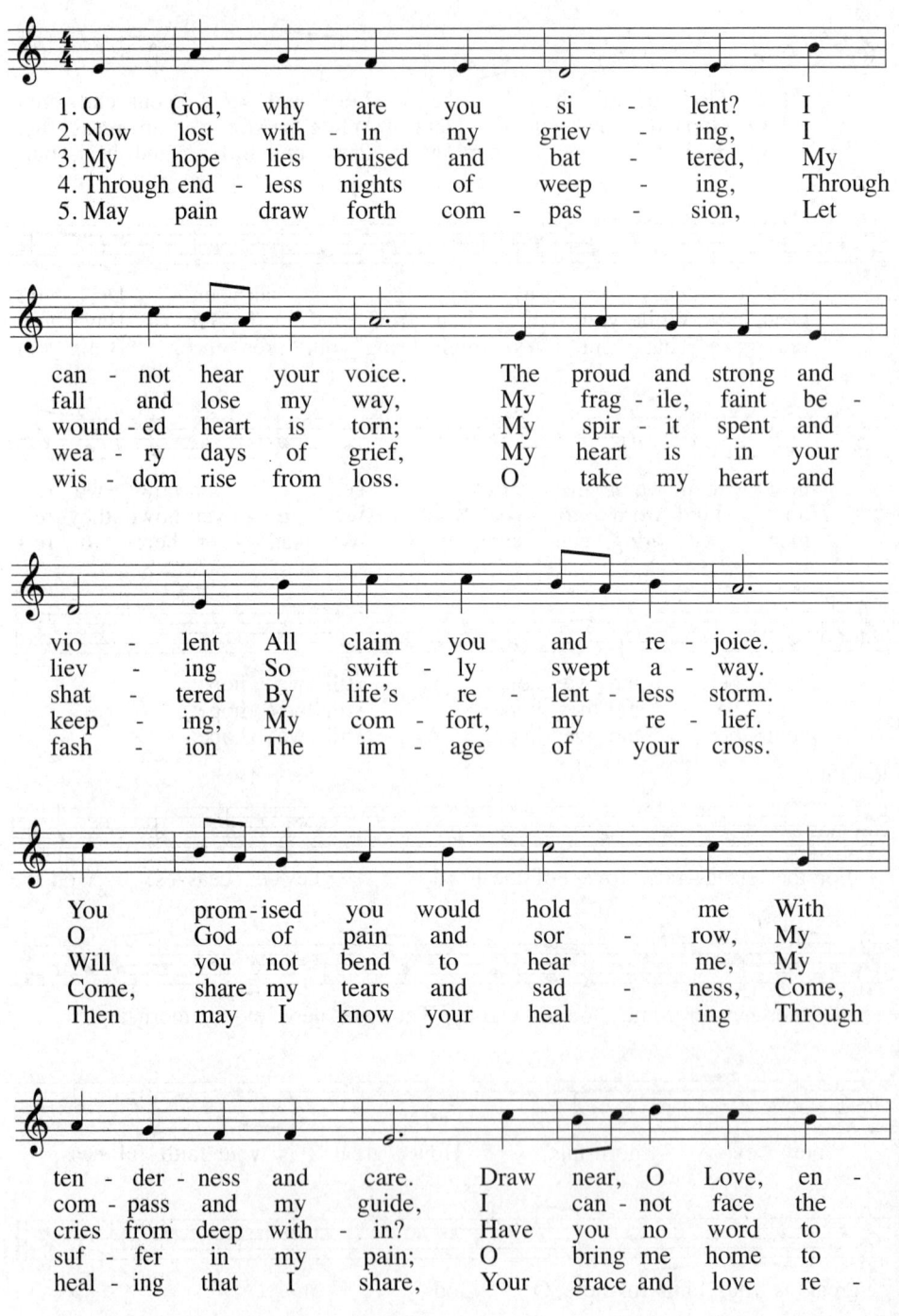

1. O God, why are you si - lent? I can - not hear your voice. The proud and strong and vio - lent All claim you and re - joice. You prom-ised you would hold me With ten - der - ness and care. Draw near, O Love, en -

2. Now lost with - in my griev - ing, I fall and lose my way, My frag - ile, faint be - liev - ing So swift - ly swept a - way. O God of pain and sor - row, My com - pass and my guide, I can - not face the

3. My hope lies bruised and bat - tered, My wound - ed heart is torn; My spir - it spent and shat - tered By life's re - lent - less storm. Will you not bend to hear me, My cries from deep with - in? Have you no word to

4. Through end - less nights of weep - ing, Through wea - ry days of grief, My heart is in your keep - ing, My com - fort, my re - lief. Come, share my tears and sad - ness, Come, suf - fer in my pain; O bring me home to

5. May pain draw forth com - pas - sion, Let wis - dom rise from loss. O take my heart and fash - ion The im - age of your cross. Then may I know your heal - ing That I share, Your grace and love re -

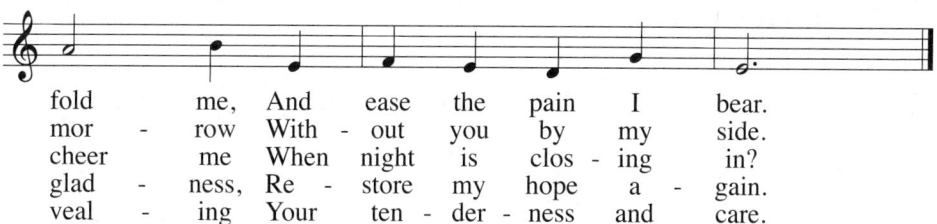

fold	me,	And	ease	the	pain	I	bear.
mor - row	With - out	you	by	my	side.
cheer	me	When	night	is	clos - ing	in?
glad - ness,	Re - store	my	hope	a - gain.
veal - ing	Your	ten - der - ness	and	care.

Text: Marty Haugen, b.1950, © 2003, GIA Publications, Inc.
Tune: PASSION CHORALE, 7 6 7 6 D; Hans Leo Hassler, 1564–1612; harm. by J. S. Bach, 1685–1750

God Remembers 777

1. God re-mem-bers pain: Nail by nail, thorn by thorn,
2. God re-mem-bers joy: Touch of love, taste of food,
3. God re-mem-bers us: All we were, all we are,

Hun - ger, thirst, and mus-cles torn. Time may dull our griefs And
All our sens-es know is good. Love and life flow by And
Lives with-in our Lov-er's care. Time may dull our minds And

heal our less - er wounds, But in e-ter-nal Love Yes-ter-day is
pre - cious days are gone, But in e-ter-nal Love Ev - 'ry day is
death will take us all, But in e-ter-nal Love Ev - 'ry life is

now, And pain is in the heart of God.
now, And joy is in the heart of God.
now: Our life is hid with Christ in God.

Text: Colossians 3:3–4; Brian Wren, b.1936, © 1993, Hope Publishing Company
Tune: GOD REMEMBERS, 5 6 7 5 6 6 6 5 8; Marty Haugen, b.1950, © 2003, GIA Publications, Inc.

778 How Long, O God

1. "How long, O God," the psalm-ist cries, A
2. The e-vil lurks with-in, with-out, It
3. Your grace, O God, seems far a-way; Will
4. How can we hope? How can we sing? O
5. "How long, O God," the psalm-ist cries, A

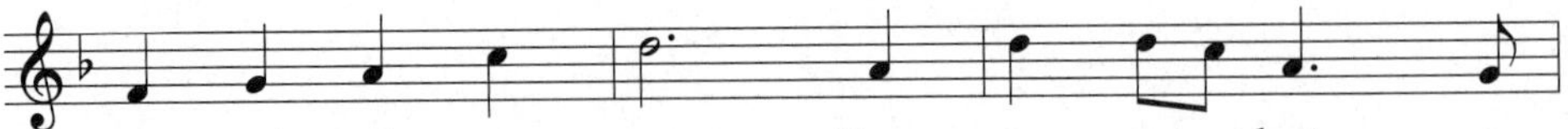

cry we make our own, For we are lost, a-
threat-ens to de-stroy The frag-ile cords that
heal-ing ev-er come? Our bro-ken lives lie
God, set free our voice To name the sor-rows,
cry we make our own. Though we are lost, a-

lone, a-fraid, And far a-way from home.
make us one, That bind our hearts in joy.
bro-ken still; Will night give way to dawn?
name the pain, That we might yet re-joice.
lone, a-fraid, Our God will lead us home.

Text: Ralph F. Smith, 1950–1994, © 2003, Augsburg Fortress
Tune: DETROIT, CM; Supplement to *Kentucky Harmony*, 1820; harm. by Gerald H. Knight, 1908–1979, © The Royal School of Church Music

779 May the Grace of Christ Our Savior

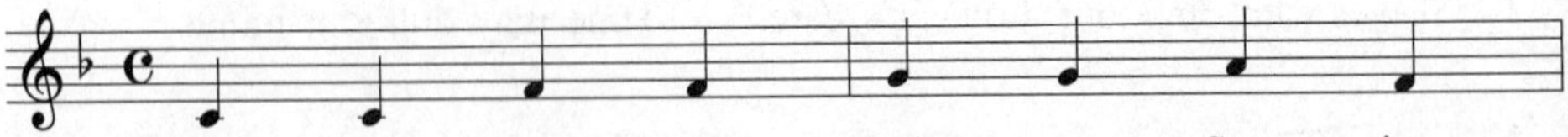

1. May the grace of Christ our Sav-ior
2. Thus may we/they a-bide in un-ion

And the Fa-ther's bound-less love With the Ho-ly
With each oth-er and the Lord, And pos-sess, in

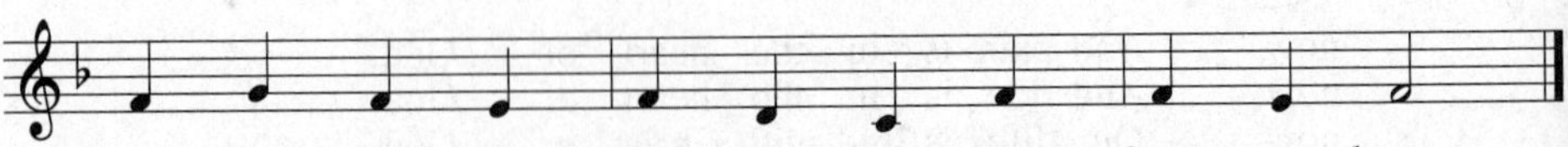

Spir-it's fa-vor, Rest up-on us/them from a-bove.
sweet com-mun-ion, Joys which earth can-not af-ford.

Text: 2 Corinthians 13:13; John Newton, 1725–1807
Tune: STUTTGART, 8 7 8 7; *Psalmodia Sacra*, 1715; adapt. and harm. by William H. Havergal, 1793–1870, alt.

May the Road Rise to Meet You 780

Refrain

May the road rise to meet you. May the wind be at your back. May the sun shine warm up-on your face,

May the rain fall soft-ly on your fields, And un-til we meet a-gain, may you

Last time

keep safe in the gen-tle, lov-ing arms of God.

Verses

1.–6. For ev-'ry thing there is a sea-son; a time for

meet-ing, a time to say good-bye.
lis-t'ning, a time to speak the truth.
laugh-ter, a time for tears and pain.
search-ing, a time for calm and peace.
lov-ing, a time for let-ting go.
liv-ing, a time for go-ing home.

In all things

D.C.

God is near, al-ways guid-ing your way.

Text: Traditional Irish blessing; verses based on Ecclesiastes 3:2–8; adapt. by Lori True, b.1961
Tune: Lori True, b.1961
© 2003, GIA Publications, Inc.

781 The Peace of the Earth / La Paz de la Tierra

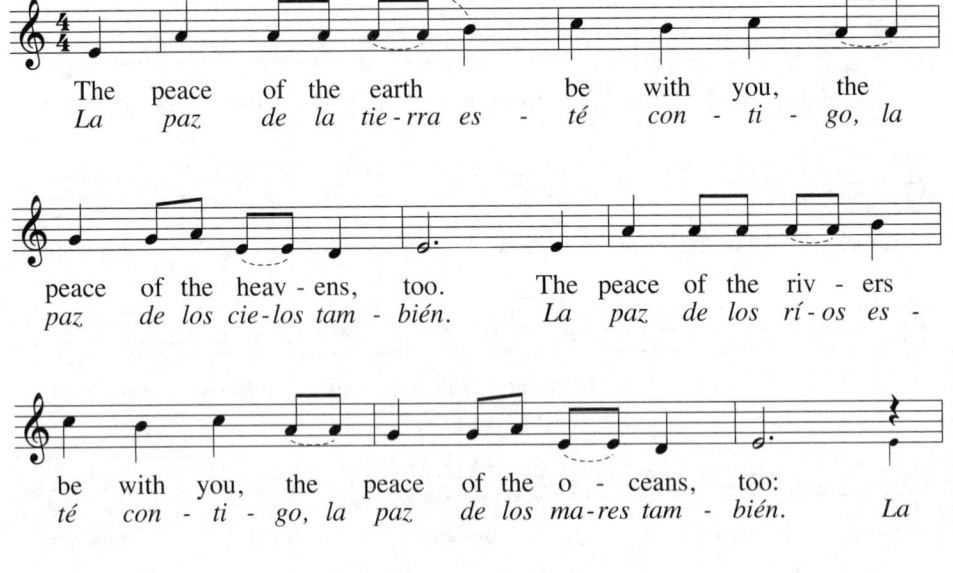

The peace of the earth be with you, the
La paz de la tie - rra es - té con - ti - go, la

peace of the heav - ens, too. The peace of the riv - ers
paz de los cie - los tam - bién. La paz de los rí - os es -

be with you, the peace of the o - ceans, too:
té con - ti - go, la paz de los ma - res tam - bién. La

deep peace fall - ing o - ver you,
paz pro - fun - da ca - yen - do so - bre ti. La

God's peace grow - ing in you.
paz pro - fun - da cre - cien - do en ti.

Text: Traditional Guatemalan; tr. by Christine Carson, © 1998, Christine Carson and Iona Community, GIA Publications, Inc., agent
Tune: Traditional Guatemalan; arr. by John L. Bell, b.1949, © 1998, Christine Carson and Iona Community, GIA Publications, Inc., agent

782 May the Peace of Christ Be with You / Kirisuto No Heiwa

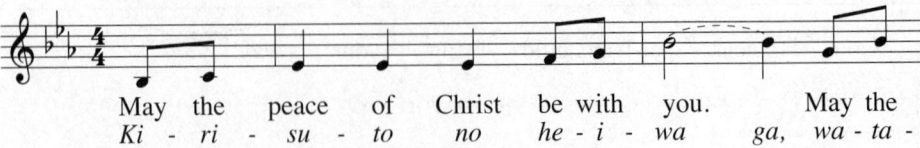

May the peace of Christ be with you. May the
Ki - ri - su - to no he - i - wa ga, wa - ta -

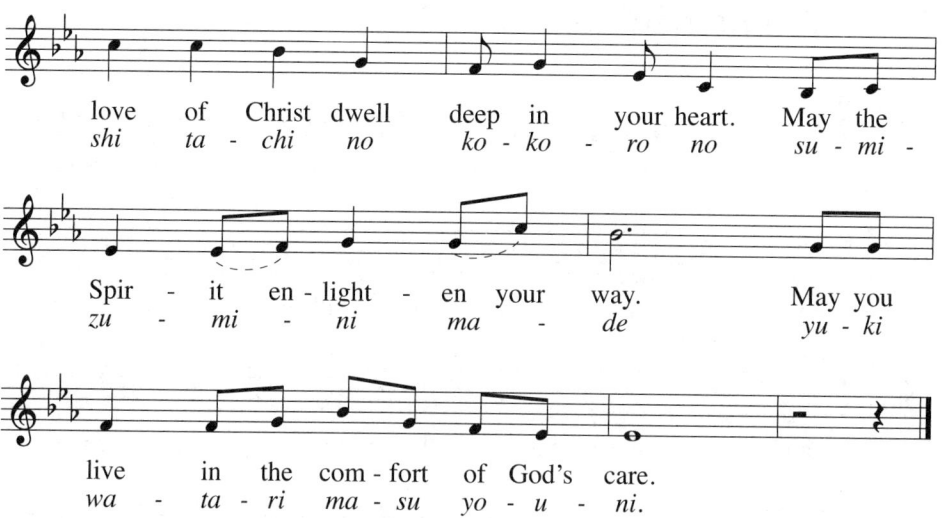

love of Christ dwell deep in your heart. May the
shi ta - chi no ko - ko - ro no su - mi -

Spir - it en - light - en your way. May you
zu - mi - ni ma - de yu - ki

live in the com - fort of God's care.
wa - ta - ri ma - su yo - u - ni.

Text: Izumi Shiota, b.1951, ©; additional text by Lori True, b.1961, © 2008, GIA Publications, Inc.
Tune: Izumi Shiota, b.1951, ©; arr. by Lori True; acc. by Mary Howarth, © 2008, 2010, GIA Publications, Inc.

We Walk by Faith 783

1., 5. We walk by faith, and not by sight; No
2. We may not touch his hands and side, Nor
3. Help then, O Lord, our un - be - lief; And
4. That, when our life of faith is done, In

gra - cious words we hear From him who spoke as
fol - low where he trod; But in his prom - ise
may our faith a - bound To call on you when
realms of clear - er light We may be - hold you

none e'er spoke; But we be - lieve him near.
we re - joice, And cry, "My Lord and God!"
you are near, And seek where you are found:
as you are, With full and end - less sight.

Text: Henry Alford, 1810–1871, alt.
Tune: SHANTI, CM; Marty Haugen, b.1950, © 1984, GIA Publications, Inc.

784 We Remember

Refrain

We re-mem-ber how you loved us to your death,
and still we cel-e-brate, for you are with us here;
and we be-lieve that we will see you when you come
in your glo-ry, Lord. We re-mem-ber, we
cel-e-brate, we be-lieve.

Verses

1. Here, a mil-lion wound-ed souls Are
2. Now we re-cre-ate your love, We
3. Christ, the Fa-ther's great "A-men" To
4. See the face of Christ re-vealed In

yearn-ing just to touch you and be healed;
bring the bread and wine to share a meal:
all the hopes and dreams of ev-'ry heart,
ev-'ry per-son stand-ing by your side:

D.C.

Gath-er all your peo-ple, and hold them to your heart.
Sign of grace and mer-cy, the pres-ence of the Lord.
Peace be-yond all tell-ing, and free-dom from all fear.
Gifts to one an-oth-er, and tem-ples of your love.

Text: Marty Haugen, b.1950
Tune: WE REMEMBER, 7 10 12 with refrain; Marty Haugen, b.1950
© 1980, GIA Publications, Inc.

Mayenziwe / Your Will Be Done 785

Xhosa phonetics:
My-yen-zee-way tahn-doe yah-koe.

Text: From the Lord's Prayer, South African (Xhosa)
Tune: South African traditional, as taught by George Mxadana; transcribed by John L. Bell, b.1949; © 1990, Iona Community,
   GIA Publications, Inc., agent

786 He Comes to Us as One Unknown

1. He comes to us as one un-known, A
2. He comes when souls in si - lence lie And
3. He comes to us in sound of seas, The
4. He comes in love as once he came By
5. He comes in truth when faith is grown; Be -

breath un - seen, un - heard; As though with - in a
thoughts of day de - part; Half seen up - on the
o - cean's fume and foam; Yet small and still up -
flesh and blood and birth; To bear with - in our
lieved, o - beyed, a - dored: The Christ in all the

heart of stone, Or shriv - eled seed in dark - ness sown, A
in - ward eye, A fall - ing star a - cross the sky Of
on the breeze, A wind that stirs the tops of trees, A
mor - tal frame A life, a death, a sav - ing Name, For
scrip-tures shown, As yet un - seen, but not un - known, Our

pulse of be - ing stirred, A pulse of be - ing stirred.
night with - in the heart, Of night with - in the heart.
voice to call us home, A voice to call us home.
ev - 'ry child of earth, For ev - 'ry child of earth.
Sav - ior and our Lord, Our Sav - ior and our Lord.

Text: Timothy Dudley-Smith, b.1926, © 1973, Hope Publishing Company
Tune: REPTON, 8 6 88 66; Charles H. H. Parry, 1848–1918

A Living Faith 787

1. Faith of our fa - thers, liv - ing still
2. Faith of our moth - ers, dar - ing faith,
3. Faith of our sis - ters, broth - ers too,
4. Faith born of God, O call us yet;

In spite of dun - geon, fire, and sword;
Your work for Christ is love re - vealed,
Who still must bear op - pres - sion's might,
Bind us with all who fol - low you,

Oh, how our hearts beat high with joy
Spread-ing God's word from pole to pole,
Rais - ing on high, in pris - ons dark,
Shar - ing the strug - gle of your cross

When - e'er we hear that glo - rious word.
Mak - ing love known and free - dom real.
The cross of Christ still burn - ing bright.
Un - til the world is made a - new.

Faith of our fa - thers, ho - ly faith,
Faith of our moth - ers, ho - ly faith,
Faith for to - day, O liv - ing faith,
Faith born of God, O liv - ing faith,

We will be true to you till death.

Text: St. 1, Frederick W. Faber, 1814–1863, alt.; sts. 2–4, Joseph R. Alfred, b.1947, alt., © 1981
Tune: ST. CATHERINE, 8 8 8 8 8 8; Henry F. Hemy, 1818–1888; adapt. by James G. Walton, 1821–1905

788   Center of My Life

Refrain

O Lord,   you   are the cen-ter of my life:

I will al-ways praise   you,   I will al-ways serve   you,

I   will   al - ways keep   you   in   my   sight.

Verses 1–3

1.   Keep me safe, O   God,   I take ref-uge in you.   I
2.   I   will bless the Lord who gives me   coun - sel,   who
3. And   so   my heart re - joic - es, my   soul is glad;

say   to   the Lord, "You are   my   God.   My
e   -   ven   at   night di - rects my   heart.   I
e   -   ven   in   safe - ty shall my   bod - y rest.   For

hap   -   pi - ness   lies in you   a - lone;   my
keep   the Lord   ev - er   in   my sight: since
you   will not leave   my   soul a - mong the dead,   nor

D.C.

hap - pi - ness   lies in   you a - lone."
he   is   at my right   hand,   I shall stand   firm.
let   your be - lov - ed know de - cay.

Verse 4

4. You will   show   me the   path of life,   the

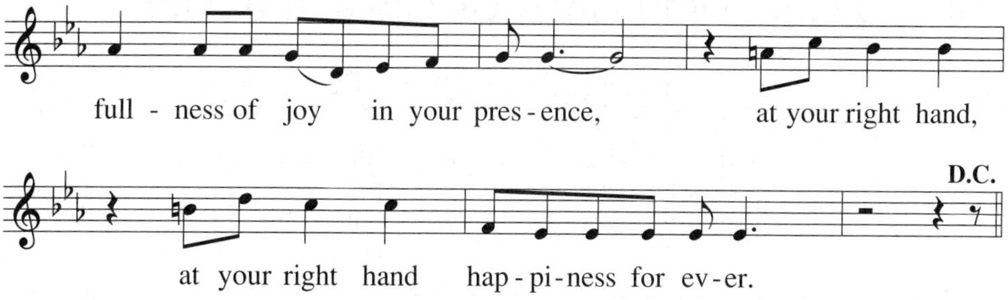
full - ness of joy in your pres - ence, at your right hand,
at your right hand hap - pi - ness for ev - er.
D.C.

Text: Psalm 16; verses trans. © 1963, The Grail, GIA Publications, Inc., agent; refrain, Paul Inwood, b.1947, © 1985, Paul Inwood
Tune: Paul Inwood, b.1947, © 1985, Paul Inwood
Published by OCP.

Keep in Mind 789

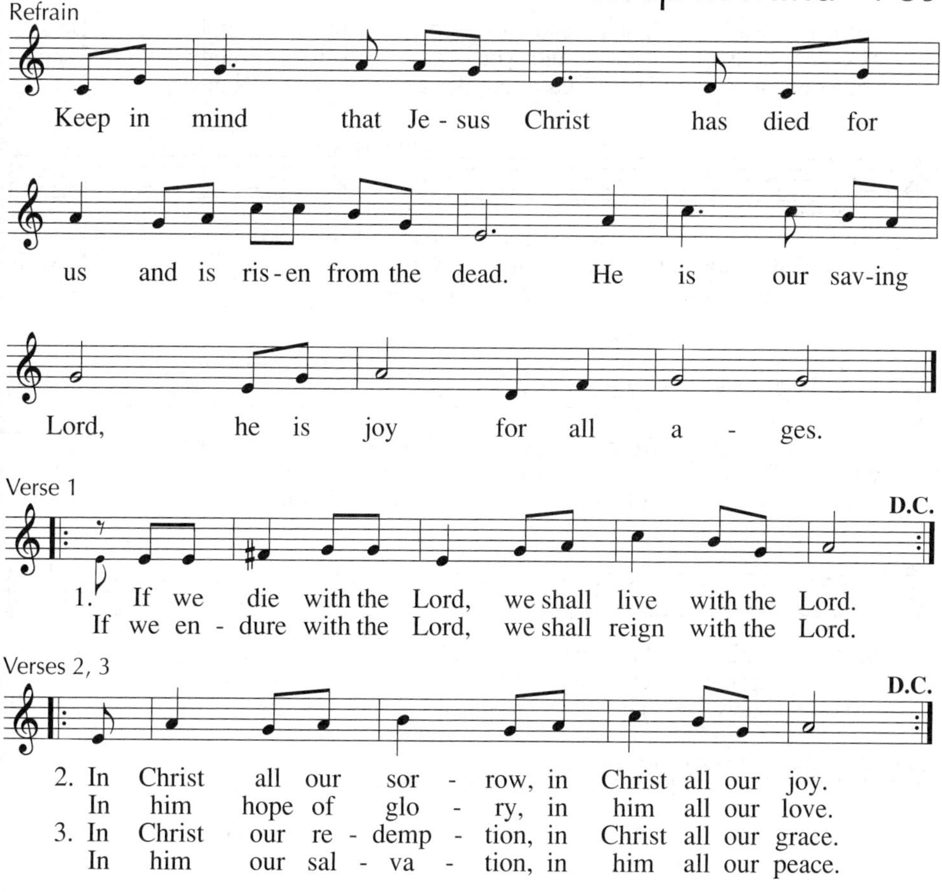
Refrain
Keep in mind that Je - sus Christ has died for
us and is ris - en from the dead. He is our sav-ing
Lord, he is joy for all a - ges.
Verse 1
D.C.
1. If we die with the Lord, we shall live with the Lord.
If we en - dure with the Lord, we shall reign with the Lord.
Verses 2, 3
D.C.
2. In Christ all our sor - row, in Christ all our joy.
In him hope of glo - ry, in him all our love.
3. In Christ our re - demp - tion, in Christ all our grace.
In him our sal - va - tion, in him all our peace.

Text: 2 Timothy 2:8–12, Lucien Deiss, CSSp, 1921–2007
Tune: Lucien Deiss, CSSp, 1921–2007

790 O God, Who Gives Us Life and Breath

1. O God, who gives us life and breath, Who
2. O God, who calls your peo-ple out, To
3. O God of cov - e - nant and law, Re -

shapes us in the womb, Who guards our lives from
ven - ture and to dare, To plumb the bleak a -
vealed in cloud and flame, Your might - y deeds e -

birth to death, Then leads us from the tomb: De -
byss of doubt And find you e - ven there: When
voke our awe; We dare not speak your Name. Yet

liv - er us from fears that kill The
we de - spair in wan - der - ing Through
we by faith are drawn to you And

life we have from you. Help us to know your
wastes of emp - ty lies, Re - fresh us with the
will your peo - ple prove, As on our hearts you

Spir - it still Is mak - ing all things new.
liv - ing spring Of hope that nev - er dies.
write a - new The cov - e - nant of love.

Text: Carl P. Daw, Jr., b.1944, © 1990, Hope Publishing Company
Tune: IN NOMINE DEI, CMD; Sally Ann Morris, b.1952, © 2009, GIA Publications, Inc.

Without Seeing You 791

Refrain

With-out see-ing you, we love you; with-out
touch-ing you, we em-brace; with-out know-ing you, we
fol-low; with-out see-ing you, we be-lieve.

Verses

1. We re - turn to you deep with - in, leave the
2. The spar - row will find a home, near to
3. For - ev - er we sing to you of your
4. For you are our shep - herd, there is
5. You will show us the path of life, you, our
6. We will tell of your works, O God, to the

past to the dust; turn to you with tears and
you, O God; how hap - py, we who
good - ness, O God; pro - claim - ing to
noth - ing that we need; in green pas - tures we will
por - tion and cup. In you we will
ends of the earth. Re - joic - ing in your

D.C.

fast - ing; you are read - y to for - give.
dwell with you, for - ev - er in your house.
all the world of your faith-ful-ness and love.
find our rest, near the wa - ters of peace.
place our trust, for - ev - er in your joy.
pres - ence, we will sing to your name.

Text: Inspired by 1 Peter 1:8; David Haas, b.1957
Tune: David Haas, b.1957
© 1993, GIA Publications, Inc.

792 Surely It Is God Who Saves Me

1. Sure - ly it is God who saves me; I shall trust and have no fear; For the Lord de - fends and shields me, And his sav - ing help is near. So re - joice as you draw wa - ter From sal - va - tion's heal - ing spring; In the day of your de - liv - 'rance Thank the Lord, his mer - cies sing.

2. Make God's deeds known to the peo - ples: Tell out his ex - alt - ed Name. Praise the Lord, who has done great things; All his works God's might pro - claim. Zi - on, lift your voice in sing - ing; For with you has come to dwell, In your ver - y midst, the great and Ho - ly One of Is - ra - el.

Text: Isaiah 12:1–6; Carl P. Daw, Jr., b.1944, © 1982, 1990, Hope Publishing Company
Tune: RAQUEL, 8 7 8 7 D; Skinner Chávez-Melo, 1944–1992, © 1987, Estate of Skinner Chávez-Melo

Alternate tune: PLEADING SAVIOR

793 How Firm a Foundation

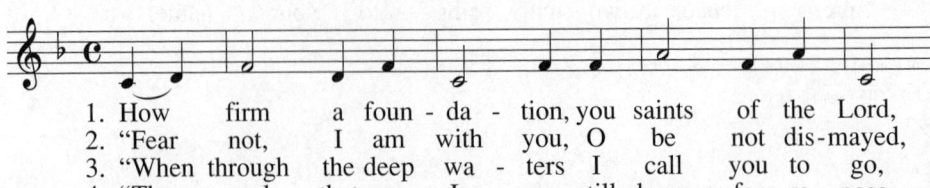

1. How firm a foun - da - tion, you saints of the Lord,
2. "Fear not, I am with you, O be not dis - mayed,
3. "When through the deep wa - ters I call you to go,
4. "The soul that on Je - sus still leans for re - pose,

Is laid for your faith in Christ Je - sus, the Word!
For I am your God, and will still give you aid;
The riv - ers of woe shall not you o - ver - flow;
I will not, I will not de - sert to its foes;

What more can God say than to you has been said,
I'll strength - en you, help you, and cause you to stand,
For I will be with you, your trou - bles to bless,
That soul, though all hell should en - deav - or to shake,

To you who for ref - uge to Je - sus have fled?
Up - held by my right - eous, om - nip - o - tent hand.
And sanc - ti - fy to you your deep - est dis - tress.
I'll nev - er, no nev - er, no nev - er for - sake!"

Text: 2 Peter 1:4; John Rippon's *A Selection of Hymns*, 1787, alt.
Tune: FOUNDATION, 11 11 11 11; Funk's *Compilation of Genuine Church Music*, 1832; harm. by Richard Proulx, 1937–2010, © 1975,
GIA Publications, Inc.

All Will Be Well 794

Ostinato Refrain

All will be well, and all will be well, all

To repeat

man - ner of things will be well.

Last time

well, will be well, will be well.

Text: *The Revelations of Divine Love*, Julian of Norwich; adapt. by Steven C. Warner, b.1954
Tune: Steven C. Warner, b.1954
© 1993, World Library Publications

795 On Eagle's Wings

Verse 1

1. You who dwell in the shel-ter of the Lord, who a-
bide in his shad-ow for life, say to the Lord: "My
ref-uge, my rock in whom I trust!"

Refrain

And he will raise you up on ea-gle's wings, bear you on the
breath of dawn, make you to shine like the sun, and

Last time to Coda   *To verses*

hold you in the palm of his hand.   2. The

Verse 2

snare of the fowl-er will nev-er cap-ture you, and
fam-ine will bring you no fear: un-der his wings your

D.S.

ref-uge, his faith-ful-ness your shield.

Verse 3

3. You need not fear the ter-ror of the night, nor the

TRUST

ar - row that flies by   day;   though thou - sands fall a -

bout you,   near   you it shall not   come.

Verse 4

4. For   to   his   an - gels   he's   giv - en a com-mand   to

guard you   in all of   your ways;   up - on their hands they will

bear you   up, lest you dash your foot a-gainst a   stone.

⊕ Coda

And hold you, hold you in the   palm   of his hand.

Text: Psalm 91; Michael Joncas, b.1951
Tune: Michael Joncas, b.1951
© 1979, OCP

O God, Keep Me Safe 796

Ostinato Refrain

O   God, keep me   safe,   for I trust in you. The path-way to
German: Be - hü - te mich, Gott,   ich ver-trau-e dir, du zeigst mir den

life you teach me. With you is peace and joy in all full-ness.   O
Weg zum Le - ben. Bei dir ist Freu-de, Freu-de in Fül - le.   Be-

Last time

Text: Taizé Community
Tune: Taizé Community
© 2007, Les Presses de Taizé, GIA Publications, Inc., agent

797 Be Not Afraid

Verse 1

1. You shall cross the bar-ren des-ert, but you shall not die of thirst. You shall wan-der far in safe-ty though you do not know the way. You shall speak your words in for-eign lands and all will un-der-stand. You shall see the face of God and live.

Refrain

Be not a-fraid. I go be-fore you al-ways. Come, fol-low me, and I will give you rest.

Verse 2

2. If you pass through rag-ing wa-ters in the sea, you shall not drown. If you walk a-mid the burn-ing flames, you shall not be harmed. If you stand be-fore the

pow'r of hell and death is at your side,

D.S.

know that I am with you through it all.

Verse 3

3. Bless-ed are your poor, for the king-dom shall be

theirs. Blest are you that weep and mourn, for

one day you shall laugh. And if wick-ed tongues in -

sult and hate you all be-cause of me,

D.S.

bless-ed, bless-ed are you!

Text: Isaiah 43:2–3, Luke 6:20ff; Bob Dufford, SJ, b.1943
Tune: Bob Dufford, SJ, b.1943; acc. by Theophane Hytrek, OSF, 1915–1992
© 1975, 1978, Robert J. Dufford, SJ, and OCP

798 Pues Si Vivimos / If We Are Living

1. Pues si vi - vi - mos, pa - ra él vi -
2. En es - ta vi - da fru - tos hay que
3. En la tris - te - za y en el do -
4. En es - te mun - do por do - quier ha -

1. *If we are liv - ing, we are in the*
2. *Through-out our lives we have fruit to*
3. *When there is sad - ness, when there is*
4. *And in this world we will al - ways*

vi - mos; Y si mo - ri - mos,
dar, Y bue - nas o - bras
lor, En la be - lle - za
brá Gen - te que llo - ra

Lord, And if we die,
bear. All of our good works
pain, In Christ the Lord,
find Those who are weep - ing,

pa - ra él mo - ri - mos. Se - a que vi -
he - mos de o - fren - dar. Se - a ya que
y en el a - mor, Se - a que su -
y sin con - so - lar. Se - a que a - yu -

we are in the Lord, For if we
are for us to share. Wheth - er we
we have love to gain. Wheth - er we
sick in heart and mind. They need our

va - mos o que mu - ra - mos,
de - mos o que re - ci - ba - mos,
fra - mos o que go - ce - mos,
de - mos o que a - li - men - te - mos,

live or if we die,
give or we re - ceive,
suf - fer or we re - joice,
help, they need our care.

So - mos del Se -

We be-long to

ñor,   so - mos del   Se - ñor.
God,   we be - long   to God.

Text: Verse 1, Romans 14:8; traditional Mexican; vss. 2–4, Roberto Escamilla, b.1931, © 1983, Abingdon Press; tr. by Deborah L. Alvarez, b.1969,
© 1994, Abingdon Press, admin. Music Services
Tune: SOMOS DEL SEÑOR, Irregular; traditional Mexican; arr. by Ronald F. Krisman, b.1946, © 2004, GIA Publications, Inc.

Bambelela / Never Give Up 799

O
no

Ostinato Refrain

Bam - be - le - la,   bam - be - le - la,
Nev - er give up,   nev - er give up,

bam - be - le - la,   bam - be - le - la,
nev - er give up,   nev - er give up,

bam - ba, bam - ba, bam - ba, bam - ba, bam - ba, O
nev - er, nev - er, nev - er, nev - er, nev - er, no

Last time

bam - ba,   bam - be - le - la.
nev - er,   nev - er give up.

Last time

Text: Traditional South African
Tune: Traditional South African; tr. by Mairi Munro and Martine Stemerick; adapt. by Mairi Munro and Philip Jakob
© 2002, JL Zwane Memorial Congregation

800 Seek Ye First

1. Seek ye first the king - dom of God
2. Ask, and it shall be giv - en un - to you,
3. You do not live by bread a - lone,
4. Where two or three are gath - ered in my name,

and his right - eous - ness,
seek, and you shall find,
but by ev - 'ry word
there am I in their midst;

and all these things shall be add - ed un - to you;
knock, and the door shall be o - pened un - to you;
that comes forth from the mouth of God;
and what - so - ev - er you ask I will do;

Al - le - lu, al - le - lu - ia.

2. *Optional Refrain, Descant, or Canon:*

Al - le - lu - ia, al - le - lu - ia,

al - le - lu - ia, al - le - lu, al - le - lu - ia.

May be sung as a two-voice canon.

Text: Matthew 6:33, 7:7; adapt. by Karen Lafferty, b.1948
Tune: SEEK YE FIRST, Irregular; Karen Lafferty, b.1948
© 1972, CCCM Music/Universal Music–Brentwood Benson Publishing (admin. CapitolCMGPublishing.com)

Nothing Is Impossible with God 801

Text: Based on Luke 1:26; James J. Chepponis, b.1956
Tune: ZUBIK, 12 15 15 with refrain; James J. Chepponis, b.1956
© 2001, GIA Publications, Inc.

802 How Can I Keep from Singing?

1. My life flows on in end-less song. A-
2. Through all the tu - mult and the strife I
3. What though my joys and com-fort die? The
4. The peace of Christ makes fresh my heart, A

bove earth's lam - en - ta - tion   I   hear the clear though
hear that mu - sic ring - ing.   It   finds an ech - o
Lord my sav - ior liv - eth.   What though the dark - ness
foun - tain ev - er spring-ing!   All   things are mine since

far - off hymn   That hails a new   cre - a - tion.
in my soul.   How can I keep   from sing-ing?
gath - er round?   Songs in the night   he giv - eth.
I am his!   How can I keep   from sing-ing?

No storm can shake my in-most calm   While to that Rock I'm

cling-ing.   Since Christ is Lord of heav-en and earth,

How can I keep from sing-ing?

Text: Robert Lowry, 1826–1899, alt.
Tune: HOW CAN I KEEP FROM SINGING, 8 7 8 7 with refrain; Robert Lowry, 1826–1899; harm. by Robert J. Batastini, b.1942, © 1988, GIA
  Publications, Inc.

In Every Age 803

Verse 1

1. Long before the mountains came to be and the land and sea and stars of the night,
   through the endless seasons of all time, you have always been, you will always be.

Refrain

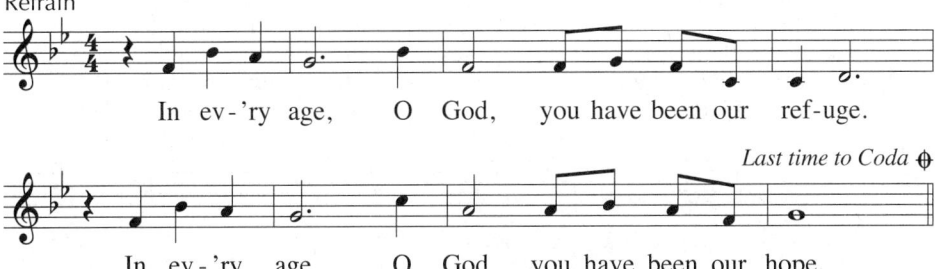

In ev-'ry age, O God, you have been our ref-uge.

Last time to Coda

In ev-'ry age, O God, you have been our hope.

Verses 2, 3

2. Destiny is cast, and at your silent word we return to dust and scatter to the wind.
   A thousand years are like a single moment gone,
   as the light that fades at the end of day.

3. Teach us to make use of the time we have. Teach us to be patient even as we wait.
   Teach us to embrace our ev'ry joy and pain,
   to sleep peacefully, and to rise up strong.

Coda

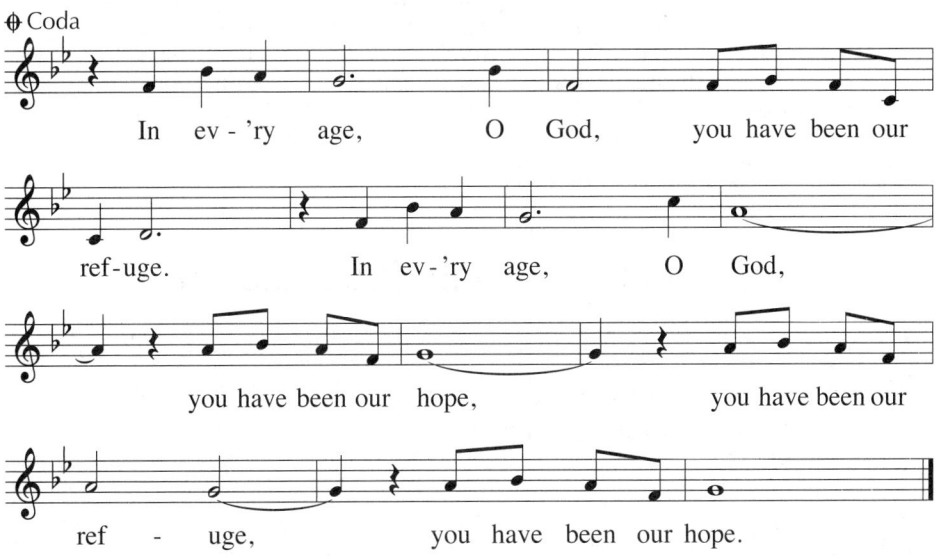

In ev - 'ry age, O God, you have been our

ref-uge. In ev-'ry age, O God,

you have been our hope, you have been our

ref - uge, you have been our hope.

Text: Based on Psalm 90:1–4, 12, Janèt Sullivan Whitaker, b.1958
Tune: Janèt Sullivan Whitaker, b.1958
© 1998, 1999, Janèt Sullivan Whitaker. Published by OCP.

804 O God, Our Help in Ages Past

1. O God, our help in a - ges past, Our
2. Un - der the shad - ow of your throne Your
3. Be - fore the hills in or - der stood, Or
4. A thou - sand a - ges in your sight Are
5. Time, like an ev - er - roll - ing stream, Bears
6. O God, our help in a - ges past, Our

hope for years to come, Our shel - ter from the
saints have dwelt se - cure; Suf - fi - cient is your
earth re - ceived its frame, From ev - er - last - ing
like an eve - ning gone, Short as the watch that
all our years a - way; They fly for - got - ten,
hope for years to come, Still be our guard while

storm - y blast, And our e - ter - nal home.
arm a - lone, And our de - fense is sure.
you are God, To end - less years the same.
ends the night Be - fore the ris - ing sun.
as a dream Dies at the o - p'ning day.
trou - bles last, And our e - ter - nal home.

Text: Psalm 90; Isaac Watts, 1674–1748, alt.
Tune: ST. ANNE, CM; attr. to William Croft, 1678–1727; harm. composite from 18th C. versions

805 Boundless Love / Tình Chúa Cao Vòi

Refrain

Far be - yond the reach of end - less sky, far be -
Tình yêu Chúa cao vòi biết bao nào con

low the depths of end - less sea, your love that has no
biết đáp đền thế nào, để cho cân xứng Chúa

end en - flames my heart a - gain.
ơi! Để cho cân xứng Chúa ơi!

Verses

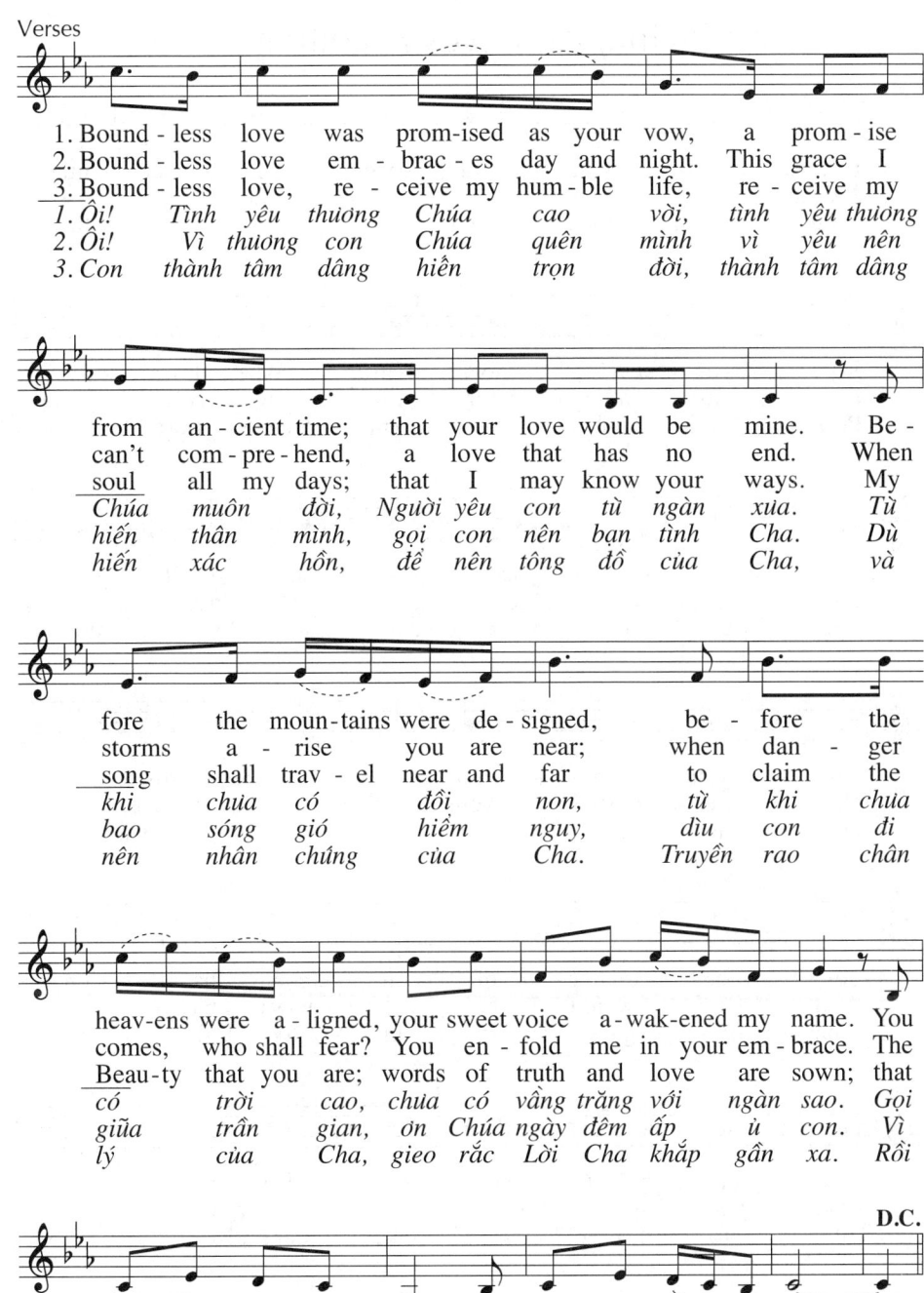

1. Bound - less love was prom-ised as your vow, a prom - ise
2. Bound - less love em - brac - es day and night. This grace I
3. Bound - less love, re - ceive my hum - ble life, re - ceive my
1. Ôi! Tình yêu thương Chúa cao vời, tình yêu thương
2. Ôi! Vì thương con Chúa quên mình vì yêu nên
3. Con thành tâm dâng hiến trọn đời, thành tâm dâng

from an - cient time; that your love would be mine. Be -
can't com - pre - hend, a love that has no end. When
soul all my days; that I may know your ways. My
Chúa muôn đời, Người yêu con từ ngàn xưa. Từ
hiến thân mình, gọi con nên bạn tình Cha. Dù
hiến xác hồn, để nên tông đồ của Cha, và

fore the moun-tains were de - signed, be - fore the
storms a - rise you are near; when dan - ger
song shall trav - el near and far to claim the
khi chưa có đồi non, từ khi chưa
bao sóng gió hiểm nguy, dìu con đi
nên nhân chứng của Cha. Truyền rao chân

heav-ens were a - ligned, your sweet voice a - wak-ened my name. You
comes, who shall fear? You en - fold me in your em - brace. The
Beau-ty that you are; words of truth and love are sown; that
có trời cao, chưa có vầng trăng với ngàn sao. Gọi
giữa trần gian, ơn Chúa ngày đêm ấp ủ con. Vì
lý của Cha, gieo rắc Lời Cha khắp gần xa. Rồi

D.C.

found me in my shame and called me out of my pain.
vi - sion of your face, no dream could ev - er re - place.
you, Most High, a - lone are source and cor - ner - stone.
con giữa muôn muôn người, tìm con giữa nơi bùn nhơ.
con Chúa quên thân mình, đời con dám mơ gì hơn.
con sẽ đi khắp miền làm nhân chứng cho tình yêu.

Text: Duy Thiên; tr. by Rufino Zaragoza, OFM
Tune: Duy Thiên; keyboard acc. by Kelly Dobbs-Mickus, b.1966
© 1987, 2000, Duy Thiên. Published by OCP.

806 Love Divine, All Loves Excelling

1. Love di - vine, all loves ex - cel - ling,
2. Come, Al - might - y, to de - liv - er,
3. Fin - ish then your new cre - a - tion,

Joy of heav'n, to earth come down!
Let us all your life re - ceive;
Pure and spot - less, gra - cious Lord.

Fix in us your hum - ble dwell - ing,
Sud - den - ly re - turn and nev - er,
Let us see your great sal - va - tion

All your faith - ful mer - cies crown.
Nev - er - more your tem - ples leave.
Per - fect - ly in you re - stored.

Je - sus, source of all com - pas - sion,
You we would be al - ways bless - ing,
Changed from glo - ry in - to glo - ry,

Love un - bound - ed, love all pure;
Serve you as your hosts a - bove,
Till in heav'n we take our place,

Vis - it us with your sal - va - tion,
Pray, and praise you with - out ceas - ing,
Till we sing be - fore the Al - might - y,

Let your love in us en - dure.
Glo - ry in your pre - cious love.
Lost in won - der, love, and praise.

Text: Charles Wesley, 1707–1788, alt.
Tune: HYFRYDOL, 8 7 8 7 D; Rowland H. Prichard, 1811–1887

What Wondrous Love Is This   807

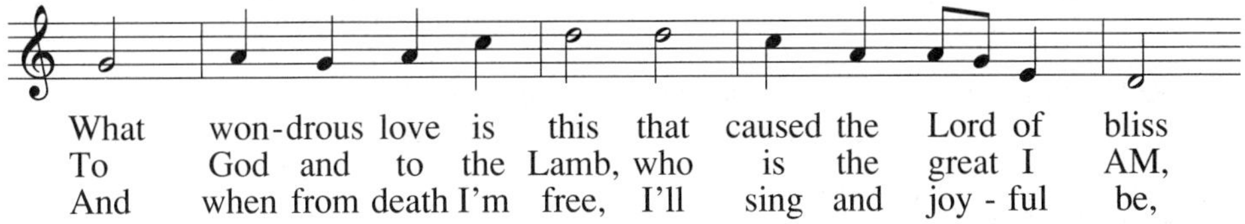

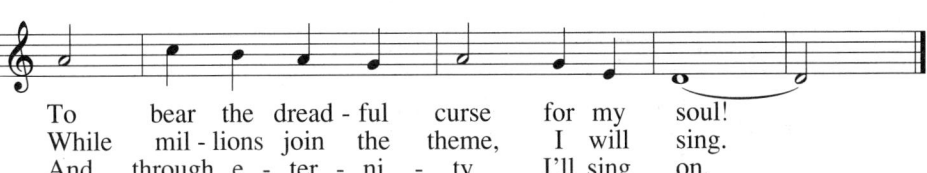

1. What won-drous love is this, O my soul, O my soul!
2. To God and to the Lamb I will sing, I will sing;
3. And when from death I'm free, I'll sing on, I'll sing on;

What won-drous love is this, O my soul!
To God and to the Lamb I will sing.
And when from death I'm free, I'll sing on.

What won-drous love is this that caused the Lord of bliss
To God and to the Lamb, who is the great I AM,
And when from death I'm free, I'll sing and joy - ful be,

To bear the dread-ful curse for my soul, for my soul;
While mil - lions join the theme, I will sing, I will sing;
And through e - ter - ni - ty I'll sing on, I'll sing on;

To bear the dread-ful curse for my soul!
While mil - lions join the theme, I will sing.
And through e - ter - ni - ty I'll sing on.

Text: Alexander Means, 1801–1883
Tune: WONDROUS LOVE, 12 9 12 12 9; *Southern Harmony,* 1835; harm. by Richard Proulx, 1937–2010, © 1975, GIA Publications, Inc.

808 Ubi Caritas

Refrain

U - bi cá - ri - tas et a - mor,
Where true char - i - ty and love a - bide,
Spanish: Don - de hay a - mor y ca - ri - dad,
Korean: 사 랑 의 나 눔 있 는 곳 에
Tagalog: Sa pag - ma - ma - hal na - ro - roon ang Diyos.

u - bi cá - ri - tas De - us i - bi est.
God is dwell - ing there; God is dwell - ing there.
don - de hay a - mor Dios a - llí es - tá.
하 느 님 께 서 계 시 도 - 다.
Sa pag - ma - ma - hal na - ro - roon ang Diyos.

Korean transliteration: Sa-lang-ui na-num iss-neun gos-e.
Ha-neu-nim-kke-seo gye-si-do—da.

Text: 1 Corinthians 13:2–8, 13; Taizé Community, 1978
Tune: Jacques Berthier, 1923–1994
© 1979, 2009, 2011, Les Presses de Taizé, GIA Publications, Inc., agent

809 Where Charity and Love Prevail

1. Where char - i - ty and love pre - vail,
2. With grate - ful joy and ho - ly fear
3. For - give we now each oth - er's faults
4. Let strife a - mong us be un - known,
5. Let us re - call that in our midst
6. No race nor creed can love ex - clude

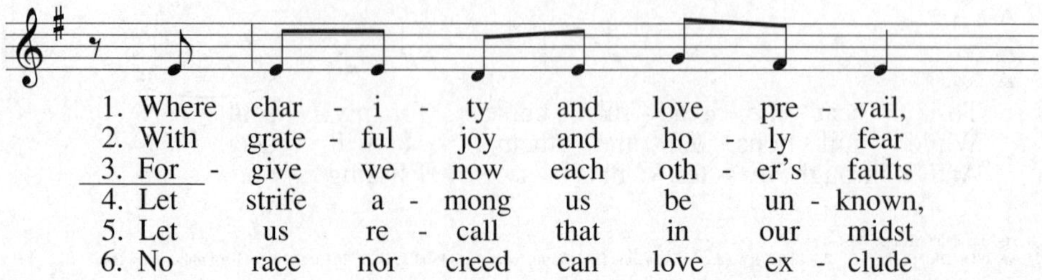

There God is ev - er found; Brought here to - geth - er
God's char - i - ty we learn; Let us with heart and
As we our faults con - fess; And let us love each
Let all con - ten - tion cease; Be God's the glo - ry
Dwells God's be - got - ten Son; As mem - bers of his
If hon - ored be God's name; Our fam - i - ly em -

by Christ's love, By love are we thus bound.
mind and soul Now love God in re - turn.
oth - er well In Chris - tian ho - li - ness.
that we seek, Be ours God's ho - ly peace.
bod - y joined, We are in Christ made one.
brac - es all Whose Fa - ther is the same.

Text: *Ubi caritas;* tr. by Omer Westendorf, 1916–1997
Tune: CHRISTIAN LOVE, CM; Paul Benoit, OSB, 1893–1979
© 1960, World Library Publications

Lord of All Nations, Grant Me Grace 810

1. Lord of all na - tions, grant me grace To love all
2. Break down the walls that would di - vide Your chil - dren,
3. For - give me, Lord, where I have erred By love - less
4. Give me your cour - age, Lord, to speak When-ev - er
5. With your own love may I be filled, And by your

peo - ple, ev - 'ry race, To see each per - son as I
Lord, on ev - 'ry side. My neigh-bor's good let me pur -
act and thought-less word. Make me to see the wrong I
strong op - press the weak. Should I my - self as vic - tim
Ho - ly Spir - it willed, That all whose lives are touched by

ought, My kin - dred, whom your love has bought.
sue; Let Chris - tian love bind warm and true.
do Will cru - ci - fy my Lord a - new.
live, Re - mem - b'ring you, may I for - give.
mine May know your heal - ing touch di - vine.

Text: Philippians 2:1–18; Olive W. Spannaus, b.1916, © 1969, 1997, Concordia Publishing House
Tune: BEATUS VIR, LM; Slovak melody, 16th C.; harm. by Richard Hillert, 1923–2010, © 1969, Concordia Publishing House

811   With Great Love

Refrain

We can do no great things, we can do no great things,

we can do no great things; on-ly

To verses | *Final ending*

small things with great love.   great love, with great love,

with great love.

Verses

1. Use us as in - stru-ments, sim-ple ves-sels of your peace.
2. Lord, make us in - stru-ments, qui - et ves-sels of your love.
3. Choose us as in - stru-ments, sa - cred ves-sels of your will.

In - spire in us pure hearts of un - der - stand - ing,
Cre - ate in us clean hearts of con - tem - pla - tion
Trans-form in us new hearts of God's com - pas - sion

to know that, in your warm em - brace, our
to see your face in those we serve, in
to live true lives of read - i - ness: We

D.C.

be - ings will find rest.
all who search for you.
lis - ten for your call.

No Greater Love 812

Refrain

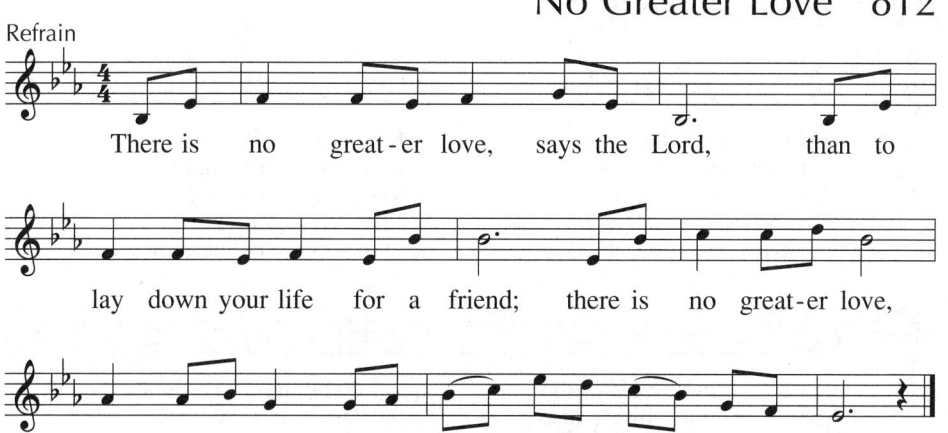

There is no great-er love, says the Lord, than to

lay down your life for a friend; there is no great-er love,

no great-er love, than to lay down your life for a friend.

Verses

1. As the Father has loved me, so I have loved you.
   Live on in my love.
   You will live in my love if you keep my commands,
   even as I have kept my Father's.

2. All this I tell you that my joy may be yours
   and your joy may be complete.
   Love one another as I have loved you:
   This is my command.

3. You are my friends if you keep my commands;
   no longer slaves but friends to me.
   All I heard from my Father,
   I have made known to you: Now I call you friends.

4. It was not you who chose me, it was I who chose you,
   chose you to go forth and bear fruit.
   Your fruit must endure, so you will receive
   all you ask the Father in my name.

Text: John 15:9–17; Michael Joncas, b.1951
Tune: Michael Joncas, b.1951
© 1988, GIA Publications, Inc.

813 Love Is His Word

1. Love is his word, love is his way.
2. Love is his way, love is his mark.
3. Love is his mark, love is his sign.
4. Love is his sign, love is his news.
5. Love is his news, love is his name.

Feast - ing with all, fast - ing a - lone,
Shar - ing his last Pass - o - ver feast.
Bread for our strength, wine for our joy.
"Do this," he said, "lest you for - get
We are his own, cho - sen and called,

Liv - ing and dy - ing, Ris - ing a - gain.
Guest at his ta - ble, Host to the Twelve,
"This is my bod - y, This is my blood."
All my deep sor - row, All my dear blood."
Fam - i - ly, breth - ren, Cous-ins and kin.

Love, on - ly love, is his way.
Love, on - ly love, is his mark.
Love, on - ly love, is his sign.
Love, on - ly love, is his news.
Love, on - ly love, is his name.

Rich - er than gold is the love of my Lord,

bet - ter than splen - dor and wealth.

Rich - er than gold is the love of my Lord,

bet - ter   than splen - dor   and   wealth.

6. Love is his name, love is his law.
   Hear his command, all who are his:
   "Love one another, I have loved you."
   Love, only love, is his law.

7. Love is his law, love is his word:
   Love of the Lord, Father and Word.
   Love of the Spirit, God ev'ry one.
   Love, only love, is his word.

Text: Luke Connaughton, 1917–1979, © 1970, Mayhew McCrimmon, Ltd.
Tune: JULINORMA, 4 4 8 5 4 7 with refrain; Robert M. Hutmacher, OFM, b.1948, © 1986, GIA Publications, Inc.

Nothing Can Ever 814

Refrain [A]

Noth - ing can ev - er come be - tween us and the love of God, the
Nun - ca na - da po - drá pri - var-nos del a - mor de Dios, a -

Last time

love of God re - vealed to us in Christ Je - sus.
mor de Dios que se re - ve - la en Cris - to.

Last time

Verses [B]

Oh,   Oh.

Text: Psalm 56:4–5, 10–14, Romans 8:39; Taizé Community
Tune: Taizé Community
© 2007, 2011, Les Presses de Taizé, GIA Publications, Inc., agent

815 Ubi Caritas

Refrain

*U - bi cá - ri - tas   est ve - ra,   est ve - ra:

De - us i - bi est,   De - us i - bi est.

Verses

1. The love of Christ joins us to - geth - er. Let
2. In true com - mu - nion let us gath - er. May
3. May we who gath - er at this ta - ble to
4. For those in need make us your mer - cy, for
5. May we one day be - hold your glo - ry and

1. U - ni - dos co - mo un so - lo cuer - po,
2. Reu - ni - dos y a - li - men - ta - dos, ya
3. Que el pan de vi - da que nos u - ne nos
4. Y pa - ra los ne - ce - si - ta - dos de a -
5. Con - cé - de - nos ya ver tu glor - ia y en

us re - joice in him, and in our love and
all di - vi - sions cease and in their place be
share the bread of life be - come a sac - ra -
those op - pressed, your might. Make us, your Church, a
see you face to face, re - joic - ing with the

en la co - mu - nión de - mos - tre - mos
li - bres del ren - cor, vi - va - mos nues - tra
cam-bie el co - ra - zón pa - ra dar al
mor y de bon - dad se - a - mos la es - pe -
tu pre - sen - cia es - tar; y u - ni - dos a los

*Where there is true charity, God is present.

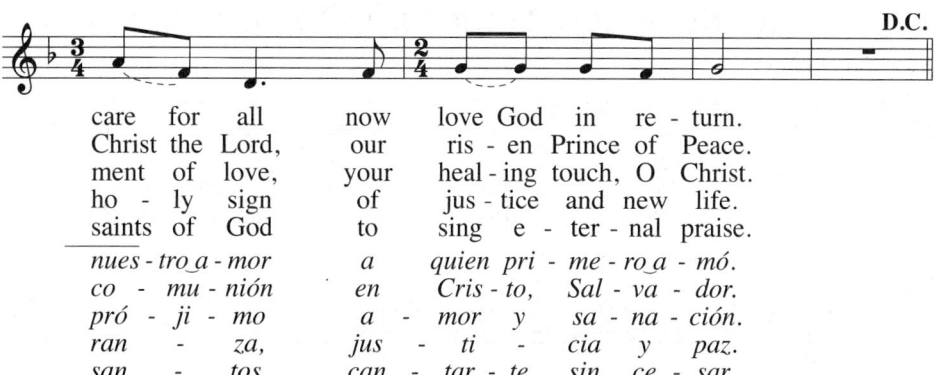

D.C.

care for all now love God in re - turn.
Christ the Lord, our ris - en Prince of Peace.
ment of love, your heal - ing touch, O Christ.
ho - ly sign of jus - tice and new life.
saints of God to sing e - ter - nal praise.
nues - tro_a - mor a quien pri - me - ro_a - mó.
co - mu - nión en Cris - to, Sal - va - dor.
pró - ji - mo a - mor y sa - na - ción.
ran - za, jus - ti - cia y paz.
san - tos, can - tar - te sin ce - sar.

Text: Refrain and vss. 1, 2 and 5 based on *Ubi Caritas*, 9th c.; vss. 3, 4, Bob Hurd, b.1950; Spanish by Pedro Rubalcava, b.1958
Tune: Bob Hurd b.1950; acc. by Craig S. Kingsbury, b.1952
© 1996, 2004, Bob Hurd. Published by OCP.

Shall Tribulation or Distress 816

1. Shall trib - u - la - tion or dis - tress, Shall per - se -
2. Shall ill - ness, hun - ger, or de - spair, Shall lone - ly
3. No, nei - ther an - gel hosts nor thrones, Nor height nor

cu - tion, fire, or sword, Or an - y per - il of this
grief or anx - ious fears, Or deeds of ha - tred and dis -
depth of e - vil's reach, Nor pres - ent things, nor things to

world— Or e - ven death, Or e - ven death— Shall an - y
dain— Or e - ven death, Or e - ven death— Shall an - y
come— Not e - ven death, Not e - ven death— Not an - y

pow'r of earth or heav'n Di - vide us from your love, O Christ?
pow'r of earth or heav'n Di - vide us from your love, O Christ?
pow'r of earth or heav'n Can part us from your love, O Christ.

Text: Based on Romans 8:35, 38; Mary Louise Bringle, b.1953
Tune: ROMANS 8, 8 8 8 4 4 8 8; Sally Ann Morris, b.1952
© 2006, GIA Publications, Inc.

817 Si Yo No Tengo Amor / If I Do Not Have Love

Estribillo / Refrain

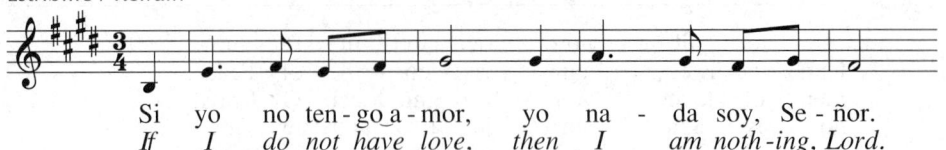

Si yo no ten-go a-mor, yo na - da soy, Se - ñor.
If I do not have love, then I am noth-ing, Lord.

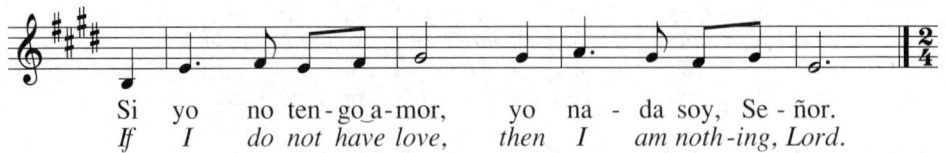

Si yo no ten-go a-mor, yo na - da soy, Se - ñor.
If I do not have love, then I am noth-ing, Lord.

Estrofas / Verses

1. El a - mor es com-pren - si - vo. El a -
2. El a - mor nun - ca se i - rri - ta. El a -
3. El a - mor dis - cul - pa to - do. El a -

1. Love is kind and un - der - stand-ing In its
2. Not quick - tem - pered or re - sent - ful, Prone to
3. Love is quick to be for - giv - ing. Spread-ing

mor es ser - vi - cial. El a - mor no tie - ne en -
mor no es des - cor - tés. El a - mor no es e - go -
mor es ca - ri - dad. No se a - le - gra de lo in -

words and in its deeds, Nev - er pomp - ous, nev - er
take of - fense or brood: Love is pa - tient and un -
love is love's de - light. Love does not re - joice at

D.C.

vi - dia. El a - mor no bus - ca el mal.
ís - ta. El a - mor nun - ca es do - blez.
jus - to. Só - lo go - za en la ver - dad.

jeal - ous, But at - tuned to oth - ers' needs.
self - ish, Nev - er boast - ful, nev - er rude.
e - vil, But re - joic - es in the right.

4. El amor soporta todo.
   El amor todo lo cree.
   El amor todo lo_espera.
   El amor es siempre fiel.

5. Aunque_el don de profecía
   O de lenguas cesará,
   El amor es algo_eterno.
   Nunca, nunca pasará.

4. *Bearing all, believing all things,*
   Love endures and love prevails.
   Ever hopeful, ever faithful,
   By God's grace, love never fails.

5. *While an end will come to gifts we use*
   To praise and prophesy,
   Love is holy and eternal
   And will never, never die.

Text: Anonymous; tr. by Mary Louise Bringle, b.1953, © 2005, GIA Publications, Inc.
Tune: Traditional; acc. by Ronald F. Krisman, b.1946, © 2005, GIA Publications, Inc.

Not for Tongues of Heaven's Angels   818

1. Not for tongues of heav-en's an - gels, Not for wis - dom
2. Love is hum - ble, love is gen - tle, Love is ten - der,
3. Nev - er jeal - ous, nev - er self - ish, Love will not re -
4. In the day this world is fad - ing Faith and hope will

to dis - cern, Not for faith that mas-ters moun-tains,
true, and kind; Love is gra-cious, ev - er pa - tient,
joice in wrong; Nev - er boast - ful nor re - sent - ful,
play their part; But when Christ is seen in glo - ry

For this bet - ter gift we yearn:
Gen - er - ous of heart and mind:
Love be - lieves and suf - fers long: May love be ours, Lord;
Love shall reign in ev - 'ry heart:

may love be ours.   May love be ours, O Lord.

Text: 1 Corinthians 13:1–13; Timothy Dudley-Smith, b.1926, © 1985, Hope Publishing Company
Tune: COMFORT, 8 7 8 7 with refrain; Michael Joncas, b.1951, © 1988, GIA Publications, Inc.

819 Eye Has Not Seen

Refrain

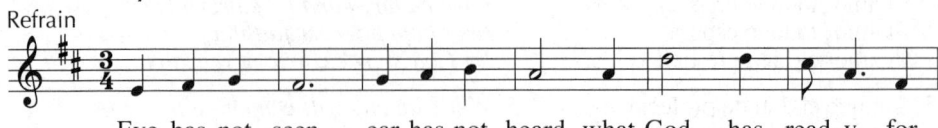

Eye has not seen, ear has not heard what God has read-y for

those who love him; Spir-it of love, come, give us the mind of

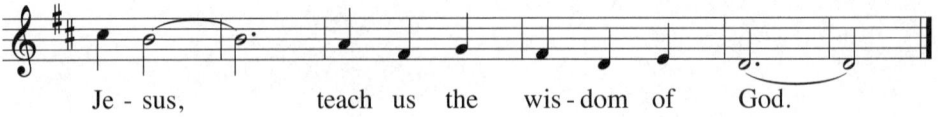

Je - sus, teach us the wis-dom of God.

Verses 1–3

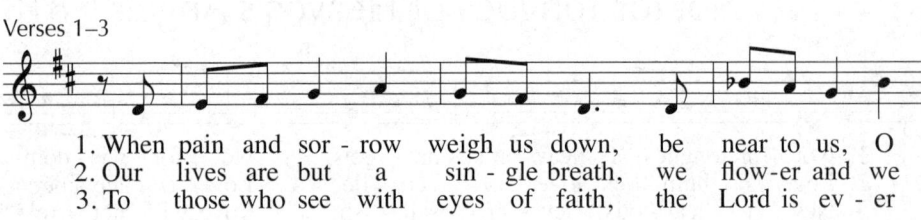

1. When pain and sor - row weigh us down, be near to us, O
2. Our lives are but a sin - gle breath, we flow-er and we
3. To those who see with eyes of faith, the Lord is ev - er

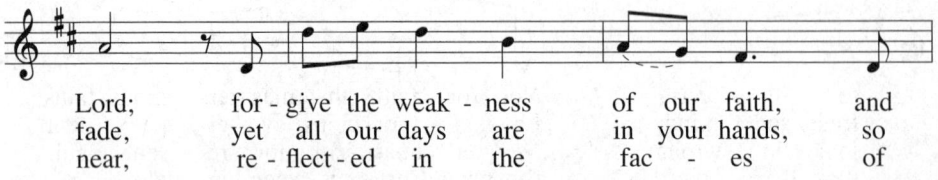

Lord; for - give the weak - ness of our faith, and
fade, yet all our days are in your hands, so
near, re - flect-ed in the fac - es of

D.C.

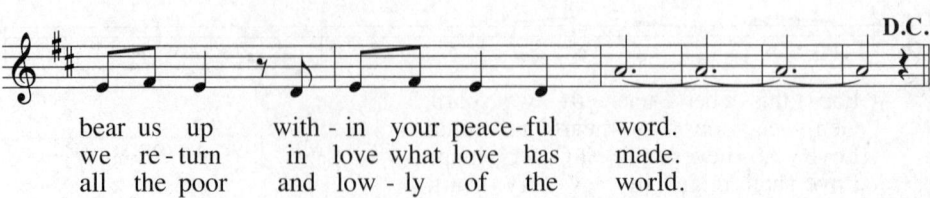

bear us up with - in your peace-ful word.
we re - turn in love what love has made.
all the poor and low - ly of the world.

Verse 4

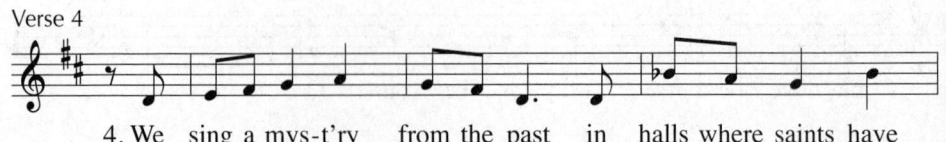

4. We sing a mys-t'ry from the past in halls where saints have

trod,   yet   ev - er new   the   mu - sic rings   to

D.C.

Je - sus, Liv - ing   Song   of   God.

Text: 1 Corinthians 2:9–10; Marty Haugen, b.1950
Tune: Marty Haugen, b.1950
© 1982, GIA Publications, Inc.

The King of Love My Shepherd Is   820

1. The   King   of   love   my   shep - herd is,   Whose
2. Where streams   of   liv - ing   wa - ter   flow,   My
3. Con - fused   and   fool - ish   oft   I strayed,   But
4. In   death's   dark   vale   I   fear   no   ill   With
5. You   spread   a   ta - ble   in   my sight,   Your
6. And   so,   through all   the length   of days   Your

good - ness fails   me   nev - er;   I   noth - ing lack   if
ran - somed soul   he's lead - ing, And, where   the   ver - dant
yet   in   love   he sought   me, And   on   his shoul - der
you,   dear Lord, be - side   me, Your   rod   and staff   my
sav - ing grace be - stow - ing; And, oh, what trans - port
good - ness fails   me   nev - er; Good Shep - herd, may   I

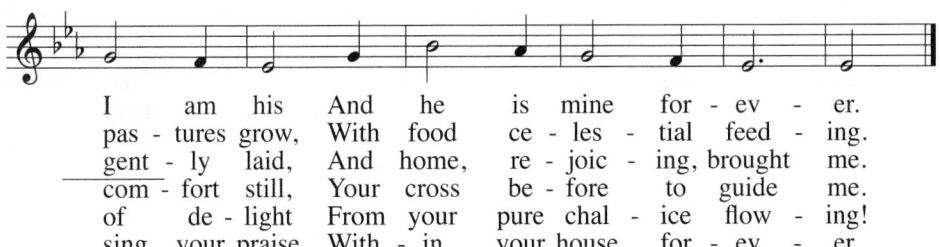

I   am   his   And   he   is mine   for - ev - er.
pas - tures grow, With food   ce - les - tial feed - ing.
gent - ly laid,   And home, re - joic - ing, brought me.
com - fort still, Your cross be - fore   to   guide   me.
of   de - light From your pure chal - ice flow - ing!
sing your praise With - in   your house   for - ev - er.

Text: Psalm 23; Henry W. Baker, 1821–1877, alt.
Tune: ST. COLUMBA, 8 7 8 7; Irish melody; harm. by A. Gregory Murray, OSB, 1905–1992, © Downside Abbey

821 I Heard the Voice of Jesus Say

1. I heard the voice of Je - sus say, "Come
2. I heard the voice of Je - sus say, "Be -
3. I heard the voice of Je - sus say, "I

un - to me and rest; Lay down, O wea - ry
hold, I free - ly give The liv - ing wa - ter;
am this dark world's light; Look un - to me, your

one, lay down Your head up - on my breast." I
thirst - y one, Stoop down and drink and live." I
morn shall rise, And all your day be bright." I

came to Je - sus as I was, So
came to Je - sus, and I drank Of
looked to Je - sus, and I found In

wea - ry, worn, and sad; I found in him a
that life - giv - ing stream; My thirst was quenched, my
him my star, my sun; And in that light of

rest - ing place, And he has made me glad.
soul re - vived, And now I live in him.
life I'll walk Till trav - 'ling days are done.

Text: Horatius Bonar, 1808–1889
Tune: KINGSFOLD, CMD; English melody; harm. by Ralph Vaughan Williams, 1872–1958

You Are Mine 822

Verses

1. I will come to you in the si - lence,
2. I am hope for all who are hope - less,
3. I am strength for all the de - spair - ing,
4. am the Word that leads all to free - dom, I

I will lift you from all your fear.
I am eyes for all who long to see. In the
heal - ing for the ones who dwell in shame.
am the peace the world can - not give.

You will hear my voice, I claim you as my choice, be
shad - ows of the night, I will be your light,
All the blind will see, the lame will all run free, and
I will call your name, em - brac - ing all your pain, stand

still and know I am here. *(To verse 2)*
come and rest in me. *(To refrain)*
all will know my name. *(To refrain)*
up, now walk, and live! *(To refrain)*

Refrain

Do not be a - fraid, I am with you. I have called you

each by name. Come and fol - low me, I will bring you

D.C.

home; I love you and you are mine.

4. I

Text: David Haas, b.1957
Tune: David Haas, b.1957
© 1991, GIA Publications, Inc.

823 Come to Me, O Weary Traveler

1. Come to me, O wea-ry trav-'ler; Come to me with
2. Do not fear, my yoke is eas-y; Do not fear, my
3. Take my yoke and leave your trou-bles; Take my yoke and
4. Rest in me, O wea-ry trav-'ler; Rest in me and

your dis-tress; Come to me, you heav-y bur-dened;
bur-den's light; Do not fear the path be-fore you;
come with me. Take my yoke, I am be-side you;
do not fear. Rest in me, my heart is gen-tle;

Come to me and find your rest.
Do not run from me in fright.
Take and learn hu-mil-i-ty.
Rest and cast a-way your care.

Text: Matthew 11:28–30; Sylvia G. Dunstan, 1955–1993, © 1991, GIA Publications, Inc.
Tune: DUNSTAN, 8 7 8 7; Bob Moore, b.1962, © 1993, GIA Publications, Inc.

Alternate tune: STUTTGART

824 Jesus, Lead the Way

1. Je-sus, lead the way Through our life's long day. When at
2. Je-sus, be our light In the midst of night. Let not
3. When we seek re-lief From a long-felt grief; When temp-
4. Je-sus, still lead on Till our rest be won. If you

times the way is cheer-less, Help us fol-low, calm and
faith-less fears o'er-take us; Let not faith and hope for-
ta-tions come al-lur-ing, Make us pa-tient and en-
lead us through rough plac-es, Grant us your re-deem-ing

fear - less.   Guide us   by   your   hand   To the prom - ised land.
sake us.   May   we   feel   you   near   As we   wor - ship here.
dur - ing.   Lord, we   seek your   grace In this   ho - ly place.
grac - es.   When our course is   o'er,   O - pen heav - en's door.

Text: *Jesu, geh voran;* Nicholas L. von Zinzendorf, 1700–1760; tr. by Jane Borthwick, 1813–1897, alt.
Tune: ROCHELLE, 55 88 55; Adam Drese, 1620–1701; harm. alt.

Nada Te Turbe   825

Ostinato Refrain

Korean transliteration: Du-lyeo-wo mal-la geog-jeong-eul mal-la
Ju-nim gye-si-ni a-swi-um eobs-ne.
Du-lyeo-wo mal-la geog-jeong-eul mal-la
Ju-nim an-e-seo.

Text: St. Teresa of Jesus; Taizé Community, 1986, 1991
Tune: Jacques Berthier, 1923–1994
© 1986, 1991, Les Presses de Taizé, GIA Publications, Inc., agent

826 Precious Lord, Take My Hand

1. Pre - cious Lord, take my hand, Lead me on, let me
2. When my way grows drear, Pre - cious Lord, lin - ger
3. When the dark - ness ap - pears And the night draws

stand, I am tired, I am weak, I am
near, When my life is al - most
near, And the day is past and

worn. Through the storm, through the
gone, Hear my cry, hear my
gone, At the riv - er I

night, Lead me on to the light. Take my
call, Hold my hand lest I fall. Take my
stand, Guide my feet, hold my hand. Take my

hand, pre - cious Lord, lead me home.
hand, pre - cious Lord, lead me home.
hand, pre - cious Lord, lead me home.

Text: Thomas A. Dorsey, 1899–1993
Tune: PRECIOUS LORD, 66 9 D; George N. Allen, 1812–1877; adapt. by Thomas A. Dorsey, 1899–1993; arr. by Kelly Dobbs-Mickus, b.1966
© 1938, (renewed), arr. © 1994, Warner-Tamerlane Publishing Corp.

My Shepherd, You Supply My Need 827

1. My Shep - herd, you sup - ply my need; Most
2. When I walk through the shades of death, Your
3. The sure pro - vi - sions of my God At -

ho - ly is your name. In pas - tures green you
pres - ence is my stay. One word of your sup -
tend me all my days. O may your house be

make me feed Be - side the liv - ing stream. You
port - ing breath Drives all my fears a - way. Your
my a - bode And all my work be praise! There

bring my wan - d'ring spir - it back When I for -
hand, in sight of all my foes, Does still my
would I find a set - tled rest, While oth - ers

sake your ways, And lead me, for your
ta - ble spread. My cup with bless - ings
go and come; No more a stran - ger

mer - cy's sake, In paths of truth and grace.
o - ver - flows; Your oil a - noints my head.
or a guest, But like a child at home.

Text: Psalm 23; Isaac Watts, 1674–1748, alt.
Tune: RESIGNATION, CMD; Funk's *Compilation of Genuine Church Music*, 1832; harm. by John L. Bell, b.1949, © 1993, Iona Community,
GIA Publications, Inc., agent

828 Do Not Let Your Hearts Be Troubled

Refrain

Do not let your hearts be trou - bled, have

faith in God and faith in me. I will go forth to pre -

pare a place for you, then I'll come back to take you

with me, that where I am, you may al - so be.

Verse 1

1. In God's house there are man - y plac - es for you a -

lone to dwell in safe - ty. You know the way to

D.C.

where I'll lead you, if you are lost, I will show the way.

Verses 2, 3

2. I am the way, the truth and the life,
3. The words I speak are not on - ly of my-self,

on - ly through me can you know what I know. If you knew
it is your God who lives with - in me. If you be -

me,   you would see the vi - sion,   if you see
lieve   that your God and I   are one,   I will pro -

D.C.

me,   you   see your God.
vide   when you call my name.

Text: John 14:1–3, 6–7, 10–14; David Haas, b.1957
Tune: David Haas, b.1957
© 1995, GIA Publications, Inc.

Do Not Be Afraid   829

Refrain

Do not be a - fraid.   I am with you   al-ways.

Do not be a - fraid.   My love is for - ev - er.

Verses

1. I know the plans I have for you, says the Lord, plans for peace and prosperity.
   Trust in me as I live in you. I give you a future and a hope.

2. Search for me with all your heart. I will let myself be found by you.
   I could never leave you orphaned. I will not abandon you!

3. Do not worry about tomorrow. Let go of all anxiety.
   If I so care for the birds in the air, I'll provide for all you need.

4. Do not let your hearts be troubled. Have faith in God and faith in me.
   I give you peace that passes understanding, peace to guard your heart and mind.

Text: Matthew 6:26, 34, John 14:1, 3, 27; Jeanne Cotter, b.1964
Tune: Jeanne Cotter, b.1964
© 2016, GIA Publications, Inc.

830 The Clouds' Veil

Refrain

E-ven though the rain hides the stars, e-ven though the
mist swirls the hills, e-ven when the dark clouds
veil the sky, God is by my side. E-ven when the
sun shall fall in sleep, e-ven when at dawn the sky shall
weep, e-ven in the night when storms shall rise,
God is by my side. God is by my side.

Verses

1. Bright the stars at night that
2. Deep the feast of life where
3. Blest are they who sing the

mir - ror heav-en's way to you. Bright the stars in
saints shall gath - er in deep peace. Deep in heav - en's
fel - low - ship of saints in light. Blest is heav - en's

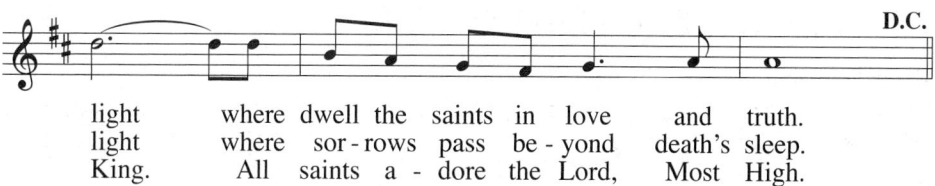

light   where dwell the saints in love   and   truth.
light   where sor-rows pass be-yond   death's sleep.
King.   All   saints a - dore the Lord,   Most High.

Text: Liam Lawton, b.1959
Tune: Liam Lawton, b.1959; arr. by John McCann, b.1961
© 1997, GIA Publications, Inc.

There Is a Balm in Gilead   831

Refrain

There is a balm   in   Gil-e-ad   To make the wound-ed   whole;

There is a balm   in   Gil-e-ad   To heal   the sin-sick soul.

Verses

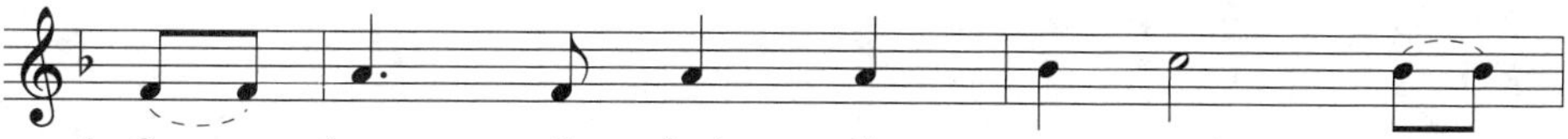

1. Some - times   I   feel   dis - cour - aged   And
2. Don't   ev - er   be   dis - cour - aged,   For
3. If you can - not preach like   Pe - ter,   If you

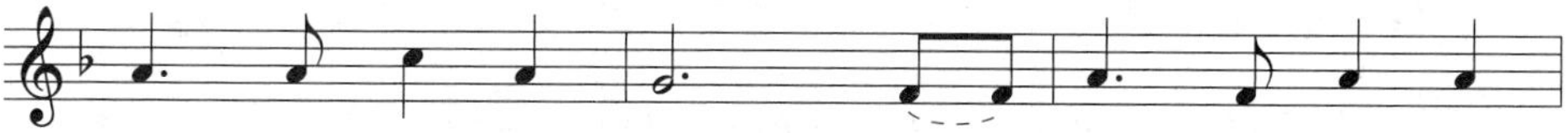

think   my work's in   vain,   But   then   the Ho - ly
Je - sus is your friend;   And   if   you lack for
can - not pray like Paul,   You can tell   the love of

D.C.

Spir - it   Re - vives   my soul a - gain.
knowl-edge,   He'll ne'er   re - fuse to   lend.
Je - sus,   And say,   "He died for   all!"

Text: African American spiritual
Tune: BALM IN GILEAD, 7 6 7 6 with refrain; African American spiritual; arr. by Nolan Williams, Jr., b.1969, © 2000, GIA Publications, Inc.

832 Within Our Darkest Night

Ostinato Refrain

Within our dark-est night, you kin - dle the
fire that nev - er dies a - way, nev - er dies a -
way. With-in our dark-est night, you kin - dle the
fire that nev - er dies a - way, nev-er dies a - way.

Text: Taizé Community, 1991
Tune: Jacques Berthier, 1923–1994

Heart of a Shepherd 833

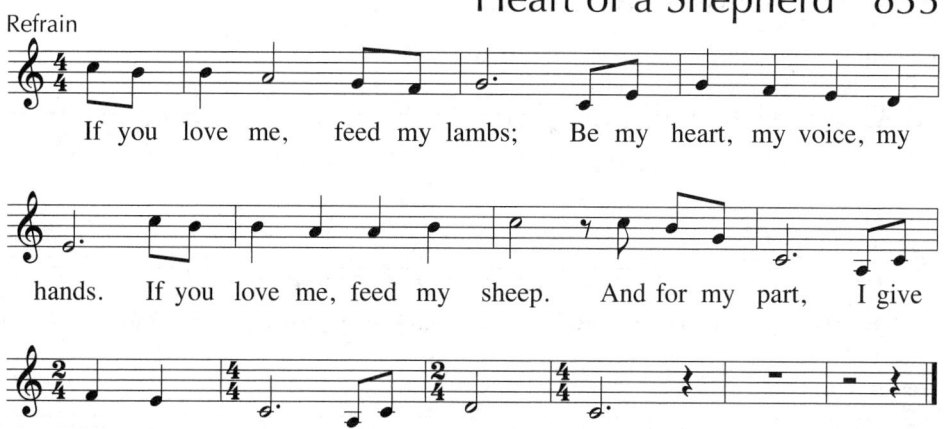

Refrain

If you love me, feed my lambs; Be my heart, my voice, my hands. If you love me, feed my sheep. And for my part, I give you the heart of a shep-herd.

Verses

1. Lord, you are my shepherd;
   there is nothing I shall want.
   Fresh and green are the pastures
   where you give me repose.
   Near restful waters you lead me,
   to revive my drooping spirit.

2. You guide me along the right path;
   you are true to your name.
   If I should walk in the valley of darkness
   no evil would I fear.
   You are there with your crook and your staff;
   with these you give me comfort.

3. You have prepared a banquet for me
   in the sight of my foes.
   My head you have anointed with oil;
   my cup is overflowing.

4. Surely goodness and kindness shall follow me
   all the days of my life.
   In the Lord's own house shall I dwell
   for ever and ever.

5. To the Father and Son give glory,
   give glory to the Spirit,
   to God who is, who was, and who will be
   for ever and ever.

Text: Refrain, Rory Cooney, b.1952, © 2005, GIA Publications, Inc.; verses, Psalm 23, The Grail, © 1963, 1993, The Grail, GIA Publications, Inc., agent
Tune: Refrain and verses arr., Rory Cooney, b.1952, © 2005, GIA Publications, Inc.; verses melody, Joseph Gelineau, SJ, 1920–2008, © 1963, 1993,
The Grail, GIA Publications, Inc., agent

834 Quietly, Peacefully

Refrain

Qui - et - ly, peace - ful - ly let me rest in you.

Qui - et - ly, peace - ful - ly lead me back to you.

Verses

1. In my weak - ness I have strayed,
2. Breathe your law deep in me,
3. Save me from my self - ish ways,
4. Lov - ing wis - dom, you a - lone
5. Hap - py is the heart that's free,
6. In the night I call to you;
7. Heal - ing Grace, take my pain,

drift - ing far from you.   In your good - ness
plant it in my soul.   Let your jus - tice
keep me from my pride.   By your grace,
know all I can be.   You, the hope my
choos - ing life with you.   Break the chains that
can you hear me cry?   Sad and fear - ful,
guard me night and day.   Show - er me

D.C.

stead - y me,   light my path to you.
be my song,   kind - ness be my goal.
bring me home, safe - ly by your side.
spir - it seeks, come and set me free.
bind my soul,   let me walk with you.
still I plead: do not pass me by.
with your love, wash my tears a - way.

Funeral Verses

1. Go in peace as the saints lead you on your way.
   May the angels take you home to God's holy place.

2. God has come to carry you to your dwelling place.
   Do not fear, Christ bids you come; meet God face to face.

3. Lay your burdens, calm your fears; you are not alone.
   Loving arms welcome you safely to God's home.

Text: Lori True, b.1961, © 2007, GIA Publications, Inc.
Tune: Antonín Dvořák, 1841–1904; adapt. by Lori True, b.1961, © 2007, GIA Publications, Inc.

Stand by Me 835

1. When the storms of life are rag-ing,
2. In the midst of trib - u - la-tions,
3. In the midst of faults and fail-ures, Stand by me,
4. In the midst of per - se - cu - tion,
5. When I'm grow - ing old and fee - ble,

When the storms of life are rag - ing,
In the midst of trib - u - la-tions,
In the midst of faults and fail-ures, Stand by me,
In the midst of per - se - cu - tion,
When I'm grow - ing old and fee - ble,

When the world is toss - ing me Like a ship up - on the
When the hosts of hell as - sail, And my strength be - gins to
When I do the best I can, And my friends mis - un - der-
When my foes in war ar - ray Un - der - take to stop my
When my life be - comes a bur - den, And I'm near - ing chill - y

sea; Thou who rul - est wind and wa - ter,
fail, Thou who nev - er lost a bat - tle,
stand, Thou who know - est all a - bout me, Stand by me.
way, Thou who saved Paul and Si - las,
Jor - dan, O thou "Lil - y of the Val - ley,"

Text: Charles A. Tindley, 1851–1933
Tune: STAND BY ME, 8 3 8 3 77 8 3; Charles A. Tindley, 1851–1933; harm. by Francis A. Clark, 1851–1933

836 Come to Me

Refrain

Come to me, come to me, come when you are wea - ry;

come to me, come to me, and I will give you rest.

Verses 1, 2

1. All who la - bor and are bur - dened,
2. Take my yoke up - on your shoul - ders,

all who la - bor and are bur - dened, let them come to me,
take my yoke up - on your shoul - ders, come and learn from me,

come to me, and I will give them rest.
learn from me, for I am gen - tle of heart.

Verse 3

3. For the heart I hold is hum - ble, yes, the

heart I hold is hum - ble, and my yoke is eas - y, my

bur - den light, and you will find rest for your souls.

Verse 4

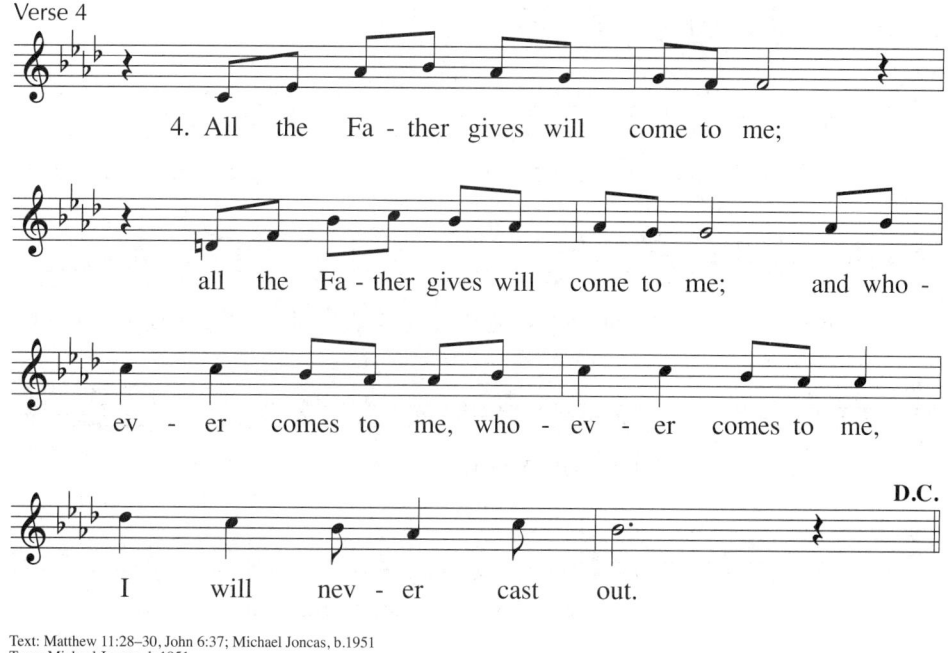

4. All the Fa - ther gives will come to me;
all the Fa - ther gives will come to me; and who -
ev - er comes to me, who - ev - er comes to me,
I will nev - er cast out.

Text: Matthew 11:28–30, John 6:37; Michael Joncas, b.1951
Tune: Michael Joncas, b.1951
© 1989, 2014, GIA Publications, Inc.

Come, Bring Your Burdens to God / 837
Woza Nomthwalo Wakho

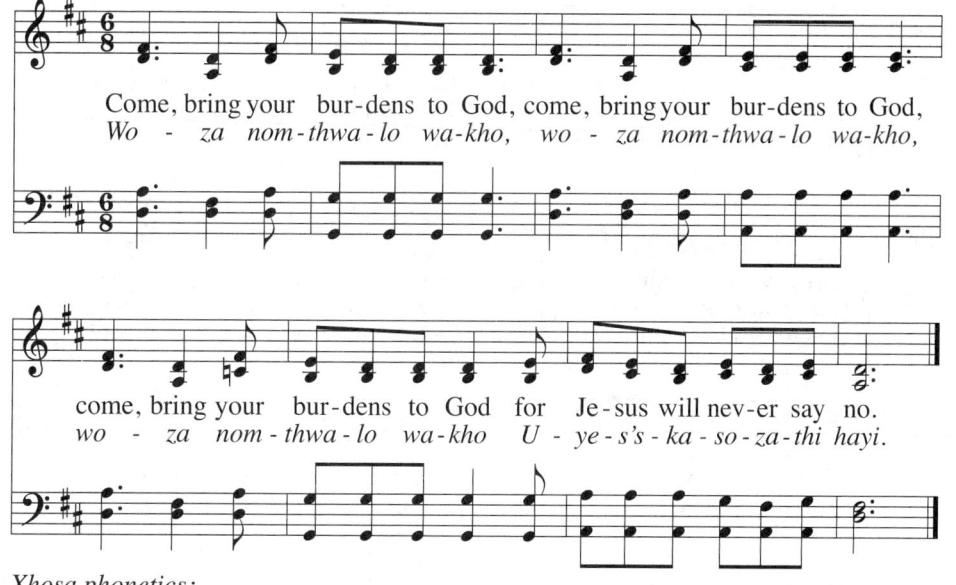

Come, bring your bur-dens to God, come, bring your bur-dens to God,
Wo - za nom-thwa-lo wa-kho, wo - za nom-thwa-lo wa-kho,

come, bring your bur-dens to God for Je-sus will nev-er say no.
wo - za nom-thwa-lo wa-kho U - ye-s's - ka - so - za - thi hayi.

Xhosa phonetics:
Woh-zah nohm-thwah-loh wah-khoh, U-yehs skah-soh-zah-thee hahyee

Text: South African (Xhosa); tr. by Barbara Clark, Mairi Munro, and Martine Stemerick, © 2008, Iona Community, GIA Publications, Inc., agent
Tune: South African melody; arr. by Welile Sigabi, © 2008, Iona Community, GIA Publications, Inc., agent

838 In the Arms of God

Refrain

Come and rest in the arms of God, leave your wor-ry and fear; make your home in the heart of God, God will dry ev-'ry tear. For the bur-den you car-ry will fade with-in God's care, come and rest in the arms of God.

Verses

1. Gen-tle is God's way and hum-ble is God's heart. God's love will light the way that leads to peace. Sure-ly you shall see God's good-ness and God's grace: Rest now in God's em-brace.

2. Do not be a-fraid; God heals the bro-ken heart. Through grief and dis-be-lief God still re-mains. God and God a-lone will be your soul's true rest: Fall in the arms of God.

3. You are not a-lone, for God is al-ways near. Come, place your doubt and fear with-in God's care. God will give you rest and soothe your wea-ry soul: Dwell in the heart of God.

D.C.

Text: Tony E. Alonso, b.1980
Tune: Tony E. Alonso, b.1980
© 2009, GIA Publications, Inc.

Blest Are They 839

Verses 1–3

1. Blest are they, the poor in spir-it; theirs is the
2. Blest are they, the low - ly ones; they shall in -
3. Blest are they who show mer-cy; mer - cy

king - dom of God. Blest are they,
her - it the earth. Blest are they who
shall be theirs. Blest are they, the

full of sor-row; they shall be con - soled.
hun-ger and thirst; they shall have their fill.
pure of heart; they shall see God.

Refrain

Re - joice and be glad! Bless-ed are you,

ho - ly are you! Re - joice and be glad!

Yours is the king - dom of God!

Verses 4, 5

4. Blest are they who seek peace; they are the
5. Blest are you who suf - fer hate, all be -

chil - dren of God. Blest are they who
cause of me. Re-joice and be glad,

D.S.

suf - fer in faith; the glo - ry of God is theirs.
yours is the king - dom; shine for all to see.

Text: Matthew 5:3–12; David Haas, b.1957
Tune: David Haas, b.1957; vocal arr. by David Haas, b.1957, Michael Joncas, b.1951
© 1985, GIA Publications, Inc.

840 The Kingdom of God

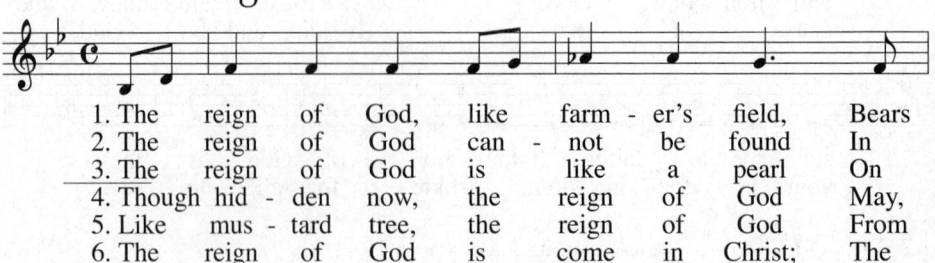

1. The king-dom of God is jus-tice and joy;
2. The king-dom of God is mer-cy and grace;
3. The king-dom of God is chal-lenge and choice:
4. God's king-dom is come, the gift and the goal;

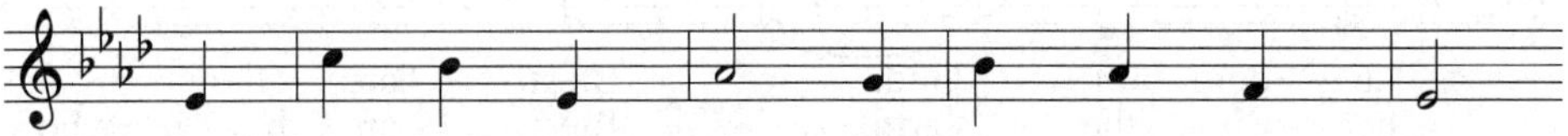

For Je-sus re - stores what sin would de - stroy.
The cap - tives are freed, the sin - ners find place,
Be - lieve the good news, re - pent and re - joice!
In Je - sus be - gun, in heav - en made whole.

God's pow - er and glo - ry in Je - sus we know;
The out - cast are wel - comed God's ban - quet to share;
God's love for us sin - ners brought Christ to his cross:
The heirs of the king - dom shall an - swer his call;

And here and here - af - ter the king-dom shall grow.
And hope is a - wak - ened in place of de - spair.
Our cri - sis of judg - ment for gain or for loss.
And all things cry "Glo - ry!" to God all in all.

Text: Bryn A. Rees, 1911–1983, © 1973, Alexander Scott
Tune: LAUDATE DOMINUM, 10 10 11 11; Charles H. H. Parry, 1848–1918

841 The Reign of God

1. The reign of God, like farm - er's field, Bears
2. The reign of God can - not be found In
3. The reign of God is like a pearl On
4. Though hid - den now, the reign of God May
5. Like mus - tard tree, the reign of God From
6. The reign of God is come in Christ; The

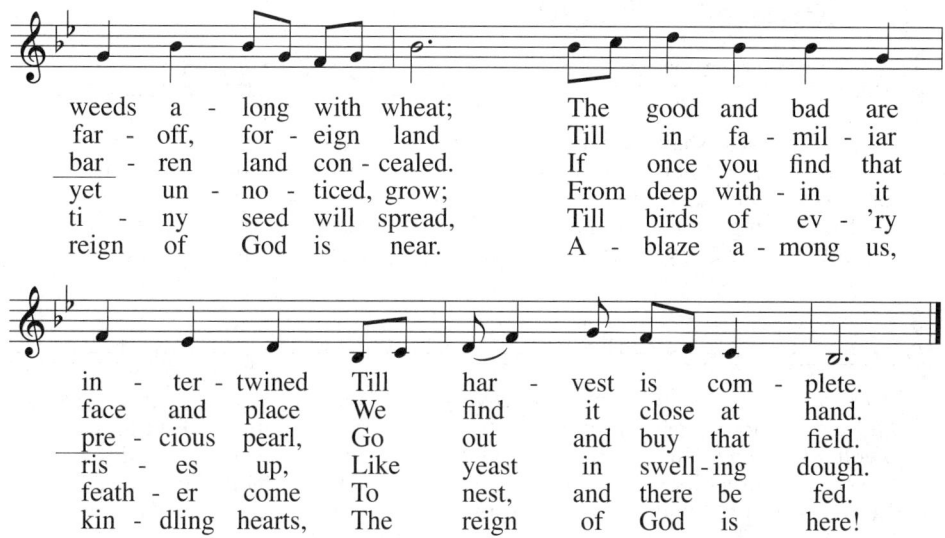

weeds	a -	long	with	wheat;	The	good	and	bad	are
far -	off,	for -	eign	land	Till	in	fa -	mil -	iar
bar -	ren	land	con -	cealed.	If	once	you	find	that
yet	un -	no -	ticed,	grow;	From	deep	with -	in	it
ti -	ny	seed	will	spread,	Till	birds	of	ev -	'ry
reign	of	God	is	near.	A -	blaze	a -	mong	us,

in -	ter -	twined	Till	har -	vest	is	com -	plete.
face	and	place	We	find	it	close	at	hand.
pre -	cious	pearl,	Go	out	and	buy	that	field.
ris -	es	up,	Like	yeast	in	swell - ing	dough.
feath -	er	come	To	nest,	and	there	be	fed.
kin -	dling	hearts,	The	reign	of	God	is	here!

Text: Matthew 13:24–33, 44–49, Mark 4:26–34; Delores Dufner, OSB, b.1939, © 1995, 2003, GIA Publications, Inc.
Tune: McKEE, CM; African American; adapt. by Harry T. Burleigh, 1866–1949

Jesus, Remember Me 842

Ostinato Refrain

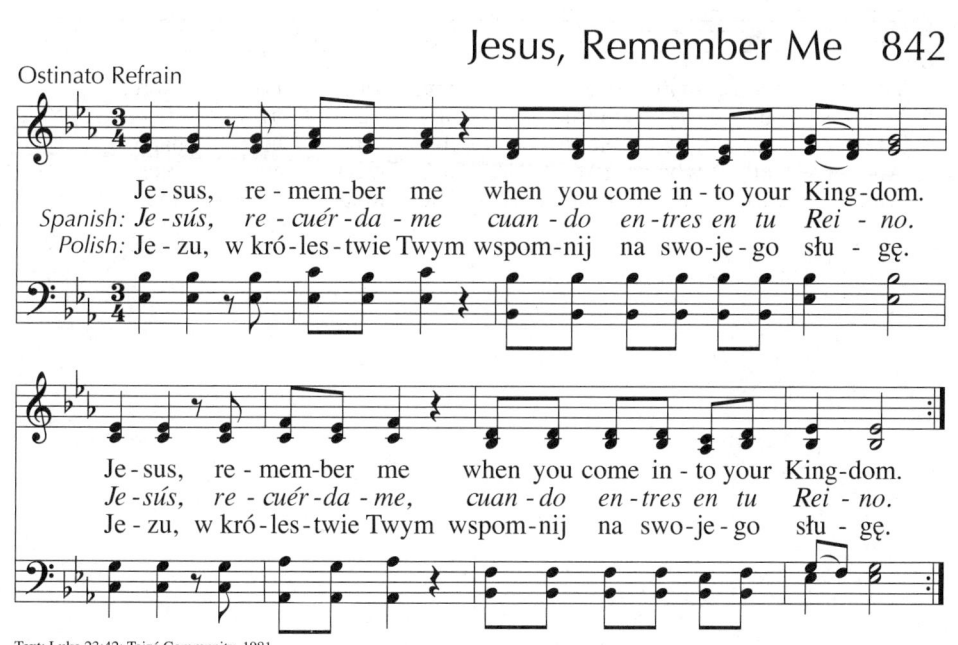

Je - sus, re - mem - ber me when you come in - to your King - dom.
Spanish: Je - sús, re - cuér - da - me cuan - do en - tres en tu Rei - no.
Polish: Je - zu, w kró - les - twie Twym wspom - nij na swo - je - go słu - gę.

Je - sus, re - mem - ber me when you come in - to your King - dom.
Je - sús, re - cuér - da - me, cuan - do en - tres en tu Rei - no.
Je - zu, w kró - les - twie Twym wspom - nij na swo - je - go słu - gę.

Text: Luke 23:42; Taizé Community, 1981
Tune: Jacques Berthier, 1923–1994
© 1981, 2005, Les Presses de Taizé, GIA Publications, Inc., agent

843 Jesus Shall Reign

1. Je - sus shall reign wher - e'er the sun
2. To him shall end - less prayer be made,
3. Peo - ple and realms of ev - 'ry tongue
4. Bless - ings a - bound wher - e'er he reigns:
5. Let ev - 'ry crea - ture rise and bring

Does its suc - ces - sive jour - neys run;
And prais - es throng to crown his head;
Dwell on his love with sweet - est song;
The pris - 'ners leap to lose their chains,
Bless - ing and hon - or to our King,

His king - dom stretch from shore to shore,
His name like sweet per - fume shall rise
And in - fant voic - es shall pro - claim
The wea - ry find e - ter - nal rest,
An - gels de - scend with songs a - gain,

Till moons shall wax and wane no more.
With ev - 'ry morn - ing sac - ri - fice.
Their ear - ly bless - ings on his name.
And all who suf - fer want are blest.
And earth re - peat the loud A - men.

Text: Isaac Watts, 1674–1748, alt.
Tune: DUKE STREET, LM; John Hatton, c.1710–1793

We Will Walk with God / 844
Caminemos con Dios / Sizohamba

We will walk with God, my broth-ers, we will walk with God.
Ca - mi - ne - mos con Dios, her - ma - nos, ca - mi - ne - mos con Dios.
Swati: Si - zo-ham-ba na - ye, wo wo wo, si - zo-ham-ba na - ye.

We will walk with God, my sis - ters, we will walk with God.
Ca - mi - ne - mos con Dios, her - ma - nas, ca - mi - ne - mos con Dios.
Si - zo-ham-ba na - ye, wo wo wo, si - zo-ham-ba na - ye.

We will go re - joic - ing till the king-dom has come.
Ca - mi - nan - do_a - le - gres has - ta_el rei - no de Dios.
Ngom-hla wen - ja - bu - la, si - zo-ham - ba na - ye.

We will go re - joic - ing till the king-dom has come.
Ca - mi - nan - do_a - le - gres has - ta_el rei - no de Dios.
Ngom-hla wen - ja - bu - la, si - zo-ham - ba na - ye.

Swati phonetics:
See-zoh-hahm-bah nah-yay, woh woh woh, see-zoh-hahm-bah nah-yay.
Ngahm-hlah wen-jah-boo-lah, see-zoh-hahm-bah nah-yay.

Text: Swaziland traditional; transcribed by Swedish Youth Exchange Project, ©; English tr. by John L. Bell, b.1949, © 2002, Iona Community, GIA Publications, Inc., agent; Spanish tr. by Ronald F. Krisman, b.1946, © 2012, GIA Publications, Inc.
Tune: SIZOHAMBA, Irregular; Swaziland traditional; transcribed by Swedish Youth Exchange Project, ©

845 Within the Reign of God

Verses

1. Come now, the feast is spread; in Je-sus' name we break the bread.
2. Stand up and do not fear, for Christ is tru-ly pres-ent here.
3. Wel-come the weak and poor, the sin-ner finds an o-pen door,
4. All fear and ha-tred ends and foes be-come our faith-ful friends,
5. Sing out the ju-bi-lee when those en-slaved are all set free,
6. One earth, one ho-ly band, one fam-'ly as our God has planned,

Here shall we all be fed
Heav-en is tru-ly near
none judged, and none ig-nored   with-in the reign of God.
just as our God in-tends
chil-dren of God are we
all share the prom-ised land

Cantor:

Come take this ho-ly food; re-ceive the bod-y and the blood.
Now at the wed-ding feast, the great-est here shall be the least.
Here shall the wea-ry rest, the stran-ger be a wel-come guest.
All you who seek God's face are wel-come in this ho-ly place;
No more can we for-get the ones who bear life's crush-ing debt;
Come now, the feast is spread, in Je-sus' name we break the bread;

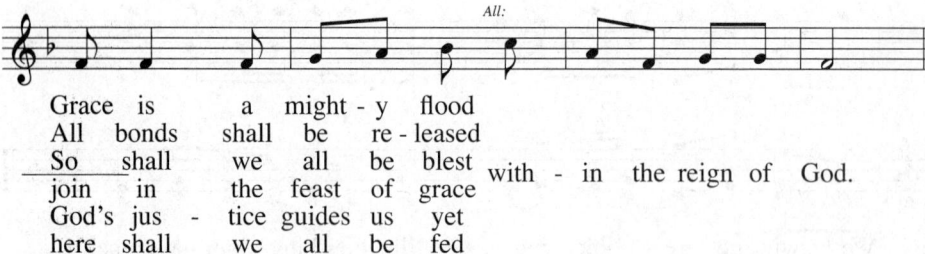

Grace is a might-y flood
All bonds shall be re-leased
So shall we all be blest   with-in the reign of God.
join in the feast of grace
God's jus-tice guides us yet
here shall we all be fed

Refrain

Bless-ed are they who will feast in the reign of God.

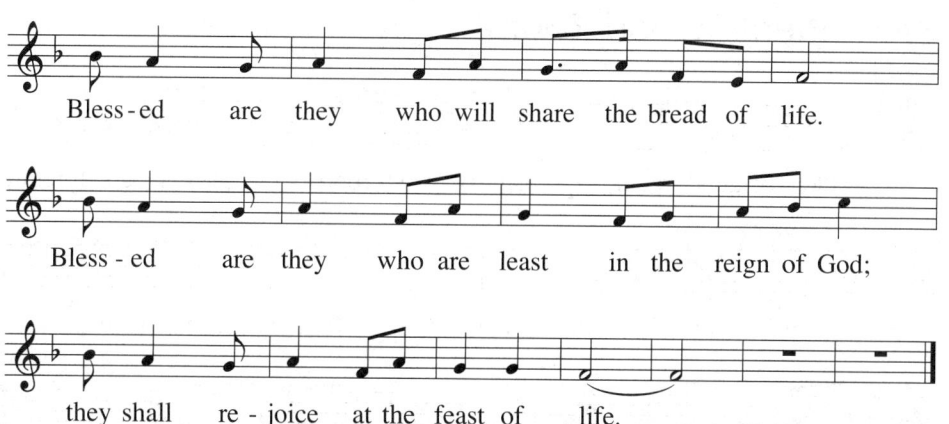

Blessed are they who will share the bread of life.

Blessed are they who are least in the reign of God;

they shall re-joice at the feast of life.

Text Marty Haugen, b.1950
Tune: Marty Haugen, b.1950
© 1999, GIA Publications, Inc.

The Kingdom of God   846

Ostinato Refrain

The king-dom of God is jus-tice and peace and
El rei - no de Dios es rei - no de paz, jus -

joy in the Ho-ly Spir - it. Come, Lord, and
ti - cia y a - le - grí - a. Ven, Dios, y

Last time

o-pen in us the gates of your king - dom.
a - bre en mí las puer - tas del rei - no.
Last time

Text: Taizé Community
Tune: Taizé Community
© 2001, 2011, Les Presses de Taizé, GIA Publications, Inc., agent

847 Plenty Good Room

Refrain

Plen-ty good room, plen-ty good room, plen-ty good room in my Fa-ther's king-dom, Plen-ty good room, plen-ty good room, just choose your seat and sit down.

Verses

1. I would not be a sin-ner,
2. I would not be a li-ar, I'll tell you the rea-son
3. I would not be a back-slid-er,

why; cause if my Lord should call on me I would-n't be read-y to die.

D.C.

Text: African American spiritual
Tune: African American spiritual; arr. by Joseph Joubert, b.1958, © 2000, GIA Publications, Inc.

Sing a New Church 848

1. Sum - moned by   the   God who made   us   Rich in
2. Ra - diant ris - en   from the   wa - ter,   Robed in
3. Trust the   good - ness   of   cre - a - tion;   Trust the
4. Bring the   hopes   of   ev - 'ry   na - tion;   Bring the
5. Draw   to - geth - er   at one   ta - ble   All   the

our   di - ver - si - ty,   Gath-ered in   the   name of
ho - li - ness and light,   Male and   fe - male   in God's
Spir - it   strong with - in.   Dare to dream   the   vi - sion
art   of   ev - 'ry race.   Weave a   song   of   peace and
hu - man   fam - i - ly;   Shape a   cir - cle   ev - er

Je - sus,   Rich - er still   in   u - ni - ty:
im - age,   Male and   fe - male,   God's de - light:
prom - ised, Sprung from seed   of   what has been.
jus - tice;   Let   it   sound through time and space.
wid - er   And   a   peo - ple   ev - er   free.

Let us bring the   gifts that dif - fer   And, in

splen - did, var - ied ways, Sing a new Church in - to

be - ing, One in faith and love and praise.

Text: Delores Dufner, OSB, b.1939, © 1991, Delores Dufner, OSB. Published by OCP.
Tune: NETTLETON, 8 7 8 7 with refrain, from Wyeth's *Repository of Sacred Music*, 1813

849 God, Bless Your Church with Strength!

1. God, bless your Church with strength! Wher - ev - er we may be, Build up your ser - vants as we work In com - mon min - is - try. Urge us from fledg - ling faith To ven - ture and to soar, Through o - pen skies to sing the praise Of Christ, whom we a - dore.

2. God, bless your Church with life! May all our branch - es thrive, Un - blem - ished, whole - some, bear - ing fruit, A - bun - dant - ly a - live. From you, one Ho - ly Vine, In free - dom may we grow. Sus - tain us in our mis - sion, Lord, Your love and peace to show.

3. God, bless your Church with hope! De - spite cha - ot - ic days May we in dark - ness shine, to light A path - way through life's maze. May jus - tice be our aim And kind - ness ours to share; And let us walk in hum - ble - ness, As - sured our God is there.

Text: John A. Dalles, b.1954, © 2000, GIA Publications, Inc.
Tune: DIADEMATA, SMD; George J. Elvey, 1816–1893

As a Fire Is Meant for Burning 850

1. As a fire is meant for burn - ing
2. We are learn - ers; we are teach - ers;
3. As a green bud in the spring - time

1. With a bright and warm-ing flame, So the Church is meant for
2. We are pil - grims on the way. We are seek - ers; we are
3. Is a sign of life re - newed, So may we be signs of

1. mis - sion, Giv - ing glo - ry to God's name.
2. giv - ers; We are ves - sels made of clay.
3. one - ness Mid earth's peo - ples, man - y hued.

1. As we wit - ness to the gos - pel, We would
2. By our gen - tle, lov - ing ac - tions, We would
3. As a rain - bow lights the heav - ens When a

1. build a bridge of care, Join - ing hands a - cross the
2. show that Christ is light. In a hum - ble, lis - t'ning
3. storm is past and gone, May our lives re - flect the

1. na - tions, Find - ing neigh - bors ev - 'ry - where.
2. Spir - it, We would live to God's de - light.
3. ra - diance Of God's new and glor - ious dawn.

Text: Ruth Duck, b.1947, © 1992, GIA Publications, Inc.
Tune: BEACH SPRING, 8 7 8 7 D; *The Sacred Harp*, 1844; harm. by Ronald A. Nelson, 1927–2014, © 1978, *Lutheran Book of Worship*,
admin. by Augsburg Fortress

851 Christ's Church Shall Glory

1. Christ's church shall glo - ry in his pow'r
2. Christ's peo - ple serve his way - ward world
3. Christ's liv - ing lamp shall bright - ly burn,
4. Christ's bod - y tri - umphs in his name;

And grow to his per - fec - tion; He is our
To whom he seems a stran - ger; He knows its
And to our earth - ly cit - y For - got - ten
One Fa - ther sov - 'reign giv - er, One Spir - it,

rock, our might - y tow'r Our life, our res - ur -
wel - come from of old, He shares our joy, our
beau - ty shall re - turn, And pu - ri - ty and
with his love a - flame, One Lord, the same for

rec - tion: So by his skill - ful hand
dan - ger: So strong, and yet so weak,
pit - y: To give the op - pressed their right
ev - er. To you, O God, our prize

The church of Christ shall stand; The mas - ter -
The church of Christ shall speak; His cross our
The church of Christ shall fight; And though the
The church of Christ shall rise Be - yond all

build - er's plan He works, as he be - gan,
great - est need, His word the vi - tal seed
years seem long He is our strength and song,
meas - ured height, To that e - ter - nal light

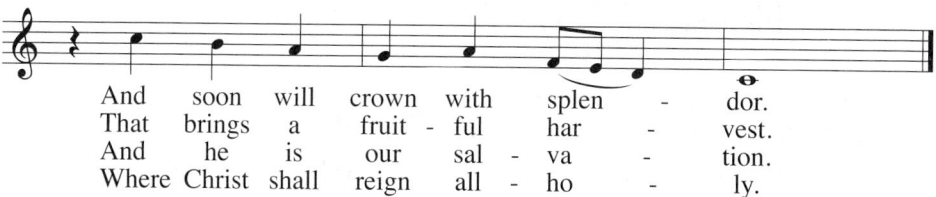

And soon will crown with splen - dor.
That brings a fruit - ful har - vest.
And he is our sal - va - tion.
Where Christ shall reign all - ho - ly.

Text: Christopher Idle, b.1938, © 1982, The Jubilate Group (admin. by Hope Publishing Company)
Tune: EIN' FESTE BURG, 8 7 8 7 66 66 7; Martin Luther, 1483–1546; harm. by J. S. Bach, 1685–1750

Christ Is Made the Sure Foundation   852

1. Christ is made the sure foun-da-tion, Christ, our Head and
2. To this tem-ple, where we call you, Come, O Lord of
3. Here be-stow on all your ser-vants What they ask of
4. Praise and hon-or to the Fa-ther, Praise and hon-or

cor - ner - stone, Cho - sen of the Lord and pre - cious,
hosts, to - day; With your stead - fast lov - ing-kind-ness,
you to gain; What they gain from you, for - ev - er
to the Son, Praise and hon - or to the Spir - it,

Bind - ing all the Church in one; Ho - ly Zi - on's
Hear your ser - vants as they pray; And your full - est
With the bless - ed to re - tain; And here - af - ter
Ev - er three and ev - er one: One in might and

help for - ev - er And our con - fi - dence a - lone.
ben - e - dic - tion Shed in all its bright ar - ray.
in your glo - ry Ev - er - more with you to reign.
one in glo - ry While un - end - ing a - ges run!

Text: *Angularis fundamentum*; 11th C.; tr. by John M. Neale, 1818–1866, alt.
Tune: WESTMINSTER ABBEY, 8 7 8 7 8 7; adapt. from an anthem of Henry Purcell, 1659–1695, by Ernest Hawkins, 1807–1868

853 A House of Prayer

Refrain

Let this be a house of prayer, shel-ter of God's love and care, shaped in-to a house of liv - ing stones by the hands of Christ, our cor - ner - stone. Let this be a house of prayer for all peo - ple.

Verses

Cantor:

1. A font of God's love o - ver-flow-ing:
2. A ref - uge in a time of trou - ble:
3. A ta - ble set for friend and stran-ger:

All:

Let this be a house of

A ho - ly ground where all find wel - come:
A ves - sel of God's grace and mer - cy:
A bod - y tak - en, blessed and bro - ken:

prayer.

A tem - ple of the
A hos - pi - tal where
A ban - quet hall for

Let this be a house of prayer.

D.C.

Ho - ly Spir - it:
wounds are treat-ed:
ev - 'ry hun-ger:

Let this be a house of prayer.

Text: Tony E. Alonso, b.1980
Tune: Tony E. Alonso, b.1980
© 2015, GIA Publications, Inc.

O Christ the Great Foundation 854

1. O Christ the great foun - da - tion On which your peo - ple stand
2. Bap - tized in one con - fes - sion, One church in all the earth,
3. Where ty - rants' hold is tight-ened, Where strong de - vour the weak,
4. This is the mo - ment glo - rious When he who once was dead

To preach your true sal - va - tion In ev - 'ry age and land:
We bear our Lord's im - pres - sion, The sign of sec - ond birth:
Where in - no - cents are fright-ened The right-eous fear to speak,
Shall lead his church vic - to - rious, Their cham-pion and their head.

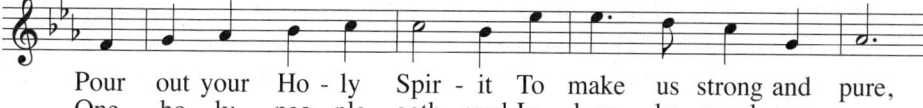

Pour out your Ho - ly Spir - it To make us strong and pure,
One ho - ly peo - ple gath - ered In love be - yond our own,
There let your church a - wak - ing At - tack the pow'rs of sin
The Lord of all cre - a - tion His heav'n - ly king-dom brings

To keep the faith un - bro - ken As long as worlds en - dure.
By grace we were in - vit - ed, By grace we make you known.
And, all their ram-parts break - ing, With you the vic - tory win.
The fi - nal con - sum - ma - tion, The glo - ry of all things.

Text: Timothy T'ingfang Lew, 1891–1947, alt., © 1977, Christian Conference of Asia, admin. by GIA Publications, Inc.
Tune: AURELIA, 7 6 7 6 D; Samuel Sebastian Wesley, 1810–1876

855 Bless These Walls

Refrain

Bless these walls, bless this space; find in us a ho-ly place.

Make us new, one in you, gath-ered here to grow in faith.

1., 2. *To verses 1, 2*

3. *To verse 3* *4.*

grow in grow in faith.

Verse 1

1. Gath-ered here in this ho-ly tem-ple, all are here: the great-est and least. You've pre-pared a place for us to dwell in last-ing peace. *D.C.*

Verse 2

2. May the doors of our church be o-pen to all who hear your call. O-pen wide the gates and let the love of Christ pour in. *D.C.*

Verse 3

faith.

3. As the spar-row finds a home and the swal-low finds its nest, our hap-pi-ness is with you, O God. In your house we shall, we shall dwell. *D.C.*

Text: Based on Psalm 84; Zack Stachowski
Tune: Zack Stachowski
© 2011, GIA Publications, Inc.

'Tis the Gift to Be Simple 856

'Tis the gift to be sim-ple, 'tis the gift to be free, 'Tis the
gift to come down where we ought to be; And
when we find our-selves in the place just right, 'Twill
be in the val - ley of love and de - light.
When true sim-plic-i - ty is gained, To bow and to bend we
shan't be a-shamed; to turn, turn, will be our de-light, Till by
turn - ing, turn - ing we come round right.

Text: Joseph Brackett, Jr., 1797–1882
Tune: SIMPLE GIFTS, Joseph Brackett, Jr., 1797–1882; acc. Margaret W. Mealy, b.1922, © 1984

857 O Blessed Are the Poor in Spirit

1. O bless-ed are the poor in spirit;
3. O bless-ed are the meek;
5. O bless-ed are the merciful;
7. O bless-ed are the peacemakers;
9. O bless-ed are you when the world re-viles you and persecutes you;

1. for theirs is the kingdom of heav - en.
3. for they shall in - her - it the earth.
5. for they shall obtain mer - cy.
7. for they shall be called the chil-dren of God.
9. and utters all manner of evil against you falsely for my sake.

2. O bless-ed are those who mourn;
4. O bless-ed are those who hunger and thirst af - ter righteousness;
6. O bless-ed are the pure in heart;
8. O bless-ed are those who are perse - cut-ed for righteousness' sake;
10. Re - joice and be ex - ceedingly glad;

2. for they shall be com - fort - ed.
4. for they shall be sat - is - fied.
6. for they shall see God.
8. for theirs is the kingdom of heav - en.
10. for great is your reward in heav - en.

Text: Matthew 5:3–12; *The Beatitudes*
Tune: KONTAKION, Irregular; Russian Orthodox Liturgy, adapt. by Richard Proulx, 1937–2010, © 1985, GIA Publications, Inc.

Journey of Faith 858

1. Mak - er of gal - ax - ies, star - dust, and all that has
2. Je - sus, of Mar - y born, bring - ing the good news as -
3. Spir - it of Je - sus and men - tor of saints through the
4. We are your fam - 'ly be - lov - ed in each gen - er -
5. Praise for the joy of be - liev - ing and jour - ney a -

be - ing, O - pen the eyes of our
tound - ing, O - pen the ears of our
a - ges, O - pen our lips with a
a - tion, Church on a pil - grim - age,
maz - ing; Praise for the good - ness and

hearts to know faith's ways of see - ing.
hearts to your Gos - pel re - sound - ing.
word that in - vites and en - gag - es.
called to em - brace trans - for - ma - tion.
beau - ty here, ev - 'ry - where blaz - ing!

Shine through the night; Lead us to ra - diance of
Hear - ing your voice, Let all the peo - ple re -
We will pro - claim Par - don and peace in Christ's
Called to this way, Grow - ing in love day by
Praise for the song, Sing - ing the faith - heart - ed

light, Vi - sion em - pow - 'ring and free - ing.
joice, Glad in your bless - ings a - bound - ing.
name Through all of life, all its stag - es.
day, We live now, Christ's new cre - a - tion.
strong; Praise for de - light in the prais - ing!

Text: Delores Dufner, OSB, b.1939, © 2012, Sisters of St. Benedict. Published by World Library Publications
Tune: LOBE DEN HERREN, 14 14 47 8; *Stralsund Gesangbuch*, 1665

859 What Does the Lord Require

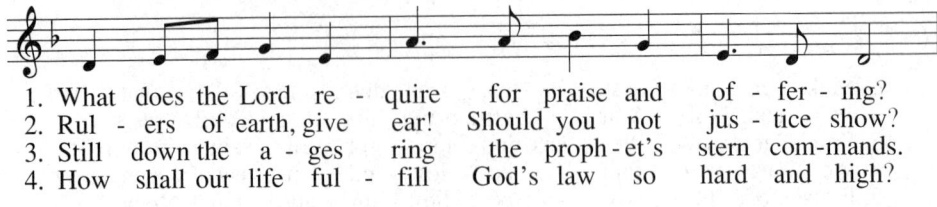

1. What does the Lord re - quire for praise and of - fer - ing?
2. Rul - ers of earth, give ear! Should you not jus - tice show?
3. Still down the a - ges ring the proph - et's stern com-mands.
4. How shall our life ful - fill God's law so hard and high?

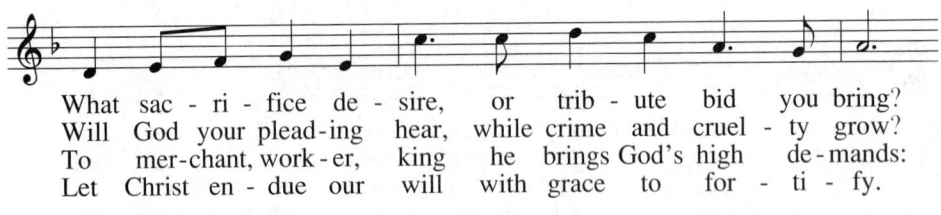

What sac - ri - fice de - sire, or trib - ute bid you bring?
Will God your plead-ing hear, while crime and cruel - ty grow?
To mer-chant, work - er, king he brings God's high de - mands:
Let Christ en - due our will with grace to for - ti - fy.

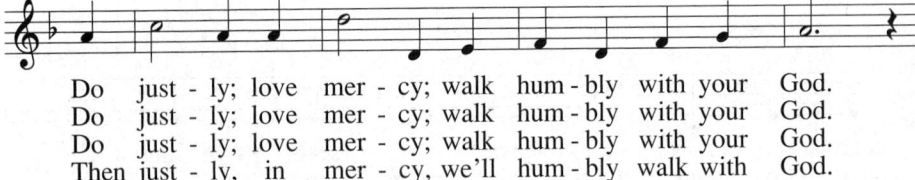

Do just - ly; love mer - cy; walk hum - bly with your God.
Do just - ly; love mer - cy; walk hum - bly with your God.
Do just - ly; love mer - cy; walk hum - bly with your God.
Then just - ly, in mer - cy, we'll hum - bly walk with God.

Text: Micah 6:6–8; Albert F. Bayly, 1901–1984, alt., © 1988, Oxford University Press
Tune: SHARPTHORNE, 12 12 12; Erik Routley, 1917–1982, © 1969, Hope Publishing Company

860 Lord, Make Us Servants of Your Peace

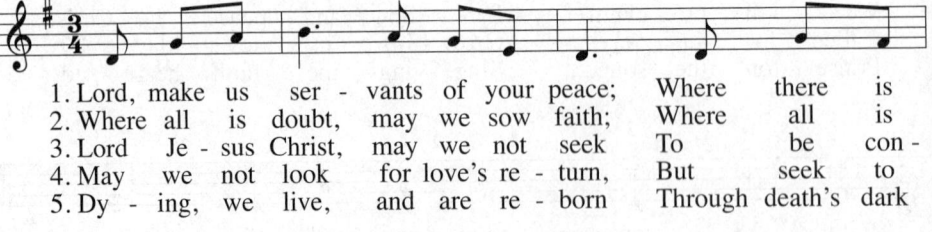

1. Lord, make us ser - vants of your peace; Where there is
2. Where all is doubt, may we sow faith; Where all is
3. Lord Je - sus Christ, may we not seek To be con -
4. May we not look for love's re - turn, But seek to
5. Dy - ing, we live, and are re - born Through death's dark

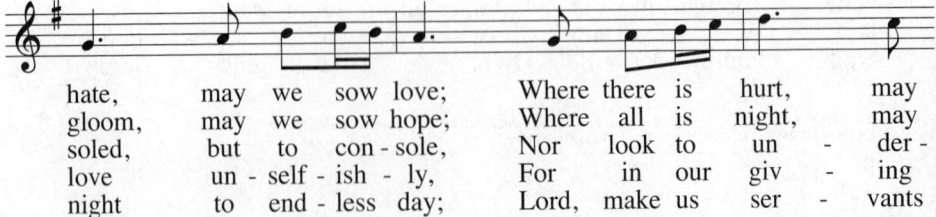

hate, may we sow love; Where there is hurt, may
gloom, may we sow hope; Where all is night, may
soled, but to con - sole, Nor look to un - der -
love un - self - ish - ly, For in our giv - ing
night to end - less day; Lord, make us ser - vants

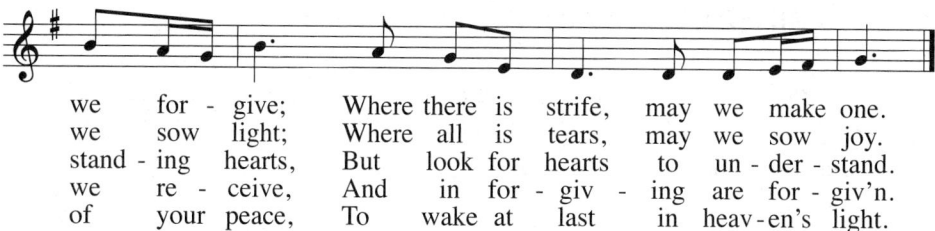

we	for - give;	Where there is	strife,	may	we	make one.
we	sow light;	Where all is	tears,	may	we	sow joy.
stand - ing	hearts,	But look for	hearts	to	un - der - stand.
we	re - ceive,	And in for - giv -	ing	are	for - giv'n.
of	your peace,	To wake at	last	in	heav-en's light.

Text: Based on a prayer attrib. to St. Francis of Assisi; James Quinn, SJ, 1919–2010, © 1994, James Quinn, SJ. Published by OCP.
Tune: O WALY WALY, LM; English melody; harm. by Martin West, b.1929, © 1983, Hope Publishing Comapny

The Servant Song 861

1., 6. Will	you	let	me	be	your	ser - vant,	Let	me	be	as
2. We	are	pil - grims	on	a	jour - ney,	We	are	trav - 'lers
3. I	will	hold	the	Christ-light	for	you	In	the	night - time
4. I	will	weep when	you	are	weep-ing;	When you	laugh	I'll
5. When we	sing	to	God	in	heav - en	We	shall	find	such

Christ	to	you;	Pray	that	I	may	have	the	grace	to
on	the	road;	We	are	here	to	help	each	oth - er
of	your	fear;	I	will	hold	my	hand	out	to	you,
laugh	with you.	I	will	share your	joy	and	sor - row
har - mo - ny,	Born	of	all	we've	known	to - geth - er

Let	you	be	my	ser -	vant,	too.
Walk	the	mile	and	bear	the	load.
Speak	the	peace	you	long	to	hear.
'Til	we've	seen	this	jour -	ney	through.
Of	Christ's	love	and	ag -	o -	ny.

Text: Richard Gillard, b.1953
Tune: Richard Gillard, b.1953; harm. by Betty Pulkingham, b.1928
© 1977, Universal Music—Brentwood Benson Publishing (admin. CapitolCMGPublishing.com)

862 Christ in Me Arise

Refrain

Christ in me a - rise and dis - pel all the dark-ness.

Christ in me a - rise with your pow - er and your strength.

Christ in me pour out your bless - ing and heal-ing.

Christ in me a - rise and I shall rise with you.

Verses

1. Be now my vi - sion; o - pen these eyes,
2. Be now my foot - steps, lead - ing the way,

show - ing me all that I must see.
tak - ing me where I must go.

On-ward to the king-dom, you are the way. A -

D.C.

rise in me and I shall rise with you.

Bridge

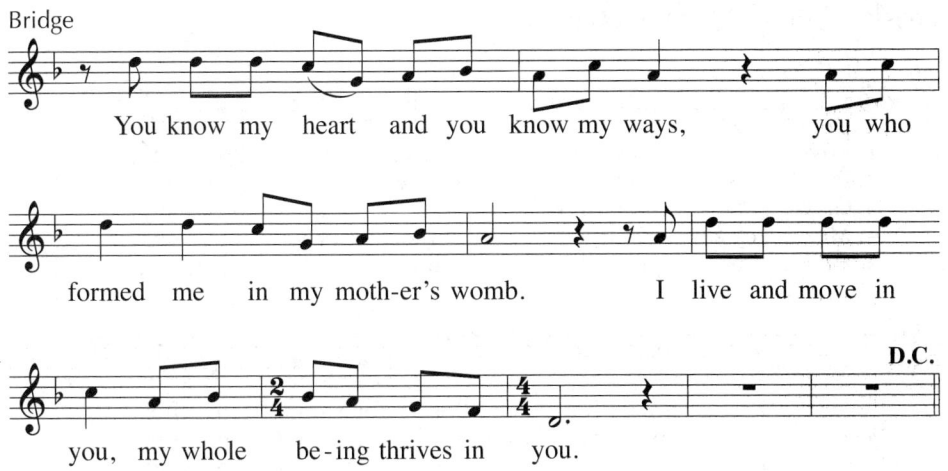

You know my heart and you know my ways, you who formed me in my moth-er's womb. I live and move in you, my whole be-ing thrives in you.

D.C.

Text: Trevor Thomson, b.1971
Tune: Trevor Thomson, b.1971; acc. by Rick Modlin, b.1966
© 2008, Trevor Thomson. Published by Spirit & Song, a division of OCP.

In Love You Summon   863

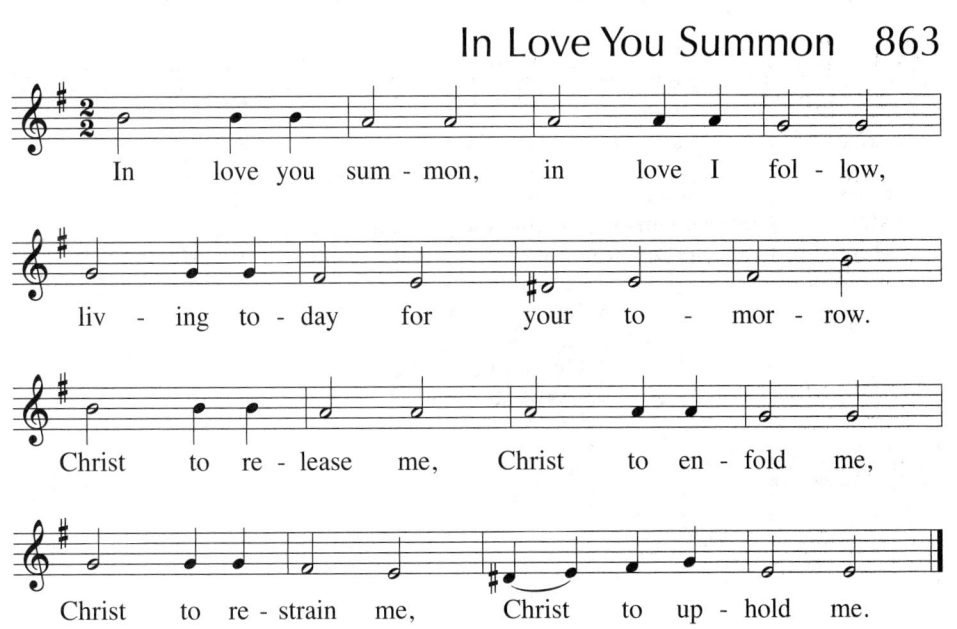

In love you sum-mon, in love I fol-low, liv-ing to-day for your to-mor-row. Christ to re-lease me, Christ to en-fold me, Christ to re-strain me, Christ to up-hold me.

Text: John L. Bell, b.1949
Tune: John L. Bell, b.1949
© 1998, Iona Community, GIA Publications, Inc., agent

864 Love Is Flowing

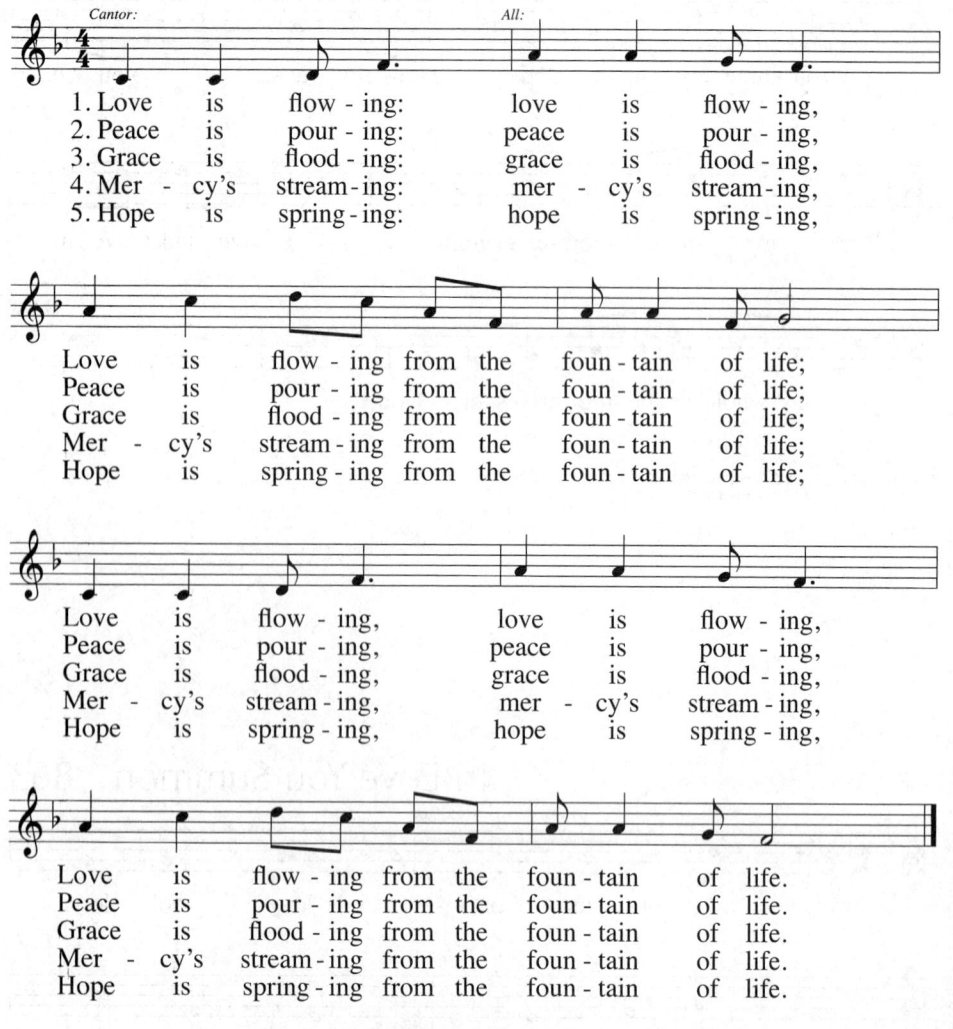

Cantor:

1. Love is flow - ing: love is flow - ing,
2. Peace is pour - ing: peace is pour - ing,
3. Grace is flood - ing: grace is flood - ing,
4. Mer - cy's stream - ing: mer - cy's stream - ing,
5. Hope is spring - ing: hope is spring - ing,

All:

Love is flow - ing from the foun - tain of life;
Peace is pour - ing from the foun - tain of life;
Grace is flood - ing from the foun - tain of life;
Mer - cy's stream - ing from the foun - tain of life;
Hope is spring - ing from the foun - tain of life;

Love is flow - ing, love is flow - ing,
Peace is pour - ing, peace is pour - ing,
Grace is flood - ing, grace is flood - ing,
Mer - cy's stream - ing, mer - cy's stream - ing,
Hope is spring - ing, hope is spring - ing,

Love is flow - ing from the foun - tain of life.
Peace is pour - ing from the foun - tain of life.
Grace is flood - ing from the foun - tain of life.
Mer - cy's stream - ing from the foun - tain of life.
Hope is spring - ing from the foun - tain of life.

6. Living water…
7. Joy unending…
8. God's sweet mercy…
9. God's strong justice…

Text: Marty Haugen, b.1950
Tune: FOUNTAIN OF LIFE, 8 10 8 10; Marty Haugen, b.1950
© 2007, GIA Publications, Inc.

We Belong to You 865

Refrain

We be - long to you, O Lord of our long - ing,
we be - long to you. In our dai - ly liv - ing,
To verses
dy - ing and ris - ing we be - long to you.

Final ending
We be - long to you. We be - long to you.

Verses

1. In the wa - ters of your mer - cy,
2. Filled with gifts and filled with good - ness,
3. When we share the bread you've bro - ken
4. We are called to share your word, Lord,

when the old be - comes the new,
Spir - it breath - ing life in - to
with the man - y and the few,
in all we say and all we do.

souls u - nit - ed in the mys - t'ry:
all who seek to find their pur - pose:
we are blessed and we are bro - ken;
As our jour - ney moves us on - ward,

D.C.

we be - long to you.

Text: Victoria Thomson, b.1969, © 2006, Victoria Thomson
Tune: Trevor Thomson, b.1971, © 2006, Trevor Thomson
Published by Spirit & Song, a division. of OCP.

866 Go Make of All Disciples

1. "Go make of all dis - ci - ples." We hear the call, O
2. "Go make of all dis - ci - ples," Bap - tiz - ing in the
3. "Go make of all dis - ci - ples." We at your feet would
4. "Go make of all dis - ci - ples." We wel-come your com -

Lord, That comes from you, our Fa - ther, In
name Of Fa - ther, Son, and Spir - it— From
stay Un - til each life's vo - ca - tion Shows
mand. "Lo, I am with you al - ways." We

your e - ter - nal Word. In - spire our ways of
age to age the same. We call each new dis -
forth your ho - ly way. We cul - ti - vate the
take your guid - ing hand. The task looms large be -

learn - ing Through earn - est, fer - vent prayer, And
ci - ple To fol - low you, O Lord, Re -
na - ture God plants in ev - 'ry heart, Re -
fore us— We fol - low with - out fear. In

let our dai - ly liv - ing Re - veal you ev - 'ry-where.
deem - ing soul and bod - y By wa - ter and the Word.
veal - ing in our wit - ness The Mas - ter Teach-er's art.
heav'n and earth your pow - er Shall bring God's king - dom here.

Text: Matthew 28:19–20; Leon M. Adkins, 1896–1986, alt. © 1964, Abingdon Press, admin. Music Services
Tune: ELLACOMBE, 7 6 7 6 D; *Gesangbuch der Herzogl,* Wirtemberg, 1784

God Has Chosen Me 867

Text: Bernadette Farrell, b.1957
Tune: Bernadette Farrell, b.1957
© 1990, Bernadette Farrell. Published by OCP.

868 Lord, Whose Love in Humble Service

1. Lord, whose love in hum-ble serv-ice Bore the weight of hu-man need, Who up-on the cross, for-sak-en, Of-fered mer-cy's per-fect deed: We, your ser-vants, bring the wor-ship Not of voice a-lone, but heart, Con-se-crat-ing to your pur-pose Ev-'ry gift that you im-part.

2. Still the chil-dren wan-der home-less, Still the hun-gry cry for bread. Still the cap-tives long for free-dom, Still in grief we mourn our dead. As you, Lord, in deep com-pas-sion Healed the sick and freed the soul, By your Spir-it kin-dles Still to save and make us whole.

3. As we wor-ship, grant us vi-sion, Till your love's re-veal-ing light In its height and depth and great-ness Dawns up-on our hu-man sight, Mak-ing known the needs and bur-dens Your com-pas-sion bids us bear, Stir-ring us to faith-ful serv-ice, Your a-bun-dant life to share.

4. Called from wor-ship in-to serv-ice, Forth in your great name we go To the child, the youth, the a-ged, Love in liv-ing deeds to show. Hope and health, good-will and com-fort, Coun-sel, aid, and peace we give That your chil-dren, Lord, in free-dom, May your mer-cy know, and live.

Text: Albert F. Bayly, 1901–1984, alt., 1988, © Oxford University Press
Tune: BEACH SPRING, 8 7 8 7 D; *The Sacred Harp*, 1844; harm. by Ronald A. Nelson, 1927–2014, © 1978, *Lutheran Book of Worship*, admin. by Augsburg Fortress

Here I Am, Lord   869

Verses

1. I, the Lord of sea and sky, I have heard my
2. I, the Lord of snow and rain, I have borne my
3. I, the Lord of wind and flame, I will tend the

peo - ple cry. All who dwell in dark and sin
peo - ple's pain. I have wept for love of them.
poor and lame. I will set a feast for them.

My hand will save. I, who made the
They turn a - way. I will break their
My hand will save. Fin - est bread I

stars of night, I will make their dark - ness bright.
hearts of stone, Give them hearts for love a - lone.
will pro - vide Till their hearts be sat - is - fied.

Who will bear my light to them? Whom shall I send?
I will speak my word to them. Whom shall I send?
I will give my life to them. Whom shall I send?

Refrain

Here I am, Lord. Is it I, Lord? I have heard you

call - ing in the night. I will go, Lord, if you

lead me. I will hold your peo - ple in my heart.

Text: Isaiah 6; Dan Schutte, b.1947
Tune: HERE I AM, LORD, 77 7 4 D with refrain; Dan Schutte, b.1947; arr. by Michael Pope, SJ, and John Weissrock
© 1981, OCP

870 God, Whose Giving Knows No Ending

1. God, whose giv - ing knows no end - ing, From your
2. Skills and time are ours for press - ing Toward the
3. Treas - ure, too, you have en - trust - ed, Gain through

rich and end - less store: Na - ture's won - der, Je - sus'
goals of Christ, your Son: All at peace in health and
pow'rs your grace con - ferred; Ours to use for home and

wis - dom, Cost - ly cross, grave's shat - tered door,
free - dom, Rac - es joined, the Church made one.
kin - dred, And to spread the gos - pel word.

Gift - ed by you, we turn to you, Of - f'ring
Now di - rect our dai - ly la - bor, Lest we
O - pen wide our hands in shar - ing, As we

up our - selves in praise; Thank - ful song shall rise for -
strive for self a - lone; Born with tal - ents, make us
heed Christ's age - less call, Heal - ing, teach - ing, and re -

ev - er, Gra - cious do - nor of our days.
ser - vants Fit to an - swer at your throne.
claim - ing, Serv - ing you by lov - ing all.

Text: Robert L. Edwards, 1915–2006, © 1961, ren. 1989, The Hymn Society (admin. by Hope Publishing Company)
Tune: RUSTINGTON, 8 7 8 7 D; Charles H. H. Parry, 1848–1918

Alternate tune: BEACH SPRING

871 The Spirit Sends Us Forth to Serve

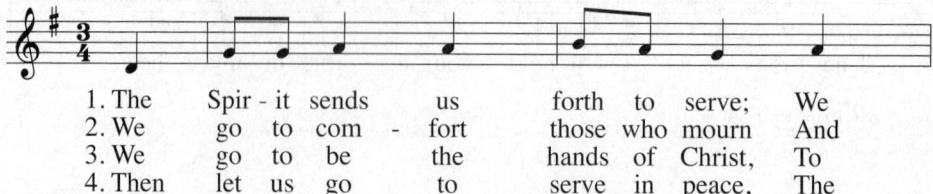

1. The Spir - it sends us forth to serve; We
2. We go to com - fort those who mourn And
3. We go to be the hands of Christ, To
4. Then let us go to serve in peace, The

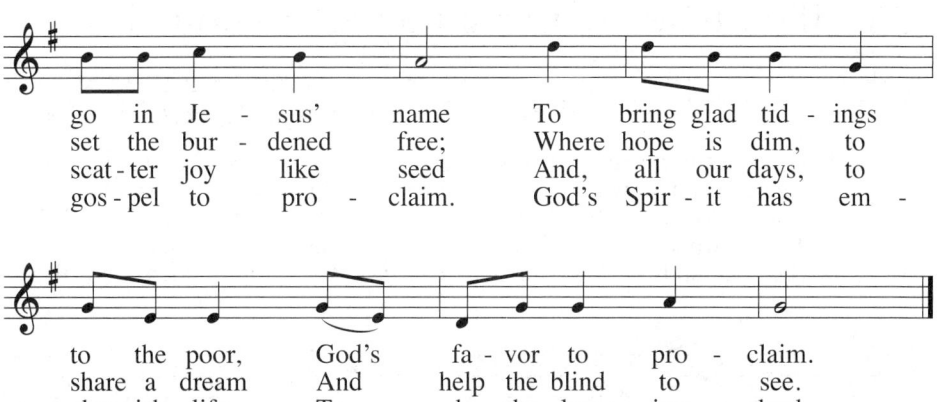

go in Je - sus' name To bring glad tid - ings
set the bur - dened free; Where hope is dim, to
scat - ter joy like seed And, all our days, to
gos - pel to pro - claim. God's Spir - it has em -

to the poor, God's fa - vor to pro - claim.
share a dream And help the blind to see.
cher - ish life, To do the lov - ing deed.
pow-ered us; We go in Je - sus' name.

Text: Delores Dufner, OSB, b.1939, © 1993, Delores Dufner, OSB. Published by OCP.
Tune: AZMON, CM; Carl G. Gläser, 1784–1829; harm. by Lowell Mason, 1792–1872

Now Let Us from This Table Rise   872

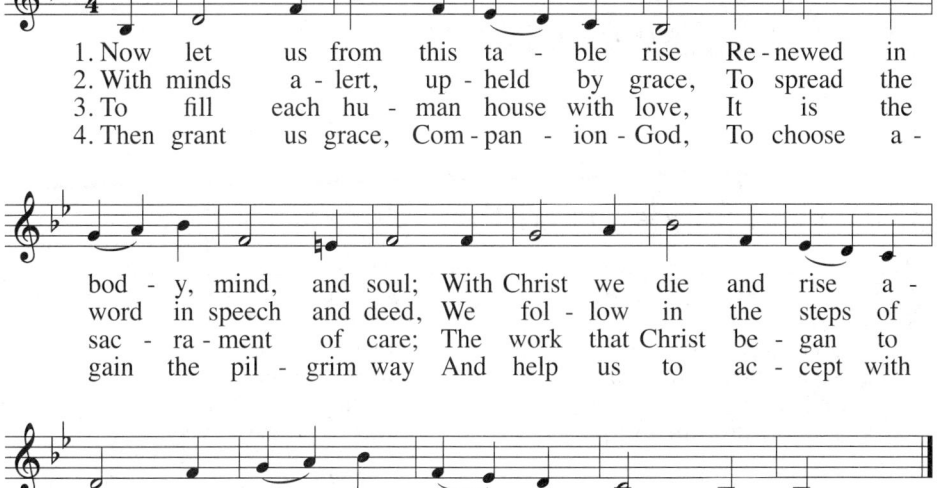

1. Now let us from this ta - ble rise Re - newed in
2. With minds a - lert, up - held by grace, To spread the
3. To fill each hu - man house with love, It is the
4. Then grant us grace, Com - pan - ion - God, To choose a -

bod - y, mind, and soul; With Christ we die and rise a -
word in speech and deed, We fol - low in the steps of
sac - ra - ment of care; The work that Christ be - gan to
gain the pil - grim way And help us to ac - cept with

gain, His self - less love has made us whole.
Christ, At one with all in hope and need.
do We hum - bly pledge our - selves to share.
joy The chal - lenge of to - mor - row's day.

Text: Fred Kaan, 1929–2009, © 1968, Hope Publishing Company
Tune: DEUS TUORUM MILITUM, LM; *Grenoble Antiphoner,* 1753; harm. by Basil Harwood, 1859–1949, © Executors of the late Dr. Basil Harwood

Alternate tune: DUKE STREET

873 The Church of Christ Cannot Be Bound

1. The Church of Christ can - not be bound By
2. True faith will o - pen up the door And
3. True love will not sit i - dly by When
4. If what we have we free - ly share To
5. The Church of Christ can - not be bound By

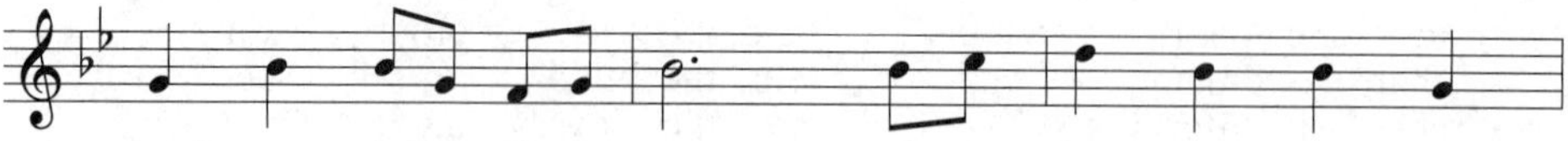

walls of wood or stone. Where char - i - ty and
step in - to the street. True serv - ice will seek
jus - tice is de - nied. True mer - cy hears the
meet our neigh - bor's need, Then we ex - tend the
walls of wood or stone. Where char - i - ty and

love are found, There can the Church be known.
out the poor And ask to wash their feet.
home - less cry And wel - comes them in - side.
Spir - it's care Through ev - 'ry self - less deed.
love are found, There can the Church be known.

Text: Adam M. L. Tice, b.1979, © 2005, GIA Publications, Inc.
Tune: McKEE, CM; African American; adapt. by Harry T. Burleigh, 1866–1949

874 God Sends Us Forth

1. God sends us forth to love and serve,
2. Nour - ished by Christ, our Word and Bread,
3. Called to the ones the world ig - nores—
4. So, with the cross to lead the way,

Make known God's name and live God's word,
Burn - ing with love and Spir - it - led,
Hun - gry and thirst - y, weak and poor—
Let us go forth in peace to - day,

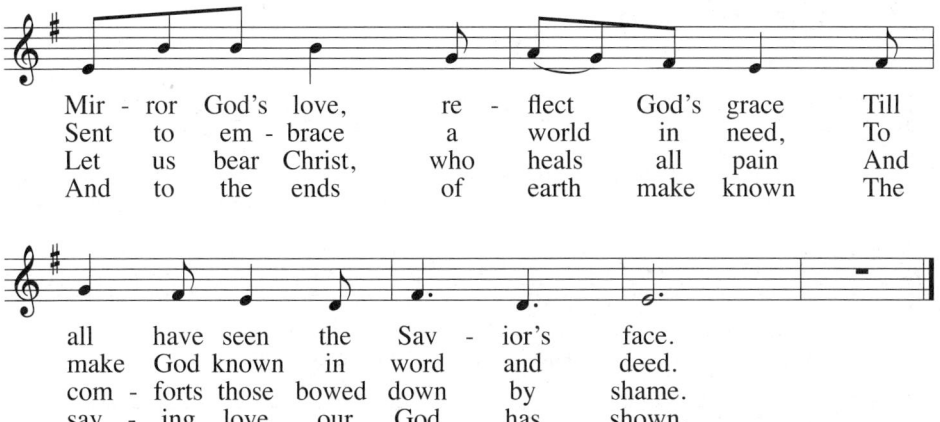

Mir - ror God's love, re - flect God's grace Till
Sent to em - brace a world in need, To
Let us bear Christ, who heals all pain And
And to the ends of earth make known The

all have seen the Sav - ior's face.
make God known in word and deed.
com - forts those bowed down by shame.
sav - ing love our God has shown.

Text: Tony E. Alonso, b.1980
Tune: GAILHAC, LM; Tony E. Alonso, b.1980
© 2009, GIA Publications, Inc.

The Joy of the Gospel 875

1. The joy of the Gos - pel in - vites us to - day,
2. The Gos - pel per - suades us to meet Je - sus' gaze,
3. The joy of the Gos - pel en - gag - es the heart,
4. The Gos - pel im - pels us, with Christ at our side,

Be - liev - ing in Je - sus, to walk in his way:
To let his Word touch us, de - light and a - maze.
Em - pow - ers dis - ci - ples and gives each a part:
Pre - pared and com - mis-sioned, with arms o - pen wide,

To love and serve oth - ers, the last and the least,
The Gos - pel a - wak - ens, en - liv - ens the soul;
To care for the poor and re - spond to their plea,
To go forth re - joic - ing in Good News to share:

To be for our world both the salt and the yeast.
It kin - dles the spir - it, makes new and makes whole.
To lift up the low - ly, from bur - dens set free.
God's love is for all and ex - tends ev - 'ry - where!

Text: Delores Dufner, OSB, b.1939, © 2016, GIA Publications, Inc.
Tune: ST. DENIO, 11 11 11 11; adapt. from a Welsh ballad in John Roberts' *Hymns of the Sanctuary*, 1839

876 City of God

Verses 1, 2

1. A-wake from your slum-ber! A - rise from your
2. We are sons of the morn-ing; we are daugh-ters of

sleep! A new day is dawn-ing
day. The One who has loved us

for all those who weep. The peo-ple in
has bright-ened our way. The Lord of all

dark-ness have seen a great light. The Lord of our
kind-ness has called us to be a light for his

long-ing has con-quered the night.
peo-ple to set their hearts free.

𝄋 Refrain

Let us build the cit-y of God. May our tears be

turned in-to danc-ing! For the Lord, our light and our

love, has turned the night in-to day!

Verse 3

3. God is light; in him there is no

dark-ness. Let us walk in his light, his

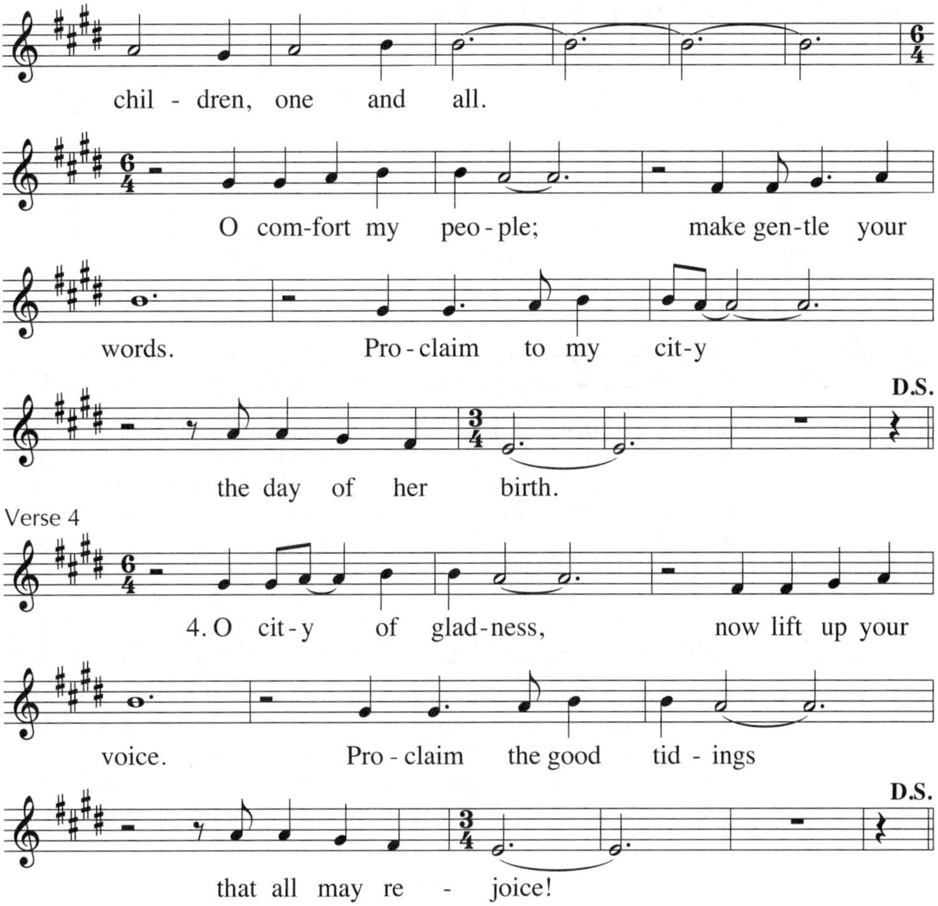

chil - dren, one and all.

O com-fort my peo - ple; make gen-tle your

words. Pro - claim to my cit-y

D.S.

the day of her birth.

Verse 4

4. O cit-y of glad-ness, now lift up your

voice. Pro - claim the good tid - ings

D.S.

that all may re - joice!

Text: Dan Schutte, b.1947
Tune: Dan Schutte, b.1947; acc. by Robert J. Batastini, b.1942
© 1981, OCP

Thuma Mina / Send Me, Jesus   877

1. Thu - ma mi-na, Thu-ma mi-na, Thu-ma mi-na So-man-dla.
2. Send me, Je-sus, send me, Je-sus, send me, Je-sus, send me, Lord.
3. Lead me, Je-sus, lead me, Je-sus, lead me, Je-sus, lead me, Lord.
4. Fill me, Je-sus, fill me, Je-sus, fill me, Je-sus, fill me, Lord.

878   Glorify the Lord by Our Lives

1. We go in peace in Je - sus' name To
2. May dai - ly la - bor, skills, and arts Give
3. Christ urg - es us to serve the poor, The
4. The heav - ens and the earth de - clare The
5. We go to serve— to heal and bless As

love and serve the Lord, A - noint - ed by the
glo - ry to the Lord. Our hands and feet, our
bless - ed of the Lord, And wel - come through our
good - ness of the Lord, And we en - coun - ter
ser - vants of the Lord. Our knees shall bow, our

Spir - it's flame To love and serve the Lord.
minds and hearts Give glo - ry to the Lord.
o - pen door The bless - ed of the Lord.
ev - 'ry - where The good - ness of the Lord.
tongues con - fess As ser - vants of the Lord.

If we live the Gos - pel we seek to pro - claim,
With wis - dom and pas - sion the Spir - it im - parts
In lov - ing the peo - ple the world would ig - nore We
As we touch cre - a - tion with heal - ing and care,
When we meet God's will for the world with our "Yes,"

glo - ri - fy the Lord by our lives.

Text: Adam M. L. Tice, b.1979
Tune: AIKENHEAD, 8 6 8 6 11 9; Tony E. Alonso, b.1980
© 2015, GIA Publications, Inc.

We Come with Joy in Jesus Christ 879

1. We come with joy in Je - sus Christ, Who
2. A lit - tle bread is all we have, So
3. Like rip - ples in a pool, our gifts, How -

knows our hu - man need, Who, moved with pit - y
mea - ger our sup - ply; A lit - tle time, a
ev - er small they are, Will reach and heal a

for the poor, Would ev - 'ry hun - ger feed.
lit - tle love Can hard - ly sat - is - fy.
need - y world, Will com - fort near and far.

He blessed the fish and bar - ley loaves Till
But let us bring the best we have, De -
For Christ will bless our bit of bread, The

food was mul - ti - plied. His boun - ty o - ver -
spite our pov - er - ty, And of - fer all our
loaves our hands pro - vide, Till emp - ty bas - kets

flowed their want And all were sat - is - fied.
gifts to Christ, Im - per - fect though they be.
o - ver - flow And all are sat - is - fied.

Text: Delores Dufner, OSB, b.1939, © 1994, GIA Publications, Inc., alt.
Tune: FOREST GREEN, CMD; English; harm. by Ralph Vaughan Williams, 1872–1958, alt.

880 Sent Forth by God's Blessing

1. Sent forth by God's bless-ing, Our true faith con-fess-ing, The peo-ple of God from this dwell-ing take leave. Our prayer here has end-ed, O now be ex-tend-ed The fruits of our wor-ship in all who be-lieve. The seed of Christ's teach-ing, Our in-ner souls reach-ing, Shall blos-som in ac-tion for God and for all. God's grace shall in-cite us, In love shall u-nite us To fur-ther God's king-dom and an-swer the call.

2. With praise and thanks-giv-ing To God who is liv-ing, The tasks of our ev-'ry-day life we em-brace. Our faith ev-er shar-ing, In love ev-er car-ing, We claim as our fam-'ly all those of each race. With grace God has fed us, One true light has led us U-nit-ing us all in the life that we share. Then may all the liv-ing With praise and thanks-giv-ing Give hon-or to Christ and his name that we bear.

Text: Omer Westendorf, 1916–1997; alt. by Alan J. Hommerding, b.1956, © 1964, 1994, World Library Publications
Tune: ASH GROVE, 66 11 66 11 D; Welsh melody

Moved by the Gospel, Let Us Move   881

1. Moved by the Gos - pel, let us move With
2. Let weav - ers form from bro - ken strands A
3. O Spir - it, breathe a - mong us here; In -

ev - 'ry gift and art. The im - age of cre -
tap - es - try of prayer. Let art - ists paint with
spire the work we do. May hands and voic - es,

a - tive love In - dwells each hu - man heart. The
skill - ful hands Their joy, la - ment, and care. Then
eye and ear At - test to life made new. In

Mak - er calls cre - a - tion good, So
mime the sto - ry: Christ has come. With
wor - ship and in dai - ly strife Cre -

let us now ex - press With sound and col - or,
rev - 'rence dance the word. With flute and or - gan,
ate a - mong us still. Great Art - ist, form our

stone and wood, The shape of ho - li - ness.
ching and drum God's praise be ev - er heard.
com - mon life Ac - cord - ing to your will.

Text: Ruth Duck, b.1947, © 1992, GIA Publications, Inc.
Tune: KINGSFOLD, CMD; English melody; harm. by Ralph Vaughan Williams, 1872–1958

882 Christ Has No Body Now But Yours

Refrain

Christ has no bod-y now but yours, no hands but yours. Here on this earth yours is the work, to serve with the joy of com-pas-sion.

Verses

1. No hands but yours to heal the wound-ed world,
2. No eyes but yours to see as Christ would see,
3. No feet but yours to jour-ney with the poor,
4. Through ev-'ry gift, give back to those in need:

    no hands but yours to soothe all its suf-f'ring,
    to find the lost, to gaze with com-pas-sion;
    to walk this world with mer-cy and jus-tice.
    As Christ has blessed, so now be his bless-ing,

    no touch but yours to bind the bro-ken
    no eyes but yours to glimpse the ho-ly
    Yours are the steps to build a last-ing
    with ev-'ry gift a ben-e-dic-tion

D.C.

    hope of the peo-ple of God.
    joy of the cit-y of God.
    peace for the chil-dren of God.
    be to the peo-ple of God.

Text: St. Teresa of Ávila, 1515–1582, adapt. by Steven C. Warner, b.1954
Tune: Steven C. Warner, b.1954
© 2003, World Library Publications

We Have Been Told 883

Refrain

We have been told, we've seen his face and heard his voice a - live in our hearts: "Live in my love with all your heart; as the Fa - ther has loved me, so I have loved you."

Verse 1

1. "I am the vine, you are the branch - es, and all who live in me will bear great fruit."

Verses 2, 3

2. "You are my friends, if you keep my com - mands; no long - er slaves, I call you friends."
3. "No great - er love is there than this: to lay down one's life for a friend."

D.C.

884 Pescador de Hombres / Lord, When You Came

Estrofas / Verses

1. Tú has ve - ni - do a la o - ri - lla,
2. Tú sa - bes bien lo que ten - go;
3. Tú ne - ce - si - tas mis ma - nos,
4. Tú, pes - ca - dor de o - tros la - gos,

1. Lord, when you came to the sea - shore
2. Lord, you knew what my boat car - ried:
3. Lord, have you need of my la - bor,
4. Lord, send me where you would have me,

No has bus - ca - do ni a sa - bios, ni a
En mi bar - ca no hay o - ro ni es -
Mi can - san - cio que a o - tros des -
An - sia e - ter - na de al - mas que es -

You weren't seek - ing the wise or the
Nei - ther mon - ey nor weap - ons for
Hands for serv - ice, a heart made for
To a vil - lage, or heart of the

ri - cos; Tan só - lo quie - res
pa - das, Tan só - lo re - des
can - se, A - mor que quie - ra
pe - ran, A - mi - go bue - no,

wealth - y, But on - ly ask - ing
fight - ing, But nets for fish - ing,
lov - ing, My arms for lift - ing
cit - y; I will re - mem - ber

que yo te si - ga.
y mi tra - ba - jo.
se - guir a - man - do.
que a - sí me lla - mas.

that I might fol - low.
my dai - ly la - bor.
the poor and bro - ken?
that you are with me.

Estribillo / Refrain

Se - ñor,   me has mi - ra - do a los   o - jos,
O   Lord,   *in my eyes you were gaz - ing,*

Son - ri - en - do   has di - cho mi
Kind -ly smil - ing,   *my name you were*

nom - bre,   En la a - re - na
say - ing;   *All I treas - ured,*

he de - ja - do mi bar - ca,   Jun - to a
I have left on the sand there;   *Close to*

ti   bus - ca - ré o - tro mar.
you,   *I will find oth - er seas.*

Text: *Pescador de Hombres*, Cesáreo Gabaráin, 1936–1991; tr. by Rev. Willard F. Jabusch, b.1930
Tune: PESCADOR DE HOMBRES, 8 10 10 with refrain; Cesáreo Gabaráin, 1936–1991; acc. by Diana Kodner, b.1957
© 1979, 1987, 1989, Cesáreo Gabaráin. Published by OCP.

885 You Walk along Our Shoreline

1. You walk a-long our shore-line, Where land meets un-known sea.
2. You call us, Christ, to gath-er The peo-ple of the earth.
3. We cast our net, O Je-sus; We cry the king-dom's name;

We hear your voice of pow-er, "Now come and fol-low me.
We can-not fish for on-ly Those lives we think have worth.
We work for love and jus-tice; We learn to hope through pain.

And if you still will fol-low Through storm and wave and shoal,
We spread your net of gos-pel A - cross the wa-ter's face,
You call us, Lord, to gath-er God's daugh-ters and God's sons,

Then I will make you fish-ers, But of the hu-man soul."
Our boat a com-mon shel-ter For all found by your grace.
To let your judg-ment heal us So that all may be one.

Text: Sylvia G. Dunstan, 1955–1993, © 1991, GIA Publications, Inc.
Tune: AURELIA, 7 6 7 6 D; Samuel S. Wesley, 1810–1876

The Summons   886

1. Will you come and fol - low me If I but
2. Will you leave your - self be - hind If I but
3. Will you let the blind - ed see If I but
4. Will you love the "you" you hide If I but
5. Lord, your sum - mons ech - oes true When you but

call your name? Will you go where
call your name? Will you care for
call your name? Will you set the
call your name? Will you quell the
call my name. Let me turn and

you don't know And nev - er be the same?
cruel and kind And nev - er be the same?
pris - 'ners free And nev - er be the same?
fear in - side And nev - er be the same?
fol - low you And nev - er be the same.

Will you let my love be shown, Will you
Will you risk the hos - tile stare Should your
Will you kiss the lep - er clean, And do
Will you use the faith you've found To re -
In your com - pa - ny I'll go Where your

let my name be known, Will you let my
life at - tract or scare? Will you let me
such as this un - seen, And ad - mit to
shape the world a - round, Through my sight and
love and foot - steps show. Thus I'll move and

life be grown In you and you in me?
an - swer prayer In you and you in me?
what I mean In you and you in me?
touch and sound In you and you in me?
live and grow In you and you in me.

Text: John L. Bell, b.1949, © 1987, Iona Community, GIA Publications, Inc., agent
Tune: KELVINGROVE, 7 6 7 6 777 6; Scottish melody; arr. by John L. Bell, b.1949, © 1987, Iona Community, GIA Publications, Inc., agent

887 I Danced in the Morning

1. I
2. I
3. I
4. I
5. They

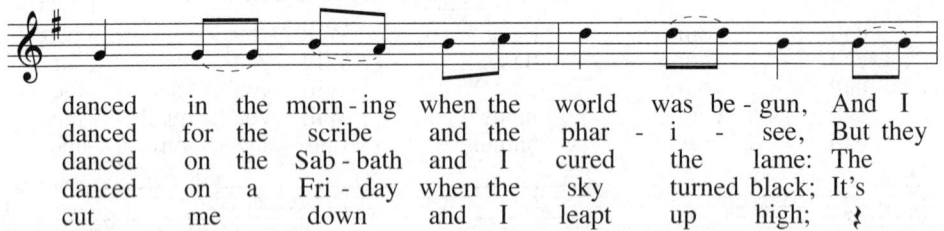

1.	danced	in	the	morn-ing	when the	world	was be-gun,	And I
2.	danced	for	the	scribe	and the	phar-i-see,		But they
3.	danced	on	the	Sab-bath	and I	cured	the lame:	The
4.	danced	on	a	Fri-day	when the	sky	turned black;	It's
5.	cut	me	down	and I	leapt	up	high;	

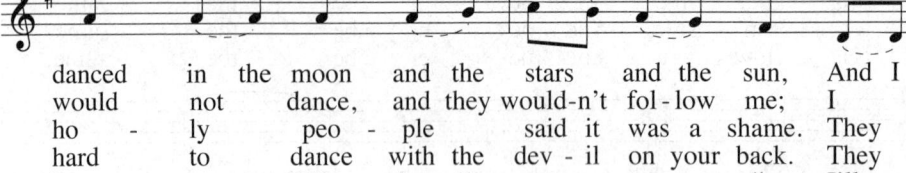

danced	in	the	moon	and the	stars	and the	sun,	And I
would	not	dance,	and they	would-n't	fol-low	me;		I
ho-ly	peo-ple	said it	was a	shame.				They
hard	to	dance	with the	dev-il	on your	back.		They
I	am	the	life	that-'ll	nev-er, nev-er	die;		I'll

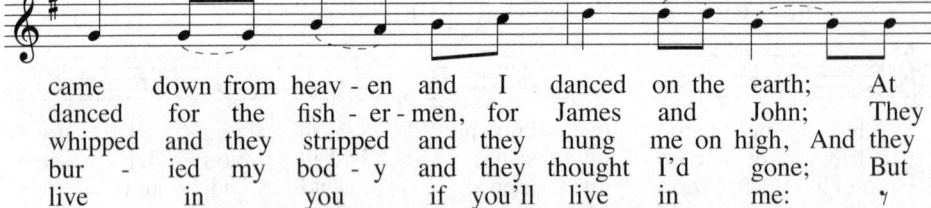

came	down from	heav-en	and	I	danced	on the	earth;	At
danced	for the	fish-er-men,	for	James	and	John;		They
whipped	and they	stripped	and they	hung	me on	high,	And they
bur-ied	my	bod-y	and they	thought	I'd	gone;		But
live	in	you	if	you'll	live	in	me:	

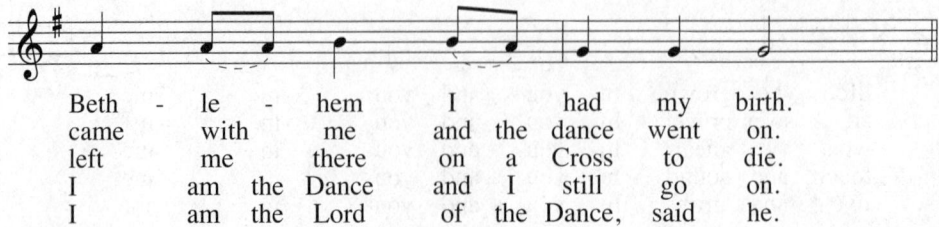

Beth-le-hem	I	had	my	birth.
came with	me	and the	dance	went on.
left	me	there	on a	Cross to die.
I	am	the Dance	and I	still go on.
I	am	the Lord	of the Dance,	said he.

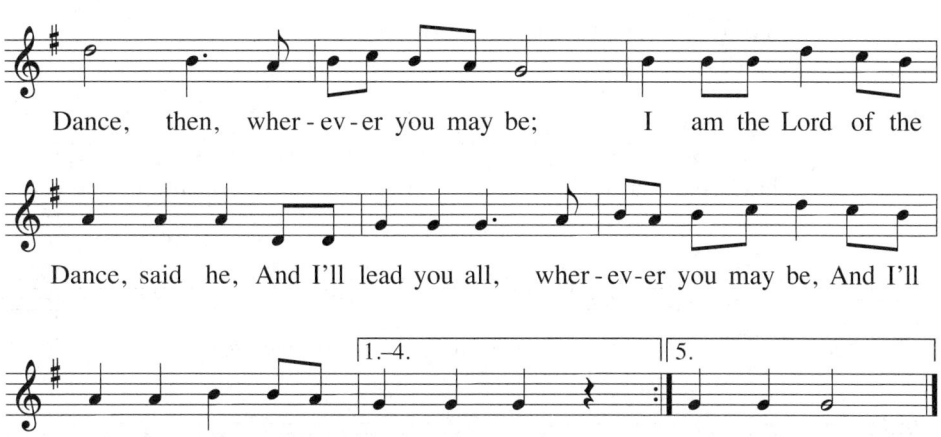

Dance, then, wher - ev - er you may be; I am the Lord of the
Dance, said he, And I'll lead you all, wher - ev - er you may be, And I'll
1.–4.
5.
lead you all in the Dance, said he. Dance, said he.

Text: Sydney Carter, 1915–2004, © 1963, Stainer & Bell, Ltd. (admin. by Hope Publishing Company)
Tune: LORD OF THE DANCE, Irregular with refrain; adapted from a traditional Shaker melody by Sydney Carter, 1915–2004, © 1963, Stainer & Bell, Ltd., (admin. by Hope Publishing Company)

Lord, Help Us Walk Your Servant Way 888

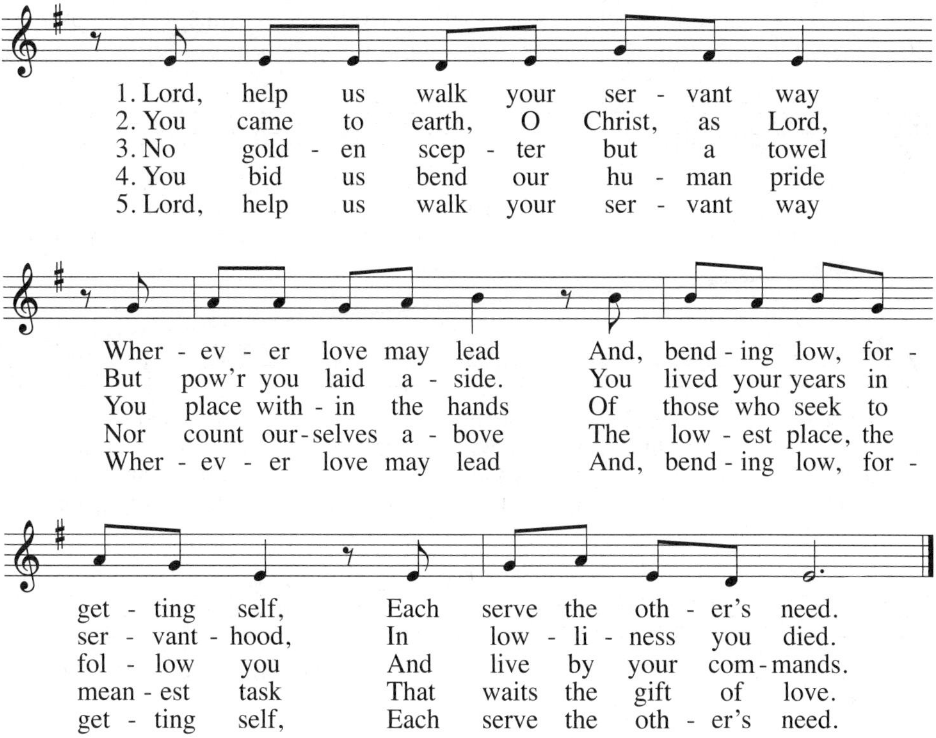
1. Lord, help us walk your ser - vant way
2. You came to earth, O Christ, as Lord,
3. No gold - en scep - ter but a towel
4. You bid us bend our hu - man pride
5. Lord, help us walk your ser - vant way
Wher - ev - er love may lead And, bend - ing low, for -
But pow'r you laid a - side. You lived your years in
You place with - in the hands Of those who seek to
Nor count our - selves a - bove The low - est place, the
Wher - ev - er love may lead And, bend - ing low, for -
get - ting self, Each serve the oth - er's need.
ser - vant - hood, In low - li - ness you died.
fol - low you And live by your com - mands.
mean - est task That waits the gift of love.
get - ting self, Each serve the oth - er's need.

Text: Herman G. Stuempfle, Jr., 1923–2007, © 1997, GIA Publications, Inc.
Tune: CHRISTIAN LOVE, CM; Paul Benoit, OSB, 1893–1979, © 1960, World Library Publications

889　Now We Remain

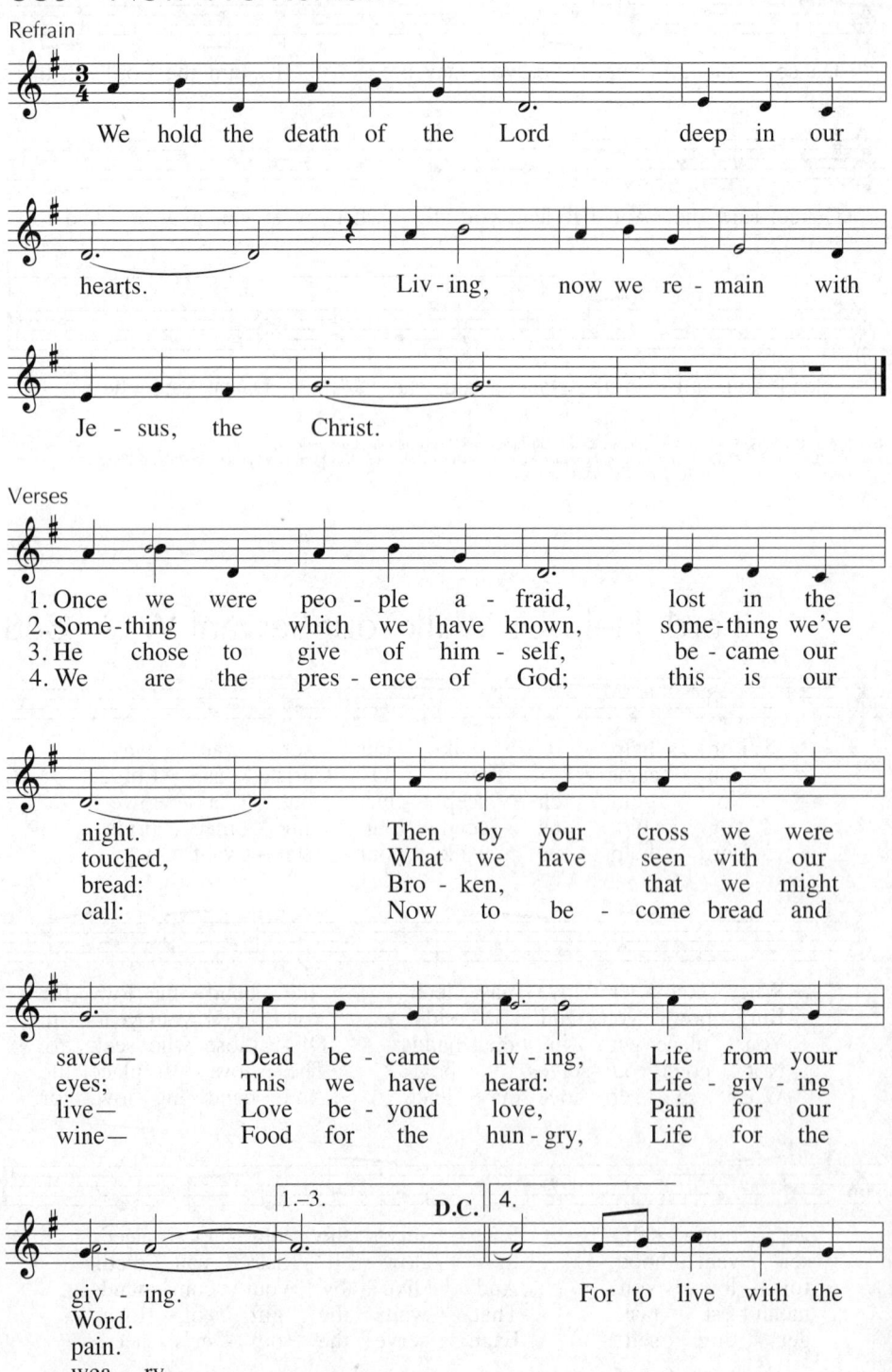

Refrain

We hold the death of the Lord deep in our hearts. Liv-ing, now we re-main with Je-sus, the Christ.

Verses

1. Once we were peo - ple a - fraid, lost in the night. Then by your cross we were saved— Dead be - came liv - ing, Life from your giv - ing.

2. Some-thing which we have known, some-thing we've touched, What we have seen with our eyes; This we have heard: Life - giv - ing, Word.

3. He chose to give of him - self, be - came our bread: Bro - ken, that we might live— Love be - yond love, Pain for our pain.

4. We are the pres - ence of God; this is our call: Now to be - come bread and wine— Food for the hun - gry, Life for the wea - ry.

1.–3. giv - ing.

D.C.

4. For to live with the

D.C.

Lord,   we must die with the   Lord.

Text: 1 Corinthians, 1 John, 2 Timothy; David Haas, b.1957
Tune: David Haas, b.1957
© 1983, GIA Publications, Inc.

Take Up Your Cross   890

1. "Take up your cross," the Sav-ior said, "If
2. Take up your cross; let not its weight Fill
3. Take up your cross, heed not the shame, And
4. Take up your cross, then, in his strength, And
5. Take up your cross and fol-low Christ, Nor

you would my dis - ci - ple be; Take up your cross with
your weak spir - it with a - larm; His strength shall bear your
let your fool-ish pride be still; The Lord for you ac -
calm - ly ev - 'ry dan - ger brave: It guides you to a
think till death to lay it down; For those who hum - bly

will - ing heart, And hum - bly fol - low af - ter me."
spir - it up, And brace your heart, and nerve your arm.
cept - ed death Up - on a cross on Cal - v'ry's hill.
bet - ter home And leads to vic - t'ry o'er the grave.
bear the cross One day will wear the glo - rious crown.

Text: Charles W. Everest, 1814–1877, alt.
Tune: ERHALT UNS HERR, LM; Klug's *Geistliche Lieder*, 1543; harm. by J. S. Bach, 1685–1750

Alternate tune: O WALY WALY

891 Those Who Love and Those Who Labor

1. Those who love and those who la-bor Fol-low in the
2. Where the man-y work to-geth-er, They with Christ him-
3. Let the seek-er nev-er fal-ter Till the truth is

way of Christ; Thus the first dis-ci-ples found him,
self a-bide, But the lone-ly work-ers al-so
found a-far With the wis-dom of the a-ges

Thus the gift of love suf-ficed. Je-sus says to
Find him ev-er at their side. Lo, the Prince of
Un-der-neath a gi-ant star, With the rich-est

those who seek him, I will nev-er pass you by;
com-mon wel-fare Dwells with-in the mar-ket strife;
and the poor-est, Of the sum of things pos-sessed,

Raise the stone and you shall find me;
Lo, the bread of heav'n is bro-ken
Like a child at first to won-der,

Cleave the wood, and there am I.
In the sac-ra-ment of life.
Like a king at last to rest.

Text: Geoffrey Dearmer, 1893–1996, alt., © Oxford University Press
Tune: HYMN TO JOY, 8 7 8 7 D; arr. from Ludwig van Beethoven, 1770–1827, by Edward Hodges, 1796–1867

Two Fishermen 892

1. Two fish-er-men, who lived a-long The Sea of Gal-i-
2. And as he walked a-long the shore, 'Twas James and John he'd
3. O Si-mon Pe-ter, An-drew, James, And John, be-lov-ed
4. And you, good Chris-tians, one and all, Who'd fol-low Je-sus'

lee, Stood by the shore to cast their nets In-
find; And these two sons of Zeb - e-dee Would
one, You heard Christ's call to speak good news Re-
way, Come, leave be-hind what keeps you bound To

to an age-less sea. Now, Je - sus watched them
leave their boats be-hind. Their work and all they
vealed to God's own Son. Su-san - na, Mar-y,
trap-pings of our day. And lis - ten as he

from a-far, Then called them each by name. It
held so dear They left be-side their nets. Their
Mag - da-lene, Who trav-eled with your Lord, You
calls your name To come and fol-low near, For

changed their lives, these sim-ple men; They'd nev-er be the same.
names they'd heard as Je-sus called; They came with-out re-gret.
min - is-tered to him with joy For he is God a-dored.
still he speaks in var-ied ways To those his call will hear.

Leave all things you have and come and fol-low

me, and come and fol-low me.

Text: Suzanne Toolan, RSM, b.1927, © 1986, GIA Publications, Inc.
Tune: LEAVE ALL THINGS, CMD with refrain; Suzanne Toolan, RSM, b.1927, © 1970, GIA Publications, Inc.

893 The Love of the Lord

1. All that I count-ed as gain
2. Rich-es and hon-ors will fade,
3. Sil-ver and gold have I none,
4. Faith is the wealth I pos-sess

Now I con-sid-er as loss,
Earth-ly de-light dis-ap-pear,
No land to count as my home, Yet
Find-ing its source in my God:

Emp-ty and worth-less to me In the
Fade like the grass of the field In the
wealth be-yond meas-ure I own In the
Faith in the prom-ise of Christ Is my

1., 3.   2., 4.

light of the love of the Lord.
light of the love of the Lord.
light of the love of the Lord.
life and my love of the Lord.

What more could bring us hope than to know the pow'r of his

life? What more could bring us peace than to

share in his suf-f'ring and death? What more could be our

fi-nal wish than to live in the love of the Lord?

Text: Philippians 3:8–14; Michael Joncas, b.1951
Tune: CARITAS DOMINI, 7 7 7 9 D with refrain; Michael Joncas, b.1951
© 1988, GIA Publications, Inc.

Unless a Grain of Wheat 894

Refrain

Un - less a grain of wheat shall fall up -
on the ground and die, it re - mains but a
sin - gle grain with no life.

Verses

1. If we have died with him, then we shall
2. If an - y - one serves me, then they must
3. Make your home in me as I make
4. If you re - main in me and my word
5. Those who love me are loved by my
6. Peace I leave with you, my peace I

live with him; if we hold firm, we shall
fol - low me; where - ev - er I am, my
mine in you; those who re - main in me
lives in you, then you will be my dis -
Fa - ther; we shall be with them and
give to you; peace which the world can - not

D.C.

reign with him.
ser - vants will be.
bear much fruit.
ci - ples.
dwell in them.
give is my gift.

Text: John 12:24; Bernadette Farrell, b.1957
Tune: Bernadette Farrell, b.1957
© 1983, Bernadette Farrell. Published by OCP.

895 Unless a Grain of Wheat Falls into the Earth

Refrain

Un-less a grain of wheat falls in-to the earth and

dies, it will re-main a sin-gle grain, but if it

dies, new life will grow, and bring forth fruit, the fruit of

Last time to Coda ⊕

love for the life of the world.

Verses

1. Je - sus Christ, lift - ed up, You draw all peo - ple
2. Je - sus Christ, ho - ly light, Dis - pel the dark - ness
3. Je - sus Christ, Seed that dies, You prom - ise us a -
4. Je - sus Christ, Bread of Life, You give your - self to
5. Je - sus Christ, Liv - ing Vine, In love you pray, "A -
6. Je - sus: Way, Truth and Life, You guide us on our

to your - self; Teach us to of - fer up our
in our minds; O - pen our eyes that we might
bun - dant life; Teach us to die to self each
feed our hearts; From man - y grains make us one
bide in me." O may our hearts a - bide in
jour - ney home. Help us to fol - low where you

D.C.

lives And bear rich fruit in you.
see Your reign with - in our midst.
day And rise a - gain in you.
loaf, Your Bod - y in the world.
you, And may our lives bear fruit.
lead, Show us the way to you.

♦ Coda

world,   the fruit of   love   for the life   of the world.

Text: John 12; Marty Haugen, b.1950
Tune: UNLESS A GRAIN, 6 8 8 6 with refrain; Marty Haugen, b.1950
© 2015, GIA Publications, Inc.

Guide My Feet 896

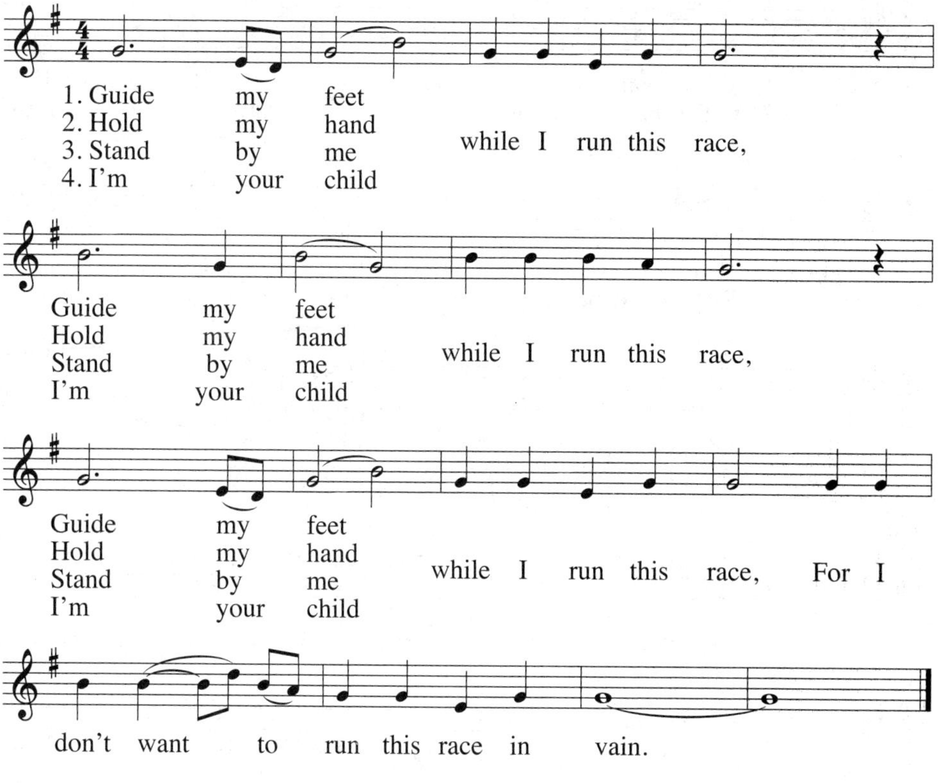

1. Guide   my   feet
2. Hold   my   hand
3. Stand   by   me   while I   run this   race,
4. I'm   your   child

Guide   my   feet
Hold   my   hand
Stand   by   me   while I   run this   race,
I'm   your   child

Guide   my   feet
Hold   my   hand
Stand   by   me   while I   run this   race,   For I
I'm   your   child

don't   want   to   run this race in   vain.

Text: African American spiritual
Tune: African American spiritual; harm. by Dr. Wendell P. Whalum, 1931–1987, © Estate of Wendell Whalum

897 I Will Be the Vine

Refrain

I will be the vine and you will be the branch-es. All
you who live in me will nev - er, nev - er die.
I will be the sign, I will of - fer man - y chanc - es; so
live, oh, live in me and you shall have new life.

Verses 1, 2

1. Re - main in me, as I re-main in
2. As the Fa - ther loved me, so have I loved

you. You may ask what you will, ask what you
you. Re - main in my love, re - main in my

D.C.

will, and you shall re - ceive.
love, and I will give you life.

Verse 3

3. If you are my friends, you will live my com -

mands. There is no great - er love, no great - er

D.C.

love than to lay down your life for your friends.

Text: Based on John 15:5–14; Liam Lawton, b.1959
Tune: Liam Lawton, b.1959; arr. by John McCann, b.1961
© 1998, GIA Publications, Inc.

For the Healing of the Nations   898

1. For the heal - ing of the na - tions, Lord, we pray with
2. Lead your peo - ple in - to free - dom, From de - spair your
3. All that kills a - bun - dant liv - ing, Let it from the
4. You, cre - a - tor God, have writ - ten Your great name on

one ac - cord; For a just and e - qual shar - ing
world re - lease That, re - deemed from war and ha - tred,
earth be banned: Pride of sta - tus, race, or school - ing,
hu - man - kind; For our grow - ing in your like - ness

Of the things that earth af - fords. To a life of
All may come and go in peace. Show us how, through
Dog - mas that ob - scure your plan. In our com - mon
Bring the life of Christ to mind, That by our re -

love in ac - tion Help us rise and pledge our word.
care and good - ness, Fear will die and hope in - crease.
quest for jus - tice May we hal - low life's brief span.
sponse and serv - ice Earth its des - ti - ny may find.

Text: Fred Kaan, 1929–2009, alt., © 1968, Hope Publishing Company
Tune: ST. THOMAS, 8 7 8 7 8 7; John Wade, 1711–1786

899 God of Day and God of Darkness

1. God of day and God of darkness, Now we stand be - fore the night; As the shad - ows stretch and deep - en, Come and make our dark - ness bright. All cre - a - tion still is groan - ing For the dawn - ing of your might, When the Sun of peace and jus - tice Fills the earth with ra - diant light.

2. Still the na - tions curse the darkness, Still the rich op - press the poor; Still the earth is bruised and bro - ken By the ones who still want more. So our hearts can - not ig - nore All your peo - ple lost and bro - ken, All your chil - dren at our door.

3. Show us Christ in one an - oth - er, Make us ser - vants strong and true; Give us all your love of jus - tice So we do what you would do. Let us call all peo - ple ho - ly, Let us pledge our lives a - new, Make us one with all the low - ly, Let us all be one in you.

4. You shall be the path that guides us, You the light that in us burns; Shin - ing deep with - in all peo - ple, Yours the love that we must learn. For our hearts shall wan - der rest - less 'Til they safe to you re - turn; Find - ing you in one an - oth - er, We shall all your face dis - cern.

5. Praise to you in day and darkness, You our source and you our end; Praise to you who love and nur - ture As a fa - ther, moth - er, friend. Grant us all a peace - ful rest - ing, Let each mind and bod - y mend, So we rise re - freshed to - mor - row, Hearts re - newed to King - dom tend.

Text: Marty Haugen, b.1950, © 1985, 1994, GIA Publications, Inc.
Tune: BEACH SPRING, 8 7 8 7 D; *The Sacred Harp*, 1844; harm. by Marty Haugen, b.1950, © 1985, GIA Publications, Inc.

A Place Called Home   900

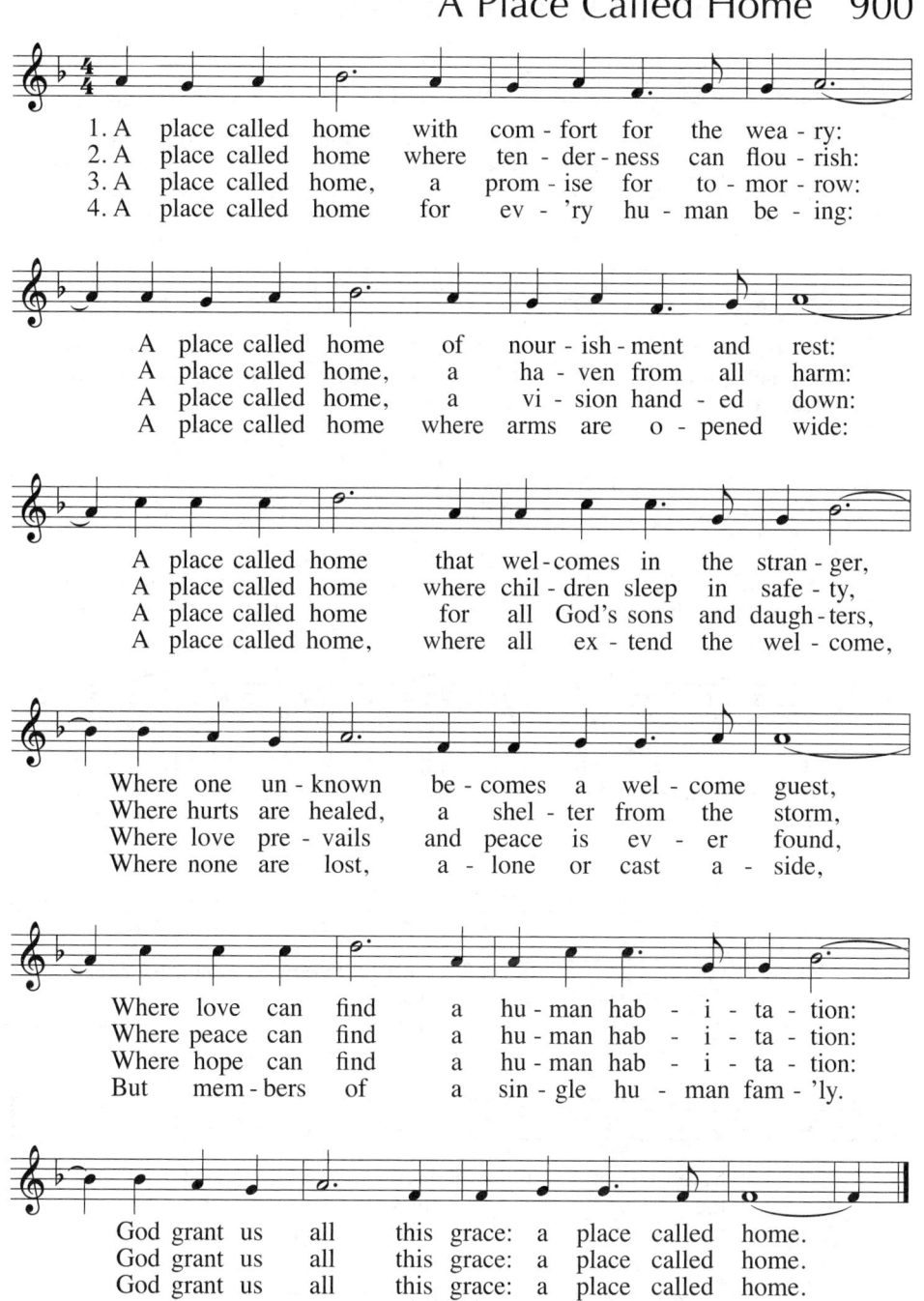

1. A place called home with com-fort for the wea-ry:
2. A place called home where ten-der-ness can flou-rish:
3. A place called home, a prom-ise for to-mor-row:
4. A place called home for ev-'ry hu-man be-ing:

A place called home of nour-ish-ment and rest:
A place called home, a ha-ven from all harm:
A place called home, a vi-sion hand-ed down:
A place called home where arms are o-pened wide:

A place called home that wel-comes in the stran-ger,
A place called home where chil-dren sleep in safe-ty,
A place called home for all God's sons and daugh-ters,
A place called home, where all ex-tend the wel-come,

Where one un-known be-comes a wel-come guest,
Where hurts are healed, a shel-ter from the storm,
Where love pre-vails and peace is ev-er found,
Where none are lost, a-lone or cast a-side,

Where love can find a hu-man hab-i-ta-tion:
Where peace can find a hu-man hab-i-ta-tion:
Where hope can find a hu-man hab-i-ta-tion:
But mem-bers of a sin-gle hu-man fam-'ly.

God grant us all this grace: a place called home.
God grant us all this grace: a place called home.
God grant us all this grace: a place called home.
God grant us grace to build a place called home.

Text: Michael Joncas, b.1951, © 2016, GIA Publications, Inc.
Tune: FINLANDIA, 11 10 11 10 11 10; Jean Sibelius, 1865–1957

901 Jesus, Our Divine Companion

1. Je - sus, our di - vine com - pan - ion, By your low - ly
2. All who tread the path of la - bor Fol - low where your
3. Ev - 'ry task, how - ev - er sim - ple, Fills the soul with

hu - man birth You have come to join all work - ers,
feet have trod; All who work with - out com - plain - ing
grace a - new; Ev - 'ry act of hu - man kind - ness

Bur - den - bear - ers of the earth. As the car - pen -
Do the ho - ly will of God. You, the peace sur -
Done in love is done to you. Je - sus, our di -

ter of Naz - 'reth, Toil - ing for your dai - ly food,
pas - sing knowl - edge, Dwell with us in dai - ly strife;
vine com - pan - ion, Help us all to do our best;

By your pa - tience and your cour - age,
You, the Bread of heav - en, bro - ken
Bless us in our dai - ly la - bor,

You have taught us work is good.
In the sac - ra - ment of life.
Lead us to the Sab - bath rest.

Text: Henry van Dyke, 1852–1933, alt.
Tune: PLEADING SAVIOR, 8 7 8 7 D; *Christian Lyre*, 1830; harm. by Richard Proulx, 1937–2010, © 1986, GIA Publications, Inc.

We Are Called   902

1. Come! Live in the light! Shine with the joy and the love of the Lord! We are called to be light for the king - dom, to live in the free - dom of the cit - y of God!

2. Come! O - pen your heart! Show your mer - cy to all those in fear! We are called to be hope for the hope - less so all ha - tred and blind - ness will be no more!

3. Sing! Sing a new song! Sing of that great day when all will be one! God will reign, and we'll walk with each oth - er as sis - ters and broth - ers u - nit - ed in love!

We are called to act with jus - tice, we are called to love ten - der - ly, we are called to serve one an - oth - er, to walk hum - bly with God!

Text: Micah 6:8; David Haas, b.1957
Tune: David Haas, b.1957
© 1988, GIA Publications, Inc.

903 Freedom Is Coming

O yes, I know.

O yes, I know.

yes, I know. O yes, I

O yes, I know. O yes, I

1. O 2.

know. O yes. I yes, I know.

Text: South African
Tune: South African
© 1984, Peace of Music Publishing AB, admin. by Walton Music Corp., a division of GIA Publications, Inc.

If You Believe and I Believe   904

If you be-lieve and I be-lieve and we to-geth-er pray,

The Ho-ly Spir-it must come down and set God's peo-ple free,

And set God's peo-ple free, and set God's peo-ple free;

The Ho-ly Spir-it must come down and set God's peo-ple free.

Text: Zimbabwean traditional
Tune: Zimbabwean traditional; adapt. of English traditional; as taught by Tarasai; arr. by John L. Bell, b.1949, © 1991, Iona Community,
   GIA Publications, Inc., agent

905 God, Whose Purpose Is to Kindle

1. God, whose pur - pose is to kin - dle,
2. God, who still a sword de - liv - ers
3. God, who in your ho - ly gos - pel

Now ig - nite us with your fire. While the earth a -
Rath - er than a plac - id peace, With your sharp-ened
Wills that all should tru - ly live, Make us sense our

waits your burn - ing, With your pas - sion us in - spire.
Word dis - turb us, From com - pla - cen - cy re - lease!
share of fail - ure, Our tran - quil - i - ty for - give.

O - ver - come our sin - ful calm - ness,
Save us now from sat - is - fac - tion,
Teach us cour - age as we strug - gle

Stir us with your sav - ing name. Bap - tize with your
When we pri - vate - ly are free, Yet are un - dis -
In all lib - er - at - ing strife. Lift the small - ness

fier - y Spir - it, Crown our lives with tongues of flame.
turbed in spir - it By our neigh - bor's mis - er - y.
of our vi - sion By your own a - bun - dant life.

Text: Luke 12:49; David E. Trueblood, 1900–1994, alt., © 1967, David Elton Trueblood
Tune: GENEVA, 8 7 8 7 D; George H. Day, 1883–1966, © 1942, The Church Pension Fund

Alternate tune: HOLY MANNA

We Shall Overcome 906

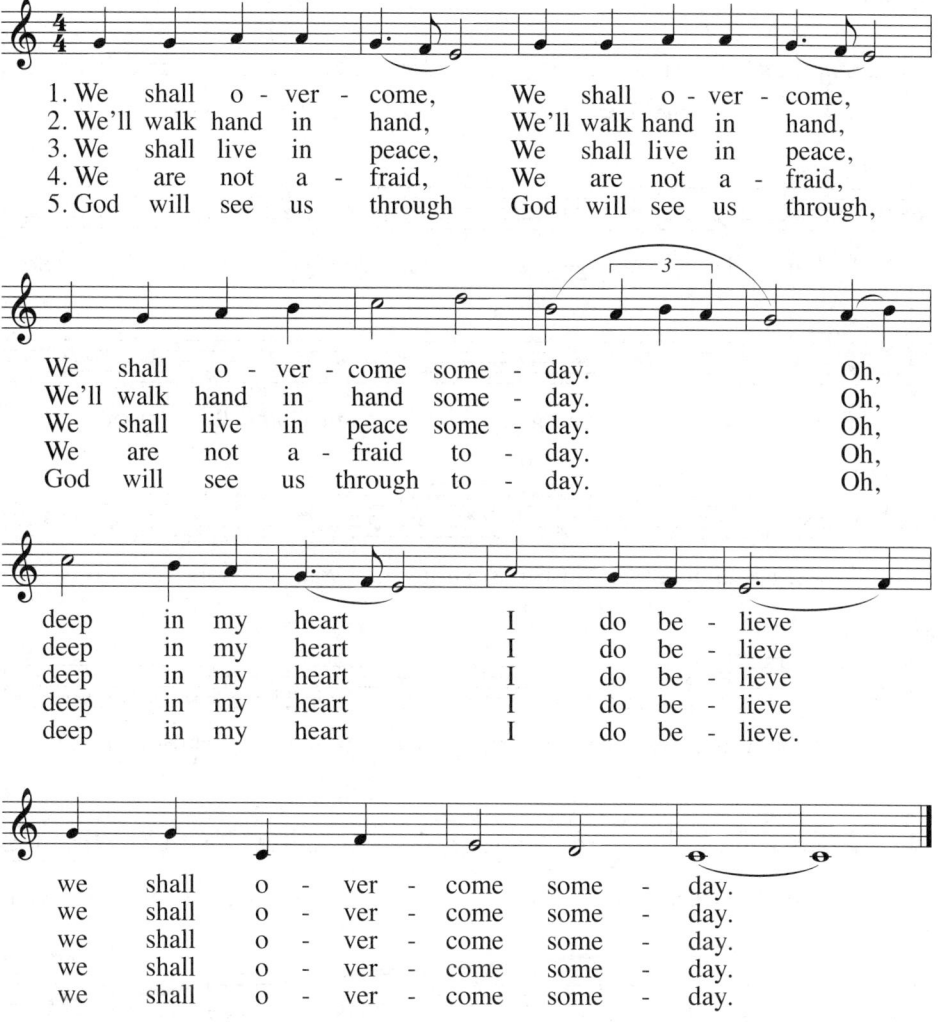

1. We shall o - ver - come, We shall o - ver - come,
2. We'll walk hand in hand, We'll walk hand in hand,
3. We shall live in peace, We shall live in peace,
4. We are not a - fraid, We are not a - fraid,
5. God will see us through God will see us through,

We shall o - ver - come some - day. Oh,
We'll walk hand in hand some - day. Oh,
We shall live in peace some - day. Oh,
We are not a - fraid to - day. Oh,
God will see us through to - day. Oh,

deep in my heart I do be - lieve
deep in my heart I do be - lieve
deep in my heart I do be - lieve
deep in my heart I do be - lieve
deep in my heart I do be - lieve.

we shall o - ver - come some - day.
we shall o - ver - come some - day.
we shall o - ver - come some - day.
we shall o - ver - come some - day.
we shall o - ver - come some - day.

6. We shall stand together...
7. The truth will make us free...
8. We shall be like him...
9. The whole wide world around...

Text: Spiritual
Tune: WE SHALL OVERCOME, 5 5 7 9 7; Spiritual; arr. by Nolan Williams, Jr., b.1969, © 2000, GIA Publications, Inc.

907 What You Have Done for Me

her - it the king - dom pre - pared for you. For

you are my chil-dren, called to serve as keep-ers of the

D.S.

vi - sion and speak-ers of the word.

Verse 3

3. I will look to you when life on earth has end - ed.

Those who give will re-ceive, those who seek will find; so

D.S.

seek my face in ev-'ry face and see the eyes of God!

Text: Based on Matthew 25:24–41; Tony E. Alonso, b.1980
Tune: Tony E. Alonso, b.1980
© 2001, GIA Publications, Inc.

908 The Thirsty Cry for Water, Lord

1. The thirst-y cry for wa-ter, Lord; The
2. The cup of wa-ter poured in love The
3. But help us al-so hear the cry Of
4. And come to us, O ris-en Christ, Our

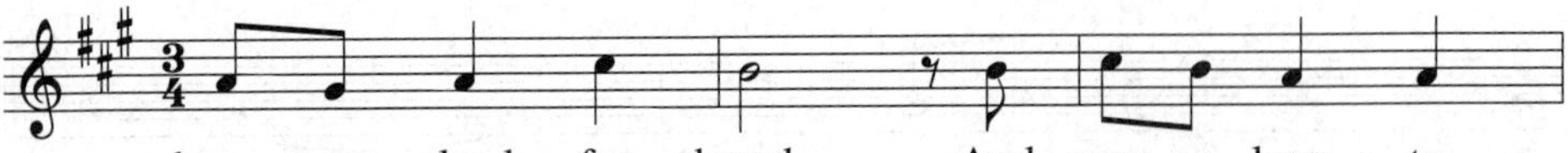

hun-gry plead for bread. And man-y long to
pangs of thirst will still. The bread of earth you
hun-g'ring, thirst-ing hearts For liv-ing wa-ter,
rest-less souls re-lieve; And sat-is-fy our

rise a-gain Where hope, cast down, lies dead.
bid us share, The fam-ished child can fill.
bread of life Your grace a-lone im-parts.
starv-ing hearts That we may rise and live.

Text: Herman G. Stuempfle, Jr., 1923–2007, © 1997, GIA Publications, Inc.
Tune: SHANTI, CM; Marty Haugen, b.1950, © 1984, GIA Publications, Inc.

909 Jesus Entered Egypt

1. Je-sus en-tered E-gypt Flee-ing Her-od's hand,
2. Je-sus was a mi-grant liv-ing as a guest
3. Je-sus cross-es bor-ders With the wan-d'ring poor,

Liv-ing as an a-lien In a for-eign land.
With the friends and stran-gers Who could of-fer rest.
Search-ing for a ref-uge, For an o-pen door.

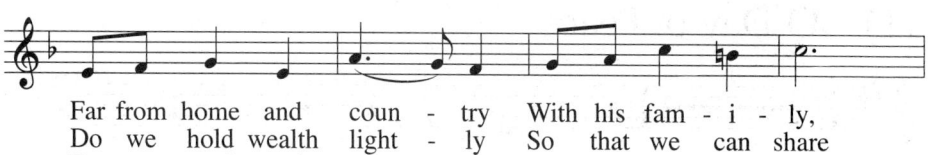

Far from home and coun - try With his fam - i - ly,
Do we hold wealth light - ly So that we can share
Do our words and ac - tions An - swer Je - sus' plea:

Was there room and wel - come For this ref - u - gee?
Shel - ter with the home - less, And a - bun - dant care?
"Give the low - ly wel - come, And you wel - come me"?

Text: Adam M. L. Tice, b.1979, © 2009, GIA Publications, Inc.
Tune: KING'S WESTON, 6 5 6 5 D; Ralph Vaughan Williams, 1872–1958, alt., © 1931, Oxford University Press

O God of Love, O King of Peace 910

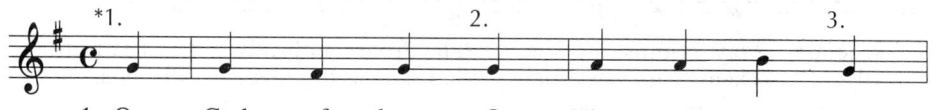

1. O God of love, O King of peace, Make
2. Re - mem - ber, Lord, your works of old, The
3. Whom shall we trust but you, O Lord? Where
4. Where saints and an - gels dwell a - bove All

wars through - out the world to cease; Our greed and vio - lent
won - ders that your peo - ple told; Re - mem - ber not our
rest but on your faith - ful word? None ev - er called on
hearts are joined in ho - ly love; Oh, bind us in that

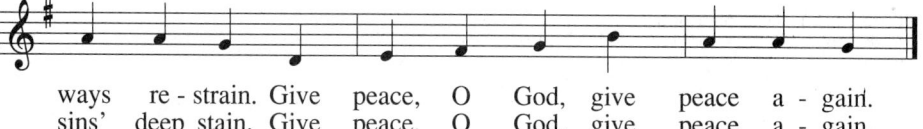

ways re - strain. Give peace, O God, give peace a - gain.
sins' deep stain. Give peace, O God, give peace a - gain.
you in vain. Give peace, O God, give peace a - gain.
heav'n - ly chain. Give peace, O God, give peace a - gain.

*May be sung as a two- or four-voice canon.

Text: Henry W. Baker, 1821–1877, alt.
Tune: TALLIS' CANON, LM; Thomas Tallis, c.1505–1585

911 O Day of Peace

1. O day of peace that dim - ly
2. Then shall the wolf dwell with the

shines Through all our hopes and prayers and dreams, Guide us to
lamb Nor shall the fierce de - vour the small; As beasts and

jus - tice, truth and love, De - liv - ered from our self - ish
cat - tle calm - ly graze, A lit - tle child shall lead them

schemes. May swords of hate fall from our hands, Our hearts from
all. Then en - e - mies shall learn to love, All crea - tures

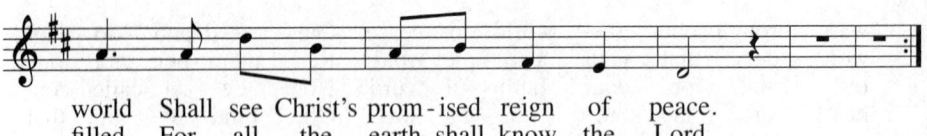

en - vy find re - lease, Till by God's grace our war - ring
find their true ac - cord; The hope of peace shall be ful -

world Shall see Christ's prom - ised reign of peace.
filled, For all the earth shall know the Lord.

Text: Carl P. Daw, Jr., b.1944, © 1982, Hope Publishing Company
Tune: JERUSALEM, LMD; Charles H. H. Parry, 1848–1918; harm. by Richard Proulx, 1937–2010, © 1986, GIA Publications, Inc.

Make Me a Channel of Your Peace   912

Verses 1, 2, 4

1. Make me a chan-nel of your peace. Where
2. Make me a chan-nel of your peace. Where
4. Make me a chan-nel of your peace. It

there is ha-tred, let me bring your love. Where
there's de-spair in life, let me bring hope. Where
is in par-don-ing that we are par-doned, in

there is in-ju-ry, your par-don, Lord, And
there is dark-ness, on-ly light, And
giv-ing of our-selves that we re-ceive, and in

where there's doubt, true faith in you.
where there's sad-ness, ev-er joy.
dy-ing that we're born to e-ter-nal life.

Verse 3

3. Oh, Mas-ter, grant that I may nev-er seek So much to be con-

soled as to con-sole. To be un-der-stood as to un-der-

stand. To be loved as to love with all my soul.

Text: *Prayer of St. Francis*; adapt. by Sebastian Temple, 1928–1997
Tune: Sebastian Temple, 1928–1997; acc. by Robert J. Batastini, b.1942
© 1967, OCP
Dedicated to Mrs. Frances Tracy

913 Prayer of Peace

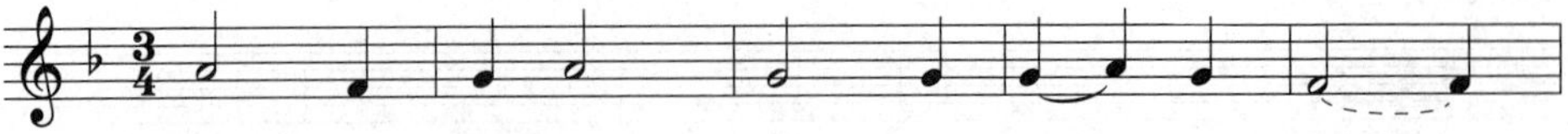

1. Peace be - fore us, peace be - hind us, peace
2. Love be - fore us, love be - hind us, love
3. Light be - fore us, light be - hind us, light
4. Christ be - fore us, Christ be - hind us, Christ
5. Al - le - lu - ia, al - le - lu - ia, al - le -
6. Peace be - fore us, peace be - hind us, peace

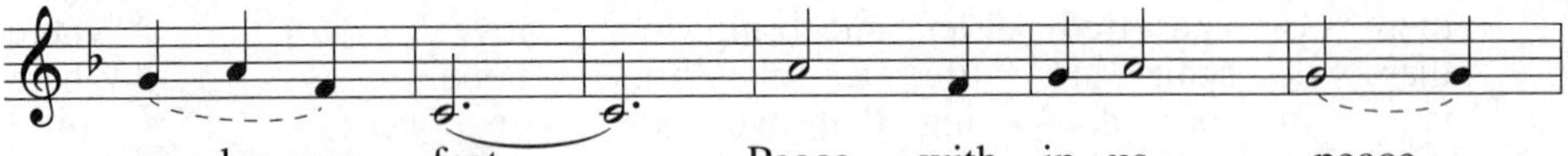

un - der our feet. Peace with - in us, peace
un - der our feet. Love with - in us, love
un - der our feet. Light with - in us, light
un - der our feet. Christ with - in us, Christ
lu - ia, Al - le - lu - ia, al - le -
un - der our feet. Peace with - in us, peace

o - ver us, let all a - round us be peace.
o - ver us, let all a - round us be love.
o - ver us, let all a - round us be light.
o - ver us, let all a - round us be Christ.
lu - ia, al - le - lu - ia.
o - ver us, let all a - round us be peace.

Text: Based on a Navajo prayer; David Haas, b.1957
Tune: David Haas, b.1957
© 1987, GIA Publications, Inc.

914 Everything That Has Voice

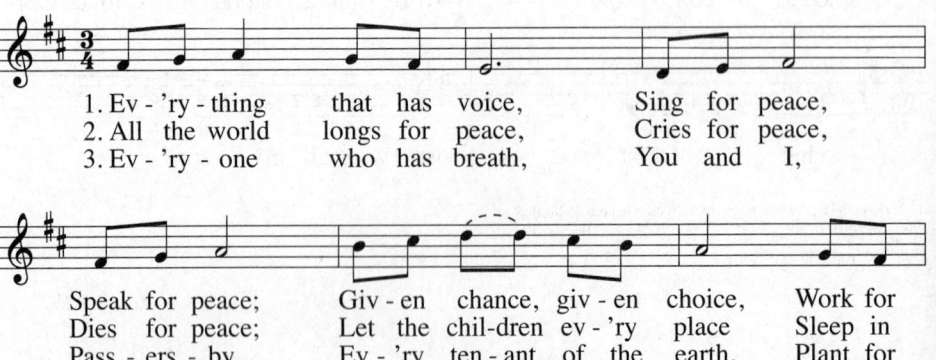

1. Ev - 'ry - thing that has voice, Sing for peace,
2. All the world longs for peace, Cries for peace,
3. Ev - 'ry - one who has breath, You and I,

Speak for peace; Giv - en chance, giv - en choice, Work for
Dies for peace; Let the chil - dren ev - 'ry place Sleep in
Pass - ers - by, Ev - 'ry ten - ant of the earth, Plant for

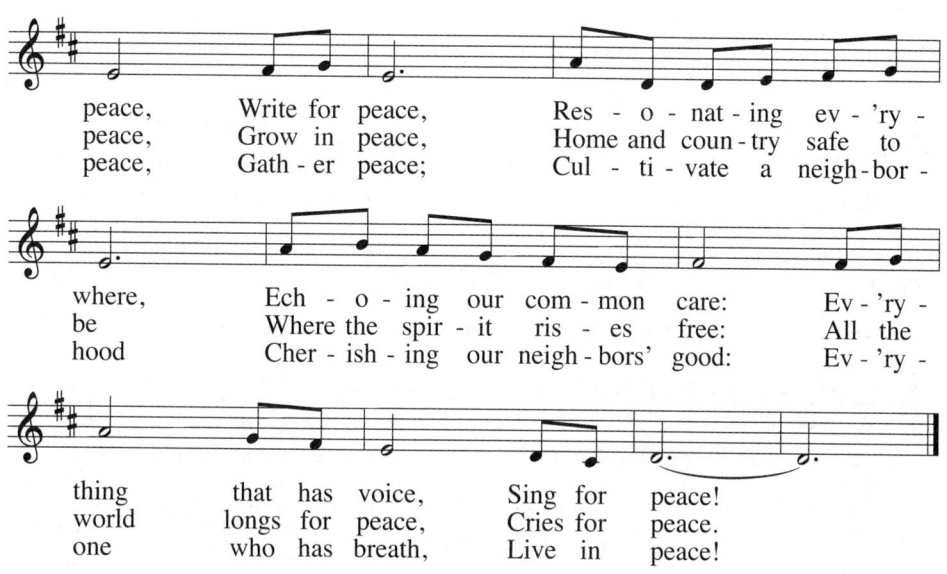

peace,   Write for peace,   Res - o - nat - ing ev - 'ry -
peace,   Grow in peace,   Home and coun - try safe to
peace,   Gath - er peace;   Cul - ti - vate a neigh - bor -

where,   Ech - o - ing our com - mon care: Ev - 'ry -
be   Where the spir - it ris - es free: All the
hood   Cher - ish - ing our neigh - bors' good: Ev - 'ry -

thing   that has voice,   Sing for peace!
world   longs for peace,   Cries for peace.
one   who has breath,   Live in peace!

Text: Shirley Erena Murray, b.1931, © 2003, Hope Publishing Company
Tune: SING FOR PEACE, 6 33 6 33 77 6 3; Marty Haugen, b.1950, © 2005, GIA Publications, Inc.

Dona Nobis Pacem 915

Canon

1. Do - na no - bis pa - cem, pa - cem.
Do - na no - bis pa - cem.

2. Do - na no - bis pa - cem.
Do - na no - bis pa - cem.

3. Do - na no - bis pa - cem.
Do - na no - bis pa - cem.

Text: *Grant us peace*
Tune: Traditional; acc. by Diana Kodner, b.1957, © 1994, GIA Publications, Inc.

916 Peace, Be Not Anxious

Refrain

Peace now I give to you. My peace I pour through you.

Not as the world gives, but ev - er more sure.

Past all un - der-stand-ing, this gra-cious com-mand - ing:

peace, be not anx - ious, God holds you se - cure.

Verses

1. Peace, be not anxious. Our Maker is gracious.
   Think now of the lilies: they toil not, nor spin.
   Fields lush with adornment, all Solomon's raiment,
   still never could rival the splendor therein.

2. Fret not for tomorrow. In joy or in sorrow,
   each tiniest sparrow God will not forget.
   Bright Spirit descending, warm comfort unending—
   peace, be not anxious: God cares for you yet.

3. In mansions of heaven, blest life will be given.
   There, one with our Maker, I'll welcome you home.
   Lo, I go before you. So, now I implore you:
   peace, be not anxious, for you are my own.

Text: Mary Louise Bringle, b.1953, alt., © 2002, GIA Publications, Inc.
Tune: Lori True, b.1961, © 2007, GIA Publications, Inc.

917 Dona Nobis Pacem Domine

Ostinato Refrain

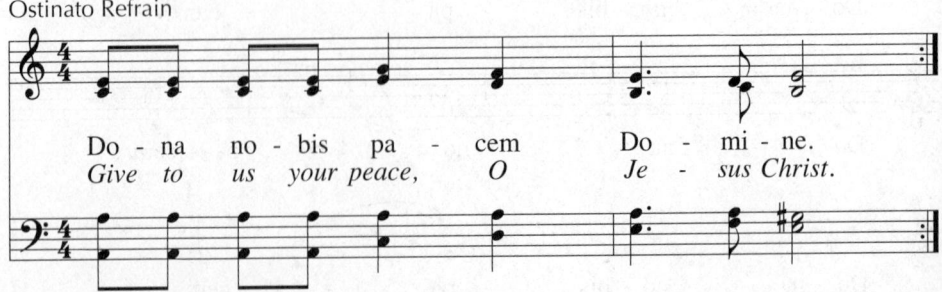

Do - na no - bis pa - cem Do - mi - ne.
Give to us your peace, O Je - sus Christ.

Text: Psalm 85:9, Matthew 5:9, John 14:27, Ephesians 2:14–17; Taizé Community
Tune: Jacques Berthier, 1923–1994
© 1982, Les Presses de Taizé, GIA Publications, Inc., agent

We Are Many Parts 918

Refrain

We are man-y parts, we are all one bod-y,

and the gifts we have we are giv-en to share.

May the Spir-it of love make us one in-deed;

one, the love that we share, one, our hope in de-

spair, one, the cross that we bear.

Verses

1. God of all, we look to you, we would be your
2. So my pain is pain for you, in your joy is
3. All you seek-ers, great and small, seek the great-est

D.C.

ser-vants true, let us be your love to all the world.
my joy, too; all is brought to-geth-er in the Lord.
gift of all; if you love, then you will know the Lord.

Text: 1 Corinthians 12, 13; Marty Haugen, b.1950
Tune: Marty Haugen, b.1950
© 1980, 1986, GIA Publications, Inc.

919 In Christ There Is No East or West

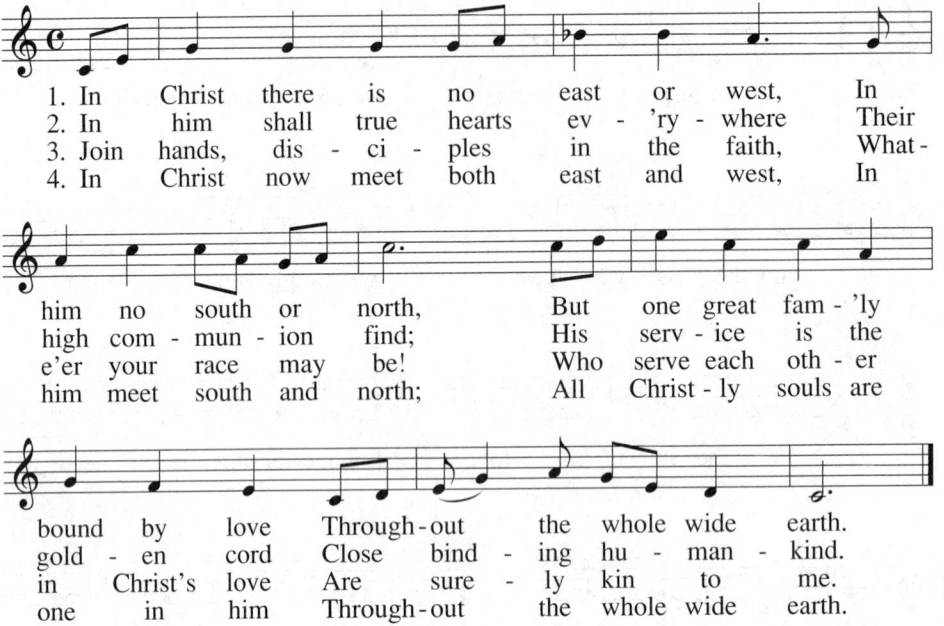

1. In Christ there is no east or west, In him no south or north, But one great fam-'ly bound by love Through-out the whole wide earth.
2. In him shall true hearts ev-'ry-where Their high com-mun-ion find; His serv-ice is the gold-en cord Close bind-ing hu-man-kind.
3. Join hands, dis-ci-ples in the faith, What-e'er your race may be! Who serve each oth-er in Christ's love Are sure-ly kin to me.
4. In Christ now meet both east and west, In him meet south and north; All Christ-ly souls are one in him Through-out the whole wide earth.

Text: Galatians 3:23; William A. Dunkerley, 1852–1941, alt.
Tune: McKEE, CM; African American; adapt. by Harry T. Burleigh, 1866–1949

920 There Is One Lord

Ostinato Refrain / Estribillo

There is one Lord, one faith, one bap-tis-m,
Hay un Se-ñor, u-na fe, un bau-tis-mo,

There is one God who is Fa-ther of all.
Un so-lo Dios, quien es Pa-dre de to-dos.

Text: Ephesians 4, adapt. by Robert J. Batastini, b.1942, and the Taizé Community, 1984
Tune: Jacques Berthier, 1923–1994
© 1984, 2007, Les Presses de Taizé, GIA Publications, Inc., agent

One Lord 921

Refrain

One Lord, one faith, one call to serve each oth - er. One heart, one mind, one com - mon ground; we stand all as one.

To verses | *Final ending*

Verses *Solo:*

1. Give us new hands, o - pen and free,
2. Give us new eyes, lov - ing and wise,
3. Give us new hearts, hum - ble yet strong,
4. Breathe out your Spir - it up - on the land.

to serve with grace and dig - ni - ty. May we be wor-
to seek the good we all have in - side. May we be wor-
to love like you our whole life long. May we be wor-
In hope and peace we'll firm - ly stand, to live lives wor-

D.C.

thy of our call.
thy of our call.
thy of our call.   We have but
thy of our call.

Text: Ephesians 4:1–24; Lori True, b.1961
Tune: Lori True, b.1961
© 2003, GIA Publications, Inc.

922 Diverse in Culture, Nation, Race

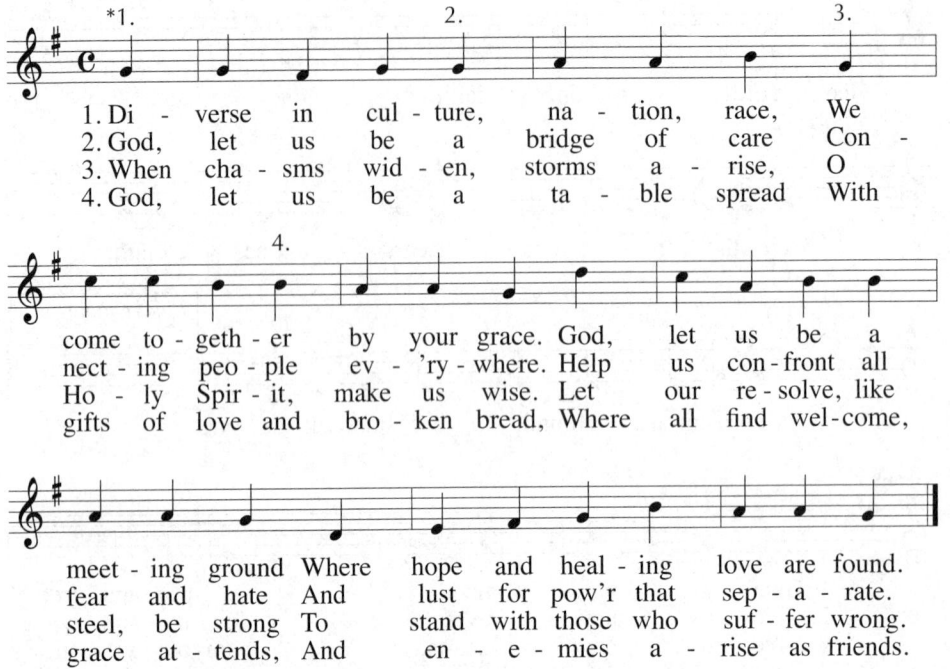

1. Di - verse in cul - ture, na - tion, race, We
2. God, let us be a bridge of care Con -
3. When cha - sms wid - en, storms a - rise, O
4. God, let us be a ta - ble spread With

come to - geth - er by your grace. God, let us be a
nect - ing peo - ple ev - 'ry - where. Help us con - front all
Ho - ly Spir - it, make us wise. Let our re - solve, like
gifts of love and bro - ken bread, Where all find wel - come,

meet - ing ground Where hope and heal - ing love are found.
fear and hate And lust for pow'r that sep - a - rate.
steel, be strong To stand with those who suf - fer wrong.
grace at - tends, And en - e - mies a - rise as friends.

*May be sung as a two- or four-voice canon.

Text: Ruth Duck, b.1947, © 1992, GIA Publications, Inc.
Tune: TALLIS' CANON, LM; Thomas Tallis, c.1505–1585

923 Come Now, O Prince of Peace

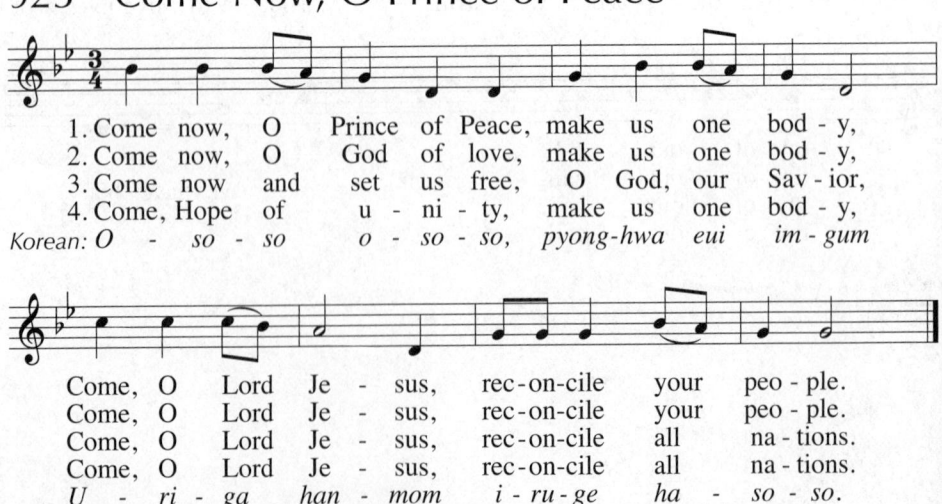

1. Come now, O Prince of Peace, make us one bod - y,
2. Come now, O God of love, make us one bod - y,
3. Come now and set us free, O God, our Sav - ior,
4. Come, Hope of u - ni - ty, make us one bod - y,
Korean: O - so - so o - so - so, pyong-hwa eui im - gum

Come, O Lord Je - sus, rec-on-cile your peo - ple.
Come, O Lord Je - sus, rec-on-cile your peo - ple.
Come, O Lord Je - sus, rec-on-cile all na - tions.
Come, O Lord Je - sus, rec-on-cile all na - tions.
U - ri - ga han - mom i - ru - ge ha - so - so.

Text: O-so-sô, Geonyong Lee, b.1947, © 1990, Geonyong Lee; para. by Marion Pope, alt., © 1990, Marion Pope
Tune: OSOSO, 11 11; Geonyong Lee, b.1947, © 1990, Geonyong Lee

As We Gather at Your Table 924

1. As we gath - er at your Ta - ble, As we
2. Turn our wor - ship in - to wit - ness In the
3. Gra - cious Spir - it, help us sum - mon Oth - er

lis - ten to your word, Help us know, O God, your
sac - ra - ment of life; Send us forth to love and
guests to share that feast Where tri - um - phant Love will

pres - ence; Let our hearts and minds be stirred. Nour - ish
serve you, Bring - ing peace where there is strife. Give us,
wel - come Those who had been last and least. There no

us with sa - cred sto - ry Till we
Christ, your great com - pas - sion To for -
more will en - vy blind us Nor will

claim it as our own; Teach us through this ho - ly
give as you for - gave; May we still be - hold your
pride our peace de - stroy, As we join with saints and

ban - quet How to make Love's vic - t'ry known.
im - age In the world you died to save.
an - gels To re - peat the sound - ing joy.

Text: Carl P. Daw, Jr. b.1944; © 1989, Hope Publishing Company
Tune: NETTLETON, 8 7 8 7 D; Wyeth's *Repository of Sacred Music*, 1813

925 All Are Welcome

1. Let us build a house where love can dwell And
2. Let us build a house where proph - ets speak, And
3. Let us build a house where love is found In
4. Let us build a house where hands will reach Be -
5. Let us build a house where all are named, Their

all can safe - ly live, A place where saints and
words are strong and true, Where all God's chil - dren
wa - ter, wine and wheat: A ban - quet hall on
yond the wood and stone To heal and strength - en,
songs and vi - sions heard And loved and treas - ured,

chil - dren tell How hearts learn to for -
dare to seek To dream God's reign a -
ho - ly ground, Where peace and jus - tice
serve and teach, And live the Word they've
taught and claimed As words with - in the

give. Built of hopes and dreams and vi - sions, Rock of
new. Here the cross shall stand as wit - ness And as
meet. Here the love of God, through Je - sus, Is re -
known. Here the out - cast and the stran - ger Bear the
Word. Built of tears and cries and laugh - ter, Prayers of

faith and vault of grace; Here the
sym - bol of God's grace; Here as
vealed in time and space; As we
im - age of God's face; Let us
faith and songs of grace, Let this

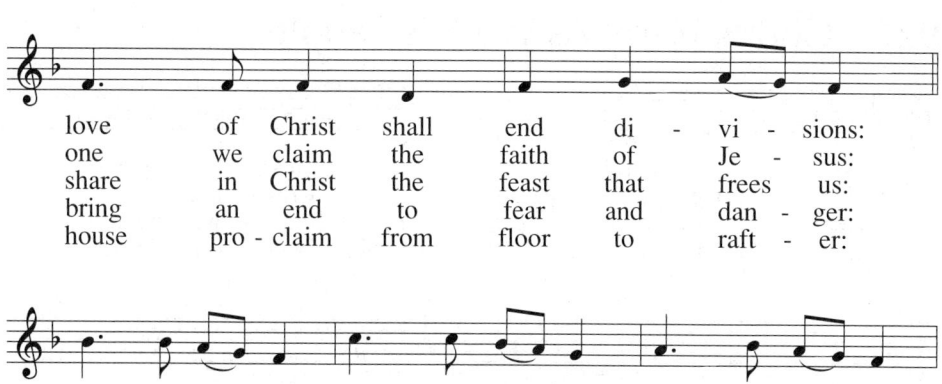

love   of   Christ   shall   end   di - vi - sions:
one   we   claim   the   faith   of   Je - sus:
share   in   Christ   the   feast   that frees us:
bring   an   end   to   fear   and dan - ger:
house   pro - claim   from   floor   to   raft - er:

All   are wel-come,   all   are wel-come,   all   are wel-come

in   this   place.

Text: Marty Haugen, b.1950
Tune: TWO OAKS, 9 6 8 6 8 7 10 with refrain; Marty Haugen, b.1950
© 1994, GIA Publications, Inc.

Uyai Mose / Come All You People   926

Ostinato Refrain

U - ya - i mo - se,   ti - na - ma - te Mwa - ri,
Come all   you peo - ple,   come and   praise your Mak - er,

U - ya - i mo - se,   ti - na - ma - te Mwa - ri,
Come all   you peo - ple,   come and   praise your Mak - er,

U - ya - i mo - se,   ti - na - ma - te Mwa - ri,
Come all   you peo - ple,   come and   praise your Mak - er,

U - ya - i   mo - se   zvi - no.
Come now   and   wor - ship   the   Lord.

Text: Alexander Gondo, b.1936
Tune: Alexander Gondo, b.1936; arr. by John L. Bell, b.1949, © 1994, Iona Community, GIA Publications, Inc., agent

927 God Is Here! As We His People

1. God is here! As we his peo-ple
2. Here are sym-bols to re-mind us
3. Here our chil-dren find a wel-come
4. Lord of all, of Church and king-dom,

Meet to of-fer praise and prayer,
Of our life-long need of grace;
In the Shep-herd's flock and fold;
In an age of change and doubt,

May we find in ful-ler meas-ure
Here are ta-ble, font, and pul-pit;
Here, as bread and wine are tak-en,
Keep us faith-ful to the Gos-pel;

What it is in Christ we share.
Here the cross has cen-tral place.
Christ sus-tains us as of old.
Help us work your pur-pose out.

Here, as in the world a-round us,
Here in hon-es-ty of preach-ing,
Here the ser-vants of the Ser-vant
Here, in this day's ded-i-ca-tion,

All our var-ied skills and arts
Here in si-lence, as in speech,
Seek in wor-ship to ex-plore
All we have to give, re-ceive;

Wait the com - ing of the Spir - it
Here, in new - ness and re - new - al,
What it means in dai - ly liv - ing
We, who can - not live with - out you,

In - to o - pen minds and hearts.
God the Spir - it comes to each.
To be - lieve and to a - dore.
We a - dore you! We be - lieve!

Text: Fred Pratt Green, 1903–2000, © 1979, Hope Publishing Company
Tune: ABBOT'S LEIGH, 8 7 8 7 D; Cyril V. Taylor, 1907–1991, © 1942, ren. 1970, Hope Publishing Company

All People That on Earth Do Dwell   928

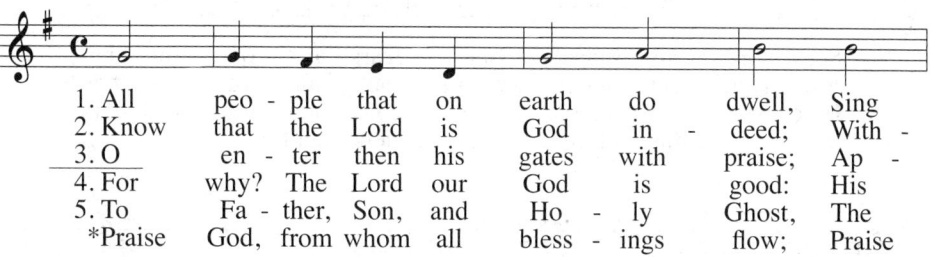

1. All peo - ple that on earth do dwell, Sing
2. Know that the Lord is God in - deed; With -
3. O en - ter then his gates with praise; Ap -
4. For why? The Lord our God is good: His
5. To Fa - ther, Son, and Ho - ly Ghost, The
*Praise God, from whom all bless - ings flow; Praise

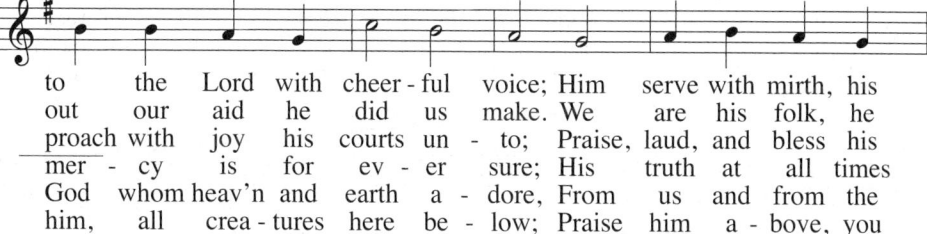

to the Lord with cheer - ful voice; Him serve with mirth, his
out our aid he did us make. We are his folk, he
proach with joy his courts un - to; Praise, laud, and bless his
mer - cy is for ev - er sure; His truth at all times
God whom heav'n and earth a - dore, From us and from the
him, all crea - tures here be - low; Praise him a - bove, you

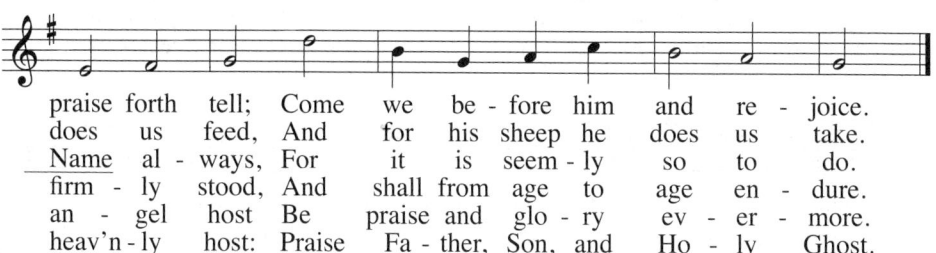

praise forth tell; Come we be - fore him and re - joice.
does us feed, And for his sheep he does us take.
Name al - ways, For it is seem - ly so to do.
firm - ly stood, And shall from age to age en - dure.
an - gel host Be praise and glo - ry ev - er - more.
heav'n - ly host: Praise Fa - ther, Son, and Ho - ly Ghost.

*May be sung alone or as an alternate to stanza 5.

Text: Psalm 100; William Kethe, d. c.1593; Doxology, Thomas Ken, 1637–1711
Tune: OLD HUNDREDTH, LM; Louis Bourgeois, c.1510–1561

929 Gather Us In

1. Here in this place new light is stream - ing,
2. We are the young— our lives are a mys - t'ry,
3. Here we will take the wine and the wa - ter,
4. Not in the dark of build - ings con - fin - ing,

Now is the dark - ness van - ished a - way,
We are the old— who yearn for your face,
Here we will take the bread of new birth,
Not in some heav - en, light - years a - way, But

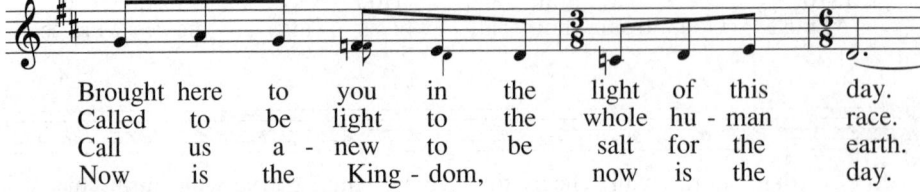

See in this space our fears and our dream-ings,
We have been sung through - out all of his - t'ry,
Here you shall call your sons and your daugh-ters,
here in this place the new light is shin - ing,

Brought here to you in the light of this day.
Called to be light to the whole hu - man race.
Call us a - new to be salt for the earth.
Now is the King - dom, now is the day.

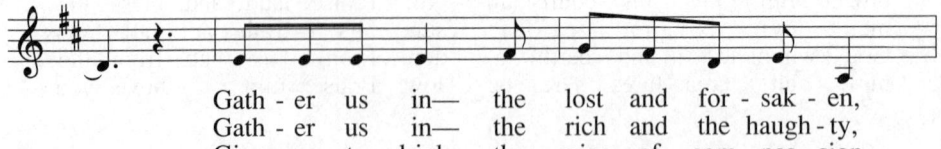

Gath - er us in— the lost and for - sak - en,
Gath - er us in— the rich and the haugh - ty,
Give us to drink the wine of com - pas - sion,
Gath - er us in and hold us for ev - er,

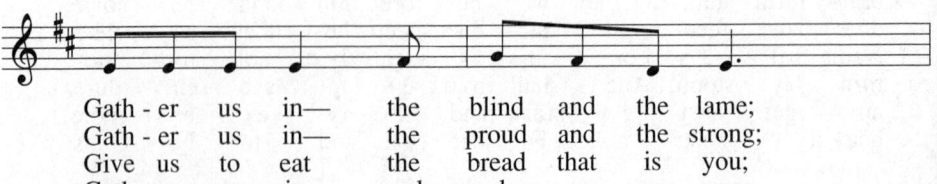

Gath - er us in— the blind and the lame;
Gath - er us in— the proud and the strong;
Give us to eat the bread that is you;
Gath - er us in and make us your own;

Call to us now, and we shall a - wak - en,
Give us a heart so meek and so low - ly,
Nour - ish us well, and teach us to fash - ion
Gath - er us in— all peo - ples to - geth - er,

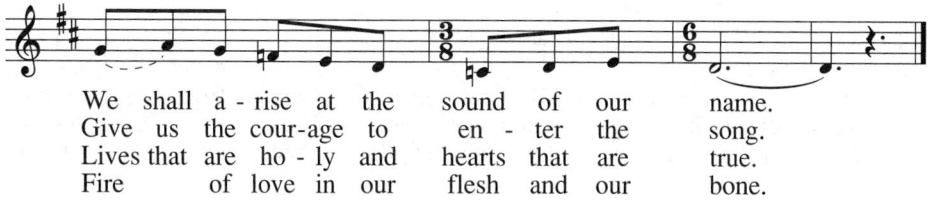

We shall a - rise at the sound of our name.
Give us the cour-age to en - ter the song.
Lives that are ho - ly and hearts that are true.
Fire of love in our flesh and our bone.

Text: Marty Haugen, b.1950
Tune: GATHER US IN, Irregular; Marty Haugen, b.1950
© 1982, GIA Publications, Inc.

Come, Rejoice before Your Maker 930

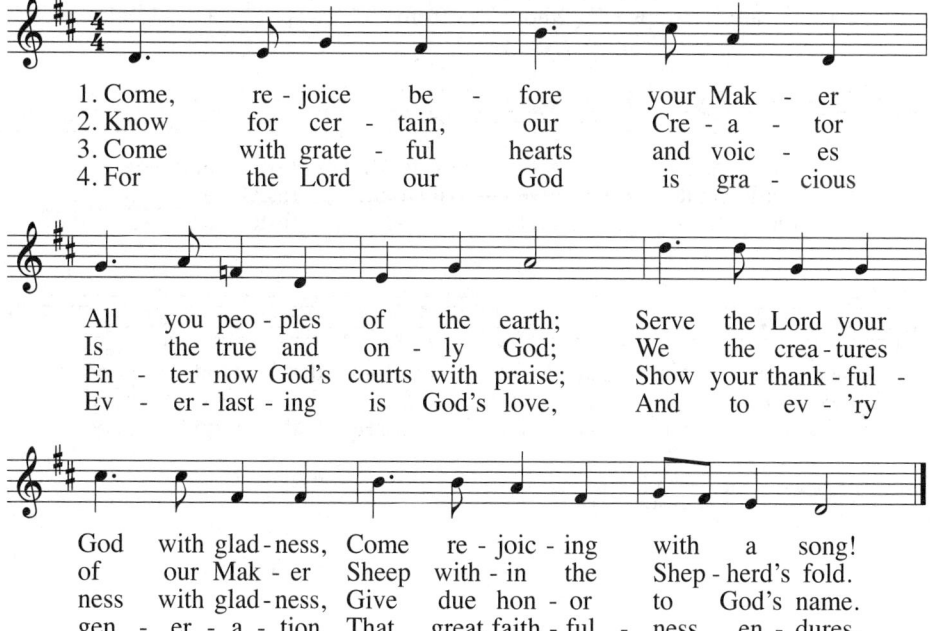

1. Come, re - joice be - fore your Mak - er
2. Know for cer - tain, our Cre - a - tor
3. Come with grate - ful hearts and voic - es
4. For the Lord our God is gra - cious

All you peo - ples of the earth; Serve the Lord your
Is the true and on - ly God; We the crea - tures
En - ter now God's courts with praise; Show your thank - ful -
Ev - er - last - ing is God's love, And to ev - 'ry

God with glad-ness, Come re - joic - ing with a song!
of our Mak - er Sheep with - in the Shep - herd's fold.
ness with glad-ness, Give due hon - or to God's name.
gen - er - a - tion That great faith - ful - ness en - dures.

Text: Psalm 100; Michael Baughen, b.1930, alt.
Tune: JUBILATE DEO, 8 7 8 7; Noel H. Tredinnick, b.1949
© 1973, The Jubilate Group (admin. by Hope Publishing Company)

931 All Who Hunger, Gather Gladly

1. All who hun - ger, gath - er glad - ly;
2. All who hun - ger, nev - er stran - gers,
3. All who hun - ger, sing to - geth - er;

Ho - ly man - na is our bread. Come from wil - der -
Seek - er, be a wel-come guest. Come from rest - less -
Je - sus Christ is liv - ing bread. Come from lone - li -

ness and wan - d'ring. Here, in truth, we will be fed.
ness and roam - ing. Here, in joy, we keep the feast.
ness and long - ing. Here, in peace, we have been led.

You that yearn for days of full - ness,
We that once were lost and scat - tered
Blest are those who from this ta - ble

All a - round us is our food. Taste and see the
In com - mun - ion's love have stood. Taste and see the
Live their days in grat - i - tude. Taste and see the

grace e - ter - nal. Taste and see that God is good.
grace e - ter - nal. Taste and see that God is good.
grace e - ter - nal. Taste and see that God is good.

Text: Sylvia G. Dunstan, 1955–1993, © 1991, GIA Publications, Inc.
Tune: HOLY MANNA, 8 7 8 7 D; William Moore, fl.1830

I Rejoiced When I Heard Them Say   932

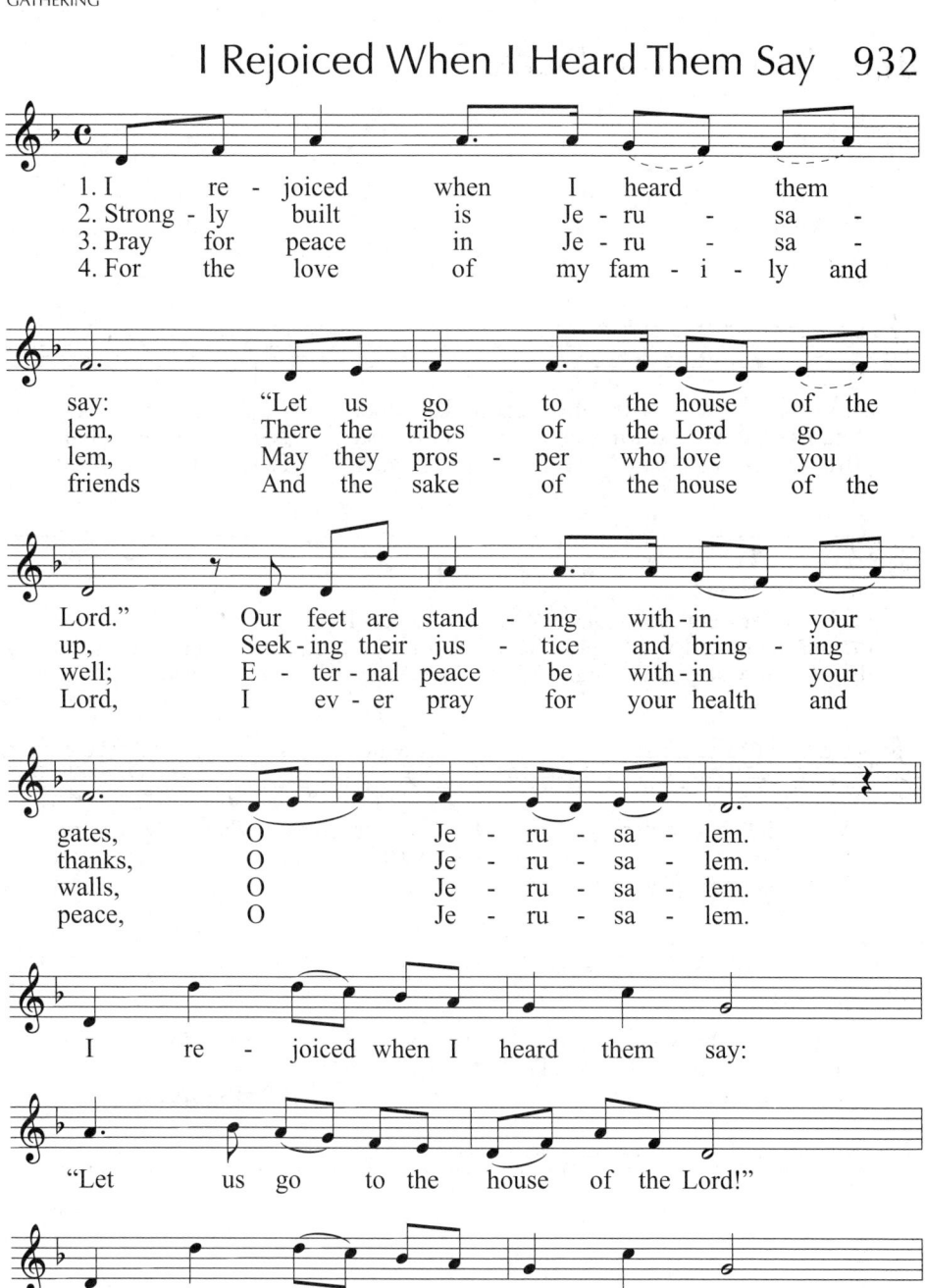

1. I re - joiced when I heard them say: "Let us go to the house of the Lord." Our feet are stand - ing with - in your gates, O Je - ru - sa - lem.

2. Strong - ly built is Je - ru - sa - lem, There the tribes of the Lord go up, Seek - ing their jus - tice and bring - ing thanks, O Je - ru - sa - lem.

3. Pray for peace in Je - ru - sa - lem, May they pros - per who love you well; E - ter - nal peace be with - in your walls, O Je - ru - sa - lem.

4. For the love of my fam - i - ly and friends And the sake of the house of the Lord, I ev - er pray for your health and peace, O Je - ru - sa - lem.

I re - joiced when I heard them say: "Let us go to the house of the Lord!"

I re - joiced when I heard them say: "Let us go to the house of the Lord!"

Text: Psalm 122; Richard Proulx, 1937–2010
Tune: MA YEDIDUT, Irregular with refrain; Hasidic melody, arr. by Richard Proulx, 1937–2010
© 1993, GIA Publications, Inc.

933 What Is This Place

1. What is this place where we are meet - ing?
2. Words from a - far, stars that are fall - ing,
3. And we ac - cept bread at his ta - ble,

On - ly a house, the earth its floor, Walls and a roof
Sparks that are sown in us like seed. Names for our God,
Bro - ken and shared, a liv - ing sign. Here in this world,

shel - ter - ing peo - ple, Win - dows for light, an o - pen door.
dreams, signs and won - ders Sent from the past are all we need.
dy - ing and liv - ing, We are each oth - er's bread and wine.

Yet it be - comes a bod - y that lives When we are
We in this place re - mem - ber and speak A - gain what
This is the place where we can re - ceive What we need

gath - ered here, And know our God is near.
we have heard: God's free re - deem - ing word.
to in - crease: God's jus - tice and God's peace.

Text: *Zomaar een dak boven wat hoofen;* Huub Oosterhuis, b.1933; tr. by David Smith, b.1933, © 1967, Gooi En Sticht, OCP, agent
Tune: KOMT NU MET ZANG, 9 8 9 8 9 66; Valerius' *Nederlandtsch Gedenckclanck*, 1626; harm. by Adriaan Engels, 1906–2003, © Gooi En Sticht, OCP, agent

934 I Come with Joy

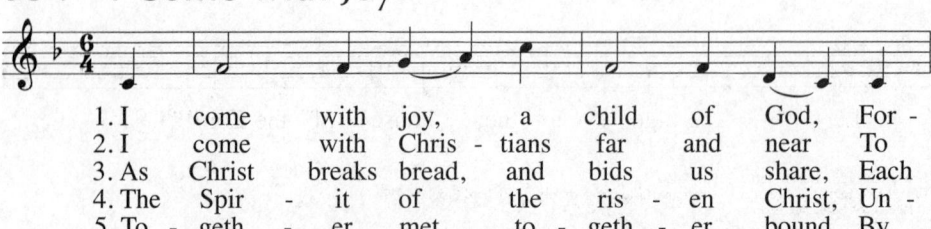

1. I come with joy, a child of God, For -
2. I come with Chris - tians far and near To
3. As Christ breaks bread, and bids us share, Each
4. The Spir - it of the ris - en Christ, Un -
5. To - geth - er met, to - geth - er bound By

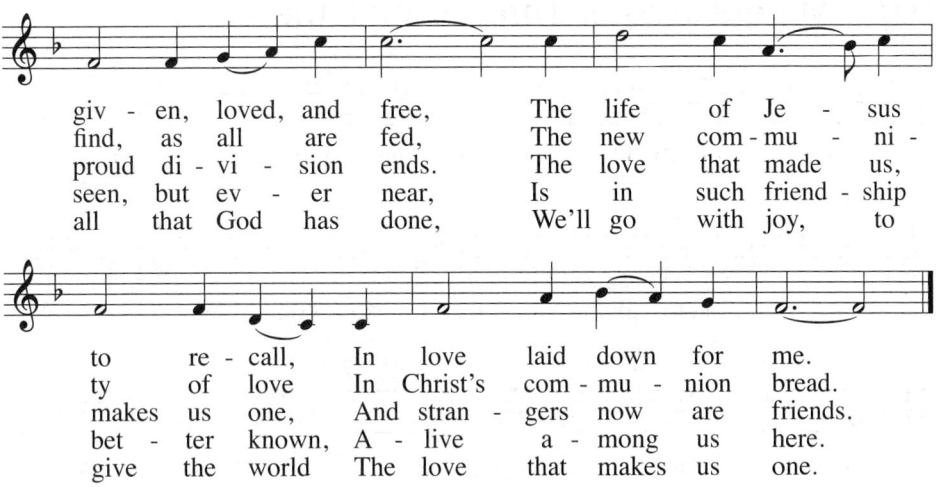

giv - en, loved, and free, The life of Je - sus
find, as all are fed, The new com - mu - ni -
proud di - vi - sion ends. The love that made us,
seen, but ev - er near, Is in such friend - ship
all that God has done, We'll go with joy, to

to re - call, In love laid down for me.
ty of love In Christ's com - mu - nion bread.
makes us one, And stran - gers now are friends.
bet - ter known, A - live a - mong us here.
give the world The love that makes us one.

Text: Brian Wren, b.1936, © 1971, rev. 1995, Hope Publishing Company
Tune: LAND OF REST, CM; American; harm. by Richard Proulx, 1937–2010, © 1975, GIA Publications, Inc.

Prepare a Room for Me   935

To be sung in alternating verses by cantor and congregation.

1. "Pre - pare a room for me, Your
2. This room we have pre - pared; The
3. "Where e - ven two or three Have
4. Lord Christ, we seek the food Your
5. "My prom - ise I will keep; Your
6. All thanks and praise to you, Our

Sav - ior, Host and Priest, Where I may gath - er
Ta - ble now is set. We wait your prom - ised
come the Meal to share, Un - seen, but liv - ing,
grace a - lone can give. We come with emp - ty,
hun - ger will be fed, For in this Meal I
Sav - ior, Lord, and Friend, That through this Loaf and

you, my friends, To cel - e - brate the feast."
pres - ence, Lord, Where we once more are met.
lov - ing still, I sure - ly will be there!"
hun - g'ring hearts That we may eat and live.
of - fer you My - self, the liv - ing Bread!"
Cup you share Your love that has no end!

Text: Herman G. Stuempfle, Jr., 1923–2007, © 2000, GIA Publications, Inc.
Tune: SOUTHWELL, SM; William Daman, *The Psalmes of David*, 1579, alt.

936 Where Two or Three Are Gathered

Refrain

Here in the Bread that is bro - ken, here in the Cup that is
poured, here in the Word that is spo - ken: Je - sus Christ is
Lord! Here where the poor find their treas - ure,
here where the great-est are least, come find a love be-yond
meas - ure in this heav'n - ly feast.

Verses

1. Where two or three are gath-ered, Gath-ered in my
2. Where two or three are gath-ered, I am there as
3. Where two or three are gath-ered, I am there with
4. Where two or three are gath-ered, Gath-ered in my
5. Where two or three are gath-ered, I am there as
6. Where two or three are gath-ered, I am there with

name, I come with words of com - fort
well, In - vit - ing my dis - ci - ples
you. I lead you in - to free - dom,
name, I wash your feet in serv - ice.
well. The bless - ings of the king - dom
you. My gifts of peace and mer - cy

D.C.

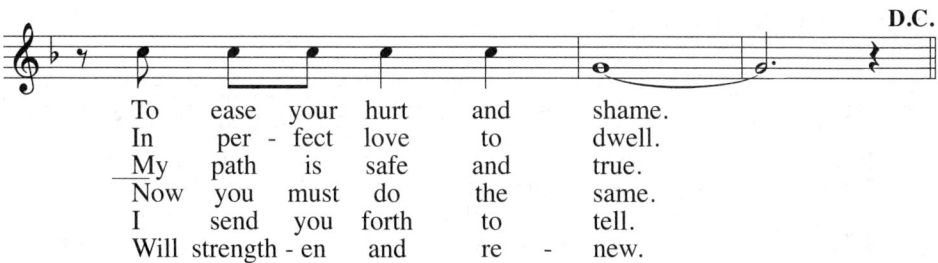

To   ease   your   hurt   and   shame.
In   per -   fect   love   to   dwell.
My   path   is   safe   and   true.
Now   you   must   do   the   same.
I   send   you   forth   to   tell.
Will   strength - en   and   re -   new.

Text: Liam Lawton, b.1959
Tune: HEAVENLY FEAST, 7 5 7 6 with refrain; Liam Lawton, b.1959; arr. by Paul A. Tate, b.1968
© 2009, Sumerset Recordings and GIA Publications, Inc.

Making Their Way   937

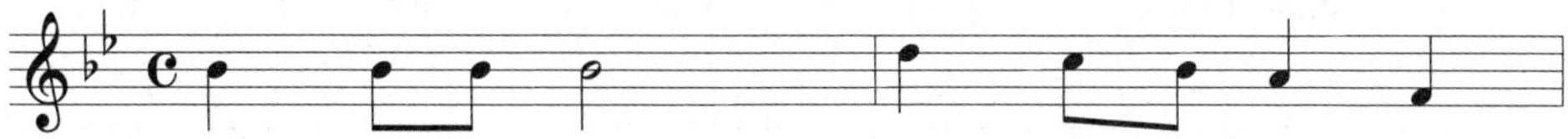

1. Mak - ing their way   down through the a - ges,
2. Mak - ing their way   all   the world o - ver,
3. Mak - ing our way   sea - son by sea - son,

Sin - ners and saints have   heard God's call: Wealth-y and poor,
Chris-tians as - sem - ble   on   this day,   Hear - ing the Word,
Pil - grims, we jour - ney   till life's end,   Trav - el-ing light,

pow - er-ful, low - ly,   Je - sus' dis - ci - ples,   one and all.
shar - ing the Ban-quet,   Learn-ing to walk in   Je - sus' way.
shar - ing the rich - es,   Car - ing for stran - ger   as for friend,

Gath - ered for wor - ship,   of - fer-ing thanks,   The   great - est
Mem - bers of Christ,   u -   nit - ed in love,   They seek our
Till in the joy   of   long - ing ful - filled,   To - geth - er

with   the   least   Have come   to   share this   feast.
God   to   know,   And so   to - geth - er   grow.
we   will   come   To   our   e - ter - nal   home.

Text: Delores Dufner, OSB, b.1939, © 2011, GIA Publications, Inc.
Tune: KOMT NU MET ZANG, 9 8 9 8 9 66; Valerius' *Nederlandtsch Gedenckclanck*, 1626; harm. by Adriaan Engels, 1906–2003,
    © 1984, Gooi En Sticht, OCP, agent

938 Holy Manna

1. Breth - ren, we have met to wor - ship And a - dore the
2. Sis - ters, will you come and help us? Mo - ses' sis - ters
3. Is there here a trem - bling jail - er, Seek - ing grace and
4. Let us love our God su - preme-ly, Let us love each

Lord our God. Will you pray with all your pow - er
aid - ed him. Will you help the trem - bling mourn-ers
filled with tears? Is there here a weep - ing Mar - y
oth - er, too. Let us love and pray for sin - ners

While we try to preach the word? All is vain un -
Who are strug - gling hard with sin? Tell them all a -
Pour - ing forth a flood of tears? Breth - ren, join your
Till our God makes all things new. Christ will call us

less the Spir - it Of the ho - ly One comes down.
bout the Sav - ior. Tell them that he will be found.
cries to help them, Sis - ters, let your prayers a - bound!
home to heav - en, At his ta - ble we'll sit down.

Breth - ren, pray, and ho - ly man - na
Sis - ters, pray, and ho - ly man - na
Pray, oh, pray, that ho - ly man - na
Christ will gird him - self and serve us

Will be show - ered all a - round.
Will be show - ered all a - round.
Will be scat - tered all a - round.
With sweet man - na all a - round.

Text: George Atkins, 1793–1827
Tune: HOLY MANNA, 8 7 8 7 D; William Moore, fl.1830

Risen Lord, We Gather Round You   939

1. Ris - en Lord, we gath - er round you, Drawn by
2. Sis - ters, broth - ers stand be - side us, Called from
3. By the loaf and cup you of - fer, Strength - en

words for - ev - er new: "Come, my peo - ple, all are
ev - 'ry land and race. One the Bread of Life that
us to fol - low you. By your bod - y, ris - en,

wel - come; Share the feast pre - pared for you!" Emp - ty
feeds us; One the Cup of brim - ming grace. Form us,
giv - en, Heal us, Christ, and make us new. Help us

hands and hearts that hun - ger, Christ, we bring to
Lord, a sin - gle bod - y, Free from en - mi -
hear your ur - gent sum - mons, Cut - ting through our

you to - day. Here you feed us with your Bod - y,
ty and strife. Je - sus, by your res - ur - rec - tion,
fear of loss: "Go, my peo - ple! Be my ser - vants!

Gift of love for which we pray.
Fill us with the Spir - it's life!
Bear with me the wait - ing cross!"

Text: Herman G. Stuempfle, Jr., 1923–2007, © 2006, GIA Publications, Inc.
Tune: DOSTER'S DANCE, 8 7 8 7 D; Tony E. Alonso, b.1980, © 2015, GIA Publications, Inc.

940 Gather Your People

Refrain

Gath-er your peo-ple, O Lord. Gath-er your peo-ple, O Lord. One bread, one bod-y, one spir-it of love. Gath-er your peo-ple, O Lord.

Verses

1. Draw us forth to the ta - ble of life:
2. We are parts of the bod - y of Christ,
3. No more harm on the moun - tain of God;
4. Wash us, Lord, in the wa - ters of life;

broth - ers and sis - ters, each of us called to
need - ing each oth - er, each of the gifts the
swords in - to plow-shares. Free us, O Lord, from
wa - ters of mer - cy, wa - ters of hope that

D.C.

walk in your light.
Spir - it pro - vides.
hard - ness of heart.
flow from your side.

Text: 1 Corinthians 12, Isaiah 2:3–4, 11:9; Bob Hurd, b.1950.
Tune: Bob Hurd. b.1950; choral arr. by Craig S. Kingsbury, b.1952; acc. by Dominic MacAller, b.1959
© 1991, Bob Hurd. Published by OCP.

Vamos Todos al Banquete / 941
Let Us Go Now to the Banquet

Estribillo / Refrain

Va - mos to - dos al ban - que - te, A la
Let us go now to the ban - quet, To the

me - sa de la cre - a - ción; Ca - da cual, con su ta - bu -
feast of the u - ni - verse. The ta - ble's set and a place is

re - te, Tie-ne_un pues - to y_u - na mi - sión.
wait - ing; Come, ev - 'ry - one, with your gifts to share.

Estrofas / Verses

1. Hoy me le - van - to muy tem - pra - no, Ya me_es -
2. Dios in - vi - ta_a to - dos los po - bres A es - ta
3. Dios nos man - da_a_ha-cer de_es - te mun - do U - na

1. *I will rise in the ear - ly morn - ing. The com -*
2. *God in - vites all the poor and hun - gry To the*
3. *May we build such a place a - mong us Where all*

pe - ra la co - mu - ni - dad. Voy su - bien - do a -
me - sa co - mún por la fe, Don - de no_hay a - ca -
me - sa don-de_ha - ya_i-gual-dad; Tra - ba - jan - do_y lu -

mu - ni - ty's wait - ing for me. With a spring in my
ban - quet of jus - tice and good, Where the har - vest will
peo - ple are e - qual in love. God has called us to

D.C.

le - gre la cues - ta, Voy en bus - ca de tu_a - mis - tad.
pa - ra - do - res Don - de to - dos pue-dan co - mer.
chan - do jun - tos, Com-par - tien - do la pro - pie - dad.

step I'm walk - ing With my friends and my fam - i - ly.
not be hoard - ed, So that no one will lack for food.
work to - geth - er And to share ev - 'ry-thing we have.

Text: *Misa Popular Salvadoreña*, Guillermo Cuéllar; tr. by Bret Hesla, b.1957, and William Dexheimer-Pharris
Tune: Guillermo Cuéllar; acc. by Ronald F. Krisman, b.1946
© 1988, tr. © 1996, acc. © 2005, GIA Publications, Inc.

942 Father, We Praise You

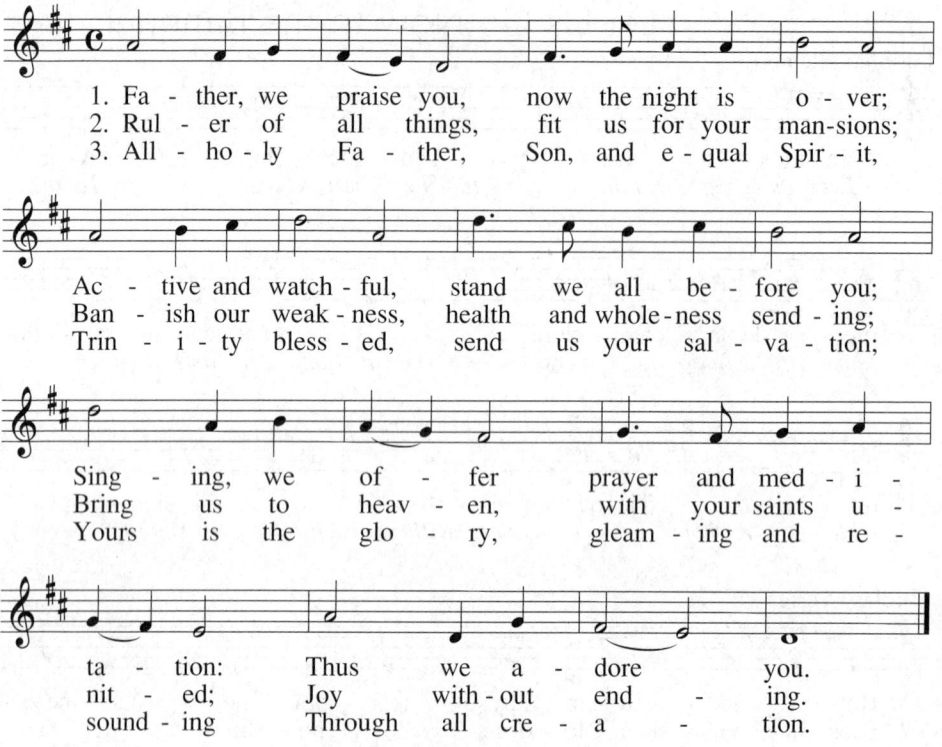

1. Fa - ther, we praise you, now the night is o - ver;
2. Rul - er of all things, fit us for your man-sions;
3. All - ho - ly Fa - ther, Son, and e - qual Spir - it,

Ac - tive and watch - ful, stand we all be - fore you;
Ban - ish our weak - ness, health and whole-ness send - ing;
Trin - i - ty bless - ed, send us your sal - va - tion;

Sing - ing, we of - fer prayer and med - i -
Bring us to heav - en, with your saints u -
Yours is the glo - ry, gleam - ing and re -

ta - tion: Thus we a - dore you.
nit - ed; Joy with - out end - ing.
sound - ing Through all cre - a - tion.

Text: *Nocte surgentes;* attr. to St. Gregory the Great, 540–604; tr. by Percy Dearmer, 1867–1936, alt.
Tune: CHRISTE SANCTORUM, 11 11 11 5; Paris *Antiphoner*, 1681

Let Us Rise 943

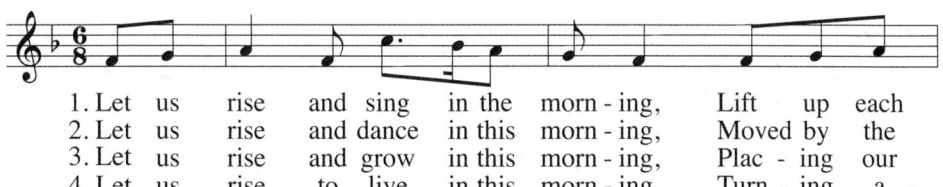

1. Let us rise and sing in the morn-ing, Lift up each
2. Let us rise and dance in this morn-ing, Moved by the
3. Let us rise and grow in this morn-ing, Plac-ing our
4. Let us rise to live in this morn-ing, Turn-ing a -

spir - it and bod - y and voice, Joined with the earth, God's
mu - sic of grace sound-ing new, Learn-ing the steps that
hope on your path - way of peace; Show us your face through
way from the a - gents of death, Plac-ing our hope in

blessed in - car - na - tion, Prais-ing the One who caused us to
lead to com - pas - sion, Act - ing in kind - ness, grate-ful and
cha - os and griev-ing, Shield us in love till sor - rows shall
all you have prom-ised, Trust-ing your love as near as each

be. Now let us sing with all of cre - a - tion And, as
true. Guide us, O God, to serve you with pas - sion: As we
cease. Lead us from fear and doubt to be - liev-ing, So in
breath. Now we shall rise and wel-come this *Sab-bath. Ho - ly

morn-ing breaks, We will rise up, re - joic - ing and free.
rise this day May we dance as the pres-ence of you.
you, each day, We find ref - uge and home and re - lief.
Spir - it, move Through its height and its depth and its breadth.

*Or: morning

Text: Marty Haugen, b.1950
Tune: LET US RISE, 9 10 10 9 10 5 9; Marty Haugen, b.1950
© 2015, GIA Publications, Inc.

944 Morning Has Broken

1. Morn-ing has bro-ken Like the first morn-ing, Black-bird has
2. Sweet the rain's new fall Sun-lit from heav-en, Like the first
3. Mine is the sun-light! Mine is the morn-ing Born of the

spo-ken Like the first bird. Praise for the sing-ing! Praise for the
dew-fall On the first grass. Praise for the sweet-ness Of the wet
one light E-den saw play! Praise with e-la-tion, Praise ev-'ry

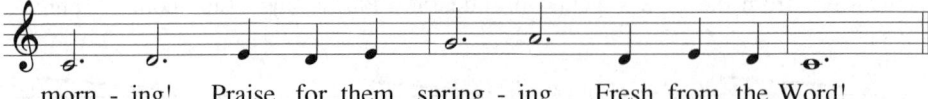

morn-ing! Praise for them, spring-ing Fresh from the Word!
gar-den, Sprung in com-plete-ness Where his feet pass.
morn-ing, God's re-cre-a-tion Of the new day!

Text: Eleanor Farjeon, 1881–1965, *The Children's Bells,* © David Higham Assoc., Ltd.
Tune: BUNESSAN, 5 5 5 4 D; Gaelic melody; acc. by Marty Haugen, b.1950, © 1987, GIA Publications, Inc.

945 God Is Alive

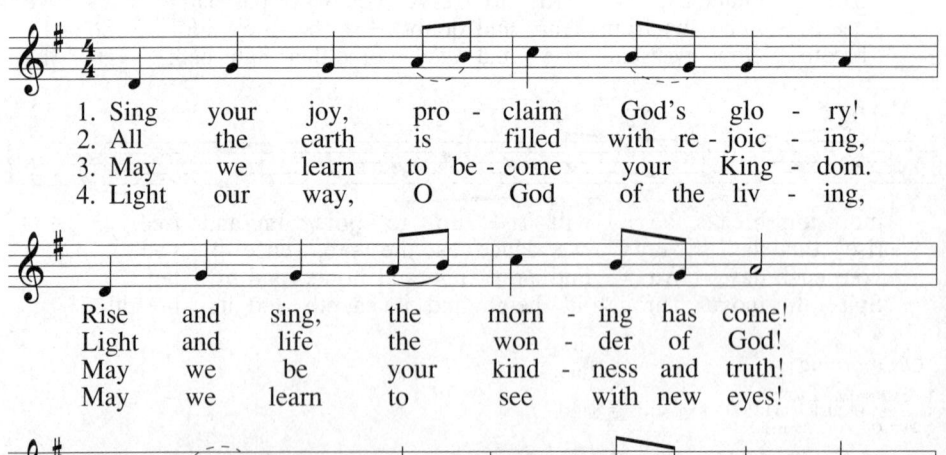

1. Sing your joy, pro-claim God's glo-ry!
2. All the earth is filled with re-joic-ing,
3. May we learn to be-come your King-dom.
4. Light our way, O God of the liv-ing,

Rise and sing, the morn-ing has come!
Light and life the won-der of God!
May we be your kind-ness and truth!
May we learn to see with new eyes!

Bless our God and praise all cre-a-tion;
Christ has tri-umphed! Ris-en for ev-er!
Love is our call-ing, gift of your pres-ence;
Je-sus the Lord, our pow-er and prom-ise;

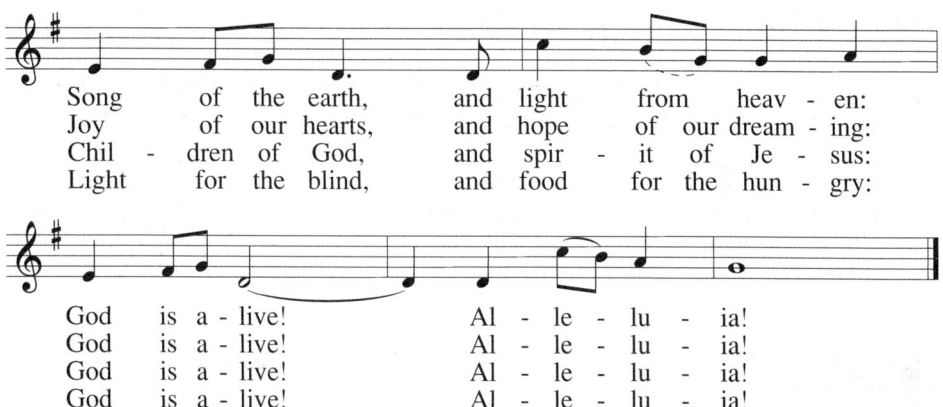

Song of the earth, and light from heav - en:
Joy of our hearts, and hope of our dream - ing:
Chil - dren of God, and spir - it of Je - sus:
Light for the blind, and food for the hun - gry:

God is a - live! Al - le - lu - ia!
God is a - live! Al - le - lu - ia!
God is a - live! Al - le - lu - ia!
God is a - live! Al - le - lu - ia!

Text: David Haas, b.1957
Tune: SUMMIT HILL, Irregular; David Haas, b.1957
© 1987, GIA Publications, Inc.

Day Is Done 946

1. Day is done, but Love un - fail - ing Dwells ev - er
2. Dark de - scends, but Light un - end - ing Shines through our
3. Eyes will close, but you un - sleep - ing Watch by our

here; Shad - ows fall, but hope, pre - vail - ing,
night; You are with us, ev - er lend - ing
side; Death may come, in Love's safe - keep - ing

Calms ev - 'ry fear. God, our Mak - er, none for - sak - ing,
New strength to sight. One in love, your truth con - fess - ing,
Still we a - bide. God of love, all e - vil quell - ing,

Take our hearts, of Love's own mak - ing; Watch our sleep - ing,
One in hope of heav - en's bless - ing, May we see, in
Sin for - giv - ing, fear dis - pel - ling, Stay with us, our

guard our wak - ing, Be al - ways near.
love's pos - sess - ing, Love's end - less light!
hearts in - dwell - ing, This e - ven - tide.

Text: James Quinn, SJ, 1919–2010, © 1969, James Quinn, SJ. Published by OCP.
Tune: AR HYD Y NOS, 8 4 8 4 888 4; Welsh melody

947 Christ, Mighty Savior

1. Christ, might - y Sav - ior, Light of all cre -
2. Now comes the day's end as the sun is
3. There - fore we come now eve - ning rites to
4. Give heed, we pray you, to our sup - pli -
5. Though bod - ies slum - ber, hearts shall keep their

a - tion, You make the day - time
set - ting: Mir - ror of day - break,
of - fer, Joy - ful - ly chant - ing
ca - tion: That you may grant us
vig - il, For ev - er rest - ing

ra - diant with the sun - light, And to the
pledge of res - ur - rec - tion; While in the
ho - ly hymns to praise you, With all cre -
par - don for of - fens - es, Strength for our
in the peace of Je - sus, In light or

night give glit - ter - ing a - dorn - ment,
heav - ens choirs of stars ap - pear - ing
a - tion join - ing hearts and voic - es,
weak hearts, rest for ach - ing bod - ies,
dark - ness wor - ship - ing our Sav - ior

Stars in the heav - ens.
Hal - low the night - fall.
Sing - ing your glo - ry.
Sooth - ing the wea - ry.
Now and for - ev - er.

Text: *Christe, lux mundi*; Mozarabic Rite, 10th C.; tr. by Alan G. McDougall, 1895–1964, rev. by Anne K. LeCroy, b.1930, and others, © 1982,
    The United Methodist Publishing House, admin. Music Services
Tune: MIGHTY SAVIOR, 11 11 11 5; David Hurd, b.1950, © 1985, GIA Publications, Inc.

Joyous Light of Heavenly Glory   948

1. Joy - ous light of heav'n - ly glo - ry, Lov - ing
2. In the stars that grace the dark - ness, In the
3. You who made the heav - en's splen - dor, Ev - 'ry

glow of God's own face, You who sing cre - a - tion's
blaz - ing sun of dawn, In the light of peace and
danc - ing star of night, Make us shine with gen - tle

sto - ry, Shine on ev - 'ry land and race.
wis - dom, We can hear your qui - et song.
jus - tice, Let us each re - flect your light.

Now as eve - ning falls a - round us, We shall
Love that fills the night with won - der, Love that
Might - y God of all cre - a - tion, Gen - tle

raise our songs to you, God of day - break, God of
warms the wea - ry soul, Love that bursts all chains a -
Christ who lights our way, Lov - ing Spir - it of sal -

shad - ows, Come and light our hearts a - new.
sun - der, Set us free and make us whole.
va - tion, Lead us on to end - less day.

Text: Marty Haugen, b.1950
Tune: JOYOUS LIGHT, 8 7 8 7 D; Marty Haugen, b.1950
© 1987, GIA Publications, Inc.

949 Abide With Me

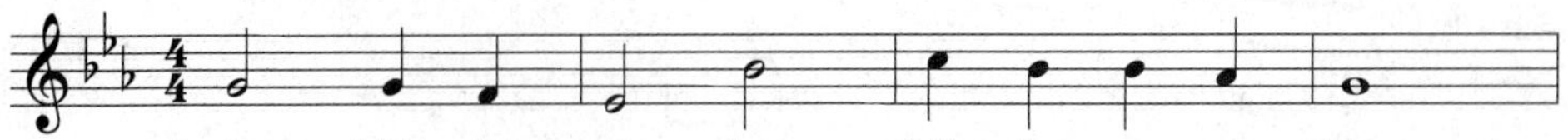

1. A - bide with me; fast falls the e - ven - tide;
2. Swift to its close ebbs out life's lit - tle day;
3. I need thy pres - ence ev - 'ry pass - ing hour;
4. I fear no foe, with thee at hand to bless;
5. Hold thou thy cross be - fore my clos - ing eyes;

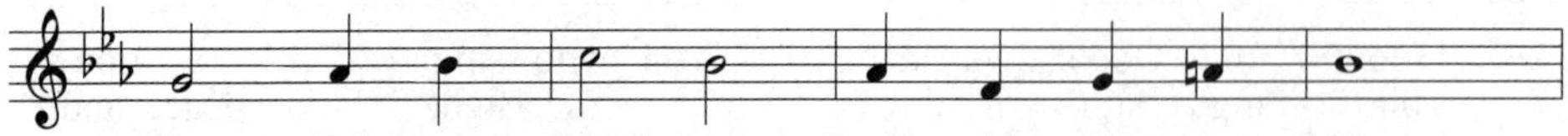

The dark - ness deep - ens; Lord, with me a - bide
Earth's joys grow dim; its glo - ries pass a - way;
What but thy grace can foil the tempt - er's pow'r?
Ills have no weight, and tears no bit - ter - ness.
Shine through the gloom and point me to the skies;

When oth - er help - ers fail and com - forts flee,
Change and de - cay in all a - round I see;
Who, like thy - self, my guide and stay can be?
Where is death's sting? Where, grave, your vic - to - ry?
Heav'n's morn - ing breaks, and earth's vain shad - ows flee;

Help of the help - less, O a - bide with me.
O thou who chang - est not, a - bide with me.
Through cloud and sun - shine, Lord, a - bide with me.
I tri - umph still, if thou a - bide with me.
In life, in death, O Lord, a - bide with me.

Text: Henry F. Lyte, 1793–1847
Tune: EVENTIDE, 10 10 10 10; William H. Monk, 1823–1889; arr. by Evelyn Simpson-Curenton, b.1953, © 2000, GIA Publications, Inc.

950 Our Darkness

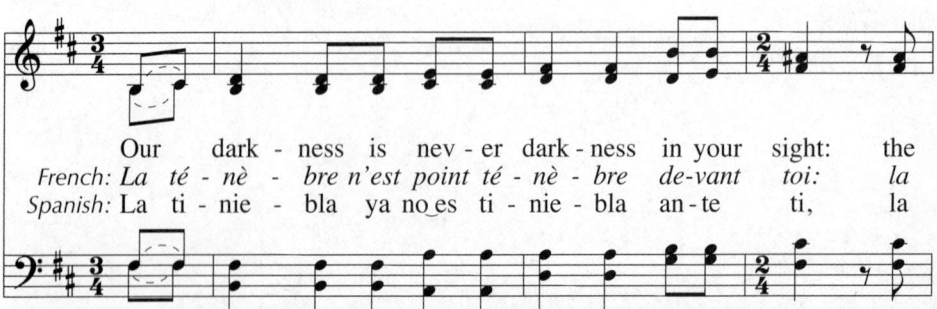

Our dark - ness is nev - er dark - ness in your sight: the
French: La té - nè - bre n'est point té - nè - bre de - vant toi: la
Spanish: La ti - nie - bla ya no es ti - nie - bla an - te ti, la

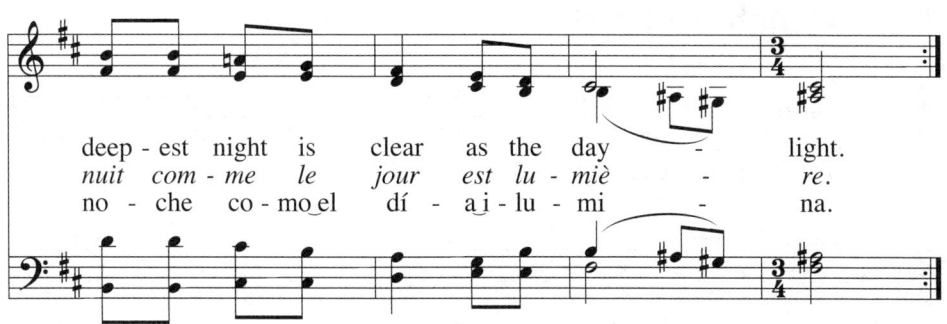

deep - est night is   clear   as the   day -   light.
nuit com - me   le   jour   est lu - miè -   re.
no - che   co - mo el   dí - a i - lu - mi -   na.

Text: Taizé Community
Tune: Jacques Berthier, 1923–1994
© 1991, Les Presses de Taizé, GIA Publications, Inc., agent

At Evening 951

1. Now it is eve - ning: Lights of the cit - y
2. Now it is eve - ning: Lit - tle ones sleep - ing
3. Now it is eve - ning: Food on the ta - ble
4. Now it is eve - ning: Here in our meet - ing

Bid us re - mem - ber Christ is our Light.
Bid us re - mem - ber Christ is our Peace.
Bids us re - mem - ber Christ is our Life.
May we re - mem - ber Christ is our Friend.

Man - y are lone - ly, Who will be neigh - bor?
Some are ne - glect - ed, Who will be neigh - bor?
Man - y are hun - gry, Who will be neigh - bor?
Some may be stran - gers, Who will be neigh - bor?

Where there is car - ing Christ is our Light.
Where there is car - ing Christ is our Peace.
Where there is shar - ing Christ is our Life.
Where there's a wel - come Christ is our Friend.

Text: Fred Pratt Green, 1903–2000, © 1974, Hope Publishing Company
Tune: EVENING HYMN, 5 5 5 4 D; David Haas, b.1957, © 1985, GIA Publications, Inc.

952 Watch, O Lord

Refrain

Watch, O Lord, with all those a-wake this night,

Watch, O Lord, with all those who weep; Give your

an-gels and saints charge o-ver all who sleep.

Verses

Cantor: *All:*   *Cantor:*

1. Tend your ail - ing ones: Rest your
2. Soothe your suf-f'ring ones: Heal af -
3. Hold your griev-ing ones: in your love, Lord;   Raise your
4. Guard your lit - tle ones: Guide your

All: *Cantor:*

wea - ry ones: Bless your
flict - ed ones: Shield your
fal - len ones: in your love, Lord;   Mend your
search - ing ones: Grant us

All: **D.C.**

dy - ing ones:
joy - ous ones:
bro - ken ones: in your love, O Lord of all.
all your peace:

Text: St. Augustine; adapt. by Marty Haugen, b.1950
Tune: Marty Haugen, b.1950

The Day You Gave Us, Lord, Is Ended   953

1. The day you gave us, Lord, is end - ed;
2. We thank you that your Church, un - sleep - ing
3. A - cross each con - ti - nent and is - land,
4. The sun, which bids us rest, is wak - ing
5. So be it, Lord! Your throne shall nev - er,

The dark - ness falls at your be - hest.
While earth rolls on - ward in - to light,
As dawn leads on an - oth - er day,
Your chil - dren un - der west - ern skies,
Like earth's proud em - pires, pass a - way;

To you our morn - ing hymns as - cend - ed;
Through all the world its watch is keep - ing,
The voice of prayer is nev - er si - lent,
And hour by hour, as day is break - ing,
Your king - dom stands, and grows for - ev - er

Your praise shall sanc - ti - fy our rest.
And nev - er rests by day or night.
Nor dies the strain of praise a - way.
Fresh hymns of thank - ful praise a - rise.
Un - til there dawns your glo - rious day.

Text: John Ellerton, 1826–1893, alt.
Tune: ST. CLEMENT, 9 8 9 8; Clement C. Scholefield, 1839–1904

954 Soon and Very Soon

1. Soon and ver-y soon we are goin' to see the King,
2. No more cry-in' there, we are goin' to see the King,
3. No more dy-in' there, we are goin' to see the King,
4. Soon and ver-y soon we are goin' to see the King,

Soon and ver-y soon we are goin' to see the King,
No more cry-in' there, we are goin' to see the King,
No more dy-in' there, we are goin' to see the King,
Soon and ver-y soon we are goin' to see the King,

Soon and ver-y soon we are goin' to see the King.
No more cry-in' there, we are goin' to see the King.
No more dy-in' there, we are goin' to see the King. Hal-le-
Soon and ver-y soon we are goin' to see the King.

1., 2.

lu - jah, hal-le-lu - jah, we're goin' to see the King!

3., 4.

Hal - le - lu - jah, hal - le - lu -

jah, hal - le - lu - jah, hal - le - lu - jah.

Text: Andraé Crouch, 1942–2015
Tune: SOON AND VERY SOON, 12 12 12 14; Andraé Crouch, 1942–2015
© 1976, Crouch Music/Bud John Songs (admin. CapitolCMGPublishing.com)

My Lord, What a Morning! 955

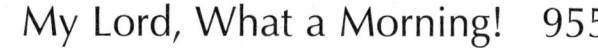

Refrain

My Lord, what a morn-ing! My Lord, what a

morn-ing! O my Lord, what a morn-ing when the

stars be-gin to fall, when the stars be-gin to fall.

Verses

1. You will hear the trum-pet sound
2. You will hear the sin-ner cry To wake the
3. You will hear the Chris-tian shout

na-tions un-der-ground, Look-ing to my God's right

D.C.

hand When the stars be-gin to fall.

Text: African American spiritual
Tune: MY LORD, WHAT A MORNING, 7 8 7 7 with refrain; African American spiritual; arr. by Melva Costen, © 1990

956   Keep Your Lamps Trimmed and Burning

1. Keep   your   lamps   trimmed and   burn - ing,   keep   your
2. Dark - er   mid - night   lies   be - fore   us,   dark - er
3. For   the   morn - ing   soon   is   break - ing,   for   the
4. Chris - tian   jour - ney   soon   be   o -   ver,   Chris - tian

lamps   trimmed   and   burn - ing,   keep   your
mid - night   lies   be - fore   us,   dark - er
morn - ing   soon   is   break - ing,   for   the
jour - ney   soon   be   o -   ver,   Chris - tian

lamps   trimmed   and   burn - ing,   the
mid - night   lies   be - fore   us,   the
morn - ing   soon   is   break - ing,   the
jour - ney   soon   be   o -   ver,   the

1.

day   is   draw - ing   nigh.   Keep   your
day   is   draw - ing   nigh.   Dark - er
day   is   draw - ing   nigh.   For   the
day   is   draw - ing   nigh.   Chris - tian

2.

Chil - dren,   don't   get   wea - ry,   chil - dren,

don't   get   wea - ry,   chil - dren,   don't   get   wea-

1.   **2.**

ry   till   your   work   is   done.   Chil - dren,   done.

Text: African American spiritual
Tune: African American spiritual; arr. by Jennifer Kerr Budziak, © 2016, GIA Publications, Inc.

O Holy City, Seen of John   957

1. O   Ho - ly   Cit - y,   seen   of   John,   Where
2. O   shame   to   us   who   rest   con - tent   While
3. Give   us,   O   God,   the   strength   to   build   The
4. Al - read - y   in   the   mind   of   God   That

Christ, the Lamb, does   reign,   With - in   those four - square
lust   and   greed   for   gain   In   street   and   shop   and
Cit - y   that   has   stood   Too   long   a   dream, whose
Cit - y   ris - es   fair: Lo,   how   its   splen - dor

walls   shall   come No   night,   nor   need,   nor   pain,   And
ten - e - ment Wring   gold   from   hu - man   pain,   And
laws   are   love, Whose   ways,   the   com - mon   good,   And
chal - leng - es   The   souls   that   great - ly   dare: Yea,

where the tears are wiped from eyes That   shall   not   weep a - gain.
bit - ter lips   in   blind de - spair Cry,   "Christ has   died   in   vain."
where the shin - ing   sun   be - comes God's   grace   for   hu - man   good.
bids   us   seize the whole of   life   And   build   its   glo - ry   there.

Text: Revelation 21; W. Russell Bowie, 1882–1969
Tune: MORNING SONG, 8 6 8 6 8 6; Wyeth's *Repository of Sacred Music*, 1813; harm. by C. Winfred Douglas, 1867–1944,
© 1940, The Church Pension Fund

958 The Trumpet in the Morning

Verses

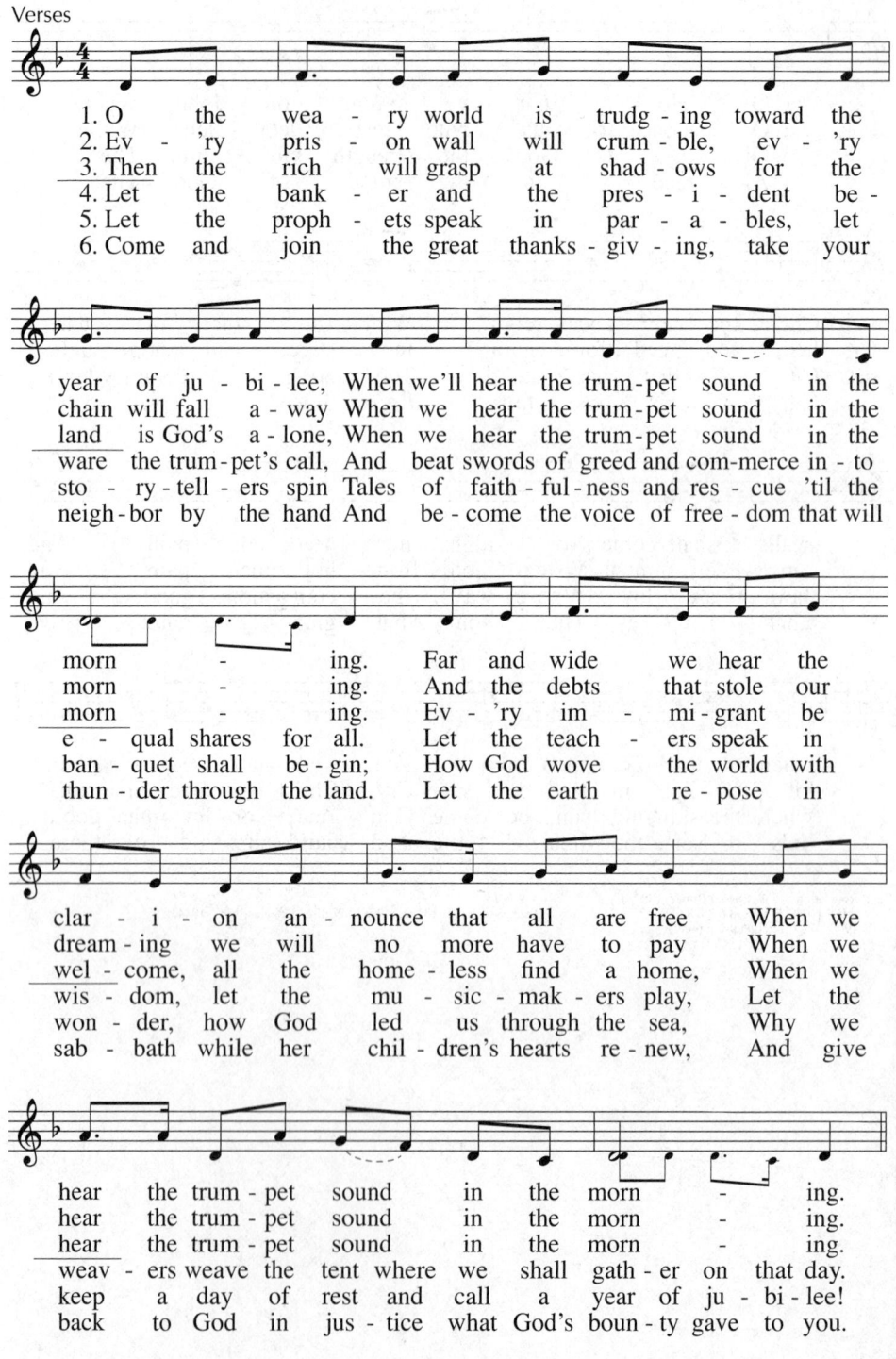

1. O the wea - ry world is trudg - ing toward the
2. Ev - 'ry pris - on wall will crum - ble, ev - 'ry
3. Then the rich will grasp at shad - ows for the
4. Let the bank - er and the pres - i - dent be -
5. Let the proph - ets speak in par - a - bles, let
6. Come and join the great thanks - giv - ing, take your

year of ju - bi - lee, When we'll hear the trum - pet sound in the
chain will fall a - way When we hear the trum - pet sound in the
land is God's a - lone, When we hear the trum - pet sound in the
ware the trum - pet's call, And beat swords of greed and com - merce in - to
sto - ry - tell - ers spin Tales of faith - ful - ness and res - cue 'til the
neigh - bor by the hand And be - come the voice of free - dom that will

morn - ing. Far and wide we hear the
morn - ing. And the debts that stole our
morn - ing. Ev - 'ry im - mi - grant be
e - qual shares for all. Let the teach - ers speak in
ban - quet shall be - gin; How God wove the world with
thun - der through the land. Let the earth re - pose in

clar - i - on an - nounce that all are free When we
dream - ing we will no more have to pay When we
wel - come, all the home - less find a home, When we
wis - dom, let the mu - sic - mak - ers play, Let the
won - der, how God led us through the sea, Why we
sab - bath while her chil - dren's hearts re - new, And give

hear the trum - pet sound in the morn - ing.
hear the trum - pet sound in the morn - ing.
hear the trum - pet sound in the morn - ing.
weav - ers weave the tent where we shall gath - er on that day.
keep a day of rest and call a year of ju - bi - lee!
back to God in jus - tice what God's boun - ty gave to you.

Refrain

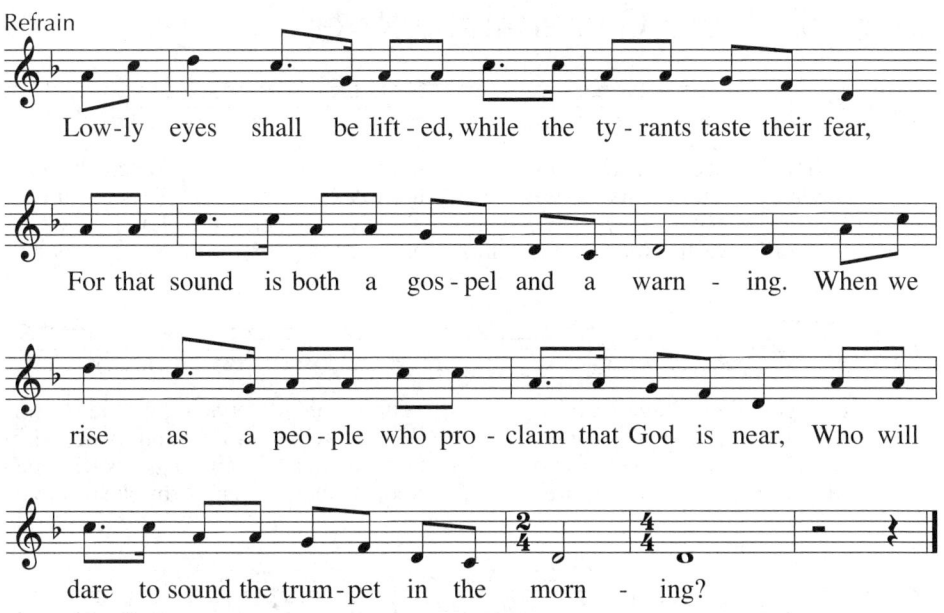

Low-ly eyes shall be lift-ed, while the ty-rants taste their fear,

For that sound is both a gos-pel and a warn - ing. When we

rise as a peo-ple who pro-claim that God is near, Who will

dare to sound the trum-pet in the morn - ing?

Text: Leviticus 25, Deuteronomy 15, Joel 2; Rory Cooney, b.1952, © 1998, GIA Publications, Inc.
Tune: MORNING TRUMPET, 15 11 15 11 with refrain; B. F. White, 1800–1879, from *Southern Harmony*; arr. by Rory Cooney, b.1952,
    © 1998, GIA Publications, Inc.

Steal Away to Jesus   959

Refrain

Steal a-way, steal a-way, steal a-way to Je-sus!

Steal a-way, steal a-way home, I ain't got long to stay here.

Verses

1. My Lord, he calls me, He calls me by the thun-der; The
2. Green trees are bend-ing, Poor sin-ners stand a trem-bling; The
3. My Lord, he calls me, He calls me by the light-ning; The

D.C.

trum-pet sounds with-in my soul; I ain't got long to stay here.

Text: African American spiritual
Tune: African American spiritual

960 Shall We Gather at the River

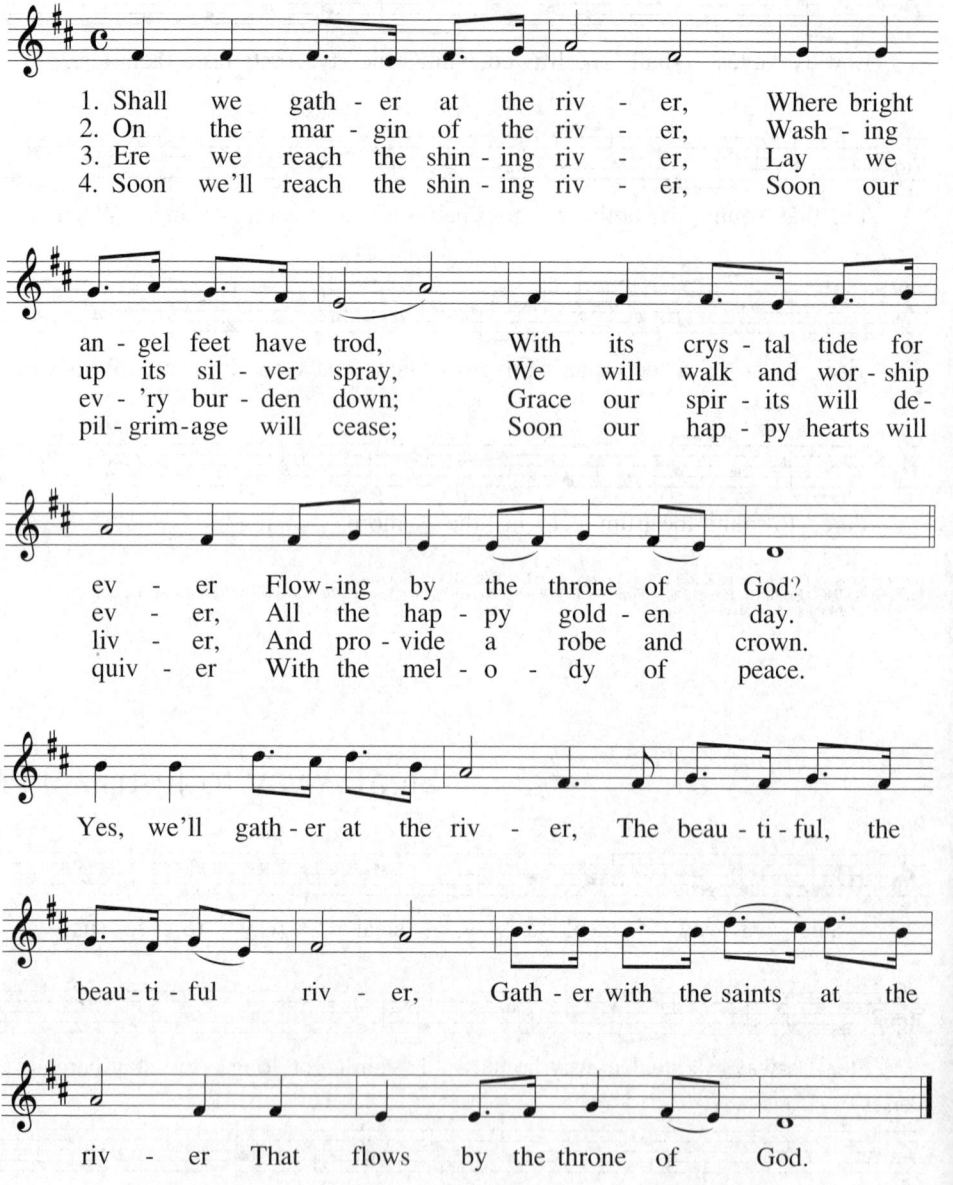

1. Shall we gath - er at the riv - er, Where bright
2. On the mar - gin of the riv - er, Wash - ing
3. Ere we reach the shin - ing riv - er, Lay we
4. Soon we'll reach the shin - ing riv - er, Soon our

an - gel feet have trod, With its crys - tal tide for
up its sil - ver spray, We will walk and wor - ship
ev - 'ry bur - den down; Grace our spir - its will de -
pil - grim-age will cease; Soon our hap - py hearts will

ev - er Flow-ing by the throne of God?
ev - er, All the hap - py gold - en day.
liv - er, And pro - vide a robe and crown.
quiv - er With the mel - o - dy of peace.

Yes, we'll gath - er at the riv - er, The beau - ti - ful, the

beau - ti - ful riv - er, Gath - er with the saints at the

riv - er That flows by the throne of God.

Text: Robert Lowry, 1826–1899
Tune: HANSON PLACE, 8 7 8 7 with refrain; Robert Lowry, 1826–1899

Lux Aeterna Litany 961

Refrain

Cantor:
Lux ae-tér - na. Do-na e-is ré - qui -

All:
Lux ae-tér - na.

em.

To Litany

Do-na e-is ré - qui - em.

Last time

A - men.

em. A - men.

Litany of Remembrance*

D.C.

(Cantor sings names from the Book of Remembrance)

We re-mem - ber.

*Sing eight names before returning to the Refrain and then continue to the next set of names.

Text: Chris de Silva, b.1967
Tune: Chris de Silva, b.1967
© 2002, Chris de Silva. Published by OCP.

962 We Shall Rise Again

1. Come to me, all you wea-ry, with your bur-dens and
2. Though we walk through the dark-ness, e-vil we do not
3. We de-pend on God's mer-cy, mer-cy which nev-er
4. Do not fear death's do-min-ion, look be-yond earth and
5. At the door there to greet us, mar-tyrs, an-gels, and

pain. Take my yoke on your shoul-ders and
fear. You are walk-ing be-side us with your
fades. We re-mem-ber our cov-e-nant and the
grave. See the bright-ness of Je-sus shin-ing
saints, And our fam-'ly and loved ones, ev-'ry-

learn from me: I am gen-tle and hum-ble,
rod and your staff. On-ly good-ness and kind-ness
prom-ise Je-sus made: If we die with Christ Je-sus,
out to light our way. Lov-ing Fa-ther and Spir-it,
one freed from their chains. We shall feel their ac-cep-tance,

and your soul will find rest, For my yoke is
fol-low us all our lives. We shall dwell in the
we shall live with him, And if we are
lov-ing Je-sus the Son, All God's peo-ple to-
and the joy of new life. We shall join in the

eas-y and my bur-den is light.
Lord's house for so man-y years to come!
faith-ful, we shall reign with him!
geth-er, we shall live on as one!
gath-er-ing, re-u-nit-ed in God's love!

We shall rise a-gain on the last day with the faith-ful, rich and

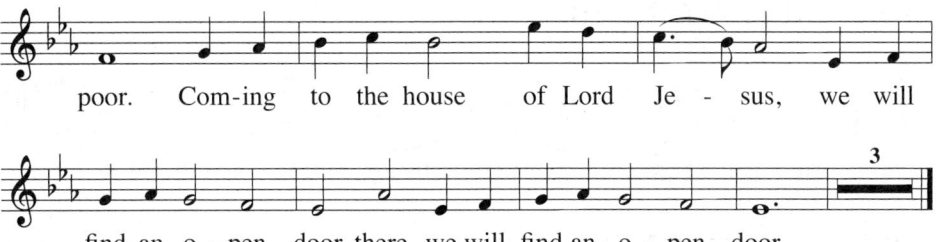

poor. Com-ing to the house of Lord Je - sus, we will

find an o - pen door there, we will find an o - pen door.

Text: Matthew 11:29–30, Psalm 23, John 11, 2 Timothy 2; Jeremy Young, b.1948
Tune: RESURRECTION; Irregular with refrain; Jeremy Young, b.1948
© 1987, GIA Publications, Inc.

Jerusalem, My Happy Home   963

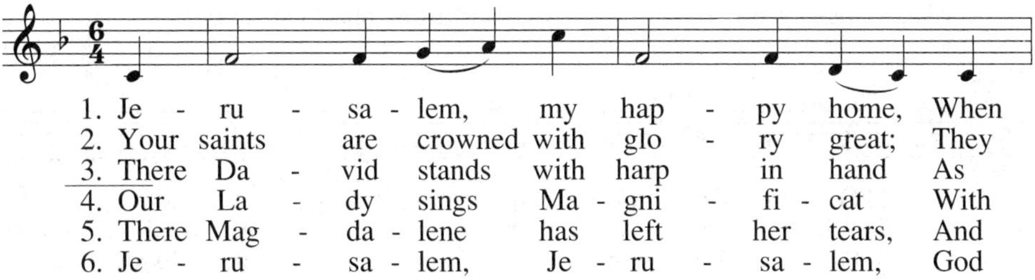

1. Je - ru - sa - lem, my hap - py home, When
2. Your saints are crowned with glo - ry great; They
3. There Da - vid stands with harp in hand As
4. Our La - dy sings Ma - gni - fi - cat With
5. There Mag - da - lene has left her tears, And
6. Je - ru - sa - lem, Je - ru - sa - lem, God

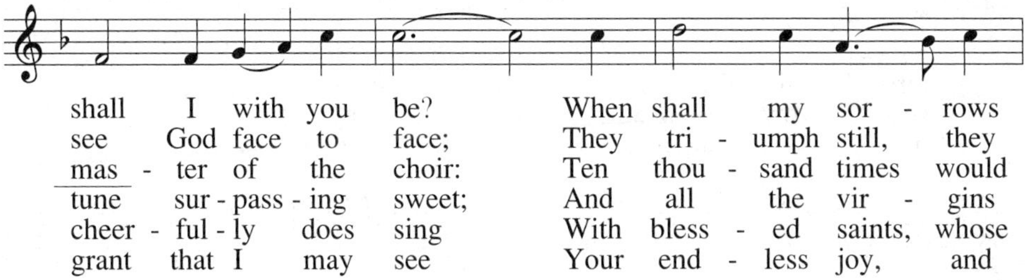

shall I with you be? When shall my sor - rows
see God face to face; They tri - umph still, they
mas - ter of the choir: Ten thou - sand times would
tune sur - pass - ing sweet; And all the vir - gins
cheer - ful - ly does sing With bless - ed saints, whose
grant that I may see Your end - less joy, and

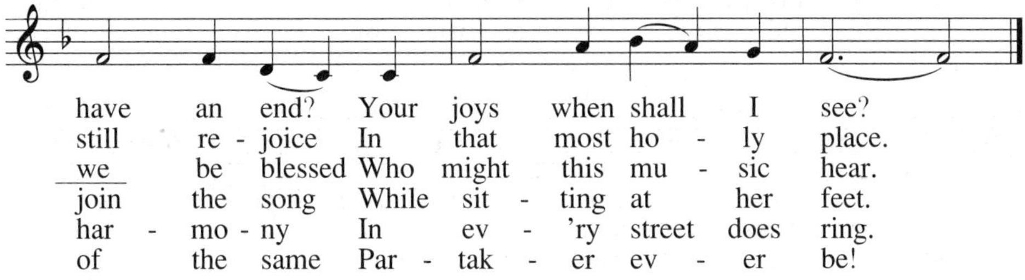

have an end? Your joys when shall I see?
still re - joice In that most ho - ly place.
we be blessed Who might this mu - sic hear.
join the song While sit - ting at her feet.
har - mo - ny In ev - 'ry street does ring.
of the same Par - tak - er ev - er be!

Text: F.B.P., 16th C., alt.
Tune: LAND OF REST, CM; American melody; harm. by Richard Proulx, 1937–2010, © 1975, GIA Publications, Inc.

964   Take Me Home

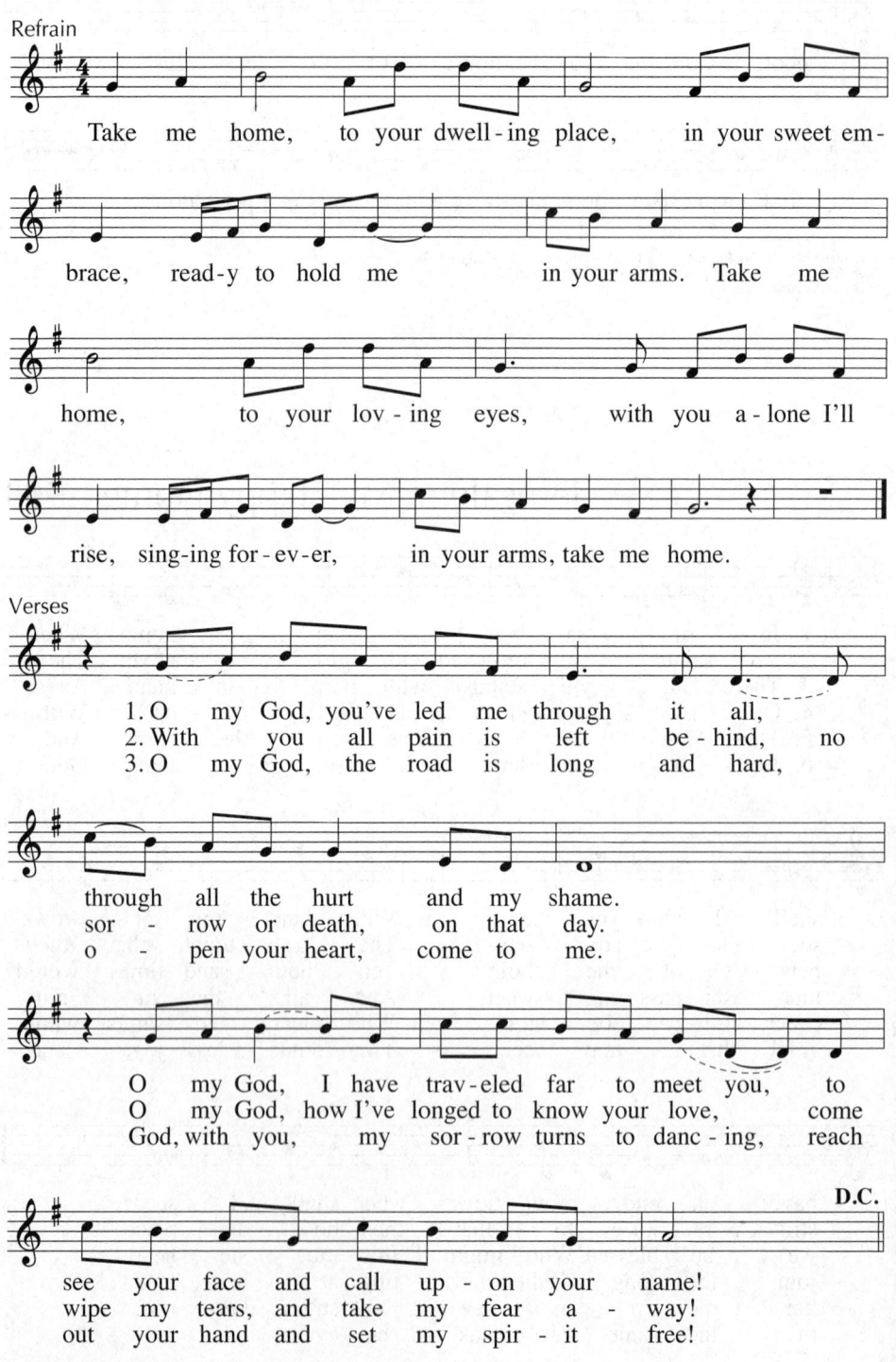

Refrain

Take me home, to your dwell-ing place, in your sweet em-brace, read-y to hold me in your arms. Take me home, to your lov-ing eyes, with you a-lone I'll rise, sing-ing for-ev-er, in your arms, take me home.

Verses

1. O my God, you've led me through it all,
2. With you all pain is left be-hind, no
3. O my God, the road is long and hard,

through all the hurt and my shame.
sor - row or death, on that day.
o - pen your heart, come to me.

O my God, I have trav-eled far to meet you, to
O my God, how I've longed to know your love, come
God, with you, my sor-row turns to danc-ing, reach

see your face and call up - on your name!
wipe my tears, and take my fear a - way!
out your hand and set my spir - it free!

D.C.

Text: David Haas, b.1957
Tune: David Haas, b.1957
© 2001, GIA Publications, Inc.

How Bright Is the Day   965

Verses

1. How bright is the day when the Chris-tian Re-
2. The an-gels stand read-y and wait-ing The
3. The saints that have gone up be-fore us All
4. And there is the bless-ed Re-deem-er, So
5. Then let us go on-ward re-joic-ing, Till

ceives the sweet mes-sage to come, To rise to the
mo-ment the spir-it is gone, To car-ry it
raise a new shout as we come, *And sing hal-le-
mild on his mer-ci-ful throne, With heart and hands
Je-sus in-vites us to come, To share in his

man-sions of glo-ry And be there for-ev-er at home.
up-ward to heav-en, And wel-come it safe-ly at home.
lu-jah the loud-er, To wel-come the trav-el-ers home.
wide-ly ex-tend-ed To wel-come his ran-som'd ones home.
glo-ri-ous king-dom, And rest in his bos-om at home.

Refrain

And be there for-ev-er at home, and be there for-ev-er at

home, to rise to the man-sions of glo-ry and

be there for-ev-er at home.

During Lent: "Sing glory and praise all the louder."

Text: S. B. Sawyer, 1808–1844
Tune: SAWYER'S EXIT, 9 8 9 8 with refrain; *The Sacred Harp*, 1860; arr. by Kyle Cothern, b.1983, © 2015, GIA Publications, Inc.

966 God, Who Made the Earth and Heaven

1. God, who made the earth and heav-en, Dark - ness and
2. And when morn a - gain shall call us To run life's
3. Guard us wak-ing, guard us sleep-ing, And, when we
4. Ho - ly Fa - ther, throned in heav-en, All - ho - ly

light: You the day for work have giv-en, For rest the
way, May we still, what-e'er be-fall us, Your will o-
die, May we in your might - y keep-ing All peace-ful
Son, Ho - ly Spir-it, free - ly giv-en, Blest Three-in-

night. May your an - gel guards de-fend us,
bey. From the pow'r of e - vil hide us,
lie. When the last dread call shall wake us,
One: Grant us grace, we now im - plore you,

Slum - ber sweet your mer - cy send us, Ho - ly dreams and
In the nar - row path - way guide us, Nev - er be your
Then, O Lord, do not for - sake us, But to reign in
Till we lay our crowns be - fore you, And in wor - thier

hopes at - tend us All through the night.
smile de - nied us All through the day.
glo - ry take us With you on high.
strains a - dore you While a - ges run.

Text: St. 1, Reginald Heber, 1783–1826, sts. 2, 4, William Mercer, 1811–1873, st. 3, Richard Whately, 1787–1863, alt.
Tune: AR HYD Y NOS, 8 4 8 4 888 4; Welsh melody; harm. by Ralph Vaughan Williams, 1872–1958

In His Temple Now Behold Him 967

1. In his tem - ple now be - hold him, See the long ex -
2. In the arms of her who bore him, Vir - gin pure, be -
3. Je - sus, by your pres - en - ta - tion, When they blest you,
4. Prince and au - thor of sal - va - tion, Be your bound - less

pect - ed Lord; An - cient proph - ets had fore - told him;
hold him lie, While his a - ged saints a - dore him
weak and poor, Make us see our great sal - va - tion,
love our theme! Je - sus, praise to you be giv - en,

God has now ful - filled his word. Now, to praise him,
Ere in faith and hope they die. Al - le - lu - ia!
Seal us with your prom - ise sure, And pre - sent us
By the world you did re - deem, With the Fa - ther

his re - deem - ed Shall break forth with one ac - cord.
Al - le - lu - ia! Lo, the in - car - nate God most high.
in your glo - ry To your Fa - ther, cleansed and pure.
and the Spir - it, Lord of maj - es - ty su - preme.

Text: Luke 2:22–24; vss. 1–3, Henry J. Pye, 1825–1903; vs. 4, William Cooke, 1821–1894
Tune: ST. THOMAS, 8 7 8 7 8 7; John F. Wade, 1711–1786

968 Long-Awaited Holy One

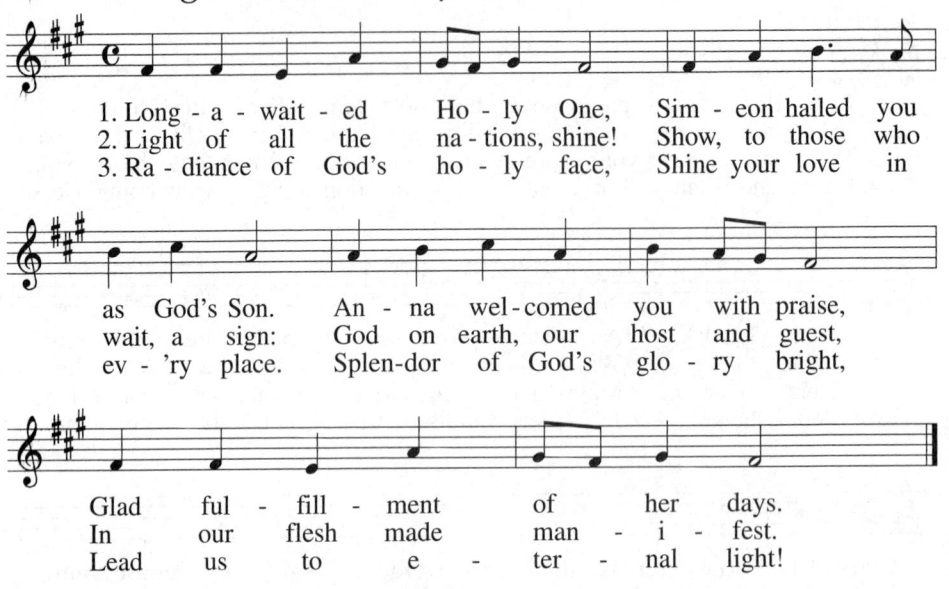

1. Long - a - wait - ed Ho - ly One, Sim - eon hailed you
2. Light of all the na - tions, shine! Show, to those who
3. Ra - diance of God's ho - ly face, Shine your love in

as God's Son. An - na wel - comed you with praise,
wait, a sign: God on earth, our host and guest,
ev - 'ry place. Splen - dor of God's glo - ry bright,

Glad ful - fill - ment of her days.
In our flesh made man - i - fest.
Lead us to e - ter - nal light!

Text: Delores Dufner, OSB, b.1939, © 1984, 1992, 2003, 2011, GIA Publications, Inc.
Tune: NUN KOMM DER HEIDEN HEILAND, 77 77; *Geistliche Gesangbüchlein*, Wittenberg, 1524

969 Come Now and Praise the Humble Saint

1. Come now and praise the hum - ble saint Of
2. The Vir - gin Mar - y's faith - ful spouse, The
3. For him there was no glo - ry here, No
4. But now with - in the Fa - ther's grace Where

Da - vid's house and line, The car - pen - ter whose
guar - dian of God's Son, Saint Jo - seph saw his
crown or mar - tyr's fame, For him there was the
saints and an - gels throng, Be - side his spouse, be -

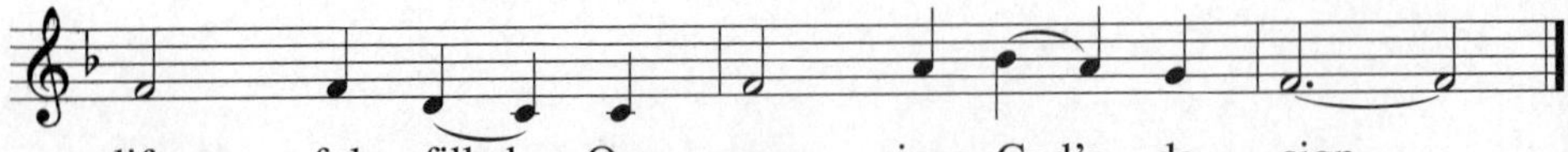

life ful - filled Our gra - cious God's de - sign.
dreams come true: The will of God was done.
pa - tient life Of faith and hum - ble name.
fore the Son, He joins the heav'n - ly song.

Text: Sts. 1, 3–4, George W. Williams, b.1922, alt., © 1979, The Hymn Society (admin. by Hope Publishing Company); st. 2, Ronald F. Krisman,
b.1946, © 2011, GIA Publications, Inc.
Tune: LAND OF REST, CM; American melody; harm. by Richard Proulx, 1937–2010, © 1975, GIA Publications, Inc.

The Hands that First Held Mary's Child   970

1. The hands that first held Mar - y's child Were hard from
2. When Jo - seph mar - veled at the size Of that small
3. "This child shall be Em - man - u - el, Not God up -
4. The tools which Jo - seph laid a - side A mob would

work - ing wood, From boards they sawed and
breath - ing frame, And gazed up - on those
on the throne, But God with us, Em -
lat - er lift And use with an - ger,

planed and filed And splin - ters they with - stood. This
bright new eyes And spoke the in - fant's name, The
man - u - el, As close as blood and bone." The
fear, and pride To cru - ci - fy God's gift. Let

day they gripped no tool of steel, They drove no
an - gel's words he once had dreamed Poured down from
ti - ny form in Jo - seph's palms Con - firmed what
us, O Lord, not on - ly hold The Child who's

i - ron nail, But cra - dled from the
heav - en's height, And like the host of
he had heard, And from his heart rose
born to - day, But charged with faith may

head to heel Our Lord, new - born and frail.
stars that beamed Blessed earth with wel - come light.
hymns and psalms For heav - en's hu - man word.
we be bold To fol - low in his way.

Text: Thomas H. Troeger, b.1945, © 1985, Oxford University Press
Tune: RESIGNATION, CMD; Funk's *Compilation of Genuine Church Music*, 1832; harm. by Richard Proulx, 1937–2010, © 1975, GIA Publications, Inc.

971 No Wind at the Window

1. No wind at the win-dow, No knock on the
2. "O Mar-y, O Mar-y, Don't hide from my
3. "This child must be born that The king-dom might
4. No pay-ment was prom-ised, No prom-is-es

door; No light from the lamp-stand, No
face. Be glad that you're fa-vored And
come: Sal-va-tion for man-y, De-
made; No wed-ding was dat-ed, No

foot on the floor; No dream born of
filled with God's grace. The time for re-
struc-tion for some; Both end and be-
blue-print dis-played. Yet Mar-y, con-

tired-ness, No ghost raised by fear: Just an
deem-ing The world has be-gun; And
gin-ning, Both mes-sage and sign; Both
sent-ing To what none could guess, Re-

an-gel and a wom-an And a voice in her ear.
you are re-quest-ed To moth-er God's son.
vic-tor and vic-tim, Both yours and di-vine."
plied with con-vic-tion, "Tell God I say yes."

Text: John L. Bell, b.1949
Tune: COLUMCILLE, Irregular; Gaelic, arr. by John L. Bell, b.1949
© 1992, Iona Community, GIA Publications, Inc., agent

The Angel Gabriel from Heaven Came   972

1. The an - gel Ga - bri - el from heav - en came,
2. "How blest a - mong all wom - en you shall be,
3. Then gen - tle Mar - y meek - ly bowed her head.
4. Of her, Em - man - u - el, the Christ, was born

With wings as drift - ed snow, with eyes as flame.
Whom ev - 'ry age will praise con - tin - ual - ly.
"To me be as it pleas - es God," she said.
In Beth - le - hem, all on a Christ - mas morn.

"All hail," said he, "O low - ly maid - en Mar - y,
Your Son shall be Em - man - u - el, by seers fore - told,
"My soul shall laud and mag - ni - fy God's ho - ly name."
And Chris - tian folk through-out the world will ev - er say:

Most high - ly fa - vored la - dy." Gló - ri - a!
Most high - ly fa - vored la - dy." Gló - ri - a!
Most high - ly fa - vored la - dy, Gló - ri - a!
"Most high - ly fa - vored la - dy." Gló - ri - a!

Text: Basque carol; para. by Sabine Baring-Gould, 1834–1924, alt.
Tune: GABRIEL'S MESSAGE, 10 10 12 10; Basque carol; harm. by Charles E. Pettman, 1865–1943

973 Praise We the Lord This Day

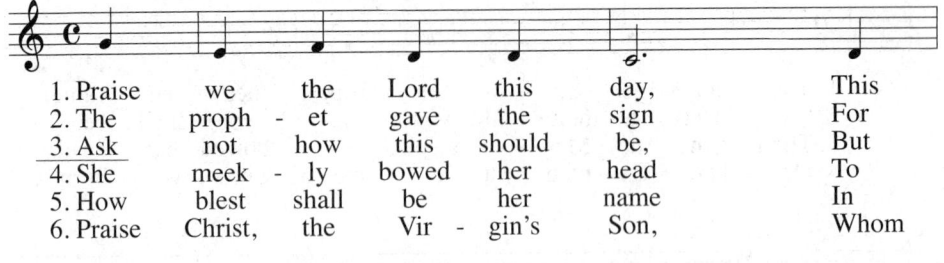

1. Praise we the Lord this day, This
2. The proph - et gave the sign For
3. Ask not how this should be, But
4. She meek - ly bowed her head To
5. How blest shall be her name In
6. Praise Christ, the Vir - gin's Son, Whom

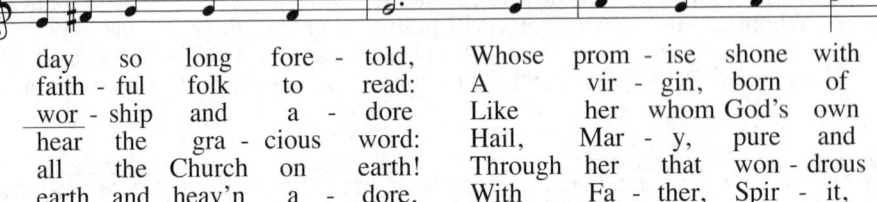

day so long fore - told, Whose prom - ise shone with
faith - ful folk to read: A vir - gin, born of
wor - ship and a - dore Like her whom God's own
hear the gra - cious word: Hail, Mar - y, pure and
all the Church on earth! Through her that won - drous
earth and heav'n a - dore, With Fa - ther, Spir - it,

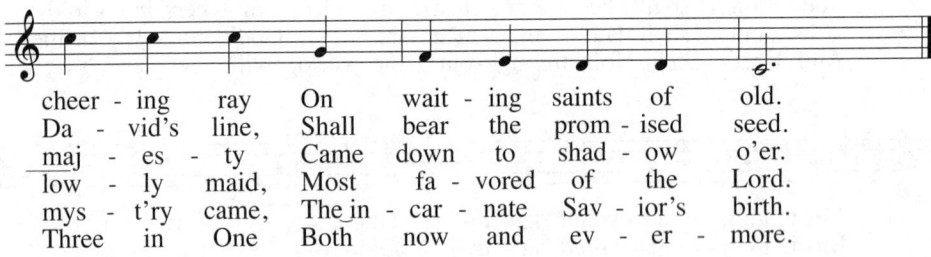

cheer - ing ray On wait - ing saints of old.
Da - vid's line, Shall bear the prom - ised seed.
maj - es - ty Came down to shad - ow o'er.
low - ly maid, Most fa - vored of the Lord.
mys - t'ry came, The in - car - nate Sav - ior's birth.
Three in One Both now and ev - er - more.

Text: Matthew 1:23; *Hymns for the Festivals and Saints' Days*, 1846, alt.
Tune: SWABIA, SM; Johann M. Speiss, 1715–1772; adapt. by William H. Havergal, 1793–1870

974 The Great Forerunner of the Morn

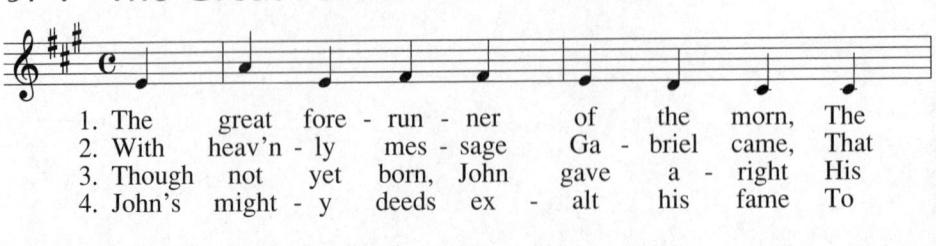

1. The great fore - run - ner of the morn, The
2. With heav'n - ly mes - sage Ga - briel came, That
3. Though not yet born, John gave a - right His
4. John's might - y deeds ex - alt his fame To

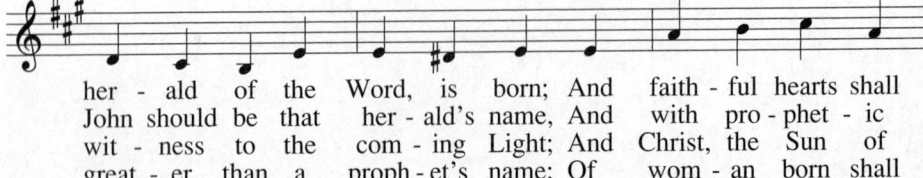

her - ald of the Word, is born; And faith - ful hearts shall
John should be that her - ald's name, And with pro - phet - ic
wit - ness to the com - ing Light; And Christ, the Sun of
great - er than a proph - et's name; Of wom - an born shall

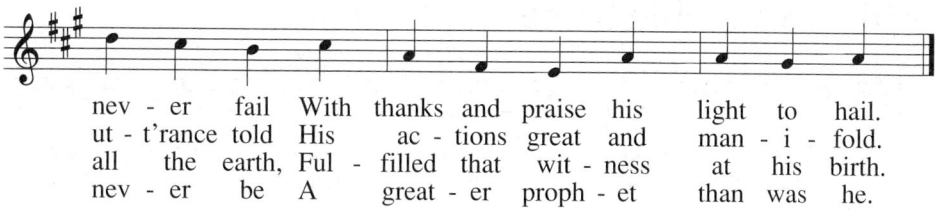

nev - er   fail   With thanks and praise his   light   to   hail.
ut - t'rance told His   ac - tions great and   man - i - fold.
all   the earth, Ful - filled that wit - ness   at   his   birth.
nev - er   be   A   great - er proph - et   than was   he.

Text: *Praecursor altus luminis*; Venerable Bede, 673–735; tr. by John M. Neale, 1818–1866, alt.
Tune: WINCHESTER NEW, LM; adapt. from *Musikalisches Handbuch*, Hamburg, 1690

When Jesus Came to Jordan   975

Verses

1. When   Je - sus   came   to   Jor - dan   To
2. He   came   to   share   re - pen - tance   With
3. He   came   to   share   temp - ta - tion,   Our
4. So   when   the   Dove   de - scend - ed   On

be   bap - tized   by   John,   He   did   not   come   for
all   who mourn   their   sins,   To   speak   the   vi - tal
ut - most woe   and   loss;   For   us   and   our   sal -
him,   the   Son   of   Man,   The   hid - den   years   had

par - don,   But   as   his   Fa - ther's   Son.
sen - tence   With   which   good news   be - gins.
va - tion   To   die   up - on   the   cross.
end - ed,   The   age   of   grace   be - gan.

Optional Refrain

Be - hold   the   Lamb   of   God,   who   takes   a - way   the

sins   of   the   world.   This   is   God's   Cho - sen   One.

Text: Verses, Fred Pratt Green, 1903–2000, © 1980, Hope Publishing Company; refrain, Lynn M. Trapp, © 2001, Hope Publishing Company
Tune: DE EERSTEN ZIJN DE LAATSTEN, 7 6 7 6; Frits Mehrtens, 1922–1975, © Interkerkelijke Stichting voor het Kerklied; refrain, Lynn M. Trapp,
  © 2001, GIA Publications, Inc.

976 Two Noble Saints

1. Two no - ble saints, both root - ed In faith and ho - ly love,
2. The words of Paul as - sure us Of Christ's re-deem-ing word;

By hope of God u - nit - ed They reach to heav'n a - bove.
The works of Pe - ter show us How we may serve the Lord.

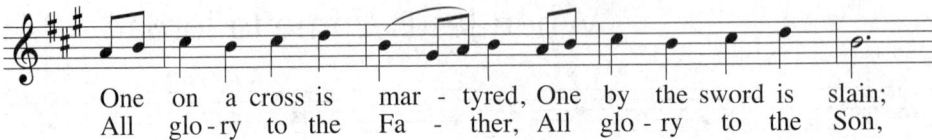

One on a cross is mar - tyred, One by the sword is slain;
All glo - ry to the Fa - ther, All glo - ry to the Son,

Both tri - umph in their dy - ing, Both glo - rious saint-hood gain.
Who with the Ho - ly Spir - it, Now reign, blest Three in One.

Text: Based on *Decora lux aeternitatis auream*, by Anne K. LeCroy, b.1930, alt., © 1982
Tune: ELLACOMBE, 7 6 7 6 D; *Gesangbuch der Herzogl*, Wirtemberg, 1784

977 Transform Us

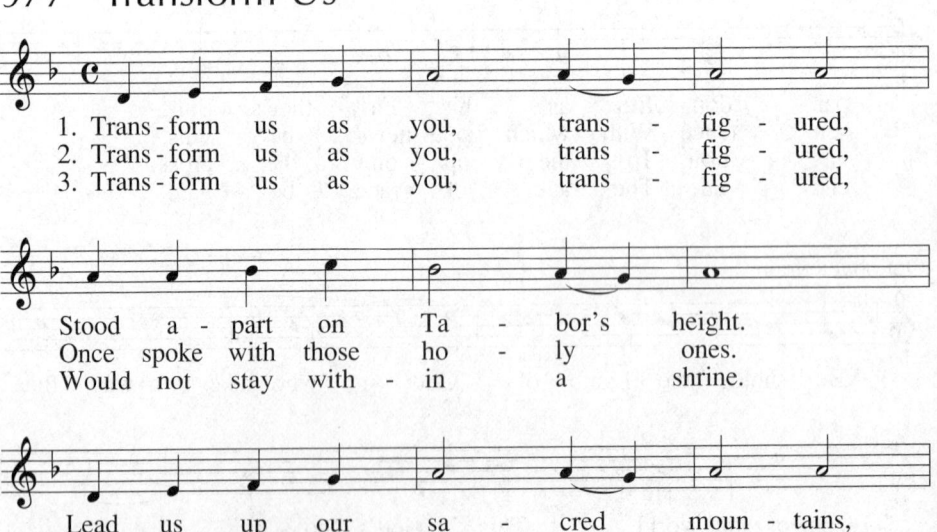

1. Trans - form us as you, trans - fig - ured,
2. Trans - form us as you, trans - fig - ured,
3. Trans - form us as you, trans - fig - ured,

Stood a - part on Ta - bor's height.
Once spoke with those ho - ly ones.
Would not stay with - in a shrine.

Lead us up our sa - cred moun - tains,
We, sur - round - ed by the wit - ness
Keep us from our great temp - ta - tion—

Search us with re - veal - ing light.
Of those saints whose work is done,
Time and truth we quick - ly bind.

Lift us from where we have fall - en,
Live in this world as your Bod - y,
Lead us down those dai - ly path - ways

Full of ques - tions, filled with fright.
Cho - sen daugh - ters, cho - sen sons.
Where our love is not con - fined.

Text: Sylvia G. Dunstan, 1955–1993, © 1993, GIA Publications, Inc.
Tune: PICARDY, 8 7 8 7 8 7; French carol; harm. by Richard Proulx, 1937–2010, © 1986, GIA Publications, Inc.

How Good, Lord, to Be Here! 978

1. How good, Lord, to be here! Your
2. How good, Lord, to be here, Your
3. Ful - fill - er of the past And
4. Be - fore we taste of death, We
5. How good, Lord, to be here! Yet

glo - ry fills the night; Your face and gar - ments,
beau - ty to be - hold Where Mo - ses and E -
hope of things to be, We hail your bod - y
see your king - dom come; We long to hold the
we may not re - main; But since you bid us

like the sun, Shine with un - bor - rowed light.
li - jah stand, Your mes - sen - gers of old.
glo - ri - fied And our re - demp - tion see.
vi - sion bright And make this hill our home.
leave the mount, Come with us to the plain.

Text: Luke 9:32–33; Joseph A. Robinson, 1858–1933, alt.
Tune: SWABIA, SM; Johann M. Speiss, 1715–1772; adapt. by William H. Havergal, 1793–1870

979 Hail, Holy Queen Enthroned Above

1. Hail, ho-ly Queen en-throned a-bove, O Ma-rí-a. Hail,
2. The cause of joy to all be-low, O Ma-rí-a. The
3. O gen-tle, lov-ing, ho-ly one, O Ma-rí-a. The

Queen of mer-cy and of love, O Ma-rí-a.
spring through which all grac-es flow, O Ma-rí-a.
God of light be-came your Son, O Ma-rí-a.

Tri-umph, all ye Cher-u-bim; Sing with us, ye
An-gels, all your prais-es bring; Earth and heav-en,
Tri-umph, all ye Cher-u-bim; Sing with us, ye

Ser-a-phim. Heav'n and earth re-sound the hymn:
with us sing; All cre-a-tion ech-o-ing:
Ser-a-phim. Heav'n and earth re-sound the hymn:

Sal-ve, Sal-ve, Sal-ve Re-gí-na.

Text: *Salve Regina, mater misericordiae*; c.1080; tr. *Roman Hymnal*, 1884; st. 2–3, adapt. by M. Owen Lee, CSB, b.1930
Tune: SALVE REGINA COELITUM, 8 4 8 4 777 4 5; *Choralmelodien zum Heiligen Gesänge*, 1808

980 Crux Fidelis

Refrain

Crux fi-dé-lis; cross of glad-ness, tree on

which our hope is hung; Let my arms be as your

branch-es! Yours, the song that must be sung.

Verses

1. The Lord Je - sus loved us and
2. The Lord Je - sus en - tered the
3. To strive for jus - tice, e - ven when
4. We keep be - fore us that which our
5. The cup is poured out! So may we
6. The road in - vites us, marked with the

gave his life for us; few of us shall be
pain and death of sin. He ac - cept - ed the
stub - born-ness pre - vails, to be one with the
kin - dred had of old: all the pain and the
drink as did our Lord, in this cup we are
steps of kin - dred past, they left foot - steps that

called to do the same. Yet all of us must
tor - ment of the cross. But with the cross he
des - p'rate of the world; to stand with those who
suf - f'ring of the cross. Yet where that cross is
called to share his fate. And let us not stand
spoke of heav - y loads. But they did not trudge

lay down our lives a - long with his: Let the
gave us the bless - ed gift of joy: Let the
cry out when we can't bring re - lief: Let that
plant - ed, the seeds of hope en - dure: Let that
back from the cross to which we're called: Let the
slow - ly! They strode a - long this path, our

D.C.

cross be our com - pan - ion as we dai - ly fol - low him.
cross be our com - pan - ion as we dai - ly fol - low him.
hope be our com - pan - ion as we dai - ly fol - low him.
hope be our com - pan - ion as we dai - ly fol - low him.
cross be our com - pan - ion as we dai - ly fol - low him.
on - ly hope be - fore us as we're called to fol - low him.

Text: Steven C. Warner, b.1954; verses adapt. from *Constitution of the Congregation of Holy Cross*
Tune: Steven C. Warner, b.1954

981 Lift High the Cross / Alcen la Cruz

Refrain

Lift high the cross, the love of Christ pro-claim till
Al-cen la cruz, em-ble-ma de su a-mor; que el

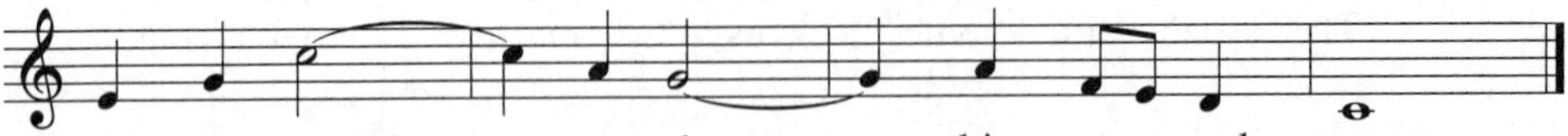

all the world a-dore his sa-cred name.
mun-do al fin co-noz - ca al Sal-va-dor.

Verses

1. Come, Chris-tians, fol-low where our Sav-ior trod, Our
2. Led on their way by this tri-um-phant sign, The
3. Each new-born ser-vant of the Cru-ci-fied Bears
4. O Lord, once lift-ed on the glo-rious tree, Your

1. Va - mos, cris-tia-nos, tras nues-tro Se-ñor; El
2. Ba - jo es-te sig-no de su gran po-der El
3. Ca - da cre-yen-te del que en cruz mu-rió En
4. Cuan - do te al-za-ron glo - rio-so en la cruz, A -

D.C.

King vic-to-rious, Christ, the Son of God.
hosts of God in con-quering ranks com-bine.
on the brow the seal of him who died.
death has bought us life e-ter-nal-ly.

rey vic-to-rio - so, Cris-to, Hi-jo de Dios.
pue-blo de Dios a - van-za sin te-mer.
su fren-te lle - va el sig-no en que ven-ció.
llí pro-me-tis - te lle-var-nos a la luz.

5. So shall our song of triumph ever be: 5. *Himnos de gloria alcemos sin cesar;*
    Praise to the Crucified for victory!   *Al rey vencedor que en cruz supo triunfar.*

Text: 1 Corinthians 1:18; George W. Kitchin, 1827–1912, and Michael R. Newbolt, 1874–1956, alt.; tr. by Dimas Planas-Belfort, 1934–1992,
    and Ángel Mattos, alt.
Tune: CRUCIFER, 10 10 with refrain; Sydney H. Nicholson, 1875–1947
© 1974, tr. © 1997, Hope Publishing Company

982 When I Survey the Wondrous Cross

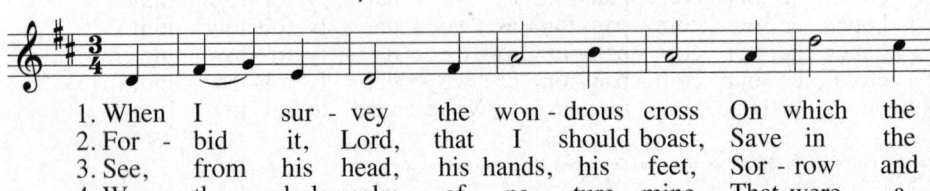

1. When I sur-vey the won-drous cross On which the
2. For-bid it, Lord, that I should boast, Save in the
3. See, from his head, his hands, his feet, Sor-row and
4. Were the whole realm of na-ture mine, That were a

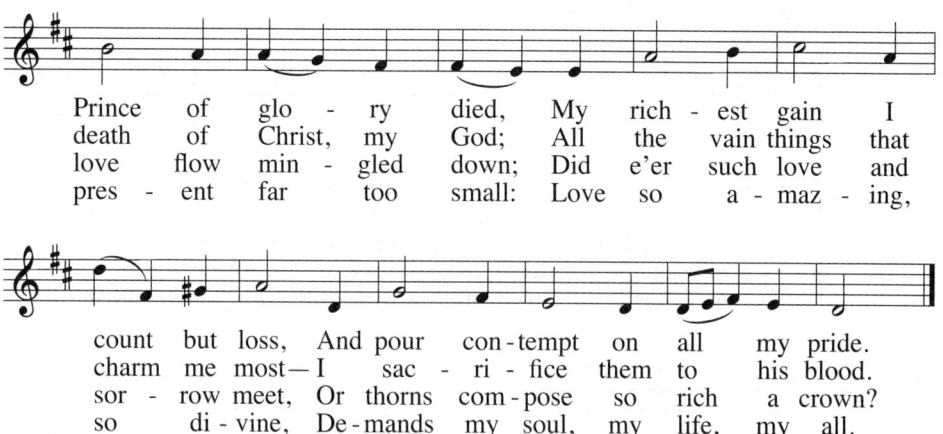

Prince	of	glo -	ry	died,	My	rich - est	gain	I
death	of	Christ,	my	God;	All	the	vain things	that
love	flow	min -	gled	down;	Did	e'er	such love	and
pres -	ent	far	too	small:	Love	so	a - maz -	ing,

count	but	loss,	And pour	con - tempt	on	all	my pride.
charm	me	most— I	sac -	ri - fice	them	to	his blood.
sor -	row	meet,	Or thorns	com - pose	so	rich	a crown?
so	di -	vine,	De - mands	my soul,	my	life,	my all.

Text: Isaac Watts, 1674–1748
Tune: ROCKINGHAM, LM; adapt. by Edward Miller, 1735–1807

As Stars Adorn the Night-Veiled Sky 983

1. As	stars	a - dorn	the	night-veiled	sky,	Ar - rayed	like
2. The	light	saints bear	is	not	their	own	But shines through
3. Through	saints	we glimpse the	light	of	Christ,	The Morn - ing
4. That	light	is	ours to	claim	and	share,	Not mere - ly
5. The	saints	in - spire	and	chal - lenge	us	Our ho - ly

jew - els	rare	and	bright,	So	shine God's	saints	in
them as	gift	and	sign:	To	show how	God	can
Star that	crowns	the	night,	Whose ris -	ing	her -	alds
praise or	gaze	up -	on:	For	all who	are	bap -
call - ing	to	em -	brace:	To	bear Christ's	light	in

ev - 'ry	age	To	give	the	world	new hope,	new light.
use and	bless	Frail	hu - man	means	for	ends	di - vine.
God's new	day,	The	prom - ised	dawn	of	life and	light.
tized be - come	Light - bear - ers	through	the	Ris - en	One.
our own	day,	To	be	the	ves -	sels	of God's grace.

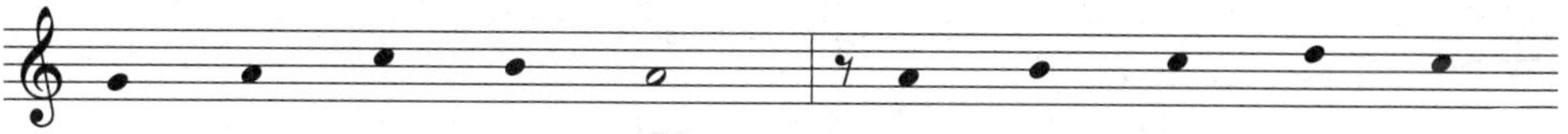

Text: Carl P. Daw, Jr., b.1944, © 1997, Hope Publishing Company
Tune: JESU DULCIS MEMORIA, LM; Mode I; acc. by Richard Proulx, 1937–2010, © 1975, GIA Publications, Inc.

984 For All the Saints

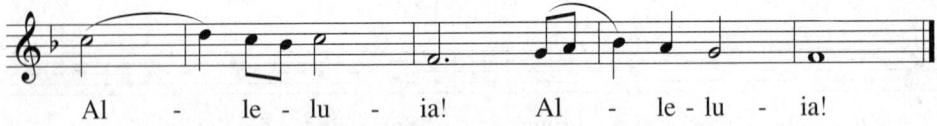

1. For all the saints, who from their la - bors rest,
2. You were their rock, their for - tress and their might;
3. O may your sol - diers, faith - ful, true, and bold,
4. O blest com - mun - ion, fel - low - ship di - vine!
5. And when the strife is fierce, the war - fare long,
6. The gold - en eve - ning bright - ens in the west;

Who to the world their faith in you con - fessed; Your
You, Lord, their Cap - tain in the well - fought fight;
Fight as the saints who no - bly fought of old, And
We fee - bly strug - gle, they in glo - ry shine; Yet
Steals on the ear the dis - tant tri - umph song, And
Soon, soon to faith - ful war - riors comes their rest;

name, O Je - sus, be for - ev - er blest.
You, in the dark - ness drear, their one true light.
win with them the vic - tor's crown of gold.
all are one with - in your great de - sign.
hearts are brave a - gain, and arms are strong.
Sweet is the calm of par - a - dise the blest.

Al - le - lu - ia! Al - le - lu - ia!

7. But then there breaks a yet more glorious day;
   The saints triumphant rise in bright array;
   The King of glory passes on his way.
   Alleluia! Alleluia!

8. From earth's wide bounds, from ocean's farthest coast,
   Through gates of pearl streams in the countless host,
   Singing to Father, Son, and Holy Ghost:
   Alleluia! Alleluia!

Text: William W. How, 1823–1897, alt.
Tune: SINE NOMINE, 10 10 10 with alleluias; Ralph Vaughan Williams, 1872–1958

For All the Faithful Women   985

1. For all the faith-ful wom-en Who served in days of old, To you shall thanks be giv-en; To all, their sto-ry told. They served with strength and glad-ness In tasks your wis-dom gave. To you their lives bore wit-ness, Pro-claimed your pow'r to save.

2. We praise your name for Mir-iam Who sang tri-um-phant-ly While Phar-oah's vaunt-ed ar-my Lay drowned be-neath the sea. As Is-rael marched to free-dom, Her chains of bond-age gone, So may we reach the king-dom Your might-y arm has won.

3. All praise for that brave war-rior Who fought at your com-mand; You made her Is-rael's sav-ior When op-pressed the land. As Deb-orah stood with val-or Up-on the bat-tle-field, Lord, teach us how to pray, Grant us her per-se-ver-ance; Lord, teach us how to pray, May we, in e-vil's ho-ur, Truth's sword with bold-ness wield.

4. To Han-nah, pray-ing child-less Be-fore the throne of grace, You gave a son whose serv-ice Would save our race. May we, with her, sur-ren-der Our-selves to your com-mand And lay up-on your al-tar Our gifts of heart and hand. To trust in your de-liv-'rance When dark-ness hides our way.

5. We sing of Mar-y, moth-er, Fair maid-en, full of grace. She bore the Christ, our broth-er, Who came to save our race. And then with joy she saw him In res-ur-rec-tion light. May we, by faith be-hold him, The day who ends all night.

6. We praise the oth-er Mar-y Who came at East-er dawn And near the tomb did tar-ry, But found her Lord was gone.

Text: Herman G. Stuempfle, Jr., 1923–2007, © 1993, GIA Publications, Inc.
Tune: AURELIA, 7 6 7 6 D; Samuel Sebastian Wesley, 1810–1876

986 By All Your Saints Still Striving

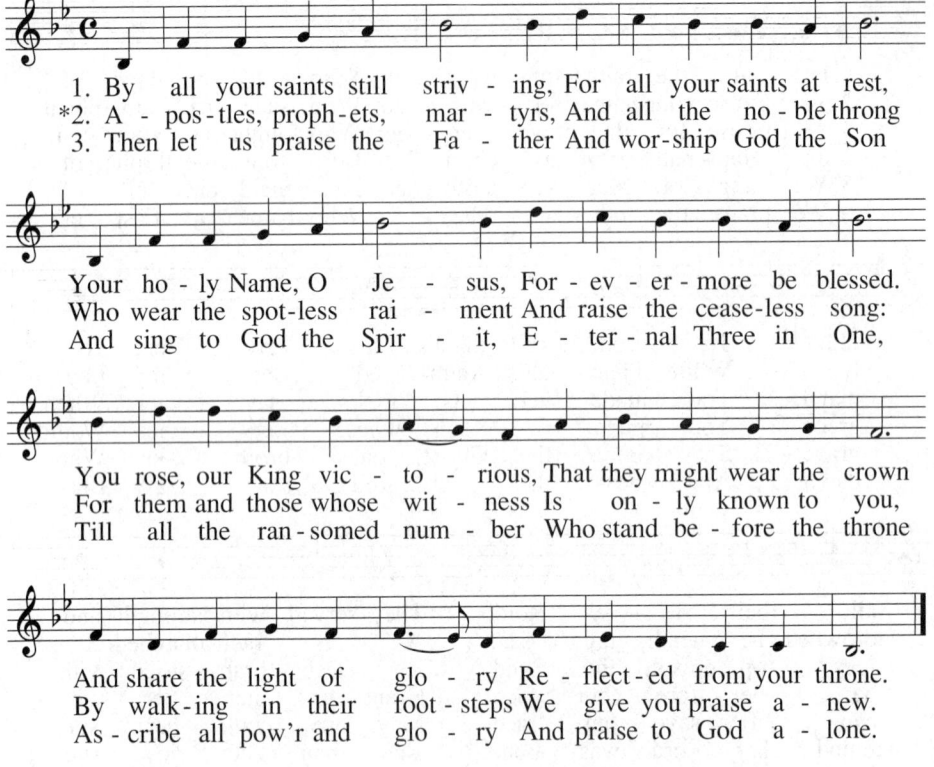

1. By all your saints still striv - ing, For all your saints at rest,
*2. A - pos - tles, proph - ets, mar - tyrs, And all the no - ble throng
3. Then let us praise the Fa - ther And wor - ship God the Son

Your ho - ly Name, O Je - sus, For - ev - er - more be blessed.
Who wear the spot-less rai - ment And raise the cease-less song:
And sing to God the Spir - it, E - ter - nal Three in One,

You rose, our King vic - to - rious, That they might wear the crown
For them and those whose wit - ness Is on - ly known to you,
Till all the ran - somed num - ber Who stand be - fore the throne

And share the light of glo - ry Re - flect - ed from your throne.
By walk - ing in their foot - steps We give you praise a - new.
As - cribe all pow'r and glo - ry And praise to God a - lone.

Stanza 2 may be replaced by an appropriate stanza taken from the following.

January 25: Conversion of Paul
Praise for the light from heaven,
Praise for the voice of awe,
Praise for the glorious vision
The persecutor saw.
O Lord, for Paul's conversion
We bless your Name today.
Come shine within our darkness
And guide us in the Way.

February 22: Chair of Peter
We praise you, Lord, for Peter,
So eager and so bold,
Thrice falling, yet repentant,
Thrice charged to feed your fold.
Lord, make your pastors faithful
To guard your flock from harm,
And hold them, when they waver,
With your almighty arm.

March 19: Joseph, Husband of Mary
All praise, O God, for Joseph,
The guardian of your Son,
Who saved him from King Herod
When safety there was none.
He taught the trade of builder,
When they to Naz'reth came,
And Joseph's love made "Father"
To be, for Christ, God's name.

March 25: Annunciation of Our Lord
We sing with joy of Mary,
Whose heart with awe was stirred
When, youthful and astonished,
She heard the angel's word.
Yet she her voice upraises
To magnify God's Name,
As once for our salvation
Your mother she became.

April 25: Mark

For Mark, O Lord, we praise you,
The weak by grace made strong;
His witness in his gospel
Becomes victorious song.
May we, in all our weakness,
Receive your pow'r divine,
And all, as fruitful branches,
Grow strong in you, the Vine.

May 3: Philip and James

We praise you, Lord, for Philip,
Blest guide to Greek and Jew,
And for young James, the faithful
Who heard and followed you.
O grant us grace to know you,
The Way, the Truth, the Life,
And wrestle with temptation
Till victors in the strife.

May 14: Matthias

For one in place of Judas,
The apostles sought God's choice;
The lot fell to Matthias,
For whom we now rejoice.
May we, as true apostles,
Your holy Church defend,
And not betray our calling,
But serve you to the end.

June 11: Barnabas

For Barnabas we praise you,
Appointed by your call,
Who, filled with faith and Spirit,
Proclaimed your word with Paul.
Give us your grace, O Savior,
That we become the same:
Companions in your mission,
Who bear the Christian name.

June 24: Birth of John the Baptist

All praise for John the Baptist,
Forerunner of the Word,
Our true Elijah, making
A highway for the Lord.
The last and greatest prophet,
He saw the dawning ray
Of light that grows in splendor
Until the perfect day.

June 29: Peter and Paul

We praise you for Saint Peter,
We praise you for Saint Paul.
They taught both Jew and Gentile
That Christ is all in all.
To cross and sword they yielded
And saw your kingdom come:
O God, your two apostles
Won life through martyrdom.

July 3: Thomas

All praise, O Lord, for Thomas,
Whose short-lived doubtings prove
Your perfect two-fold nature,
The depth of your true love.
May all who live with questions
Have faith in you restored.
Grant us the grace to know you,
Made flesh, yet God and Lord.

July 22: Mary Magdalene

For Magdalene we praise you,
Steadfast at cross and tomb.
Your "Mary!" in the garden
Dispelled her tears and gloom.
Apostle to the apostles,
She ran to spread the word;
Send us to shout the good news
That we have seen the Lord.

July 25: James

For James, O Lord, we praise you,
Who fell to Herod's sword.
He drank your cup of suff'ring
And thus fulfilled your word.
Lord, curb our vain impatience
For glory and for fame;
Equip us for such suff'rings
As glorify your Name.

August 24: Bartholomew

We praise you for Nathanael,
Surnamed Bartholomew.
We know not his achievements
But know that he was true;
For he at the Ascension
Was an apostle still.
May we discern your presence
And seek, like him, your will.

September 21: Matthew

We praise you, Lord, for Matthew,
Whose gospel words declare
That, worldly gain forsaking,
Your path of life we share.
From greed and love of money
O raise our eyes anew,
That we, whate'er our calling,
May rise and follow you.

October 18: Luke

For Luke, belov'd physician,
All praise, whose gospel shows
The healer of the nations,
The one who shares our woes.
Your wine and oil, O Savior,
Upon our spirits pour,
And with true balm of Gilead
Anoint us evermore.

October 28: Simon and Jude

Praise, Lord, for your apostles,
Saint Simon and Saint Jude.
One love, one hope impelled them
To tread the way, renewed.
May we with zeal as earnest
The faith of Christ maintain,
Be bound in love together,
And life eternal gain.

November 30: Andrew

All praise, O Lord, for Andrew,
The first to follow you;
He witnessed to his brother,
"This is Messiah true."
You called him from his fishing
Upon Lake Galilee;
He rose to meet your challenge,
"Leave all and follow me."

December 26: Stephen

All praise, O Lord, for Stephen
Who, martyred, saw you stand
To help in time of torment,
To plead at God's right hand.
Like you, our suff'ring Savior,
His enemies he blessed,
With "Lord, receive my spirit,"
His faith, in death, confessed.

December 27: John

For John, belov'd disciple,
Exiled to Patmos' shore,
And for his faithful record,
We praise you evermore.
Praise for the mystic vision
His words to us unfold.
Instill in us his longing,
Your glory to behold.

December 28: Holy Innocents

We praise you for the infants,
Whom your mysterious love
Called early from life's conflicts
To share your peace above.
O Rachel, cease your weeping;
They rest from earthly cares.
Lord, grant us crowns as brilliant
And lives as pure as theirs.

Text: Based on Horatio Nelson, 1823–1913, by Jerry D. Godwin, b.1944, © 1985, The Church Pension Fund; stanzas for Barnabas and
    Mary Magdalene, © 2006, Augsburg Fortress
Tune: ST. THEODULPH, 7 6 7 6 D; Melchior Teschner, 1584–1635

Blessed Feasts of Blessed Martyrs 987

1. Bless - ed feasts of bless - ed mar-tyrs, Ho - ly wom - en,
2. Faith pre - vail-ing, hope un - fail-ing, Lov - ing Christ with
3. There-fore, you co - heirs of glo - ry, All who dwell with

ho - ly men, With the mem - 'ry of their wit-ness
sin - gle heart, Thus they, glo - rious and vic - to-rious,
Christ on high, Join to ours your sup - pli - ca-tion

Greet we your re - turn a - gain. Wor - thy deeds are
Brave-ly bore the mar - tyr's part, By con-tempt of
When be - fore him we draw nigh, Pray - ing that, this

theirs, and won - ders, Wor - thy of the name they bore;
ev - 'ry an - guish, By un - yield-ing bat - tle done;
life com - plet - ed, All its fleet - ing mo - ments past,

We, our joy - ful prais - es sing - ing,
Vic - tors at the last, they tri - umph,
By his grace we may be wor - thy

Hon - or them for - ev - er - more.
With the host of an - gels one.
Of e - ter - nal bliss at last.

Text: *O beata beatorum*, Latin, 12th. C.; tr. John M. Neale, 1818–1866, alt.
Tune: IN BABILONE, 8 7 8 7 D; *Oude en Nieuwe Hollantse Boerenlieties en Contredansen*, c.1710

988 Come and See the Many Wonders

1. Come and see the man - y won - ders
2. Come and name the men and wom - en
3. Go and live as Christ's dis - ci - ples.

God has worked through man - y hands.
Called by Christ and by him sent.
Go and be his face and hands,

Come and count the man - y bless-ings,
They pro - claimed the King - dom's com - ing
And pro - claim by word and ac - tion

Wo - ven from so man - y strands.
In his Word and Sac - ra - ment.
That God's love is Christ's com - mand.

We have seen the face of Je - sus,
Sing of found - ers and of build - ers,
Raise a song of glad thanks - giv - ing;

Who has dwelt a - mong us here:
Pas - tors, teach - ers, ser - vants all,
Let it ring that all may hear:

Christ, the source of all our bless-ings,
Who by lives of faith and serv - ice
Praise the Fa - ther, Son, and Spir - it,

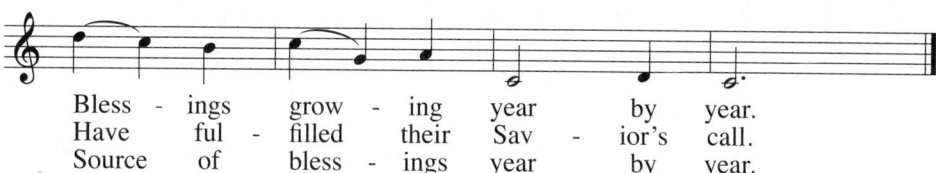

Bless - ings grow - ing year by year.
Have ful - filled their Sav - ior's call.
Source of bless - ings year by year.

Text: Harry Hagan, OSB, © 2010, Saint Meinrad's Abbey
Tune: ABBOT'S LEIGH, 8 7 8 7 D; Cyril V. Taylor, 1907–1991, © 1942, ren. 1970, Hope Publishing Company

Ye Watchers and Ye Holy Ones 989

1. Ye watch - ers and ye ho - ly ones, Bright
2. O high - er than the cher - u - bim, More
3. Re - spond, ye souls in end - less rest, Ye
4. O friends, in glad - ness let us sing, Su -

ser - aphs, cher - u - bim, and thrones, Raise the
glo - rious than the ser - a - phim, Lead their
pa - tri - archs and proph - ets blest: "Al - le -
per - nal an - thems ech - o - ing: "Al - le -

glad strain: "Al - le - lu - ia!" Cry out, do - min - ions, prince-doms,
prais - es: "Al - le - lu - ia!" O bear - er of the e - ter - nal
lu - ia, Al - le - lu - ia!" Ye ho - ly twelve, ye mar - tyrs
lu - ia, Al - le - lu - ia!" To God the Fa - ther, God the

pow'rs, Vir - tues, arch - an - gels, an - gels' choirs:
Word, Most gra - cious, mag - ni - fy the Lord:
strong, All saints tri - um - phant, raise the song:
Son, And God the Spir - it, Three in One:

"Al - le - lu - ia! Al - le - lu - ia!" Al - le - lu - ia,

al - le - lu - ia, al - le - lu - ia!

Text: John A. Riley, 1858–1945
Tune: LASST UNS ERFREUEN, LM with alleluias; *Geistliche Kirchengesänge*, Cologne, 1623; harm. by Ralph Vaughan Williams, 1872–1958

990 For the Faithful Who Have Answered

1. For the faith - ful who have an - swered
2. Man - y eyes have glimpsed the prom - ise.
3. For this cloud of faith - ful wit - ness,

When they heard your call to serve, For the man - y
Man - y hearts have yearned to see. Man - y ears have
For the com - mon life we share, For the work of

ways you led them Test - ing will and stretch-ing nerve,
heard you call - ing Us to great - er lib - er - ty.
peace and jus - tice, For the gos - pel that we bear,

For their work and for their wit - ness As they strove a -
Some have fal - len in the strug - gle. Oth - ers still are
For the vi - sion that our home-land Is your love— deep,

gainst the odds, For their cour - age and o - be-dience
fight - ing on. You are not a - shamed to own us.
high, and broad— For the dif - f'rent roads we trav - el

We give thanks and praise, O God.
We give thanks and praise, O God.
We give thanks and praise, O God.

Text: Sylvia Dunstan, 1955–1993, © 1991, GIA Publications, Inc.
Tune: PLEADING SAVIOR, 8 7 8 7 D; *Christian Lyre*, 1830; harm. by Richard Proulx, 1937–2010, © 1986, GIA Publications, Inc.

A Great Cloud of Witnesses 991

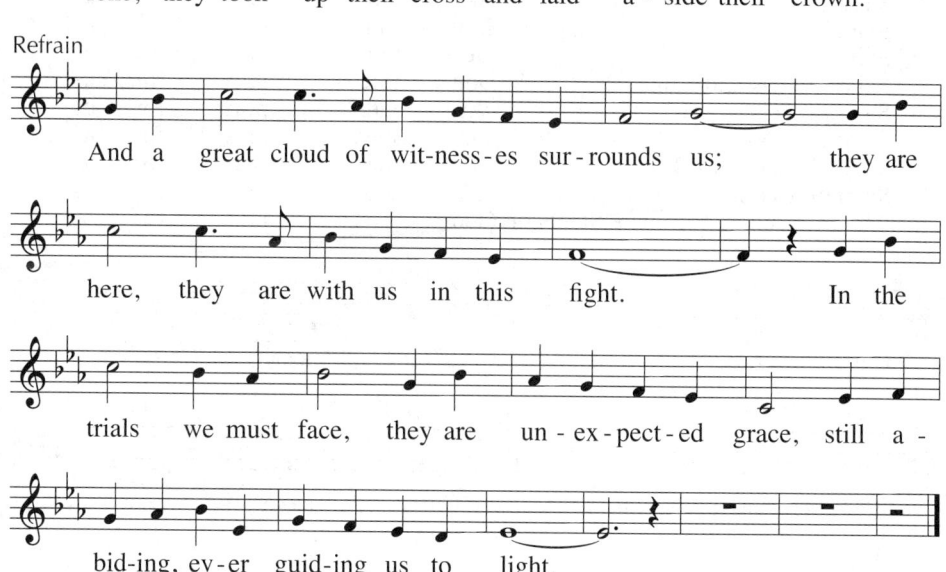

Verses

1. By God's grace we were blessed to have he-roes, strong and
2. We give thanks and re-joice for the gra-cious lives they
3. So by faith we go forth on a path as yet un-

true, shin-ing bright through our long and wea-ry nights.
led, for the strength and the wis-dom they passed on.
known, hold-ing fast to the prom-ise hand-ed down

E-ven now they are near, in our hearts they shine a-
Once, they sang with God's voice, and our spir-its still are
from the ones who stood firm; though for-sak-en and a-

new, still a-bid-ing, ev-er guid-ing us to light.
fed on our jour-ney toward the reign where all are one.
lone, they took up their cross and laid a-side their crown.

Refrain

And a great cloud of wit-ness-es sur-rounds us; they are

here, they are with us in this fight. In the

trials we must face, they are un-ex-pect-ed grace, still a-

bid-ing, ev-er guid-ing us to light.

Text: Hebrews, 12:1–3; Marty Haugen, b.1950
Tune: Marty Haugen, b.1950

992 Litany of the Saints

Cantor: / *Assembly:*

Lord, have mer - cy. Lord, have mer - cy.
Christ, have mer - cy. Christ, have mer - cy.
Lord, have mer - cy. Lord, have mer - cy.

		pray for us.
Holy Mary, Mother of	God,	pray for us.
Saint	Mich - ael,	pray for us.
Holy Angels of	God,	pray for us.
Saint John the	Bap - tist,	pray for us.
Saint	Jo - seph,	pray for us.
Saint Peter and Saint	Paul,	pray for us.
Saint	An - drew,	pray for us.
Saint	John,	pray for us.
Saint Mary	Mag - dalene,	pray for us.
Saint	Ste - phen,	pray for us.
Saint Ignatius of	An - tioch,	pray for us.
Saint	Law - rence,	pray for us.
Saint Perpetua and Saint Fe -	lic - ity,	pray for us.
Saint	Ag - nes,	pray for us.
Saint	Gre - gory,	pray for us.
Saint Au -	gus - tine,	pray for us.
Saint Atha -	na - sius,	pray for us.
Saint	Ba - sil,	pray for us.
Saint	Mar - tin,	pray for us.
Saint	Ben - edict,	pray for us.
Saint Francis and Saint	Dom - inic,	pray for us.
Saint Francis	Xa - vier,	pray for us.
Saint John Vi -	an - ney,	pray for us.
Saint Catherine of Si -	e - na,	pray for us.
Saint Teresa of	Je - sus,	pray for us.
All holy men and women, Saints of God,		pray for us.

Cantor: / *Assembly:*
Christ, hear us. Christ, hear us.

Christ, gra-cious-ly hear us. Christ, gra-cious-ly hear us.

Text: *Litany of the Saints, Roman Missal*
Music: *Litany of the Saints, Roman Missal*
© 2010, ICEL

Immaculate Mary 993

1. Im - mac - u - late Mar - y, your prais - es we sing;
2. Pre - des - tined for Christ by e - ter - nal de - cree,
3. To you by an an - gel, the Lord God made known
4. Most blest of all wom - en, you heard and be - lieved;
5. The an - gels re - joiced when you brought forth God's Son;

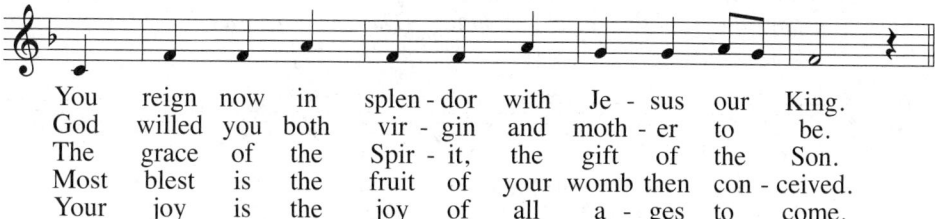

You reign now in splen - dor with Je - sus our King.
God willed you both vir - gin and moth - er to be.
The grace of the Spir - it, the gift of the Son.
Most blest is the fruit of your womb then con - ceived.
Your joy is the joy of all a - ges to come.

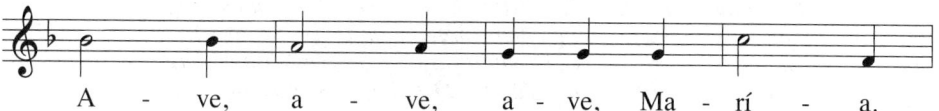

A - ve, a - ve, a - ve, Ma - rí - a.

A - ve, a - ve, Ma - rí - a.

6. Your child is the Savior, all hope lies in him:
   He gives us new life and redeems us from sin.

7. In glory for ever now close to your Son,
   All ages will praise you for all God has done.

Text: St. 1, Jeremiah Cummings, 1814–1866, alt.; sts. 2–7, Brian Foley, 1919–2000, © 1971, Faber Music Ltd.
Tune: LOURDES HYMN, 11 11 with refrain; French melody, Grenoble, 1882

994 Desde el Cielo / From the Heavens

Estribillo: Des - de_el cie - lo_u - na_her - mo - sa ma - ña - na,
1. Su - pli - can - te jun - ta - ba las ma - nos,
2. Su lle - ga - da lle - nó de_a - le - grí - a,
3. Jun - to_al mon - te pa - sa - ba Juan Die - go,

Refrain: From the heav'ns on a beau - ti - ful morn - ing,
1. She was clasp - ing her hands, soft - ly pray - ing,
2. Her ar - ri - val brought joy o - ver - flow - ing,
3. From the hill - side Juan Die - go was round - ing,

Des - de_el cie - lo_u - na_her - mo - sa ma - ña - na,
Su - pli - can - te jun - ta - ba las ma - nos.
Su lle - ga - da lle - nó de_a - le - grí - a,
Jun - to_al mon - te pa - sa - ba Juan Die - go.
From the heav'ns on a beau - ti - ful morn - ing,
She was clasp - ing her hands, soft - ly pray - ing,
Her ar - ri - val brought joy o - ver - flow - ing,
From the hill - side Juan Die - go was round - ing,

La Gua - da - lu - pa - na, la Gua - da - lu - pa - na,
Y_e - ran me - xi - ca - nos, y_e - ran me - xi - ca - nos,
De paz y_ar - mo - ní - a, de paz y_ar - mo - ní - a,
Y_a - cer - có - se lue - go, y_a - cer - có - se lue - go,
Ra - diant light was pour - ing, ra - diant light was pour - ing,
Face and pos - ture say - ing, face and pos - ture say - ing,
Peace and con - cord grow - ing, peace and con - cord grow - ing,
Mu - sic sweet - ly sound - ing, mu - sic sweet - ly sound - ing,

| 1. | 2. |

La Gua - da - lu - pa - na ba - jó_al Te - pe - yac. yac.
Y_e - ran me - xi - ca - nos su por - te_y su faz. faz.
De paz y_ar - mo - ní - a to - do_el A - ná - huac. huac.
Y_a - cer - có - se lue - go al o - ír can - tar. tar.
La Gua - da - lu - pa - na came to Te - pe - yac. yac.
She was Me - xi - ca - na, like the peo - ple there. there.
Peace and con - cord grow - ing in the A - ná - huac. huac.
Mu - sic sweet - ly sound - ing filled the cool, crisp air. air.

4. "Juan Dieguito," la Virgen le dijo,
"Juan Dieguito," la Virgen le dijo,
"Este cerro elijo, este cerro elijo,
Este cerro elijo para hacer mi altar."
"Este cerro elijo, este cerro elijo,
Este cerro elijo para hacer mi altar."

5. Y en la tilma entre rosas pintadas,
Y en la tilma entre rosas pintadas,
Su imagen amada, su imagen amada,
Su imagen amada se dignó dejar.
Su imagen amada, su imagen amada,
Su imagen amada se dignó dejar.

6. Desde entonces para el Mexicano,
Desde entonces para la Mexicana,
Ser Guadalupano, ser Guadalupana,
Ser Guadalupanos es algo esencial.
Ser Guadalupano, ser Guadalupana,
Ser Guadalupanos es algo esencial.

7. Madrecita de los Mexicanos,*
Madrecita de los Mexicanos,
Que estás en el cielo, que estás en
el cielo,
Que estás en el cielo, ruega a Dios
por nos.
Que estás en el cielo, que estás en
el cielo,
Que estás en el cielo, ruega a Dios
por nos.

8. En sus penas se postra de hinojos,
En sus penas se postra de hinojos,
Y eleva sus ojos, y eleva sus ojos,
Y eleva sus ojos hacia el Tepeyac.
Y eleva sus ojos, y eleva sus ojos,
Y eleva sus ojos hacia el Tepeyac.

4. *"Juan Dieguito," the Virgin called gently.*
"Juan Dieguito," the Virgin called gently.
Telling him intently, telling him intently,
"This hill I have chosen for my holy shrine."
Telling him intently, telling him intently,
"This hill I have chosen for my holy shrine."

5. *Roses fell from his cloak, brightly tinted,*
Roses fell from his cloak, brightly tinted,
Leaving there imprinted, leaving there
imprinted,
Leaving there the image of the Virgin fair.
Leaving there imprinted, leaving there
imprinted
Leaving there the image of the Virgin fair.

6. *From that time forward, each Mexicano,*
From that time forward, each Mexicana,
True Guadalupano, true Guadalupana,
True Guadalupanos all are born to be.
True Guadalupano, true Guadalupana,
True Guadalupanos all are born to be.

7. *Madrecita† to all peoples given,*
Madrecita to all peoples given,
As the Queen of Heaven, as the Queen
of Heaven,
As the Queen of Heaven, kindly pray
for us.
As the Queen of Heaven, as the Queen
of Heaven,
As the Queen of Heaven, kindly pray
for us.

8. *We approach you in love, humbly kneeling,*
We approach you in love, humbly kneeling,
Earnestly appealing, earnestly appealing,
Lifting up our eyes and hearts to Tepeyac.
Earnestly appealing, earnestly appealing,
Lifting up our eyes and hearts to Tepeyac.

Texto alternativo / alternate text: Madrecita de todos nosotros *(2x)*
†Dearest Mother

Text: Traditional; tr. by Mary Louise Bringle, b.1953, © 2005, GIA Publications, Inc.
Tune: APARACIONES GUADALUPANAS, 10 10 10 12 11 D; traditional; harm. by Ronald F. Krisman, b.1946, © 2005, GIA Publications, Inc.

995 Mañanitas a la Virgen de Guadalupe / Morning Praises to the Virgin of Guadalupe

Estrofas 1–4 / Verses 1–4

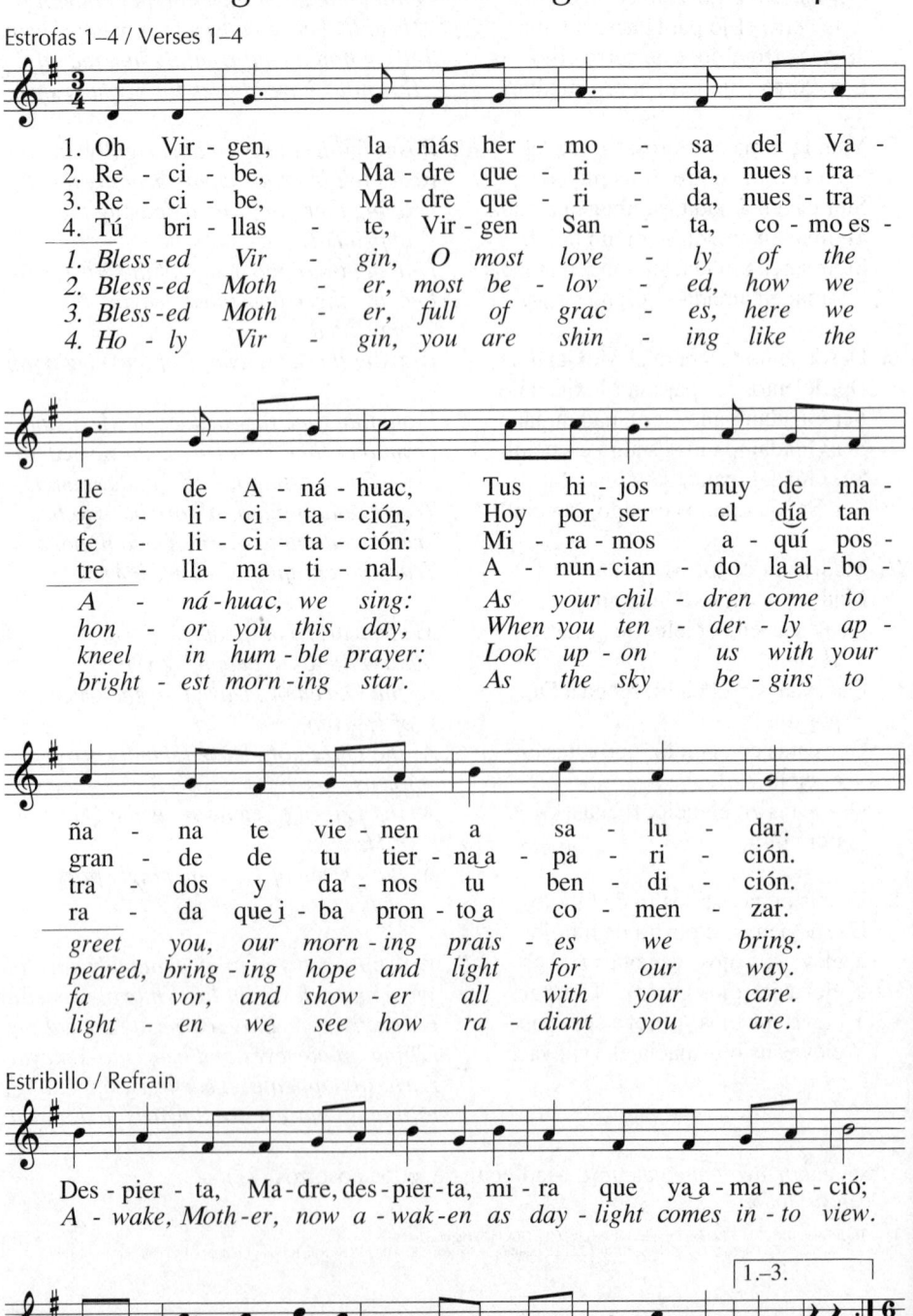

1. Oh Vir - gen, la más her - mo - sa del Va -
2. Re - ci - be, Ma - dre que - ri - da, nues - tra
3. Re - ci - be, Ma - dre que - ri - da, nues - tra
4. Tú bri - llas - te, Vir - gen San - ta, co - mo es -

1. Bless -ed Vir - gin, O most love - ly of the
2. Bless -ed Moth - er, most be - lov - ed, how we
3. Bless -ed Moth - er, full of grac - es, here we
4. Ho - ly Vir - gin, you are shin - ing like the

lle de A - ná - huac, Tus hi - jos muy de ma -
fe - li - ci - ta - ción, Hoy por ser el día tan
fe - li - ci - ta - ción: Mi - ra - mos a - quí pos -
tre - lla ma - ti - nal, A - nun - cian - do la al - bo -

A - ná -huac, we sing: As your chil - dren come to
hon - or you this day, When you ten - der - ly ap -
kneel in hum - ble prayer: Look up - on us with your
bright - est morn -ing star. As the sky be - gins to

ña - na te vie - nen a sa - lu - dar.
gran - de de tu tier - na a - pa - ri - ción.
tra - dos y da - nos tu ben - di - ción.
ra - da que i - ba pron - to a co - men - zar.

greet you, our morn - ing prais - es we bring.
peared, bring - ing hope and light for our way.
fa - vor, and show - er all with your care.
light - en we see how ra - diant you are.

Estribillo / Refrain

Des - pier - ta, Ma - dre, des - pier - ta, mi - ra que ya a - ma - ne - ció;
A - wake, Moth -er, now a - wak -en as day - light comes in - to view.

1.–3.

Mi -ra es - te ra - mo de flo - res que pa - ra ti trai - go yo.
See this bright bou -quet of flow -ers we bring to of - fer to you.

yo. / you.

Estrofa 5 / Verse 5

5. Ya vie - ne al - bo - ran - do el dí - a, qué lin-
El ce - rro del Te - pe - yac es - co-
5. *The dawn is spread - ing its col - ors to sa -*
In Te - pe - yac, on a hill - side, you have

da es - tá la ma - ña - na, Sa - lu - de-
gis - te por mo - ra - da, Por e - so
lute you, fair Ma - don - na. We, too, would
graced us, fair Ma - don - na. For choos - ing

mos a Ma - rí - a: bue - nos dí - as, Gua - da - lu - pa - na.
te sa - lu - da - mos, bue - nos dí - as, Gua - da - lu - pa - na.
of - fer our prais - es as we greet you, Gua - da - lu - pa - na.
this as your dwell - ing, we now hail you, Gua - da - lu - pa - na.

Ya vie - ne a - ma - ne - cien - do, ya la
The morn - ing light is break - ing with the

luz del dí - a nos dio; Le - ván - ta - te, Vir - gen-
daz - zling gift of the sun. Now a - rise, O dear - est

ci - ta, mi - ra que ya a - ma - ne - ció.
Vir - gin: for a new day has be - gun!

Text: Traditional; tr. by Mary Louise Bringle, b.1953, © 2012, GIA Publications, Inc.
Tune: Traditional; harm. by Ronald F. Krisman, b.1946, © 2012, GIA Publications, Inc.

996 Buenos Días, Paloma Blanca / Fairest Dove, Most Lovely Maiden

1. Bue - nos días, *Pa - lo - ma Blan - ca,
2. Ni - ña lin - da, ni - ña san - ta,
3. Qué lin - da es - tá la ma - ña - na,
4. Cie - lo a - zul yo te con - vi - do

1. Fair - est Dove, most love - ly maid - en
2. Love - ly maid - en, chaste and ho - ly,
3. O how love - ly is the morn - ing:
4. Blu - est sky, I now in - vite you,

Hoy te ven - go a sa - lu - dar,
Tu dul - ce nom - bre a - la - bar;
El a - ro - ma de las flo - res
En es - te di - cho - so dí - a

On your bright ce - les - tial throne,
I de - light to sing your fame.
Ev - 'ry flow'r from sleep a - wakes,
In these pre - cious morn - ing hours,

Sa - lu - dan - do tu be - lle - za
Por - que e - res tan sa - cro - san - ta,
Des - pi - den sua - ves o - lo - res
A que pres - tes tu her - mo - su - ra

Now re - ceive the morn - ing greet - ings
You are set a - part in splen - dor,
Send - ing forth its sweet - est fra - grance,
To in - fuse your ra - diant beau - ty

En tu tro - no ce - les - tial.
Hoy te ven - go a sa - lu - dar.
An - tes de rom - per el al - ba.
A las flo - res de Ma - rí - a.

That I bring to you a - lone.
And I praise your dear - est name.
As the qui - et day - light breaks.
In - to Ho - ly Mar - y's flow'rs.

*Paloma Blanca, literally "white dove," is a title used for the Blessed Virgin Mary in several hymns from Mexico.
*"Paloma Blanca" es un título usado para la Santísima Virgen María en varios himnos de México.

E - res Ma - dre del Crea - dor
Re - lu - cien - te co - mo_el al - ba,
Mi pe - cho con voz u - fa - na,
Ma - dre mía de Gua - da - lu - pe,
You, our great Cre - a - tor's moth - er,
You, who shine like bright - est morn - ing,
With a voice that swells with glad - ness,
Vir - gin pure of Gua - da - lu - pe,

Y_a mi co - ra - zón en - can - tas;
Pu - ra, sen - ci - lla_y sin man - cha.
Gra - cias te da, Ma - dre mí - a;
Dá - me ya tu ben - di - ción;
You en - chant my heart with love,
I can nev - er praise e - nough.
Som - ber night, my heart for - sakes.
All your bless - ings now im - part,

Gra - cias te doy con a - mor.
¡Qué gus - to re - ci - be mi al - ma!
En es - te di - cho - so dí - a
Re - ci - be_es - tas ma - ña - ni - tas
So I of - fer my thanks - giv - ing
With what joy my soul is fill - ing
I give thanks to you, my moth - er,
And re - ceive the morn - ing prais - es

Bue - nos días, Pa - lo - ma Blan - ca.
Bue - nos días, Pa - lo - ma Blan - ca.
An - tes de rom - per el al - ba.
De_un hu - mil - de co - ra - zón.
As I greet you, Fair - est Dove.
As I greet you, Fair - est Dove.
As the joy - ous morn - ing breaks.
Pour - ing from my hum - ble heart.

Text: Traditional; tr. by Mary Louise Bringle, b.1953, © 2012, GIA Publications, Inc.
Tune: Traditional; acc. by Ronald F. Krisman, b.1946, © 2012, GIA Publications, Inc.

997 For Builders Bold

1. For build - ers bold whose vi - sion pure Saw
2. As here they raised a soar - ing spire Which
3. We come, O Lord, in - her - i - tors From

more than brick or stone, Who laid in hope foun -
thrusts toward worlds a - bove, So may our prayers, like
those whose work is done. Lord, make us now con -

da - tions sure With Christ the cor - ner - stone; For
tongues of fire, Leap kin - dled by your love. And
trib - u - tors To years be - yond our own. Let

those who hon - ored your com - mands And
let your liv - ing Word de - scend As
faith's en - kin - dled flame not fail; Let

trust - ed your strong Word, Who of - fered faith - ful
seed on wait - ing hearts And, fruit - ful there, its
love's best gifts in - crease. Let hope in Christ's sure

hearts and hands, We give you thanks, O Lord.
grace ex - tend To earth's most dis - tant parts.
Word pre - vail Till earth and time shall cease.

Text: Herman G. Stuempfle, Jr., 1923–2007, © 1993, GIA Publications, Inc.
Tune: FOREST GREEN, CMD; English melody; harm. by Ralph Vaughan Williams, 1872–1958, alt.

998 How Blessed Is This Place

1. How bless - ed is this place, O Lord, Where you are
2. Here let your sa - cred fire of old De - scend to
3. Here let your wea - ry one find rest, The trou - bled
4. Here your an - gel - ic spir - its send Their sol - emn

wor - shiped and a - dored; In faith we here an al - tar
kin - dle spir - its cold; And may our prayers, when here we
heart, your com - fort blest, The guilt - y one, a sure re -
praise with ours to blend, And grant the vi - sion, in - ly

raise To your great glo - ry, God of praise.
bend, Like in - cense sweet to you as - cend.
treat, The sin - ner, par - don at your feet.
giv'n, Of this your house, the gate of heav'n.

Text: Ernest E. Ryden, 1886–1981, alt., sts. 1–3, © *Lutheran Church in America*; st. 4, © 1958, *Service Book and Hymnal*
Tune: O WALY WALY, LM; English; harm. by Martin West, b.1929, © 1983, Hope Publishing Company

Among All 999

Refrain

A-mong all, you are blessed, and full of grace and ho-

li-ness. A-mong all, you said yes to do God's will

with o - pen-ness. O La-dy, full of grace, Mar-y,

Moth-er of God, be with us, pray for us.

Verses

1. You teach us to o - bey the liv - ing word of God. You show us
2. You teach us how to serve God's king-dom here on earth. You bring to
3. You teach us how to pray with hum - ble-ness of heart. You guide us

D.C.

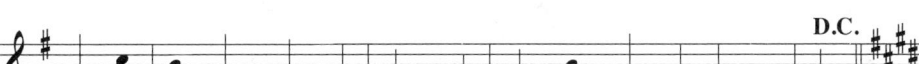

how to lis-ten to his voice that calls us each by name.
birth a wil-ling-ness to share our lives with joy and love.
to be in-stru-ments of peace and hope for all the world.

Text: Chris de Silva, b.1967
Tune: Chris de Silva, b.1967
© 2007, GIA Publications, Inc.

1000 Salve Regina / Hail, Queen of Heaven

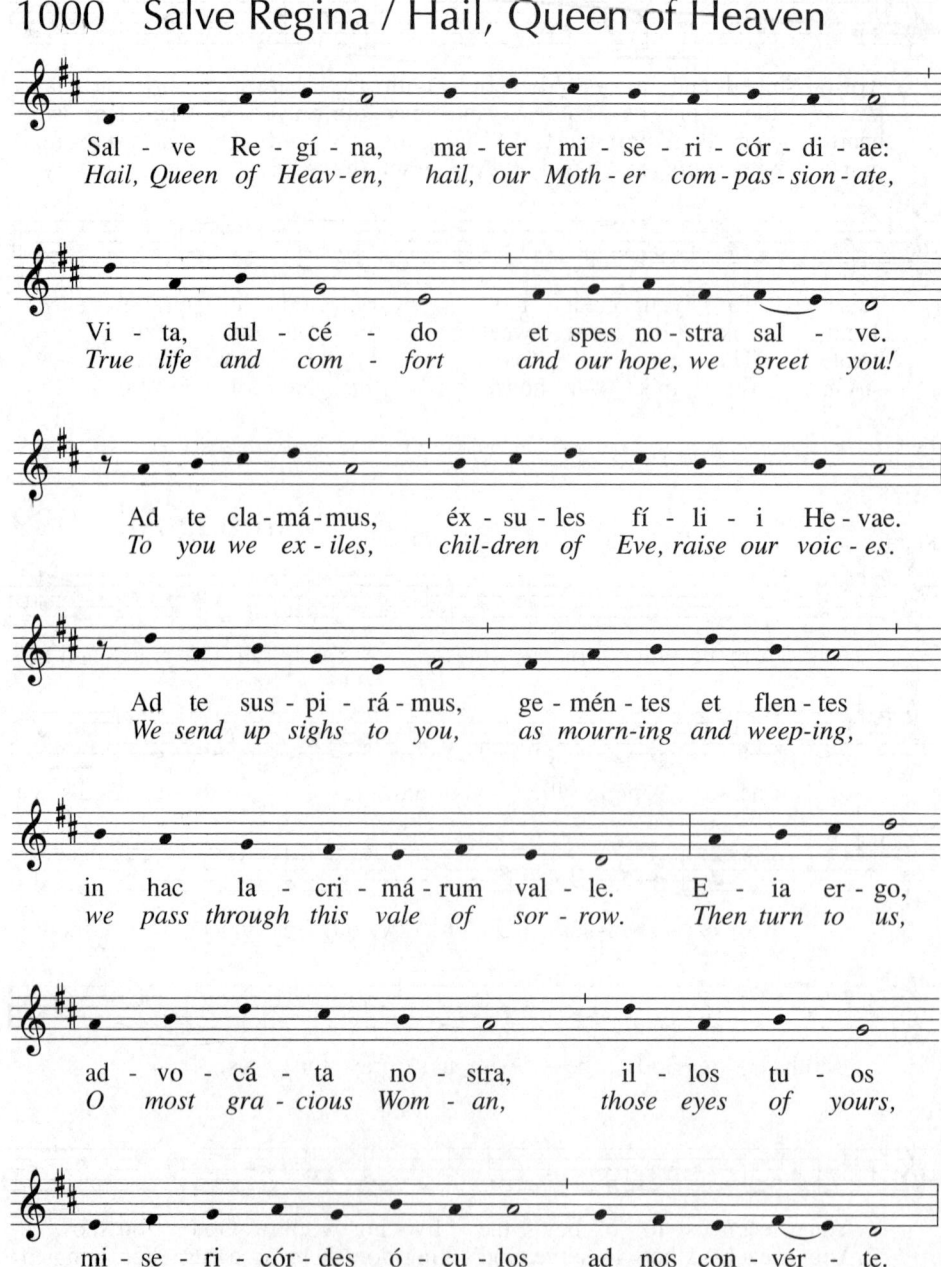

Sal - ve Re - gí - na, ma - ter mi - se - ri - cór - di - ae:
Hail, Queen of Heav - en, hail, our Moth - er com - pas - sion - ate,

Vi - ta, dul - cé - do et spes no - stra sal - ve.
True life and com - fort and our hope, we greet you!

Ad te cla - má - mus, éx - su - les fí - li - i He - vae.
To you we ex - iles, chil - dren of Eve, raise our voic - es.

Ad te sus - pi - rá - mus, ge - mén - tes et flen - tes
We send up sighs to you, as mourn - ing and weep - ing,

in hac la - cri - má - rum val - le. E - ia er - go,
we pass through this vale of sor - row. Then turn to us,

ad - vo - cá - ta no - stra, il - los tu - os
O most gra - cious Wom - an, those eyes of yours,

mi - se - ri - cór - des ó - cu - los ad nos con - vér - te.
so full of love and ten - der - ness, so full of pit - y.

Et Je - sum, be - ne - dí - ctum fru - ctum ven - tris tu - i,
And grant us af - ter these, our days of lone - ly ex - ile,

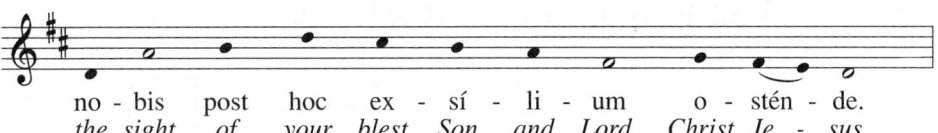

no - bis post hoc ex - sí - li - um o - stén - de.
the sight of your blest Son and Lord, Christ Je - sus.

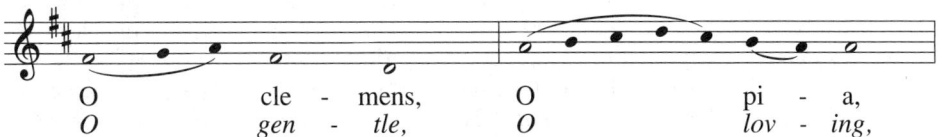

O cle - mens, O pi - a,
O gen - tle, O lov - ing,

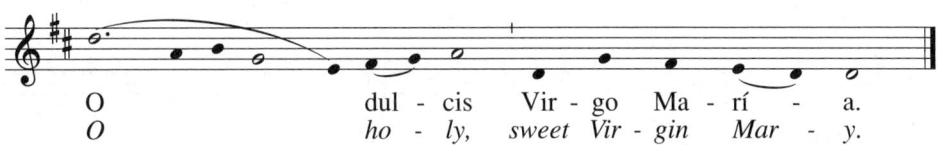

O dul - cis Vir - go Ma - rí - a.
O ho - ly, sweet Vir - gin Mar - y.

Text: *Salve Regina, mater misericordiae,* c.1080, tr. by John C. Selner, SS, 1904–1992, © 1954, GIA Publications, Inc.
Tune: SALVE REGINA, Irregular; Mode V; acc. by Gerard Farrell, OSB, 1919–2000, alt., © 1986, GIA Publications, Inc.

Ave Maria 1001

A - ve Ma - rí - a, grá - ti - a ple - na,

Dó - mi - nus te - cum, be - ne - dí - cta tu in mu - li - é -

ri - bus, et be - ne - dí - ctus fru - ctus ven - tris tu - i, Je - sus.

San - cta Ma - rí - a, Ma - ter De - i, o - ra pro no - bis pec - ca -

tó - ri - bus, nunc et in ho - ra mor - tis no - strae. A - men.

Text: *Hail, Mary, full of grace,* Luke 1:29; Latin, 13th C.
Tune: AVE MARIA, Irregular; Mode I; acc. by Robert LeBlanc, b.1948, © 1986, GIA Publications, Inc.

1002 O Sanctissima / O Most Holy One

1. O san - ctís - si - ma, O pi - ís - si - ma,
2. Tu so - lá - ti - um Et re - fú - gi - um,
3. Ec - ce dé - bi - les, Per quam flé - bi - les,
4. Vir - go ré - spi - ce, Ma - ter, á - spi - ce,

1. O most ho - ly one, O most low - ly one,
2. Com - fort in our tears, Ref - uge in our fears,
3. See us pow - er - less. In our hope - less - ness
4. Maid - en, look on us, Moth - er, care for us.

Dul - cis vir - go Ma - rí - a!
Vir - go ma - ter Ma - rí - a!
Sal - va nos, O Ma - rí - a!
Au - di nos, O Ma - rí - a!

Praise to you, vir - gin Mar - y!
Vir - gin moth - er, sweet Mar - y!
Save us! Aid us, O Mar - y!
Hear our plead - ing, O Mar - y!

Ma - ter a - má - ta, In - te - me - rá - ta,
Quid - quid o - ptá - mus, Per te spe - rá - mus,
Tol - le lan - guó - res, Sa - na do - ló - res,
Tu me - di - cí - nam, Por - tas di - ví - nam;

Kind, lov - ing Moth - er, Graced like no oth - er,
What - e'er our souls need Grant us, as we plead:
Come, take our sad - ness; Fill us with glad - ness.
You bring us heal - ing, God's love re - veal - ing.

O - ra, o - ra pro no - bis.
O - ra, o - ra pro no - bis.
O - ra, o - ra pro no - bis.
O - ra, o - ra pro no - bis.

Pray, O pray for us, Mar - y!
Pray, O pray for us, Mar - y!
Pray, O pray for us, Mar - y!
Pray, O pray for us, Mar - y!

Text: St. 1, *Stimmen der Völker in Liedern*, 1807; st. 2, *Arundel Hymnal*, 1902; tr. Neil Borgstrom, b.1953, © 1994, 2011, GIA Publications, Inc.
Tune: O DU FRÖLICHE, 55 7 55 7; Tattersall's *Improved Psalmody*, 1794

Sing We of the Blessed Mother 1003

1. Sing we of the Bless-ed Moth-er, Who re-ceived the
2. Sing we, too, of Mar-y's sor-rows, Of the sword that
3. Sing a-gain the joys of Mar-y When she saw the
4. Sing the great-est joy of Mar-y When on earth her

an - gel's word And, o-be-dient to the sum-mons,
pierced her through, When be-neath the cross of Je - sus
ris - en Lord, And in prayer with Christ's a - pos - tles
work was done, And the Lord of all cre - a - tion

Bore in love the in-fant Lord. Sing we of the
She his weight of suf-f'ring knew, Looked up-on her
Wait - ed on his prom-ised word. From on high the
Brought her to his heav'n-ly home. Vir - gin Moth-er,

joys of Mar - y, At whose breast that child was fed,
Son and Sav - ior Reign-ing from the aw - ful tree,
blaz - ing glo - ry Of the Spir - it's pres - ence came:
Mar - y bless-ed, Raised on high and crowned with grace,

Who is Son of God e - ter - nal
Saw the price of our re - demp - tion
Heav'n - ly breath of God's own be - ing
May your Son, the world's re - deem - er,

And the ev - er - last - ing Bread.
Paid to set the sin - ner free.
To - kened in the wind and flame.
Grant us all to see his face.

Text: George B. Timms, 1910–1997, alt., © 1975, Oxford University Press
Tune: ALLE TAGE SING UND SAGE, 8 7 8 7 D; Trier *Gesangbuch*, 1695

1004 Mary, First among Believers

1. Mar - y, first a - mong be - liev - ers, Trust - ing in the
*2. Mar - y, first a - mong the ex - iles, Seek - ing ref - uge
3. Mar - y, first a - mong dis - ci - ples, Lis - t'ning, learn - ing
*4. Mar - y, first a - mong the suf - f'ring, Stand - ing bowed be -
5. Mar - y, first a - mong the bless - ed, Robed in heav - en's

an - gel's word, You con - sent - ed and, con - ceiv - ing,
in the night, You left home with spouse and In - fant,
from your Son, You held dear his words and ac - tions,
neath the cross, You knew all the pain and an - guish
beau - ty bright, You re - joice with saints and an - gels

Brought to birth the Son of God. Moth - er now of
Flee - ing Her - od's sword in fright. Moth - er now of
Pon - d'ring each, for - get - ting none. Moth - er now of
Of op - pres - sion, grief, and loss. Moth - er now of
In your Son's re - splen - dent light. Moth - er now of

all be - liev - ers, Give our frag - ile faith in - crease;
all the ex - iles, Give them sleep with - out a - larm;
all dis - ci - ples, Help us lis - ten day by day;
all the suf - f'ring, May we show Com - pas - sion's face;
all the bless - ed, Make your pil - grim peo - ple strong;

May we, trust - ing in God's prom - ise,
Give them cloth - ing, food, and shel - ter;
O - pen to the Spir - it's prompt - ing,
May the vic - tims of in - jus - tice
Keep us faith - ful till we join you,

*Stanzas 2 and 4 may be omitted.

Doubts   and   use - less   fears   re - lease.
Keep   them   safe   and   free   from   harm.
Help   us   fol - low   Je - sus' way.
Know,   through us,   God's   love   and   grace.
Prais - ing God   in   end - less   song.

Text: Delores Dufner, OSB, b.1939, © 2011, GIA Publications, Inc.
Tune: PLEADING SAVIOR, 8 7 8 7 D; *Christian Lyre*, 1830; harm. by Richard Proulx, 1937–2010, © 1986, GIA Publications, Inc.

All Who Claim the Faith of Jesus   1005

1. All   who   claim   the   faith of   Je - sus   Sing the
2. Bless - ed were   the   cho - sen peo - ple   Out of
3. There - fore let   all   faith - ful peo - ple   Sing the
4. "Mag - ni - fy, my   soul, God's great - ness;   In my

won - ders that were done   When the   love   of   God the   Fa - ther
whom the   Lord did come;   Bless - ed was   the land of   prom - ise
hon - or   of   her name;   Let   the   Church, in her fore - shad-owed,
Sav - ior   I   re - joice;   All   the   a - ges call me   bless - ed,

O'er our   sins   the   vic - t'ry   won,   When God   made   the
Fash-ioned for   his   earth - ly   home; But more   bless - ed
Part in   her thanks-giv - ing   claim; What Christ's moth - er
In   his   praise I   lift   my   voice; God has   cast   down

Vir - gin   Mar - y   Moth - er   of   the   on - ly   Son.
far   the   moth - er,   She   who bore him   in her womb.
sang in   glad - ness Let Christ's peo - ple sing the   same:
all   the   might - y,   And   the   low - ly are his choice."

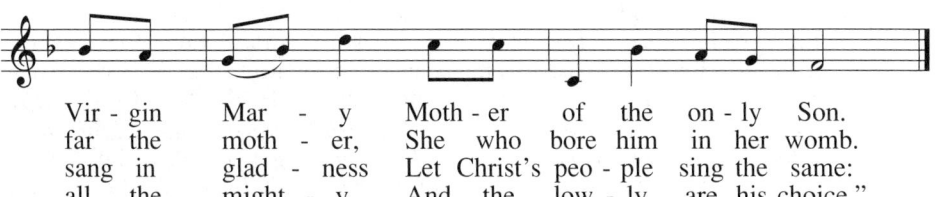

Text: Sts. 1–3, Vincent Stuckey Stratton Coles, 1845–1929, alt.; st. 4, F. Bland Tucker, 1895–1984
Tune: TILLFLYKT, 8 7 8 7 8 7; *Sionstoner*, 1889; harm. by Marty Haugen, b.1950, © 1987, GIA Publications, Inc.

1006 Como Estrella en Claro Cielo / As a Star on Cloudless Evenings

1. Co - mo_es - tre - lla_en   cla - ro
2. Fue   un   án - gel   quien   le
3. De   la   pa - ja   al   ma -
4. Glo - ria_al   Pa - dre   y   al

1. *As   a   star   on   cloud -less*
2. *When the   an - gel   spoke to*
3. *From the   sta - ble   to   the*
4. *To   the   Fa - ther,   Son, and*

cie - lo   De   ful - gen - te   res - plan - dor,   Es - co -
die - ra   Be - llas   nue - vas   de   sa - lud,   Y_a   me -
de - ro   Fue_a   su   hi - jo   siem - pre   fiel   Y_en - tre
Hi - jo,   Y_al   Es - pí - ri - tu_en   ver - dad,   Co - mo

eve - nings Will   with   great - er   bril - liance   shine,   So   re -
Mar - y,   His   good news brought great   de - light: He fore -
hill - side   Mar - y's   faith   would   nev - er   dim: In   her
Spir - it,   Glo - ry,   hon - or,   thanks, and   praise,   As   it

gi - da   fue   Ma - rí - a   Por   de - sig - nio   del   Se -
dia - dos   de_u - na   no - che   Dios   al   mun - do_en - vió   la
lá - gri - mas   y   ri - sas   Con - sa - gró   su   vi - da_a
e - ra   al   prin - ci - pio,   Es   a - ho - ra   y   se -

splen -dent   was   the   maid - en   Cho - sen   for   the   Lord's de -
told   the Light's ap - pear - ance When but   half - spent was   the
tears   and   in   her laugh - ter   She   had pledged her   life   to
was   in   the   be - gin - ning   And   shall   be   for   end - less

ñor.   Es   cual   ro - sa   que   flo - re - ce   En - tre
luz.   Es   su   fru - to   en - gen - dra - do,   Del   Crea -
él.   Hoy ce - le - bro   su_a - le - grí - a,   Hoy   ce -
rá.   Mi_a - la - ban - za_a   Dios se_e - le - va   Co - mo_in -

sign: Fair -est   rose   in   all earth's gar - den,   Bloom -ing
night.   It   was God's   on - ly - be - got - ten,   The   Cre -
Him.   As   we   cel - e - brate her   glad - ness,   We   re -
days.   Let   our prayers   rise   up   like   in - cense   To   the

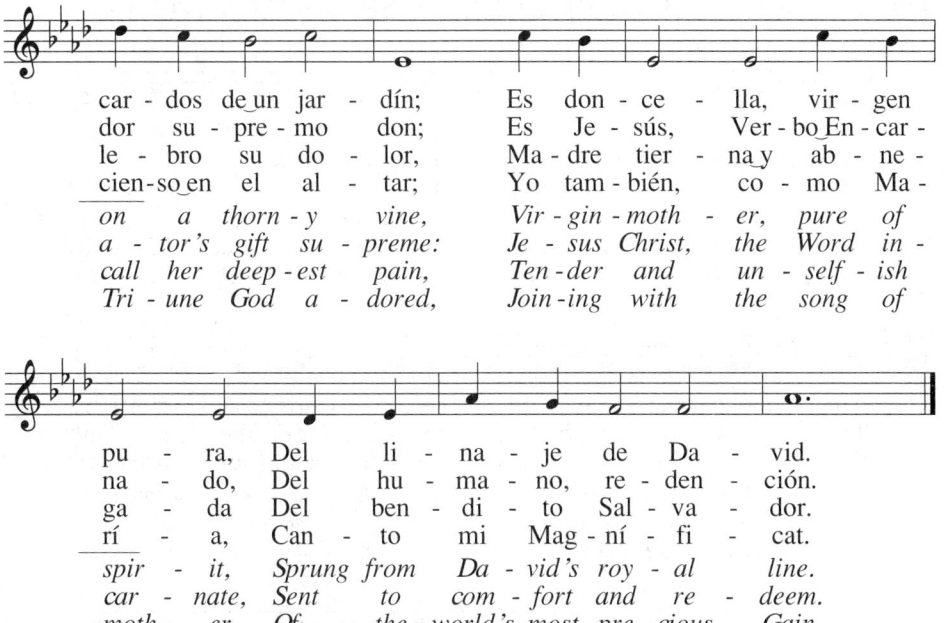

car - dos de un jar - dín; Es don - ce - lla, vir - gen
dor su - pre - mo don; Es Je - sús, Ver - bo En - car -
le - bro su do - lor, Ma - dre tier - na y ab - ne -
cien - so en el al - tar; Yo tam - bién, co - mo Ma -
on a thorn - y vine, Vir - gin - moth - er, pure of
a - tor's gift su - preme: Je - sus Christ, the Word in -
call her deep - est pain, Ten - der and un - self - ish
Tri - une God a - dored, Join - ing with the song of

pu - ra, Del li - na - je de Da - vid.
na - do, Del hu - ma - no, re - den - ción.
ga - da Del ben - di - to Sal - va - dor.
rí - a, Can - to mi Mag - ní - fi - cat.
spir - it, Sprung from Da - vid's roy - al line.
car - nate, Sent to com - fort and re - deem.
moth - er Of the world's most pre - cious Gain.
Mar - y As we mag - ni - fy the Lord.

Text: Skinner Chávez-Melo, 1944–1992, © 1987, Estate of Skinner Chávez-Melo; tr. by Ronald F. Krisman, b.1946, © 2005, GIA Publications, Inc.
Tune: RAQUEL, 8 7 8 7 D; Skinner Chávez-Melo, 1944–1992, © 1987, Estate of Skinner Chávez-Melo

1007 Stainless the Maiden / Serdeczna Matko

1. Stain - less the Maid - en whom he chose for moth - er;
2. Lan - tern in dark - ness, when the sick are sigh - ing,
3. Je - sus has con - quered; to his side he raised her;
1. Ser - de-czna Ma - tko, O - pie - kun - ko lu - dzi,
2. Do ko - góż ma - my, wzdy - chać nę - dzne dzia - tki?
3. Za - słu - ży - li - śmy, to praw - da, przez zło - ści,

Nine months she wait - ed, bear - ing Christ, our broth - er;
Thresh - old of bright - ness, com - fort for the dy - ing,
Queen of the an - gels, ev - 'ry saint has praised her.
Niech Cię płacz sie - rot do li - to - ści wzbu - dzi!
Tyl - ko do Cie - bie, u - ko - cha - nej Ma - tki:
By nas Bóg ka - rał ró - zgą su - ro - wo - ści

Think of her glad - ness when at last she saw him:
High she is hold - ing for a world a - dor - ing,
Yet, in her splen - dor, Mar - y goes on draw - ing
Wy - gnań - cy E - wy, do Cie - bie wo - ła - my:
U któ - rej Ser - ce o - twar - te ka - żde - mu,
Lecz kie - dy Oj - ciec ro - zgnie-wa - ny sie - cze,

Repeat ad lib.

God in a man - ger, Beth - le - hem a heav - en!
Hope of the na - tions, Je - sus Christ, our broth - er.
Sin - ners and ex - iles to their prom - ised glo - ry.
Zli - tuj się, zli - tuj, niech się nie tu - ła - my!
A o - so - bli - wie nę - dzą stra - pio - ne - mu!
Szczę - śli - wy kto się do Ma - tki u - cie - cze.

Text: Polish traditional; English paraphrase by Rev. Willard F. Jabusch, b.1930, © 1976, Rev. Willard F. Jabusch. Published by OCP.
Tune: SERDECZNA MATKO, 11 11 D; Polish traditional; adapt. by Kelly Dobbs-Mickus, b.1966, from an arr. by Richard Proulx, 1937–2010,
© 2011, GIA Publications, Inc.

I Sing a Maid 1008

1. I sing a maid of ten - der years To
2. She watched him grow to man - hood's strength To
3. And if the song had end - ed then, Our

whom an an - gel came, And knelt, as to a
meet his des - ti - ny. And when the dan - ger
eyes would fill with tears, But ah! the song had

might - y queen, And bowed bright wings of
of his truth Brought him to Cal - va -
just be - gun To ech - o down the

flame: A na - tion's hope in her re - ply, This
ry, She stood by him all pow - er - less To
years! Now lift your voic - es, hearts and souls, To

maid of match - less grace; For God's own son be -
ease his dy - ing pain, 'Til in the dark - est
sing with one ac - cord To hon - or Mar - y,

came her child, And she his rest - ing place.
hour of all, She held her son a - gain.
Moth - er of The Christ, the Ris - en Lord!

Text: M. D. Ridge, b.1938, © 1987, GIA Publications, Inc.
Tune: THE FLIGHT OF THE EARLS, CMD; traditional Celtic melody; harm. by Michael Joncas, b.1951, © 1987, GIA Publications, Inc.

1009 Ave Maria

Verses

1. Hail Mar - y full of grace, the
2. Ho - ly Mar - y moth-er of God, the

Lord is with you.
Lord is with you.

Bless - ed are you a - mong all wom-en,
Pray for us sin - ners, pray for us sin - ners,

Blest is the fruit of your womb.
Now and at the hour of our death.

Refrain

Je - sus, formed in your faith, A - ve Ma - rí - a al - le -

lu - ia. Je - sus, born in your love,

A - ve Ma - rí - a al - le - lu - ia.

Text: Hail Mary; additional text by Dan Kantor, b.1960
Tune: Dan Kantor, b.1960; arr. by Rob Glover, b.1950
© 1993, GIA Publications, Inc.

We Sing with Holy Mary   1010

1. O God, your Church is sing - ing in praise to you, Most
2. We sing with ho - ly Mar - y in spir - it, heart, and

High. Our thank - ful bless-ings ring - ing; you, Lord, we mag - ni -
voice. Your Word in - car - nate bear - ing, in you our souls re -

fy. The whole cre - a - tion gath - ers with Mar - y full of
joice! You chose her for your moth - er and named her "fa-vored

grace, With proph - ets, saints, and mar - tyrs who
one" For Christ, our Lord and broth - er, your

see you face to face. She crowns their song un -
own be - lov - ed Son. Grace us to live her

dy - ing a - round the Lamb en - throned, The
sto - ry: to serve you as we ought; To

Bride and Spir - it cry - ing: "Lord Je - sus, quick - ly come!"
sing, in end - less glo - ry, our own Ma - gni - fi - cat!

Text: Alan J. Hommerding, b.1956, © 2007, World Library Publications
Tune: THAXTED, 13 13 13 13 13 13; Gustav Holst, 1874–1934

1011 Litany of Mary /
Letanía de la Santísima Virgen María

Cantor:

1. Holy Mary, *Response 1*
   Mother of God, *Response 1*
   Mother of the Church, *Response 2*

Cantor:

1. *Santa María,* Response 1
   Madre de Dios, Response 1
   Madre de la Iglesia, Response 2

Cantor:

2. Mother of good counsel, *Response 1*
   Mother most pure, *Response 1*
   Mirror of justice, *Response 2*

3. Refuge of sinners, *Response 1*
   Morning star, *Response 1*
   Mary, Queen of peace, *Response 2*

4. Gate of heaven, *Response 1*
   Queen of angels, *Response 1*
   Health of the sick, *Response 2*

Cantor:

2. *Madre del buen consejo,* Response 1
   Madre purísima, Response 1
   Espejo de justicia, Response 2

3. *Refugio de los pecadores,* Response 1
   Estrella de la mañana, Response 1
   Reina de la paz, Response 2

4. *Puerta del cielo,* Response 1
   Reina de los ángeles, Response 1
   Salud de los enfermos, Response 2

Text: Based on the Litany of Loretto; Tony E. Alonso, b.1980
Tune: Refrain based on LOURDES HYMN; Tony E. Alonso, b.1980
© 2008, GIA Publications, Inc.

1012 Come and Be Sealed

Ostinato Refrain

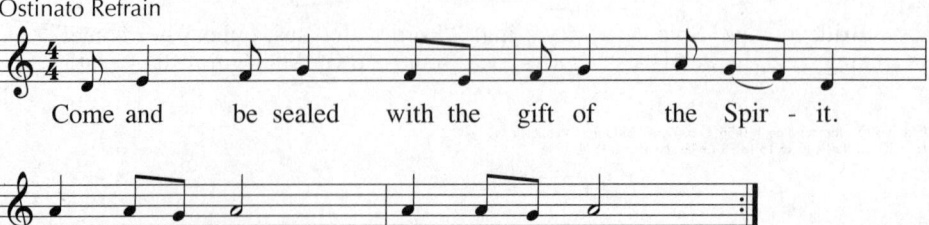

Text: Tony E. Alonso, b.1980
Tune: Tony E. Alonso, b.1980
© 2007, GIA Publications, Inc.

Blessed Be God, Who Chose You in Christ 1013

Refrain

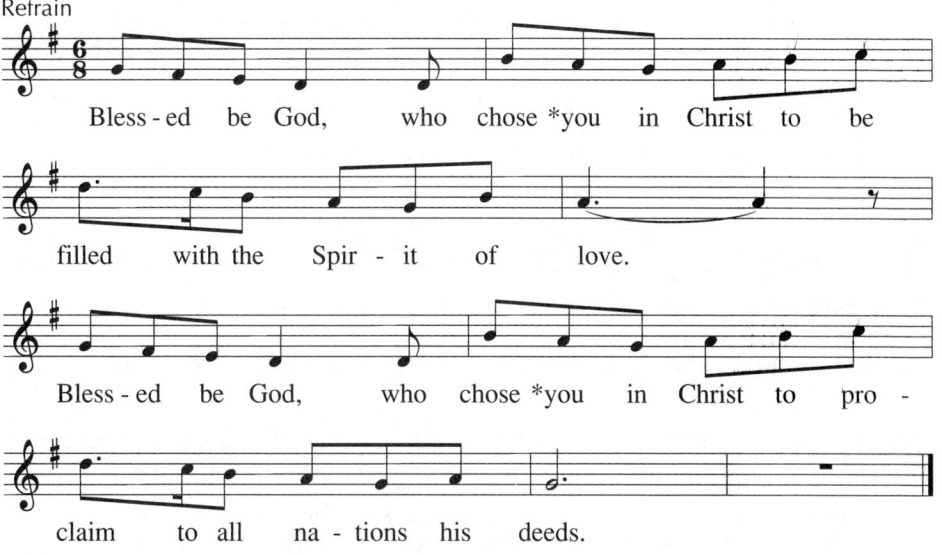

Bless - ed be God, who chose *you in Christ to be filled with the Spir - it of love. Bless - ed be God, who chose *you in Christ to pro - claim to all na - tions his deeds.

Verses

1. We come to you, Lord Jesus.
   You have called us to new life,
   as children of the Father, and one in you.

The cantor concludes each verse:
Send forth your Holy Spirit, renew the face of the earth.

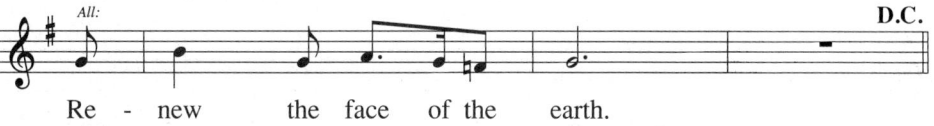

Re - new the face of the earth.

2. From all who have been baptized in water and the Holy Spirit,
   you have formed one people,
   united in your Son, Jesus Christ.
   Send forth...

3. Come and set us free, and fill our hearts
   with the Spirit of your love,
   that we may live in your peace.
   Send forth...

4. You call those who have been baptized
   to announce the Good News of Jesus Christ
   to people ev'rywhere.
   Send forth...

Or: us

Text: Adapted from the *Rite of Baptism*, James J. Chepponis, b.1956
Tune: James J. Chepponis, b.1956
© 1982, GIA Publications, Inc.

1014 Wash, O God, Our Sons and Daughters

1. Wash, O God, our sons and daugh - ters, Where your
2. We who bring them long for nur - ture; By your
3. O how deep your ho - ly wis - dom! Un - i -

cleans - ing wa - ters flow. Num - ber them a - mong your
milk may we be fed. Let us join your feast, par -
mag - ined, all your ways! To your name be glo - ry,

peo - ple; Bless as Christ blessed long a - go.
tak - ing Cup of bless - ing, liv - ing bread.
hon - or! With our lives we wor - ship, praise!

Weave them gar - ments bright and spar - kling; Com - pass
God, re - new us, guide our foot - steps; Free from
We your peo - ple stand be - fore you, Wa - ter -

them with love and light. Fill, a - noint them;
sin and all its snares, One with Christ in
washed and Spir - it - born. By your grace, our

send your Spir - it, Ho - ly dove and heart's de - light.
liv - ing, dy - ing, By your Spir - it, chil - dren, heirs.
lives we of - fer. Re - cre - ate us; God, trans - form!

Text: Ruth Duck, b.1947, © 1989, The United Methodist Publishing House, admin. Music Services
Tune: BEACH SPRING, 8 7 8 7 D, *The Sacred Harp*; harm. by Ronald A. Nelson, 1927–2014, © 1978, *Lutheran Book of Worship*,
   admin. by Augsburg Fortress

Alternate tune: HYMN TO JOY

We Have Put on Christ   1015

Refrain (or Canon)

*We have put on Christ, in him *we have been bap-tized.

Al - le - lu - ia, al - le - lu - ia.

Verses

Cantor:

1. Springs of wa - ter, bless the Lord! Now through Christ is
2. Now through Christ is life re - stored! Praise the faith - ful,
3. Springs and foun - tains, shout for joy! All your tal - ents
4. Praise the Fount of life and grace: God of ev - 'ry
5. Streams and show - ers, find your voice! Brooks and tor - rents,
6. Tell of all that God has done: Now in Christ our
7. Might - y riv - ers, swift and broad, Chant the won - ders
8. Now the Lamb who once was slain God has raised to

All:

life re - stored!
liv - ing Lord!
now em - ploy!
time and space!   Sing out your praise to God!
all re - joice!
vic - t'ry won!
of our God!
life a - gain!

D.C.

Al - le - lu - ia!

*Or: You

Text: Refrain, ICEL, © 1969; verses by Marty Haugen, b.1950, © 1997, GIA Publications, Inc.
Tune: Refrain, Howard Hughes, SM, b.1930, © 1977, ICEL; verses and arr. by David Sanders, © 2012, GIA Publications, Inc.

1016 Covenant Hymn

1. Wher - ev - er you go, I will fol - low, Wher-
2. What - ev - er you dream, I am with you, When
3. And though you should fall, you will find me, When
4. Wher - ev - er you die, I will be there To
5. Wher - ev - er you go, I will fol - low, Be -

ev - er you live is my home. Though
stars call your name in the night. Though
no oth - er friend can you claim, When
sing you to sleep with a psalm, To
hold! The ho - ri - zon shines clear. The

days be of bless - ing or sor - row, Though
shad - ows and mist cloud the fu - ture, To -
foes beat you down or be - tray you And
soothe you with tales of our jour - ney, Your
pos - si - ble gleams like a cit - y: To -

house be of can - vas or stone, Though
geth - er we bear there a light. Like
oth - ers de - sert you in shame. When
fears and your doubts I will calm. We'll
geth - er we've noth - ing to fear. So

E - den be lost to the past, Though
A - bram and Sar - ah we stand, With
home and dreams aren't e - nough, And
live when jour - neys are done For -
speak with words bold and true The

moun - tains be - fore us be vast, Wher -
on - ly a prom - ise in hand. But
you run a - way from my love, I'll
ev - er in mem - 'ry as one. And
mes - sage my heart speaks to you. You

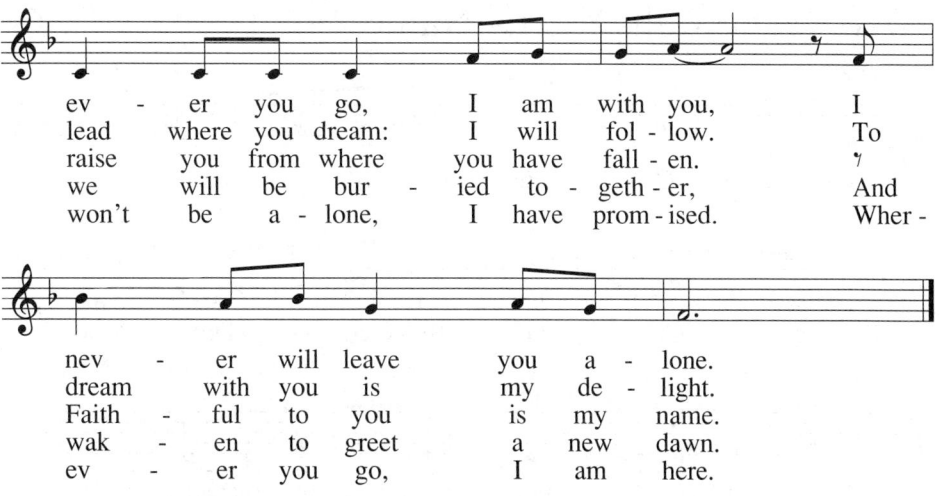

ev - er you go, I am with you, I
lead where you dream: I will fol - low. To
raise you from where you have fall - en.
we will be bur - ied to - geth - er, And
won't be a - lone, I have prom - ised. Wher -

nev - er will leave you a - lone.
dream with you is my de - light.
Faith - ful to you is my name.
wak - en to greet a new dawn.
ev - er you go, I am here.

Text: Ruth 1:16; Rory Cooney, b.1952
Tune: Gary Daigle, b.1957
© 1993, GIA Publications, Inc.

Down to the River to Pray   1017

As I went down to the riv - er to pray,

stud-y-ing a-bout that good old way. And who shall wear the

star - ry crown, good Lord, show me the way.

Oh, *broth-er, let's go down, come on down, don't you

want to go down? Oh, broth - er, let's go down,

down to the riv - er to pray.

*Sister, father, mother.

Text: American folk song
Tune: American folk song; arr. by Robert J. Batastini, b.1942, © 2003, GIA Publications, Inc.

1018 Who Calls You by Name

Refrain

Cantor:
Bless-ed be God! O Bless-ed be God!

All:
Bless-ed be God! O Bless-ed be God! Who

calls you by name! Who calls you by name!

Cantor:
Ho - ly and cho - sen one!

All:
Ho - ly and cho - sen one!

Verses

1. Come, and re - turn to the Lord!
2. Seek to be chil - dren of light!
3. Sing now with all your heart!

Live by the Word of God, who
Live in the love of God, who
Praise and glo - ry be to our God, who

D.C.

calls you by name! Who calls you by name!
calls you by name! Who calls you by name!
calls you by name! Who calls you by name!

Text: David Haas, b.1957
Tune: David Haas, b.1957

We Know That Christ Is Raised 1019

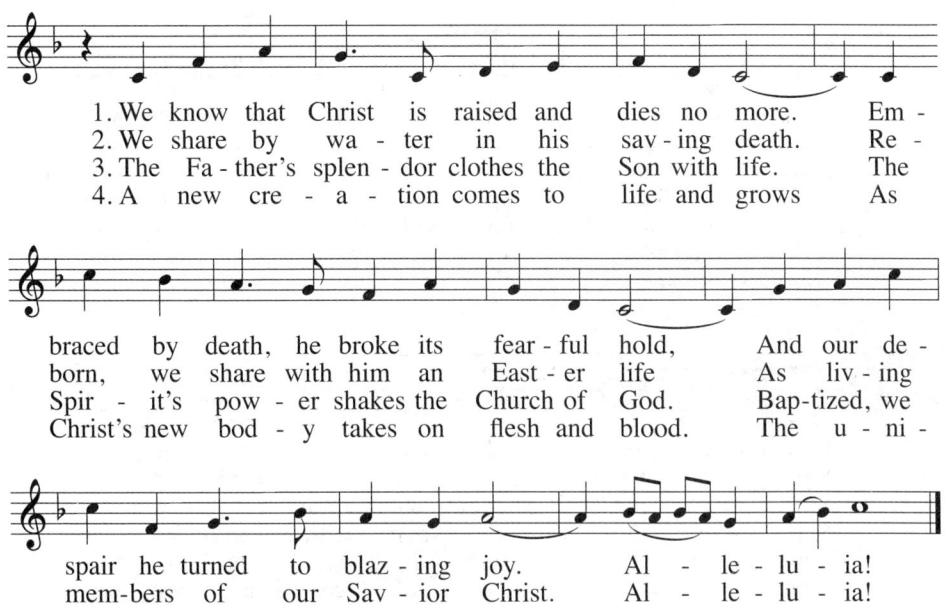

1. We know that Christ is raised and dies no more. Em-
2. We share by wa-ter in his sav-ing death. Re-
3. The Fa-ther's splen-dor clothes the Son with life. The
4. A new cre-a-tion comes to life and grows As

braced by death, he broke its fear-ful hold, And our de-
born, we share with him an East-er life As liv-ing
Spir-it's pow-er shakes the Church of God. Bap-tized, we
Christ's new bod-y takes on flesh and blood. The u-ni-

spair he turned to blaz-ing joy. Al - le-lu - ia!
mem-bers of our Sav-ior Christ. Al - le-lu - ia!
live with God the Three in One. Al - le-lu - ia!
verse re-stored and whole will sing: Al - le-lu - ia!

Text: Romans 6:4, 9; John B. Geyer, b.1932, © 1972, John B. Geyer
Tune: ENGELBERG, 10 10 10 with alleluia; Charles V. Stanford, 1852–1924

Baptized in Water 1020

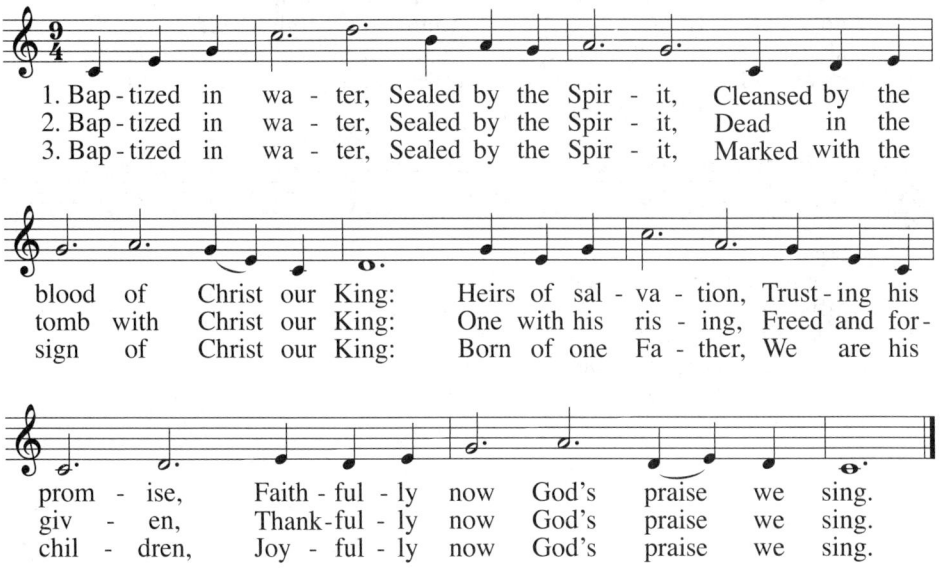

1. Bap-tized in wa-ter, Sealed by the Spir-it, Cleansed by the
2. Bap-tized in wa-ter, Sealed by the Spir-it, Dead in the
3. Bap-tized in wa-ter, Sealed by the Spir-it, Marked with the

blood of Christ our King: Heirs of sal-va-tion, Trust-ing his
tomb with Christ our King: One with his ris-ing, Freed and for-
sign of Christ our King: Born of one Fa-ther, We are his

prom-ise, Faith-ful-ly now God's praise we sing.
giv-en, Thank-ful-ly now God's praise we sing.
chil-dren, Joy-ful-ly now God's praise we sing.

Text: Michael Saward, b.1932, © 1982, The Jubilate Group (admin. by Hope Publishing Company)
Tune: BUNESSAN, 5 5 8 D; Gaelic melody; acc. by A. Gregory Murray, OSB, 1905–1992, © Downside Abbey

1021 Easter Vigil Initiation Acclamations

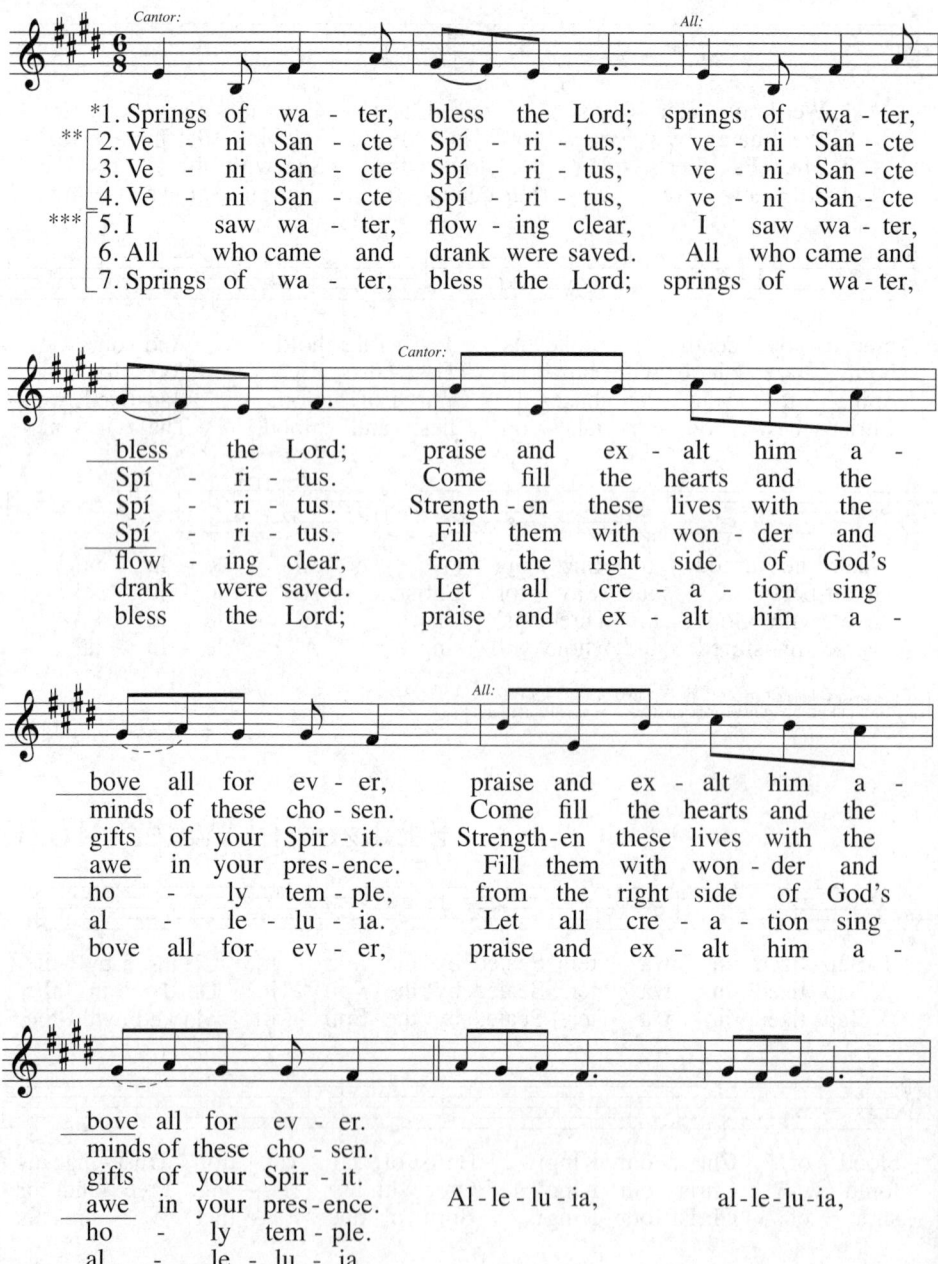

*1. Springs of wa - ter, bless the Lord; springs of wa - ter,
** ⌈2. Ve - ni San - cte Spí - ri - tus, ve - ni San - cte
   │3. Ve - ni San - cte Spí - ri - tus, ve - ni San - cte
   ⌊4. Ve - ni San - cte Spí - ri - tus, ve - ni San - cte
*** ⌈5. I saw wa - ter, flow - ing clear, I saw wa - ter,
   │6. All who came and drank were saved. All who came and
   ⌊7. Springs of wa - ter, bless the Lord; springs of wa - ter,

_ bless the Lord; praise and ex - alt him a -
 Spí - ri - tus. Come fill the hearts and the
 Spí - ri - tus. Strength - en these lives with the
 Spí - ri - tus. Fill them with won - der and
 flow - ing clear, from the right side of God's
 drank were saved. Let all cre - a - tion sing
 bless the Lord; praise and ex - alt him a -

_ bove all for ev - er, praise and ex - alt him a -
 minds of these cho - sen. Come fill the hearts and the
 gifts of your Spir - it. Strength-en these lives with the
 awe in your pres-ence. Fill them with won - der and
 ho - ly tem - ple, from the right side of God's
 al - le - lu - ia. Let all cre - a - tion sing
 bove all for ev - er, praise and ex - alt him a -

_ bove all for ev - er.
 minds of these cho - sen.
 gifts of your Spir - it.
 awe in your pres-ence. Al - le - lu - ia, al - le - lu - ia,
 ho - ly tem - ple.
 al - le - lu - ia.
 bove all for ev - er.

*Blessing of water
**During the anointing
***Rite of Sprinkling

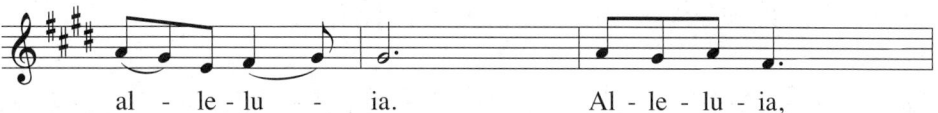

al - le - lu - ia.   Al - le - lu - ia,

al - le - lu - ia,   al - le - lu - ia.

Text: Verses 1, 7, ICEL, © 2010; verses 2–6, Tony E. Alonso, b.1980, © 2012, World Library Publications
Tune: Tony E. Alonso, b.1980, © 2012, World Library Publications

Wade in the Water 1022

Refrain

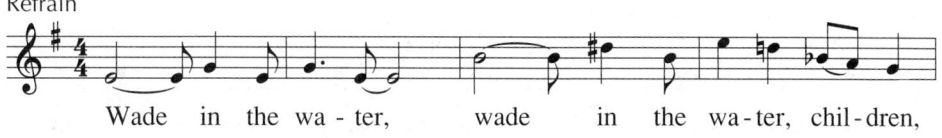

Wade   in the wa - ter,   wade   in the wa - ter, chil - dren,

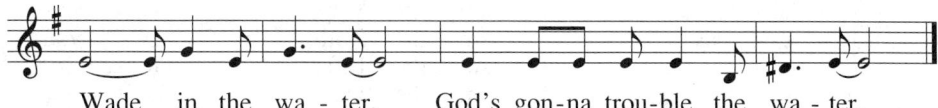

Wade   in the wa - ter,   God's gon-na trou-ble the wa - ter.

Verses

Solo: *All:*

1. See   that   host   all dressed in white,
2. See   that   band   all dressed in red,   God's gon-na trou-ble the
3. Look   o - ver yon-der, what   do   I   see?
4. If you don't be - lieve I've   been re - deemed,

Solo:

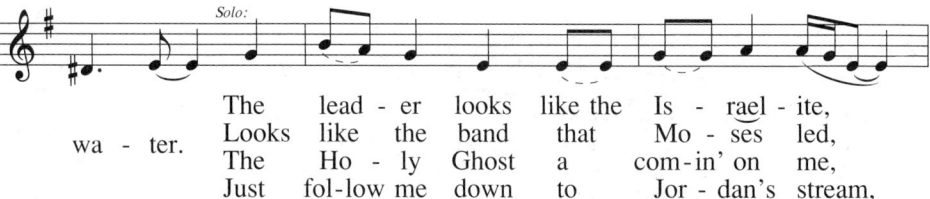

wa - ter.
            The   lead - er   looks   like the   Is - rael - ite,
            Looks like   the   band   that   Mo - ses   led,
            The   Ho - ly Ghost   a   com-in' on me,
            Just   fol-low me down   to   Jor - dan's stream,

All: D.C.

God's   gon - na trou - ble   the   wa - ter.

Text: African American spiritual
Tune: WADE IN THE WATER, 7 8 8 8 with refrain; African American spiritual; arr. by James Abbington, b.1960, © 2000, GIA Publications, Inc.

1023   I Receive the Living God

Refrain

I re - ceive the liv-ing God, And my heart is full of joy. I re - ceive the liv-ing God, And my heart is full of joy.

Verses

1. Je - sus says: I am the Bread Sent to
2. Je - sus says: I am the Vine, Far from
3. Je - sus says: I am the Way, And my
4. Je - sus says: I am the Truth. If you
5. Je - sus says: I am the Life, Raised in
6. Je - sus says: I am the Day, Shin - ing

1. you from God Most High. Take and eat, and you will
2. whom no life can grow. If you join your-self to
3. path is straight and true. Fol - low me to where I
4. fol - low close to me, You will know me in your
5. tri - umph from the dead. As one Bod - y now re -
6. bright - ly through your night. Wel - come me, and you will

D.C.

1. live; You need nev - er fear to die.
2. me, A rich har - vest you will know.
3. lead; There my Fa - ther waits for you.
4. heart, And my word will make you free.
5. main, Mem - bers joined to me, the Head.
6. walk By the Spir - it's guid - ing light.

7. Jesus says: I am the Love
   Which can bind you close to me.
   Those who know this gift I bring
   Will find true community.

8. Jesus says: I am the Peace
   Which the world cannot bestow.
   Learn to love and live in me,
   And in you my Reign will grow.

9. Jesus says: I am the Lamb,
   And my death set sinners free.
   Those who drink the cup I drink
   Must take up this work with me.

Text: Vss. 1–3, 5–9, Bernard Geoffroy, b.1946; tr. by Ronald F. Krisman, b.1946, © 2011, GIA Publications, Inc.; vs. 4, anonymous
Tune: LIVING GOD, 7 7 7 7 with refrain; Dom Clément Jacob, OSB, 1906–1977, adapt.; harm. by Richard Proulx, 1937–2010, © 1986,
GIA Publications, Inc.

At That First Eucharist 1024

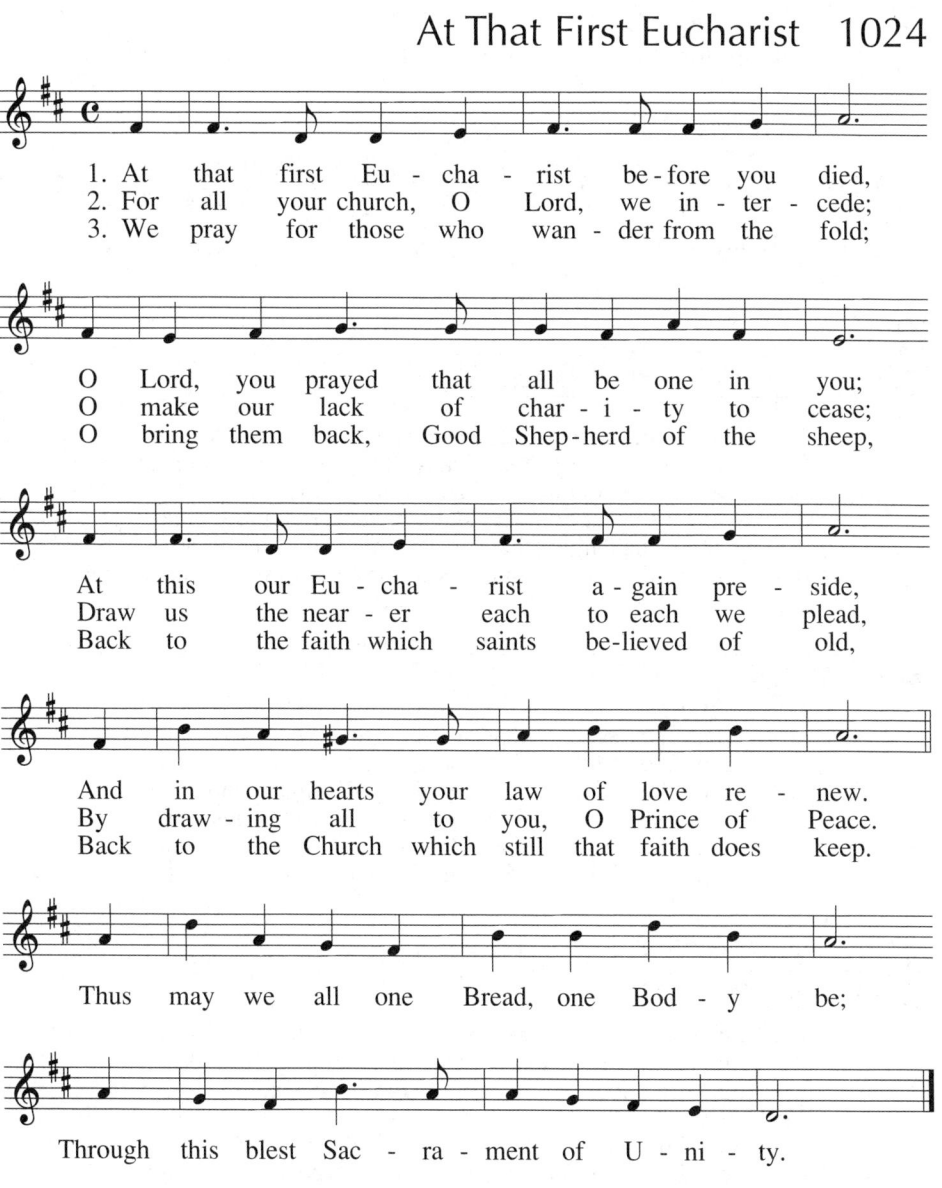

1. At that first Eu - cha - rist be - fore you died,
2. For all your church, O Lord, we in - ter - cede;
3. We pray for those who wan - der from the fold;

O Lord, you prayed that all be one in you;
O make our lack of char - i - ty to cease;
O bring them back, Good Shep - herd of the sheep,

At this our Eu - cha - rist a - gain pre - side,
Draw us the near - er each to each we plead,
Back to the faith which saints be - lieved of old,

And in our hearts your law of love re - new.
By draw - ing all to you, O Prince of Peace.
Back to the Church which still that faith does keep.

Thus may we all one Bread, one Bod - y be;

Through this blest Sac - ra - ment of U - ni - ty.

Text: William H. Turton, 1859–1938, alt.
Tune: UNDE ET MEMORES, 10 10 10 10 with refrain; William H. Monk, 1823–1889, alt.

1025 Take and Eat

Refrain

Take and eat; take and eat: this is my bod - y
giv - en up for you. Take and drink; take and drink:
this is my blood giv - en up for you.

Verses

1. I am the Word that spoke and light was made;
2. I am the way that leads the ex - ile home;
3. I am the Lamb that takes a - way your sin;
4. I am the cor - ner - stone that God has laid;
5. I am the light that came in - to the world;
6. I am the first and last, the Liv - ing One;

I am the seed that died to be re - born;
I am the truth that sets the cap - tive free;
I am the gate that guards you night and day;
A cho - sen stone and pre - cious in his eyes;
I am the light that dark - ness can - not hide;
I am the Lord who died that you might live;

I am the bread that comes from heav'n a - bove;
I am the life that rais - es up the dead;
You are my flock: you know the shep - herd's voice;
You are God's dwell - ing place, on me you rest;
I am the morn - ing star that nev - er sets;
I am the bride - groom, this my wed - ding song;

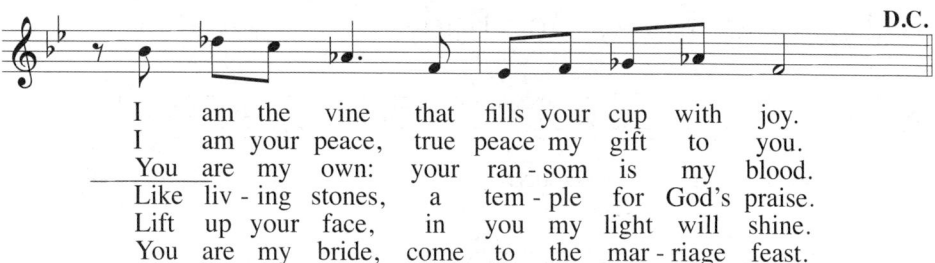

D.C.

I am the vine that fills your cup with joy.
I am your peace, true peace my gift to you.
You are my own: your ran - som is my blood.
Like liv - ing stones, a tem - ple for God's praise.
Lift up your face, in you my light will shine.
You are my bride, come to the mar - riage feast.

Text: Verse text, James Quinn, SJ, 1919–2010, © 1969, James Quinn, SJ. Published by OCP; refrain text, Michael Joncas, b.1951,
© 1989, GIA Publications, Inc.
Tune: CORPUS DOMINI, 10 10 10 10 with refrain; Michael Joncas, b.1951, © 1989, GIA Publications, Inc.

As the Bread of Life Is Broken 1026

Refrain

As the bread of life is bro - ken, the cup of love out - poured,

We are one in Christ, our Sav - ior, and sent to serve the Lord.

Verses

1. We, the man - y who are gath - ered, are u -
2. In the word of God pro - claimed here the good
3. In the bread of life here giv - en, we be -
4. Sent as bless - ing for God's peo - ple, to go

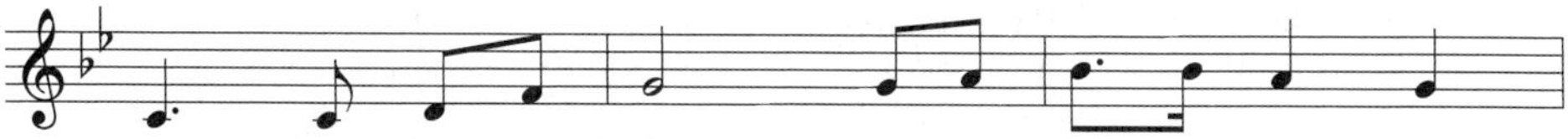

nit - ed now as one. In this joy - ful cel - e -
news of truth is heard. In the tell - ing of the
come what we re - ceive. In the cup of love here
forth in love and peace, In our wit - ness to God's

D.C.

bra - tion, we re - call what God has done.
sto - ries, we are o - pen to God's word.
of - fered, we af - firm what we be - lieve.
king - dom, may our char - i - ty in - crease.

Text: James J. Chepponis, b.1956, © 2002, Birnamwood Publications, a div. of MorningStar Music Publishers, Inc.
Tune: THAXTED, 14 14 15 15; Gustav Holst, 1874–1934

1027   One Bread, One Body

Refrain

One bread, one bod-y, one Lord of all, one cup of bless-ing which we bless. And we, though man-y, through-out the earth, we are one bod-y in this one Lord.

Verses

1. Gen - tile   or   Jew,   Ser - vant   or   free,
2. Man - y   the   gifts,   Man - y   the   works,
3. Grain for   the   fields,   Scat-tered and grown,

D.C.

Wom-an   or   man   no   more.
One in   the Lord   of   all.
Gath-ered   to   one   for   all.

Text: 1 Corinthians 10:16–17, 12:4, 12–13, 20; Galatians 3:28; Ephesians 4:4–6; the *Didache* 9; John Foley, SJ, b.1939
Tune: ONE BREAD, ONE BODY, 4 4 6 with refrain; John Foley, SJ, b.1939
© 1978, John B. Foley, SJ. Published by OCP.

You Satisfy the Hungry Heart   1028

Refrain

You sat - is - fy the hun - gry heart   With

gift of fin - est wheat;   Come give to us,   O

sav - ing Lord,   The bread   of life to   eat.

Verses

1. As when the shep - herd calls his sheep, They
2. With joy - ful lips we sing to you Our
3. Is not the cup we bless and share The
4. The mys - t'ry of your pres - ence, Lord, No
5. You give your - self to us, O Lord; Then

know and heed his voice; So when you call your
praise and grat - i - tude, That you should count us
blood of Christ out - poured? Do not one cup, one
mor - tal tongue can tell: Whom all the world can -
self - less let us be, To serve each oth - er

D.C.

fam - 'ly, Lord, We fol - low and re - joice.
wor - thy, Lord, To share this heav'n - ly food.
loaf, de - clare Our one - ness in the Lord?
not con - tain Comes in our hearts to dwell.
in your name In truth and char - i - ty.

Text: Omer Westendorf, 1916–1997
Tune: BICENTENNIAL, CM with refrain; Robert E. Kreutz, 1922–1996

1029 I Am the Bread of Life / Yo Soy el Pan de Vida

Verses

1. I am the Bread of life. You who
2. The bread that I will give is my
3. Un - less you eat of the
4. I am the Res - ur - rec - tion,
5. Yes, Lord, we be - lieve that

1. Yo soy el Pan de Vi - da. A mí
2. El pan que yo da - ré es mi
3. Si us - te - des no co - men la
4. Yo soy la Re - su - rrec-ción,
5. Sí, Se - ñor, cre - e - mos que

come to me shall not hun - ger; and who be -
flesh for the life of the world, and if you
flesh of the Son of Man and
I am the life. If you be -
you are the Christ, the

ven - gan: no ten-drán ham - bre. En mí
car - ne, la vi - da del mun - do. Los que
car - ne del Hi - jo del Hom - bre, y no
Yo soy la Vi - da. Si en
tú e - res el Me - sí - as, el

lieve in me shall not thirst. No one can come to
eat of this bread, you shall live for
drink of his blood, and drink of his
lieve in me, e - ven though you
Son of God, Who has

cre - an: no ten-drán sed. Na - die vie - ne a
co - men de es - te pan vi - vi - rán por
be - ben de su san - gre, no be - ben de su
mí us - te - des cre - en, aun - que ha - yan
Hi - jo de Dios, que has ve - ni - do al

me   un - less   the   Fa - ther   beck - ons.
ev - er,————   you   shall   live   for   ev - er.
blood,   you   shall   not have life   with - in   you.
die,————   you   shall   live   for   ev - er.
come   in - to————   the————   world.——

mí   si mi Pa - dre   no lo̲a - tra - e.
siem - pre,————   vi - vi - rán   por   siem - pre.
san - gre,   no po-drán   te - ner   mi   vi - da.
muer - to,————   vi - vi - rán   por   siem - pre.
mun - do————   pa - ra   re - di - mir - nos.

Refrain

And I will raise   you up,   and I will
Yo los re - su - ci - ta - ré,   Yo los re -

raise   you up,   and I will raise   you
su - ci - ta - ré,   Yo los re - su - ci - ta -

up   on   the   last   day.
ré   en   el   dí - a   fi - nal.

Text: John 6 and 11; Suzanne Toolan, RSM, b.1927; tr. anon., rev. by Ronald F. Krisman, b.1946
Tune: BREAD OF LIFE, Irregular with refrain; Suzanne Toolan, RSM, b.1927
© 1966, 1970, 1986, 1993, 2005, GIA Publications, Inc.

1030 Alleluia! Sing to Jesus!

1. Al - le - lu - ia! Sing to Je - sus! His the
2. Al - le - lu - ia! Not as or - phans Are we
3. Al - le - lu - ia! Bread of an - gels, Here on
4. Al - le - lu - ia! King e - ter - nal, You the

scep - ter, his the throne. Al - le - lu - ia! His the
left in sor - row now; Al - le - lu - ia! He is
earth our food, our stay! Al - le - lu - ia! Here the
Lord of lords we own; Al - le - lu - ia! Born of

tri - umph, His the vic - to - ry a - lone.
near us; Faith be - lieves, nor ques - tions how.
sin - ful Flee to you from day to day.
Mar - y, Earth your foot - stool, heav'n your throne.

Hark! The songs of peace - ful Zi - on Thun - der
Though the cloud from sight re - ceived him When the
In - ter - ces - sor, friend of sin - ners, Earth's re -
You with - in the veil have en - tered, Robed in

like a might - y flood: "Je - sus out of ev - 'ry
for - ty days were o'er, Shall our hearts for - get his
deem - er, plead for me, Where the songs of all the
flesh, our great high priest; Here on earth both priest and

na - tion Has re - deemed us by his blood."
prom - ise: "I am with you ev - er - more"?
sin - less Sweep a - cross the crys - tal sea.
vic - tim In the eu - cha - ris - tic feast.

Text: Revelation 5:9; William C. Dix, 1837–1898
Tune: HYFRYDOL, 8 7 8 7 D; Rowland H. Prichard, 1811–1887

Taste and See 1031

Refrain

Taste and see, taste and see the good - ness of the Lord. O taste and see, taste and see the good - ness of the Lord, of the Lord.

Verses

1. I will bless the Lord at all times.
2. Glo - ri - fy the Lord with me.
3. Wor - ship the Lord, all you peo - ple.

Praise shall al - ways be on my lips;
To - geth - er let us all praise God's name.
You'll want for noth - ing if you ask.

my soul shall glo - ry in the Lord
I called the Lord who an - swered me;
Taste and see that the Lord is good;

for God has been so good to me.
from all my trou - bles I was set free.
in God we need put all our trust.

D.C.

Text: Psalm 34; James E. Moore, Jr., b.1951
Tune: James E. Moore, Jr., b.1951
© 1983, GIA Publications, Inc.

1032 All Who Hunger

Verses

1. All who hun-ger, gath - er glad - ly; Ho - ly man - na
2. All who hun-ger, nev - er stran-gers; Seek-er, be a
3. All who hun-ger, sing to-geth - er; Je - sus Christ is

is our bread. Come from wil - der-ness and wan-d'ring.
wel-come guest. Come from rest - less-ness and roam - ing.
liv - ing bread. Come from lone - li - ness and long - ing.

Here, in truth, we will be fed. You that yearn for
Here, in joy, we keep the feast. We that once were
Here, in peace, we have been led. Blest are those who

days of full - ness, All a - round us is our food.
lost and scat-tered In com - mun-ion's love have stood.
from this ta - ble Live their days in grat - i - tude.

Refrain

Taste and see the grace e - ter-nal. Taste and see that God is good.

Text: Sylvia G. Dunstan, 1955–1993, © 1991, GIA Publications, Inc.
Tune: GRACE ETERNAL, 8 7 8 7 8 7 with refrain; Bob Moore, b.1962, © 1993, GIA Publications, Inc.

1033 Eat This Bread

Refrain

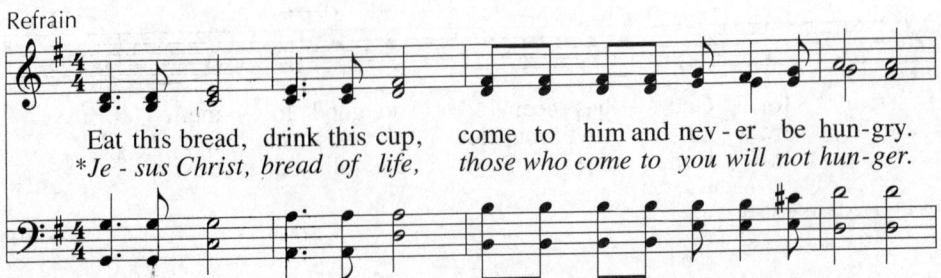

Eat this bread, drink this cup, come to him and nev - er be hun-gry.
Je - sus Christ, bread of life, those who come to you will not hun-ger.

Alternate Refrain

Eat this bread, drink this cup, trust in him and you will not thirst.
Je - sus Christ, Ris - en Lord, those who trust in you will not thirst.

Text: John 6; adapt. by Robert J. Batastini, b.1942
Tune: Jacques Berthier, 1923–1994
© 1984, 2005, Les Presses de Taizé, GIA Publications, Inc., agent

Amén. El Cuerpo de Cristo   1034

Refrain

A - mén. El Cuer - po de Cris - to. A - mén. La

San - gre del Se - ñor. *Eat - ing your Bod - y, drink - ing your Blood, we be -*

come what we re - ceive. A - mén. A - mén.

Verses

1. A - mén. *We re - mem - ber your dy - ing*
2. A - mén. *Now we of - fer the sac - ri -*
3. A - mén. *Lord, you make us one bod - y*
4. A - mén. *We find you when we serve the*
5. A - mén. *We look for - ward to your re -*

and your ris - ing. A - mén. Y con - ti - go, Se -
fice you gave us. A - mén. Te o - fre - ce - mos, Se -
and one spir - it. A - mén. En tu cuer - po, Se -
poor and low - ly. A - mén. A ti mis - mo ser -
turn in glo - ry. A - mén. Es - pe - ra - mos el

D.C.

ñor, re - su - ci - ta - mos. A - mén.
ñor, to - do lo que so - mos. A - mén.
ñor, un pue - blo san - to. A - mén.
vi - mos en los po - bres. A - mén.
día de tu ve - ni - da. A - mén.

Text: John Schiavone, b.1947
Tune: John Schiavone, b.1947
© 1995, John Schiavone. Published by OCP.

1035 Bread of Life from Heaven / Pan de Vida Eterna

Refrain / Estribillo

Bread of life from heav-en, your blood and bod - y giv - en, we
Pan de vi - da e - ter - na, nos das tu cuer - po y san - gre.

eat this bread and drink this cup un - til you come a - gain.
Has - ta que vuel - vas tú, Se - ñor, co - me - mos en tu a - mor.

Verses / Estrofas

1. Break now the bread of Christ's sac - ri - fice; Giv - ing
2. Seek not the food that will pass a - way; Set your
3. Love as the One who, in love for you, Gave him -
4. Take in the light that will nev - er dim, Taste the
5. Dwell in the One who now dwells in you; Make your
6. Drink of this cup and de - clare his death; Eat this
7. *Ven y com-par - te el di - vi - no pan;* De - mos
8. *Es - te mis - te - rio es el máx - i - mo* Sa - cri -
9. *Ven a la me - sa de com - pa - sión,* Re - cor -
10. *Hoy que co - me - mos del pan de a - mor* So - mos
11. *Ce - na que nos re - pre - sen - ta hoy* La vi - da,

thanks, hun - gry ones gath - er 'round. Eat all of you, and be
hearts on the food that en - dures. Come, learn the true and the
self for the life of the world. Come to the One who is
life that is strong - er than death. Live in the One who will
home in the life - giv - ing Word. Know on - ly Christ, Ho - ly
bread and be - lieve Eas - ter morn; Trust his re - turn and, with
gra - cias con gran co - ra - zón. *Cris - to es sus - ten - to que*
fi - cio de fe y de a - mor. *Pan que nos lla - ma a con -*
de - mos a Cris - to Je - sús. *Él nos da vi - da con*
u - no en Cris - to Je - sús. *Ce - na que es fuen - te de in -*
muer - te, y re - su - rrec - ción *De Je - su - cris - to, que es*

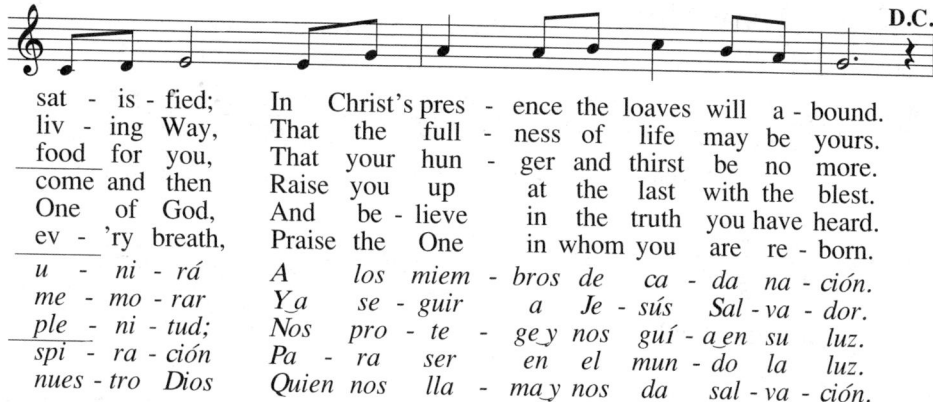

D.C.

sat - is - fied;	In Christ's pres - ence the loaves will a - bound.
liv - ing Way,	That the full - ness of life may be yours.
food for you,	That your hun - ger and thirst be no more.
come and then	Raise you up at the last with the blest.
One of God,	And be - lieve in the truth you have heard.
ev - 'ry breath,	Praise the One in whom you are re - born.
u - ni - rá	*A los miem - bros de ca - da na - ción.*
me - mo - rar	*Y a se - guir a Je - sús Sal - va - dor.*
ple - ni - tud;	*Nos pro - te - ge y nos guí - a en su luz.*
spi - ra - ción	*Pa - ra ser en el mun - do la luz.*
nues - tro Dios	*Quien nos lla - ma y nos da sal - va - ción.*

Text: Based on John 6; adapt. by Susan R. Briehl, b.1952; tr. by Jaime Cortez, b.1963
Tune: ARGENTINE SANTO, 9 9 9 9 with refrain; Argentine folk melody; adapt. and verses by Marty Haugen, b.1950
© 2001, GIA Publications, Inc.

This Is the Body of Christ 1036

This is the Bod-y of Christ, bro-ken that we may be

whole; this cup, as prom-ised by God, true to his word,

cra-dles our Lord: food for the good of the soul.

Text: John L. Bell, b.1949
Tune: John L. Bell, b.1949
© 1998, Iona Community, GIA Publications, Inc., agent

1037 Draw Near

Refrain

Draw near, draw near! Take the Bod-y of your Lord. Draw near, draw near!

Drink the Blood for you out-poured.

Verses

1. Draw near and take the Bod-y of the Lord,
2. Christ, our Re-deem - er, God's e - ter - nal Son,
3. Let us ap-proach with faith-ful hearts sin - cere
4. With heav'n-ly bread Christ makes the hun-gry whole;

And drink with faith the Blood for you out-poured.
Has by his cross and blood the vic - t'ry won.
And claim the prom - ise of sal - va - tion here.
His liv - ing wa - ter fills the thirst - ing soul.

Saved by his Bod - y and his ho - ly Blood, With
He spent his life for great - est and for least. Praise
Christ rules our hearts, and all his saints de - fends; He
Al - pha - O - me - ga, un - to whom shall bow All

D.C.

souls re - freshed we give our thanks to God.
Christ the Pas - chal Vic - tim, Christ the Priest.
gives be - liev - ers life that nev - er ends.
na - tions of the earth, be with us now.

Text: *Sancti, venite, Christi corpus sumite*, 7th C.; tr. by John M. Neale, 1818–1866, alt.
Tune: NEALE, 10 10 10 10 with refrain; Steven R. Janco, b.1961, © 1992, World Library Publications

Life-Giving Bread, Saving Cup 1038

Refrain

Life - giv-ing Bread, sav - ing Cup, we of-fer in thanks-giv-ing, O God. Life - giv-ing Bread, sav - ing Cup, we of-fer as a sign of our love.

Verses

1. For bread that is bro - ken, we give thanks; For
2. We thank you, O Fa - ther, for your name, Which
3. Cre - a - tor of all, we of - fer thanks; You
4. Re - mem - ber your Church, which sings your praise; Per -

wine that is poured, we give praise. For
you give to dwell in our hearts. You
give us a share in your life. You
fect it in truth and in love. And

life and for knowl-edge of the king - dom: All
bring us to - geth - er as one fam - 'ly: All
strength - en our bod - y and our spir - it: All
gath - er your peo - ple all to - geth - er To

D.C.

praise to you un - til the end of time!
praise to you un - til the end of time!
praise to you un - til the end of time!
praise you un - til the end of time!

Text: Adapted from the *Didache*, 2nd C.; James J. Chepponis, b.1956
Tune: LIFE-GIVING BREAD, 9 8 10 10 with refrain; James J. Chepponis, b.1956
© 1987, GIA Publications, Inc.

1039 Come to Me, All Pilgrims Thirsty

1. "Come to me, all pil-grims thirst-y; Drink the wa-ter I will give. If you knew what gift I of-fer, You would come to me and live."
2. "Come to me, all trav-'lers wea-ry; Come that I may give you rest. Drink the cup of life I of-fer, At this ta-ble be my guest."
3. "Come to me, be-liev-ers bur-dened; Find re-fresh-ment in this place. Come, re-ceive the gift I of-fer; Turn to me and seek my face."
4. "Come to me, re-pent-ant sin-ners; Leave be-hind your guilt and shame. If you knew di-vine com-pas-sion, You would turn and call my name."
5. "Come to me, dis-tressed and need-y; I will be your trust-ed friend. Seek the gift of life I of-fer; Come, your o-pen hands ex-tend."
6. "Come to me, a-ban-doned, or-phaned; Lone-ly ways no long-er roam. Come, ac-cept the gift I of-fer; Come and make in me your home."

Je-sus, ev-er-flow-ing foun-tain, give us wa-ter from your well. In the gra-cious gift you of-fer there is joy no tongue can tell.

Text: Delores Dufner, OSB, b.1939, © 2008, GIA Publications, Inc.
Tune: HOLY MANNA, 8 7 8 7 with refrain; William Moore, fl. 1830; harm. by Charles Anders, b.1929, © 1969, *Contemporary Worship I*, admin. Augsburg Fortress

Many and Great 1040

Verses

1. Man - y and great are bear-ers of the Word:
2. Man - y and great are seeds up-on the field:
3. Man - y and great are voic-es of de-spair:
4. Man - y and great are peb-bles in the sand:

The Christ speaks; the heart seeks.
The hand sows; the seeds grow.
The rain falls; the voice calls.
The sun glows; the wind blows.

Gath - ered as one, we lis-ten to the Word
Take now and eat the cov-e-nant ful-filled,
Take now and drink the wine of hope and care;
Take now and spread the Word to ev-'ry land,

And share the meal of new birth.
The bread of prom-ise and life.
Our cup of bless-ing we share.
The Word of good-ness and hope.

Refrain

The wheat grows from spring-time to fall; the wine flows; in Christ we re-call the shar-ing of our lives with one and all.

Text: Ricky Manalo, CSP, b.1965
Tune: Ricky Manalo, CSP, b.1965
© 1995, Ricky Manalo, CSP. Published by OCP.

1041 Now in This Banquet

Refrain *1.   2.

Now   in   this   ban - quet,   Christ   is   our   bread;
Advent: God   of   our   jour - neys,   day - break   to   night;
Lent: Lord,   you   can   o - pen   hearts   that   are   stone;

Here   shall   all   hun - gers   be   fed.
Lead   us   to   jus - tice   and   light.
Live   in   our   flesh   and   our   bone;

Bread   that   is   bro - ken,   wine   that   is   poured,
Grant   us   com - pas - sion,   strength   for   the   day,
Lead   us   to   won - der,   mys - t'ry   and   grace,

Love   is   the   sign   of   our   Lord.
Wis - dom   to   walk   in   your   way.
One   in   your   lov - ing   em -   brace.

Verses 1, 2

1. You who have touched us and graced us with love,
2. Let our hearts burn with the fire of your love;

D.C.

make us your peo - ple of good - ness and light.
o - pen our eyes to the glo - ry of God.

May be sung in canon.

Verse 3

3. God who makes the blind to see, God who makes the lame to walk, bring us danc - ing in - to day, lead your peo - ple in your way.

D.C.

Verse 4

4. Hope for the hope - less, light for the blind, "Strong" is your name, Lord, "Gen - tle" and "Kind."

D.C.

Verse 5

5. Call us to be your light, call us to be your love, make us your peo - ple a - gain.

D.C.

Verse 6

6. Come, O Spir - it! re - new our hearts! We shall a - rise to be chil - dren of light.

D.C.

Text: Marty Haugen, b.1950
Tune: Marty Haugen, b.1950

1042 Song of the Body of Christ /
Canción del Cuerpo de Cristo

Estrofas

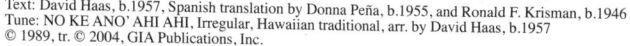

1. Hoy ve - ni - mos por - que so - mos tu pue - blo, re - na -
2. A sa - nar al en - fer - mo nos lla - mas, al an -
3. Pan de vi - da y san - gre de la a - lian - za, haz - nos
4. Nos guia - rás y te se - gui - re - mos. Nues - tro a -
5. Vi - vi - re - mos can - tan - do "A - lo - ja." "A - le -

ci - dos por tu per - dón, re - u - ni - dos
sio - so, tu es - pe - ran - za tra - er, y al ham - brien - to,
u - no en es - ta co - mu - nión. Que tu rei - no
lien - to vi - tal tú se - rás. Nues - tra luz, en el
lu - ya" es nues - tra can - ción. Que vi - va - mos por

D.C.

en tu a - mor, y de un co - ra - zón.
nues - tro a - li - men - to o - fre - cer.
ven - ga en nues - tra trans - for - ma - ción.
dí - a y en la no - che bri - lla - rás.
siem - pre en paz y fra - ter - na u - nión.

Text: David Haas, b.1957, Spanish translation by Donna Peña, b.1955, and Ronald F. Krisman, b.1946
Tune: NO KE ANO' AHI AHI, Irregular, Hawaiian traditional, arr. by David Haas, b.1957
© 1989, tr. © 2004, GIA Publications, Inc.

In Memory of You   1043

Lord, Je - sus! You are here with us.

This we do in mem - o - ry of you.

Verses

Ave verum Corpus natum de María Vírgine:	Hail, true body, born of the Virgin Mary,
Vere passum, immolátum in cruce pro hómine:	Truly suffering, sacrificed on the cross for us.
Cuius latus perforátum fluxit aqua et sánguine:	Whose side, when pierced, flowed with water and blood:
Esto nobis praegustátum mortis in exámine.	Be for us a foretaste in death's agony.
O Jesu dulcis! O Jesu pie! O Jesu fili Maríae.	O Jesu sweet, O Jesu pure, O Jesu, Son of Mary.

Text: Alexander Peloquin, 1918–1997
Tune: Alexander Peloquin, 1918–1997
© 1976, GIA Publications, Inc.

1044   Gusten y Vean / Taste and See

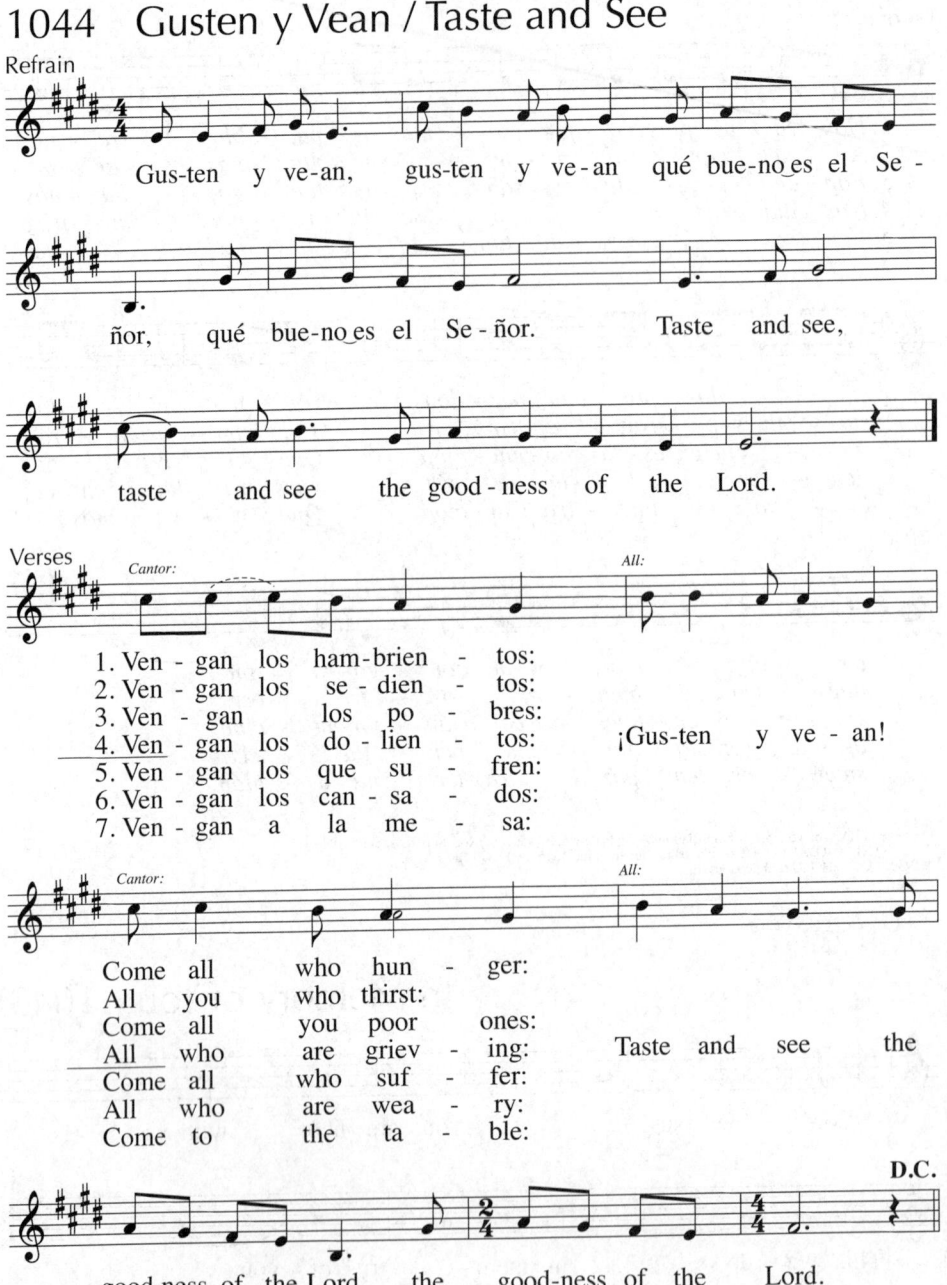

Refrain

Gus-ten y ve-an, gus-ten y ve-an qué bue-no_es el Señor, qué bue-no_es el Se-ñor. Taste and see,
taste and see the good-ness of the Lord.

Verses

Cantor:

1. Ven - gan los ham-brien - tos:
2. Ven - gan los se - dien - tos:
3. Ven - gan los po - bres:
4. Ven - gan los do - lien - tos: ¡Gus-ten y ve - an!
5. Ven - gan los que su - fren:
6. Ven - gan los can - sa - dos:
7. Ven - gan a la me - sa:

Cantor:

Come all who hun - ger:
All you who thirst:
Come all you poor ones:
All who are griev - ing: Taste and see the
Come all who suf - fer:
All who are wea - ry:
Come to the ta - ble:

good-ness of the Lord, the good-ness of the Lord.

Text: Based on Psalm 34; Tony E. Alonso, b.1980
Tune: Tony E. Alonso, b.1980
© 2008, GIA Publications, Inc.

O Blessed Savior 1045

Refrain

O bless-ed Sav-ior, now be - hold the grate-ful gath-'ring of your fold in joy - ful med i - ta - tion. Our thirst-ing souls, our hun-gry hearts now seek the food which life im-parts, the bread of our sal - va - tion.

Verses

Cantor:

1. O Lord, our God, the source of love, All good gifts come from you,
2. To us you say, "Take this and eat!" Now yearn - ing hearts are fed;
3. O lov - ing God, the source of life, You are the Ho - ly One
4. As once you fed the mul - ti - tude When loaves and fish were few,
5. O Lord, you know our hu - man plight; You bid us come to you;

Who once sent man - na from a - bove
Come, fill us with the best of wheat;
Who gives to us the sav - ing cup,
O feed us now with bread and wine
Your yoke is mild, your bur - den light;

D.C.

To feed your cho - sen few.
Give us the liv - ing bread.
Je - sus, your on - ly Son.
That makes us one in you.
Re - fresh our souls a - new.

Text: Omer Westendorf, 1916–1997, © 1990, World Library Publications
Tune: Jerry R. Brubaker, b.1946, © 1990, Jerry R, Brubaker, published by World Library Publications

1046 From the Many, Make Us One

Verses

1. Je - sus prayed be - fore he died,
2. Je - sus washed their feet and cried,
3. Love the world so loved by God:
4. Walk with all who walked be - fore:
5. Dy - ing seeds have made our bread:
6. Eat and drink and so pro - claim:

To this ta-ble now we come.

"Make them one this whole world wide!
grieved the deeds that would di - vide.
Tat - tered, scat - tered, worn and trod.
wea - ry, bur - dened, bro - ken, poor,
Christ the first - born from the dead.
In Christ's dy - ing, death is slain!

From the man - y, make us one.

Ev - 'ry shade and tribe and tongue,
Bow us down now, each to all;
Come to wel - come ta - ble here!
saints of ev - 'ry age and place,
From the vine - yard comes a flood:
Call to mind we too have died:

To this ta - ble now we come.

male and fe - male, old and young!"
make this world a ban - quet hall.
Doors wide o - pen, noth - ing fear.
ev - 'ry col - or, ev - 'ry grace.
cup of bless - ing, Sav - ior's blood.
Liv - ing wa - ters from Christ's side.

From the

Refrain

man-y, make us one. When we sing and when we cry, as we live and as we die: To this ta-ble now we come. From the man-y, make us one.

Text: Gabe Huck, b.1941
Tune: Tony E. Alonso, b.1980
© 2015, GIA Publications, Inc.

Draw Us in the Spirit's Tether 1047

1. Draw us in the Spir-it's teth - er, For when
2. As dis - ci - ples used to gath - er In the
3. All our meals and all our liv - ing Make as

hum - bly in your name Two or
name of Christ to sup, Then with
sac - ra - ments of you, That by

three are met to - geth - er, You are in the
thanks to God the Fa - ther Break the bread and
car - ing, help-ing, giv - ing, We may be dis -

midst of them. Al - le - lu - ia! Al - le - lu - ia!
bless the cup. Al - le - lu - ia! Al - le - lu - ia!
ci - ples true. Al - le - lu - ia! Al - le - lu - ia!

Touch we now your gar - ment's hem.
So now bind our friend - ship up.
We will serve with faith a - new.

Text: Percy Dearmer, 1867–1936, alt., © 1931, Oxford University Press
Tune: UNION SEMINARY, 8 7 8 7 44 7; Harold Friedell, 1905–1958, © 1957, ren., The H. W. Gray Company, admin. Alfred Music; harm. by
    Jet Turner, 1928–1984, © 1967, Chalice Press

1048 May We Be One (Communion Litany)

Cantor(s):

1. Lamb of God, you take a - way the sins of the world:
2. Lamb of God, un - blem - ished of - f'ring made for our sin:
3. Lamb of God, de - stroyed that all who eat might be healed:
4. Lamb of God, whose blood will save your peo - ple from death:
5. Lamb of God, our com - mon mem - 'ry, cov - e - nant feast:
6. Lamb of God, our free - dom won, re - mem - bered for ev - er:

All:

have mer - cy on us, have mer - cy on us.

Last time

Cantor(s):

Lamb of God, you take a - way the sins of the world,

All:

grant us peace, grant us peace.

Additional invocations:

Lamb of God, the shepherd of all who hunger and thirst…
Lamb of God, joy of the martyrs, song of the saints…
Lamb of God, all peoples will sing your victory song…
Lamb of God, unconquered light of the city of God…
Lamb of God, how blessed are those who are called to your feast…

Text: *Agnus Dei;* additional text by Rory Cooney
Music: Gary Daigle
© 1993, GIA Publications, Inc.

May We Be One (Communion Hymn) 1049

Text: Rory Cooney, b.1952
Tune: Gary Daigle, b.1957
© 1993, GIA Publications, Inc.

1050　Broken for the Broken

Refrain

Bro-ken for the bro-ken,　poured out for the poor:

Bless-ed feast of God's cre - a - tion, giv-en for us all.

Bro-ken for the bro-ken,　shared for hu-man-kind,　we pro-

claim your death, O Lord:　God's sac-ri-fice and　sign.

Verses

1. For　the hun-gry ones,　for the thirst-y　ones,
2. For　the ones a-bused,　for the ones con-fused,
3. For　the voice-less ones,　for the help-less ones,
4. For　the wound-ed ones,　for the shat-tered ones,
5. For　the ones in chains,　for the ones in　fear,
6. For　the ail-ing ones,　for the hurt-ing　ones,
7. As　we break this bread,　as we take this　cup,
8. As　we trust your word,　as we live your way,
9. Change our hearts, O　Lord,　give us will-ing hearts,

for　the lone-ly ones, you call　us to serve,　to be
for　the ones re-fused, you call　us to love,　to be
for　the home-less ones, you call　us to speak,　to be
for　the ti - red ones, you call　us to help,　to be
for　the ones in debt, you call　us to give,　to be
for　the dy-ing ones, you call　us to care,　to be
as　we share this meal, you call　us to change,　to be
as　we walk by faith, you call　us to share,　to be
hearts that rec - og - nize the cour - age to serve　and share

D.C.

1.–8. Christ for each oth - er, bro-ken for the world.
9. Christ with each oth - er, bro-ken for the world.

Text: Chris de Silva, b.1967
Tune: Chris de Silva, b.1967
© 2012, GIA Publications, Inc.

At the Table of Jesus   1051

Refrain

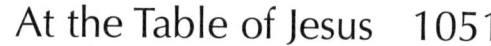

At the ta - ble of Je-sus we are nour - ished and fed   By the

bless - ing   cup   and   heav - en's liv - ing bread.   At the

ta - ble of Je - sus earth and   heav - en are wed.   To a

hun - gry   world,   by our   God   we are led.

Verses

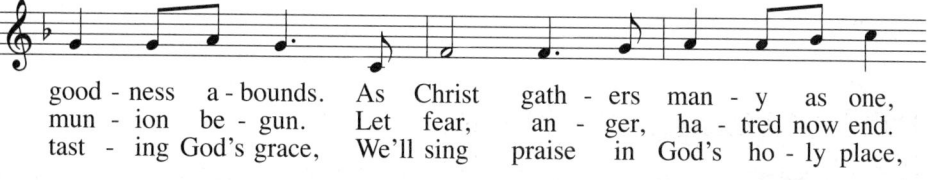

1. Where love and char - i - ty are found There God is   a - mong us; God's
2. Now,   as   we gath-er all as one, Di - vi - sion   is end - ed, com-
3. Joined with   the   an - gels and the saints, Be - hold-ing God's glo - ry and

good - ness   a - bounds.   As   Christ   gath - ers   man - y   as one,
mun - ion   be - gun.   Let   fear,   an - ger,   ha - tred now end.
tast - ing God's grace,   We'll sing   praise   in   God's ho - ly place,

D.C.

Let   our   hearts   be   glad   and   re - flect God's love.
Let   us   dwell   in   love   as   our   God   in - tends.
And with   heav - en's hosts we'll come face   to   face.

Text: Based on *Ubi Caritas*; Tony E. Alonso, b.1980
Tune: SIMPLE GIFTS, Irregular with refrain; Joseph Brackett, Jr., 1797–1882; arr. by Marty Haugen, b.1950
© 2010, GIA Publications, Inc.

1052 Stop By, Lord

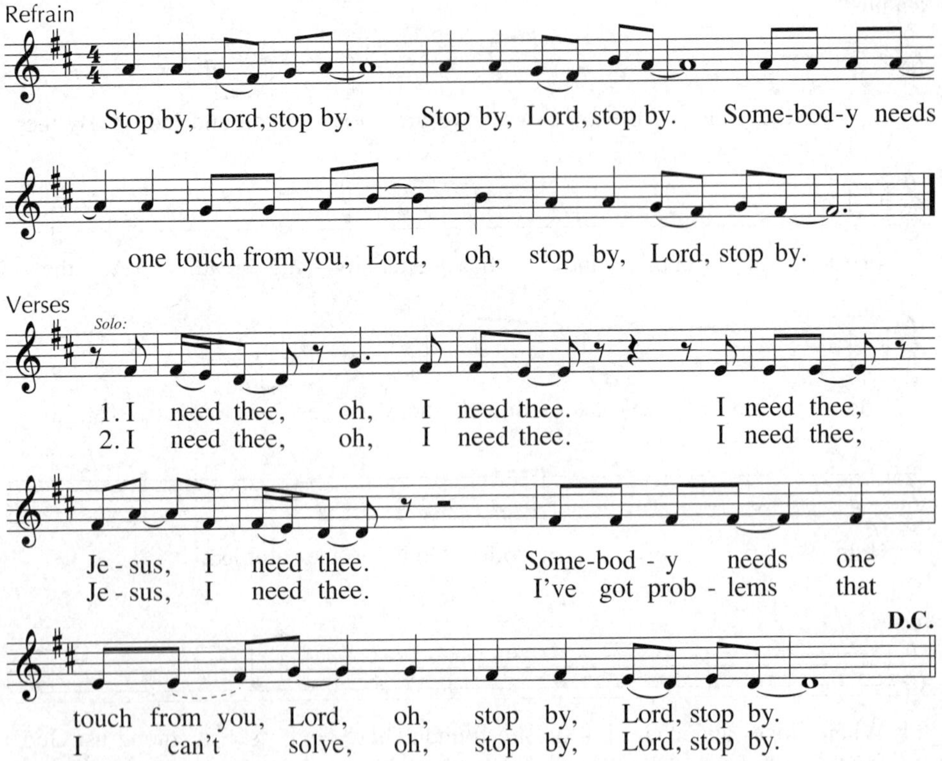

Refrain

Stop by, Lord, stop by.   Stop by, Lord, stop by.   Some-bod-y needs

one touch from you, Lord,   oh,   stop by, Lord, stop by.

Verses

Solo:

1. I   need thee,   oh,   I   need thee.   I   need thee,
2. I   need thee,   oh,   I   need thee.   I   need thee,

Je-sus,   I   need thee.   Some-bod-y   needs   one
Je-sus,   I   need thee.   I've got prob-lems   that

D.C.

touch from you, Lord,   oh,   stop by,   Lord, stop by.
I   can't   solve,   oh,   stop by,   Lord, stop by.

Text: Doris Wesley Bettis, b.1954
Tune: Doris Wesley Bettis, b.1954
© 2001, GIA Publications, Inc.

1053 O Christ, the Healer

1. O   Christ,   the   heal - er,   we   have   come   To
2. From   ev - 'ry   ail - ment   flesh   en - dures   Our
3. How   strong,   O   Lord,   are   our   de - sires,   How
4. In   con - flicts   that   de - stroy   our   health   We
5. Grant   that   we   all,   made   one   in   faith,   In

pray for health, to   plead   for friends. How   can   we   fail   to
bod - ies clam - or   to   be   freed; Yet   in   our   hearts we
weak our knowl-edge   of   our-selves! Re - lease   in   us   those
rec - og - nize   the world's dis - ease;   Our   com - mon   life   de -
your com-mun - i - ty   may   find   The   whole - ness   that,   en -

be   re - stored, When reached by   love   that   nev - er   ends?
would con - fess That   whole - ness is   our   deep - est   need.
heal - ing   truths Un - con - scious pride re - sists or shelves.
clares our   ills: Is   there   no   cure, O   Christ, for these?
rich - ing   us, Shall   reach   the   whole of   hu - man - kind.

Text: Fred Pratt Green, 1903–2000, © 1969, Hope Publishing Company
Tune: ERHALT UNS HERR, LM; Klug's *Geistliche Lieder*, 1543; harm. by J. S. Bach, 1685–1750

Hold Us, Jesus   1054

Refrain

Hold us, Je - sus, help us, Je - sus, heal us, Je-sus, we pray.

Hold us, Je - sus, help us, Je - sus, heal us, Je-sus, we pray.

Ky-ri-e, e-le - i - son,   Chri-ste, e-le - i - son.

Verses

Cantor: *Cantor:*
                                                                 In the
All:

1. In the des - ert of de-spair,
2. In the des - ert of   pain,   be with us, Lord, quench our thirst.
3. In the des - ert of   sin,

All:

dark - ness of   doubt,
dark - ness of a - buse,   walk with us, Lord, light our path.
dark - ness of   hate,

D.C.

Give us hope,   give us peace,   give us   strength.

Text: Chris de Silva, b.1967
Tune: Chris de Silva, b.1967
© 2007, GIA Publications, Inc.

1055 More Than Watchers for the Morning

1. Sit - ting with a child in sick - ness, List - 'ning
2. Yearn - ing for a graced for - give - ness; Sore, re -
3. Thirst - ing for a day of jus - tice, Hun - g'ring,

for a cry of pain, Bear - ing with a
pent - ing; deep in need; Wan - d'ring through a
plead-ing, now we kneel; Griev - ing for a

friend through sor - row, Keep - ing vig - il,
maze of ques - tions, Won - d'ring where our
world that's bro - ken, Pray - ing for its

we re - main:
paths will lead: More than watch - ers for the morn - ing,
wounds to heal:

we a - wait with wake - ful care, hop - ing through the

night of weep - ing God will lift us from de - spair.

Text: Mary Louise Bringle, b.1953, © 2002, GIA Publications, Inc.
Tune: GENEVA, 8 7 8 7 with refrain; George H. Day, 1883–1966, © 1942, The Church Pension Fund

Lord Jesus Christ, Lover of All   1056

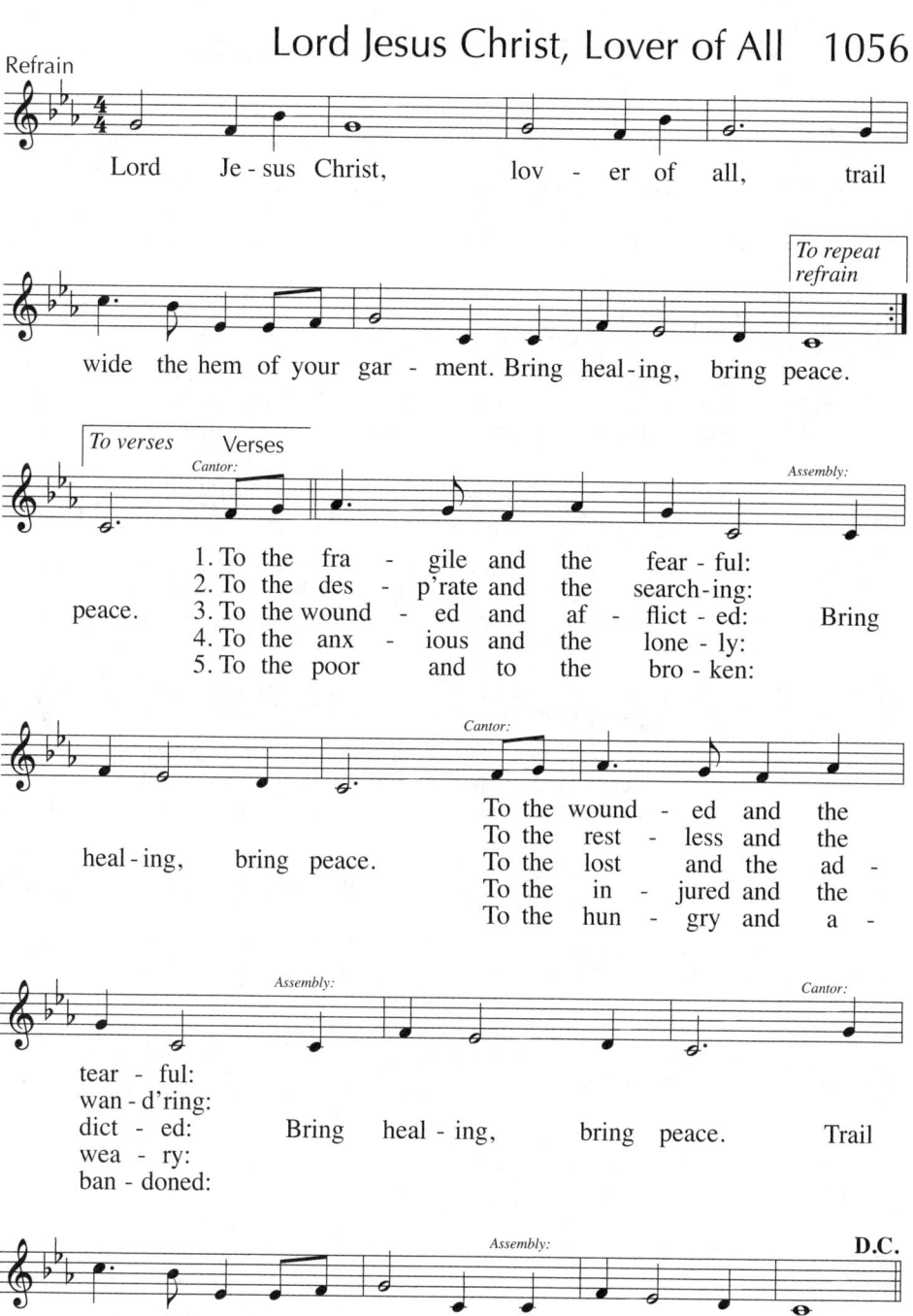

Text: Refrain, John L. Bell, b.1949, © 1987, Iona Community, GIA Publications, Inc., agent; verses, Tony E. Alonso, b.1980, © 2016, GIA Publications, Inc.
Tune: Refrain, John L. Bell, b.1949, © 1987, Iona Community, GIA Publications, Inc., agent; verses and refrain vocal harmony, Tony E. Alonso, b.1980, © 2016, GIA Publications, Inc.

1057 We Cannot Measure How You Heal

1. We can-not meas-ure how you heal Or
2. The pain that will not go a - way, The
3. So some have come who need your help, And

an - swer ev - 'ry suf - f'rer's prayer, Yet
guilt that clings from things long past, The
some have come to make a - mends, As

we be - lieve your grace re - sponds Where faith and
fear of what the fu - ture holds, Are pres - ent
hands which shaped and saved the world Are pres - ent

doubt u - nite to care. Your hands, though blood - ied
as if meant to last. But pres - ent too is
in the touch of friends. Lord, let your Spir - it

on the cross, Sur - vive to hold and heal and
love which tends The hurt we nev - er hoped to
meet us here To mend the bod - y, mind, and

warn, To car - ry all through death to
find, The pri - vate ag - o - nies in -
soul, To dis - en - tan - gle peace from

life And cra - dle chil - dren yet un - born.
side, The mem - o - ries that haunt the mind.
pain, And make your bro - ken peo - ple whole.

Text: John L. Bell, b.1949
Tune: YE BANKS AND BRAES, 8 8 8 8 D; Scottish traditional; arr. by John L. Bell, b.1949
© 1989, Iona Community, GIA Publications, Inc., agent

The God of Second Chances 1058

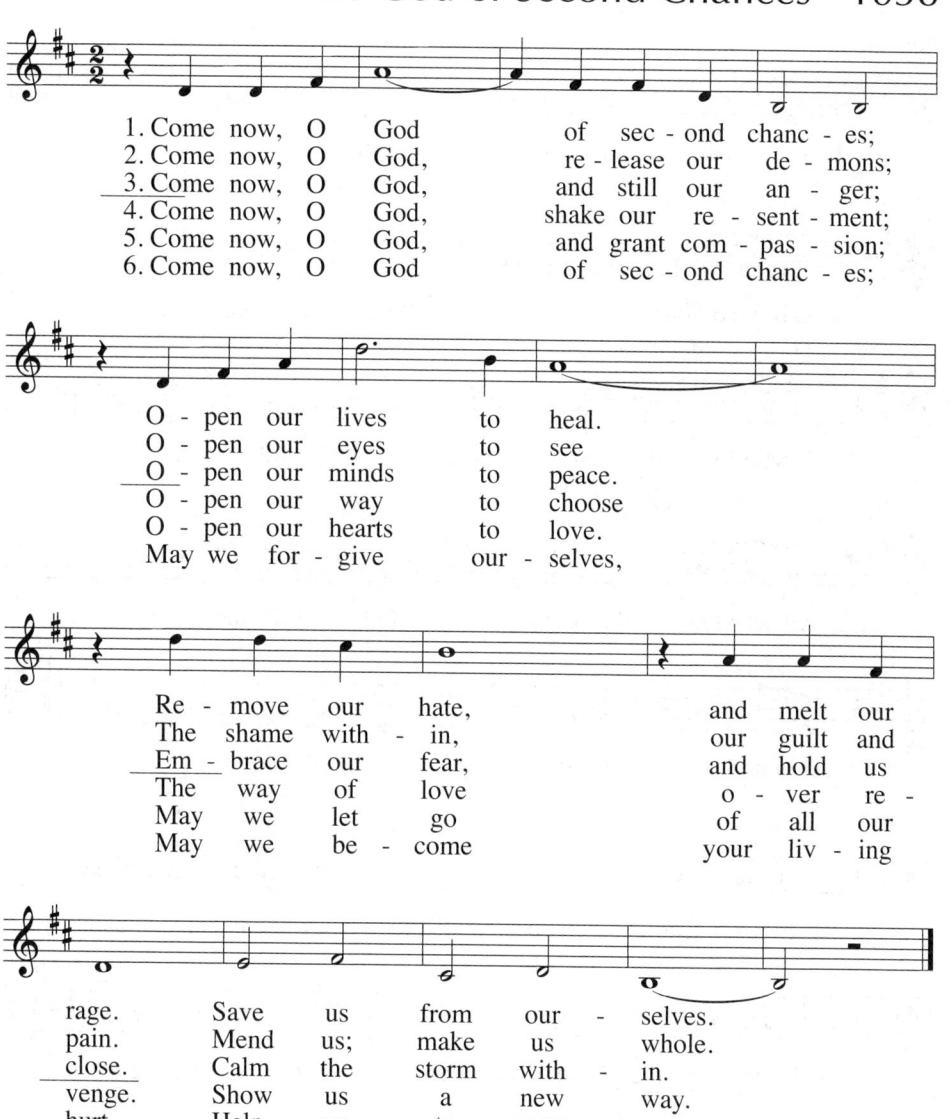

1. Come now, O God of sec - ond chanc - es;
2. Come now, O God, re - lease our de - mons;
3. Come now, O God, and still our an - ger;
4. Come now, O God, shake our re - sent - ment;
5. Come now, O God, and grant com - pas - sion;
6. Come now, O God of sec - ond chanc - es;

O - pen our lives to heal.
O - pen our eyes to see
O - pen our minds to peace.
O - pen our way to choose
O - pen our hearts to love.
May we for - give our - selves,

Re - move our hate, and melt our
The shame with - in, our guilt and
Em - brace our fear, and hold us
The way of love o - ver re -
May we let go of all our
May we be - come your liv - ing

rage. Save us from our - selves.
pain. Mend us; make us whole.
close. Calm the storm with - in.
venge. Show us a new way.
hurt. Help us to move on.
sign: Chil - dren of God's love.

Text: David Haas, b.1957
Tune: NEW BEGINNING, 9 6 8 5; David Haas, b.1957
© 2005, GIA Publications, Inc.

1059 Jesus, Heal Us

Refrain

Je-sus, heal us; Je-sus. Je-sus, hear us now.

Verse 1

1. All who fear the Lord: Wait for God's mer-cy.

D.C.

All who love the Lord: Come, he will fill you.

Verse 2

2. All who fear the Lord: Fol-low the way.

D.C.

All who love the Lord: Hope in God's good-ness.

Verse 3

3. All who fear the Lord: Keep your hearts pre-pared.

D.C.

All who love the Lord: Be hum-bled in God's pres-ence.

Verse 4

4. All who trust the Lord: God will up-hold you. Let us

D.C.

cling to our God; let us fall in the arms of the Lord!

Text: David Haas, b.1957
Tune: David Haas, b.1957
© 1988, GIA Publications, Inc.

Softly and Tenderly Jesus Is Calling   1060

1. Soft - ly and ten - der - ly   Je - sus   is   call - ing,
2. Why should we   tar - ry   when Je - sus   is   plead - ing,
3. Time   is   now fleet - ing,   the   mo - ments are pass - ing,
4. O   for   the   won - der - ful   love   he   has prom - ised,

Call - ing   for   you   and   for   me;
Plead - ing   for   you   and   for   me?
Pass - ing   from   you   and   from   me;
Prom - ised   for   you   and   for   me;

See,   on   the   por - tals he's   wait - ing and watch - ing,
Why should we lin - ger   and   heed   not   his   mer - cies,
Shad - ows are gath - er - ing, death - beds are com - ing,
Though we have sinned he   has   mer - cy   and par - don,

Watch - ing   for   you   and for   me.
Mer - cies   for   you   and for   me?
Com - ing   for   you   and for   me.
Par - don   for   you   and for   me.

Come home,   come home,   Ye who are wea - ry,   come

home;   Ear - nest - ly,   ten - der - ly,

Je - sus is call - ing —   Call - ing,   "O sin - ner, come   home!"

Text: Will L. Thompson, 1847–1909
Tune: Will L. Thompson, 1847–1909

1061 Come, You Sinners, Poor and Needy

1. Come, you sin - ners, poor and need - y,
2. Come, you thirst - y, come, and wel - come,
3. Come, you wea - ry, heav - y lad - en,

Weak and wound - ed, sick and sore, Je - sus, Son of
God's free boun - ty glo - ri - fy: True be - lief and
Lost and ru - ined by the fall; If you tar - ry

God, will save you, Full of pit - y, love, and pow'r.
true re - pen - tance, Ev - 'ry grace that brings you nigh.
till you're bet - ter, You will nev - er come at all.

I will a-rise and go to Je - sus, He will em-brace me

in his arms; In the arms of my dear

Sav - ior, Oh, there are ten thou - sand charms.

Text: Verses, Joseph Hart, 1712–1768, *Hymns Composed on Various Subjects*, 1759, alt.; refrain anonymous
Tune: RESTORATION, 8 7 8 7 with refrain; *Southern Harmony*, 1835; harm. by George E. Mims, b.1938, © 1979, George E. Mims

Forgive Our Sins 1062

1. "For - give our sins as we for - give," You
2. How can your par - don reach and bless The
3. In blaz - ing light your cross re - veals The
4. Lord, cleanse the depths with - in our souls And

taught us, Lord, to pray; But you a - lone can
un - for - giv - ing heart That broods on wrongs and
truth we dim - ly knew: How small are oth - ers'
bid re - sent - ment cease. Then, by your mer - cy

grant us grace To live the words we say.
will not let Old bit - ter - ness de - part?
debts to us, How great our debt to you!
rec - on - ciled, Our lives will spread your peace.

Text: Rosamond E. Herklots, 1905–1987, alt., © Oxford University Press
Tune: DETROIT, CM; Supplement to *Kentucky Harmony*, 1820; harm. by Gerald H. Knight, 1908–1979, © The Royal School of Church Music

Alternate tune: MORNING SONG

God Is Forgiveness 1063

Ostinato Refrain

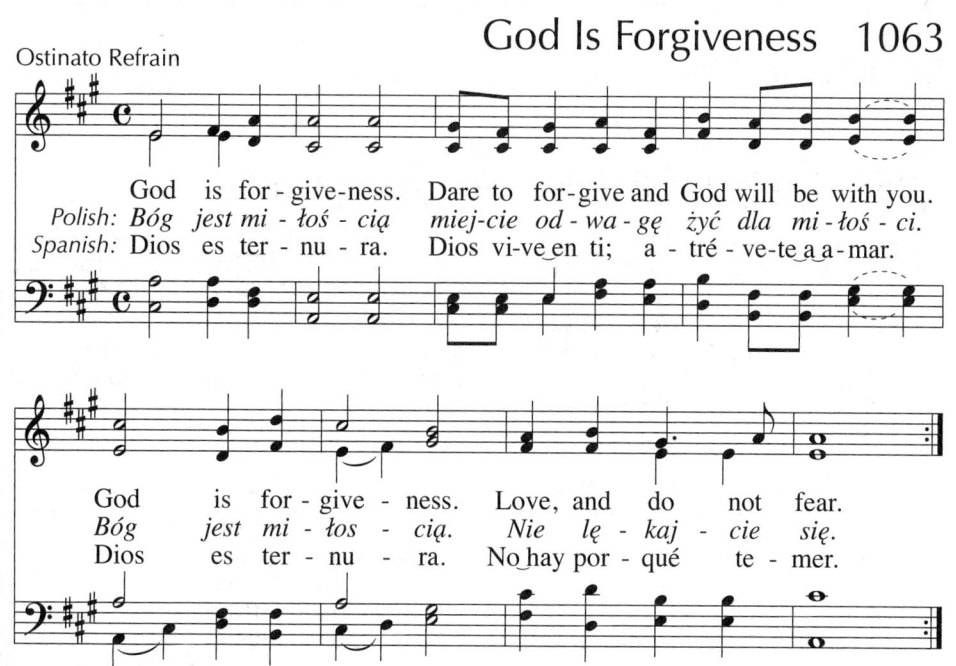

God is for - give-ness. Dare to for-give and God will be with you.
Polish: Bóg jest mi - łoś - cią miej-cie od - wa - gę żyć dla mi - łoś - ci.
Spanish: Dios es ter - nu - ra. Dios vi-ve en ti; a - tré - ve-te a a - mar.

God is for - give - ness. Love, and do not fear.
Bóg jest mi - łos - cią. Nie lę - kaj - cie się.
Dios es ter - nu - ra. No hay por - qué te - mer.

Text: Taizé Community
Tune: Taizé Community
© 2007, 2011, Les Presses de Taizé, GIA Publications, Inc., agent

1064 Our Father, We Have Wandered

1. Our Fa-ther, we have wan-dered And hid-den from your face;
2. And now at length dis-cern-ing The e-vil that we do,
3. O Lord of all the liv-ing, Both ban-ished and re-stored,

In fool-ish-ness have squan-dered Your leg-a-cy of grace.
Be-hold us, Lord, re-turn-ing With hope and trust to you.
Com-pas-sion-ate, for-giv-ing, And ev-er-car-ing Lord,

But now, in ex-ile dwell-ing, We rise with fear and shame,
In haste you come to meet us And home re-joic-ing bring,
Grant now that our trans-gress-ing, Our faith-less-ness may cease.

As, dis-tant but com-pell-ing, We hear you call our name.
In glad-ness there to greet us With calf and robe and ring.
Stretch out your hand in bless-ing, In par-don, and in peace.

Text: Kevin Nichols, 1929–2006, © 1980, ICEL
Tune: PASSION CHORALE, 7 6 7 6 D; Hans Leo Hassler, 1564–1612; harm. by J. S. Bach, 1685–1750

1065 Help Us Forgive, Forgiving Lord

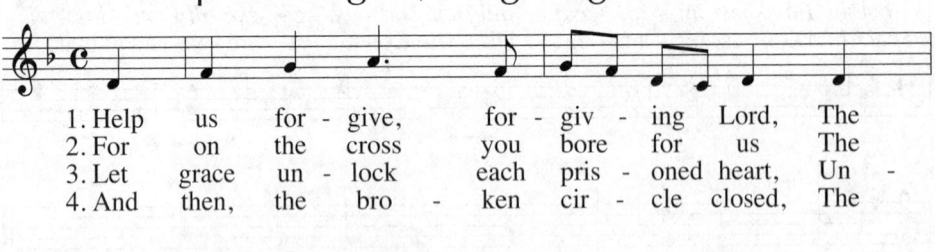

1. Help us for-give, for-giv-ing Lord, The
2. For on the cross you bore for us The
3. Let grace un-lock each pris-oned heart, Un -
4. And then, the bro-ken cir-cle closed, The

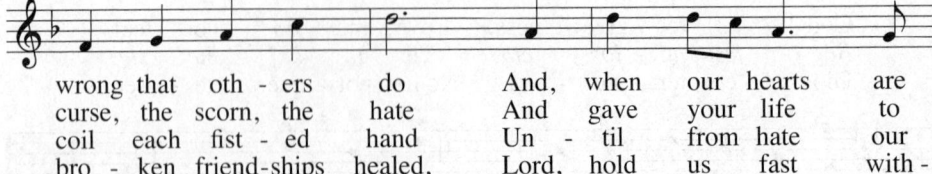

wrong that oth-ers do And, when our hearts are
curse, the scorn, the hate And gave your life to
coil each fist-ed hand Un-til from hate our
bro-ken friend-ships healed, Lord, hold us fast with-

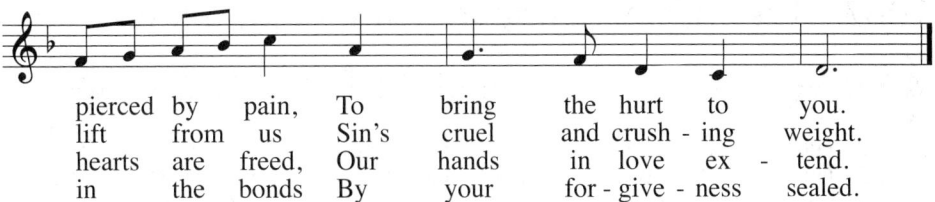

pierced by pain, To bring the hurt to you.
lift from us Sin's cruel and crush - ing weight.
hearts are freed, Our hands in love ex - tend.
in the bonds By your for - give - ness sealed.

Text: Herman G. Stuempfle, Jr., 1923–2007, © 1997, GIA Publications, Inc.
Tune: DETROIT, CM; Supplement to *Kentucky Harmony*, 1820; harm. by Gerald H. Knight, 1908–1979, © The Royal School of Church Music

Healer of Our Every Ill   1066

Refrain

Heal - er of our ev - 'ry ill, Light of each to - mor - row,

Give us peace be - yond our fear And hope be - yond our sor - row.

Verses

1. You who know our fears and sad - ness,
2. In the pain and joy, be - hold - ing
3. Give us strength to love each oth - er,
4. You who know each thought and feel - ing,

Grace us with your peace and glad - ness.
How your grace is still un - fold - ing,
Ev - 'ry sis - ter, ev - 'ry broth - er.
Teach us all your way of heal - ing.

D.C.

Spir - it of all com - fort, fill our hearts.
Give us all your vi - sion, God of love.
Spir - it of all kind - ness, be our guide.
Spir - it of com - pas - sion, fill each heart.

Text: Marty Haugen, b.1950
Tune: HEALER OF OUR EVERY ILL, 88 9 with refrain; Marty Haugen, b.1950
© 1987, GIA Publications, Inc.

1067 The Master Came to Bring Good News

1. The Mas - ter came to bring good news, The
2. The Law's ful - filled through Je - sus Christ, The
3. To seek the sin - ners Je - sus came, To
4. For - give us, Lord, as we for - give And

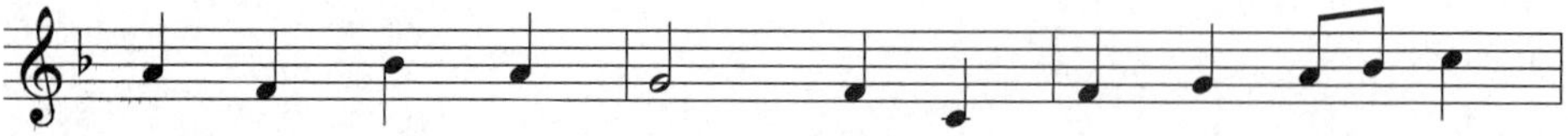

news of love and free - dom, To heal the sick and
man who lived for oth - ers. The law of Christ is:
live a - mong the friend - less, To show them love that
seek to help each oth - er. For - give us, Lord, and

seek the poor, To build the peace - ful king - dom.
Serve in love Our sis - ters and our broth - ers.
they might share The king - dom that is end - less.
we shall live To pray and work to - geth - er.

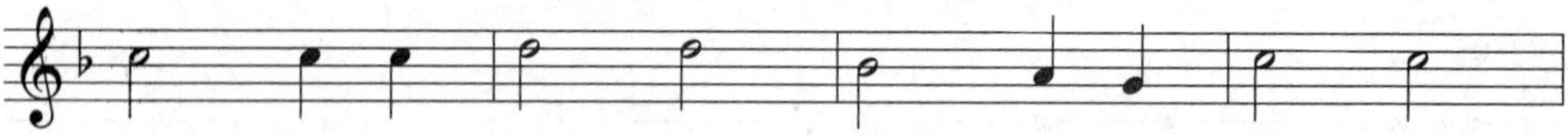

Fa - ther, for - give us! Through Je - sus hear us!

As we for - give one an - oth - er!

Text: Ralph Finn, b.1941, © 1965, GIA Publications, Inc.
Tune: ICH GLAUB AN GOTT, 8 7 8 7 with refrain; Mainz *Gesangbuch*, 1870; harm. by Richard Proulx, 1937–2010, © 1986, GIA Publications, Inc.

1068 God of Mercy and Compassion

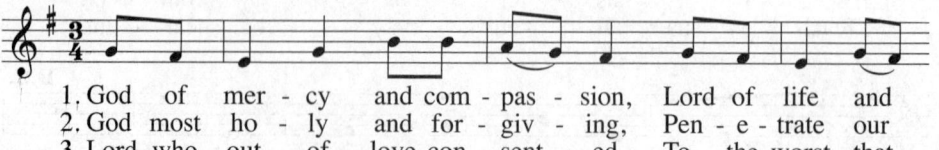

1. God of mer - cy and com - pas - sion, Lord of life and
2. God most ho - ly and for - giv - ing, Pen - e - trate our
3. Lord, who out of love con - sent - ed To the worst that

blind - ing light, Truth whom crea - tures would re - fash - ion, Place on
pride and sloth; On a peo - ple part - ly liv - ing, Place the
we could do; Lord, a - ban - doned and tor - ment - ed, Let us

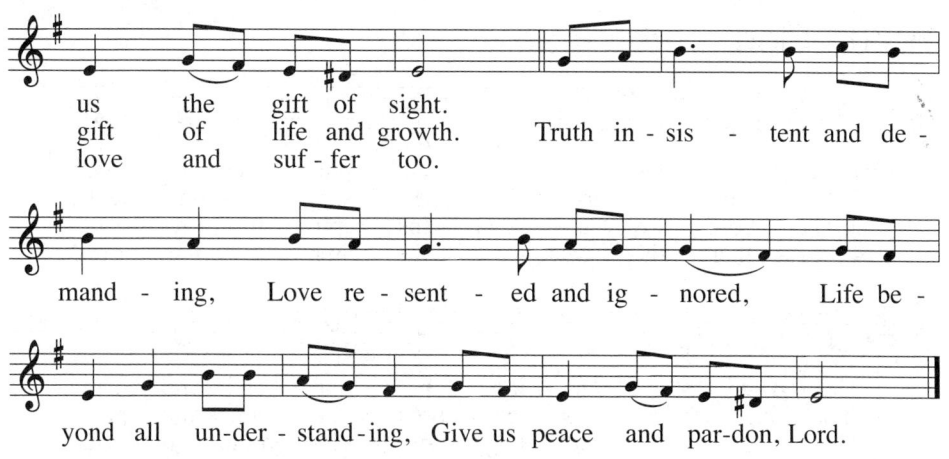

us the gift of sight.
gift of life and growth. Truth in - sis - tent and de -
love and suf - fer too.

mand - ing, Love re - sent - ed and ig - nored, Life be -

yond all un - der - stand - ing, Give us peace and par - don, Lord.

Text: Michael Hodgetts, alt., ©
Tune: AU SANG QU'UN DIEU, 8 7 8 7 with refrain; French melody, adapt. from G. B. Pergolesi, 1710–1736

Yes, I Shall Arise 1069

Refrain

Yes, I shall a - rise and re - turn to my Fa - ther!

Verses

1. To you, O Lord, I lift up my
2. Look down on me, have mer - cy, O
3. My heart and soul shall yearn for your
4. Do not with - hold your good - ness from
5. To you I pray; have pit - y on

D.C.

soul; In you, O my God, I place all my trust.
Lord; For - give me my sins, be - hold all my grief.
face; Be gra - cious to me and an - swer my plea.
me; O Lord, may your love be deep in my soul.
me; My God, I have sinned a - gainst your great love.

6. Mercy I cry, O Lord, wash me clean; And cleaner than snow my spirit shall be.

7. Give me again the joy of your help; Now open my lips, your praise I will sing.

8. Happy are they, forgiven by God; Their sins blotted out, their guilt is no more.

9. You are my joy, my refuge and strength; Let all upright hearts give praise to the Lord.

10. My soul will sing, my heart will rejoice; The blessings of God will fill all my days.

Text: Psalm 51; Lucien Deiss, CSSp, 1921–2007
Tune: PRODIGAL, 9 10 with refrain; Lucien Deiss, CSSp, 1921–2007

1070 God, in the Planning

1. God, in the plan - ning and pur - pose of life,
2. Je - sus was found, at a sim - i - lar feast,
3. There - fore we pray that his spir - it pre - side
4. Praise then the Mak - er, the Spir - it, the Son,

Hal - lowed the un - ion of hus - band and wife:
Tak - ing the roles of both ser - vant and priest,
O - ver the wed - ding of bride - groom and bride,
Source of the love through which two are made one.

This we em - bod - y where love is dis - played,
Turn - ing cre - at - ed things in - to di - vine,
Help - ing them share what is ten - der and true,
God's is the glo - ry, the good - ness, and grace

Rings are pre - sent - ed and prom - is - es made.
Tears in - to laugh - ter and wa - ter to wine.
Light - ing with love all they dream of and do.
Seen in this mar - riage and known in this place.

Text: John L. Bell, b.1949, © 1989, Iona Community, GIA Publications, Inc., agent
Tune: SLANE, 10 10 10 10; Irish melody; harm. by Erik Routley, 1917–1982, © 1975, Hope Publishing Company

1071 When Love Is Found

1. When love is found and hope comes home, Sing and be
2. When love has flow'red in trust and care, Build both each
3. When love is tried as loved ones change, Hold still to
4. When love is torn, and trust be - trayed, Pray strength to
5. Praise God for love, praise God for life, In age or

glad that two are one. When love ex - plodes and
day, that love may dare To reach be - yond home's
hope, though all seems strange, Till ease re - turns and
love till tor - ments fade, Till lov - ers keep no
youth, in calm or strife. Lift up your hearts! Let

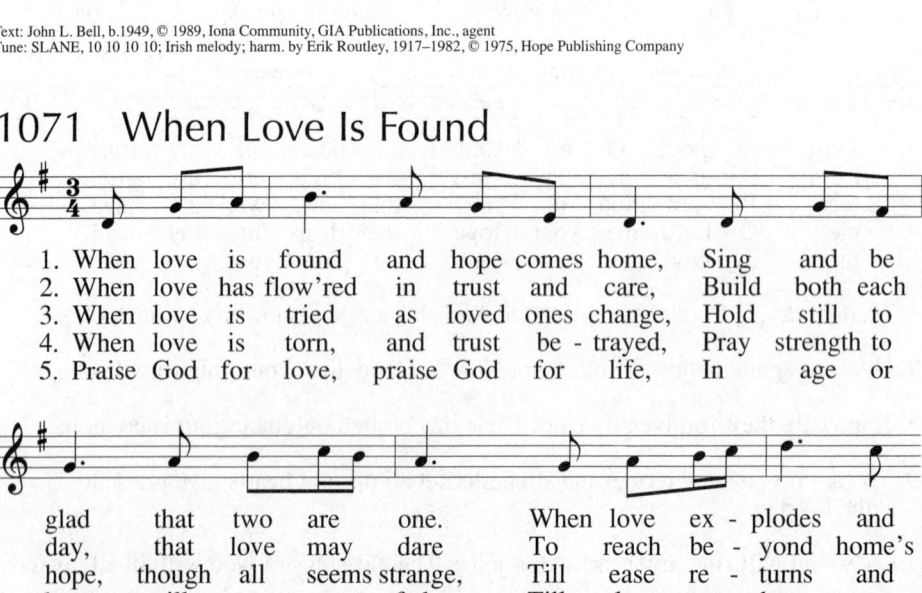

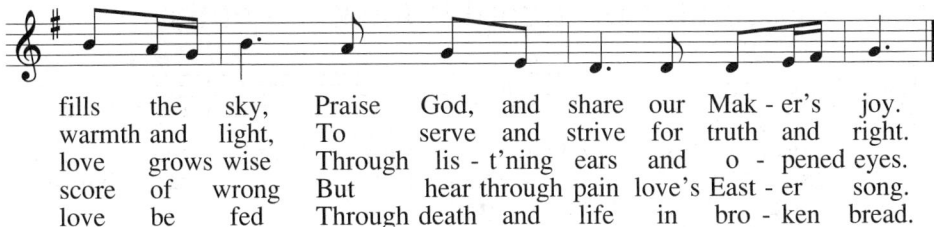

fills	the	sky,	Praise	God,	and	share	our	Mak -	er's	joy.
warmth	and	light,	To	serve	and	strive	for	truth	and	right.
love	grows	wise	Through	lis - t'ning	ears	and	o -	pened	eyes.
score	of	wrong	But	hear	through	pain	love's	East -	er	song.
love	be	fed	Through	death	and	life	in	bro -	ken	bread.

Text: Brian Wren, b.1936, © 1983, Hope Publishing Company
Tune: O WALY WALY, LM; English melody; harm. by Martin West, b.1929, © 1983, Hope Publishing Company

Wherever You Go 1072

Verses

1. Come, set me like a seal upon your heart; a seal protecting your arm.
   Deep waters cannot quench this love; the ocean will not sweep it away.

2. Arise my beloved, come to me; the rains are gone, the winter is past.
   The flowers appear, the vines are pruned, and the dove's song is heard in our land.

3. Wherever you stay, I will stay; your people will be my people.
   Wherever you die, so will I die with you in the arms of God!

Text: Ruth 1:16–17; Song of Songs 2:10–12, 7:6–7; David Haas, b.1957
Tune: David Haas, b.1957
© 1993, GIA Publications, Inc.

1073 Love Has Brought Us Here Together

1. Love has brought us here to-geth - er:
2. Love is gen - tle, love is pa - tient,
3. Love does not re - joice at e - vil;

Love of fam - 'ly, love of friends;
Soft in words and kind in deeds.
Love re - joic - es in the right.

Love, our vow till death should part us;
Love is strong and nev - er pom - pous;
Keen in giv - ing and for - giv - ing,

Love, God's gift, that nev - er ends.
Love puts first the oth - er's needs.
Spread - ing love is love's de - light.

From our birth, through - out our life - time,
Not quick - tem - pered or re - sent - ful,
When two peo - ple pledge their un - ion,

Love's in - sis - tence calls our name.
Prone to take of - fense or brood,
All who wit - ness are re - newed,

Floods of wa - ters can - not drown it
Love ex - cels in grace and mer - cy,
Feast - ing at love's earth - ly ban - quet,

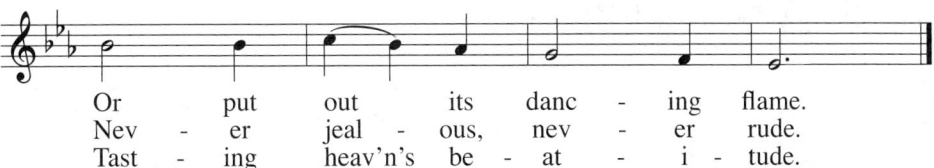

Or   put   out   its   danc - ing   flame.
Nev - er   jeal - ous,   nev - er   rude.
Tast - ing   heav'n's   be - at - i - tude.

Text: Mary Louise Bringle, b.1953, © 2010, GIA Publications, Inc.
Tune: HYFRYDOL, 8 7 8 7 D; Rowland H. Prichard, 1811–1887

God of Love, Embrace Your People   1074

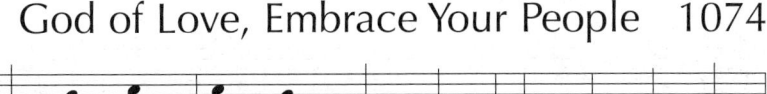

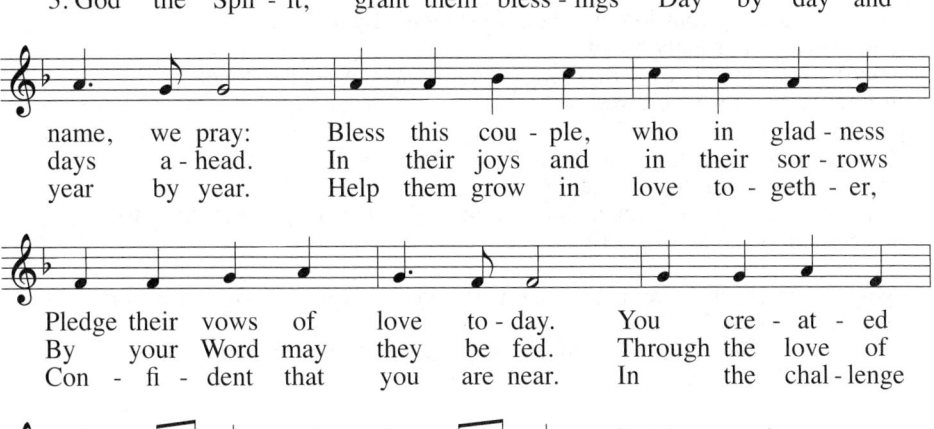

1. God   of   love, em - brace your   peo - ple.   Gath - ered   in   your
2. Christ our   light, shine   forth   in   splen - dor;   Lead these two   in
3. God   the   Spir - it,   grant them   bless - ings   Day   by   day and

name,   we pray: Bless   this   cou - ple,   who   in   glad - ness
days   a - head.   In   their   joys   and   in   their   sor - rows
year   by   year.   Help   them grow   in   love   to - geth - er,

Pledge their   vows   of   love   to - day.   You   cre - at - ed
By   your   Word may   they   be   fed.   Through the   love   of
Con - fi - dent   that   you   are near.   In   the   chal - lenge

man   and   wom - an   In   your   im - age,   to   be   one.
friends   and   fam - 'ly   Let   them know your   love   out-poured;
of   to - mor - row   Guide them   ev - er   in   your ways.

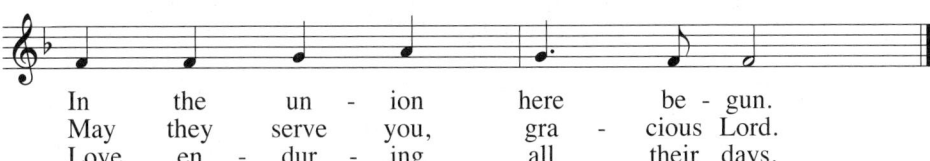

May   your   love   be   al - ways   pres - ent
In   the   Church,   where   all   find   wel - come,
May   their   prom - ise   last   for - ev - er,

In   the   un - ion   here   be - gun.
May   they   serve   you,   gra - cious Lord.
Love   en - dur - ing   all   their days.

Text: James J. Chepponis, b.1956, © 2011, GIA Publications, Inc.
Tune: HYMN TO JOY, 8 7 8 7 D; arr. from Ludwig van Beethoven, 1770–1827, by Edward Hodges, 1796–1867

1075   A Nuptial Blessing

Refrain

May God bless you, hold and keep you; may God's mer-cy shine on you, guide your work and guard your rest-ing, keep your love for ev-er new.

Verses

1. May God satisfy your longing, be refreshment at your table,
   and provide your daily bread,
   guard your going and your coming, be the solace in your silence:
   life within the lives you wed.

2. May God join your hopeful spirits, fill your hearts with truth and courage,
   trust to share both joy and tears,
   teach love to your children's children; may your household learn to witness
   living faith through all your years.

3. May God make your home a refuge where you warmly welcome strangers
   and the lowly find a place;
   make you caring, kind companions, help you meet the needs of neighbors,
   finding Christ in every face.

Text: Vicki Klima, b.1952; adapt. by Michael Joncas, b.1951, and George Szews, b.1951
Tune: Michael Joncas, b.1951
© 1989, GIA Publications, Inc.

1076   A Litany of Love

Responses

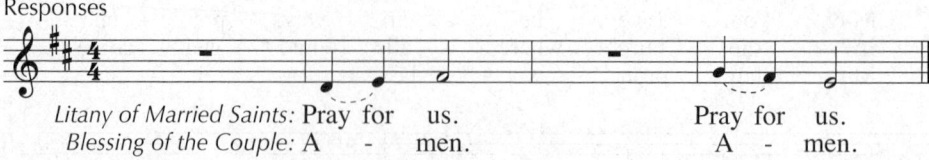

Litany of Married Saints: Pray for us.   Pray for us.
Blessing of the Couple: A - men.   A - men.

Text: Tony E. Alonso, b.1980
Tune: Based on *Canon in D*, Johann Pachelbel, 1653–1706; arr. by Tony E. Alonso, b.1980
© 2010, GIA Publications, Inc.

Love Is the Sunlight 1077

1. Love is the sun - light Shaped of your splen - dor,
2. Love is the spa - cious Qui - et of shad - ows,
3. May we in glad - ness Grow in your sun - shine,

Love is the star bright Born of your hand,
Love is the gra - cious Shade of re - lease,
May we in sad - ness Rest in your shade,

Bless - ing of heav - en Gra - cious - ly giv - en,
Mist of the morn - ing, Mid - day a - dorn - ing,
Giv - ing and gain - ing, Ev - er re - main - ing,

Ra - diant with glo - ry From your com - mand.
Cool with the twi - light Breath of your peace.
One in the mar - riage Your love has made.

Text: Borghild Jacobson, © 1981, Concordia Publishing House
Tune: BUNESSAN, 5 5 5 4 D; Gaelic melody; acc. by Marty Haugen, b.1950, © 1987, GIA Publications, Inc.

May the Angels Lead You into Paradise 1078

Cantor, then all:

May the an - gels lead you in - to par - a - dise;

may the mar - tyrs come to wel - come you and

take you to the ho - ly cit - y, the

new and e - ter - nal Je - ru - sa - lem.

Text: *In paradisum; Rite of Funerals,* © 1970, ICEL
Tune: Howard Hughes, SM, b.1930, © 1977, ICEL

1079 God of Love, Whose Mercies Daily

1. God of love, whose mer-cies dai-ly Like the morn-ing are re-born, Look on us, your gath-ered peo-ple: Heart-sick, trou-bled, wea-ry, worn, Who be-fore you raise our voic-es, Nam-ing those called from our sight, Con-fi-dent that each is pre-cious And is pres-ent in your light.

2. Christ, who lived through earth-ly suf-f'ring, Loss, be-tray-al, fear and death, Ev-er-faith-ful to your call-ing, Serv-ing till your fi-nal breath: In your name we make me-mo-rial Of those gath-ered at your hand; Freed from pain, de-spair and sor-row, Ris-en Lord, with you they stand.

3. Ho-ly Spir-it, whose in-dwell-ing Makes a tem-ple of each heart, Par-a-clete of strength-'ning pow-er, Be with us and ne'er de-part; As we name each name be-fore you, All are known and loved and count-ed; For-ti-fy us with your grace That we strive to live in whole-ness Till in heav'n we see your face.

4. God of mer-cy, love and mem-'ry, Give us strength to fol-low you; Let us trust that our de-part-ed, Now at rest, their strug-gle through, All are known and loved and count-ed; As we name them, so may we, Joined with them in one com-mun-ion, Lov-ing, serv-ing ev-er be.

Text: J. Michael Thompson, b.1953, © 1994, World Library Publications
Tune: BEACH SPRING, 8 7 8 7 D; *The Sacred Harp*, 1844; harm. by Ronald A. Nelson, 1927–2014, © 1978, *Lutheran Book of Worship*, admin. by Augsburg Fortress

There Is a Place   1080

1. There is a place pre - pared for lit - tle
2. There is a place where hands which held ours
3. There is a place where all the lost po -
4. There is a place where God will hear our
5. Je - sus, who bids us be like lit - tle

chil - dren, Those we once lived for, those we deep - ly
tight - ly Now are re - leased be - yond all hurt and
ten - tial Yields its full prom - ise, finds its true in -
ques - tions, Suf - fer our an - ger, share our speech-less
chil - dren, Shields those our arms are yearn-ing to em -

mourn, Those who from play, from learn - ing and from
fear, Healed by that love which al - so feels our
tent; Si - lenced no more, young voic - es ech - o
grief, Gen - tly re - pair the in - no-cence of
brace. God will en - sure that all are re - u -

laugh - ter, Cruel - ly were torn.
sor - row Tear af - ter tear.
free - ly As they were meant.
lov - ing And of be - lief.
nit - ed; There is a place.

Text: John L. Bell, b.1949
Tune: DUNBLANE PRIMARY, 11 10 11 4; John L. Bell, b.1949
© 1996, Iona Community, GIA Publications, Inc., agent

1081 O Lord, You Died That All Might Live

1. O Lord, you died that all might live And
2. Lord, bless our friend who died in you. As
3. In green and pleas - ant pas - tures feed The
4. Per - fect us, Lord of pow'r and might, That,

rise to see the per - fect day. The full - ness of your
you have giv - en him/her re - lease, So raise him/her up, your
sheep that you have sum - moned hence; And by the still, cool
with our friend, we all may come To dwell with - in your

mer - cy give To this our friend for whom we pray.
ser - vant true, And give him/her ev - er - last - ing peace.
wa - ters lead Your flock in lov - ing prov - i - dence.
cit - y bright, Je - ru - sa - lem, our heav'n - ly home.

O Lamb of God, Re - deem - er blest, Grant

him/her e - ter - nal light and rest.

Text: Richard F. Littledale, 1833–1890, alt.
Tune: MELITA, LM with refrain; John B. Dykes, 1823–1876

1082 May Holy Angels Lead You

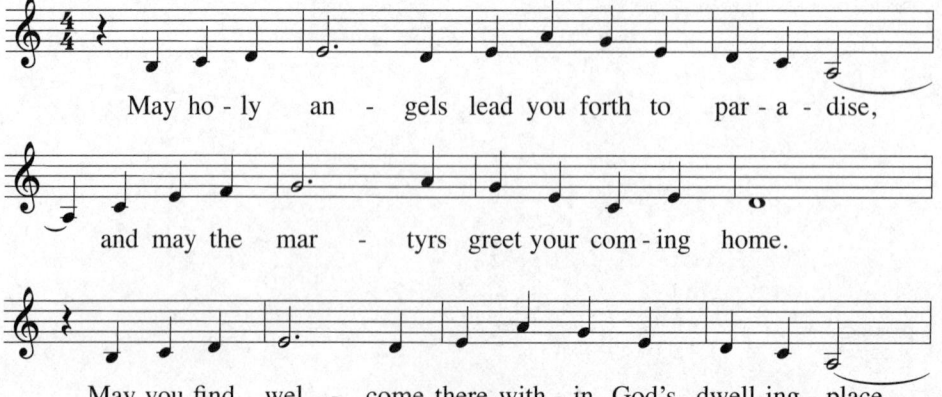

May ho - ly an - gels lead you forth to par - a - dise,

and may the mar - tyrs greet your com - ing home.

May you find wel - come there with - in God's dwell-ing - place, the rad - iant cit - y, New Je - ru - sa - lem.

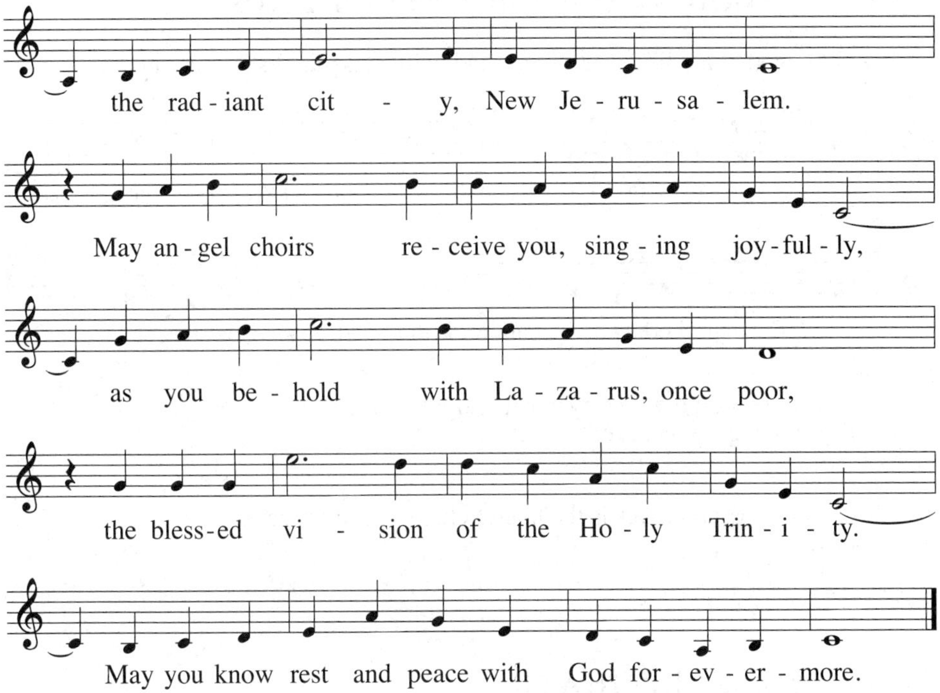

May an - gel choirs re - ceive you, sing - ing joy - ful - ly,

as you be - hold with La - za - rus, once poor,

the bless - ed vi - sion of the Ho - ly Trin - i - ty.

May you know rest and peace with God for - ev - er - more.

Text: *In paradisum* and *Chorus angelorum*; Latin 11th C.; para. by Ronald F. Krisman, b.1946, © 2011, GIA Publications, Inc.
Tune: LONDONDERRY AIRE, 11 10 11 10 D; arr. by John L. Bell, b.1949, © 1996, Iona Community, GIA Publications, Inc., agent

Rest Eternal 1083

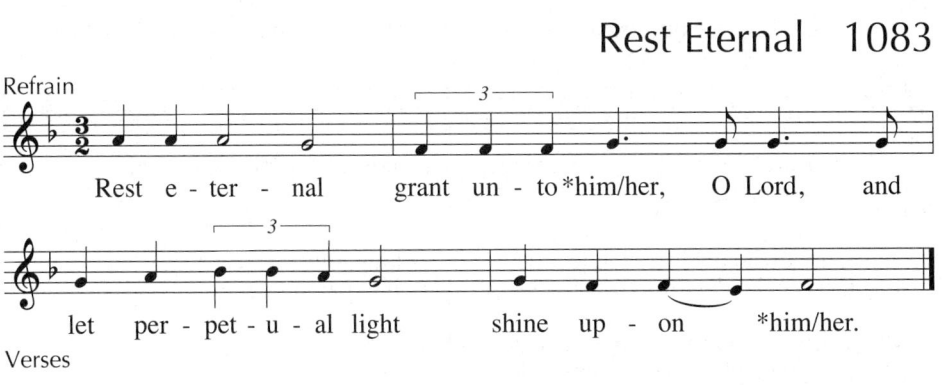

Refrain

Rest e - ter - nal grant un - to *him/her, O Lord, and

let per - pet - u - al light shine up - on *him/her.

Verses

1. It is fitting to sing a hymn to you in Zion:
   all flesh shall come to you.

2. For the souls of the just are in the hands of God:
   no pain shall reach them there.

3. Like a deer that longs for running streams,
   so longs my soul for you.

Or: them

Text: Refrain, Requiem Mass; vs. 1, Psalm 65; vs. 2, Wisdom 3; adapt. by Gail Gillispie, © 2007, World Library Publications;
vs. 3; *Lectionary for Mass*, © 1969, 1981, 1977, ICEL
Music: Gail Gillispie, © 2007, World Library Publications

1084   I Know That My Redeemer Lives

Cantor: I know that my Redeemer lives, and on the last day I shall rise again;

in my bod - y I shall look on God, my Sav - ior,

in my bod - y I shall look on God, my Sav - ior.

Cantor:
I myself shall see him; my own eyes will gaze on him,
my own eyes will gaze on him;
in my body...

This is the hope I cherish, this is the hope I cherish in my heart;
in my body...

Text: *Rite of Funerals,* © 1970, ICEL
Tune: Howard Hughes, SM, b.1930, © 1977, ICEL

1085   Song of Farewell

Refrain

Dy-ing you de-stroyed our death!   Ris-ing you re - stored our life!

Lord Je - sus,   Lord Je - sus, come in glo - ry!

Verses

1. May Christ who died for you lead you into his kingdom;
   may Christ who died for you lead you this day into paradise.

2. May Christ, the Good Shepherd, lead you home today
   and give you a place within his flock.

Alternate children's verse:
2. May Christ, the Good Shepherd, take you on his shoulders
   and bring you home, bring you home today.

3. May the angels lead you into paradise;
   may the martyrs come to welcome you
   and take you to the Holy City, the new and eternal Jerusalem.

4. May the choirs of angels come to meet you,
   may the choirs of angels come to meet you;
   where Lazarus is poor no longer, may you have eternal life in Christ.

Alternate children's verse:
4. May the choirs of angels come to meet you,
   may the choirs of angels come to meet you;
   and with all God's children may you have eternal life in Christ.

Text: Memorial Acclamation, © 1973, ICEL; *In paradisum;* Michael Marchal, b.1951, © 1988, GIA Publications, Inc.
Tune: Michael Joncas, b.1951, © 1988, GIA Publications, Inc.

This Is My Song 1086

1. This is my song, O God of all the na - tions,
2. My coun - try's skies are blu - er than the o - cean,
3. This is my prayer, O Lord of all earth's king - doms:

A song of peace for lands a - far and mine.
And sun - light beams on clo - ver - leaf and pine.
Your king - dom come; on earth your will be done.

This is my home, the coun - try where my heart is;
But oth - er lands have sun - light too, and clo - ver,
Let Christ be lift - ed up till all shall serve him,

Here are my hopes, my dreams, my ho - ly shrine.
And skies are ev - 'ry - where as blue as mine.
And hearts u - nit - ed learn to live as one.

But oth - er hearts in oth - er lands are beat - ing
So hear my song, O God of all the na - tions,
So hear my prayer, O God of all the na - tions.

With hopes and dreams as true and high as mine.
A song of peace for their land and for mine.
My - self I give you; let your will be done.

Text: Sts. 1, 2, Lloyd Stone, 1912–1993; st. 3, Georgia Harkness, 1891–1974, © 1964, Lorenz Publishing Co.
Tune: FINLANDIA, 11 10 11 10 11 10; Jean Sibelius, 1865–1957

1087 America the Beautiful

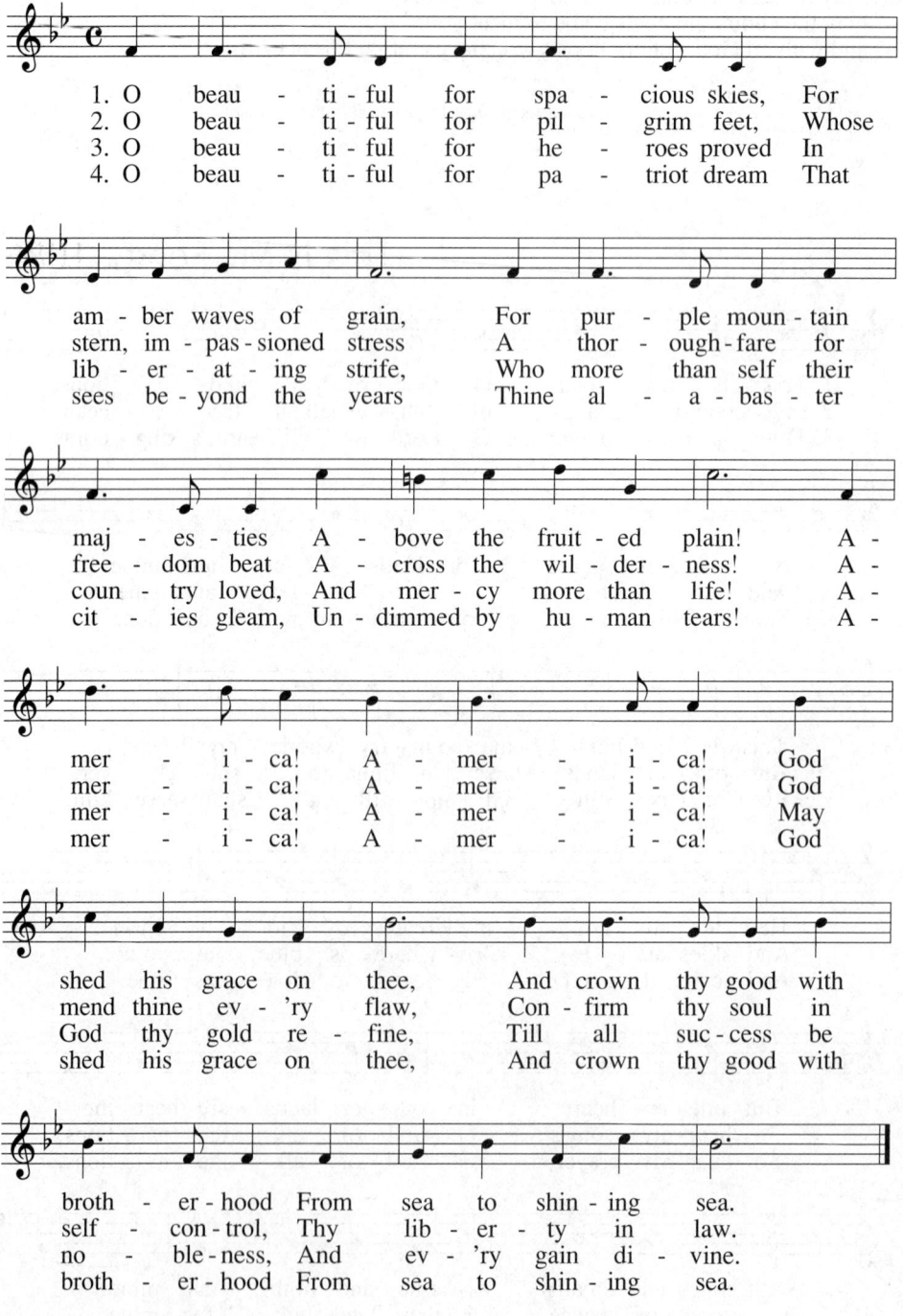

1. O beau - ti - ful for spa - cious skies, For
2. O beau - ti - ful for pil - grim feet, Whose
3. O beau - ti - ful for he - roes proved In
4. O beau - ti - ful for pa - triot dream That

am - ber waves of grain, For pur - ple moun - tain
stern, im - pas - sioned stress A thor - ough - fare for
lib - er - at - ing strife, Who more than self their
sees be - yond the years Thine al - a - bas - ter

maj - es - ties A - bove the fruit - ed plain! A -
free - dom beat A - cross the wil - der - ness! A -
coun - try loved, And mer - cy more than life! A -
cit - ies gleam, Un - dimmed by hu - man tears! A -

mer - i - ca! A - mer - i - ca! God
mer - i - ca! A - mer - i - ca! God
mer - i - ca! A - mer - i - ca! May
mer - i - ca! A - mer - i - ca! God

shed his grace on thee, And crown thy good with
mend thine ev - 'ry flaw, Con - firm thy soul in
God thy gold re - fine, Till all suc - cess be
shed his grace on thee, And crown thy good with

broth - er - hood From sea to shin - ing sea.
self - con - trol, Thy lib - er - ty in law.
no - ble - ness, And ev - 'ry gain di - vine.
broth - er - hood From sea to shin - ing sea.

Text: Katherine L. Bates, 1859–1929
Tune: MATERNA, CMD; Samuel A. Ward, 1848–1903

The God of All Eternity 1088

1. The God of all e - ter - ni - ty, Un - bound by
2. What shall we of - fer God to - day— Our dreams of
3. God does not share our doubts and fears, Nor shrinks from
4. Let faith or for - tune rise or fall, Let dreams and
5. God grant that we, in this new year, May show the

space yet al - ways near, Is pres - ent where his
what we can - not see, Or, with eyes fas - tened
the un - known or strange: The one who fash - ioned
dread both have their day; Those whom God loves walk
world the King - dom's face, And let our work and

peo - ple meet To cel - e - brate the com - ing year.
to the past, Our dread of what is yet to be?
heav'n and earth Makes all things new and ush - ers change.
un - a - fraid With Christ their guide and Christ their way.
wor - ship thrive As signs of hope and means of grace.

Text: John L. Bell, b.1949, © 1989, Iona Community, GIA Publications, Inc., agent
Tune: PUER NOBIS, LM; adapt. by Michael Praetorius, 1571–1621

Lectionary

1089 Advent / Christmas

In various ways and various places the Church has marked the days around the winter solstice (or the summer solstice in the southern hemisphere) in late December and early January. Customs, traditions, and rituals from the world's cultures have quite naturally found a home around the many-faceted celebration of the Word-made-flesh, the manifestation of God-with-us.

The present Roman calendar observes the season of Advent for three to four weeks prior to December 25. This season has a two-fold focus: the second coming of Jesus Christ at the end of human history and the historical incarnation of Jesus two thousand years ago.

Advent is filled with beautiful scripture readings, songs, prayers and gestures. These abound with images of God's promise and human longing, the beauty present in both darkness and light, the earth's sorrows and its fullness, and the goodness and mystery of time.

At Christmas this spirit blossoms in acclamation: the stories of nativity and epiphany, of Mary and of the Innocents, of Jesus baptized and of water become wine. Until well into January the songs and sights and smells of Christmas surround the Church not with sentimental fantasies but with everyday faith in a gracious God. The festivals of the Christmas season bear their own reflection of what is proclaimed on every Sunday of the year and in every baptism: our lives are caught up now in Jesus who was born of the virgin Mary, who suffered, died and has been raised.

The lectionary of Advent/Christmas is the foundation of these winter days. These scripture readings, proclaimed and pondered year after year, turn the Christian and the Church toward that peace and glory we name but do not yet know.

1090 FIRST SUNDAY OF ADVENT / A

READING I   *Isaiah 2:1–5 / 1*

This is what Isaiah, son of Amoz,
saw concerning Judah and Jerusalem.
  In days to come,
the mountain of the LORD's house
  shall be established as the highest

mountain
  and raised above the hills.
All nations shall stream toward it;
  many peoples shall come and say:

"Come, let us climb the LORD's mountain,
  to the house of the God of Jacob,
that he may instruct us in his ways,
  and we may walk in his paths."
For from Zion shall go forth instruction,
  and the word of the LORD from
    Jerusalem.
He shall judge between the nations,
  and impose terms on many peoples.

They shall beat their swords into
    plowshares
  and their spears into pruning hooks;
one nation shall not raise the sword
    against another,
  nor shall they train for war again.
O house of Jacob, come,
  let us walk in the light of the LORD!

RESPONSORIAL PSALM   *Psalm 122:1–2, 3–4ab, 4cd–5, 6–7, 8–9*

Let us go re - joic - ing to the house, to the house of the Lord.

I rejoiced when they said to me,
  "Let us go to the house of the
    LORD."
And now our feet are standing
  within your gates, O Jerusalem. ℟.

Jerusalem is built as a city
  bonded as one together.
It is there that the tribes go up,
  the tribes of the LORD. ℟.

For Israel's witness it is
  to praise the name of the LORD.
There were set the thrones for judgment,

the thrones of the house of David. ℟.

For the peace of Jerusalem pray,
  "May they prosper, those who love
    you."
May peace abide in your walls,
  and security be in your towers. ℟.

For the sake of my family and friends,
  let me say, "Peace upon you."
For the sake of the house of the LORD,
  our God,
  I will seek good things for you. ℟.

READING II   *Romans 13:11–14*

Brothers and sisters: You know the time; it is the hour now for you to awake from sleep. For our salvation is nearer now than when we first believed; the night is advanced, the day is at hand. Let us then throw off the works of darkness and put on the armor of light; let us conduct ourselves properly as in the day, not in orgies and drunkenness, not in promiscuity and lust, not in rivalry and jealousy. But put on the Lord Jesus Christ, and make no provision for the desires of the flesh.

GOSPEL   *Matthew 24:37–44*

Jesus said to his disciples: "As it was in the days of Noah, so it will be at the coming of the Son of Man. In those days before the flood, they were eating and drinking, marrying and giving in marriage, up to the day that Noah entered the ark. They did not know until the flood came and carried them all away. So will it be also at the coming of the Son of Man. Two men will be out in the field; one will be taken, and one will be left. Two women will be grinding at the mill; one will be taken, and one will be left. Therefore, stay awake! For you do not know on which day your Lord will come. Be sure of this: if the master of the house had known the hour of night when the thief was coming, he would have stayed awake and not let his house be broken into. So too, you also must be prepared, for at an hour you do not expect, the Son of Man will come."

1091 FIRST SUNDAY OF ADVENT / B

READING I

Isaiah 63:16b–17, 19b; 64:2–7 / 2

You, LORD, are our father,
  our redeemer you are named forever.
Why do you let us wander, O LORD,
    from your ways,
    and harden our hearts so that we fear
      you not?
Return for the sake of your servants,
  the tribes of your heritage.
Oh, that you would rend the heavens
    and come down,
    with the mountains quaking before
      you,
while you wrought awesome deeds we
    could not hope for,
    such as they had not heard of from
      of old.
No ear has ever heard, no eye ever seen,
    any God but you
    doing such deeds for those who
      wait for him.
Would that you might meet us doing
    right,
that we were mindful of you in our
  ways!
Behold, you are angry, and we are
  sinful;
all of us have become like unclean
  people,
all our good deeds are like polluted
  rags;
we have all withered like leaves,
  and our guilt carries us away like
    the wind.
There is none who calls upon your
  name,
  who rouses himself to cling to you;
for you have hidden your face from us
  and have delivered us up to our
    guilt.
Yet, O LORD, you are our father;
  we are the clay and you the potter:
  we are all the work of your hands.

RESPONSORIAL PSALM

Psalm 80:2ac and 3b, 15–16, 18–19

HH, adapt.

Lord, make us turn to you; let us see your face and we shall be saved.

O shepherd of Israel, hear us,
  enthroned on the cherubim, shine
    forth.
  Rouse up your might and come
    to save us. ℟.

God of hosts, turn again, we implore;
  look down from heaven and see.
Visit this vine and protect it,
  the vine your right hand has planted,
  the son of man you have claimed
    for yourself. ℟.

May your hand be on the man at your
    right hand,
  the son of man you have confirmed
    as your own.

And we shall never forsake you again;
  give us life that we may call upon
  your name. ℟.

READING II
1 Corinthians 1:3–9

Brothers and sisters: Grace to you and peace from God our Father and the Lord Jesus
Christ.

    I give thanks to my God always on your account for the grace of God bestowed
on you in Christ Jesus, that in him you were enriched in every way, with all discourse
and all knowledge, as the testimony to Christ was confirmed among you, so that you
are not lacking in any spiritual gift as you wait for the revelation of our Lord Jesus
Christ. He will keep you firm to the end, irreproachable on the day of our Lord Jesus
Christ. God is faithful, and by him you were called to fellowship with his Son, Jesus
Christ our Lord.

GOSPEL
Mark 13:33–37

Jesus said to his disciples: "Be watchful! Be alert! You do not know when the time
will come. It is like a man traveling abroad. He leaves home and places his servants
in charge, each with his own work, and orders the gatekeeper to be on the watch.
Watch, therefore; you do not know when the lord of the house is coming, whether in
the evening, or at midnight, or at cockcrow, or in the morning. May he not come suddenly and find you sleeping. What I say to you, I say to all: 'Watch!'"

FIRST SUNDAY OF ADVENT / C   1092

READING I
Jeremiah 33:14–16 / 3

The days are coming, says the LORD,
  when I will fulfill the promise
  I made to the house of Israel and
    Judah.
In those days, in that time,
  I will raise up for David a just shoot;

he shall do what is right and just in
  the land.
In those days Judah shall be safe
  and Jerusalem shall dwell secure;
  this is what they shall call her:
  "The LORD our justice."

RESPONSORIAL PSALM
Psalm 25:4–5, 8–9, 10 and 14

To you, O Lord, I lift my soul.

O LORD, make me know your ways.
  Teach me your paths.
Guide me in your truth, and teach me;
  for you are the God of my salvation.
I have hoped in you all day long. ℟.

Good and upright is the LORD;
  he shows the way to sinners.
He guides the humble in right judgment;
  to the humble he teaches his way. ℟.

All the LORD's paths are mercy
    and faithfulness,
        for those who keep his covenant
        and commands.

The LORD's secret is for those
    who fear him;
        to them he reveals his covenant. ℟.

READING II   *1 Thessalonians 3:12—4:2*

Brothers and sisters: May the Lord make you increase and abound in love for one another and for all, just as we have for you, so as to strengthen your hearts, to be blameless in holiness before our God and Father at the coming of our Lord Jesus with all his holy ones. Amen.

Finally, brothers and sisters, we earnestly ask and exhort you in the Lord Jesus that, as you received from us how you should conduct yourselves to please God — and as you are conducting yourselves — you do so even more. For you know what instructions we gave you through the Lord Jesus.

GOSPEL   *Luke 21:25-28, 34-36*

Jesus said to his disciples: "There will be signs in the sun, the moon, and the stars, and on earth nations will be in dismay, perplexed by the roaring of the sea and the waves. People will die of fright in anticipation of what is coming upon the world, for the powers of the heavens will be shaken. And then they will see the Son of Man coming in a cloud with power and great glory. But when these signs begin to happen, stand erect and raise your heads because your redemption is at hand.

"Beware that your hearts do not become drowsy from carousing and drunkenness and the anxieties of daily life, and that day catch you by surprise like a trap. For that day will assault everyone who lives on the face of the earth. Be vigilant at all times and pray that you have the strength to escape the tribulations that are imminent and to stand before the Son of Man."

1093 SECOND SUNDAY OF ADVENT / A

READING I   *Isaiah 11:1–10 / 4*

On that day, a shoot shall sprout from
    the stump of Jesse,
        and from his roots a bud shall
        blossom.
The spirit of the Lord shall rest upon him:
    a spirit of wisdom and of
        understanding,
a spirit of counsel and of strength,
    a spirit of knowledge and of fear of
        the LORD,
    and his delight shall be the fear of
        the LORD.
Not by appearance shall he judge,
    nor by hearsay shall he decide,
but he shall judge the poor with justice,

and decide aright for the land's
    afflicted.
He shall strike the ruthless with the rod
    of his mouth,
    and with the breath of his lips he
        shall slay the wicked.
Justice shall be the band around his waist,
    and faithfulness a belt upon his hips.
Then the wolf shall be a guest of the
    lamb,
    and the leopard shall lie down with
        the kid;
the calf and the young lion shall browse
    together,
    with a little child to guide them.

The cow and the bear shall be neighbors,
together their young shall rest;
the lion shall eat hay like the ox.
The baby shall play by the cobra's den,
and the child lay his hand on the
adder's lair.
There shall be no harm or ruin on all my
holy mountain;

for the earth shall be filled with
knowledge of the LORD,
as water covers the sea.
On that day, the root of Jesse,
set up as a signal for the nations,
the Gentiles shall seek out,
for his dwelling shall be glorious.

RESPONSORIAL PSALM

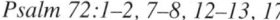

Psalm 72:1–2, 7–8, 12–13, 17

O God, give your judgment to the king,
to a king's son your justice,
that he may judge your people in justice,
and your poor in right judgment. ℟.

In his days shall justice flourish,
and great peace till the moon is no
more.
He shall rule from sea to sea,
from the River to the bounds
of the earth. ℟.

For he shall save the needy when
they cry,
the poor, and those who are helpless.

He will have pity on the weak and
the needy,
and save the lives of the needy. ℟.

May his name endure forever,
his name continue like the sun.
Every tribe shall be blest in him,
all nations shall call him blessed. ℟.

READING II

Romans 15:4–9

Brothers and sisters: Whatever was written previously was written for our instruction, that by endurance and by the encouragement of the Scriptures we might have hope. May the God of endurance and encouragement grant you to think in harmony with one another, in keeping with Christ Jesus, that with one accord you may with one voice glorify the God and Father of our Lord Jesus Christ.

Welcome one another, then, as Christ welcomed you, for the glory of God. For I say that Christ became a minister of the circumcised to show God's truthfulness, to confirm the promises to the patriarchs, but so that the Gentiles might glorify God for his mercy. As it is written:

Therefore, I will praise you among the Gentiles
and sing praises to your name.

GOSPEL *Matthew 3:1–12*

John the Baptist appeared, preaching in the desert of Judea and saying, "Repent, for the kingdom of heaven is at hand!" It was of him that the prophet Isaiah had spoken when he said:

A voice of one crying out in the desert,
Prepare the way of the Lord,
 make straight his paths.

John wore clothing made of camel's hair and had a leather belt around his waist. His food was locusts and wild honey. At that time Jerusalem, all Judea, and the whole region around the Jordan were going out to him and were being baptized by him in the Jordan River as they acknowledged their sins.

When he saw many of the Pharisees and Sadducees coming to his baptism, he said to them, "You brood of vipers! Who warned you to flee from the coming wrath? Produce good fruit as evidence of your repentance. And do not presume to say to yourselves, 'We have Abraham as our father.' For I tell you, God can raise up children to Abraham from these stones. Even now the ax lies at the root of the trees. Therefore every tree that does not bear good fruit will be cut down and thrown into the fire. I am baptizing you with water, for repentance, but the one who is coming after me is mightier than I. I am not worthy to carry his sandals. He will baptize you with the Holy Spirit and fire. His winnowing fan is in his hand. He will clear his threshing floor and gather his wheat into his barn, but the chaff he will burn with unquenchable fire."

1094 SECOND SUNDAY OF ADVENT / B

READING I *Isaiah 40:1–5, 9–11 / 5*

Comfort, give comfort to my people,
 says your God.
Speak tenderly to Jerusalem, and
 proclaim to her
 that her service is at an end,
 her guilt is expiated;
indeed, she has received from the hand
 of the LORD
 double for all her sins.

A voice cries out:
In the desert prepare the way of
 the LORD!
Make straight in the wasteland a
 highway for our God!
Every valley shall be filled in,
 every mountain and hill shall be
 made low;
the rugged land shall be made a plain,
 the rough country, a broad valley.
Then the glory of the LORD shall be
 revealed,

and all people shall see it together;
for the mouth of the LORD has
 spoken.

Go up on to a high mountain,
 Zion, herald of glad tidings;
cry out at the top of your voice,
 Jerusalem, herald of good news!
Fear not to cry out
 and say to the cities of Judah:
 Here is your God!
Here comes with power
 the Lord GOD,
 who rules by his strong arm;
here is his reward with him,
 his recompense before him.
Like a shepherd he feeds his flock;
 in his arms he gathers the lambs,
carrying them in his bosom,
 and leading the ewes with care.

RESPONSORIAL PSALM *Psalm 85:9ab and 10, 11–12, 13–14*

Lord, let us see your kind-ness, and grant us your sal - va-tion.

I will hear what the LORD God speaks;
   he speaks of peace for his people
     and his faithful.
His salvation is near for those who fear him,
   and his glory will dwell in our land. ℟.

Merciful love and faithfulness have met;
   justice and peace have kissed.

Faithfulness shall spring from the earth,
   and justice look down from
     heaven. ℟.

Also the LORD will bestow his bounty,
   and our earth shall yield its increase.
Justice will march before him,
   and guide his steps on the way. ℟.

READING II *2 Peter 3:8–14*

Do not ignore this one fact, beloved, that with the Lord one day is like a thousand years and a thousand years like one day. The Lord does not delay his promise, as some regard "delay," but he is patient with you, not wishing that any should perish but that all should come to repentance. But the day of the Lord will come like a thief, and then the heavens will pass away with a mighty roar and the elements will be dissolved by fire, and the earth and everything done on it will be found out.

Since everything is to be dissolved in this way, what sort of persons ought you to be, conducting yourselves in holiness and devotion, waiting for and hastening the coming of the day of God, because of which the heavens will be dissolved in flames and the elements melted by fire. But according to his promise we await new heavens and a new earth in which righteousness dwells. Therefore, beloved, since you await these things, be eager to be found without spot or blemish before him, at peace.

GOSPEL *Mark 1:1–8*

The beginning of the gospel of Jesus Christ the Son of God.

As it is written in Isaiah the prophet:
   Behold, I am sending my messenger ahead of you;
     he will prepare your way.
   A voice of one crying out in the desert:
     "Prepare the way of the Lord,
     make straight his paths."
John the Baptist appeared in the desert proclaiming a baptism of repentance for the forgiveness of sins. People of the whole Judean countryside and all the inhabitants of Jerusalem were going out to him and were being baptized by him in the Jordan River as they acknowledged their sins. John was clothed in camel's hair, with a leather belt around his waist. He fed on locusts and wild honey. And this is what he proclaimed: "One mightier than I is coming after me. I am not worthy to stoop and loosen the thongs of his sandals. I have baptized you with water; he will baptize you with the Holy Spirit."

1095 SECOND SUNDAY OF ADVENT / C

READING I   *Baruch 5:1–9 / 6*

Jerusalem, take off your robe of
    mourning and misery;
    put on the splendor of glory from
    God forever:
wrapped in the cloak of justice from
    God,
    bear on your head the mitre
    that displays the glory of the eternal
    name.
For God will show all the earth your
    splendor:
    you will be named by God forever
    the peace of justice, the glory of
    God's worship.

Up, Jerusalem! stand upon the heights;
    look to the east and see your
    children
gathered from the east and the west
    at the word of the Holy One,
    rejoicing that they are remembered
    by God.

Led away on foot by their enemies they
    left you:
    but God will bring them back to you
    borne aloft in glory as on royal
    thrones.
For God has commanded
    that every lofty mountain be made
    low,
and that the age-old depths and gorges
    be filled to level ground,
    that Israel may advance secure in
    the glory of God.
The forests and every fragrant kind of
    tree
    have overshadowed Israel at God's
    command;
for God is leading Israel in joy
    by the light of his glory,
    with his mercy and justice for
    company.

RESPONSORIAL PSALM   *Psalm 126:1–2ab, 2cd–3, 4–5, 6*

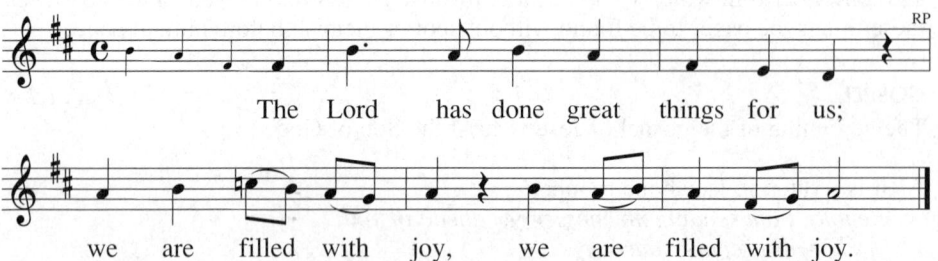

The Lord has done great things for us;
we are filled with joy, we are filled with joy.

When the LORD brought back the
    exiles of Sion,
    we thought we were dreaming.
Then was our mouth filled with
    laughter;
    on our tongues, songs of joy. ℟.

Then the nations themselves said,
    "What great deeds the LORD
    worked for them!"
What great deeds the LORD worked
    for us!
    Indeed, we were glad. ℟.

Bring back our exiles, O LORD,
    as streams in the south.
Those who are sowing in tears
    will sing when they reap. ℟.

They go out, they go out, full of tears,
    bearing seed for the sowing;
they come back, they come back with
    a song,
    bearing their sheaves. ℟.

READING II   *Philippians 1:4–6, 8–11*

Brothers and sisters: I pray always with joy in my every prayer for all of you, because of your partnership for the gospel from the first day until now. I am confident of this, that the one who began a good work in you will continue to complete it until the day of Christ Jesus. God is my witness, how I long for all of you with the affection of Christ Jesus. And this is my prayer: that your love may increase ever more and more in knowledge and every kind of perception, to discern what is of value, so that you may be pure and blameless for the day of Christ, filled with the fruit of righteousness that comes through Jesus Christ for the glory and praise of God.

GOSPEL   *Luke 3:1–6*

In the fifteenth year of the reign of Tiberius Caesar, when Pontius Pilate was governor of Judea, and Herod was tetrarch of Galilee, and his brother Philip tetrarch of the region of Ituraea and Trachonitis, and Lysanias was tetrarch of Abilene, during the high priesthood of Annas and Caiaphas, the word of God came to John the son of Zechariah in the desert. John went throughout the whole region of the Jordan, proclaiming a baptism of repentance for the forgiveness of sins, as it is written in the book of the words of the prophet Isaiah:

A voice of one crying out in the desert:
"Prepare the way of the Lord,
*   make straight his paths.*
Every valley shall be filled
*   and every mountain and hill shall be made low.*
The winding roads shall be made straight,
*   and the rough ways made smooth,*
and all flesh shall see the salvation of God."

THIRD SUNDAY OF ADVENT / A   1096

READING I   *Isaiah 35:1–6a, 10 / 7*

The desert and the parched land will exult;
   the steppe will rejoice and bloom.
They will bloom with abundant flowers,
   and rejoice with joyful song.
The glory of Lebanon will be given to them,
   the splendor of Carmel and Sharon;
they will see the glory of the LORD,
   the splendor of our God.
Strengthen the hands that are feeble,
   make firm the knees that are weak,
say to those whose hearts are frightened:
   Be strong, fear not!
Here is your God,
he comes with vindication;
with divine recompense
he comes to save you.
Then will the eyes of the blind be opened,
   the ears of the deaf be cleared;
then will the lame leap like a stag,
   then the tongue of the mute will sing.

Those whom the LORD has ransomed will return
   and enter Zion singing,
   crowned with everlasting joy;
they will meet with joy and gladness,
   sorrow and mourning will flee.

RESPONSORIAL PSALM   *Psalm 146:6c–7, 8–9a, 9bc–10*

Or: Alleluia.

Lord, come and save us.

It is the LORD who preserves fidelity
forever,
who does justice to those who are
oppressed.
It is he who gives bread to the hungry,
the LORD who sets prisoners free. ℟.

The LORD who opens the eyes of the blind,
the LORD who raises up those who
are bowed down.

It is the LORD who loves the just,
the LORD who protects the
stranger. ℟.

The LORD upholds the orphan and
the widow,
but thwarts the path of the wicked.
The LORD will reign forever,
the God of Sion from age to age. ℟.

READING II   *James 5:7–10*
Be patient, brothers and sisters, until the coming of the Lord. See how the farmer
waits for the precious fruit of the earth, being patient with it until it receives the early
and the late rains. You too must be patient. Make your hearts firm, because the coming of the Lord is at hand. Do not complain, brothers and sisters, about one another,
that you may not be judged. Behold, the Judge is standing before the gates. Take as
an example of hardship and patience, brothers and sisters, the prophets who spoke in
the name of the Lord.

GOSPEL   *Matthew 11:2–11*
When John the Baptist heard in prison of the works of the Christ, he sent his disciples
to Jesus with this question, "Are you the one who is to come, or should we look for
another?" Jesus said to them in reply, "Go and tell John what you hear and see: the
blind regain their sight, the lame walk, lepers are cleansed, the deaf hear, the dead are
raised, and the poor have the good news proclaimed to them. And blessed is the one
who takes no offense at me."

As they were going off, Jesus began to speak to the crowds about John, "What
did you go out to the desert to see? A reed swayed by the wind? Then what did you
go out to see? Someone dressed in fine clothing? Those who wear fine clothing are in
royal palaces. Then why did you go out? To see a prophet? Yes, I tell you, and more
than a prophet. This is the one about whom it is written:
Behold, I am sending my messenger ahead of you;
he will prepare your way before you.
Amen, I say to you, among those born of women there has been none greater than
John the Baptist; yet the least in the kingdom of heaven is greater than he."

THIRD SUNDAY OF ADVENT / B   1097

READING I   *Isaiah 61:1–2a, 10–11 / 8*

The spirit of the Lord GOD is upon me,
  because the LORD has anointed me;
he has sent me to bring glad tidings to
    the poor,
  to heal the brokenhearted,
to proclaim liberty to the captives
  and release to the prisoners,
to announce a year of favor from the LORD
  and a day of vindication by our God.

I rejoice heartily in the LORD,
  in my God is the joy of my soul;
for he has clothed me with a robe of
salvation
and wrapped me in a mantle of
    justice,
like a bridegroom adorned with a
    diadem,
like a bride bedecked with her
    jewels.
As the earth brings forth its plants,
  and a garden makes its growth
      spring up,
so will the Lord GOD make justice and
    praise
  spring up before all the nations.

RESPONSORIAL PSALM   *Luke 1:46–48, 49–50, 53–54*

RJB

My soul re - joic - es,   my soul re - joic - es   in   my   God.

My soul glorifies the Lord,
  my spirit rejoices in God, my savior.
He looks on his servant in her
      nothingness;
  henceforth all ages will call me
      blessed. ℟.

The Almighty works marvels for me.
  Holy his name!

His mercy is from age to age,
  on those who fear him. ℟.

He fills the starving with good things,
  sends the rich away empty.
He protects Israel his servant,
  remembering his mercy. ℟.

READING II   *1 Thessalonians 5:16–24*

Brothers and sisters: Rejoice always. Pray without ceasing. In all circumstances give thanks, for this is the will of God for you in Christ Jesus. Do not quench the Spirit. Do not despise prophetic utterances. Test everything; retain what is good. Refrain from every kind of evil.

   May the God of peace make you perfectly holy and may you entirely, spirit, soul, and body, be preserved blameless for the coming of our Lord Jesus Christ. The one who calls you is faithful, and he will also accomplish it.

GOSPEL   *John 1:6–8, 19–28*

A man named John was sent from God. He came for testimony, to testify to the light, so that all might believe through him. He was not the light, but came to testify to the light.

   And this is the testimony of John. When the Jews from Jerusalem sent priests and Levites to him to ask him, "Who are you?" he admitted and did not deny it, but admitted, "I am not the Christ." So they asked him, "What are you then? Are you

Elijah?" And he said, "I am not." "Are you the Prophet?" He answered, "No." So they said to him, "Who are you, so we can give an answer to those who sent us? What do you have to say for yourself?" He said:

"I am *the voice of one crying out in the desert,*
make straight the way of the Lord,

as Isaiah the prophet said." Some Pharisees were also sent. They asked him, "Why then do you baptize if you are not the Christ or Elijah or the Prophet?" John answered them, "I baptize with water; but there is one among you whom you do not recognize, the one who is coming after me, whose sandal strap I am not worthy to untie." This happened in Bethany across the Jordan, where John was baptizing.

1098 THIRD SUNDAY OF ADVENT / C

READING I   *Zephaniah 3:14–18a / 9*

Shout for joy, O daughter Zion!
  Sing joyfully, O Israel!
Be glad and exult with all your heart,
  O daughter Jerusalem!
The LORD has removed the judgment
    against you
  he has turned away your enemies;
the King of Israel, the LORD, is in your
    midst,
  you have no further misfortune to
    fear.

On that day, it shall be said to
  Jerusalem:
  Fear not, O Zion, be not
    discouraged!
The LORD, your God, is in your midst,
  a mighty savior;
he will rejoice over you with gladness,
  and renew you in his love,
he will sing joyfully because of you,
  as one sings at festivals.

RESPONSORIAL PSALM   *Isaiah 12:2–3, 4bcd, 5–6*

Cry out with joy and gladness: for among you is the great and Holy One of Israel.

Truly, God is my salvation,
  I trust, I shall not fear.
For the Lord is my strength, my song,
  he became my savior.
With joy you will draw water
  from the wells of salvation. ℟.

Give thanks to the Lord,
  give praise to his name!
Make his mighty deeds

known to the peoples!
Declare the greatness of his name.
  Sing a psalm to the Lord! ℟.

For he has done glorious deeds,
  make them known to all the earth!
People of Zion,
  sing and shout for joy
for great in your midst
  is the Holy One of Israel. ℟.

READING II   *Philippians 4:4–7*

Brothers and sisters: Rejoice in the Lord always. I shall say it again: rejoice! Your kindness should be known to all. The Lord is near. Have no anxiety at all, but in everything, by prayer and petition, with thanksgiving, make your requests known to God. Then the peace of God that surpasses all understanding will guard your hearts and minds in Christ Jesus.

GOSPEL   *Luke 3:10–18*

The crowds asked John the Baptist, "What should we do?" He said to them in reply, "Whoever has two cloaks should share with the person who has none. And whoever has food should do likewise." Even tax collectors came to be baptized and they said to him, "Teacher, what should we do?" He answered them, "Stop collecting more than what is prescribed." Soldiers also asked him, "And what is it that we should do?" He told them, "Do not practice extortion, do not falsely accuse anyone, and be satisfied with your wages."

Now the people were filled with expectation, and all were asking in their hearts whether John might be the Christ. John answered them all, saying, "I am baptizing you with water, but one mightier than I is coming. I am not worthy to loosen the thongs of his sandals. He will baptize you with the Holy Spirit and fire. His winnowing fan is in his hand to clear his threshing floor and to gather the wheat into his barn, but the chaff he will burn with unquenchable fire." Exhorting them in many other ways, he preached good news to the people.

FOURTH SUNDAY OF ADVENT / A   1099

READING I   *Isaiah 7:10–14 / 10*

The Lord spoke to Ahaz, saying: Ask for a sign from the Lord, your God; let it be deep as the netherworld, or high as the sky! But Ahaz answered, "I will not ask! I will not tempt the Lord!" Then Isaiah said: Listen, O house of David! Is it not enough for you to weary people, must you also weary my God? Therefore the Lord himself will give you this sign: the virgin shall conceive, and bear a son, and shall name him Emmanuel.

RESPONSORIAL PSALM   *Psalm 24:1–2, 3–4ab, 5–6*

Let the Lord en-ter; he is king of glo-ry.

The Lord's is the earth and its fullness,
   the world, and those who dwell in it.
It is he who set it on the seas;
   on the rivers he made it firm. ℟.

Who shall climb the mountain of the
      Lord?
   Who shall stand in his holy place?
The clean of hands and pure of heart,

whose soul is not set on vain
   things. ℟.

Blessings from the Lord shall he receive,
   and right reward from the God who
      saves him.
Such are the people who seek him,
   who seek the face of the God of
      Jacob. ℟.

READING II   *Romans 1:1–7*

Paul, a slave of Christ Jesus, called to be an apostle and set apart for the gospel of God, which he promised previously through his prophets in the holy Scriptures, the gospel about his Son, descended from David according to the flesh, but established as Son of God in power according to the Spirit of holiness through resurrection from the dead, Jesus Christ our Lord. Through him we have received the grace of apostleship, to bring about the obedience of faith, for the sake of his name, among all the Gentiles, among whom are you also, who are called to belong to Jesus Christ; to all the beloved of God in Rome, called to be holy. Grace to you and peace from God our Father and the Lord Jesus Christ.

GOSPEL   *Matthew 1:18–24*

This is how the birth of Jesus Christ came about. When his mother Mary was betrothed to Joseph, but before they lived together, she was found with child through the Holy Spirit. Joseph her husband, since he was a righteous man, yet unwilling to expose her to shame, decided to divorce her quietly. Such was his intention when, behold, the angel of the Lord appeared to him in a dream and said, "Joseph, son of David, do not be afraid to take Mary your wife into your home. For it is through the Holy Spirit that this child has been conceived in her. She will bear a son and you are to name him Jesus, because he will save his people from their sins." All this took place to fulfill what the Lord had said through the prophet:

Behold, the virgin shall conceive and bear a son,
and they shall name him Emmanuel,

which means "God is with us." When Joseph awoke, he did as the angel of the Lord had commanded him and took his wife into his home.

1100   FOURTH SUNDAY OF ADVENT / B

READING I   *2 Samuel 7:1–5, 8b–12, 14a, 16 / 11*

When King David was settled in his palace, and the LORD had given him rest from his enemies on every side, he said to Nathan the prophet, "Here I am living in a house of cedar, while the ark of God dwells in a tent!" Nathan answered the king, "Go, do whatever you have in mind, for the LORD is with you." But that night the LORD spoke to Nathan and said: "Go, tell my servant David, 'Thus says the LORD: Should you build me a house to dwell in?

"'It was I who took you from the pasture and from the care of the flock to be commander of my people Israel. I have been with you wherever you went, and I have destroyed all your enemies before you. And I will make you famous like the great ones of the earth. I will fix a place for my people Israel; I will plant them so that they may dwell in their place without further disturbance. Neither shall the wicked continue to afflict them as they did of old, since the time I first appointed judges over my people Israel. I will give you rest from all your enemies. The LORD also reveals to you that he will establish a house for you. And when your time comes and you rest with your ancestors, I will raise up your heir after you, sprung from your loins, and I will make his kingdom firm. I will be a father to him, and he shall be a son to me. Your house and your kingdom shall endure forever before me; your throne shall stand firm forever.'"

RESPONSORIAL PSALM   *Psalm 89:2–3, 4–5, 27 and 29*

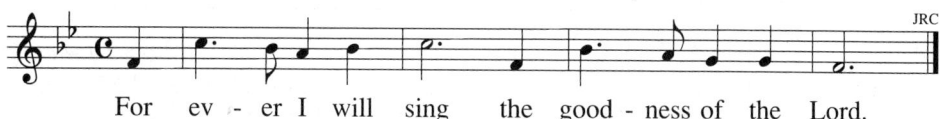

For ev - er I will sing the good - ness of the Lord.

I will sing forever of your mercies,
    O LORD;
    through all ages my mouth will
      proclaim your fidelity.
I have declared your mercy is
    established forever;
    your fidelity stands firm as the
    heavens. ℟.

"With my chosen one I have made a
    covenant;
    I have sworn to David my servant:

I will establish your descendants
    forever,
    and set up your throne through all
    ages." ℟.

"He will call out to me, 'You are my
    father,
    my God, the rock of my salvation.'
I will keep my faithful love for him
    always;
    with him my covenant shall last." ℟.

READING II   *Romans 16:25–27*

Brothers and sisters: To him who can strengthen you, according to my gospel and the proclamation of Jesus Christ, according to the revelation of the mystery kept secret for long ages but now manifested through the prophetic writings and, according to the command of the eternal God, made known to all nations to bring about the obedience of faith, to the only wise God, through Jesus Christ be glory forever and ever. Amen.

GOSPEL   *Luke 1:26–38*

The angel Gabriel was sent from God to a town of Galilee called Nazareth, to a virgin betrothed to a man named Joseph, of the house of David, and the virgin's name was Mary. And coming to her, he said, "Hail, full of grace! The Lord is with you." But she was greatly troubled at what was said and pondered what sort of greeting this might be. Then the angel said to her, "Do not be afraid, Mary, for you have found favor with God.

"Behold, you will conceive in your womb and bear a son, and you shall name him Jesus. He will be great and will be called Son of the Most High, and the Lord God will give him the throne of David his father, and he will rule over the house of Jacob forever, and of his kingdom there will be no end." But Mary said to the angel, "How can this be, since I have no relations with a man?" And the angel said to her in reply, "The Holy Spirit will come upon you, and the power of the Most High will overshadow you. Therefore the child to be born will be called holy, the Son of God. And behold, Elizabeth, your relative, has also conceived a son in her old age, and this is the sixth month for her who was called barren; for nothing will be impossible for God." Mary said, "Behold, I am the handmaid of the Lord. May it be done to me according to your word." Then the angel departed from her.

1101 FOURTH SUNDAY OF ADVENT / C

READING I *Micah 5:1–4a / 12*

Thus says the LORD:
You, Bethlehem-Ephrathah
    too small to be among the clans of
      Judah,
from you shall come forth for me
    one who is to be ruler in Israel;
whose origin is from of old,
    from ancient times.
Therefore the Lord will give them up,
    until the time
    when she who is to give birth has
      borne,

and the rest of his kindred shall return
    to the children of Israel.
He shall stand firm and shepherd his
    flock
    by the strength of the LORD,
    in the majestic name of the LORD,
    his God;
and they shall remain, for now his
    greatness
    shall reach to the ends of the earth;
    he shall be peace.

RESPONSORIAL PSALM *Psalm 80:2ac and 3b, 15–16, 18–19*

HH, adapt.

Lord, make us turn to you; let us see your face and we shall be saved.

O shepherd of Israel, hear us,
    enthroned on the cherubim, shine
      forth.
    Rouse up your might and come to
      save us. ℟.

God of hosts, turn again, we implore;
    look down from heaven and see.
Visit this vine and protect it,
    the vine your right hand has planted,
    the son of man you have claimed
      for yourself. ℟.

May your hand be on the man at your
    right hand,
    the son of man you have confirmed
    as your own.
And we shall never forsake you again;
    give us life that we may call upon
    your name. ℟.

READING II *Hebrews 10:5–10*

Brothers and sisters: When Christ came into the world, he said:
    "Sacrifice and offering you did not desire,
      but a body you prepared for me;
    in holocausts and sin offerings you took no delight.
    Then I said, 'As is written of me in the scroll,
    behold, I come to do your will, O God.'"

First he says, "Sacrifices and offerings, holocausts and sin offerings, you neither desired nor delighted in." These are offered according to the law. Then he says, "Behold, I come to do your will." He takes away the first to establish the second. By this "will," we have been consecrated through the offering of the body of Jesus Christ once for all.

GOSPEL
Luke 1:39–45

Mary set out and traveled to the hill country in haste to a town of Judah, where she entered the house of Zechariah and greeted Elizabeth. When Elizabeth heard Mary's greeting, the infant leaped in her womb, and Elizabeth, filled with the Holy Spirit, cried out in a loud voice and said, "Blessed are you among women, and blessed is the fruit of your womb. And how does this happen to me, that the mother of my Lord should come to me? For at the moment the sound of your greeting reached my ears, the infant in my womb leaped for joy. Blessed are you who believed that what was spoken to you by the Lord would be fulfilled."

DECEMBER 25: CHRISTMAS—VIGIL MASS / ABC   1102

READING I
Isaiah 62:1–5 / 13

For Zion's sake I will not be silent,
   for Jerusalem's sake I will not be
     quiet,
until her vindication shines forth like
     the dawn
   and her victory like a burning torch.

Nations shall behold your vindication,
   and all the kings your glory;
you shall be called by a new name
   pronounced by the mouth of the
     LORD.
You shall be a glorious crown in the
hand of the LORD,
   a royal diadem held by your God.
No more shall people call you
     "Forsaken,"
   or your land "Desolate,"
but you shall be called "My Delight,"
   and your land "Espoused."
For the LORD delights in you
   and makes your land his spouse.
As a young man marries a virgin,
   your Builder shall marry you;
and as a bridegroom rejoices in his bride
   so shall your God rejoice in you.

RESPONSORIAL PSALM
Psalm 89:4–5, 16–17, 27 and 29

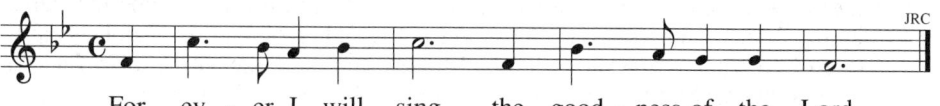

For ev - er I will sing the good - ness of the Lord.

"With my chosen one I have made a
   covenant;
I have sworn to David my servant:
I will establish your descendants forever,
   and set up your throne through all
     ages." ℟.

How blessed the people who know your
praise,
   who walk, O LORD, in the light of
     your face,
who find their joy every day in your
     name,
   who make your justice their joyful
     acclaim. ℟.

"He will call out to me, 'You are my father,   always;
   my God, the rock of my salvation.'   with him my covenant shall last." ℟.
I will keep my faithful love for him

READING II   *Acts 13:16–17, 22–25*

When Paul reached Antioch in Pisidia and entered the synagogue, he stood up, motioned with his hand, and said, "Fellow Israelites and you others who are God-fearing, listen. The God of this people Israel chose our ancestors and exalted the people during their sojourn in the land of Egypt. With uplifted arm he led them out of it. Then he removed Saul and raised up David as king; of him he testified, 'I have found David, son of Jesse, a man after my own heart; he will carry out my every wish.' From this man's descendants God, according to his promise, has brought to Israel a savior, Jesus. John heralded his coming by proclaiming a baptism of repentance to all the people of Israel; and as John was completing his course, he would say, 'What do you suppose that I am? I am not he. Behold, one is coming after me; I am not worthy to unfasten the sandals of his feet.'"

GOSPEL   *Matthew 1:1–25 or 1:18–25*

For short form read only the part in brackets.

The book of the genealogy of Jesus Christ, the son of David, the son of Abraham.

Abraham became the father of Isaac, Isaac the father of Jacob, Jacob the father of Judah and his brothers. Judah became the father of Perez and Zerah, whose mother was Tamar. Perez became the father of Hezron, Hezron the father of Ram, Ram the father of Amminadab. Amminadab became the father of Nahshon, Nahshon the father of Salmon, Salmon the father of Boaz, whose mother was Rahab. Boaz became the father of Obed, whose mother was Ruth. Obed became the father of Jesse, Jesse the father of David the king.

David became the father of Solomon, whose mother had been the wife of Uriah. Solomon became the father of Rehoboam, Rehoboam the father of Abijah, Abijah the father of Asaph. Asaph became the father of Jehoshaphat, Jehoshaphat the father of Joram, Joram the father of Uzziah. Uzziah became the father of Jotham, Jotham the father of Ahaz, Ahaz the father of Hezekiah. Hezekiah became the father of Manasseh, Manasseh the father of Amos, Amos the father of Josiah. Josiah became the father of Jechoniah and his brothers at the time of the Babylonian exile.

After the Babylonian exile, Jechoniah became the father of Shealtiel, Shealtiel the father of Zerubbabel, Zerubbabel the father of Abiud. Abiud became the father of Eliakim, Eliakim the father of Azor, Azor the father of Zadok. Zadok became the father of Achim, Achim the father of Eliud, Eliud the father of Eleazar. Eleazar became the father of Matthan, Matthan the father of Jacob, Jacob the father of Joseph, the husband of Mary. Of her was born Jesus who is called the Christ.

Thus the total number of generations from Abraham to David is fourteen generations; from David to the Babylonian exile, fourteen generations; from the Babylonian exile to the Christ, fourteen generations.

Now [this is how the birth of Jesus Christ came about. When his mother Mary was betrothed to Joseph, but before they lived together, she was found with child through the Holy Spirit. Joseph her husband, since he was a righteous man, yet unwilling to expose her to shame, decided to divorce her quietly. Such was his intention when, behold, the angel of the Lord appeared to him in a dream and said, "Joseph, son of David, do not be afraid to take Mary your wife into your home. For it is through the

Holy Spirit that this child has been conceived in her. She will bear a son and you are to name him Jesus, because he will save his people from their sins." All this took place to fulfill what the Lord had said through the prophet:

Behold, the virgin shall conceive and bear a son,
and they shall name him Emmanuel,

which means "God is with us." When Joseph awoke, he did as the angel of the Lord had commanded him and took his wife into his home. He had no relations with her until she bore a son, and he named him Jesus.]

DEC. 25: CHRISTMAS—MASS DURING THE NIGHT / ABC   1103

READING I   *Isaiah 9:1–6 / 14*

The people who walked in darkness
    have seen a great light;
upon those who dwelt in the land of
    gloom
    a light has shone.
You have brought them abundant joy
    and great rejoicing,
as they rejoice before you as at the
    harvest,
    as people make merry when
    dividing spoils.
For the yoke that burdened them,
    the pole on their shoulder,
and the rod of their taskmaster
    you have smashed, as on the day of
    Midian.
For every boot that tramped in battle,

every cloak rolled in blood,
    will be burned as fuel for flames.
For a child is born to us, a son is given
    us;
    upon his shoulder dominion rests
They name him Wonder-Counselor,
    God-Hero,
    Father-Forever, Prince of Peace.
His dominion is vast
    and forever peaceful,
from David's throne, and over his
    kingdom,
    which he confirms and sustains
by judgment and justice,
    both now and forever.
The zeal of the LORD of hosts will do
    this!

RESPONSORIAL PSALM   *Psalm 96:1–2a, 2b–3, 11–12, 13*

To - day   is   born our Sav - ior,   Christ the Lord.

O sing a new song to the LORD;
    sing to the LORD, all the earth.
    O sing to the LORD; bless his name. ℟.

Proclaim his salvation day by day.
    Tell among the nations his glory,
    and his wonders among all the
    peoples. ℟.

Let the heavens rejoice and earth be
    glad;

let the sea and all within it thunder
    praise.
Let the land and all it bears rejoice.
Then will all the trees of the wood
    shout for joy. ℟.

At the presence of the LORD, for he
    comes,
    he comes to judge the earth.
He will judge the world with justice;
    he will govern the peoples with his
    truth. ℟.

READING II   *Titus 2:11–14*

Beloved: The grace of God has appeared, saving all and training us to reject godless ways and worldly desires and to live temperately, justly, and devoutly in this age, as we await the blessed hope, the appearance of the glory of our great God and savior Jesus Christ, who gave himself for us to deliver us from all lawlessness and to cleanse for himself a people as his own, eager to do what is good.

GOSPEL   *Luke 2:1–14*

In those days a decree went out from Caesar Augustus that the whole world should be enrolled. This was the first enrollment, when Quirinius was governor of Syria. So all went to be enrolled, each to his own town. And Joseph too went up from Galilee from the town of Nazareth to Judea, to the city of David that is called Bethlehem, because he was of the house and family of David, to be enrolled with Mary, his betrothed, who was with child. While they were there, the time came for her to have her child, and she gave birth to her firstborn son. She wrapped him in swaddling clothes and laid him in a manger, because there was no room for them in the inn.

Now there were shepherds in that region living in the fields and keeping the night watch over their flock. The angel of the Lord appeared to them and the glory of the Lord shone around them, and they were struck with great fear. The angel said to them, "Do not be afraid; for behold, I proclaim to you good news of great joy that will be for all the people. For today in the city of David a savior has been born for you who is Christ and Lord. And this will be a sign for you: you will find an infant wrapped in swaddling clothes and lying in a manger." And suddenly there was a multitude of the heavenly host with the angel, praising God and saying:

"Glory to God in the highest
    and on earth peace to those on whom his favor rests."

1104   DEC. 25: CHRISTMAS—MASS AT DAWN / ABC

READING I   *Isaiah 62:11–12 / 15*

See, the Lord proclaims
    to the ends of the earth:
say to daughter Zion,
    your savior comes!
Here is his reward with him,

his recompense before him.
They shall be called the holy people,
    the redeemed of the Lord,
and you shall be called "Frequented,"
    a city that is not forsaken.

RESPONSORIAL PSALM   *Psalm 97:1 and 6, 11–12*

A light will shine on us this day: the Lord is born for us.

The Lord is king, let earth rejoice;
    let the many islands be glad.
The skies proclaim his justice;
    all peoples see his glory. ℟.

Light shines forth for the just one,
    and joy for the upright of heart.
Rejoice in the Lord, you just;
    to the memory of his holiness give
        thanks. ℟.

READING II   *Titus 3:4–7*

Beloved:

When the kindness and generous love
  of God our savior appeared,
not because of any righteous deeds
    we had done
  but because of his mercy,
he saved us through the bath of
    rebirth

and renewal by the Holy Spirit,
  whom he richly poured out on us
    through Jesus Christ our savior,
so that we might be justified by his
    grace
  and become heirs in hope of
    eternal life.

GOSPEL   *Luke 2:15–20*

When the angels went away from them to heaven, the shepherds said to one another,
"Let us go, then, to Bethlehem to see this thing that has taken place, which the Lord
has made known to us." So they went in haste and found Mary and Joseph, and the
infant lying in the manger. When they saw this, they made known the message that
had been told them about this child. All who heard it were amazed by what had been
told them by the shepherds. And Mary kept all these things, reflecting on them in her
heart. Then the shepherds returned, glorifying and praising God for all they had heard
and seen, just as it had been told to them.

DEC. 25: CHRISTMAS—MASS DURING THE DAY / ABC   1105

READING I   *Isaiah 52:7–10 / 16*

How beautiful upon the mountains
  are the feet of him who brings
    glad tidings,
announcing peace, bearing good news,
  announcing salvation, and saying
    to Zion,
  "Your God is King!"

Hark! Your sentinels raise a cry,
  together they shout for joy,

for they see directly, before their eyes,
  the LORD restoring Zion.
Break out together in song,
  O ruins of Jerusalem!
For the LORD comforts his people,
  he redeems Jerusalem.
The LORD has bared his holy arm
  in the sight of all the nations;
all the ends of the earth will behold
  the salvation of our God.

RESPONSORIAL PSALM   *Psalm 98:1, 2–3ab, 3cd–4, 5–6*

All the ends of the earth have seen the sav-ing pow-er of God.

O sing a new song to the LORD,
  for he has worked wonders.
His right hand and his holy arm
  have brought salvation. ℟.

The LORD has made known his
    salvation,
  has shown his deliverance to the
    nations.
He has remembered his merciful love
  and his truth for the house of
    Israel. ℟.

All the ends of the earth have seen
  the salvation of our God.
Shout to the LORD, all the earth;
  break forth into joyous song,
  and sing out your praise. ℟.

Sing psalms to the LORD with the harp,
  with the harp and the sound of song.
With trumpets and the sound of the
  horn,
  raise a shout before the King,
  the LORD. ℟.

READING II
Hebrews 1:1–6

Brothers and sisters: In times past, God spoke in partial and various ways to our ancestors through the prophets; in these last days, he has spoken to us through the Son, whom he made heir of all things and through whom he created the universe,
  who is the refulgence of his glory, the very imprint of his being,
  and who sustains all things by his mighty word.
  When he had accomplished purification from sins,
  he took his seat at the right hand of the Majesty on high,
  as far superior to the angels
  as the name he has inherited is more excellent than theirs.

For to which of the angels did God ever say:
  You are my son; this day I have begotten you?
Or again:
  I will be a father to him, and he shall be a son to me?
And again, when he leads the firstborn into the world, he says:
  Let all the angels of God worship him.

GOSPEL
John 1:1–18 or 1:1–5, 9–14

For short form read only the parts in brackets.

[In the beginning was the Word,
  and the Word was with God,
  and the Word was God.
He was in the beginning with God.
All things came to be through him,
  and without him nothing came to be.
What came to be through him was life,
  and this life was the light of the human race;
  the light shines in the darkness,
  and the darkness has not overcome it.]
A man named John was sent from God. He came for testimony, to testify to the light, so that all might believe through him. He was not the light, but came to testify to the light. [The true light, which enlightens everyone, was coming into the world.
  He was in the world,
  and the world came to be through him,
  but the world did not know him.
He came to what was his own,
  but his own people did not accept him.

But to those who did accept him he gave power to become children of God, to those who believe in his name, who were born not by natural generation nor by human choice nor by a man's decision but of God.

And the Word became flesh
  and made his dwelling among us,
  and we saw his glory,
  the glory as of the Father's only Son,
  full of grace and truth.]
John testified to him and cried out, saying, "This was he of whom I said, 'The one who is coming after me ranks ahead of me because he existed before me.'" From his fullness we have all received, grace in place of grace, because while the law was given through Moses, grace and truth came through Jesus Christ. No one has ever seen God. The only Son, God, who is at the Father's side, has revealed him.

HOLY FAMILY OF JESUS, MARY AND JOSEPH / ABC   1106

READING I   *Sirach 3:2–6, 12–14 / 17*

God sets a father in honor over his
  children;
  a mother's authority he confirms
  over her sons.
Whoever honors his father atones
  for sins,
  and preserves himself from them.
When he prays, he is heard;
  he stores up riches who reveres
  his mother.
Whoever honors his father is
  gladdened by children,
  and, when he prays, is heard.
Whoever reveres his father will live a
long life;
he who obeys his father brings
  comfort to his mother.

My son, take care of your father when
  he is old;
  grieve him not as long as he lives.
Even if his mind fail, be considerate of
  him;
  revile him not all the days of his life;
kindness to a father will not be forgotten,
  firmly planted against the debt of
  your sins
—a house raised in justice to you.

RESPONSORIAL PSALM   *Psalm 128:1–2, 3, 4–5*

O bless-ed are those who fear the Lord and walk in his ways.

Blessed are all who fear the LORD,
  and walk in his ways!
By the labor of your hands you shall eat.
  You will be blessed and prosper. ℟.

Your wife like a fruitful vine
  in the heart of your house;
your children like shoots of the olive
  around your table. ℟.

Indeed thus shall be blessed
  the man who fears the LORD.
May the LORD bless you from Sion.
  May you see Jerusalem prosper
  all the days of your life! ℟.

READING II   *Colossians 3:12–21 or 3:12–17*

For short form read only the part in brackets.

[Brothers and sisters: Put on, as God's chosen ones, holy and beloved, heartfelt compassion, kindness, humility, gentleness, and patience, bearing with one another and forgiving one another, if one has a grievance against another; as the Lord has forgiven you, so must you also do. And over all these put on love, that is, the bond of perfection. And let the peace of Christ control your hearts, the peace into which you were also called in one body. And be thankful. Let the word of Christ dwell in you richly, as in all wisdom you teach and admonish one another, singing psalms, hymns, and spiritual songs with gratitude in your hearts to God. And whatever you do, in word or in deed, do everything in the name of the Lord Jesus, giving thanks to God the Father through him.]

Wives, be subordinate to your husbands, as is proper in the Lord. Husbands, love your wives, and avoid any bitterness toward them. Children, obey your parents in everything, for this is pleasing to the Lord. Fathers, do not provoke your children, so they may not become discouraged.

GOSPEL / A   *Matthew 2:13–15, 19–23*

When the magi had departed, behold, the angel of the Lord appeared to Joseph in a dream and said, "Rise, take the child and his mother, flee to Egypt, and stay there until I tell you. Herod is going to search for the child to destroy him." Joseph rose and took the child and his mother by night and departed for Egypt. He stayed there until the death of Herod, that what the Lord had said through the prophet might be fulfilled, *Out of Egypt I called my son.*

When Herod had died, behold, the angel of the Lord appeared in a dream to Joseph in Egypt and said, "Rise, take the child and his mother and go to the land of Israel, for those who sought the child's life are dead." He rose, took the child and his mother, and went to the land of Israel. But when he heard that Archelaus was ruling over Judea in place of his father Herod, he was afraid to go back there. And because he had been warned in a dream, he departed for the region of Galilee. He went and dwelt in a town called Nazareth, so that what had been spoken through the prophets might be fulfilled, *He shall be called a Nazorean.*

GOSPEL / B   *Luke 2:22–40 or 2:22, 39–40*

For short form read only the parts in brackets.

[When the days were completed for their purification according to the law of Moses, they took him up to Jerusalem to present him to the Lord,] just as it is written in the law of the Lord, *Every male that opens the womb shall be consecrated to the Lord,* and to offer the sacrifice of *a pair of turtledoves or two young pigeons,* in accordance with the dictate in the law of the Lord.

Now there was a man in Jerusalem whose name was Simeon. This man was righteous and devout, awaiting the consolation of Israel, and the Holy Spirit was upon him. It had been revealed to him by the Holy Spirit that he should not see death before he had seen the Christ of the Lord. He came in the Spirit into the temple; and when the parents brought in the child Jesus to perform the custom of the law in regard to him, he took him into his arms and blessed God, saying:

"Now, Master, you may let your servant go

in peace, according to your word,
for my eyes have seen your salvation,
  which you prepared in sight of all the peoples,
a light for revelation to the Gentiles,
  and glory for your people Israel."

The child's father and mother were amazed at what was said about him; and Simeon blessed them and said to Mary his mother, "Behold, this child is destined for the fall and rise of many in Israel, and to be a sign that will be contradicted—and you yourself a sword will pierce—so that the thoughts of many hearts may be revealed." There was also a prophetess, Anna, the daughter of Phanuel, of the tribe of Asher. She was advanced in years, having lived seven years with her husband after her marriage, and then as a widow until she was eighty-four. She never left the temple, but worshiped night and day with fasting and prayer. And coming forward at that very time, she gave thanks to God and spoke about the child to all who were awaiting the redemption of Jerusalem.

[When they had fulfilled all the prescriptions of the law of the Lord, they returned to Galilee, to their own town of Nazareth. The child grew and became strong, filled with wisdom; and the favor of God was upon him.]

GOSPEL / C   *Luke 2:41–52*

Each year Jesus' parents went to Jerusalem for the feast of Passover, and when he was twelve years old, they went up according to festival custom. After they had completed its days, as they were returning, the boy Jesus remained behind in Jerusalem, but his parents did not know it. Thinking that he was in the caravan, they journeyed for a day and looked for him among their relatives and acquaintances, but not finding him, they returned to Jerusalem to look for him. After three days they found him in the temple, sitting in the midst of the teachers, listening to them and asking them questions, and all who heard him were astounded at his understanding and his answers. When his parents saw him, they were astonished, and his mother said to him, "Son, why have you done this to us? Your father and I have been looking for you with great anxiety." And he said to them, "Why were you looking for me? Did you not know that I must be in my Father's house?" But they did not understand what he said to them. He went down with them and came to Nazareth, and was obedient to them; and his mother kept all these things in her heart. And Jesus advanced in wisdom and age and favor before God and man.

IN YEAR B, THESE READINGS MAY BE USED   1107

READING I   *Genesis 15:1–6; 21:1–3*

The word of the LORD came to Abram in a vision, saying:
  "Fear not, Abram!
    I am your shield;
    I will make your reward very great."
But Abram said, "O Lord GOD, what good will your gifts be, if I keep on being child-less and have as my heir the steward of my house, Eliezer?" Abram continued, "See, you have given me no offspring, and so one of my servants will be my heir." Then the word of the LORD came to him: "No, that one shall not be your heir; your own issue shall be your heir." The Lord took Abram outside and said, "Look up at the sky and

count the stars, if you can. Just so," he added, "shall your descendants be." Abram put his faith in the LORD, who credited it to him as an act of righteousness.

The LORD took note of Sarah as he had said he would; he did for her as he had promised. Sarah became pregnant and bore Abraham a son in his old age, at the set time that God had stated. Abraham gave the name Isaac to this son of his whom Sarah bore him.

RESPONSORIAL PSALM   *Psalm 105:1–2, 3–4, 6–7, 8–9*

The Lord re-mem-bers his cov-e-nant for ev - er.

Give thanks to the LORD; proclaim his name.
  Make known his deeds among the peoples.
O sing to him, sing his praise;
  tell all his wonderful works! ℟.

Glory in his holy name;
  let the hearts that seek the LORD rejoice.
Turn to the LORD and his strength;
  constantly seek his face. ℟.

O children of Abraham, his servant,
  O descendants of the Jacob he chose,
he, the LORD, is our God;
  his judgments are in all the earth. ℟.

He remembers his covenant forever:
  the promise he ordained for a thousand generations,
the covenant he made with Abraham,
  the oath he swore to Isaac. ℟.

READING II   *Hebrews 11:8, 11–12, 17–19*

Brothers and sisters: By faith Abraham obeyed when he was called to go out to a place that he was to receive as an inheritance; he went out, not knowing where he was to go. By faith he received power to generate, even though he was past the normal age—and Sarah herself was sterile—for he thought that the one who had made the promise was trustworthy. So it was that there came forth from one man, himself as good as dead, descendants as numerous as the stars in the sky and as countless as the sands on the seashore.

By faith Abraham, when put to the test, offered up Isaac, and he who had received the promises was ready to offer his only son, of whom it was said, "Through Isaac descendants shall bear your name." He reasoned that God was able to raise even from the dead, and he received Isaac back as a symbol.

1108 IN YEAR C, THESE READINGS MAY BE USED

READING I   *1 Samuel 1:20–22, 24–28*

In those days Hannah conceived, and at the end of her term bore a son whom she called Samuel, since she had asked the LORD for him. The next time her husband Elkanah was going up with the rest of his household to offer the customary sacrifice to the LORD and to fulfill his vows, Hannah did not go, explaining to her husband, "Once the child is weaned, I will take him to appear before the LORD and to remain there forever; I will offer him as a perpetual nazirite."

Once Samuel was weaned, Hannah brought him up with her, along with a three-year-old bull, an ephah of flour, and a skin of wine, and presented him at the temple of the LORD in Shiloh. After the boy's father had sacrificed the young bull, Hannah, his mother, approached Eli and said: "Pardon, my lord! As you live, my lord, I am the woman who stood near you here, praying to the LORD. I prayed for this child, and the LORD granted my request. Now I, in turn, give him to the LORD; as long as he lives, he shall be dedicated to the LORD." Hannah left Samuel there.

RESPONSORIAL PSALM   *Psalm 84:2–3, 5–6, 9–10*

Bless - ed,   bless - ed are they   who dwell in your house,   O Lord.

How lovely is your dwelling place,
   O LORD of hosts.
My soul is longing and yearning
   for the courts of the LORD.
My heart and my flesh cry out
   to the living God. ℟.

Blessed are they who dwell in your house,
   forever singing your praise.

Blessed the people whose strength is in
   you,
   whose heart is set on pilgrim
   ways. ℟.

O LORD God of hosts, hear my prayer;
   give ear, O God of Jacob.
Turn your eyes, O God, our shield;
   look on the face of your anointed. ℟.

READING II   *1 John 3:1–2, 21–24*

Beloved: See what love the Father has bestowed on us that we may be called the children of God. And so we are. The reason the world does not know us is that it did not know him. Beloved, we are God's children now; what we shall be has not yet been revealed. We do know that when it is revealed we shall be like him, for we shall see him as he is.

Beloved, if our hearts do not condemn us, we have confidence in God and receive from him whatever we ask, because we keep his commandments and do what pleases him. And his commandment is this: we should believe in the name of his Son, Jesus Christ, and love one another just as he commanded us. Those who keep his commandments remain in him, and he in them, and the way we know that he remains in us is from the Spirit he gave us.

JAN. 1: SOLEMNITY OF MARY, HOLY MOTHER OF GOD / ABC 1109

READING I   *Numbers 6:22–27 / 18*

The LORD said to Moses: "Speak to Aaron and his sons and tell them: This is how you shall bless the Israelites. Say to them:
   The LORD bless you and keep you!
   The LORD let his face shine upon you, and be gracious to you!
   The LORD look upon you kindly and give you peace!
So shall they invoke my name upon the Israelites, and I will bless them."

RESPONSORIAL PSALM *Psalm 67:2–3, 5, 6 and 8*

RJB

May God bless us in his mer - cy,

may God bless us in his mer - cy.

O God, be gracious and bless us
 and let your face shed its light upon us.
So will your ways be known upon earth
 and all nations learn your salvation. ℟.

Let the nations be glad and shout for joy,
 with uprightness you rule the
 peoples;
 you guide the nations on earth. ℟.

Let the peoples praise you, O God;
 let all the peoples praise you.
May God still give us his blessing
 that all the ends of the earth may
 revere him. ℟.

READING II *Galatians 4:4–7*

Brothers and sisters: When the fullness of time had come, God sent his Son, born of a woman, born under the law, to ransom those under the law, so that we might receive adoption as sons. As proof that you are sons, God sent the Spirit of his Son into our hearts, crying out, "Abba, Father!" So you are no longer a slave but a son, and if a son then also an heir, through God.

GOSPEL *Luke 2:16–21*

The shepherds went in haste to Bethlehem and found Mary and Joseph, and the infant lying in the manger. When they saw this, they made known the message that had been told them about this child. All who heard it were amazed by what had been told them by the shepherds. And Mary kept all these things, reflecting on them in her heart. Then the shepherds returned, glorifying and praising God for all they had heard and seen, just as it had been told to them.

When eight days were completed for his circumcision, he was named Jesus, the name given him by the angel before he was conceived in the womb.

1110 EPIPHANY OF THE LORD / ABC

READING I *Isaiah 60:1–6 / 20*

Rise up in splendor, Jerusalem! Your
 light has come,
 the glory of the Lord shines upon
 you.
See, darkness covers the earth,
 and thick clouds cover the peoples;

but upon you the LORD shines,
 and over you appears his glory.
Nations shall walk by your light,
 and kings by your shining radiance.
Raise your eyes and look about;
 they all gather and come to you:

your sons come from afar,
and your daughters in the arms of
their nurses.

Then you shall be radiant at what
you see,
your heart shall throb and overflow,
for the riches of the sea shall be
emptied out before you,

the wealth of nations shall be
brought to you.
Caravans of camels shall fill you,
dromedaries from Midian and Ephah;
all from Sheba shall come
bearing gold and frankincense,
and proclaiming the praises of the
LORD.

RESPONSORIAL PSALM

Psalm 72:1–2, 7–8, 10–11, 12–13

Lord, ev - 'ry na - tion on earth will a - dore you.

O God, give your judgment to the king,
to a king's son your justice,
that he may judge your people in justice,
and your poor in right judgment. ℟.

In his days shall justice flourish,
and great peace till the moon is no
more.
He shall rule from sea to sea,
from the River to the bounds of the
earth. ℟.

The kings of Tarshish and the islands
shall pay him tribute.
The kings of Sheba and Seba
shall bring him gifts.
Before him all kings shall fall prostrate,
all nations shall serve him. ℟.

For he shall save the needy when they
cry,
the poor, and those who are helpless.
He will have pity on the weak and the
needy,
and save the lives of the needy. ℟.

READING II

Ephesians 3:2–3a, 5–6

Brothers and sisters: You have heard of the stewardship of God's grace that was given to me for your benefit, namely, that the mystery was made known to me by revelation. It was not made known to people in other generations as it has now been revealed to his holy apostles and prophets by the Spirit: that the Gentiles are coheirs, members of the same body, and copartners in the promise in Christ Jesus through the gospel.

GOSPEL

Matthew 2:1–12

When Jesus was born in Bethlehem of Judea, in the days of King Herod, behold, magi from the east arrived in Jerusalem, saying, "Where is the newborn king of the Jews? We saw his star at its rising and have come to do him homage." When King Herod heard this, he was greatly troubled, and all Jerusalem with him. Assembling all the chief priests and the scribes of the people, he inquired of them where the Christ was to be born. They said to him, "In Bethlehem of Judea, for thus it has been written through the prophet:
And you, Bethlehem, land of Judah,
are by no means least among the rulers of Judah;
since from you shall come a ruler,
who is to shepherd my people Israel."

Then Herod called the magi secretly and ascertained from them the time of the star's appearance. He sent them to Bethlehem and said, "Go and search diligently for the child. When you have found him, bring me word, that I too may go and do him homage." After their audience with the king they set out. And behold, the star that they had seen at its rising preceded them, until it came and stopped over the place where the child was. They were overjoyed at seeing the star, and on entering the house they saw the child with Mary his mother. They prostrated themselves and did him homage. Then they opened their treasures and offered him gifts of gold, frankincense, and myrrh. And having been warned in a dream not to return to Herod, they departed for their country by another way.

1111   BAPTISM OF THE LORD / ABC

READING I   *Isaiah 42:1–4, 6–7 / 21*

Thus says the LORD:
Here is my servant whom I uphold,
  my chosen one with whom I am
    pleased,
upon whom I have put my spirit;
  he shall bring forth justice to the
    nations,
not crying out, not shouting,
  not making his voice heard in the
    street.
A bruised reed he shall not break,
  and a smoldering wick he shall not
    quench,
until he establishes justice on the earth;

the coastlands will wait for his
  teaching.

I, the LORD, have called you for the
  victory of justice,
I have grasped you by the hand;
I formed you, and set you
  as a covenant of the people,
  a light for the nations,
to open the eyes of the blind,
  to bring out prisoners from
    confinement,
  and from the dungeon, those who
    live in darkness.

RESPONSORIAL PSALM   *Psalm 29:1a and 2, 3ac–4, 3b and 9b–10*

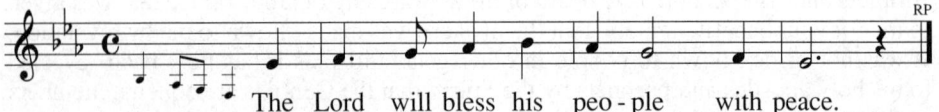

The Lord will bless his peo-ple with peace.

Ascribe to the LORD, you heavenly powers,
  ascribe to the LORD glory and strength.
Ascribe to the LORD the glory of his name;
  bow down before the LORD, majestic
    in holiness. ℟.

The voice of the LORD upon the waters,
  the LORD on the immensity of waters;
the voice of the LORD full of power;

the voice of the LORD full of
  splendor. ℟.

The God of glory thunders;
  in his temple they all cry, "Glory!"
The LORD sat enthroned above the
    flood;
  the LORD sits as king forever. ℟.

READING II   *Acts 10:34–38*

Peter proceeded to speak to those gathered in the house of Cornelius, saying: "In truth, I see that God shows no partiality. Rather, in every nation whoever fears him and acts uprightly is acceptable to him. You know the word that he sent to the Israelites as he proclaimed peace through Jesus Christ, who is Lord of all, what has happened all over Judea, beginning in Galilee after the baptism that John preached, how God anointed Jesus of Nazareth with the Holy Spirit and power. He went about doing good and healing all those oppressed by the devil, for God was with him."

GOSPEL / A
Matthew 3:13–17

Jesus came from Galilee to John at the Jordan to be baptized by him. John tried to prevent him, saying, "I need to be baptized by you, and yet you are coming to me?" Jesus said to him in reply, "Allow it now, for thus it is fitting for us to fulfill all righteousness." Then he allowed him. After Jesus was baptized, he came up from the water and behold, the heavens were opened for him, and he saw the Spirit of God descending like a dove and coming upon him. And a voice came from the heavens, saying, "This is my beloved Son, with whom I am well pleased."

GOSPEL / B
Mark 1:7–11

This is what John the Baptist proclaimed:

"One mightier than I is coming after me. I am not worthy to stoop and loosen the thongs of his sandals. I have baptized you with water; he will baptize you with the Holy Spirit."

It happened in those days that Jesus came from Nazareth of Galilee and was baptized in the Jordan by John. On coming up out of the water he saw the heavens being torn open and the Spirit, like a dove, descending upon him. And a voice came from the heavens, "You are my beloved Son; with you I am well pleased."

GOSPEL / C
Luke 3:15–16, 21–22

The people were filled with expectation, and all were asking in their hearts whether John might be the Christ. John answered them all, saying, "I am baptizing you with water, but one mightier than I is coming. I am not worthy to loosen the thongs of his sandals. He will baptize you with the Holy Spirit and fire."

After all the people had been baptized and Jesus also had been baptized and was praying, heaven was opened and the Holy Spirit descended upon him in bodily form like a dove. And a voice came from heaven, "You are my beloved Son; with you I am well pleased."

IN YEAR B, THESE READINGS MAY BE USED   1112

READING I
Isaiah 55:1–11

Thus says the LORD:
All you who are thirsty,
    come to the water!
You who have no money,
    come, receive grain and eat;
come, without paying and without cost,
    drink wine and milk!
Why spend your money for what is
    not bread,
your wages for what fails to satisfy?
Heed me, and you shall eat well,
    you shall delight in rich fare.
Come to me heedfully,
    listen, that you may have life.
I will renew with you the everlasting
    covenant,
    the benefits assured to David.

As I made him a witness to the peoples,
a leader and commander of nations,
so shall you summon a nation you
knew not,
and nations that knew you not
shall run to you,
because of the LORD, your God
the Holy One of Israel, who has
glorified you.

Seek the LORD while he may be found,
call him while he is near.
Let the scoundrel forsake his way,
and the wicked man his thoughts;
let him turn to the LORD for mercy;
to our God, who is generous in
forgiving.
For my thoughts are not your thoughts,
nor are your ways my ways, says
the LORD.

As high as the heavens are above the
earth
so high are my ways above your
ways
and my thoughts above your
thoughts.

For just as from the heavens
the rain and snow come down
and do not return there
till they have watered the earth,
making it fertile and fruitful,
giving seed to the one who sows
and bread to the one who eats,
so shall my word be
that goes forth from my mouth;
my word shall not return to me void,
but shall do my will,
achieving the end for which I sent it.

RESPONSORIAL PSALM *Isaiah 12:2–3, 4bcd, 5–6*

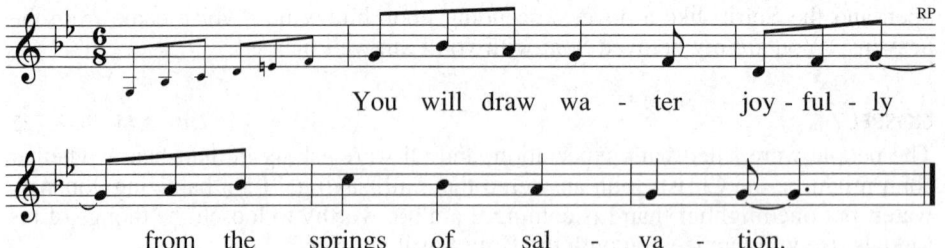

You will draw wa - ter joy - ful - ly

from the springs of sal - va - tion.

Truly, God is my salvation,
I trust, I shall not fear.
For the Lord is my strength, my song,
he became my savior.
With joy you will draw water
from the wells of salvation. ℟.

Give thanks to the Lord,
give praise to his name!
Make his mighty deeds

known to the peoples!
Declare the greatness of his name.
Sing a psalm to the Lord! ℟.

For he has done glorious deeds,
make them known to all the earth!
People of Zion,
sing and shout for joy
for great in your midst
is the Holy One of Israel. ℟.

READING II *1 John 5:1–9*

Beloved: Everyone who believes that Jesus is the Christ is begotten by God, and everyone who loves the Father loves also the one begotten by him. In this way we know
that we love the children of God when we love God and obey his commandments. For
the love of God is this, that we keep his commandments. And his commandments are

not burdensome, for whoever is begotten by God conquers the world. And the victory that conquers the world is our faith. Who indeed is the victor over the world but the one who believes that Jesus is the Son of God?

This is the one who came through water and blood, Jesus Christ, not by water alone, but by water and blood. The Spirit is the one who testifies, and the Spirit is truth. So there are three that testify, the Spirit, the water, and the blood, and the three are of one accord. If we accept human testimony, the testimony of God is surely greater. Now the testimony of God is this, that he has testified on behalf of his Son.

IN YEAR C, THESE READINGS MAY BE USED — 1113

READING I   *Isaiah 40:1–5, 9–11*

Comfort, give comfort to my people,
  says your God.
Speak tenderly to Jerusalem, and
    proclaim to her
  that her service is at an end,
  her guilt is expiated;
indeed, she has received from the hand
    of the LORD
  double for all her sins.

  A voice cries out:
In the desert prepare the way of the
  LORD!
  Make straight in the wasteland a
  highway for our God!
Every valley shall be filled in,
  every mountain and hill shall be
    made low;
  the rugged land shall be made a plain,
  the rough country, a broad valley.
Then the glory of the LORD shall be

revealed
and all people shall see it together;
for the mouth of the LORD has
  spoken.

Go up onto a high mountain,
  Zion, herald of glad tidings;
cry out at the top of your voice,
  Jerusalem, herald of good news!
Fear not to cry out
  and say to the cities of Judah:
  Here is your God!
Here comes with power
  the Lord GOD,
  who rules by a strong arm;
here is his reward with him,
  his recompense before him.
Like a shepherd he feeds his flock;
  in his arms he gathers the lambs,
carrying them in his bosom,
  and leading the ewes with care.

RESPONSORIAL PSALM   *Psalm 104:1b–2, 3–4, 24–25, 27–28, 29–30*

O bless the Lord, bless the Lord, my soul, O my soul.

O LORD my God, how great you are,
  clothed in majesty and honor,
wrapped in light as with a robe!
  You stretch out the heavens like a
    tent. ℟.

On the waters you establish your
    dwelling.
  You make the clouds your chariot;
  you ride on the wings of the wind.
You make the winds your messengers,
  flame and fire your servants. ℟.

How many are your works, O Lord!
   In wisdom you have made them all.
   The earth is full of your creatures.
Vast and wide is the span of the sea,
   with its creeping things past counting,
   living things great and small. ℟.

All of these look to you
   to give them their food in due season.
You give it, they gather it up;
   you open wide your hand, they are
      well filled. ℟.

You take away their breath, they die,
   returning to the dust from which
      they came.
You send forth your spirit, and they
   are created,
and you renew the face of the
   earth. ℟.

READING II   *Titus 2:11–14; 3:4–7*

Beloved: The grace of God has appeared, saving all and training us to reject godless ways and worldly desires and to live temperately, justly, and devoutly in this age, as we await the blessed hope, the appearance of the glory of our great God and savior Jesus Christ, who gave himself for us to deliver us from all lawlessness and to cleanse for himself a people as his own, eager to do what is good.

When the kindness and generous love
   of God our savior appeared,
not because of any righteous deeds we had done
   but because of his mercy,
He saved us through the bath of rebirth
   and renewal by the Holy Spirit,
whom he richly poured out on us
   through Jesus Christ our savior,
so that we might be justified by his grace
   and become heirs in hope of eternal life.

On a Wednesday in February or early March the Church enters into prayer and fasting and almsgiving, attending with great seriousness to its calling. Forty days later on a Thursday evening, that season of Lent ends. From Holy Thursday night until Easter Sunday afternoon, the Church keeps the Paschal Triduum, the "Easter Three Days." Good Friday and Holy Saturday find Christians fasting, keeping vigil, remembering the passion, death and resurrection of the Lord until, at the great Vigil liturgy, the Church celebrates this paschal mystery in baptism, confirmation and eucharist. Then, for the fifty days of Eastertime the Church again sings the alleluia and rejoices to bring God's peace to the world.

The origins of Lent are bound up with the final stages in the initiation of those seeking to be baptized. After months or years of learning gradually the Christian way of life, the catechumens were called to spend the last weeks before baptism in fasting and prayer. The whole Church stayed by the catechumens in these days. The lenten season was also kept intensely by those doing penance for their sins. Today both catechumens and penitents keep Lent with the whole Church. Lent's scriptures, prayers and rites give clarity and strength to the life-long struggle against evil. That struggle is waged with many forms of prayer and fasting and practices of charity.

The origins of the fifty days of Eastertime are even more ancient. This is the springtime rejoicing of people who know their dependence on fields and flocks. It is the rejoicing of Israel remembering the exodus from slavery to freedom. It became the rejoicing of the Church in the resurrection of Jesus and the presence of that risen life in the newly baptized. The Eastertime lectionary is filled with a lively peace and the quiet exuberance of those who believe that evil is not finally triumphant. When the fifty days conclude at Pentecost the Church knows again how disturbing, how restless, how strong is the Spirit given by Christ.

ASH WEDNESDAY 1115

READING I *Joel 2:12–18 / 219*

Even now, says the LORD,
    return to me with your whole heart,
    with fasting, and weeping, and
        mourning;
Rend your hearts, not your garments,
    and return to the LORD, your God.
For gracious and merciful is he,
    slow to anger, rich in kindness,
    and relenting in punishment.
Perhaps he will again relent
    and leave behind him a blessing,
Offerings and libations,
    for the LORD, your God.

Blow the trumpet in Zion!
    proclaim a fast,
    call an assembly;
Gather the people,
    notify the congregation;

Assemble the elders,
    gather the children
    and the infants at the breast;
Let the bridegroom quit his room,
    and the bride her chamber.
Between the porch and the altar
    let the priests, the ministers of the
        LORD, weep,
And say, "Spare, O LORD, your people,
    and make not your heritage a
        reproach,
    with the nations ruling over them!
Why should they say among the
        peoples,
    'Where is their God?'"

Then the LORD was stirred to concern
    for his land
and took pity on his people.

RESPONSORIAL PSALM   *Psalm 51:3–4, 5–6a, 12–13, 14 and 17*

Be mer - ci - ful, O Lord, for we have sinned.

Have mercy on me, O God,
  according to your merciful love;
according to your great compassion,
  blot out my transgressions.
Wash me completely from my iniquity,
  and cleanse me from my sin. ℟.

My transgressions, truly I know them;
  my sin is always before me.
Against you, you alone, have I sinned;
  what is evil in your sight I have
    done. ℟.

Create a pure heart for me, O God;
  renew a steadfast spirit within me.
Do not cast me away from your presence;
  take not your holy spirit from me. ℟.

Restore in me the joy of your salvation;
  sustain in me a willing spirit.
O Lord, open my lips
  and my mouth shall proclaim your
    praise. ℟.

READING II   *2 Corinthians 5:20—6:2*

Brothers and sisters: We are ambassadors for Christ, as if God were appealing through us. We implore you on behalf of Christ, be reconciled to God. For our sake he made him to be sin who did not know sin, so that we might become the righteousness of God in him.

Working together, then, we appeal to you not to receive the grace of God in vain. For he says:

In an acceptable time I heard you,
  and on the day of salvation I helped you.

Behold, now is a very acceptable time; behold, now is the day of salvation.

GOSPEL   *Matthew 6:1–6, 16–18*

Jesus said to his disciples: "Take care not to perform righteous deeds in order that people may see them; otherwise, you will have no recompense from your heavenly Father. When you give alms, do not blow a trumpet before you, as the hypocrites do in the synagogues and in the streets to win the praise of others. Amen, I say to you, they have received their reward. But when you give alms, do not let your left hand know what your right is doing, so that your almsgiving may be secret. And your Father who sees in secret will repay you.

"When you pray, do not be like the hypocrites, who love to stand and pray in the synagogues and on street corners so that others may see them. Amen, I say to you, they have received their reward. But when you pray, go to your inner room, close the door, and pray to your Father in secret. And your Father who sees in secret will repay you.

"When you fast, do not look gloomy like the hypocrites. They neglect their appearance, so that they may appear to others to be fasting. Amen, I say to you, they have received their reward. But when you fast, anoint your head and wash your face, so that you may not appear to be fasting, except to your Father who is hidden. And your Father who sees what is hidden will repay you."

FIRST SUNDAY OF LENT / A 1116

READING I *Genesis 2:7–9; 3:1–7 / 22*

The LORD God formed man out of the clay of the ground and blew into his nostrils the breath of life, and so man became a living being.

Then the LORD God planted a garden in Eden, in the east, and placed there the man whom he had formed. Out of the ground the LORD God made various trees grow that were delightful to look at and good for food, with the tree of life in the middle of the garden and the tree of the knowledge of good and evil.

Now the serpent was the most cunning of all the animals that the LORD God had made. The serpent asked the woman, "Did God really tell you not to eat from any of the trees in the garden?" The woman answered the serpent: "We may eat of the fruit of the trees in the garden; it is only about the fruit of the tree in the middle of the garden that God said, 'You shall not eat it or even touch it, lest you die.'" But the serpent said to the woman: "You certainly will not die! No, God knows well that the moment you eat of it your eyes will be opened and you will be like gods who know what is good and what is evil." The woman saw that the tree was good for food, pleasing to the eyes, and desirable for gaining wisdom. So she took some of its fruit and ate it; and she also gave some to her husband, who was with her, and he ate it. Then the eyes of both of them were opened, and they realized that they were naked; so they sewed fig leaves together and made loincloths for themselves.

RESPONSORIAL PSALM *Psalm 51:3–4, 5–6a, 12–13, 14 and 17*

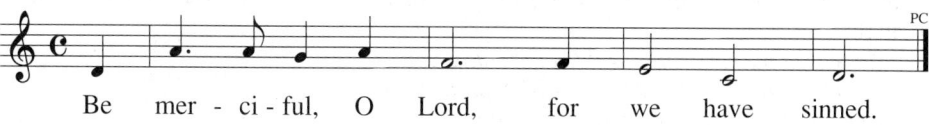

Be mer - ci - ful, O Lord, for we have sinned.

Have mercy on me, O God,
  according to your merciful love;
according to your great compassion,
  blot out my transgressions.
Wash me completely from my iniquity,
  and cleanse me from my sin. ℟.

My transgressions, truly I know them;
  my sin is always before me.
Against you, you alone, have I sinned;
  what is evil in your sight I have
    done. ℟.

Create a pure heart for me, O God;
  renew a steadfast spirit within me.
Do not cast me away from your presence;
  take not your holy spirit from me. ℟.

Restore in me the joy of your salvation;
  sustain in me a willing spirit.
O Lord, open my lips
  and my mouth shall proclaim your
    praise. ℟.

READING II *Romans 5:12–19 or 5:12, 17–19*

For short form read only the parts in brackets.

[Brothers and sisters: Through one man sin entered the world, and through sin, death, and thus death came to all men, inasmuch as all sinned—] for up to the time of the law, sin was in the world, though sin is not accounted when there is no law. But death reigned from Adam to Moses, even over those who did not sin after the pattern of the trespass of Adam, who is the type of the one who was to come.

But the gift is not like the transgression. For if by the transgression of the one, the many died, how much more did the grace of God and the gracious gift of the one man Jesus Christ overflow for the many. And the gift is not like the result of the one who sinned. For after one sin there was the judgment that brought condemnation; but the gift, after many transgressions, brought acquittal. [For if, by the transgression of the one, death came to reign through that one, how much more will those who receive the abundance of grace and of the gift of justification come to reign in life through the one Jesus Christ. In conclusion, just as through one transgression condemnation came upon all, so, through one righteous act, acquittal and life came to all. For just as through the disobedience of the one man the many were made sinners, so, through the obedience of the one, the many will be made righteous.]

GOSPEL   *Matthew 4:1–11*

At that time Jesus was led by the Spirit into the desert to be tempted by the devil. He fasted for forty days and forty nights, and afterwards he was hungry. The tempter approached and said to him, "If you are the Son of God, command that these stones become loaves of bread."
He said in reply, "It is written:
One does not live on bread alone,
but on every word that comes forth
from the mouth of God."

Then the devil took him to the holy city, and made him stand on the parapet of the temple, and said to him, "If you are the Son of God, throw yourself down. For it is written:
He will command his angels concerning you
and with their hands they will support you,
lest you dash your foot against a stone."
Jesus answered him, "Again it is written, *You shall not put the Lord, your God, to the test.*" Then the devil took him up to a very high mountain, and showed him all the kingdoms of the world in their magnificence, and he said to him, "All these I shall give to you, if you will prostrate yourself and worship me." At this, Jesus said to him, "Get away, Satan! It is written:
The Lord, your God, shall you worship
and him alone shall you serve."

Then the devil left him and, behold, angels came and ministered to him.

RITE OF ELECTION
At the beginning of Lent, it is the responsibility of the bishop to call those who are judged ready to prepare for the sacraments of initiation at Easter. The bishop is to consult first with the pastors, catechists and others. The rite may take place at the cathedral. If the rite takes place in the parish church, the bishop may designate the pastor to act in his place.
This rite is also called the "Enrollment of Names." Each candidate now gives his/her name, or writes it down. When all have been enrolled, the bishop says: "You have been chosen to be initiated into the sacred mysteries at the Easter Vigil." He then speaks to them and to their sponsors about their lenten preparation for baptism.
The faithful join in prayers of intercession for the elect, as the catechumens are now called. If the eucharist is to be celebrated, the elect are first dismissed.

FIRST SUNDAY OF LENT / B 1117

READING I *Genesis 9:8–15 / 23*

God said to Noah and to his sons with him: "See, I am now establishing my covenant with you and your descendants after you and with every living creature that was with you: all the birds, and the various tame and wild animals that were with you and came out of the ark. I will establish my covenant with you, that never again shall all bodily creatures be destroyed by the waters of a flood; there shall not be another flood to devastate the earth." God added: "This is the sign that I am giving for all ages to come, of the covenant between me and you and every living creature with you: I set my bow in the clouds to serve as a sign of the covenant between me and the earth. When I bring clouds over the earth, and the bow appears in the clouds, I will recall the covenant I have made between me and you and all living beings, so that the waters shall never again become a flood to destroy all mortal beings."

RESPONSORIAL PSALM *Psalm 25:4–5ab, 6 and 7bc, 8–9*

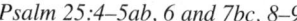

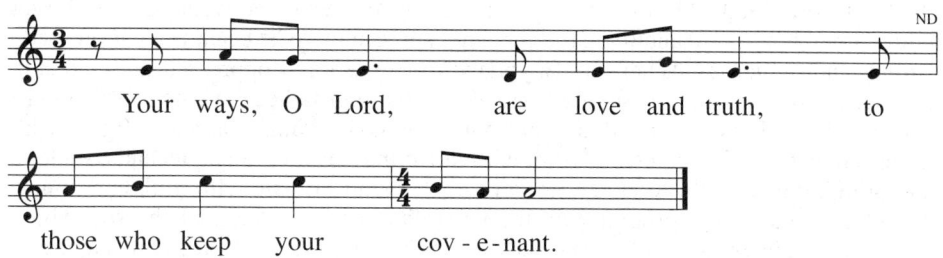

Your ways, O Lord, are love and truth, to those who keep your cov‑e‑nant.

O Lord, make me know your ways.
  Teach me your paths.
Guide me in your truth, and teach me;
  for you are the God of my
    salvation. ℟.

Remember your compassion, O Lord,
  and your merciful love,
  for they are from of old.
In your merciful love remember me,

because of your goodness,
  O Lord. ℟.

Good and upright is the Lord;
  he shows the way to sinners.
He guides the humble in right
    judgment;
  to the humble he teaches his
    way. ℟.

READING II *1 Peter 3:18–22*

Beloved: Christ suffered for sins once, the righteous for the sake of the unrighteous, that he might lead you to God. Put to death in the flesh, he was brought to life in the Spirit. In it he also went to preach to the spirits in prison, who had once been disobedient while God patiently waited in the days of Noah during the building of the ark, in which a few persons, eight in all, were saved through water. This prefigured baptism, which saves you now. It is not a removal of dirt from the body but an appeal to God for a clear conscience, through the resurrection of Jesus Christ, who has gone into heaven and is at the right hand of God, with angels, authorities, and powers subject to him.

GOSPEL   *Mark 1:12–15*

The Spirit drove Jesus out into the desert, and he remained in the desert for forty days, tempted by Satan. He was among wild beasts, and the angels ministered to him.

After John had been arrested, Jesus came to Galilee proclaiming the gospel of God: "This is the time of fulfillment. The kingdom of God is at hand. Repent, and believe in the gospel."

RITE OF ELECTION

See no. 1116

1118 FIRST SUNDAY OF LENT / C

READING I   *Deuteronomy 26:4–10 / 24*

Moses spoke to the people, saying: "The priest shall receive the basket from you and shall set it in front of the altar of the LORD, your God. Then you shall declare before the LORD, your God, 'My father was a wandering Aramean who went down to Egypt with a small household and lived there as an alien. But there he became a nation great, strong, and numerous. When the Egyptians maltreated and oppressed us, imposing hard labor upon us, we cried to the LORD, the God of our fathers, and he heard our cry and saw our affliction, our toil, and our oppression. He brought us out of Egypt with his strong hand and outstretched arm, with terrifying power, with signs and wonders; and bringing us into this country, he gave us this land flowing with milk and honey. Therefore, I have now brought you the firstfruits of the products of the soil which you, O LORD, have given me.' And having set them before the Lord, your God, you shall bow down in his presence."

RESPONSORIAL PSALM   *Psalm 91:1–2, 10–11, 12–13, 14–15*

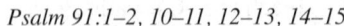

Be with me, Lord, when I am in trou - ble.

He who dwells in the shelter of the
    Most High,
and abides in the shade of the
    Almighty,
says to the LORD, "My refuge,
    my stronghold, my God in whom I
    trust!" ℟.

Upon you no evil shall fall,
    no plague approach your tent.
For you has he commanded his angels
    to keep you in all your ways. ℟.

They shall bear you upon their hands,
    lest you strike your foot against a
    stone.
On the lion and the viper you will tread,
    and trample the young lion and the
    serpent. ℟.

Since he clings to me in love, I will
    free him,
    protect him, for he knows my name.
When he calls on me, I will answer
    him;
    I will be with him in distress;
    I will deliver him, and give him
    glory. ℟.

READING II   *Romans 10:8–13*

Brothers and sisters: What does Scripture say?

The word is near you,
    in your mouth and in your heart

—that is, the word of faith that we preach—, for, if you confess with your mouth that Jesus is Lord and believe in your heart that God raised him from the dead, you will be saved. For one believes with the heart and so is justified, and one confesses with the mouth and so is saved. For the Scripture says, *No one who believes in him will be put to shame*. For there is no distinction between Jew and Greek; the same Lord is Lord of all, enriching all who call upon him. For "everyone who calls on the name of the Lord will be saved."

GOSPEL   *Luke 4:1–13*

Filled with the Holy Spirit, Jesus returned from the Jordan and was led by the Spirit into the desert for forty days, to be tempted by the devil. He ate nothing during those days, and when they were over he was hungry. The devil said to him, "If you are the Son of God, command this stone to become bread." Jesus answered him, "It is written, *One does not live on bread alone*." Then he took him up and showed him all the kingdoms of the world in a single instant. The devil said to him, "I shall give to you all this power and glory; for it has been handed over to me, and I may give it to whomever I wish. All this will be yours, if you worship me." Jesus said to him in reply, "It is written:

You shall worship the Lord, your God,
    and him alone shall you serve."

Then he led him to Jerusalem, made him stand on the parapet of the temple, and said to him, "If you are the Son of God, throw yourself down from here, for it is written:

He will command his angels concerning you, to guard you,

and:

With their hands they will support you,
    lest you dash your foot against a stone."

Jesus said to him in reply, "It also says, *You shall not put the Lord, your God, to the test*." When the devil had finished every temptation, he departed from him for a time.

RITE OF ELECTION
See no. 1116

SECOND SUNDAY OF LENT / A   1119

READING I   *Genesis 12:1–4a / 25*

The Lord said to Abram: "Go forth from the land of your kinsfolk and from your father's house to a land that I will show you.

"I will make of you a great nation,
    and I will bless you;
I will make your name great,
    so that you will be a blessing.

I will bless those who bless you
    and curse those who curse you.
All the communities of the earth
    shall find blessing in you."

Abram went as the LORD directed him.

RESPONSORIAL PSALM   *Psalm 33:4–5, 18–19, 20 and 22*

Lord, let your mer-cy be on us, as we place our trust in you.

The word of the LORD is faithful,
    and all his works to be trusted.
The LORD loves justice and right,
    and his merciful love fills the earth. ℟.

Yes, the LORD's eyes are on those who
    fear him,
    who hope in his merciful love,

to rescue their souls from death,
    to keep them alive in famine. ℟.

Our soul is waiting for the LORD.
    He is our help and our shield.
May your merciful love be upon us,
    as we hope in you, O LORD. ℟.

READING II   *2 Timothy 1:8b–10*

Beloved: Bear your share of hardship for the gospel with the strength that comes from God.

He saved us and called us to a holy life, not according to our works but according to his own design and the grace bestowed on us in Christ Jesus before time began, but now made manifest through the appearance of our savior Christ Jesus, who destroyed death and brought life and immortality to light through the gospel.

GOSPEL   *Matthew 17:1–9*

Jesus took Peter, James, and John his brother, and led them up a high mountain by themselves. And he was transfigured before them; his face shone like the sun and his clothes became white as light. And behold, Moses and Elijah appeared to them, conversing with him. Then Peter said to Jesus in reply, "Lord, it is good that we are here. If you wish, I will make three tents here, one for you, one for Moses, and one for Elijah." While he was still speaking, behold, a bright cloud cast a shadow over them, then from the cloud came a voice that said, "This is my beloved Son, with whom I am well pleased; listen to him." When the disciples heard this, they fell prostrate and were very much afraid. But Jesus came and touched them, saying, "Rise, and do not be afraid." And when the disciples raised their eyes, they saw no one else but Jesus alone.

As they were coming down from the mountain, Jesus charged them, "Do not tell the vision to anyone until the Son of Man has been raised from the dead."

SECOND SUNDAY OF LENT / B

1120

READING I   *Genesis 22:1–2, 9a, 10–13, 15–18 / 26*

God put Abraham to the test. He called to him, "Abraham!" "Here I am!" he replied. Then God said: "Take your son Isaac, your only one, whom you love, and go to the land of Moriah. There you shall offer him up as a holocaust on a height that I will point out to you."

When they came to the place of which God had told him, Abraham built an altar there and arranged the wood on it. Then he reached out and took the knife to slaughter his son. But the LORD's messenger called to him from heaven, "Abraham, Abraham!" "Here I am!" he answered. "Do not lay your hand on the boy," said the messenger. "Do not do the least thing to him. I know now how devoted you are to God, since you did not withhold from me your own beloved son." As Abraham looked about, he spied a ram caught by its horns in the thicket. So he went and took the ram and offered it up as a holocaust in place of his son.

Again the LORD's messenger called to Abraham from heaven and said: "I swear by myself, declares the LORD, that because you acted as you did in not withholding from me your beloved son, I will bless you abundantly and make your descendants as countless as the stars of the sky and the sands of the seashore; your descendants shall take possession of the gates of their enemies, and in your descendants all the nations of the earth shall find blessing—all this because you obeyed my command."

RESPONSORIAL PSALM   *Psalm 116:10 and 15, 16–17, 18–19*

RP

I will walk be - fore the Lord, in the land of the liv - ing.

I trusted, even when I said,
  "I am sorely afflicted."
How precious in the eyes of the LORD
  is the death of his faithful. ℟.

Your servant, LORD, your servant am I,
  the son of your handmaid;
  you have loosened my bonds.

A thanksgiving sacrifice I make;
  I will call on the name of the
  LORD. ℟.

My vows to the LORD I will fulfill
  before all his people,
in the courts of the house of the LORD,
  in your midst, O Jerusalem. ℟.

READING II   *Romans 8:31b–34*

Brothers and sisters: If God is for us, who can be against us? He who did not spare his own Son but handed him over for us all, how will he not also give us everything else along with him?

Who will bring a charge against God's chosen ones? It is God who acquits us. Who will condemn? Christ Jesus it is who died—or, rather, was raised—who also is at the right hand of God, who indeed intercedes for us.

GOSPEL   *Mark 9:2–10*

Jesus took Peter, James, and John and led them up a high mountain apart by them-selves. And he was transfigured before them, and his clothes became dazzling white, such as no fuller on earth could bleach them. Then Elijah appeared to them along with Moses, and they were conversing with Jesus. Then Peter said to Jesus in reply, "Rabbi, it is good that we are here! Let us make three tents: one for you, one for Moses, and one for Elijah." He hardly knew what to say, they were so terrified. Then a cloud came, casting a shadow over them; from the cloud came a voice, "This is my beloved Son. Listen to him." Suddenly, looking around, they no longer saw anyone but Jesus alone with them.

As they were coming down from the mountain, he charged them not to relate what they had seen to anyone, except when the Son of Man had risen from the dead. So they kept the matter to themselves, questioning what rising from the dead meant.

1121 SECOND SUNDAY OF LENT / C

READING I   *Genesis 15:5–12, 17–18 / 27*

The Lord God took Abram outside and said, "Look up at the sky and count the stars, if you can. Just so," he added, "shall your descendants be." Abram put his faith in the LORD, who credited it to him as an act of righteousness.

He then said to him, "I am the LORD who brought you from Ur of the Chaldeans to give you this land as a possession." "O Lord GOD," he asked, "how am I to know that I shall possess it?" He answered him, "Bring me a three-year-old heifer, a three-year-old she-goat, a three-year-old ram, a turtledove, and a young pigeon." Abram brought him all these, split them in two, and placed each half opposite the other; but the birds he did not cut up. Birds of prey swooped down on the carcasses, but Abram stayed with them. As the sun was about to set, a trance fell upon Abram, and a deep, terrifying darkness enveloped him.

When the sun had set and it was dark, there appeared a smoking fire pot and a flaming torch, which passed between those pieces. It was on that occasion that the LORD made a covenant with Abram, saying: "To your descendants I give this land, from the Wadi of Egypt to the Great River, the Euphrates."

RESPONSORIAL PSALM   *Psalm 27:1, 7–8, 9abc, 13–14*

RP

The Lord is my light and my sal - va - tion.

The LORD is my light and my salvation;
  whom shall I fear?
The LORD is the stronghold of my life;
  whom should I dread? ℟.

O LORD, hear my voice when I call;
  have mercy and answer me.
Of you my heart has spoken, "Seek his
    face."
  It is your face, O LORD, that I seek. ℟.

Hide not your face from me.
  Dismiss not your servant in anger;
you have been my help.
  Do not abandon or forsake me. ℟.

I believe I shall see the LORD's goodness
  in the land of the living.
Wait for the LORD; be strong;
  be stouthearted, and wait for the
    LORD! ℟.

READING II   *Philippians 3:17—4:1 or 3:20—4:1*
For short form read only the parts in brackets.

Join with others in being imitators of me, [brothers and sisters,] and observe those
who thus conduct themselves according to the model you have in us. For many, as I
have often told you and now tell you even in tears, conduct themselves as enemies of
the cross of Christ. Their end is destruction. Their God is their stomach; their glory is
in their "shame." Their minds are occupied with earthly things. But [our citizenship is
in heaven, and from it we also await a savior, the Lord Jesus Christ. He will change
our lowly body to conform with his glorified body by the power that enables him also
to bring all things into subjection to himself.

    Therefore, my brothers and sisters, whom I love and long for, my joy and crown,
*in this way stand firm in the Lord.

In the short form, this last line is: . . . in this way stand firm in the Lord, beloved.

GOSPEL   *Luke 9:28b–36*
Jesus took Peter, John, and James and went up the mountain to pray. While he was
praying his face changed in appearance and his clothing became dazzling white. And
behold, two men were conversing with him, Moses and Elijah, who appeared in glory
and spoke of his exodus that he was going to accomplish in Jerusalem. Peter and his
companions had been overcome by sleep, but becoming fully awake, they saw his
glory and the two men standing with him. As they were about to part from him, Peter
said to Jesus, "Master, it is good that we are here; let us make three tents, one for you,
one for Moses, and one for Elijah." But he did not know what he was saying. While
he was still speaking, a cloud came and cast a shadow over them, and they became
frightened when they entered the cloud. Then from the cloud came a voice that said,
"This is my chosen Son; listen to him." After the voice had spoken, Jesus was found
alone. They fell silent and did not at that time tell anyone what they had seen.

THIRD SUNDAY OF LENT / A   1122

READING I   *Exodus 17:3–7 / 28*
In those days, in their thirst for water, the people grumbled against Moses, saying,
"Why did you ever make us leave Egypt? Was it just to have us die here of thirst with
our children and our livestock?" So Moses cried out to the LORD, "What shall I do
with this people? A little more and they will stone me!" The LORD answered Moses,
"Go over there in front of the people, along with some of the elders of Israel, holding
in your hand, as you go, the staff with which you struck the river. I will be standing
there in front of you on the rock in Horeb. Strike the rock, and the water will flow
from it for the people to drink." This Moses did, in the presence of the elders of Israel.
The place was called Massah and Meribah, because the Israelites quarreled there and
tested the LORD, saying, "Is the LORD in our midst or not?"

RESPONSORIAL PSALM *Psalm 95:1–2, 6–7c, 7d–9*

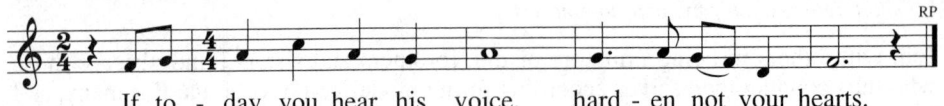

If to - day you hear his voice, hard - en not your hearts.

Come, let us ring out our joy to the LORD;
  hail the rock who saves us.
Let us come into his presence, giving
      thanks;
  let us hail him with a song of praise. ℟.

O come; let us bow and bend low.
  Let us kneel before the God who
      made us,
for he is our God and we

the people who belong to his pasture,
the flock that is led by his hand. ℟.

O that today you would listen to his
  voice!
"Harden not your hearts as at Meribah,
  as on that day at Massah in the desert
when your forebears put me to the test;
  when they tried me, though they saw
  my work." ℟.

READING II *Romans 5:1–2, 5–8*

Brothers and sisters: Since we have been justified by faith, we have peace with God through our Lord Jesus Christ, through whom we have gained access by faith to this grace in which we stand, and we boast in hope of the glory of God.

And hope does not disappoint, because the love of God has been poured out into our hearts through the Holy Spirit who has been given to us. For Christ, while we were still helpless, died at the appointed time for the ungodly. Indeed, only with difficulty does one die for a just person, though perhaps for a good person one might even find courage to die. But God proves his love for us in that while we were still sinners Christ died for us.

GOSPEL *John 4:5–42 or 4:5–15, 19b–26, 39a, 40–42*

For short form read only the parts in brackets.

[Jesus came to a town of Samaria called Sychar, near the plot of land that Jacob had given to his son Joseph. Jacob's well was there. Jesus, tired from his journey, sat down there at the well. It was about noon.

A woman of Samaria came to draw water. Jesus said to her, "Give me a drink." His disciples had gone into the town to buy food. The Samaritan woman said to him, "How can you, a Jew, ask me, a Samaritan woman, for a drink?" —For Jews use nothing in common with Samaritans.— Jesus answered and said to her, "If you knew the gift of God and who is saying to you, 'Give me a drink,' you would have asked him and he would have given you living water." The woman said to him, "Sir, you do not even have a bucket and the cistern is deep; where then can you get this living water? Are you greater than our father Jacob, who gave us this cistern and drank from it himself with his children and his flocks?" Jesus answered and said to her, "Everyone who drinks this water will be thirsty again; but whoever drinks the water I shall give will never thirst; the water I shall give will become in him a spring of water welling up to eternal life." The woman said to him, "Sir, give me this water, so that I may not be thirsty or have to keep coming here to draw water."]

Jesus said to her, "Go call your husband and come back." The woman answered and said to him, "I do not have a husband." Jesus answered her, "You are right in saying, 'I do not have a husband.' For you have had five husbands, and the one you have now is not your husband. What you have said is true." The woman said to him, "Sir, [I can see that you are a prophet. Our ancestors worshiped on this mountain; but you people say that the place to worship is in Jerusalem." Jesus said to her, "Believe me, woman, the hour is coming when you will worship the Father neither on this mountain nor in Jerusalem. You people worship what you do not understand; we worship what we understand, because salvation is from the Jews. But the hour is coming, and is now here, when true worshipers will worship the Father in Spirit and truth; and indeed the Father seeks such people to worship him. God is Spirit, and those who worship him must worship in Spirit and truth." The woman said to him, "I know that the Messiah is coming, the one called the Christ; when he comes, he will tell us everything." Jesus said to her, "I am he, the one speaking with you."]

At that moment his disciples returned, and were amazed that he was talking with a woman, but still no one said, "What are you looking for?" or "Why are you talking with her?" The woman left her water jar and went into the town and said to the people, "Come see a man who told me everything I have done. Could he possibly be the Christ?" They went out of the town and came to him. Meanwhile, the disciples urged him, "Rabbi, eat." But he said to them, "I have food to eat of which you do not know." So the disciples said to one another, "Could someone have brought him something to eat?" Jesus said to them, "My food is to do the will of the one who sent me and to finish his work. Do you not say, 'In four months the harvest will be here'? I tell you, look up and see the fields ripe for the harvest. The reaper is already receiving payment and gathering crops for eternal life, so that the sower and reaper can rejoice together. For here the saying is verified that 'One sows and another reaps.' I sent you to reap what you have not worked for; others have done the work, and you are sharing the fruits of their work."

[Many of the Samaritans of that town began to believe in him] because of the word of the woman who testified, "He told me everything I have done." [When the Samaritans came to him, they invited him to stay with them; and he stayed there two days. Many more began to believe in him because of his word, and they said to the woman, "We no longer believe because of your word; for we have heard for ourselves, and we know that this is truly the savior of the world."]

FIRST SCRUTINY

During Lent, the elect (those catechumens who have been called to prepare for baptism at Easter) are called to come before the community for exorcisms and prayers. This takes place after the liturgy of the word on the Third, Fourth, and Fifth Sundays of Lent. These rites are intended to purify the hearts and minds of the elect, to strengthen them against temptation, to help them progress in the love of God.

The presider asks the assembly to pray in silence for the elect, then to join in intercessions for them. The presider lays hands on each of the elect and prays that the elect be delivered from the power of evil and become witnesses to the gospel. A song or psalm may be sung, then the elect are dismissed as usual and the faithful continue with the liturgy of the eucharist.

THIRD SUNDAY OF LENT / B   1123

READING I   *Exodus 20:1–17 or 20:1–3, 7–8, 12–17 / 29*
For short form read only the parts in brackets.

[In those days, God delivered all these commandments: "I, the LORD, am your God, who brought you out of the land of Egypt, that place of slavery. You shall not have other gods besides me.] You shall not carve idols for yourselves in the shape of anything in the sky above or on the earth below or in the waters beneath the earth; you shall not bow down before them or worship them. For I, the LORD, your God, am a jealous God, inflicting punishment for their fathers' wickedness on the children of those who hate me, down to the third and fourth generation; but bestowing mercy down to the thousandth generation on the children of those who love me and keep my commandments.

["You shall not take the name of the LORD, your God, in vain. For the LORD will not leave unpunished the one who takes his name in vain.

"Remember to keep holy the sabbath day.] Six days you may labor and do all your work, but the seventh day is the sabbath of the LORD, your God. No work may be done then either by you, or your son or daughter, or your male or female slave, or your beast, or by the alien who lives with you. In six days the LORD made the heavens and the earth, the sea and all that is in them; but on the seventh day he rested. That is why the LORD has blessed the sabbath day and made it holy.

["Honor your father and your mother, that you may have a long life in the land which the LORD, your God, is giving you.

You shall not kill.

You shall not commit adultery.

You shall not steal.

You shall not bear false witness against your neighbor.

You shall not covet your neighbor's house. You shall not covet your neighbor's wife, nor his male or female slave, nor his ox or ass, nor anything else that belongs to him."]

RESPONSORIAL PSALM   *Psalm 19:8, 9, 10, 11*

Lord, you have the words of ev-er-last - ing life.

The law of the LORD is perfect; it revives the soul. The decrees of the LORD are steadfast; they give wisdom to the simple. ℟.	The fear of the LORD is pure, abiding forever. The judgments of the LORD are true; they are, all of them, just. ℟.
The precepts of the LORD are right; they gladden the heart. The command of the LORD is clear; it gives light to the eyes. ℟.	They are more to be desired than gold, than quantities of gold. And sweeter are they than honey, than honey flowing from the comb. ℟.

READING II   *1 Corinthians 1:22–25*

Brothers and sisters: Jews demand signs and Greeks look for wisdom, but we proclaim Christ crucified, a stumbling block to Jews and foolishness to Gentiles, but to those who are called, Jews and Greeks alike, Christ the power of God and the wisdom of God. For the foolishness of God is wiser than human wisdom, and the weakness of God is stronger than human strength.

GOSPEL   *John 2:13–25*

Since the Passover of the Jews was near, Jesus went up to Jerusalem. He found in the temple area those who sold oxen, sheep, and doves, as well as the money changers seated there. He made a whip out of cords and drove them all out of the temple area, with the sheep and oxen, and spilled the coins of the money changers and overturned their tables, and to those who sold doves he said, "Take these out of here, and stop making my Father's house a marketplace." His disciples recalled the words of Scripture, *Zeal for your house will consume me.* At this the Jews answered and said to him, "What sign can you show us for doing this?" Jesus answered and said to them, "Destroy this temple and in three days I will raise it up." The Jews said, "This temple has been under construction for forty-six years, and you will raise it up in three days?" But he was speaking about the temple of his body. Therefore, when he was raised from the dead, his disciples remembered that he had said this, and they came to believe the Scripture and the word Jesus had spoken.

While he was in Jerusalem for the feast of Passover, many began to believe in his name when they saw the signs he was doing. But Jesus would not trust himself to them because he knew them all, and did not need anyone to testify about human nature. He himself understood it well.

FIRST SCRUTINY
See no. 1122

THIRD SUNDAY OF LENT / C   1124

READING I   *Exodus 3:1–8a, 13–15 / 30*

Moses was tending the flock of his father-in-law Jethro, the priest of Midian. Leading the flock across the desert, he came to Horeb, the mountain of God. There an angel of the LORD appeared to Moses in fire flaming out of a bush. As he looked on, he was surprised to see that the bush, though on fire, was not consumed. So Moses decided, "I must go over to look at this remarkable sight, and see why the bush is not burned."

When the LORD saw him coming over to look at it more closely, God called out to him from the bush, "Moses! Moses!" He answered, "Here I am." God said, "Come no nearer! Remove the sandals from your feet, for the place where you stand is holy ground. I am the God of your fathers," he continued, "the God of Abraham, the God of Isaac, the God of Jacob." Moses hid his face, for he was afraid to look at God. But the LORD said, "I have witnessed the affliction of my people in Egypt and have heard their cry of complaint against their slave drivers, so I know well what they are suffering. Therefore I have come down to rescue them from the hands of the Egyptians and lead them out of that land into a good and spacious land, a land flowing with milk and honey."

Moses said to God, "But when I go to the Israelites and say to them, 'The God of your fathers has sent me to you,' if they ask me, 'What is his name?' what am I to tell them?" God replied, "I am who am." Then he added, "This is what you shall tell the Israelites: I AM sent me to you."

God spoke further to Moses, "Thus shall you say to the Israelites: The LORD, the God of your fathers, the God of Abraham, the God of Isaac, the God of Jacob, has sent me to you.

"This is my name forever;
thus am I to be remembered through all generations."

RESPONSORIAL PSALM *Psalm 103:1–2, 3–4, 6–7, 8 and 11*

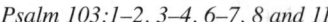

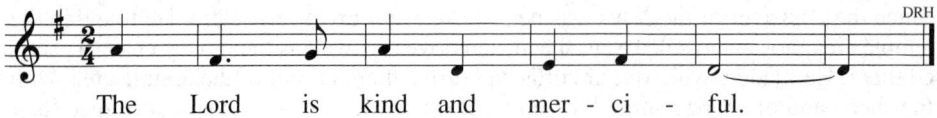

The Lord is kind and mer - ci - ful.

Bless the LORD, O my soul,
  and all within me, his holy name.
Bless the LORD, O my soul,
  and never forget all his benefits. ℟.

It is the Lord who forgives all your sins,
  who heals every one of your ills,
who redeems your life from the grave,
  who crowns you with mercy and
    compassion. ℟.

The LORD does just deeds,
  gives full justice to all who are
oppressed.
He made known his ways to Moses,
  and his deeds to the children of
    Israel. ℟.

The LORD is compassionate and
    gracious,
  slow to anger and rich in mercy.
For as the heavens are high above
    the earth,
  so strong his mercy for those
    who fear him. ℟.

READING II *1 Corinthians 10:1–6, 10–12*

I do not want you to be unaware, brothers and sisters, that our ancestors were all under the cloud and all passed through the sea, and all of them were baptized into Moses in the cloud and in the sea. All ate the same spiritual food, and all drank the same spiritual drink, for they drank from a spiritual rock that followed them, and the rock was the Christ. Yet God was not pleased with most of them, for they were struck down in the desert.

These things happened as examples for us, so that we might not desire evil things, as they did. Do not grumble as some of them did, and suffered death by the destroyer. These things happened to them as an example, and they have been written down as a warning to us, upon whom the end of the ages has come. Therefore, whoever thinks he is standing secure should take care not to fall.

GOSPEL *Luke 13:1–9*

Some people told Jesus about the Galileans whose blood Pilate had mingled with the blood of their sacrifices. Jesus said to them in reply, "Do you think that because these Galileans suffered in this way they were greater sinners than all other Galileans? By no means! But I tell you, if you do not repent, you will all perish as they did! Or those eighteen people who were killed when the tower at Siloam fell on them—do you think they were more guilty than everyone else who lived in Jerusalem? By no means! But I tell you, if you do not repent, you will all perish as they did!"

And he told them this parable: "There once was a person who had a fig tree planted in his orchard, and when he came in search of fruit on it but found none, he said to the gardener, 'For three years now I have come in search of fruit on this fig tree but have found none. So cut it down. Why should it exhaust the soil?' He said to him in reply, 'Sir, leave it for this year also, and I shall cultivate the ground around it and fertilize it; it may bear fruit in the future. If not you can cut it down.'"

FIRST SCRUTINY
See no. 1122

FOURTH SUNDAY OF LENT / A   1125

READING I   *1 Samuel 16:1b, 6–7, 10–13a / 31*

The LORD said to Samuel: "Fill your horn with oil, and be on your way. I am sending you to Jesse of Bethlehem, for I have chosen my king from among his sons."

As Jesse and his sons came to the sacrifice, Samuel looked at Eliab and thought, "Surely the LORD's anointed is here before him." But the LORD said to Samuel: "Do not judge from his appearance or from his lofty stature, because I have rejected him. Not as man sees does God see, because man sees the appearance but the LORD looks into the heart." In the same way Jesse presented seven sons before Samuel, but Samuel said to Jesse, "The LORD has not chosen any one of these." Then Samuel asked Jesse, "Are these all the sons you have?" Jesse replied, "There is still the youngest, who is tending the sheep." Samuel said to Jesse, "Send for him; we will not begin the sacrificial banquet until he arrives here." Jesse sent and had the young man brought to them. He was ruddy, a youth handsome to behold and making a splendid appearance. The LORD said, "There—anoint him, for this is the one!" Then Samuel, with the horn of oil in hand, anointed David in the presence of his brothers; and from that day on, the spirit of the LORD rushed upon David.

RESPONSORIAL PSALM   *Psalm 23:1–3a, 3b–4, 5, 6*

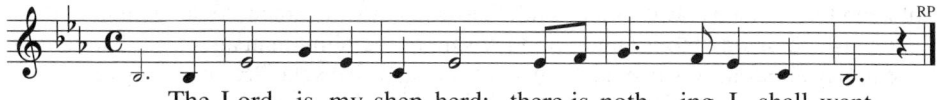

The Lord is my shep-herd; there is noth - ing I shall want.

The LORD is my shepherd;
    there is nothing I shall want.
Fresh and green are the pastures
    where he gives me repose.
Near restful waters he leads me;
    he revives my soul. ℟.

He guides me along the right path,
    for the sake of his name.
Though I should walk in the valley of
      the shadow of death,
    no evil would I fear, for you are
      with me.

Your crook and your staff will give
    me comfort. ℟.

You have prepared a table before me
    in the sight of my foes.
My head you have anointed with oil;
    my cup is overflowing. ℟.

Surely goodness and mercy shall
    follow me
    all the days of my life.
In the LORD's own house shall I dwell
    for length of days unending. ℟.

READING II   *Ephesians 5:8–14*

Brothers and sisters: You were once darkness, but now you are light in the Lord. Live as children of light, for light produces every kind of goodness and righteousness and truth. Try to learn what is pleasing to the Lord. Take no part in the fruitless works of darkness; rather expose them, for it is shameful even to mention the things done by them in secret; but everything exposed by the light becomes visible, for everything that becomes visible is light. Therefore, it says:
    "Awake, O sleeper,
    and arise from the dead,
    and Christ will give you light."

GOSPEL   *John 9:1–41 or 9:1, 6–9, 13–17, 34–38*

For short form read only the parts in brackets.

[As Jesus passed by he saw a man blind from birth.] His disciples asked him, "Rabbi, who sinned, this man or his parents, that he was born blind?" Jesus answered, "Neither he nor his parents sinned; it is so that the works of God might be made visible through him. We have to do the works of the one who sent me while it is day. Night is coming when no one can work. While I am in the world, I am the light of the world." When he had said this, [he spat on the ground and made clay with the saliva, and smeared the clay on his eyes, and said to him, "Go wash in the Pool of Siloam" — which means Sent—. So he went and washed, and came back able to see.

His neighbors and those who had seen him earlier as a beggar said, "Isn't this the one who used to sit and beg?" Some said, "It is," but others said, "No, he just looks like him." He said, "I am."] So they said to him, "How were your eyes opened?" He replied, "The man called Jesus made clay and anointed my eyes and told me, 'Go to Siloam and wash.' So I went there and washed and was able to see." And they said to him, "Where is he?" He said, "I don't know."

[They brought the one who was once blind to the Pharisees. Now Jesus had made clay and opened his eyes on a sabbath. So then the Pharisees also asked him how he was able to see. He said to them, "He put clay on my eyes, and I washed, and now I can see." So some of the Pharisees said, "This man is not from God, because he does not keep the sabbath." But others said, "How can a sinful man do such signs?" And there was a division among them. So they said to the blind man again, "What do you have to say about him, since he opened your eyes?" He said, "He is a prophet."]

Now the Jews did not believe that he had been blind and gained his sight until they summoned the parents of the one who had gained his sight. They asked them, "Is this your son, who you say was born blind? How does he now see?" His parents answered and said, "We know that this is our son and that he was born blind. We do not know how he sees now, nor do we know who opened his eyes. Ask him, he is of age; he can speak for himself." His parents said this because they were afraid of the Jews, for the Jews had already agreed that if anyone acknowledged him as the Christ, he would be expelled from the synagogue. For this reason his parents said, "He is of age; question him."

So a second time they called the man who had been blind and said to him, "Give God the praise! We know that this man is a sinner." He replied, "If he is a sinner, I do not know. One thing I do know is that I was blind and now I see." So they said to him, "What did he do to you? How did he open your eyes?" He answered them, "I told you already and you did not listen. Why do you want to hear it again? Do you want to become his disciples, too?" They ridiculed him and said, "You are that man's disciple; we are disciples of Moses! We know that God spoke to Moses, but we do not know where this one is from." The man answered and said to them, "This is what is so amazing, that you do not know where he is from, yet he opened my eyes. We know that God does not listen to sinners, but if one is devout and does his will, he listens to him. It is unheard of that anyone ever opened the eyes of a person born blind. If this man were not from God, he would not be able to do anything." [They answered and said to him, "You were born totally in sin, and are you trying to teach us?" Then they threw him out.

When Jesus heard that they had thrown him out, he found him and said, "Do you believe in the Son of Man?" He answered and said, "Who is he, sir, that I may believe in him?" Jesus said to him, "You have seen him, the one speaking with you is he." He said, "I do believe, Lord," and he worshiped him.] Then Jesus said, "I came into this world for judgment, so that those who do not see might see, and those who do see might become blind."

Some of the Pharisees who were with him heard this and said to him, "Surely we are not also blind, are we?" Jesus said to them, "If you were blind, you would have no sin; but now you are saying, 'We see,' so your sin remains."

SECOND SCRUTINY

During Lent, the elect (those catechumens who have been called to prepare for baptism at Easter) are called to come before the community for exorcisms and prayers. This takes place after the liturgy of the word on the Third, Fourth, and Fifth Sundays of Lent. These rites are intended to purify the hearts and minds of the elect, to strengthen them against temptation, to help them progress in the love of God.

The presider asks the assembly to pray in silence for the elect, then to join in intercessions for them. The presider lays hands on each of the elect and prays that the elect be delivered from the power of evil and become witnesses to the gospel. A song or psalm may be sung, then the elect are dismissed as usual and the faithful continue with the liturgy of the eucharist.

FOURTH SUNDAY OF LENT / B   1126

READING I   *2 Chronicles 36:14–16, 19–23 / 32*

In those days, all the princes of Judah, the priests, and the people added infidelity to infidelity, practicing all the abominations of the nations and polluting the LORD's temple which he had consecrated in Jerusalem.

Early and often did the LORD, the God of their fathers, send his messengers to them, for he had compassion on his people and his dwelling place. But they mocked the messengers of God, despised his warnings, and scoffed at his prophets, until the anger of the LORD against his people was so inflamed that there was no remedy. Their enemies burnt the house of God, tore down the walls of Jerusalem, set all its palaces afire, and destroyed all its precious objects. Those who escaped the sword were carried captive to Babylon, where they became servants of the king of the Chaldeans and his sons until the kingdom of the Persians came to power. All this was to fulfill the word of the LORD spoken by Jeremiah: "Until the land has retrieved its lost sabbaths, during all the time it lies waste it shall have rest while seventy years are fulfilled."

In the first year of Cyrus, king of Persia, in order to fulfill the word of the LORD spoken by Jeremiah, the LORD inspired King Cyrus of Persia to issue this proclamation throughout his kingdom, both by word of mouth and in writing: "Thus says Cyrus, king of Persia: All the kingdoms of the earth the LORD, the God of heaven, has given to me, and he has also charged me to build him a house in Jerusalem, which is in Judah. Whoever, therefore, among you belongs to any part of his people, let him go up, and may his God be with him!"

RESPONSORIAL PSALM

Psalm 137:1–2, 3, 4–5, 6

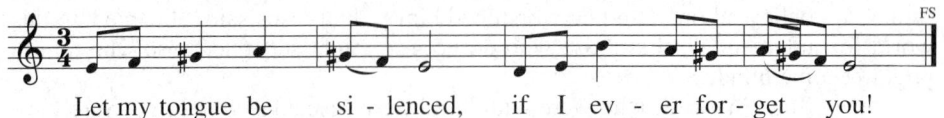

Let my tongue be si - lenced, if I ev - er for - get you!

By the rivers of Babylon
  there we sat and wept,
  remembering Sion;
on the poplars that grew there
  we hung up our harps. ℟.

For it was there that they asked us,
  our captors, for songs,
  our oppressors, for joy.
"Sing to us," they said,
  "one of Sion's songs." ℟.

O how could we sing
  the song of the LORD
  on foreign soil?
If I forget you, Jerusalem,
  let my right hand wither! ℟.

O let my tongue
  cleave to my palate
  if I remember you not,
if I prize not Jerusalem
  as the first of my joys! ℟.

READING II

Ephesians 2:4–10

Brothers and sisters: God, who is rich in mercy, because of the great love he had for us, even when we were dead in our transgressions, brought us to life with Christ —by grace you have been saved—, raised us up with him, and seated us with him in the heavens in Christ Jesus, that in the ages to come he might show the immeasurable riches of his grace in his kindness to us in Christ Jesus. For by grace you have been saved through faith, and this is not from you; it is the gift of God; it is not from works, so no one may boast. For we are his handiwork, created in Christ Jesus for the good works that God has prepared in advance, that we should live in them.

GOSPEL

John 3:14–21

Jesus said to Nicodemus: "Just as Moses lifted up the serpent in the desert, so must the Son of Man be lifted up, so that everyone who believes in him may have eternal life."

For God so loved the world that he gave his only Son, so that everyone who believes in him might not perish but might have eternal life. For God did not send his Son into the world to condemn the world, but that the world might be saved through him. Whoever believes in him will not be condemned, but whoever does not believe has already been condemned, because he has not believed in the name of the only Son of God. And this is the verdict, that the light came into the world, but people preferred darkness to light, because their works were evil. For everyone who does wicked things hates the light and does not come toward the light, so that his works might not be exposed. But whoever lives the truth comes to the light, so that his works may be clearly seen as done in God.

SECOND SCRUTINY

See no. 1125

FOURTH SUNDAY OF LENT / C   1127

READING I   *Joshua 5:9a, 10–12 / 33*

The LORD said to Joshua, "Today I have removed the reproach of Egypt from you."

While the Israelites were encamped at Gilgal on the plains of Jericho, they celebrated the Passover on the evening of the fourteenth of the month. On the day after the Passover, they ate of the produce of the land in the form of unleavened cakes and parched grain. On that same day after the Passover, on which they ate of the produce of the land, the manna ceased. No longer was there manna for the Israelites, who that year ate of the yield of the land of Canaan.

RESPONSORIAL PSALM   *Psalm 34:2–3, 4–5, 6–7*

Taste and see the good - ness of the Lord.

I will bless the LORD at all times;
   praise of him is always in my mouth.
In the LORD my soul shall make its boast;
   the humble shall hear and be glad. ℟.

Glorify the LORD with me;
   together let us praise his name.
I sought the LORD, and he answered me;

from all my terrors he set me free. ℟.

Look toward him and be radiant;
   let your faces not be abashed.
This lowly one called; the LORD heard,
   and rescued him from all his
   distress. ℟.

READING II   *2 Corinthians 5:17–21*

Brothers and sisters: Whoever is in Christ is a new creation: the old things have passed away; behold, new things have come. And all this is from God, who has reconciled us to himself through Christ and given us the ministry of reconciliation, namely, God was reconciling the world to himself in Christ, not counting their trespasses against them and entrusting to us the message of reconciliation. So we are ambassadors for Christ, as if God were appealing through us. We implore you on behalf of Christ, be reconciled to God. For our sake he made him to be sin who did not know sin, so that we might become the righteousness of God in him.

GOSPEL   *Luke 15:1–3, 11–32*

Tax collectors and sinners were all drawing near to listen to Jesus, but the Pharisees and scribes began to complain, saying, "This man welcomes sinners and eats with them." So to them Jesus addressed this parable: "A man had two sons, and the younger son said to his father, 'Father give me the share of your estate that should come to me.' So the father divided the property between them. After a few days, the younger son collected all his belongings and set off to a distant country where he squandered his inheritance on a life of dissipation. When he had freely spent everything, a severe famine struck that country, and he found himself in dire need. So he hired himself out to one of the local citizens who sent him to his farm to tend the swine. And he longed to eat his fill of the pods on which the swine fed, but nobody gave him any. Coming to his senses he thought, 'How many of my father's hired workers have more than enough food to eat, but here am I, dying from hunger. I shall get up and go to my father and I shall say to him, "Father, I have sinned against heaven and against you.

I no longer deserve to be called your son; treat me as you would treat one of your hired workers.'" So he got up and went back to his father. While he was still a long way off, his father caught sight of him, and was filled with compassion. He ran to his son, embraced him and kissed him. His son said to him, 'Father, I have sinned against heaven and against you; I no longer deserve to be called your son.' But his father ordered his servants, 'Quickly bring the finest robe and put it on him; put a ring on his finger and sandals on his feet. Take the fattened calf and slaughter it. Then let us celebrate with a feast, because this son of mine was dead, and has come to life again; he was lost, and has been found.' Then the celebration began. Now the older son had been out in the field and, on his way back, as he neared the house, he heard the sound of music and dancing. He called one of the servants and asked what this might mean. The servant said to him, 'Your brother has returned and your father has slaughtered the fattened calf because he has him back safe and sound.' He became angry, and when he refused to enter the house, his father came out and pleaded with him. He said to his father in reply, 'Look, all these years I served you and not once did I disobey your orders; yet you never gave me even a young goat to feast on with my friends. But when your son returns who swallowed up your property with prostitutes, for him you slaughter the fattened calf.' He said to him, 'My son, you are here with me always; everything I have is yours. But now we must celebrate and rejoice, because your brother was dead and has come to life again; he was lost and has been found.'"

SECOND SCRUTINY
See no. 1125

1128 FIFTH SUNDAY OF LENT / A

READING I   *Ezekiel 37:12–14 / 34*

Thus says the Lord GOD: O my people, I will open your graves and have you rise from them, and bring you back to the land of Israel. Then you shall know that I am the LORD, when I open your graves and have you rise from them, O my people! I will put my spirit in you that you may live, and I will settle you upon your land; thus you shall know that I am the LORD. I have promised, and I will do it, says the LORD.

RESPONSORIAL PSALM   *Psalm 130:1–2, 3–4, 5–6ab and 7a, 7b–8*

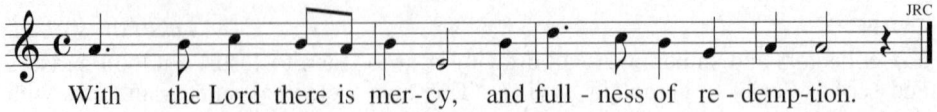

With the Lord there is mer-cy, and full-ness of re-demp-tion.

Out of the depths I cry to you, O LORD;
  Lord, hear my voice!
O let your ears be attentive
  to the sound of my pleadings. ℟.

If you, O LORD, should mark iniquities,
  Lord, who could stand?
But with you is found forgiveness,
  that you may be revered. ℟.

I long for you, O LORD,
  my soul longs for his word.
My soul hopes in the Lord
  more than watchmen for daybreak.
Let Israel hope for the LORD. ℟.

For with the LORD there is mercy,
  in him is plentiful redemption.
It is he who will redeem Israel
  from all its iniquities. ℟.

READING II   *Romans 8:8–11*

Brothers and sisters: Those who are in the flesh cannot please God. But you are not in the flesh; on the contrary, you are in the spirit, if only the Spirit of God dwells in you. Whoever does not have the Spirit of Christ does not belong to him. But if Christ is in you, although the body is dead because of sin, the spirit is alive because of righteousness. If the Spirit of the one who raised Jesus from the dead dwells in you, the one who raised Christ from the dead will give life to your mortal bodies also, through his Spirit dwelling in you.

GOSPEL   *John 11:1–45 or 11:3–7, 17, 20–27, 33b–45*
For short form read only the parts in brackets. The words in parentheses are omitted in the long form.

Now a man was ill, Lazarus from Bethany, the village of Mary and her sister Martha. Mary was the one who had anointed the Lord with perfumed oil and dried his feet with her hair; it was her brother Lazarus who was ill. So [the sisters (of Lazarus) sent word to Jesus saying, "Master, the one you love is ill." When Jesus heard this he said, "This illness is not to end in death, but is for the glory of God, that the Son of God may be glorified through it." Now Jesus loved Martha and her sister and Lazarus. So when he heard that he was ill, he remained for two days in the place where he was. Then after this he said to his disciples, "Let us go back to Judea."] The disciples said to him, "Rabbi, the Jews were just trying to stone you, and you want to go back there?" Jesus answered, "Are there not twelve hours in a day? If one walks during the day, he does not stumble, because he sees the light of this world. But if one walks at night, he stumbles, because the light is not in him." He said this, and then told them, "Our friend Lazarus is asleep, but I am going to awaken him." So the disciples said to him, "Master, if he is asleep, he will be saved." But Jesus was talking about his death, while they thought that he meant ordinary sleep. So then Jesus said to them clearly, "Lazarus has died. And I am glad for you that I was not there, that you may believe. Let us go to him." So Thomas, called Didymus, said to his fellow disciples, "Let us also go to die with him."

[When Jesus arrived, he found that Lazarus had already been in the tomb for four days.] Now Bethany was near Jerusalem, only about two miles away. And many of the Jews had come to Martha and Mary to comfort them about their brother. [When Martha heard that Jesus was coming, she went to meet him; but Mary sat at home. Martha said to Jesus, "Lord, if you had been here, my brother would not have died. But even now I know that whatever you ask of God, God will give you." Jesus said to her, "Your brother will rise." Martha said to him, "I know he will rise, in the resurrection on the last day." Jesus told her, "I am the resurrection and the life; whoever believes in me, even if he dies, will live, and everyone who lives and believes in me will never die. Do you believe this?" She said to him, "Yes, Lord. I have come to believe that you are the Christ, the Son of God, the one who is coming into the world."]

When she had said this, she went and called her sister Mary secretly, saying, "The teacher is here and is asking for you." As soon as she heard this, she rose quickly and went to him. For Jesus had not yet come into the village, but was still where Martha had met him. So when the Jews who were with her in the house comforting her saw Mary get up quickly and go out, they followed her, presuming that she was going to the tomb to weep there. When Mary came to where Jesus was and saw him, she fell at his feet and said to him, "Lord, if you had been here, my brother would not have died." When Jesus saw her weeping and the Jews who had come with her weeping, [he became perturbed and deeply troubled, and said, "Where have you laid him?" They said to him, "Sir, come and see." And Jesus wept. So the Jews said, "See how he loved him." But some of them said, "Could not the one who opened the eyes of the blind man have done something so that this man would not have died?"

So Jesus, perturbed again, came to the tomb. It was a cave, and a stone lay across it. Jesus said, "Take away the stone." Martha, the dead man's sister, said to him, "Lord, by now there will be a stench; he has been dead for four days." Jesus said to her, "Did I not tell you that if you believe you will see the glory of God?" So they took away the stone. And Jesus raised his eyes and said, "Father, I thank you for hearing me. I know that you always hear me; but because of the crowd here I have said this, that they may believe that you sent me." And when he had said this, he cried out in a loud voice, "Lazarus, come out!" The dead man came out, tied hand and foot with burial bands, and his face was wrapped in a cloth. So Jesus said to them, "Untie him and let him go."

Now many of the Jews who had come to Mary and seen what he had done began to believe in him.]

THIRD SCRUTINY

During Lent, the elect (those catechumens who have been called to prepare for baptism at Easter) are called to come before the community for exorcisms and prayers. This takes place after the liturgy of the word on the Third, Fourth, and Fifth Sundays of Lent. These rites are intended to purify the hearts and minds of the elect, to strengthen them against temptation, to help them progress in the love of God.

The presider asks the assembly to pray in silence for the elect, then to join in intercessions for them. The presider lays hands on each of the elect and prays that the elect be delivered from the power of evil and become witnesses to the gospel. A song or psalm may be sung, then the elect are dismissed as usual and the faithful continue with the liturgy of the eucharist.

1129 FIFTH SUNDAY OF LENT / B

READING I
Jeremiah 31:31–34 / 35

The days are coming, says the LORD, when I will make a new covenant with the house of Israel and the house of Judah. It will not be like the covenant I made with their fathers the day I took them by the hand to lead them forth from the land of Egypt; for they broke my covenant, and I had to show myself their master, says the LORD. But this is the covenant that I will make with the house of Israel after those days, says the LORD. I will place my law within them and write it upon their hearts; I will be their God, and they shall be my people. No longer will they have need to teach their friends and relatives how to know the LORD. All, from least to greatest, shall know me, says the LORD, for I will forgive their evildoing and remember their sin no more.

RESPONSORIAL PSALM
Psalm 51:3–4, 12–13, 14–15

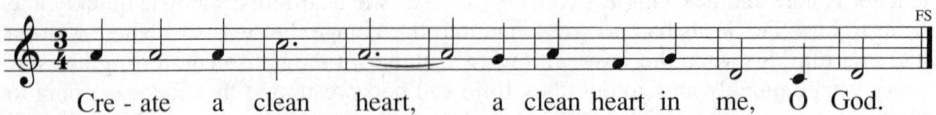

Cre - ate a clean heart, a clean heart in me, O God.

Have mercy on me, O God,
　according to your merciful love;
according to your great compassion,
　blot out my transgressions.
Wash me completely from my iniquity,
　and cleanse me from my sin. ℟.

Create a pure heart for me, O God;
　renew a steadfast spirit within me.

Do not cast me away from your
　presence;
　take not your holy spirit from me. ℟.

Restore in me the joy of your salvation;
　sustain in me a willing spirit.
I will teach transgressors your ways,
　that sinners may return to you. ℟.

READING II
Hebrews 5:7–9

In the days when Christ Jesus was in the flesh, he offered prayers and supplications with loud cries and tears to the one who was able to save him from death, and he was heard because of his reverence. Son though he was, he learned obedience from what he suffered; and when he was made perfect, he became the source of eternal salvation for all who obey him.

GOSPEL
John 12:20–33

Some Greeks who had come to worship at the Passover Feast came to Philip, who was from Bethsaida in Galilee, and asked him, "Sir, we would like to see Jesus." Philip went and told Andrew; then Andrew and Philip went and told Jesus. Jesus answered them, "The hour has come for the Son of Man to be glorified. Amen, amen, I say to you, unless a grain of wheat falls to the ground and dies, it remains just a grain of wheat; but if it dies, it produces much fruit. Whoever loves his life loses it, and whoever hates his life in this world will preserve it for eternal life. Whoever serves me must follow me, and where I am, there also will my servant be. The Father will honor whoever serves me.

"I am troubled now. Yet what should I say? 'Father, save me from this hour'? But it was for this purpose that I came to this hour. Father, glorify your name." Then a voice came from heaven, "I have glorified it and will glorify it again." The crowd there heard it and said it was thunder; but others said, "An angel has spoken to him." Jesus answered and said, "This voice did not come for my sake but for yours. Now is the time of judgment on this world; now the ruler of this world will be driven out. And when I am lifted up from the earth, I will draw everyone to myself." He said this indicating the kind of death he would die.

THIRD SCRUTINY
See no. 1128

FIFTH SUNDAY OF LENT / C
1130

READING I
Isaiah 43:16–21 / 36

Thus says the LORD,
　who opens a way in the sea
　and a path in the mighty waters,
who leads out chariots and horsemen,
　a powerful army,
till they lie prostrate together, never to
　rise,

snuffed out and quenched like a wick.
Remember not the events of the past,
　the things of long ago consider not;
see, I am doing something new!
　Now it springs forth, do you not
　perceive it?
In the desert I make a way,

in the wasteland, rivers.
Wild beasts honor me,
  jackals and ostriches,
for I put water in the desert

and rivers in the wasteland
  for my chosen people to drink,
the people whom I formed for myself,
  that they might announce my praise.

RESPONSORIAL PSALM *Psalm 126:1–2ab, 2cd–3, 4–5, 6*

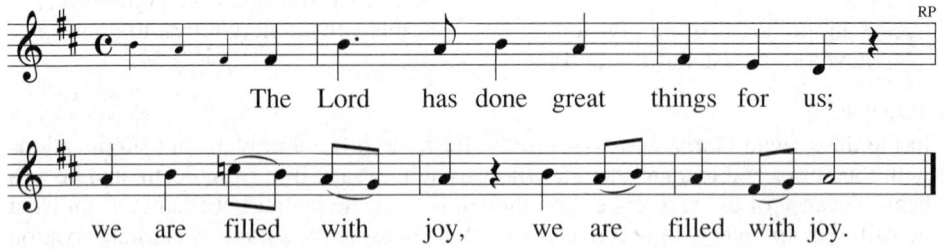

The Lord has done great things for us;
we are filled with joy, we are filled with joy.

When the LORD brought back the exiles
  of Sion,
  we thought we were dreaming.
Then was our mouth filled with laughter;
  on our tongues, songs of joy. ℟.

Then the nations themselves said,
  "What great deeds
  the LORD worked for them!"
What great deeds the LORD worked for us!
  Indeed, we were glad. ℟.

Bring back our exiles, O LORD,
  as streams in the south.
Those who are sowing in tears
  will sing when they reap. ℟.

They go out, they go out, full of tears,
  bearing seed for the sowing;
they come back, they come back with
  a song,
  bearing their sheaves. ℟.

READING II *Philippians 3:8–14*

Brothers and sisters: I consider everything as a loss because of the supreme good of knowing Christ Jesus my Lord. For his sake I have accepted the loss of all things and I consider them so much rubbish, that I may gain Christ and be found in him, not having any righteousness of my own based on the law but that which comes through faith in Christ, the righteousness from God, depending on faith to know him and the power of his resurrection and the sharing of his sufferings by being conformed to his death, if somehow I may attain the resurrection from the dead.

It is not that I have already taken hold of it or have already attained perfect maturity, but I continue my pursuit in hope that I may possess it, since I have indeed been taken possession of by Christ Jesus. Brothers and sisters, I for my part do not consider myself to have taken possession. Just one thing: forgetting what lies behind but straining forward to what lies ahead, I continue my pursuit toward the goal, the prize of God's upward calling, in Christ Jesus.

GOSPEL *John 8:1–11*

Jesus went to the Mount of Olives. But early in the morning he arrived again in the temple area, and all the people started coming to him, and he sat down and taught them. Then the scribes and the Pharisees brought a woman who had been caught in adultery and made her stand in the middle. They said to him, "Teacher, this woman was caught in the very act of committing adultery. Now in the law, Moses commanded us to stone such women. So what do you say?" They said this to test him, so that they could have some charge to bring against him. Jesus bent down and began to write on the ground with his finger. But when they continued asking him, he straightened up and said to them, "Let the one among you who is without sin be the first to throw a stone at her." Again he bent down and wrote on the ground. And in response, they went away one by one, beginning with the elders. So he was left alone with the woman before him. Then Jesus straightened up and said to her, "Woman, where are they? Has no one condemned you?" She replied, "No one, sir." Then Jesus said, "Neither do I condemn you. Go, and from now on do not sin any more."

THIRD SCRUTINY
See no. 1128

PALM SUNDAY OF THE PASSION OF THE LORD   1131

Passion or Palm Sunday is the last Sunday in Lent. Its closeness to the end of Lent has given this liturgy two distinct features: the procession with palms and the gospel reading of the Lord's passion. The blessing and carrying of palms celebrates Jesus' entrance into Jerusalem to accomplish his paschal mystery. The reading of the passion comes as a conclusion to all the gospel readings of the lenten Sundays: these scriptures yearly prepare catechumens and the faithful to approach the celebration of Christ's death and resurrection. That celebration takes place most especially in the sacraments of initiation at the Easter Vigil.

COMMEMORATION OF THE LORD'S ENTRANCE INTO JERUSALEM

This rite may be very simple or may involve the entire assembly in a procession with the blessing of palms and the gospel reading of Jesus' entrance into Jerusalem. Depending on the local Church, then, some of the following hymns, psalms and readings will be used.

OPENING ANTIPHON   1132
The following or another appropriate acclamation may be sung.

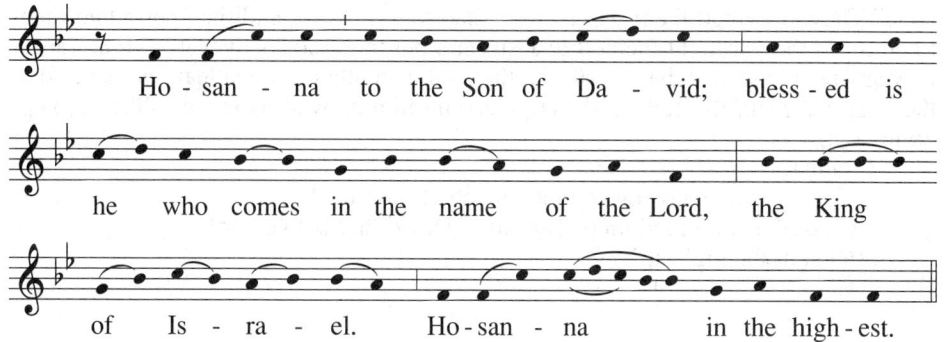

Ho-san-na to the Son of Da-vid; bless-ed is he who comes in the name of the Lord, the King of Is-ra-el. Ho-san-na in the high-est.

Text: ICEL, © 2010
Music: ICEL, © 2010; acc. by Richard Proulx, © 1985, 2011, GIA Publications, Inc.

1133 BLESSING OF BRANCHES

All hold branches as these are blessed. The branches may be of palm or from a tree that is native to the area. The green or flowering branches signify the victory of life.

1134 GOSPEL / A   *Matthew 21:1–11 / 37*

When Jesus and the disciples drew near Jerusalem and came to Bethphage on the Mount of Olives, Jesus sent two disciples, saying to them, "Go into the village opposite you, and immediately you will find an ass tethered, and a colt with her. Untie them and bring them here to me. And if anyone should say anything to you, reply, 'The master has need of them.' Then he will send them at once." This happened so that what had been spoken through the prophet might be fulfilled:

Say to daughter Zion,
"Behold, your king comes to you,
    meek and riding on an ass,
    and on a colt, the foal of a beast of burden."

The disicples went and did as Jesus had ordered them. They brought the ass and the colt and laid their cloaks over them, and he sat upon them. The very large crowd spread their cloaks on the road, while others cut branches from the trees and strewed them on the road. The crowds preceding him and those following kept crying out and saying:

"Hosanna to the Son of David;
    blessed is he who comes in the name of the Lord;
    hosanna in the highest."

And when he entered Jerusalem the whole city was shaken and asked, "Who is this?" And the crowds replied, "This is Jesus the prophet, from Nazareth in Galilee."

1135 GOSPEL / B   *Mark 11:1–10*

When Jesus and his disciples drew near to Jerusalem, to Bethphage and Bethany at the Mount of Olives, he sent two of his disciples and said to them, "Go into the village opposite you, and immediately on entering it, you will find a colt tethered on which no one has ever sat. Untie it and bring it here. If anyone should say to you, 'Why are you doing this?' reply, 'The Master has need of it and will send it back here at once.'" So they went off and found a colt tethered at a gate outside on the street, and they untied it. Some of the bystanders said to them, "What are you doing, untying the colt?" They answered them just as Jesus had told them to, and they permitted them to do it. So they brought the colt to Jesus and put their cloaks over it. And he sat on it. Many people spread their cloaks on the road, and others spread leafy branches that they had cut from the fields. Those preceding him as well as those following kept crying out:

"Hosanna!
    Blessed is he who comes in the name of the Lord!
    Blessed is the kingdom of our father David that is to come!
Hosanna in the highest!"

Or:

GOSPEL / B   *John 12:12–16*

When the great crowd that had come to the feast heard that Jesus was coming to Jerusalem, they took palm branches and went out to meet him, and cried out:

"Hosanna!
"Blessed is he who comes in the name of the Lord,
the king of Israel."

Jesus found an ass and sat upon it, as is written:
Fear no more, O daughter Zion;
see, your king comes, seated upon an ass's colt.
His disciples did not understand this at first, but when Jesus had been glorified they
remembered that these things were written about him and that they had done this for him.

GOSPEL / C — *Luke 19:28–40* 1136

Jesus proceeded on his journey up to Jerusalem. As he drew near to Bethphage and
Bethany at the place called the Mount of Olives, he sent two of his disciples. He said,
"Go into the village opposite you, and as you enter it you will find a colt tethered on
which no one has ever sat. Untie it and bring it here. And if anyone should ask you,
'Why are you untying it?' you will answer, 'The Master has need of it.'" So those
who had been sent went off and found everything just as he had told them. And as
they were untying the colt, its owners said to them, "Why are you untying this colt?"
They answered, "The Master has need of it." So they brought it to Jesus, threw their
cloaks over the colt, and helped Jesus to mount. As he rode along, the people were
spreading their cloaks on the road; and now as he was approaching the slope of the
Mount of Olives, the whole multitude of his disciples began to praise God aloud with
joy for all the mighty deeds they had seen. They proclaimed:
"Blessed is the king who comes
in the name of the Lord.
Peace in heaven
and glory in the highest."
Some of the Pharisees in the crowd said to him, "Teacher, rebuke your disciples." He
said in reply, "I tell you, if they keep silent, the stones will cry out!"

PROCESSION 1137

*All join in the procession or at least in the song. Such a movement of people expresses the experi-
ence of Lent: the Church has been called to move on, to go ever further toward the paschal mystery
of death and resurrection. Hymn no. 585, or another appropriate hymn or song may be sung.*

This dialogue may be used:

Priest, deacon, or other minister: Let us go forth in peace.

In the name of Christ.   A - men.

*The commemoration of the Lord's entrance into Jerusalem, whether this is done in a simple or sol-
emn manner, concludes with the opening prayer of the Mass.*

1138 LITURGY OF THE WORD / ABC

READING I

Isaiah 50:4–7 / 38

The Lord GOD has given me
a well-trained tongue,
that I might know how to speak to the
weary
a word that will rouse them.
Morning after morning
he opens my ear that I may hear;
and I have not rebelled,
have not turned back.
I gave my back to those who beat me,
my cheeks to those who plucked my
beard;
my face I did not shield
from buffets and spitting.

The Lord GOD is my help,
therefore I am not disgraced;
I have set my face like flint,
knowing that I shall not be put to
shame.

RESPONSORIAL PSALM

Psalm 22:8–9, 17–18a, 19–20, 23–24

FS

My God, my God, why have you a - ban-doned me?

All who see me deride me;
they curl their lips, they toss their
heads:
"He trusted in the LORD, let him save him;
let him release him, for in him he
delights." ℟.

For dogs have surrounded me;
a band of the wicked besets me.
They tear holes in my hands and my feet;
I can count every one of my bones. ℟.

They divide my clothing among them,
they cast lots for my robe.
But you, O LORD, do not stay afar off;
my strength, make haste to help me! ℟.

I will tell of your name to my kin,
and praise you in the midst of the
assembly;
"You who fear the LORD, give him praise;
all descendants of Jacob, give him
glory;
revere him, all you descendants of
Israel." ℟.

READING II

Philippians 2:6–11

Christ Jesus, though he was in the form
of God,
did not regard equality with God
something to be grasped.
Rather, he emptied himself,
taking the form of a slave,
coming in human likeness;
and found human in appearance,
he humbled himself,
becoming obedient to the point of
death,
even death on a cross.
Because of this, God greatly exalted him
and bestowed on him the name
which is above every name,
that at the name of Jesus
every knee should bend,
of those in heaven and on earth and
under the earth,
and every tongue confess that
Jesus Christ is Lord,
to the glory of God the Father.

GOSPEL / A *Matthew 26:14—27:66 or 27:11–54* 1139

For short form read only the part in brackets.

The symbols of the following passion narrative represent:
  + Christ;   N narrator;   V voice;   C crowd.

N The Passion of our Lord Jesus Christ according to Matthew.

N One of the Twelve, who was called Judas Iscariot, went to the chief priests and said,

V "What are you willing to give me if I hand him over to you?"

N They paid him thirty pieces of silver, and from that time on he looked for an opportunity to hand him over.

On the first day of the Feast of Unleavened Bread, the disciples approached Jesus and said,

V "Where do you want us to prepare for you to eat the Passover?"

N He said,

+ "Go into the city to a certain man and tell him, 'The teacher says, "My appointed time draws near; in your house I shall celebrate the Passover with my disciples."'"

N The disciples then did as Jesus had ordered, and prepared the Passover.

When it was evening, he reclined at table with the Twelve. And while they were eating, he said,

+ "Amen, I say to you, one of you will betray me."

N Deeply distressed at this, they began to say to him one after another,

V "Surely it is not I, Lord?"

N He said in reply,

+ "He who has dipped his hand into the dish with me is the one who will betray me. The Son of Man indeed goes, as it is written of him, but woe to that man by whom the Son of Man is betrayed. It would be better for that man if he had never been born."

N Then Judas, his betrayer, said in reply,

V "Surely it is not I, Rabbi?"

N He answered,

+ "You have said so."

N While they were eating, Jesus took bread, said the blessing, broke it, and giving it to his disciples said,

+ "Take and eat; this is my body."

N Then he took a cup, gave thanks, and gave it to them, saying,

+ "Drink from it, all of you, for this is my blood of the covenant, which will be shed on behalf of many for the forgiveness of sins. I tell you, from now on I shall not drink this fruit of the vine until the day when I drink it with you new in the kingdom of my Father."

N Then, after singing a hymn, they went out to the Mount of Olives.

Then Jesus said to them,

+ "This night all of you will have your faith in me shaken, for it is written:
  I will strike the shepherd,
    and the sheep of the flock will
    be dispersed;
  but after I have been raised up, I shall go before you to Galilee."

N Peter said to him in reply,

V "Though all may have their faith in you shaken, mine will never be."

N Jesus said to him,

+ "Amen, I say to you, this very night before the cock crows, you will deny me three times."

N Peter said to him,

V "Even though I should have to die with you, I will not deny you."

N And all the disciples spoke likewise.

Then Jesus came with them to a place called Gethsemane, and he said to his disciples,

+ "Sit here while I go over there and pray."

N He took along Peter and the two sons of Zebedee, and began to feel sorrow and distress. Then he said to them,

+ "My soul is sorrowful even to death. Remain here and keep watch with me."

N He advanced a little and fell prostrate in prayer, saying,

+ "My Father, if it is possible, let this cup pass from me; yet, not as I will, but as you will."

N When he returned to his disciples he found them asleep. He said to Peter,

+ "So you could not keep watch with me for one hour? Watch and pray that you may not undergo the test. The spirit is willing, but the flesh is weak."

N Withdrawing a second time, he prayed again,

+ "My Father, if it is not possible that this cup pass without my drinking it, your will be done!"

N Then he returned once more and found them asleep, for they could not keep their eyes open. He left them and withdrew again and prayed a third time, saying the same thing again. Then he returned to his disciples and said to them,

+ "Are you still sleeping and taking your rest? Behold, the hour is at hand when the Son of Man is to be handed over to sinners. Get up, let us go. Look, my betrayer is at hand."

N While he was still speaking, Judas, one of the Twelve, arrived, accompanied by a large crowd, with swords and clubs, who had come from the chief priests and the elders of the people. His betrayer had arranged a sign with them, saying,

V "The man I shall kiss is the one; arrest him."

N Immediately he went over to Jesus and said,

V "Hail, Rabbi!"

N and he kissed him. Jesus answered him,

+ "Friend, do what you have come for."

N Then stepping forward they laid hands on Jesus and arrested him. And behold, one of those who accompanied Jesus put his hand to his sword, drew it, and struck the high priest's servant, cutting off his ear. Then Jesus said to him,

+ "Put your sword back into its sheath, for all who take the sword will perish by the sword. Do you think that I cannot call upon my Father and he will not provide me at this moment with more than twelve legions of angels? But then how would the Scriptures be fulfilled which say that it must come to pass in this way?"

N At that hour Jesus said to the crowds,

+ "Have you come out as against a robber, with swords and clubs to seize me? Day after day I sat teaching in the temple area, yet you did not arrest me. But all this has come to pass that the writings of the prophets may be fulfilled."

N Then all the disciples left him and fled.

Those who had arrested Jesus led him away to Caiaphas the high priest, where the scribes and the elders were assembled. Peter was following him at a distance as far as the high priest's courtyard, and going inside he sat down with the servants to see the outcome. The chief priests and the entire Sanhedrin kept trying to obtain false testimony against Jesus in order to put him to death, but they found none, though many false witnesses came forward. Finally two came forward who stated,

C "This man said, 'I can destroy the temple of God and within three days rebuild it.'"

N The high priest rose and addressed him,

V "Have you no answer? What are these men testifying against you?"

N But Jesus was silent. Then the high priest said to him,

V "I order you to tell us under oath before the living God whether you are the Christ, the Son of God."

N Jesus said to him in reply,

+ "You have said so. But I tell you: From now on you will see 'the Son of Man

  seated at the right hand of the Power' and 'coming on the clouds of heaven.'"

N Then the high priest tore his robes and said,

V "He has blasphemed! What further need have we of witnesses? You have now heard the blasphemy; what is your opinion?"

N They said in reply,

C "He deserves to die!"

N Then they spat in his face and struck him, while some slapped him, saying,

C "Prophesy for us, Christ: who is it that struck you?"

N Now Peter was sitting outside in the courtyard. One of the maids came over to him and said,

C "You too were with Jesus the Galilean."

N But he denied it in front of everyone, saying,

V "I do not know what you are talking about!"

N As he went out to the gate, another girl saw him and said to those who were there,

C "This man was with Jesus the Nazorean."

N Again he denied it with an oath,

V "I do not know the man!"

N A little later the bystanders came over and said to Peter,

C "Surely you too are one of them; even your speech gives you away."

N At that he began to curse and to swear,

V "I do not know the man."

N And immediately a cock crowed. Then Peter remembered the word that Jesus had spoken: "Before the cock crows you will deny me three times." He went out and began to weep bitterly.

When it was morning, all the chief priests and the elders of the people took counsel against Jesus to put him to death. They bound him, led him away, and handed him over to Pilate, the governor.

Then Judas, his betrayer, seeing that Jesus had been condemned, deeply regretted what he had done. He returned the thirty pieces of silver to the chief priests and elders, saying,

V "I have sinned in betraying innocent blood."

N They said,

C "What is that to us? Look to it yourself."

N Flinging the money into the temple, he departed and went off and hanged himself. The chief priests gathered up the money, but said,

C "It is not lawful to deposit this in the temple treasury, for it is the price of blood."

N After consultation, they used it to buy the potter's field as a burial place for foreigners. That is why that field even today is called the Field of Blood. Then was fulfilled what had been said through Jeremiah the prophet, *And they took the thirty pieces of silver, the value of a man with a price on his head, a price set by some of the Israelites, and they paid it out for the potter's field just as the Lord had commanded me.*

Now [Jesus stood before the governor, and he questioned him,

V "Are you the king of the Jews?"

N Jesus said,

+ "You say so."

N And when he was accused by the chief priests and elders, he made no answer. Then Pilate said to him,

V "Do you not hear how many things they are testifying against you?"

N But he did not answer him one word, so that the governor was greatly amazed.

Now on the occasion of the feast the governor was accustomed to release to the crowd one prisoner whom they wished. And at that time they had a notorious prisoner called Barabbas. So when they had assembled, Pilate said to them,

V "Which one do you want me to release to you, Barabbas, or Jesus called Christ?"

N For he knew that it was out of envy that they had handed him over. While he was still seated on the bench, his wife sent him a message, "Have nothing to do with that righteous man. I suffered much in a dream today because of him." The chief priests and the elders persuaded the crowds to ask for Barabbas but to destroy Jesus. The governor said to them in reply,

V "Which of the two do you want me to release to you?"

N They answered,

C "Barabbas!"

N Pilate said to them,

V "Then what shall I do with Jesus called Christ?"

N They all said,

C "Let him be crucified!"

N But he said,

V "Why? What evil has he done?"

N They only shouted the louder,

C "Let him be crucified!"

N When Pilate saw that he was not succeeding at all, but that a riot was breaking out instead, he took water and washed his hands in the sight of the crowd, saying,

V "I am innocent of this man's blood. Look to it yourselves."

N And the whole people said in reply,

C "His blood be upon us and upon our children."

N Then he released Barabbas to them, but after he had Jesus scourged, he handed him over to be crucified.

Then the soldiers of the governor took Jesus inside the praetorium and gathered the whole cohort around him. They stripped off his clothes and threw a scarlet military cloak about him. Weaving a crown out of thorns, they placed it on his head, and a reed in his right hand. And kneeling before him, they mocked him, saying,

C "Hail, King of the Jews!"

N They spat upon him and took the reed and kept striking him on the head. And when they had mocked him, they stripped him of the cloak, dressed him in his own clothes, and led him off to crucify him.

As they were going out, they met a Cyrenian named Simon; this man they pressed into service to carry his cross.

And when they came to a place called Golgotha —which means Place of the Skull—, they gave Jesus wine to drink mixed with gall. But when he had tasted it, he refused to drink. After they had crucified him, they divided his garments by casting lots; then they sat down and kept watch over him there. And they placed over his head the written charge against him: This is Jesus, the King of the Jews. Two revolutionaries were crucified with him, one on his right and the other on his left. Those passing by reviled him, shaking their heads and saying,

C "You who would destroy the temple and rebuild it in three days, save yourself, if you are the Son of God, and come down from the cross!"

N Likewise the chief priests with the scribes and elders mocked him and said,

C "He saved others; he cannot save himself. So he is the king of Israel! Let him come down from the cross now, and we will believe in him. He trusted in God; let him deliver him now if he wants him. For he said, 'I am the Son of God.'"

N The revolutionaries who were crucified with him also kept abusing him in the same way.

From noon onward, darkness came over the whole land until three in the afternoon. And about three o'clock Jesus cried out in a loud voice,

+ *"Eli, Eli, lema sabachthani?"*

N which means,

+ "My God, my God, why have you forsaken me?"

N Some of the bystanders who heard it said,

C "This one is calling for Elijah."

N Immediately one of them ran to get a sponge; he soaked it in wine, and putting it on a reed, gave it to him to drink. But the rest said,

C "Wait, let us see if Elijah comes to save him."

N But Jesus cried out again in a loud voice, and gave up his spirit.

Here all kneel and pause for a short time.

N And behold, the veil of the sanctuary was torn in two from top to bottom. The earth quaked, rocks were split, tombs were opened, and the bodies of many saints who had fallen asleep were raised. And coming forth from their tombs after his resurrection, they entered the holy city and appeared to many. The centurion and the men with him who were keeping watch over Jesus feared greatly when they saw the earthquake and all that was happening, and they said,

C "Truly, this was the Son of God!"]

N There were many women there, looking on from a distance, who had followed Jesus from Galilee, ministering to him. Among them were Mary Magdalene and Mary the mother of James and Joseph, and the mother of the sons of Zebedee.

When it was evening, there came a rich man from Arimathea named Joseph, who was himself a disciple of Jesus. He went to Pilate and asked for the body of Jesus; then Pilate ordered it to be handed over. Taking the body, Joseph wrapped it in clean linen and laid it in his new tomb that he had hewn in the rock. Then he rolled a huge stone across the entrance to the tomb and departed. But Mary Magdalene and the other Mary remained sitting there, facing the tomb.

The next day, the one following the day of preparation, the chief priests and the Pharisees gathered before Pilate and said,

C "Sir, we remember that this impostor while still alive said, 'After three days I will be raised up.' Give orders, then, that the grave be secured until the third day, lest his disciples come and steal him and say to the people, 'He has been raised from the dead.' This last imposture would be worse than the first."

N Pilate said to them,

V "The guard is yours; go, secure it as best you can."

N So they went and secured the tomb by fixing a seal to the stone and setting the guard.

1140 GOSPEL / B

For short form read only the part in brackets.

The symbols of the following passion narrative represent:
    + Christ;   N *narrator;*   V *voice;*   C *crowd.*

N The Passion of our Lord Jesus Christ according to Mark.

N The Passover and the Feast of Unleavened Bread were to take place in two days' time. So the chief priests and the scribes were seeking a way to arrest him by treachery and put him to death. They said,

C "Not during the festival, for fear that there may be a riot among the people."

N When he was in Bethany reclining at table in the house of Simon the leper, a woman came with an alabaster jar of perfumed oil, costly genuine spikenard. She broke the alabaster jar and poured it on his head. There were some who were indignant.

C "Why has there been this waste of perfumed oil? It could have been sold for more than three hundred days' wages and the money given to the poor."

N They were infuriated with her. Jesus said,

+ "Let her alone. Why do you make trouble for her? She has done a good thing for me. The poor you will always have with you, and whenever you wish you can do good to them, but you will not always have me. She has done what she could. She has anticipated anointing my body for burial. Amen, I say to you, wherever the gospel is proclaimed to the whole world, what she has done will be told in memory of her."

N Then Judas Iscariot, one of the Twelve, went off to the chief priests to hand him over to them. When they heard him they were pleased and promised to pay him money. Then he looked for an opportunity to hand him over.

On the first day of the Feast of Unleavened Bread, when they sacrificed the Passover lamb, his disciples said to him,

V "Where do you want us to go and prepare for you to eat the Passover?"

N He sent two of his disciples and said to them,

+ "Go into the city and a man will meet you, carrying a jar of water. Follow him. Wherever he enters, say to the master of the house, 'The Teacher says, "Where is my guest room where I may eat the Passover with my disciples?"' Then he will show you a large upper room furnished and ready. Make the preparations for us there."

N The disciples then went off, entered the city, and found it just as he had told them; and they prepared the Passover.

When it was evening, he came with the Twelve. And as they reclined at table and were eating, Jesus said,

+ "Amen, I say to you, one of you will betray me, one who is eating with me."

N They began to be distressed and to say to him, one by one,

V "Surely it is not I?"

N He said to them,

+ "One of the Twelve, the one who dips with me into the dish. For the Son of Man indeed goes, as it is written of him, but woe to that man by whom the Son of Man is betrayed. It would be better for that man if he had never been born."

N While they were eating, he took bread, said the blessing, broke it, and gave it to them, and said,

+ "Take it; this is my body."

N Then he took a cup, gave thanks, and gave it to them, and they all drank from it. He said to them,

+ "This is my blood of the covenant, which will be shed for many. Amen, I say to you, I shall not drink again the fruit of the vine until the day when I drink it new in the kingdom of God."

N Then, after singing a hymn, they went out to the Mount of Olives.

Then Jesus said to them,

+ "All of you will have your faith shaken, for it is written:
  I will strike the shepherd,
  and the sheep will be
  dispersed.
  But after I have been raised up, I shall go before you to Galilee."

N Peter said to him,

V "Even though all should have their faith shaken, mine will not be."

N Then Jesus said to him,

+ "Amen, I say to you, this very night before the cock crows twice you will deny me three times."

N But he vehemently replied,

V "Even though I should have to die with you, I will not deny you."

N And they all spoke similarly.

Then they came to a place named Gethsemane, and he said to his disciples,

+ "Sit here while I pray."

N He took with him Peter, James, and John, and began to be troubled and distressed. Then he said to them,

+ "My soul is sorrowful even to death. Remain here and keep watch."

N He advanced a little and fell to the ground and prayed that if it were possible the hour might pass by him; he said,

+ "Abba, Father, all things are possible to you. Take this cup away from me, but not what I will but what you will."

N When he returned he found them asleep. He said to Peter,

+ "Simon, are you asleep? Could you not keep watch for one hour? Watch and pray that you may not undergo the test. The spirit is willing but the flesh is weak."

N Withdrawing again, he prayed, saying the same thing. Then he returned once more and found them asleep, for they could not keep their eyes open and did not know what to answer him. He returned a third time and said to them,

+ "Are you still sleeping and taking your rest? It is enough. The hour has come. Behold, the Son of Man is to be handed over to sinners. Get up, let us go. See, my betrayer is at hand."

N Then, while he was still speaking, Judas, one of the Twelve, arrived, accompanied by a crowd with swords and clubs who had come from the chief priests, the scribes, and the elders. His betrayer had arranged a signal with them, saying,

V "The man I shall kiss is the one; arrest him and lead him away securely."

N He came and immediately went over to him and said,

V "Rabbi."

N And he kissed him. At this they laid hands on him and arrested him. One of the bystanders drew his sword, struck the high priest's servant, and cut off his ear. Jesus said to them in reply,

+ "Have you come out as against a robber, with swords and clubs, to seize me? Day after day I was with you teaching in the temple area, yet you did not arrest me; but that the Scriptures may be fulfilled."

N And they all left him and fled. Now a young man followed him wearing nothing but a linen cloth about his body. They seized him, but he left the cloth behind and ran off naked.

They led Jesus away to the high priest, and all the chief priests and the elders and the scribes came together. Peter followed him at a distance into the high priest's courtyard and was seated with the guards, warming himself at the fire. The chief priests and the entire Sanhedrin kept trying to obtain testimony against Jesus in order to put him to death, but they found none. Many gave false witness against him, but their testimony did not agree. Some took the stand and testified falsely against him, alleging,

C "We heard him say, 'I will destroy this temple made with hands and within three days I will build another not made with hands.'"

N Even so their testimony did not agree. The high priest rose before the assembly and questioned Jesus, saying,

V "Have you no answer? What are these men testifying against you?"

N But he was silent and answered nothing. Again the high priest asked him and said to him,

V "Are you the Christ, the son of the Blessed One?"

N Then Jesus answered,

+ "I am;
  and 'you will see the Son of Man seated at the right hand of the Power
  and coming with the clouds of heaven.'"

N At that the high priest tore his garments and said,

V "What further need have we of witnesses? You have heard the blasphemy. What do you think?"

N They all condemned him as deserving to die. Some began to spit on him. They blindfolded him and struck him and said to him,

C "Prophesy!"

N And the guards greeted him with blows.

While Peter was below in the courtyard, one of the high priest's maids came along. Seeing Peter warming himself, she looked intently at him and said,

C "You too were with the Nazarene, Jesus."

N But he denied it saying,

V "I neither know nor understand what you are talking about."

N So he went out into the outer court. Then the cock crowed. The maid saw him and began again to say to the bystanders,

C "This man is one of them."

N Once again he denied it. A little later the bystanders said to Peter once more,

C "Surely you are one of them; for you too are a Galilean."

N He began to curse and to swear,

V "I do not know this man about whom you are talking."

N And immediately a cock crowed a second time. Then Peter remembered the word that Jesus had said to him, "Before the cock crows twice you will deny me three times." He broke down and wept.

[As soon as morning came, the chief priests with the elders and the scribes, that is, the whole Sanhedrin held a council. They bound Jesus, led him away, and handed him over to Pilate. Pilate questioned him,

V "Are you the king of the Jews?"

N He said to him in reply,

+ "You say so."

N The chief priests accused him of many things. Again Pilate questioned him,

V "Have you no answer? See how many things they accuse you of."

N Jesus gave him no further answer, so that Pilate was amazed.

Now on the occasion of the feast he used to release to them one prisoner whom they requested. A man called Barabbas was then in prison along with the rebels who had committed murder in a rebellion. The crowd came forward and began to ask him to do for them as he was accustomed. Pilate answered,

V "Do you want me to release to you the king of the Jews?"

N For he knew that it was out of envy that the chief priests had handed him over. But the chief priests stirred up the crowd to have him release Barabbas for them instead. Pilate again said to them in reply,

V "Then what do you want me to do with the man you call the king of the Jews?"

N They shouted again,

C "Crucify him."

N Pilate said to them,

V "Why? What evil has he done?"

N They only shouted the louder,

C "Crucify him."

N So Pilate, wishing to satisfy the crowd, released Barabbas to them and, after he had Jesus scourged, handed him over to be crucified.

The soldiers led him away inside the palace, that is, the praetorium, and assembled the whole cohort. They clothed him in purple and, weaving a crown of thorns, placed it on him. They began to salute him with,

C "Hail, King of the Jews!"

N and kept striking his head with a reed and spitting upon him. They knelt before him in homage. And when they had mocked him, they stripped him of the purple cloak, dressed him in his own clothes, and led him out to crucify him.

They pressed into service a passer-by, Simon, a Cyrenian, who was coming in from the country, the father of Alexander and Rufus, to carry his cross.

They brought him to the place of Golgotha—which is translated Place of the Skull—. They gave him wine drugged with myrrh, but he did not take it. Then they crucified him and divided his garments by casting lots for them to see what each should take. It was nine o'clock in the morning when they crucified him. The inscription of the charge against him read, "The King of the Jews." With him they crucified two revolutionaries, one on his right and one on his left. Those passing by reviled him, shaking their heads and saying,

C "Aha! You who would destroy the temple and rebuild it in three days, save yourself by coming down from the cross."

N Likewise the chief priests, with the scribes, mocked him among themselves and said,

C "He saved others; he cannot save himself. Let the Christ, the King of Israel, come down now from the cross that we may see and believe."

N Those who were crucified with him also kept abusing him.

At noon darkness came over the whole land until three in the afternoon. And at three o'clock Jesus cried out in a loud voice,

+ *"Eloi, Eloi, lema sabachthani?"*

N which is translated,

+ "My God, my God, why have you forsaken me?"

N Some of the bystanders who heard it said,

C "Look, he is calling Elijah."

N One of them ran, soaked a sponge with wine, put it on a reed and gave it to him to drink saying,

V "Wait, let us see if Elijah comes to take him down."

N Jesus gave a loud cry and breathed his last.

Here all kneel and pause for a short time.

N The veil of the sanctuary was torn in two from top to bottom. When the centurion who stood facing him saw how he breathed his last he said,

V "Truly this man was the Son of God!"]

N There were also women looking on from a distance. Among them were Mary Magdalene, Mary the mother of the younger James and of Joses, and Salome. These women had followed him when he was in Galilee and ministered to him. There were also many other women who had come up with him to Jerusalem.

When it was already evening, since it was the day of preparation, the day before the sabbath, Joseph of Arimathea, a distinguished member of the council, who was himself awaiting the kingdom of God, came and courageously went to Pilate and asked for the body of Jesus. Pilate was amazed that he was already dead. He summoned the centurion and asked him if Jesus had already died. And when he learned of it from the centurion, he gave the body to Joseph. Having bought a linen cloth, he took him down, wrapped him in the linen cloth, and laid him in a tomb that had been hewn out of the rock. Then he rolled a stone against the entrance to the tomb. Mary Magdalene and Mary the mother of Joses watched where he was laid.

1141 GOSPEL / C

Luke 22:14—23:56 or 23:1–49

For short form read only the part in brackets.

The symbols of the following passion narrative represent:
   + Christ; N narrator; V voice; C crowd.

N The Passion of our Lord Jesus Christ according to Luke.

N When the hour came, Jesus took his place at table with the apostles. He said to them,

+ "I have eagerly desired to eat this Passover with you before I suffer, for, I tell you, I shall not eat it again until there is fulfillment in the kingdom of God."

N Then he took a cup, gave thanks, and said,

+ "Take this and share it among yourselves; for I tell you that from this time on I shall not drink of the fruit of the vine until the kingdom of God comes."

N Then he took the bread, said the blessing, broke it, and gave it to them, saying,

+ "This is my body, which will be given for you; do this in memory of me."

N And likewise the cup after they had eaten, saying,

+ "This cup is the new covenant in my blood, which will be shed for you.

"And yet behold, the hand of the one who is to betray me is with me on the table; for the Son of Man indeed goes as it has been determined; but woe to that man by whom he is betrayed."

N And they began to debate among themselves who among them would do such a deed.

Then an argument broke out among them about which of them should be regarded as the greatest. He said to them,

+ "The kings of the Gentiles lord it over them and those in authority over them are addressed as 'Benefactors'; but among you it shall not be so. Rather, let the greatest among you be as the youngest, and the leader as the servant. For who is greater: the one seated at table or the one who serves? Is it not the one seated at table? I am among you as the one who serves. It is you who have stood by me in my trials; and I confer a kingdom on you, just as my Father has conferred one on me, that you may eat and drink at my table in my kingdom; and you will sit on thrones judging the twelve tribes of Israel.

"Simon, Simon, behold Satan has demanded to sift all of you like wheat, but I have prayed that your own faith may not fail; and once you have turned back, you must strengthen your brothers."

N He said to him,

V "Lord, I am prepared to go to prison and to die with you."

N But he replied,

+ "I tell you, Peter, before the cock crows this day, you will deny three times that you know me."

N He said to them,

+ "When I sent you forth without a money bag or a sack or sandals, were you in need of anything?"

C "No, nothing,"

N they replied. He said to them,

+ "But now one who has a money bag should take it, and likewise a sack, and one who does not have a sword should sell his cloak and buy one. For I tell you that this Scripture must be fulfilled in me, namely, *He was counted among the wicked*; and indeed what is written about me is coming to fulfillment."

N Then they said,

V "Lord, look, there are two swords here."

N But he replied,

+ "It is enough!"

N Then going out, he went, as was his custom, to the Mount of Olives, and the disciples followed him. When he arrived at the place he said to them,

+ "Pray that you may not undergo the test."

N After withdrawing about a stone's throw from them and kneeling, he prayed, saying,

+ "Father, if you are willing, take this cup away from me; still, not my will but yours be done."

N And to strengthen him an angel from heaven appeared to him. He was in such agony and he prayed so fervently that his sweat became like drops of blood falling on the ground. When he rose from prayer and returned to his disciples, he found them sleeping from grief. He said to them,

+ "Why are you sleeping? Get up and pray that you may not undergo the test."

N While he was still speaking, a crowd approached and in front was one of the Twelve, a man named Judas. He went up to Jesus to kiss him. Jesus said to him,

+ "Judas, are you betraying the Son of Man with a kiss?"

N His disciples realized what was about to happen, and they asked,

V "Lord, shall we strike with a sword?"

N And one of them struck the high priest's servant and cut off his right ear. But Jesus said in reply,

+ "Stop, no more of this!"

N Then he touched the servant's ear and healed him. And Jesus said to the chief priests and temple guards and elders who had come for him,

+ "Have you come out as against a robber, with swords and clubs? Day after day I was with you in the temple area, and you did not seize me; but this is your hour, the time for the power of darkness."

N After arresting him they led him away and took him into the house of the high priest; Peter was following at a distance. They lit a fire in the middle of the courtyard and sat around it, and Peter sat down with them. When a maid saw him seated in the light, she looked intently at him and said,

C "This man too was with him."

N But he denied it saying,

V "Woman, I do not know him."

N A short while later someone else saw him and said,

C "You too are one of them";

N but Peter answered,

V "My friend, I am not."

N About an hour later, still another insisted,

C "Assuredly, this man too was with him, for he also is a Galilean."

N But Peter said,

V "My friend, I do not know what you are talking about."

N Just as he was saying this, the cock crowed, and the Lord turned and looked at Peter; and Peter remembered the word of the Lord, how he had said to him, "Before the cock crows today, you will deny me three times." He went out and began to weep bitterly. The men who held Jesus in custody were ridiculing and beating him. They blindfolded him and questioned him, saying,

C "Prophesy! Who is it that struck you?"

N And they reviled him in saying many other things against him.

When day came the council of elders of the people met, both chief priests and scribes, and they brought him before their Sanhedrin. They said,

C "If you are the Christ, tell us,"

N but he replied to them,

+ "If I tell you, you will not believe, and if I question, you will not respond. But from this time on the Son of Man will be seated at the right hand of the power of God."

N They all asked,

C "Are you then the Son of God?"

N He replied to them,

+ "You say that I am."

N Then they said,

C "What further need have we for testimony? We have heard it from his own mouth."

[N *Short form begins:* The elders of the people, chief priests and scribes, arose and brought Jesus before Pilate.]

N Then the whole assembly of them arose and brought him before Pilate. [They brought charges against him, saying,

C "We found this man misleading our people; he opposes the payment of taxes to Caesar and maintains that he is the Christ, a king."

N Pilate asked him,

V "Are you the king of the Jews?"

N He said to him in reply,

+ "You say so."

N Pilate then addressed the chief priests and the crowds,

V "I find this man not guilty."

N But they were adamant and said,

C "He is inciting the people with his teaching throughout all Judea, from Galilee where he began even to here."

N On hearing this Pilate asked if the man was a Galilean; and upon learning that he was under Herod's jurisdiction, he sent him to Herod who was in Jerusalem at that time. Herod was very glad to see Jesus; he had been wanting to see him for a long time, for he had heard about him and had been hoping to see him perform some sign. He questioned him at length, but he gave him no answer. The chief priests and scribes, meanwhile, stood by accusing him harshly. Herod and his soldiers treated him contemptuously and mocked him, and after clothing him in resplendent garb, he sent him back to Pilate. Herod and Pilate became friends that very day, even though they had been enemies formerly. Pilate then summoned the chief priests, the rulers, and the people and said to them,

V "You brought this man to me and accused him of inciting the people to revolt. I have conducted my investigation in your presence and have not found this man guilty of the charges you have brought against him, nor did Herod, for he sent him back to us. So no capital crime has been committed by him. Therefore I shall have him flogged and then release him."

N But all together they shouted out,
C "Away with this man! Release Barabbas to us."
N —Now Barabbas had been imprisoned for a rebellion that had taken place in the city and for murder.— Again Pilate addressed them, still wishing to release Jesus, but they continued their shouting,
C "Crucify him! Crucify him!"
N Pilate addressed them a third time,
V "What evil has this man done? I found him guilty of no capital crime. Therefore I shall have him flogged and then release him."
N With loud shouts, however, they persisted in calling for his crucifixion, and their voices prevailed. The verdict of Pilate was that their demand should be granted. So he released the man who had been imprisoned for rebellion and murder, for whom they asked, and he handed Jesus over to them to deal with as they wished.

As they led him away they took hold of a certain Simon, a Cyrenian, who was coming in from the country; and after laying the cross on him, they made him carry it behind Jesus.

A large crowd of people followed Jesus, including many women who mourned and lamented him. Jesus turned to them and said,

+ "Daughters of Jerusalem, do not weep for me; weep instead for yourselves and for your children for indeed, the days are coming when people will say, 'Blessed are the barren, the wombs that never bore and the breasts that never nursed.' At that time people will say to the mountains, 'Fall upon us!' and to the hills, 'Cover us!' for if these things are done when the wood is green what will happen when it is dry?"

N Now two others, both criminals, were led away with him to be executed.

When they came to the place called the Skull, they crucified him and the criminals there, one on his right, the other on his left. Then Jesus said,

+ "Father, forgive them, they know not what they do."

N They divided his garments by casting lots. The people stood by and watched; the rulers, meanwhile, sneered at him and said,

C "He saved others, let him save himself if he is the chosen one, the Christ of God."

N Even the soldiers jeered at him. As they approached to offer him wine they called out,

C "If you are King of the Jews, save yourself."

N Above him there was an inscription that read, "This is the King of the Jews."

Now one of the criminals hanging there reviled Jesus, saying,

V "Are you not the Christ? Save yourself and us."

N The other, however, rebuking him, said in reply,

V "Have you no fear of God, for you are subject to the same condemnation?

And indeed, we have been condemned justly, for the sentence we received corresponds to our crimes, but this man has done nothing criminal."

N Then he said,

V "Jesus, remember me when you come into your kingdom."

N He replied to him,

+ "Amen, I say to you, today you will be with me in Paradise."

N It was now about noon and darkness came over the whole land until three in the afternoon because of an eclipse of the sun. Then the veil of the temple was torn down the middle. Jesus cried out in a loud voice,

+ "Father, into your hands I commend my spirit";

N and when he had said this he breathed his last.

Here all kneel and pause for a short time.

N The centurion who witnessed what had happened glorified God and said,

V "This man was innocent beyond doubt."

N When all the people who had gathered for this spectacle saw what had happened, they returned home beating their breasts; but all his acquaintances stood at a distance, including the women who had followed him from Galilee and saw these events.]

Now there was a virtuous and righteous man named Joseph who, though he was a member of the council, had not consented to their plan of action. He came from the Jewish town of Arimathea and was awaiting the kingdom of God. He went to Pilate and asked for the body of Jesus. After he had taken the body down, he wrapped it in a linen cloth and laid him in a rock-hewn tomb in which no one had yet been buried. It was the day of preparation, and the sabbath was about to begin. The women who had come from Galilee with him followed behind, and when they had seen the tomb and the way in which his body was laid in it, they returned and prepared spices and perfumed oils. Then they rested on the sabbath according to the commandment.

"The Easter Triduum of the passion and resurrection of Christ is...the culmination of the entire liturgical year. What Sunday is to the week, the solemnity of Easter is to the liturgical year" (General Norms for the Liturgical Year, #18).

Lent ends quietly on Thursday afternoon. The Church enters the Triduum ("three days"). On Thursday night the Church begins a time of prayer and fasting, a time of keeping watch, that lasts into the great Vigil between Saturday and Sunday. The Church emphasizes that the fasting of Good Friday and, if possible, Holy Saturday is integral to the keeping of these days and the preparation for the sacraments of initiation celebrated at the Vigil. On Thursday night and on Friday afternoon or evening the Church gathers to pray and to remember the many facets of the single mystery.

THURSDAY OF THE LORD'S SUPPER: EVENING MASS 1143

On Thursday night Lent has ended and the Church, at this Mass of the Lord's Supper, enters into the Paschal Triduum. From the very first moment the all-embracing experience of these three days is proclaimed: "We should glory in the Cross of our Lord Jesus Christ, in whom is our salvation, life and resurrection, through whom we are saved and delivered." This is the whole of the great Triduum. On Thursday night, the liturgy draws us toward this through Scripture, through the mandatum or washing of feet, which is the direct expression of our service to one another and the world, and through the eucharistic banquet itself.

LITURGY OF THE WORD / ABC

READING I
Exodus 12:1–8, 11–14 / 39

The LORD said to Moses and Aaron in the land of Egypt, "This month shall stand at the head of your calendar; you shall reckon it the first month of the year. Tell the whole community of Israel: On the tenth of this month every one of your families must procure for itself a lamb, one apiece for each household. If a family is too small for a whole lamb, it shall join the nearest household in procuring one and shall share in the lamb in proportion to the number of persons who partake of it. The lamb must be a year-old male and without blemish. You may take it from either the sheep or the goats. You shall keep it until the fourteenth day of this month, and then, with the whole assembly of Israel present, it shall be slaughtered during the evening twilight. They shall take some of its blood and apply it to the two doorposts and the lintel of every house in which they partake of the lamb. That same night they shall eat its roasted flesh with unleavened bread and bitter herbs.

"This is how you are to eat it: with your loins girt, sandals on your feet and your staff in hand, you shall eat like those who are in flight. It is the Passover of the LORD. For on this same night I will go through Egypt, striking down every firstborn of the land, both man and beast, and executing judgment on all the gods of Egypt—I, the LORD! But the blood will mark the houses where you are. Seeing the blood, I will pass over you; thus, when I strike the land of Egypt, no destructive blow will come upon you.

"This day shall be a memorial feast for you, which all your generations shall celebrate with pilgrimage to the LORD, as a perpetual institution."

RESPONSORIAL PSALM   *Psalm 116:12–13, 15 and 16bc, 17–18*

Our bless-ing - cup   is   a com-mun-ion with the Blood   of   Christ.

How can I repay the LORD
    for all his goodness to me?
The cup of salvation I will raise;
    I will call on the name of the LORD. ℟.

How precious in the eyes of the LORD
    is the death of his faithful.
Your servant am I, the son of your

handmaid;
you have loosened my bonds. ℟.

A thanksgiving sacrifice I make;
    I will call on the name of the LORD.
My vows to the LORD I will fulfill
    before all his people. ℟.

READING II   *1 Corinthians 11:23–26*

Brothers and sisters: I received from the Lord what I also handed on to you, that the Lord Jesus, on the night he was handed over, took bread, and, after he had given thanks, broke it and said, "This is my body that is for you. Do this in remembrance of me." In the same way also the cup, after supper, saying, "This cup is the new covenant in my blood. Do this, as often as you drink it, in remembrance of me." For as often as you eat this bread and drink the cup, you proclaim the death of the Lord until he comes.

GOSPEL   *John 13:1–15*

Before the feast of Passover, Jesus knew that his hour had come to pass from this world to the Father. He loved his own in the world and he loved them to the end. The devil had already induced Judas, son of Simon the Iscariot, to hand him over. So, during supper, fully aware that the Father had put everything into his power and that he had come from God and was returning to God, he rose from supper and took off his outer garments. He took a towel and tied it around his waist. Then he poured water into a basin and began to wash the disciples' feet and dry them with the towel around his waist. He came to Simon Peter, who said to him, "Master, are you going to wash my feet?" Jesus answered and said to him, "What I am doing, you do not understand now, but you will understand later." Peter said to him, "You will never wash my feet." Jesus answered him, "Unless I wash you, you will have no inheritance with me." Simon Peter said to him, "Master, then not only my feet, but my hands and head as well." Jesus said to him, "Whoever has bathed has no need except to have his feet washed, for he is clean all over; so you are clean, but not all." For he knew who would betray him; for this reason, he said, "Not all of you are clean."

So when he had washed their feet and put his garments back on and reclined at table again, he said to them, "Do you realize what I have done for you? You call me 'teacher' and 'master,' and rightly so, for indeed I am. If I, therefore, the master and teacher, have washed your feet, you ought to wash one another's feet. I have given you a model to follow, so that as I have done for you, you should also do."

WASHING OF FEET   1144

The homily is followed by the washing of feet, the mandatum (from the Latin word for "command": "A new commandment I give to you..."). This is a simple gesture of humble service: the priest, assisted by other ministers, washes the feet of various members of the assembly. Such a gesture, with the song which accompanies it, speaks directly of the way of life Christians seek. The following or another appropriate hymn or song may be sung.

Man - dá - tum no - vum do vo - bis,

di - cit Dó - mi - nus, di - cit Dó - mi - nus.

Text: *I give you a new commandment*; Taizé Community, 1979
Tune: Jacques Berthier, 1923–1994
© 1979, Les Presses de Taizé, GIA Publications, Inc., agent

The Mass continues with the Prayer of the Faithful.

1145 TRANSFER OF THE MOST BLESSED SACRAMENT

When the communion rite is concluded, the eucharistic bread that remains is solemnly carried from the altar to a specially prepared place of repose. The following hymn accompanies the procession.

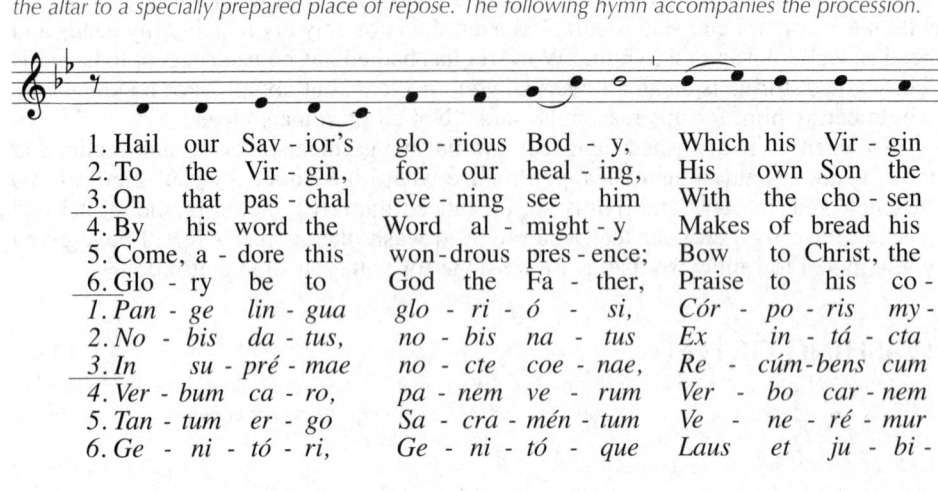

1. Hail our Sav - ior's glo - rious Bod - y, Which his Vir - gin
2. To the Vir - gin, for our heal - ing, His own Son the
3. On that pas - chal eve - ning see him With the cho - sen
4. By his word the Word al - might - y Makes of bread his
5. Come, a - dore this won - drous pres - ence; Bow to Christ, the
6. Glo - ry be to God the Fa - ther, Praise to his co -

1. Pan - ge lin - gua glo - ri - ó - si, Cór - po - ris my -
2. No - bis da - tus, no - bis na - tus Ex in - tá - cta
3. In su - pré - mae no - cte coe - nae, Re - cúm - bens cum
4. Ver - bum ca - ro, pa - nem ve - rum Ver - bo car - nem
5. Tan - tum er - go Sa - cra - mén - tum Ve - ne - ré - mur
6. Ge - ni - tó - ri, Ge - ni - tó - que Laus et ju - bi -

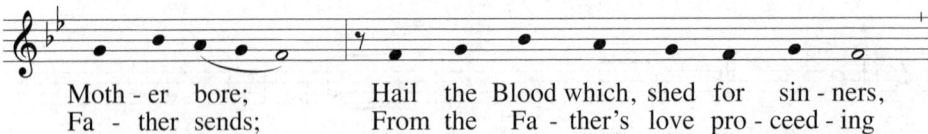

Moth - er bore; Hail the Blood which, shed for sin - ners,
Fa - ther sends; From the Fa - ther's love pro - ceed - ing
twelve re - cline, To the old law still o - be - dient
flesh in - deed; Wine be - comes his ver - y life-blood;
source of grace! Here is kept the an - cient prom - ise
e - qual Son, Ad - o - ra - tion to the Spir - it,

sté - ri - um San - gui - nís - que pre - ti - ó - si,
Vír - gi - ne, Et in mun - do con - ver - sá - tus,
frá - tri - bus, Ob - ser - vá - ta le - ge ple - ne
éf - fi - cit: Fit - que san - guis Chri - sti me - rum,
cér - nu - i: Et an - tí - quum do - cu - mén - tum
lá - ti - o, Sa - lus, ho - nor, vir - tus quo - que

Did a bro - ken world re - store; Hail the sac - ra -
Sow - er, seed and word de - scends; Won - drous life of
In its feast of love di - vine; Love di - vine, the
Faith God's liv - ing Word must heed! Faith a - lone may
Of God's earth - ly dwell - ing place. Sight is blind be -
Bond of love, in God - head one. Blest be God by

Quem in mun - di pré - ti - um Fru - ctus ven - tris
Spar - so ver - bi sé - mi - ne, Su - i mo - ras
Ci - bis in le - gá - li - bus, Ci - bum tur - bae
Et si sen - sus dé - fi - cit, Ad fir - mán - dum
No - vo ce - dat rí - tu - i; Prae - stet fi - des
Sit et be - ne - dí - cti - o: Pro - ce - dén - ti

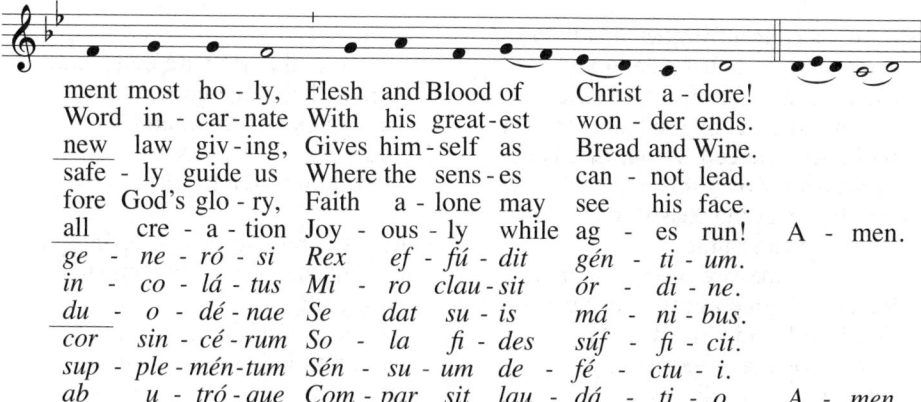

ment most ho - ly,	Flesh	and Blood of	Christ	a - dore!	
Word in - car - nate	With	his great - est	won - der ends.	
new law giv - ing,	Gives	him - self as	Bread and Wine.	
safe - ly guide us	Where	the sens - es	can - not lead.	
fore God's glo - ry,	Faith	a - lone may	see	his face.	
all cre - a - tion	Joy - ous - ly while	ag - es run!	A - men.
ge - ne - ró - si	*Rex*	*ef - fú - dit*	*gén - ti - um.*	
in - co - lá - tus	*Mi - ro clau - sit*	*ór - di - ne.*	
du - o - dé - nae	*Se*	*dat su - is*	*má - ni - bus.*	
cor sin - cé - rum	*So - la fi - des*	*súf - fi - cit.*	
sup - ple - mén - tum	*Sén - su - um de - fé - ctu - i.*	
ab u - tró - que	*Com - par sit lau - dá - ti - o.*	*A - men.*

Text: *Pange lingua*, Thomas Aquinas, 1227–1274; tr. by James Quinn, SJ, 1919–2010, © 1969. James Quinn, SJ. Published by OCP.
Tune: PANGE LINGUA GLORIOSI, 8 7 8 7; Mode III; acc. by Eugene Lapierre, 1899–1970, © 1964, GIA Publications, Inc.

The liturgy has no concluding rite, no dismissal. Rather, the Church continues to watch and pray throughout the Triduum.

GOOD FRIDAY: CELEBRATION OF THE PASSION OF THE LORD 1146

In Good Friday's liturgy of the word and adoration of the cross there is great solemnity as the Church ponders the "mystery of faith": the passion, death and resurrection of our Lord Jesus Christ. Fasting and praying during these days, the catechumens and the baptized assemble on Good Friday in the afternoon or evening for the Passion liturgy, which begins in silence.

LITURGY OF THE WORD / ABC

READING I

Isaiah 52:13—53:12 / 40

See, my servant shall prosper,
    he shall be raised high and greatly
        exalted.
Even as many were amazed at him—
    so marred was his look beyond
        human semblance
    and his appearance beyond that of
        the sons of man—
so shall he startle many nations,
    because of him kings shall stand
        speechless;
for those who have not been told shall
        see,
    those who have not heard shall
        ponder it.

Who would believe what we have heard?

To whom has the arm of the LORD
        been revealed?
He grew up like a sapling before him,
    like a shoot from the parched earth;
there was in him no stately bearing to
        make us look at him,
    nor appearance that would attract us
        to him.
He was spurned and avoided by people,
    a man of suffering, accustomed to
        infirmity,
one of those from whom people hide
        their faces,
    spurned, and we held him in no
        esteem.

Yet it was our infirmities that he bore,
　　our sufferings that he endured,
while we thought of him as stricken,
　　as one smitten by God and afflicted.
But he was pierced for our offenses,
　　crushed for our sins;
upon him was the chastisement that
　　　makes us whole,
　　by his stripes we were healed.
We had all gone astray like sheep,
　　each following his own way;
but the LORD laid upon him
　　the guilt of us all.

Though he was harshly treated, he
　　submitted
　　and opened not his mouth;
like a lamb led to the slaughter
　　or a sheep before the shearers,
　　he was silent and opened not his mouth.
Oppressed and condemned, he was
　　taken away,
　　and who would have thought any
　　　more of his destiny?
When he was cut off from the land of
　　the living,
　　and smitten for the sin of his people,
a grave was assigned him among the

wicked
　　and a burial place with evildoers,
though he had done no wrong
　　nor spoken any falsehood.
But the LORD was pleased
　　to crush him in infirmity.

If he gives his life as an offering for sin,
　　he shall see his descendants in a
　　　long life,
　　and the will of the LORD shall be
　　accomplished through him.

Because of his affliction
　　he shall see the light in fullness of
　　　days;
through his suffering, my servant shall
　　justify many,
　　and their guilt he shall bear.
Therefore I will give him his portion
　　among the great,
　　and he shall divide the spoils with
　　the mighty,
because he surrendered himself to death
　　and was counted among the wicked;
and he shall take away the sins of many,
　　and win pardon for their offenses.

RESPONSORIAL PSALM　　　　　　　　*Psalm 31:2 and 6, 12–13, 15–16, 17 and 25*

Fa - ther, in - to your hands I com-mend my spir-it, my spir-it.

In you, O LORD, I take refuge.
　　Let me never be put to shame.
　　In your justice, set me free.
Into your hands I commend my spirit.
　　You will redeem me, O LORD,
　　　O faithful God. ℟.

Because of all my foes
　　I have become a reproach,
an object of scorn to my neighbors
　　and of fear to my friends.
Those who see me in the street
　　flee from me.
I am forgotten, like someone dead,

and have become like a broken
　　vessel. ℟.

But as for me, I trust in you, O LORD;
　　I say, "You are my God.
My lot is in your hands, deliver me
　　from the hands of my enemies
　　and those who pursue me. ℟.

"Let your face shine on your servant.
　　Save me in your merciful love."
Be strong, let your heart take courage,
　　all who hope in the LORD. ℟.

READING II

Hebrews 4:14–16; 5:7–9

Brothers anvd sisters: Since we have a great high priest who has passed through the heavens, Jesus, the Son of God, let us hold fast to our confession. For we do not have a high priest who is unable to sympathize with our weaknesses, but one who has similarly been tested in every way, yet without sin. So let us confidently approach the throne of grace to receive mercy and to find grace for timely help.

In the days when Christ was in the flesh, he offered prayers and supplications with loud cries and tears to the one who was able to save him from death, and he was heard because of his reverence. Son though he was, he learned obedience from what he suffered; and when he was made perfect, he became the source of eternal salvation for all who obey him.

GOSPEL

John 18:1 – 19:42

The symbols of the following passion narrative represent:
   + *Christ*;   N *narrator*;   V *voice*;   C *crowd*.

N The Passion of our Lord Jesus Christ according to John.

N Jesus went out with his disciples across the Kidron valley to where there was a garden, into which he and his disciples entered. Judas his betrayer also knew the place, because Jesus had often met there with his disciples. So Judas got a band of soldiers and guards from the chief priests and the Pharisees and went there with lanterns, torches, and weapons. Jesus, knowing everything that was going to happen to him, went out and said to them,

+ "Whom are you looking for?"

N They answered him,

C "Jesus the Nazorean."

N He said to them,

+ "I AM."

N Judas his betrayer was also with them. When he said to them, "I AM," they turned away and fell to the ground. So he again asked them,

+ "Whom are you looking for?"

N They said,

C "Jesus the Nazorean."

N Jesus answered,

+ "I told you that I AM. So if you are looking for me, let these men go."

N This was to fulfill what he had said, "I have not lost any of those you gave me." Then Simon Peter, who had a sword, drew it, struck the high priest's slave, and cut off his right ear. The slave's name was Malchus. Jesus said to Peter,

+ "Put your sword into its scabbard. Shall I not drink the cup that the Father gave me?"

N So the band of soldiers, the tribune, and the Jewish guards seized Jesus, bound him, and brought him to Annas first. He was the father-in-law of Caiaphas, who was high priest that year. It was Caiaphas who had counseled the Jews that it was better that one man should die rather than the people.

Simon Peter and another disciple followed Jesus. Now the other disciple was known to the high priest, and he entered the courtyard of the high priest with Jesus. But Peter stood at the gate outside. So the other disciple, the acquaintance of the high priest, went out and spoke to the gatekeeper and brought Peter in. Then the maid who was the gatekeeper said to Peter,

C "You are not one of this man's disciples, are you?"

N He said,

V "I am not."

N Now the slaves and the guards were

standing around a charcoal fire that they had made, because it was cold, and were warming themselves. Peter was also standing there keeping warm.

The high priest questioned Jesus about his disciples and about his doctrine. Jesus answered him,

+ "I have spoken publicly to the world. I have always taught in a synagogue or in the temple area where all the Jews gather, and in secret I have said nothing. Why ask me? Ask those who heard me what I said to them. They know what I said."

N When he had said this, one of the temple guards standing there struck Jesus and said,

V "Is this the way you answer the high priest?"

N Jesus answered him,

+ "If I have spoken wrongly, testify to the wrong; but if I have spoken rightly, why do you strike me?"

N Then Annas sent him bound to Caiaphas the high priest.

Now Simon Peter was standing there keeping warm. And they said to him,

C "You are not one of his disciples, are you?"

N He denied it and said,

V "I am not."

N One of the slaves of the high priest, a relative of the one whose ear Peter had cut off, said,

C "Didn't I see you in the garden with him?"

N Again Peter denied it. And immediately the cock crowed.

Then they brought Jesus from Caiaphas to the praetorium. It was morning. And they themselves did not enter the praetorium, in order not to be defiled so that they could eat the Passover. So Pilate came out to them and said,

V "What charge do you bring against this man?"

N They answered and said to him,

C "If he were not a criminal, we would not have handed him over to you."

N At this, Pilate said to them,

V "Take him yourselves, and judge him according to your law."

N The Jews answered him,

C "We do not have the right to execute anyone,"

N in order that the word of Jesus might be fulfilled that he said indicating the kind of death he would die. So Pilate went back into the praetorium and summoned Jesus and said to him,

V "Are you the King of the Jews?"

N Jesus answered,

+ "Do you say this on your own or have others told you about me?"

N Pilate answered,

V "I am not a Jew, am I? Your own nation and the chief priests handed you over to me. What have you done?"

N Jesus answered,

+ "My kingdom does not belong to this world. If my kingdom did belong to this world, my attendants would be fighting to keep me from being handed over to the Jews. But as it is, my kingdom is not here."

N So Pilate said to him,

V "Then you are a king?"

N Jesus answered,

+ "You say I am a king. For this I was born and for this I came into the world, to testify to the truth. Everyone who belongs to the truth listens to my voice."

N Pilate said to him,

V "What is truth?"

N When he had said this, he again went out to the Jews and said to them,

V "I find no guilt in him. But you have a custom that I release one prisoner to you at Passover. Do you want me to release to you the King of the Jews?"

N They cried out again,

C "Not this one but Barabbas!"

N Now Barabbas was a revolutionary.

Then Pilate took Jesus and had him scourged. And the soldiers wove a crown out of thorns and placed it on his head, and clothed him in a purple cloak, and they came to him and said,

C "Hail, King of the Jews!"

N And they struck him repeatedly. Once more Pilate went out and said to them,

V "Look, I am bringing him out to you, so that you may know that I find no guilt in him."

N So Jesus came out, wearing the crown of thorns and the purple cloak. And Pilate said to them,

V "Behold, the man!"

N When the chief priests and the guards saw him they cried out,

C "Crucify him, crucify him!"

N Pilate said to them,

V "Take him yourselves and crucify him. I find no guilt in him."

N The Jews answered,

C "We have a law, and according to that law he ought to die, because he made himself the Son of God."

N Now when Pilate heard this statement, he became even more afraid, and went back into the praetorium and said to Jesus,

V "Where are you from?"

N Jesus did not answer him. So Pilate said to him,

V "Do you not speak to me? Do you not know that I have power to release you and I have power to crucify you?"

N Jesus answered him,

+ "You would have no power over me if it had not been given to you from above. For this reason the one who handed me over to you has the greater sin."

N Consequently, Pilate tried to release him; but the Jews cried out,

C "If you release him, you are not a Friend of Caesar. Everyone who makes himself a king opposes Caesar."

N When Pilate heard these words he brought Jesus out and seated him on the judge's bench in the place called Stone Pavement, in Hebrew, Gabbatha. It was preparation day for Passover, and it was about noon. And he said to the Jews,

V "Behold, your king!"

N They cried out,

C "Take him away, take him away! Crucify him!"

N Pilate said to them,

V "Shall I crucify your king?"

N The chief priests answered,

C "We have no king but Caesar."

N Then he handed him over to them to be crucified.

So they took Jesus, and, carrying the cross himself, he went out to what is called the Place of the Skull, in Hebrew, Golgotha. There they crucified him, and with him two others, one on either side, with Jesus in the middle. Pilate also had an inscription written and put on the cross. It read, "Jesus the Nazorean, the King of the Jews." Now many of the Jews read this inscription, because the place where Jesus was crucified was near the city; and it was written in Hebrew, Latin, and Greek. So the chief priests of the Jews said to Pilate,

C "Do not write 'The King of the Jews,' but that he said, 'I am the King of the Jews'."

N Pilate answered,

V "What I have written, I have written."

N When the soldiers had crucified Jesus, they took his clothes and divided them into four shares, a share for each soldier. They also took his tunic, but the tunic was seamless, woven in one piece from the top down. So they said to one another,

C "Let's not tear it, but cast lots for it to see whose it will be,"

N in order that the passage of Scripture might be fulfilled that says:

They divided my garments among them,
   and for my vesture they cast lots.
This is what the soldiers did. Standing by the cross of Jesus were his mother and his mother's sister, Mary the wife of Clopas, and Mary of Magdala. When Jesus saw his mother and the disciple there whom he loved he said to his mother,

+ "Woman, behold, your son."

N Then he said to the disciple,

+ "Behold, your mother."

N And from that hour the disciple took her into his home.

After this, aware that everything was now finished, in order that the Scripture might be fulfilled, Jesus said,

+ "I thirst."

N There was a vessel filled with common wine. So they put a sponge soaked in wine on a sprig of hyssop and put it up to his mouth. When Jesus had taken the wine, he said,

+ "It is finished."

N And bowing his head, he handed over the spirit.

Here all kneel and pause for a short time.

N Now since it was preparation day, in order that the bodies might not remain on the cross on the sabbath, for the sabbath day of that week was a solemn one, the Jews asked Pilate that their legs be broken and that they be taken down. So the soldiers came and broke the legs of the first and then of the other one who was crucified with Jesus. But when they came to Jesus and saw that he was already dead, they did not break his legs, but one soldier thrust his lance into his side, and immediately blood and water flowed out. An eyewitness has testified, and his testimony is true; he knows that he is speaking the truth, so that you also may come to believe. For this happened so that the Scripture passage might be fulfilled:

Not a bone of it will be broken.
And again another passage says:
They will look upon him whom they have pierced.

After this, Joseph of Arimathea, secretly a disciple of Jesus for fear of the Jews, asked Pilate if he could remove the body of Jesus. And Pilate permitted it. So he came and took his body. Nicodemus, the one who had first come to him at night, also came bringing a mixture of myrrh and aloes weighing about one hundred pounds. They took the body of Jesus and bound it with burial cloths along with the spices, according to the Jewish burial custom. Now in the place where he had been crucified there was a garden, and in the garden a new tomb, in which no one had yet been buried. So they laid Jesus there because of the Jewish preparation day; for the tomb was close by.

SOLEMN INTERCESSIONS

As at Sunday liturgy, the word service concludes with prayers of intercession. Today these prayers take a more solemn form as the Church lifts up to God its own needs and those of the world.

ADORATION OF THE HOLY CROSS

An ancient liturgical text reads: "See here the true and most revered Tree. Hasten to kiss it and to cry out with faith: You are our help, most revered Cross." For many centuries the Church has solemnly venerated the relic or image of the cross on Good Friday. It is not present as a picture of suffering only but as a symbol of Christ's passover, where "dying he destroyed our death and rising restored our life." It is the glorious, the life-giving cross that the faithful venerate with song, prayer, kneeling and a kiss.

As the cross is shown to the assembly, one of the following is sung.

1147

Music: Howard Hughes, SM, © 1979, 1985, GIA Publications, Inc.

Or:

1148

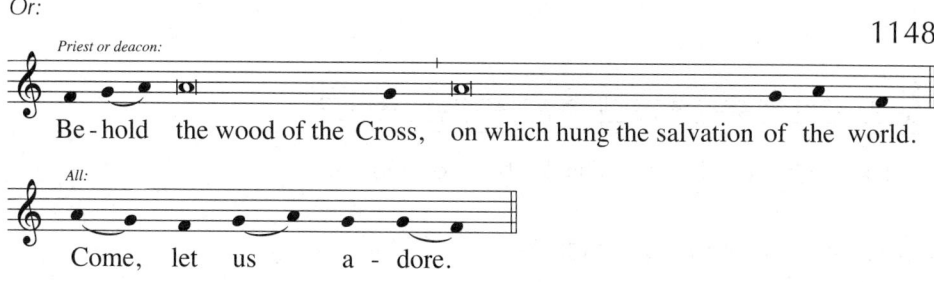

As the assembly comes forward to venerate the cross, the following or other hymns and songs may be sung.

1149

Text: *We adore you, Lord*; Taizé Community, 1979
Tune: Jacques Berthier, 1923–1994
© 1979, Les Presses de Taizé, GIA Publications, Inc., agent

1150 HOLY COMMUNION

This liturgy concludes with a simple communion rite. All recite the Lord's Prayer and receive Holy Communion. There is no concluding rite or dismissal for the Church continues to be at prayer throughout the Triduum.

1151 HOLY SATURDAY

The Church continues to fast and pray and to make ready for this night's great Vigil. Saturday is a day of great quiet and reflection. Catechumens, sponsors and some of the faithful may assemble during the day for prayer, the recitation of the Creed, and for the rite of Ephphetha (opening of ears and mouth).

1152 EASTER VIGIL IN THE HOLY NIGHT

The long preparation of the catechumens, the lenten disciplines and fast of the faithful, the vigiling and fasting and prayer that have gone on since Thursday night—all culminate in the great liturgy of this night. On this night the Church assembles to spend much time listening to Scripture, praying psalms, acclaiming the death and resurrection of the Lord. Only then are the catechumens called forward and prayed over, challenged to renounce evil and affirm their faith in God, led to the font and baptized in the blessed water. The newly baptized are then anointed with chrism and the entire assembly joins in intercession and finally in the Eucharist.

LUCERNARIUM

BLESSING OF THE FIRE AND PREPARATION OF THE PASCHAL CANDLE
The night vigil begins with the kindling of new fire and the lighting of the paschal candle.

PROCESSION
The ministers and assembly go in procession to the place where Scripture will be read. The following is sung during the procession.

The Light of Christ. Thanks be to God.

EASTER PROCLAMATION: THE EXSULTET
In this ancient text the Church gives thanks and praise to God for all that is recalled this night: Adam's fall, the deliverance from Egypt, the passover of Christ, the wedding of earth and heaven, our reconciliation.

LITURGY OF THE WORD / ABC

At the Vigil, the liturgy of the word is an extended time of readings, silence and the singing of psalms. On this night when the faithful know the death and resurrection of the Lord in baptism and eucharist, the Church needs first to hear these scripture readings, which are the foundation of our life together: the creation story, Abraham and Isaac, the dividing of the sea, the poetry of Isaiah and Baruch and Ezekiel, the proclamation of Paul to the Romans and the gospel account of Jesus' resurrection.

READING I

For short form read only the parts in brackets.

[In the beginning, when God created the heavens and the earth,] the earth was a formless wasteland, and darkness covered the abyss, while a mighty wind swept over the waters.

Then God said, "Let there be light," and there was light. God saw how good the light was. God then separated the light from the darkness. God called the light "day," and the darkness he called "night." Thus evening came, and morning followed — the first day.

Then God said, "Let there be a dome in the middle of the waters, to separate one body of water from the other." And so it happened: God made the dome, and it separated the water above the dome from the water below it. God called the dome "the sky." Evening came, and morning followed — the second day.

Then God said, "Let the water under the sky be gathered into a single basin, so that the dry land may appear." And so it happened: the water under the sky was gathered into its basin, and the dry land appeared. God called the dry land "the earth," and the basin of the water he called "the sea." God saw how good it was. Then God said, "Let the earth bring forth vegetation: every kind of plant that bears seed and every kind of fruit tree on earth that bears fruit with its seed in it." And so it happened: the earth brought forth every kind of plant that bears seed and every kind of fruit tree on earth that bears fruit with its seed in it. God saw how good it was. Evening came, and morning followed — the third day.

Then God said: "Let there be lights in the dome of the sky, to separate day from night. Let them mark the fixed times, the days and the years, and serve as luminaries in the dome of the sky, to shed light upon the earth." And so it happened: God made the two great lights, the greater one to govern the day, and the lesser one to govern the night; and he made the stars. God set them in the dome of the sky, to shed light upon the earth, to govern the day and the night, and to separate the light from the darkness. God saw how good it was. Evening came, and morning followed — the fourth day.

Then God said, "Let the water teem with an abundance of living creatures, and on the earth let birds fly beneath the dome of the sky." And so it happened: God created the great sea monsters and all kinds of swimming creatures with which the water teems, and all kinds of winged birds. God saw how good it was, and God blessed them, saying, "Be fertile, multiply, and fill the water of the seas; and let the birds multiply on the earth." Evening came, and morning followed — the fifth day.

Then God said, "Let the earth bring forth all kinds of living creatures: cattle, creeping things, and wild animals of all kinds." And so it happened: God made all kinds of wild animals, all kinds of cattle, and all kinds of creeping things of the earth. God saw how good it was. Then [God said: "Let us make man in our image, after our likeness. Let them have dominion over the fish of the sea, the birds of the air, and the cattle, and over all the wild animals and all the creatures that crawl on the ground."

God created man in his image;
in the image of God he created him;
male and female he created them.

God blessed them, saying: "Be fertile and multiply; fill the earth and subdue it. Have dominion over the fish of the sea, the birds of the air, and all the living things that move on the earth." God also said: "See, I give you every seed-bearing plant all over the earth and every tree that has seed-bearing fruit on it to be your food; and to all the animals of the land, all the birds of the air, and all the living creatures that crawl on the ground, I give all the green plants for food." And so it happened. God looked at everything he had made, and he found it very good.] Evening came, and morning followed—the sixth day.

Thus the heavens and the earth and all their array were completed. Since on the seventh day God was finished with the work he had been doing, he rested on the seventh day from all the work he had undertaken.

RESPONSORIAL PSALM   *1. Psalm 104:1–2a, 5–6, 10 and 12, 13–14, 24 and 35c*

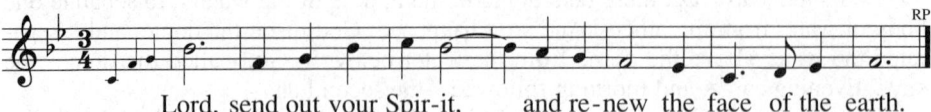

Lord, send out your Spir-it, and re-new the face of the earth.

Bless the LORD, O my soul!
   O LORD my God, how great you are,
clothed in majesty and honor,
   wrapped in light as with a robe! ℟.

You set the earth on its foundation,
   immovable from age to age.
You wrapped it with the depths like a
   cloak;
   the waters stood higher than the
   mountains. ℟.

You make springs gush forth in the
   valleys;
   they flow in between the hills.

There the birds of heaven build their
   nests;
   from the branches they sing their
   song. ℟.

From your dwelling you water the hills;
   by your works the earth has its fill.
You make the grass grow for the cattle
   and plants to serve mankind's need,
   that he may bring forth bread from
   the earth. ℟.

How many are your works, O LORD!
   In wisdom you have made them all.
The earth is full of your creatures.
   Bless the LORD, O my soul. ℟.

Or:

RESPONSORIAL PSALM   *2. Psalm 33:4–5, 6–7, 12–13, 20 and 22*

The earth is full of the good-ness, the good-ness of the Lord.

The word of the LORD is faithful,
   and all his works to be trusted.
The LORD loves justice and right,
   and his merciful love fills the earth. ℟.

By the word of the LORD the heavens
   were made,
   by the breath of his mouth all their
   host.
As in a flask, he collects the waves of
   the ocean;
   he stores up the depths of the sea. ℟.

Blessed the nation whose God is the
   LORD,
   the people he has chosen as his
   heritage.
From the heavens the Lord looks forth;
   he sees all the children of men. ℟.

Our soul is waiting for the LORD.
   He is our help and our shield.
May your merciful love be upon us,
   as we hope in you, O LORD. ℟.

READING II

Genesis 22:1–18 or 22:1–2, 9a, 10–13, 15–18 1154

For short form read only the parts in brackets.

[God put Abraham to the test. He called to him, "Abraham!" "Here I am," he replied. Then God said: "Take your son Isaac, your only one, whom you love, and go to the land of Moriah. There you shall offer him up as a holocaust on a height that I will point out to you."] Early the next morning Abraham saddled his donkey, took with him his son Isaac and two of his servants as well, and with the wood that he had cut for the holocaust, set out for the place of which God had told him.

On the third day Abraham got sight of the place from afar. Then he said to his servants: "Both of you stay here with the donkey, while the boy and I go on over yonder. We will worship and then come back to you." Thereupon Abraham took the wood for the holocaust and laid it on his son Isaac's shoulders, while he himself carried the fire and the knife. As the two walked on together, Isaac spoke to his father Abraham: "Father!" Isaac said. "Yes, son," he replied. Isaac continued, "Here are the fire and the wood, but where is the sheep for the holocaust?" "Son," Abraham answered, "God himself will provide the sheep for the holocaust." Then the two continued going forward.

[When they came to the place of which God had told him, Abraham built an altar there and arranged the wood on it.] Next he tied up his son Isaac, and put him on top of the wood on the altar. [Then he reached out and took the knife to slaughter his son. But the LORD's messenger called to him from heaven, "Abraham, Abraham!" "Here I am," he answered. "Do not lay your hand on the boy," said the messenger. "Do not do the least thing to him. I know now how devoted you are to God, since you did not withhold from me your own beloved son." As Abraham looked about, he spied a ram caught by its horns in the thicket. So he went and took the ram and offered it up as a holocaust in place of his son.] Abraham named the site Yahweh-yireh; hence people now say, "On the mountain the LORD will see."

[Again the LORD's messenger called to Abraham from heaven and said: "I swear by myself, declares the LORD, that because you acted as you did in not withholding from me your beloved son, I will bless you abundantly and make your descendants as countless as the stars of the sky and the sands of the seashore; your descendants shall take possession of the gates of their enemies, and in your descendants all the nations of the earth shall find blessing—all this because you obeyed my command."]

RESPONSORIAL PSALM

Psalm 16:5 and 8, 9–10, 11

You are my in-her-i-tance, O Lord, O Lord.

O LORD, it is you who are my portion
    and cup;
  you yourself who secure my lot.
I keep the LORD before me always;
    with him at my right hand, I shall
      not be moved. ℟.

And so, my heart rejoices, my soul is
    glad;
  even my flesh shall rest in hope.

For you will not abandon my soul to
    hell,
  nor let your holy one see
    corruption. ℟.

You will show me the path of life,
    the fullness of joy in your presence,
  at your right hand, bliss forever. ℟.

1155 READING III
Exodus 14:15—15:1

The LORD said to Moses, "Why are you crying out to me? Tell the Israelites to go forward. And you, lift up your staff and, with hand outstretched over the sea, split the sea in two, that the Israelites may pass through it on dry land. But I will make the Egyptians so obstinate that they will go in after them. Then I will receive glory through Pharaoh and all his army, his chariots and charioteers. The Egyptians shall know that I am the LORD, when I receive glory through Pharaoh and his chariots and charioteers."

The angel of God, who had been leading Israel's camp, now moved and went around behind them. The column of cloud also, leaving the front, took up its place behind them, so that it came between the camp of the Egyptians and that of Israel. But the cloud now became dark, and thus the night passed without the rival camps coming any closer together all night long. Then Moses stretched out his hand over the sea, and the LORD swept the sea with a strong east wind throughout the night and so turned it into dry land. When the water was thus divided, the Israelites marched into the midst of the sea on dry land, with the water like a wall to their right and to their left.

The Egyptians followed in pursuit; all Pharaoh's horses and chariots and charioteers went after them right into the midst of the sea. In the night watch just before dawn the LORD cast through the column of the fiery cloud upon the Egyptian force a glance that threw it into a panic; and he so clogged their chariot wheels that they could hardly drive. With that the Egyptians sounded the retreat before Israel, because the LORD was fighting for them against the Egyptians.

Then the LORD told Moses, "Stretch out your hand over the sea, that the water may flow back upon the Egyptians, upon their chariots and their charioteers." So Moses stretched out his hand over the sea, and at dawn the sea flowed back to its normal depth. The Egyptians were fleeing head on toward the sea, when the LORD hurled them into its midst. As the water flowed back, it covered the chariots and the charioteers of Pharaoh's whole army which had followed the Israelites into the sea. Not a single one of them escaped. But the Israelites had marched on dry land through the midst of the sea, with the water like a wall to their right and to their left. Thus the LORD saved Israel on that day from the power of the Egyptians. When Israel saw the Egyptians lying dead on the seashore and beheld the great power that the LORD had shown against the Egyptians, they feared the LORD and believed in him and in his servant Moses.

Then Moses and the Israelites sang this song to the LORD:

I will sing to the LORD, for he is gloriously triumphant;
horse and chariot he has cast into the sea.

RESPONSORIAL PSALM
Exodus 15:1–2, 3–4, 5–6, 17–18

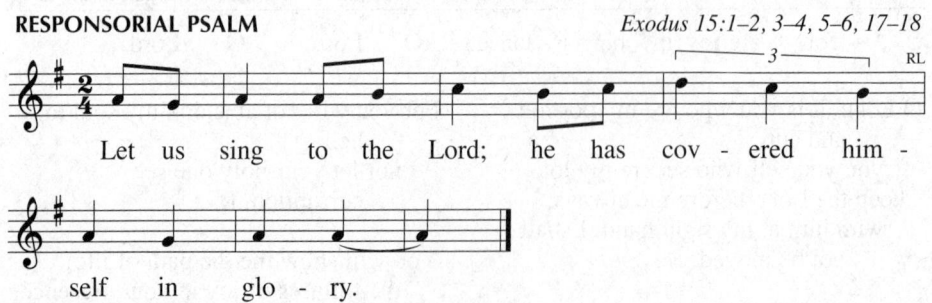

Let us sing to the Lord; he has cov - ered him - self in glo - ry.

I will sing to the Lord; glorious his
triumph!
Horse and rider he has thrown into
the sea!
The Lord is my strength, my song,
my salvation.
This is my God and I extol him,
my father's God and I give him
praise. ℟.

The LORD is a warrior! The LORD is his
name.
The chariots of Pharaoh he hurled into
the sea,
the flower of his army is drowned
in the sea. ℟.

The deeps hide them; they sank like a
stone.
Your right hand, Lord, glorious in its
power,
your right hand, Lord, has
shattered the enemy. ℟.

The people you have redeemed pass by.
You will lead them and plant them on
your mountain,
the place, O LORD, where you have
made your home,
the sanctuary, LORD, which your
hands have made.
The Lord will reign for ever and
ever! ℟.

READING IV

Isaiah 54:5–14 1156

The One who has become your
husband is your Maker;
his name is the LORD of hosts;
your redeemer is the Holy One of Israel,
called God of all the earth.
The LORD calls you back,
like a wife forsaken and grieved
in spirit,
a wife married in youth and then
cast off,
says your God.
For a brief moment I abandoned you,
but with great tenderness I will
take you back.
In an outburst of wrath, for a moment
I hid my face from you;
but with enduring love I take pity on you,
says the LORD, your redeemer.
This is for me like the days of Noah,
when I swore that the waters of Noah
should never again deluge the earth;
so I have sworn not to be angry with you,

or to rebuke you.
Though the mountains leave their place
and the hills be shaken,
my love shall never leave you
nor my covenant of peace be shaken,
says the LORD, who has mercy on
you.
O afflicted one, storm-battered and
unconsoled,
I lay your pavements in carnelians,
and your foundations in sapphires;
I will make your battlements of rubies,
your gates of carbuncles,
and all your walls of precious stones.
All your children shall be taught by the
LORD,
and great shall be the peace of your
children.
In justice shall you be established,
far from the fear of oppression,
where destruction cannot come near
you.

RESPONSORIAL PSALM

Psalm 30:2 and 4, 5–6, 11 and 12a and 13b

JRC

I will praise you, Lord, for you have res - cued me.

I will extol you, LORD, for you have
raised me up,
and have not let my enemies rejoice
over me.

O LORD, you have lifted up my soul
from the grave,
restored me to life from those who
sink into the pit. ℟.

Sing psalms to the LORD, you faithful
 ones;
  give thanks to his holy name.
His anger lasts a moment; his favor
  all through life.
  At night come tears, but dawn
  brings joy. ℟.

Hear, O LORD, and have mercy on me;
  be my helper, O LORD.
You have changed my mourning into
  dancing.
  O LORD my God, I will thank you
  forever. ℟.

1157 READING V

Isaiah 55:1–11

Thus says the LORD:
All you who are thirsty,
 come to the water!
You who have no money,
 come, receive grain and eat;
come, without paying and without
 cost,
 drink wine and milk!
Why spend your money for what is
 not bread,
 your wages for what fails to
 satisfy?
Heed me, and you shall eat well,
 you shall delight in rich fare.
Come to me heedfully,
 listen, that you may have life.
I will renew with you the everlasting
 covenant,
 the benefits assured to David.
As I made him a witness to the peoples,
 a leader and commander of nations,
so shall you summon a nation you
 knew not,
 and nations that knew you not
 shall run to you,
because of the LORD, your God,
 the Holy One of Israel, who has
 glorified you.

Seek the LORD while he may be found,

call him while he is near.
Let the scoundrel forsake his way,
 and the wicked man his thoughts;
let him turn to the LORD for mercy;
 to our God, who is generous in
 forgiving.
For my thoughts are not your thoughts,
 nor are your ways my ways, says the
 LORD.
As high as the heavens are above the
 earth,
 so high are my ways above your
 ways
 and my thoughts above your
 thoughts.

For just as from the heavens
 the rain and snow come down
and do not return there
 till they have watered the earth,
 making it fertile and fruitful,
giving seed to the one who sows
 and bread to the one who eats,
so shall my word be
 that goes forth from my mouth;
my word shall not return to me void,
 but shall do my will,
 achieving the end for which I sent it.

RESPONSORIAL PSALM

Isaiah 12:2–3, 4bcd, 5–6

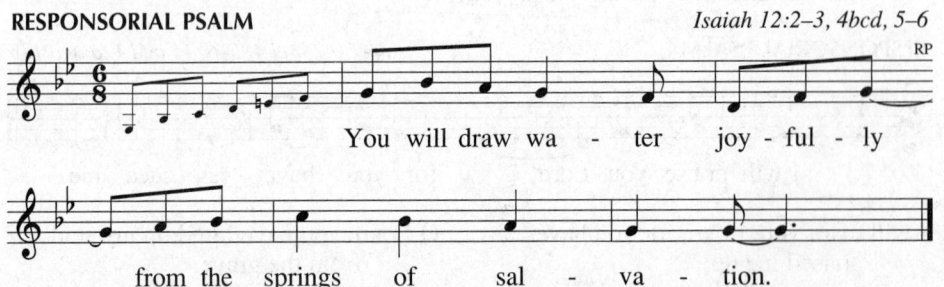

You will draw water joy-ful-ly
from the springs of sal-va-tion.

Truly, God is my salvation,
  I trust, I shall not fear.
For the Lord is my strength, my song,
  he became my savior.
With joy you will draw water
  from the wells of salvation. ℟.

Give thanks to the Lord,
  give praise to his name!
Make his mighty deeds

known to the peoples!
Declare the greatness of his name.
  Sing a psalm to the Lord! ℟.

For he has done glorious deeds,
  make them known to all the earth!
People of Zion,
  sing and shout for joy,
for great in your midst
  is the Holy One of Israel. ℟.

READING VI

Baruch 3:9–15, 32—4:4 1158

Hear, O Israel, the commandments of
  life:
  listen, and know prudence!
How is it, Israel,
  that you are in the land of your foes,
  grown old in a foreign land,
defiled with the dead,
  accounted with those destined for
  the netherworld?
You have forsaken the fountain of
  wisdom!
  Had you walked in the way of God,
  you would have dwelt in enduring
  peace.
Learn where prudence is,
  where strength, where understanding;
that you may know also
  where are length of days, and life,
  where light of the eyes, and peace.
Who has found the place of wisdom,
  who has entered into her treasuries?

The One who knows all things knows
  her;
  he has probed her by his knowledge—
the One who established the earth for
  all time,
  and filled it with four-footed beasts;

he who dismisses the light, and it
  departs,
  calls it, and it obeys him trembling;
before whom the stars at their posts
  shine and rejoice;
when he calls them, they answer, "Here
  we are!"
  shining with joy for their Maker.
Such is our God;
  no other is to be compared to him:
he has traced out the whole way of
  understanding,
  and has given her to Jacob, his
  servant,
  to Israel, his beloved son.

Since then she has appeared on earth,
  and moved among people.
She is the book of the precepts of God,
  the law that endures forever;
all who cling to her will live,
  but those will die who forsake her.
Turn, O Jacob, and receive her:
  walk by her light toward splendor.
Give not your glory to another,
  your privileges to an alien race.
Blessed are we, O Israel;
  for what pleases God is known to us!

RESPONSORIAL PSALM

Psalm 19:8, 9, 10, 11

RP

Lord, you have the words of ev-er-last - ing life.

The law of the LORD is perfect;
  it revives the soul.
The decrees of the LORD are steadfast;
  they give wisdom to the simple. ℟.

The precepts of the LORD are right;
  they gladden the heart.
The command of the LORD is clear;
  it gives light to the eyes. ℟.

The fear of the LORD is pure,
  abiding forever.
The judgments of the LORD are true;
  they are, all of them, just. ℟.

They are more to be desired than gold,
  than quantities of gold.
And sweeter are they than honey,
  than honey flowing from the comb. ℟.

1159 READING VII

Ezekiel 36:16–17a, 18–28

The word of the LORD came to me, saying: Son of man, when the house of Israel lived in their land, they defiled it by their conduct and deeds. Therefore I poured out my fury upon them because of the blood that they poured out on the ground, and because they defiled it with idols. I scattered them among the nations, dispersing them over foreign lands; according to their conduct and deeds I judged them. But when they came among the nations wherever they came, they served to profane my holy name, because it was said of them: "These are the people of the LORD, yet they had to leave their land." So I have relented because of my holy name which the house of Israel profaned among the nations where they came. Therefore say to the house of Israel: Thus says the Lord GOD: Not for your sakes do I act, house of Israel, but for the sake of my holy name, which you profaned among the nations to which you came. I will prove the holiness of my great name, profaned among the nations, in whose midst you have profaned it. Thus the nations shall know that I am the LORD, says the Lord GOD, when in their sight I prove my holiness through you. For I will take you away from among the nations, gather you from all the foreign lands, and bring you back to your own land. I will sprinkle clean water upon you to cleanse you from all your impurities, and from all your idols I will cleanse you. I will give you a new heart and place a new spirit within you, taking from your bodies your stony hearts and giving you natural hearts. I will put my spirit within you and make you live by my statutes, careful to observe my decrees. You shall live in the land I gave your fathers; you shall be my people, and I will be your God.

RESPONSORIAL PSALM

Psalm 42:3, 5bcd; 43:3, 4

When baptism is celebrated:

Like a deer that longs for run - ning
streams, my soul longs for you, my God.

My soul is thirsting for God,
  the living God;
when can I enter and appear
  before the face of God? ℟.

For I would go to the place
  of your wondrous tent,
  all the way to the house of God,
amid cries of gladness and thanksgiving,
  the throng keeping joyful festival. ℟.

O send forth your light and your truth;
  they will guide me on.
They will bring me to your holy
  mountain,
  to the place where you dwell. ℟.

And I will come to the altar of God,
  to God, my joy and gladness.
To you will I give thanks on the harp,
  O God, my God. ℟.

When baptism is not celebrated: Isaiah 12:2–3, 4bcd, 5–6

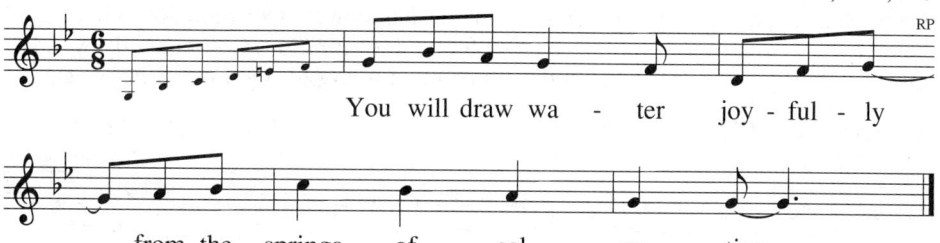

You will draw wa - ter joy - ful - ly

from the springs of sal - va - tion.

Truly, God is my salvation,
  I trust, I shall not fear.
For the Lord is my strength, my song,
  he became my savior.
With joy you will draw water
  from the wells of salvation. ℟.

Give thanks to the Lord,
  give praise to his name!
Make his mighty deeds

known to the peoples!
Declare the greatness of his name.
  Sing a psalm to the Lord! ℟.

For he has done glorious deeds,
  make them known to all the earth!
People of Zion,
  sing and shout for joy,
for great in your midst
  is the Holy One of Israel. ℟.

Or: Psalm 51:12–13, 14–15, 18–19

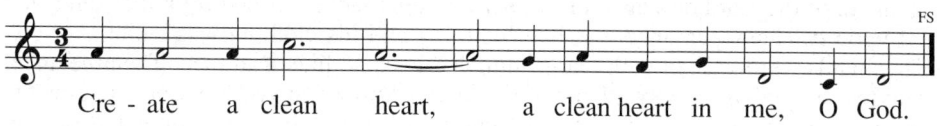

Cre - ate a clean heart, a clean heart in me, O God.

Create a pure heart for me, O God;
  renew a steadfast spirit within me.
Do not cast me away from your
    presence;
  take not your holy spirit from me. ℟.

Restore in me the joy of your salvation;
  sustain in me a willing spirit.
I will teach transgressors your ways,

that sinners may return to you. ℟.

For in sacrifice you take no delight;
  burnt offering from me would not
    please you.
My sacrifice to God, a broken spirit:
  a broken and humbled heart,
  O God, you will not spurn. ℟.

GLORIA

PRAYER

EPISTLE *Romans 6:3–11* 1160

Brothers and sisters: Are you unaware that we who were baptized into Christ Jesus were baptized into his death? We were indeed buried with him through baptism into death, so that, just as Christ was raised from the dead by the glory of the Father, we too might live in newness of life.

For if we have grown into union with him through a death like his, we shall also be united with him in the resurrection. We know that our old self was crucified with him, so that our sinful body might be done away with, that we might no longer be in slavery to sin. For a dead person has been absolved from sin. If, then, we have died with Christ, we believe that we shall also live with him. We know that Christ, raised from the dead, dies no more; death no longer has power over him. As to his death, he died to sin once and for all; as to his life, he lives for God. Consequently, you too must think of yourselves as being dead to sin and living for God in Christ Jesus.

RESPONSORIAL PSALM   *Psalm 118:1–2, 16–17, 22–23*

Chant Mode VIII

Al - le - lu - ia.

Give praise to the LORD, for he is good;
   his mercy endures forever.
Let the house of Israel say,
   "His mercy endures forever." ℟.

"The LORD's right hand has done mighty
     deeds;
   his right hand is exalted."

I shall not die, I shall live
   and recount the deeds of the
     LORD. ℟.

The stone that the builders rejected
   has become the cornerstone.
By the LORD has this been done,
   a marvel in our eyes. ℟.

GOSPEL / A   *Matthew 28:1–10*
After the sabbath, as the first day of the week was dawning, Mary Magdalene and the other Mary came to see the tomb. And behold, there was a great earthquake; for an angel of the Lord descended from heaven, approached, rolled back the stone, and sat upon it. His appearance was like lightning and his clothing was white as snow. The guards were shaken with fear of him and became like dead men. Then the angel said to the women in reply, "Do not be afraid! I know that you are seeking Jesus the crucified. He is not here, for he has been raised just as he said. Come and see the place where he lay. Then go quickly and tell his disciples, 'He has been raised from the dead, and he is going before you to Galilee; there you will see him.' Behold, I have told you." Then they went away quickly from the tomb, fearful yet overjoyed, and ran to announce this to his disciples. And behold, Jesus met them on their way and greeted them. They approached, embraced his feet, and did him homage. Then Jesus said to them, "Do not be afraid. Go tell my brothers to go to Galilee, and there they will see me."

GOSPEL / B   *Mark 16:1–7*
When the sabbath was over, Mary Magdalene, Mary, the mother of James, and Salome bought spices so that they might go and anoint him. Very early when the sun had risen, on the first day of the week, they came to the tomb. They were saying to one another, "Who will roll back the stone for us from the entrance to the tomb?" When they looked up, they saw that the stone had been rolled back; it was very large. On entering the tomb they saw a young man sitting on the right side, clothed in a white robe, and they were utterly amazed. He said to them, "Do not be amazed! You seek Jesus of Nazareth, the crucified. He has been raised; he is not here. Behold the place where they laid him. But go and tell his disciples and Peter, 'He is going before you to Galilee; there you will see him, as he told you.'"

GOSPEL / C   *Luke 24:1–12*
At daybreak on the first day of the week the women who had come from Galilee with Jesus took the spices they had prepared and went to the tomb. They found the

stone rolled away from the tomb; but when they entered, they did not find the body of the Lord Jesus. While they were puzzling over this, behold, two men in dazzling garments appeared to them. They were terrified and bowed their faces to the ground. They said to them, "Why do you seek the living one among the dead? He is not here, but he has been raised. Remember what he said to you while he was still in Galilee, that the Son of Man must be handed over to sinners and be crucified, and rise on the third day." And they remembered his words. Then they returned from the tomb and announced all these things to the eleven and to all the others. The women were Mary Magdalene, Joanna, and Mary the mother of James; the others who accompanied them also told this to the apostles, but their story seemed like nonsense and they did not believe them. But Peter got up and ran to the tomb, bent down, and saw the burial cloths alone; then he went home amazed at what had happened.

BAPTISMAL LITURGY 1161

After the homily the catechumens are called forward. The assembly chants the litany of the saints, invoking the holy women and men of all centuries. Patron saints of the Church and of the catechumens and the faithful may be included in the litany.

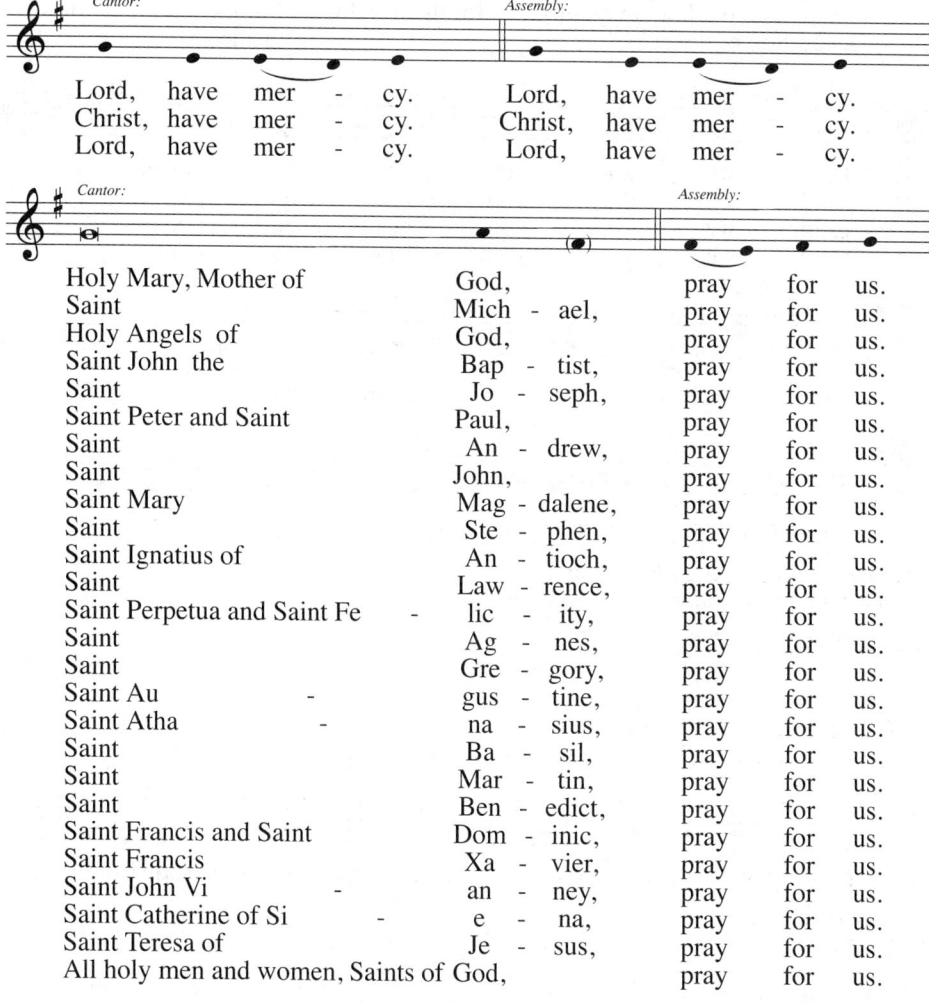

Cantor:					Assembly:				
Lord,	have	mer	-	cy.	Lord,	have	mer	-	cy.
Christ,	have	mer	-	cy.	Christ,	have	mer	-	cy.
Lord,	have	mer	-	cy.	Lord,	have	mer	-	cy.

Cantor:			Assembly:		
Holy Mary, Mother of	God,		pray	for	us.
Saint	Mich - ael,		pray	for	us.
Holy Angels of	God,		pray	for	us.
Saint John the	Bap - tist,		pray	for	us.
Saint	Jo - seph,		pray	for	us.
Saint Peter and Saint	Paul,		pray	for	us.
Saint	An - drew,		pray	for	us.
Saint	John,		pray	for	us.
Saint Mary	Mag - dalene,		pray	for	us.
Saint	Ste - phen,		pray	for	us.
Saint Ignatius of	An - tioch,		pray	for	us.
Saint	Law - rence,		pray	for	us.
Saint Perpetua and Saint Fe -	lic - ity,		pray	for	us.
Saint	Ag - nes,		pray	for	us.
Saint	Gre - gory,		pray	for	us.
Saint Au -	gus - tine,		pray	for	us.
Saint Atha -	na - sius,		pray	for	us.
Saint	Ba - sil,		pray	for	us.
Saint	Mar - tin,		pray	for	us.
Saint	Ben - edict,		pray	for	us.
Saint Francis and Saint	Dom - inic,		pray	for	us.
Saint Francis	Xa - vier,		pray	for	us.
Saint John Vi -	an - ney,		pray	for	us.
Saint Catherine of Si -	e - na,		pray	for	us.
Saint Teresa of	Je - sus,		pray	for	us.
All holy men and women, Saints of God,			pray	for	us.

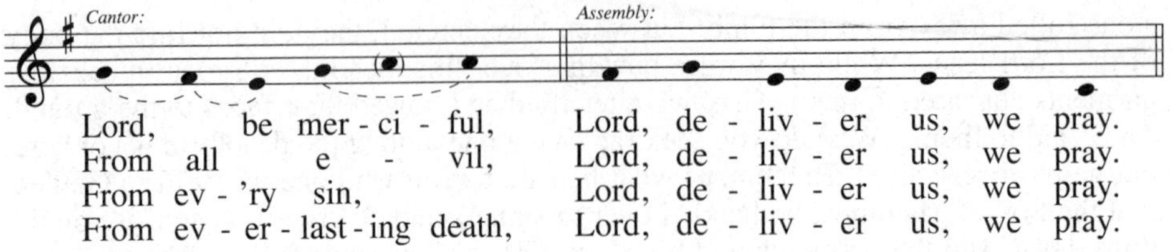

Cantor:
Assembly:

Lord, be mer - ci - ful, Lord, de - liv - er us, we pray.
From all e - vil, Lord, de - liv - er us, we pray.
From ev - 'ry sin, Lord, de - liv - er us, we pray.
From ev - er - last - ing death, Lord, de - liv - er us, we pray.

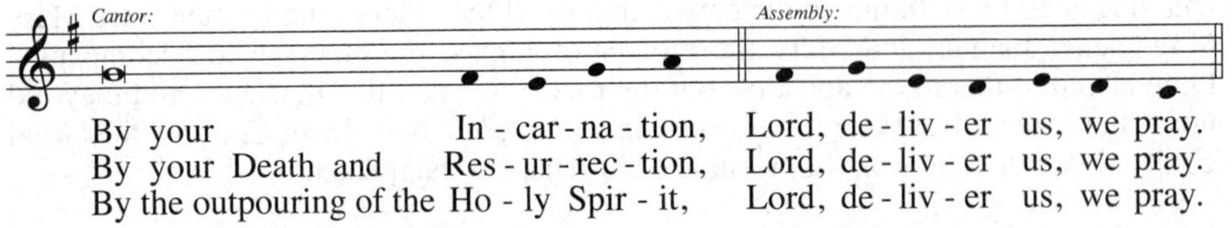

Cantor:
Assembly:

By your In - car - na - tion, Lord, de - liv - er us, we pray.
By your Death and Res - ur - rec - tion, Lord, de - liv - er us, we pray.
By the outpouring of the Ho - ly Spir - it, Lord, de - liv - er us, we pray.

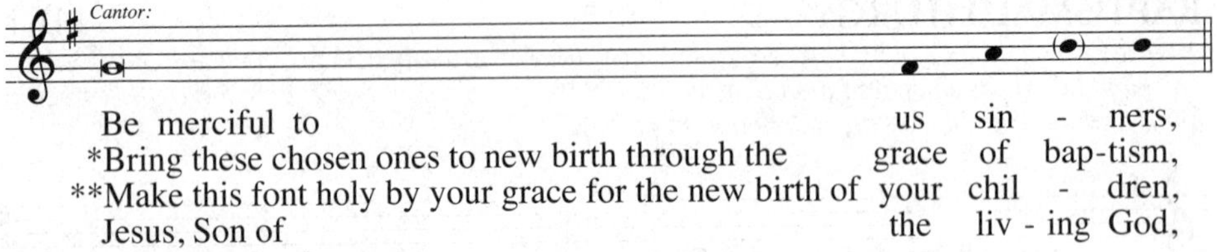

Cantor:

Be merciful to us sin - ners,
*Bring these chosen ones to new birth through the grace of bap-tism,
**Make this font holy by your grace for the new birth of your chil - dren,
Jesus, Son of the liv - ing God,

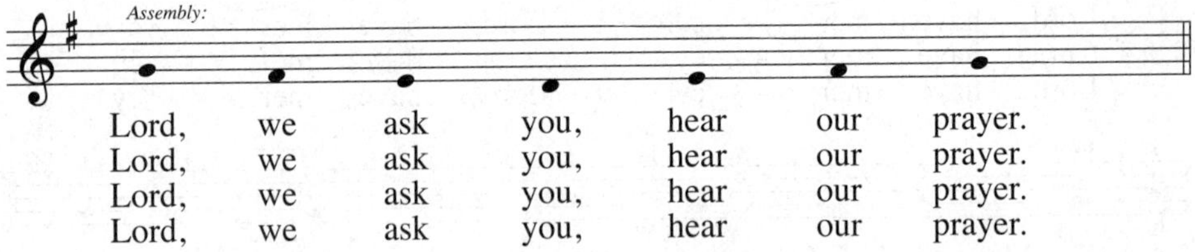

Assembly:

Lord, we ask you, hear our prayer.
Lord, we ask you, hear our prayer.
Lord, we ask you, hear our prayer.
Lord, we ask you, hear our prayer.

Cantor:
Assembly:

Christ, hear us. Christ, hear us.

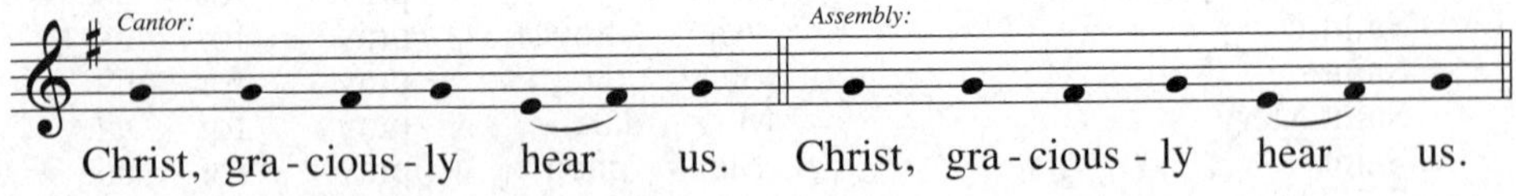

Cantor:
Assembly:

Christ, gra - cious - ly hear us. Christ, gra - cious - ly hear us.

*If there are candidates to be baptized.
**If there are no candidates to be baptized.

Text: *Litany of the Saints, Roman Missal*
Music: *Litany of the Saints, Roman Missal*
© 2010, ICEL

1162 BLESSING OF WATER

The priest gives thanks and praise to God over the waters of baptism. This acclamation is sung by all.

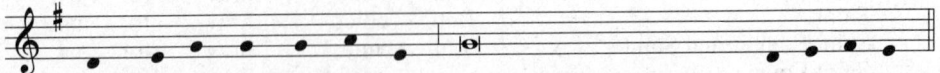

Springs of wa - ter, bless the Lord; praise and exalt him above all for ev-er.

Text: *Roman Missal*
Music: *Roman Missal*
© 2010, ICEL

RENUNCIATION OF SIN AND PROFESSION OF FAITH
Each candidate for baptism is asked to reject sin and the ways of evil and to testify to faith in Father, Son and Holy Spirit.

THE BAPTISMS   1163
One by one the candidates are led into the waters, or they bend over the font, and water is poured over them as the priest says: "N., I baptize you in the name of the Father, and of the Son, and of the Holy Spirit." After each baptism, the assembly sings an acclamation.

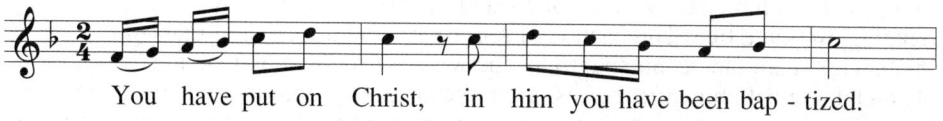

You have put on Christ, in him you have been bap - tized.

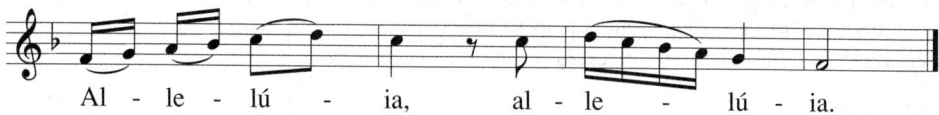

Al - le - lú - ia, al - le - lú - ia.

Text: ICEL, © 1969
Music: Howard Hughes, SM, © 1977, ICEL

Each of the newly baptized is then clothed in a baptismal garment.

RECEPTION INTO FULL COMMUNION
Those who have been previously baptized are now called forward to profess their faith and to be received into the full communion of the Catholic Church.

CONFIRMATION
Infants who have been baptized are anointed with chrism. Children and adults are usually confirmed: the priest prays and lays hands on them, then anoints each of the newly baptized with chrism saying: "N., be sealed with the Gift of the Holy Spirit."

RENEWAL OF BAPTISMAL PROMISES
All of the faithful repeat and affirm the rejection of sin made at baptism and profess faith in the Father, Son and Holy Spirit. The assembly is sprinkled with the baptismal water. The newly baptized then take their places in the assembly and, for the first time, join in the prayer of the faithful, the prayers of intercession.

LITURGY OF THE EUCHARIST   1164
The gifts and table are prepared and the eucharist is celebrated in the usual way.

CONCLUDING RITE
The dismissal is sung with "alleluia," and all respond.

Assembly:

Thanks be to God, al - le - lú - ia, al - le - lú - ia.

1165 EASTER SUNDAY / ABC

READING I *Acts 10:34a, 37–43 / 42*

Peter proceeded to speak and said: "You know what has happened all over Judea, beginning in Galilee after the baptism that John preached, how God anointed Jesus of Nazareth with the Holy Spirit and power. He went about doing good and healing all those oppressed by the devil, for God was with him. We are witnesses of all that he did both in the country of the Jews and in Jerusalem. They put him to death by hanging him on a tree. This man God raised on the third day and granted that he be visible, not to all the people, but to us, the witnesses chosen by God in advance, who ate and drank with him after he rose from the dead. He commissioned us to preach to the people and testify that he is the one appointed by God as judge of the living and the dead. To him all the prophets bear witness, that everyone who believes in him will receive forgiveness of sins through his name."

RESPONSORIAL PSALM *Psalm 118:1–2, 16–17, 22–23*

Or: Alleluia.

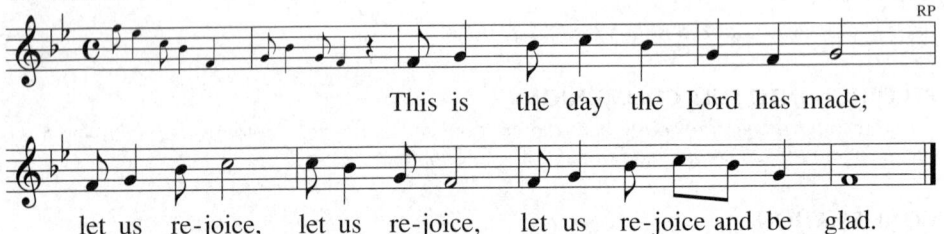

This is the day the Lord has made; let us re-joice, let us re-joice, let us re-joice and be glad.

Give praise to the LORD, for he is good;
　his mercy endures forever.
Let the house of Israel say,
　"His mercy endures forever." ℟.

"The LORD's right hand has done mighty
　deeds;
　his right hand is exalted."

I shall not die, I shall live
　and recount the deeds of the LORD. ℟.

The stone that the builders rejected
　has become the cornerstone.
By the LORD has this been done,
　a marvel in our eyes. ℟.

READING II *Colossians 3:1–4*

Brothers and sisters: If then you were raised with Christ, seek what is above, where Christ is seated at the right hand of God. Think of what is above, not of what is on earth. For you have died, and your life is hidden with Christ in God. When Christ your life appears, then you too will appear with him in glory.

Or:

READING II *1 Corinthians 5:6b–8*

Brothers and sisters: Do you not know that a little yeast leavens all the dough? Clear out the old yeast, so that you may become a fresh batch of dough, inasmuch as you are unleavened. For our paschal lamb, Christ, has been sacrificed. Therefore, let us celebrate the feast, not with the old yeast, the yeast of malice and wickedness, but with the unleavened bread of sincerity and truth.

SEQUENCE *(An alternate setting is found at no. 626.)* 1166

*1. Chris-tians, praise the Pas-chal Vic-tim! Of-fer thank-ful sac-ri-fice!
*1. Ví - cti - mae Pa-schá-li lau-des ím-mo-lent Chri-sti-á-ni.

2. Christ the Lamb has saved the sheep, Christ the just one paid the
3. Death and life fought bit-ter-ly for this won-drous vic-to-
2. A - gnus re-dé-mit o-ves: Chri-stus ín-no-cens Pa-
3. Mors et vi-ta du-él-lo con-fli-xé-re mi-rán-

price, re-con-cil-ing sin-ners to the Fa-ther.
ry; the Lord of life who died reigns glo-ri-fied!
tri re-con-ci-li-á-vit pec-ca-tó-res.
do: dux vi-tae mór-tu-us, re-gnat vi-vus.

4. O Mar-y, come and say what you saw at break of day.
6. Bright an-gels tes-ti-fied, shroud and grave clothes side by side!
4. Dic no-bis Ma-rí-a, quid vi-dí-sti in vi-a?
6. An-gé-li-cos te-stes, su-dá-ri-um, et ve-stes.

5. "The emp-ty tomb of my liv-ing Lord!
7. "Yes, Christ my hope rose glo-ri-ous-ly.
5. Se - púl-crum Chri-sti vi-vén-tis,
7. Sur-ré-xit Chri-stus spes me-a:

I saw Christ Je-sus ri-sen and a-dored!
He goes be-fore you in-to Gal-i-lee."
et gló-ri-am vi-di re-sur-gén-tis:
prae-cé-det su-os in Ga-li-láe-am.

8. Share the good news, sing joy-ful-ly: His death is vic-to-ry!
8. Sci-mus Chri-stum sur-re-xís-se a mór-tu-is ve-re:

Lord Je-sus, Vic-tor King, Show us mer-cy.
tu no-bis vi-ctor Rex, mi-se-ré-re. A - men. Al-le-lú-ia.

Verse 1 may be used as an assembly refrain after verses 3, 6, and 8.

Text: *Víctimae pascháli laudes*, ascr. to Wipo of Burgundy, d.1048; tr. by Peter J. Scagnelli, b.1949, © 1983, Peter J. Scagnelli. Published by World Library Publications.
Tune: VICTIMAE PASCHALI LAUDES, Irregular; Mode I; acc. by Richard Proulx, 1937–2010, © 1975, GIA Publications, Inc.

At an afternoon or evening Mass, another Gospel may be read (see Lectionary for Mass).

GOSPEL *John 20:1–9*

On the first day of the week, Mary of Magdala came to the tomb early in the morning, while it was still dark, and saw the stone removed from the tomb. So she ran and went to Simon Peter and to the other disciple whom Jesus loved, and told them, "They have taken the Lord from the tomb, and we don't know where they put him." So Peter and the other disciple went out and came to the tomb. They both ran, but the other disciple ran faster than Peter and arrived at the tomb first; he bent down and saw the burial cloths there, but did not go in. When Simon Peter arrived after him, he went into the tomb and saw the burial cloths there, and the cloth that had covered his head, not with the burial cloths but rolled up in a separate place. Then the other disciple also went in, the one who had arrived at the tomb first, and he saw and believed. For they did not yet understand the Scripture that he had to rise from the dead.

The rite of renewal of baptismal promises may take place after the homily, in which case the creed is omitted.

1167   SECOND SUNDAY OF EASTER / ABC

READING I / A *Acts 2:42–47 / 43*

They devoted themselves to the teaching of the apostles and to the communal life, to the breaking of bread and to the prayers. Awe came upon everyone, and many wonders and signs were done through the apostles. All who believed were together and had all things in common; they would sell their property and possessions and divide them among all according to each one's need. Every day they devoted themselves to meeting together in the temple area and to breaking bread in their homes. They ate their meals with exultation and sincerity of heart, praising God and enjoying favor with all the people. And every day the Lord added to their number those who were being saved.

READING I / B *Acts 4:32–35 / 44*

The community of believers was of one heart and mind, and no one claimed that any of his possessions was his own, but they had everything in common. With great power the apostles bore witness to the resurrection of the Lord Jesus, and great favor was accorded them all. There was no needy person among them, for those who owned property or houses would sell them, bring the proceeds of the sale, and put them at the feet of the apostles, and they were distributed to each according to need.

READING I / C *Acts 5:12–16 / 45*

Many signs and wonders were done among the people at the hands of the apostles. They were all together in Solomon's portico. None of the others dared to join them, but the people esteemed them. Yet more than ever, believers in the Lord, great numbers of men and women, were added to them. Thus they even carried the sick out into the streets and laid them on cots and mats so that when Peter came by, at least his shadow might fall on one or another of them. A large number of people from the towns in the vicinity of Jerusalem also gathered, bringing the sick and those disturbed by unclean spirits, and they were all cured.

RESPONSORIAL PSALM

Psalm 118:2–4, 13–15, 22–24

Or: Alleluia.

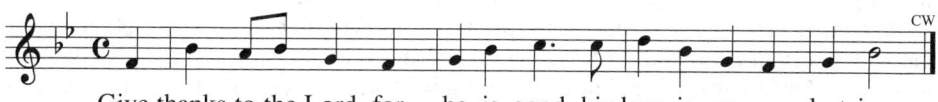

Give thanks to the Lord for he is good, his love is ev - er - last-ing.

Let the house of Israel say,
"His mercy endures forever."
Let the house of Aaron say,
"His mercy endures forever."
Let those who fear the LORD say,
"His mercy endures forever." R̃.

I was thrust down, thrust down and falling,
but the LORD was my helper.
The LORD is my strength and my song;

he was my savior.
There are shouts of joy and salvation
in the tents of the just. R̃.

The stone that the builders rejected
has become the cornerstone.
By the LORD has this been done,
a marvel in our eyes.
This is the day the LORD has made;
let us rejoice in it and be glad. R̃.

READING II / A

1 Peter 1:3–9

Blessed be the God and Father of our Lord Jesus Christ, who in his great mercy gave us a new birth to a living hope through the resurrection of Jesus Christ from the dead, to an inheritance that is imperishable, undefiled, and unfading, kept in heaven for you who by the power of God are safeguarded through faith, to a salvation that is ready to be revealed in the final time. In this you rejoice, although now for a little while you may have to suffer through various trials, so that the genuineness of your faith, more precious than gold that is perishable even though tested by fire, may prove to be for praise, glory, and honor at the revelation of Jesus Christ. Although you have not seen him you love him; even though you do not see him now yet believe in him, you rejoice with an indescribable and glorious joy, as you attain the goal of your faith, the salvation of your souls.

READING II / B

1 John 5:1–6

Beloved: Everyone who believes that Jesus is the Christ is begotten by God, and everyone who loves the Father loves also the one begotten by him. In this way we know that we love the children of God when we love God and obey his commandments. For the love of God is this, that we keep his commandments. And his commandments are not burdensome, for whoever is begotten by God conquers the world. And the victory that conquers the world is our faith. Who indeed is the victor over the world but the one who believes that Jesus is the Son of God?

This is the one who came through water and blood, Jesus Christ, not by water alone, but by water and blood. The Spirit is the one that testifies, and the Spirit is truth.

READING II / C

Revelation 1:9–11a, 12–13, 17–19

I, John, your brother, who share with you the distress, the kingdom, and the endurance we have in Jesus, found myself on the island called Patmos because I proclaimed God's word and gave testimony to Jesus. I was caught up in spirit on the Lord's day and heard behind me a voice as loud as a trumpet, which said, "Write on a scroll what you see." Then I turned to see whose voice it was that spoke to me, and when I turned, I saw seven gold lampstands and in the midst of the lampstands one like a son of man, wearing an ankle-length robe, with a gold sash around his chest.

When I caught sight of him, I fell down at his feet as though dead. He touched me with his right hand and said, "Do not be afraid. I am the first and the last, the one who lives. Once I was dead, but now I am alive forever and ever. I hold the keys to death and the netherworld. Write down, therefore, what you have seen, and what is happening, and what will happen afterwards."

GOSPEL   *John 20:19–31*

On the evening of that first day of the week, when the doors were locked, where the disciples were, for fear of the Jews, Jesus came and stood in their midst and said to them, "Peace be with you." When he had said this, he showed them his hands and his side. The disciples rejoiced when they saw the Lord. Jesus said to them again, "Peace be with you. As the Father has sent me, so I send you." And when he had said this, he breathed on them and said to them, "Receive the Holy Spirit. Whose sins you forgive are forgiven them, and whose sins you retain are retained."

Thomas, called Didymus, one of the Twelve, was not with them when Jesus came. So the other disciples said to him, "We have seen the Lord." But he said to them, "Unless I see the mark of the nails in his hands and put my finger into the nailmarks and put my hand into his side, I will not believe."

Now a week later his disciples were again inside and Thomas was with them. Jesus came, although the doors were locked, and stood in their midst and said, "Peace be with you." Then he said to Thomas, "Put your finger here and see my hands, and bring your hand and put it into my side, and do not be unbelieving, but believe." Thomas answered and said to him, "My Lord and my God!" Jesus said to him, "Have you come to believe because you have seen me? Blessed are those who have not seen and have believed."

Now, Jesus did many other signs in the presence of his disciples that are not written in this book. But these are written that you may come to believe that Jesus is the Christ, the Son of God, and that through this belief you may have life in his name.

1168   THIRD SUNDAY OF EASTER / A

READING I   *Acts 2:14, 22–33 / 46*

Then Peter stood up with the Eleven, raised his voice, and proclaimed: "You who are Jews, indeed all of you staying in Jerusalem. Let this be known to you, and listen to my words. You who are Israelites, hear these words. Jesus the Nazarene was a man commended to you by God with mighty deeds, wonders, and signs, which God worked through him in your midst, as you yourselves know. This man, delivered up by the set plan and foreknowledge of God, you killed, using lawless men to crucify him. But God raised him up, releasing him from the throes of death, because it was impossible for him to be held by it. For David says of him:

I saw the Lord ever before me,
  with him at my right hand I shall not be disturbed.
Therefore my heart has been glad and my tongue has exulted;
  my flesh, too, will dwell in hope,
because you will not abandon my soul to the netherworld,
  nor will you suffer your holy one to see corruption.
You have made known to me the paths of life;
  you will fill me with joy in your presence.

"My brothers, one can confidently say to you about the patriarch David that he died and was buried, and his tomb is in our midst to this day. But since he was a prophet and knew that God had sworn an oath to him that he would set one of his descendants upon his throne, he foresaw and spoke of the resurrection of the Christ, that neither was he abandoned to the netherworld nor did his flesh see corruption. God raised this Jesus; of this we are all witnesses. Exalted at the right hand of God, he received the promise of the Holy Spirit from the Father and poured him forth, as you see and hear."

RESPONSORIAL PSALM   *Psalm 16:1–2a and 5, 7–8, 9–10, 11*

Or: Alleluia.

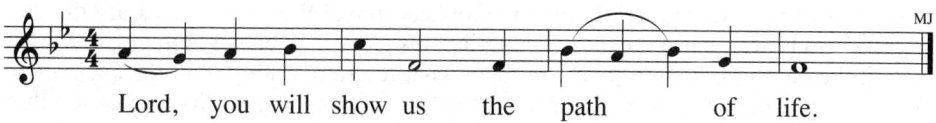

Lord, you will show us the path of life.

Preserve me, O God, for in you I take
  refuge.
  I say to the LORD, "You are my Lord."
O LORD, it is you who are my portion
  and cup;
  you yourself who secure my lot. ℟.

I will bless the LORD who gives me
  counsel,
  who even at night directs my heart.
I keep the LORD before me always;
  with him at my right hand, I shall
  not be moved. ℟.

And so, my heart rejoices, my soul is
  glad;
  even my flesh shall rest in hope.
For you will not abandon my soul to
  hell,
  nor let your holy one see
  corruption. ℟.

You will show me the path of life,
  the fullness of joy in your presence,
  at your right hand, bliss forever. ℟.

READING II   *1 Peter 1:17–21*

Beloved: If you invoke as Father him who judges impartially according to each one's works, conduct yourselves with reverence during the time of your sojourning, realizing that you were ransomed from your futile conduct, handed on by your ancestors, not with perishable things like silver or gold but with the precious blood of Christ as of a spotless unblemished lamb.

He was known before the foundation of the world but revealed in the final time for you, who through him believe in God who raised him from the dead and gave him glory, so that your faith and hope are in God.

GOSPEL *Luke 24:13–35*

That very day, the first day of the week, two of Jesus' disciples were going to a village seven miles from Jerusalem called Emmaus, and they were conversing about all the things that had occurred. And it happened that while they were conversing and debating, Jesus himself drew near and walked with them, but their eyes were prevented from recognizing him. He asked them, "What are you discussing as you walk along?" They stopped, looking downcast. One of them, named Cleopas, said to him in reply, "Are you the only visitor to Jerusalem who does not know of the things that have taken place there in these days?" And he replied to them, "What sort of things?" They said to him, "The things that happened to Jesus the Nazarene, who was a prophet mighty in deed and word before God and all the people, how our chief priests and rulers both handed him over to a sentence of death and crucified him. But we were hoping that he would be the one to redeem Israel; and besides all this, it is now the third day since this took place. Some women from our group, however, have astounded us: they were at the tomb early in the morning and did not find his body; they came back and reported that they had indeed seen a vision of angels who announced that he was alive. Then some of those with us went to the tomb and found things just as the women had described, but him they did not see." And he said to them, "Oh, how foolish you are! How slow of heart to believe all that the prophets spoke! Was it not necessary that the Christ should suffer these things and enter into his glory?" Then beginning with Moses and all the prophets, he interpreted to them what referred to him in all the Scriptures. As they approached the village to which they were going, he gave the impression that he was going on farther. But they urged him, "Stay with us, for it is nearly evening and the day is almost over." So he went in to stay with them. And it happened that, while he was with them at table, he took bread, said the blessing, broke it, and gave it to them. With that their eyes were opened and they recognized him, but he vanished from their sight. Then they said to each other, "Were not our hearts burning within us while he spoke to us on the way and opened the Scriptures to us?" So they set out at once and returned to Jerusalem where they found gathered together the eleven and those with them who were saying, "The Lord has truly been raised and has appeared to Simon!" Then the two recounted what had taken place on the way and how he was made known to them in the breaking of bread.

1169 THIRD SUNDAY OF EASTER / B

READING I *Acts 3:13–15, 17–19 / 47*

Peter said to the people: "The God of Abraham, the God of Isaac, and the God of Jacob, the God of our fathers, has glorified his servant Jesus, whom you handed over and denied in Pilate's presence when he had decided to release him. You denied the Holy and Righteous One and asked that a murderer be released to you. The author of life you put to death, but God raised him from the dead; of this we are witnesses. Now I know, brothers, that you acted out of ignorance, just as your leaders did; but God has thus brought to fulfillment what he had announced beforehand through the mouth of all the prophets, that his Christ would suffer. Repent, therefore, and be converted, that your sins may be wiped away."

RESPONSORIAL PSALM   *Psalm 4:2, 4, 7b–8a, 9*

Or: Alleluia.

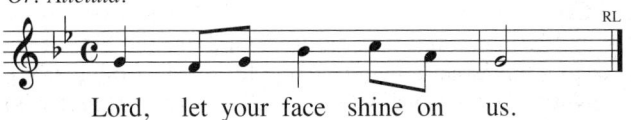

Lord, let your face shine on us.

I called, the God of justice gave me answer;
from anguish you released me,
have mercy and hear me! ℟.

Know that the LORD works wonders for his faithful one;
the LORD will hear me whenever I call him. ℟.

Lift up the light of your face on us, O LORD.
You have put into my heart a greater joy. ℟.

In peace I will lie down and fall asleep, for you alone, O LORD, make me dwell in safety. ℟.

READING II   *1 John 2:1–5a*

My children, I am writing this to you so that you may not commit sin. But if anyone does sin, we have an Advocate with the Father, Jesus Christ the righteous one. He is expiation for our sins, and not for our sins only but for those of the whole world. The way we may be sure that we know him is to keep his commandments. Those who say, "I know him," but do not keep his commandments are liars, and the truth is not in them. But whoever keeps his word, the love of God is truly perfected in him.

GOSPEL   *Luke 24:35–48*

The two disciples recounted what had taken place on the way, and how Jesus was made known to them in the breaking of bread.

While they were still speaking about this, he stood in their midst and said to them, "Peace be with you." But they were startled and terrified and thought that they were seeing a ghost. Then he said to them, "Why are you troubled? And why do questions arise in your hearts? Look at my hands and my feet, that it is I myself. Touch me and see, because a ghost does not have flesh and bones as you can see I have." And as he said this, he showed them his hands and his feet. While they were still incredulous for joy and were amazed, he asked them, "Have you anything here to eat?" They gave him a piece of baked fish; he took it and ate it in front of them.

He said to them, "These are my words that I spoke to you while I was still with you, that everything written about me in the law of Moses and in the prophets and psalms must be fulfilled." Then he opened their minds to understand the Scriptures. And he said to them, "Thus it is written that the Christ would suffer and rise from the dead on the third day and that repentance, for the forgiveness of sins, would be preached in his name to all the nations, beginning from Jerusalem. You are witnesses of these things."

THIRD SUNDAY OF EASTER / C   1170

READING I   *Acts 5:27–32, 40b–41 / 48*

When the captain and the court officers had brought the apostles in and made them stand before the Sanhedrin, the high priest questioned them, "We gave you strict orders, did we not, to stop teaching in that name? Yet you have filled Jerusalem with your teaching and want to bring this man's blood upon us." But Peter and the apostles said in reply, "We must obey God rather than men. The God of our ancestors raised Jesus, though you had him killed by hanging him on a tree. God exalted him at his right hand as leader and savior to grant Israel repentance and forgiveness of sins. We are witnesses of these things, as is the Holy Spirit whom God has given to those who obey him."

The Sanhedrin ordered the apostles to stop speaking in the name of Jesus, and dismissed them. So they left the presence of the Sanhedrin, rejoicing that they had been found worthy to suffer dishonor for the sake of the name.

RESPONSORIAL PSALM   *Psalm 30:2 and 4, 5–6, 11 and 12a and 13b*

Or: Alleluia.

I will praise you, Lord, for you have res-cued me.

I will extol you, LORD, for you have
    raised me up,
and have not let my enemies rejoice
    over me.
O LORD, you have lifted up my soul
    from the grave,
    restored me to life from those who
    sink into the pit. ℟.

Sing psalms to the LORD, you faithful
    ones;
    give thanks to his holy name.

His anger lasts a moment; his favor all
    through life.
At night come tears, but dawn
    brings joy. ℟.

Hear, O LORD, and have mercy on me;
    be my helper, O LORD.
You have changed my mourning into
    dancing.
O LORD my God, I will thank you
    forever. ℟.

READING II   *Revelation 5:11–14*

I, John, looked and heard the voices of many angels who surrounded the throne and the living creatures and the elders. They were countless in number, and they cried out in a loud voice:
    "Worthy is the Lamb that was slain
        to receive power and riches, wisdom and strength,
        honor and glory and blessing."
Then I heard every creature in heaven and on earth and under the earth and in the sea, everything in the universe, cry out:
    "To the one who sits on the throne and to the Lamb
        be blessing and honor, glory and might,
        forever and ever."
The four living creatures answered, "Amen," and the elders fell down and worshiped.

GOSPEL   *John 21:1–19 or 21:1–14*
For short form read only the part in brackets.

[At that time, Jesus revealed himself again to his disciples at the Sea of Tiberias. He revealed himself in this way. Together were Simon Peter, Thomas called Didymus,

Nathanael from Cana in Galilee, Zebedee's sons, and two others of his disciples. Simon Peter said to them, "I am going fishing." They said to him, "We also will come with you." So they went out and got into the boat, but that night they caught nothing. When it was already dawn, Jesus was standing on the shore; but the disciples did not realize that it was Jesus. Jesus said to them, "Children, have you caught anything to eat?" They answered him, "No." So he said to them, "Cast the net over the right side of the boat and you will find something." So they cast it, and were not able to pull it in because of the number of fish. So the disciple whom Jesus loved said to Peter, "It is the Lord." When Simon Peter heard that it was the Lord, he tucked in his garment, for he was lightly clad, and jumped into the sea. The other disciples came in the boat, for they were not far from shore, only about a hundred yards, dragging the net with the fish. When they climbed out on shore, they saw a charcoal fire with fish on it and bread. Jesus said to them, "Bring some of the fish you just caught." So Simon Peter went over and dragged the net ashore full of one hundred fifty-three large fish. Even though there were so many, the net was not torn. Jesus said to them, "Come, have breakfast." And none of the disciples dared to ask him, "Who are you?" because they realized it was the Lord. Jesus came over and took the bread and gave it to them, and in like manner the fish. This was now the third time Jesus was revealed to his disciples after being raised from the dead.]

When they had finished breakfast, Jesus said to Simon Peter, "Simon, son of John, do you love me more than these?" Simon Peter answered him, "Yes, Lord, you know that I love you." Jesus said to him, "Feed my lambs." He then said to Simon Peter a second time, "Simon, son of John, do you love me?" Simon Peter answered him, "Yes, Lord, you know that I love you." Jesus said to him, "Tend my sheep." Jesus said to him the third time, "Simon, son of John, do you love me?" Peter was distressed that Jesus had said to him a third time, "Do you love me?" and he said to him, "Lord, you know everything; you know that I love you." Jesus said to him, "Feed my sheep. Amen, amen, I say to you, when you were younger, you used to dress yourself and go where you wanted; but when you grow old, you will stretch out your hands, and someone else will dress you and lead you where you do not want to go." He said this signifying by what kind of death he would glorify God. And when he had said this, he said to him, "Follow me."

FOURTH SUNDAY OF EASTER / A   1171

READING I   *Acts 2:14a, 36–41 / 49*

Then Peter stood up with the Eleven, raised his voice, and proclaimed: "Let the whole house of Israel know for certain that God has made both Lord and Christ, this Jesus whom you crucified."

Now when they heard this, they were cut to the heart, and they asked Peter and the other apostles, "What are we to do, my brothers?" Peter said to them, "Repent and be baptized, every one of you, in the name of Jesus Christ for the forgiveness of your sins; and you will receive the gift of the Holy Spirit. For the promise is made to you and to your children and to all those far off, whomever the Lord our God will call." He testified with many other arguments, and was exhorting them, "Save yourselves from this corrupt generation." Those who accepted his message were baptized, and about three thousand persons were added that day.

RESPONSORIAL PSALM
Psalm 23:1–3a, 3b–4, 5, 6

Or: Alleluia.

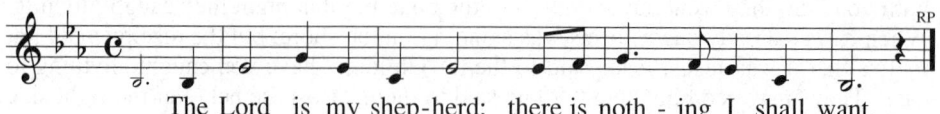

The Lord is my shep-herd; there is noth - ing I shall want.

The LORD is my shepherd;
  there is nothing I shall want.
Fresh and green are the pastures
  where he gives me repose.
Near restful waters he leads me;
  he revives my soul. ℟.

He guides me along the right path,
  for the sake of his name.
Though I should walk in the valley of
    the shadow of death,
  no evil would I fear, for you are
    with me.

Your crook and your staff will give
  me comfort. ℟.

You have prepared a table before me
  in the sight of my foes.
My head you have anointed with oil;
  my cup is overflowing. ℟.

Surely goodness and mercy shall
    follow me
  all the days of my life.
In the LORD's own house shall I dwell
  for length of days unending. ℟.

READING II
1 Peter 2:20b–25

Beloved: If you are patient when you suffer for doing what is good, this is a grace before God. For to this you have been called, because Christ also suffered for you, leaving you an example that you should follow in his footsteps.
  He committed no sin, and no deceit was found in his mouth.

When he was insulted, he returned no insult; when he suffered, he did not threaten; instead, he handed himself over to the one who judges justly. He himself bore our sins in his body upon the cross, so that, free from sin, we might live for righteousness. By his wounds you have been healed. For you had gone astray like sheep, but you have now returned to the shepherd and guardian of your souls.

GOSPEL
John 10:1–10

Jesus said: "Amen, amen, I say to you, whoever does not enter a sheepfold through the gate but climbs over elsewhere is a thief and a robber. But whoever enters through the gate is the shepherd of the sheep. The gatekeeper opens it for him, and the sheep hear his voice, as the shepherd calls his own sheep by name and leads them out. When he has driven out all his own, he walks ahead of them, and the sheep follow him, because they recognize his voice. But they will not follow a stranger; they will run away from him, because they do not recognize the voice of strangers." Although Jesus used this figure of speech, the Pharisees did not realize what he was trying to tell them.

So Jesus said again, "Amen, amen, I say to you, I am the gate for the sheep. All who came before me are thieves and robbers, but the sheep did not listen to them. I am the gate. Whoever enters through me will be saved, and will come in and go out and find pasture. A thief comes only to steal and slaughter and destroy; I came so that they might have life and have it more abundantly."

FOURTH SUNDAY OF EASTER / B 1172

READING I *Acts 4:8–12 / 50*

Peter, filled with the Holy Spirit, said: "Leaders of the people and elders: If we are being examined today about a good deed done to a cripple, namely, by what means he was saved, then all of you and all the people of Israel should know that it was in the name of Jesus Christ the Nazorean whom you crucified, whom God raised from the dead; in his name this man stands before you healed. He is *the stone rejected by you, the builders, which has become the cornerstone.* There is no salvation through anyone else, nor is there any other name under heaven given to the human race by which we are to be saved."

RESPONSORIAL PSALM *Psalm 118:1 and 8–9, 21–23, 26 and 21 and 29*

Or: Alleluia.

The stone re-ject-ed by the build-ers has be-come the cor-ner - stone.

Give praise to the LORD, for he is good;
   his mercy endures forever.
It is better to take refuge in the LORD
   than to trust in man;
it is better to take refuge in the LORD
   than to trust in princes. ℟.

I will thank you, for you have
   answered,
   and you are my savior.
The stone that the builders rejected
   has become the cornerstone.

By the LORD has this been done,
   a marvel in our eyes. ℟.

Blest is he who comes in the name of
   the LORD.
   We bless you from the house of the
   LORD.
I will thank you, for you have answered,
   and you are my savior.
Give praise to the LORD, for he is good;
   his mercy endures forever. ℟.

READING II *1 John 3:1–2*

Beloved: See what love the Father has bestowed on us that we may be called the children of God. Yet so we are. The reason the world does not know us is that it did not know him. Beloved, we are God's children now; what we shall be has not yet been revealed. We do know that when it is revealed we shall be like him, for we shall see him as he is.

GOSPEL *John 10:11–18*

Jesus said: "I am the good shepherd. A good shepherd lays down his life for the sheep. A hired man, who is not a shepherd and whose sheep are not his own, sees a wolf coming and leaves the sheep and runs away, and the wolf catches and scatters them. This is because he works for pay and has no concern for the sheep. I am the good shepherd, and I know mine and mine know me, just as the Father knows me and I know the Father; and I will lay down my life for the sheep. I have other sheep that do not belong to this fold. These also I must lead, and they will hear my voice, and there will be one flock, one shepherd. This is why the Father loves me, because I lay down my life in order to take it up again. No one takes it from me, but I lay it down on my own. I have power to lay it down, and power to take it up again. This command I have received from my Father."

1173   FOURTH SUNDAY OF EASTER / C

READING I   *Acts 13:14, 43–52 / 51*

Paul and Barnabas continued on from Perga and reached Antioch in Pisidia. On the sabbath they entered the synagogue and took their seats. Many Jews and worshipers who were converts to Judaism followed Paul and Barnabas, who spoke to them and urged them to remain faithful to the grace of God.

On the following sabbath almost the whole city gathered to hear the word of the Lord. When the Jews saw the crowds, they were filled with jealousy and with violent abuse contradicted what Paul said. Both Paul and Barnabas spoke out boldly and said, "It was necessary that the word of God be spoken to you first, but since you reject it and condemn yourselves as unworthy of eternal life, we now turn to the Gentiles. For so the Lord has commanded us, *I have made you a light to the Gentiles, that you may be an instrument of salvation to the ends of the earth."*

The Gentiles were delighted when they heard this and glorified the word of the Lord. All who were destined for eternal life came to believe, and the word of the Lord continued to spread through the whole region. The Jews, however, incited the women of prominence who were worshipers and the leading men of the city, stirred up a persecution against Paul and Barnabas, and expelled them from their territory. So they shook the dust from their feet in protest against them, and went to Iconium. The disciples were filled with joy and the Holy Spirit.

RESPONSORIAL PSALM   *Psalm 100:1–2, 3, 5*

Or: Alleluia.

We are his peo - ple, the sheep of his flock.

Cry out with joy to the LORD, all the earth.
  Serve the LORD with gladness.
  Come before him, singing for joy. ℟.

Know that he, the LORD, is God.
  He made us; we belong to him.

We are his people, the sheep of his flock. ℟.

Indeed, how good is the LORD,
  eternal his merciful love.
  He is faithful from age to age. ℟.

READING II   *Revelation 7:9, 14b–17*

I, John, had a vision of a great multitude, which no one could count, from every nation, race, people, and tongue. They stood before the throne and before the Lamb, wearing white robes and holding palm branches in their hands.

Then one of the elders said to me, "These are the ones who have survived the time of great distress; they have washed their robes and made them white in the blood of the Lamb.

"For this reason they stand before God's throne
    and worship him day and night in his temple.
The one who sits on the throne will shelter them.
They will not hunger or thirst anymore,
    nor will the sun or any heat strike them.
For the Lamb who is in the center of the throne
    will shepherd them
    and lead them to springs of life-giving water,
    and God will wipe away every tear from their eyes."

GOSPEL *John 10:27–30*

Jesus said: "My sheep hear my voice; I know them, and they follow me. I give them eternal life, and they shall never perish. No one can take them out of my hand. My Father, who has given them to me, is greater than all, and no one can take them out of the Father's hand. The Father and I are one."

FIFTH SUNDAY OF EASTER / A 1174

READING I *Acts 6:1–7 / 52*

As the number of disciples continued to grow, the Hellenists complained against the Hebrews because their widows were being neglected in the daily distribution. So the Twelve called together the community of the disciples and said, "It is not right for us to neglect the word of God to serve at table. Brothers, select from among you seven reputable men, filled with the Spirit and wisdom, whom we shall appoint to this task, whereas we shall devote ourselves to prayer and to the ministry of the word." The proposal was acceptable to the whole community, so they chose Stephen, a man filled with faith and the Holy Spirit, also Philip, Prochorus, Nicanor, Timon, Parmenas, and Nicholas of Antioch, a convert to Judaism. They presented these men to the apostles who prayed and laid hands on them. The word of God continued to spread, and the number of the disciples in Jerusalem increased greatly; even a large group of priests were becoming obedient to the faith.

RESPONSORIAL PSALM *Psalm 33:1–2, 4–5, 18–19*

Or: Alleluia.

Lord, let your mer-cy be on us, as we place our trust in you.

Ring out your joy to the LORD, O you just;
    for praise is fitting for the upright.
Give thanks to the LORD upon the harp;
    with a ten-stringed lute sing him
        songs. ℟.

For the word of the LORD is faithful,
    and all his works to be trusted.
The LORD loves justice and right,
    and his merciful love fills the
        earth. ℟.

Yes, the LORD's eyes are on those who
    fear him,
    who hope in his merciful love,
to rescue their souls from death,
    to keep them alive in famine. ℟.

READING II   *1 Peter 2:4–9*

Beloved: Come to him, a living stone, rejected by human beings but chosen and precious in the sight of God, and, like living stones, let yourselves be built into a spiritual house to be a holy priesthood to offer spiritual sacrifices acceptable to God through Jesus Christ. For it says in Scripture:

Behold, I am laying a stone in Zion,
a cornerstone, chosen and precious,
and whoever believes in it shall not be put to shame.

Therefore, its value is for you who have faith, but for those without faith:

The stone that the builders rejected
has become the cornerstone,

and

A stone that will make people stumble,
and a rock that will make them fall.

They stumble by disobeying the word, as is their destiny.

You are "a chosen race, a royal priesthood, a holy nation, a people of his own, so that you may announce the praises" of him who called you out of darkness into his wonderful light.

GOSPEL   *John 14:1–12*

Jesus said to his disciples: "Do not let your hearts be troubled. You have faith in God; have faith also in me. In my Father's house there are many dwelling places. If there were not, would I have told you that I am going to prepare a place for you? And if I go and prepare a place for you, I will come back again and take you to myself, so that where I am you also may be. Where I am going you know the way." Thomas said to him, "Master, we do not know where you are going; how can we know the way?" Jesus said to him, "I am the way and the truth and the life. No one comes to the Father except through me. If you know me, then you will also know my Father. From now on you do know him and have seen him." Philip said to him, "Master, show us the Father, and that will be enough for us." Jesus said to him, "Have I been with you for so long a time and you still do not know me, Philip? Whoever has seen me has seen the Father. How can you say, 'Show us the Father'? Do you not believe that I am in the Father and the Father is in me? The words that I speak to you I do not speak on my own. The Father who dwells in me is doing his works. Believe me that I am in the Father and the Father is in me, or else, believe because of the works themselves. Amen, amen, I say to you, whoever believes in me will do the works that I do, and will do greater ones than these, because I am going to the Father."

1175   FIFTH SUNDAY OF EASTER / B

READING I   *Acts 9:26–31 / 53*

When Saul arrived in Jerusalem he tried to join the disciples, but they were all afraid of him, not believing that he was a disciple. Then Barnabas took charge of him and brought him to the apostles, and he reported to them how he had seen the Lord, and that he had spoken to him, and how in Damascus he had spoken out boldly in the name of Jesus. He moved about freely with them in Jerusalem, and spoke out boldly in the name of the Lord. He also spoke and debated with the Hellenists, but they tried to kill him. And when the brothers learned of this, they took him down to Caesarea and sent him on his way to Tarsus.

The church throughout all Judea, Galilee, and Samaria was at peace. It was being built up and walked in the fear of the Lord, and with the consolation of the Holy Spirit it grew in numbers.

RESPONSORIAL PSALM   *Psalm 22:26b–27, 28 and 30, 31–32*

Or: Alleluia.

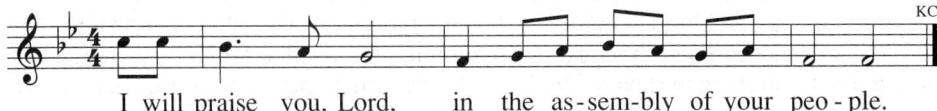

I will praise you, Lord, in the as-sem-bly of your peo - ple.

My vows I will pay before those who
    fear him.
    The poor shall eat and shall have
      their fill.
They shall praise the LORD, those who
    seek him.
    May their hearts live on forever and
      ever! ℞.

All the earth shall remember and return
    to the LORD,
    all families of the nations worship
      before him.

They shall worship him, all the mighty
    of the earth;
    before him shall bow all who go
      down to the dust. ℞.

And my soul shall live for him, my
    descendants serve him.
    They shall tell of the LORD to
      generations yet to come,
declare his saving justice to peoples
    yet unborn:
    "These are the things the LORD
      has done." ℞.

READING II   *1 John 3:18–24*

Children, let us love not in word or speech but in deed and truth.

Now this is how we shall know that we belong to the truth and reassure our hearts before him in whatever our hearts condemn, for God is greater than our hearts and knows everything. Beloved, if our hearts do not condemn us, we have confidence in God and receive from him whatever we ask, because we keep his commandments and do what pleases him. And his commandment is this: we should believe in the name of his Son, Jesus Christ, and love one another just as he commanded us. Those who keep his commandments remain in him, and he in them, and the way we know that he remains in us is from the Spirit he gave us.

GOSPEL   *John 15:1–8*

Jesus said to his disciples: "I am the true vine, and my Father is the vine grower. He takes away every branch in me that does not bear fruit, and every one that does he prunes so that it bears more fruit. You are already pruned because of the word that I spoke to you. Remain in me, as I remain in you. Just as a branch cannot bear fruit on its own unless it remains on the vine, so neither can you unless you remain in me. I am the vine, you are the branches. Whoever remains in me and I in him will bear much fruit, because without me you can do nothing. Anyone who does not remain in me will be thrown out like a branch and wither; people will gather them and throw them into a fire and they will be burned. If you remain in me and my words remain in you, ask for whatever you want and it will be done for you. By this is my Father glorified, that you bear much fruit and become my disciples."

1176 FIFTH SUNDAY OF EASTER / C

READING I   *Acts 14:21–27 / 54*

After Paul and Barnabas had proclaimed the good news to that city and made a consider-
able number of disciples, they returned to Lystra and to Iconium and to Antioch. They
strengthened the spirits of the disciples and exhorted them to persevere in the faith, saying, "It is necessary for us to undergo many hardships to enter the kingdom of God."
They appointed elders for them in each church and, with prayer and fasting, commended them to the Lord in whom they had put their faith. Then they traveled through
Pisidia and reached Pamphylia. After proclaiming the word at Perga they went down
to Attalia. From there they sailed to Antioch, where they had been commended to the
grace of God for the work they had now accomplished. And when they arrived, they
called the church together and reported what God had done with them and how he had
opened the door of faith to the Gentiles.

RESPONSORIAL PSALM   *Psalm 145:8–9, 10–11, 12–13ab*

Or: Alleluia.

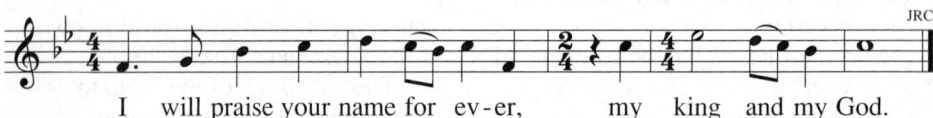

I will praise your name for ev-er,   my king and my God.

The Lᴏʀᴅ is kind and full of compassion,
   slow to anger, abounding in mercy.
How good is the Lᴏʀᴅ to all,
   compassionate to all his creatures. ℟.

All your works shall thank you, O Lᴏʀᴅ,
   and all your faithful ones bless you.
They shall speak of the glory of your
   reign,

and declare your mighty deeds. ℟.

To make known your might to the
   children of men,
   and the glorious splendor of your
   reign.
Your kingdom is an everlasting kingdom;
   your rule endures for all
   generations. ℟.

READING II   *Revelation 21:1–5a*

Then I, John, saw a new heaven and a new earth. The former heaven and the former
earth had passed away, and the sea was no more. I also saw the holy city, a new
Jerusalem, coming down out of heaven from God, prepared as a bride adorned for
her husband. I heard a loud voice from the throne saying, "Behold, God's dwelling
is with the human race. He will dwell with them and they will be his people and God
himself will always be with them as their God. He will wipe every tear from their
eyes, and there shall be no more death or mourning, wailing or pain, for the old order
has passed away."

    The One who sat on the throne said, "Behold, I make all things new."

GOSPEL   *John 13:31–33a, 34–35*

When Judas had left them, Jesus said, "Now is the Son of Man glorified, and God is
glorified in him. If God is glorified in him, God will also glorify him in himself, and
God will glorify him at once. My children, I will be with you only a little while longer.

I give you a new commandment: love one another. As I have loved you, so you also should love one another. This is how all will know that you are my disciples, if you have love for one another."

SIXTH SUNDAY OF EASTER / A   1177

READING I   *Acts 8:5–8, 14–17 / 55*

Philip went down to the city of Samaria and proclaimed the Christ to them. With one accord, the crowds paid attention to what was said by Philip when they heard it and saw the signs he was doing. For unclean spirits, crying out in a loud voice, came out of many possessed people, and many paralyzed or crippled people were cured. There was great joy in that city.

Now when the apostles in Jerusalem heard that Samaria had accepted the word of God, they sent them Peter and John, who went down and prayed for them, that they might receive the Holy Spirit, for it had not yet fallen upon any of them; they had only been baptized in the name of the Lord Jesus. Then they laid hands on them and they received the Holy Spirit.

RESPONSORIAL PSALM   *Psalm 66:1–3a, 4–5, 6–7a, 16 and 20*

Or: Alleluia.

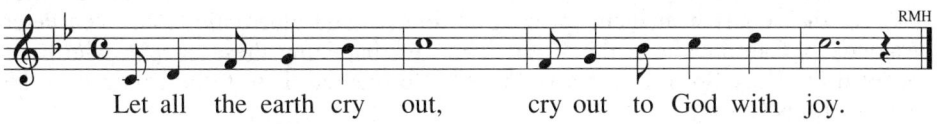

Let all the earth cry out, cry out to God with joy.

Cry out with joy to God, all the earth;
    O sing to the glory of his name.
O render him glorious praise.
    Say to God, "How awesome your
    deeds! ℟.

"Before you all the earth shall bow down,
    shall sing to you, sing to your name!"
Come and see the works of God:
    awesome his deeds among the
    children of men. ℟.

He turned the sea into dry land;
    they passed through the river on foot.
Let our joy, then, be in him;
    he rules forever by his might. ℟.

Come and hear, all who fear God;
    I will tell what he did for my soul.
Blest be God, who did not reject my
    prayer,
    nor withhold from me his merciful
    love. ℟.

READING II   *1 Peter 3:15–18*

Beloved: Sanctify Christ as Lord in your hearts. Always be ready to give an explanation to anyone who asks you for a reason for your hope, but do it with gentleness and reverence, keeping your conscience clear, so that, when you are maligned, those who defame your good conduct in Christ may themselves be put to shame. For it is better to suffer for doing good, if that be the will of God, than for doing evil. For Christ also suffered for sins once, the righteous for the sake of the unrighteous, that he might lead you to God. Put to death in the flesh, he was brought to life in the Spirit.

GOSPEL *John 14:15–21*

Jesus said to his disciples: "If you love me, you will keep my commandments. And I will ask the Father, and he will give you another Advocate to be with you always, the Spirit of truth, whom the world cannot accept, because it neither sees nor knows him. But you know him, because he remains with you, and will be in you. I will not leave you orphans; I will come to you. In a little while the world will no longer see me, but you will see me, because I live and you will live. On that day you will realize that I am in my Father and you are in me and I in you. Whoever has my commandments and observes them is the one who loves me. And whoever loves me will be loved by my Father, and I will love him and reveal myself to him."

1178   SIXTH SUNDAY OF EASTER / B

READING I *Acts 10:25–26, 34–35, 44–48 / 56*

When Peter entered, Cornelius met him and, falling at his feet, paid him homage. Peter, however, raised him up, saying, "Get up. I myself am also a human being."

Then Peter proceeded to speak and said, "In truth, I see that God shows no partiality. Rather, in every nation whoever fears him and acts uprightly is acceptable to him."

While Peter was still speaking these things, the Holy Spirit fell upon all who were listening to the word. The circumcised believers who had accompanied Peter were astounded that the gift of the Holy Spirit should have been poured out on the Gentiles also, for they could hear them speaking in tongues and glorifying God. Then Peter responded, "Can anyone withhold the water for baptizing these people, who have received the Holy Spirit even as we have?" He ordered them to be baptized in the name of Jesus Christ.

RESPONSORIAL PSALM *Psalm 98:1, 2–3ab, 3cd–4*

Or: Alleluia.

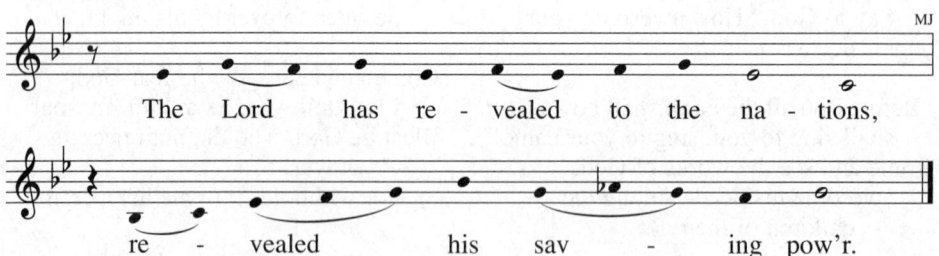

The Lord has re-vealed to the na-tions, re-vealed his sav-ing pow'r.

O sing a new song to the LORD,
    for he has worked wonders.
His right hand and his holy arm
    have brought salvation. ℞.

The LORD has made known his salvation,
    has shown his deliverance to the
        nations.
He has remembered his merciful love

and his truth for the house of
    Israel. ℞.

All the ends of the earth have seen
    the salvation of our God.
Shout to the LORD, all the earth;
    break forth into joyous song,
    and sing out your praise. ℞.

READING II   *1 John 4:7–10*

Beloved, let us love one another, because love is of God; everyone who loves is begotten by God and knows God. Whoever is without love does not know God, for God is love. In this way the love of God was revealed to us: God sent his only Son into the world so that we might have life through him. In this is love: not that we have loved God, but that he loved us and sent his Son as expiation for our sins.

GOSPEL   *John 15:9–17*

Jesus said to his disciples: "As the Father loves me, so I also love you. Remain in my love. If you keep my commandments, you will remain in my love, just as I have kept my Father's commandments and remain in his love.

"I have told you this so that my joy may be in you and your joy might be complete. This is my commandment: love one another as I love you. No one has greater love than this, to lay down one's life for one's friends. You are my friends if you do what I command you. I no longer call you slaves, because a slave does not know what his master is doing. I have called you friends, because I have told you everything I have heard from my Father. It was not you who chose me, but I who chose you and appointed you to go and bear fruit that will remain, so that whatever you ask the Father in my name he may give you. This I command you: love one another."

SIXTH SUNDAY OF EASTER / C   1179

READING I   *Acts 15:1–2, 22–29 / 57*

Some who had come down from Judea were instructing the brothers, "Unless you are circumcised according to the Mosaic practice, you cannot be saved." Because there arose no little dissension and debate by Paul and Barnabas with them, it was decided that Paul, Barnabas, and some of the others should go up to Jerusalem to the apostles and elders about this question.

The apostles and elders, in agreement with the whole church, decided to choose representatives and to send them to Antioch with Paul and Barnabas. The ones chosen were Judas, who was called Barsabbas, and Silas, leaders among the brothers. This is the letter delivered by them:

"The apostles and the elders, your brothers, to the brothers in Antioch, Syria, and Cilicia of Gentile origin: greetings. Since we have heard that some of our number who went out without any mandate from us have upset you with their teachings and disturbed your peace of mind, we have with one accord decided to choose representatives and to send them to you along with our beloved Barnabas and Paul, who have dedicated their lives to the name of our Lord Jesus Christ. So we are sending Judas and Silas who will also convey this same message by word of mouth: 'It is the decision of the Holy Spirit and of us not to place on you any burden beyond these necessities, namely, to abstain from meat sacrificed to idols, from blood, from meats of strangled animals, and from unlawful marriage. If you keep free of these, you will be doing what is right. Farewell.'"

RESPONSORIAL PSALM   *Psalm 67:2–3, 5, 6 and 8*

Or: Alleluia.

O   God,   O   God,   let   all   the na - tions   praise you!

O God, be gracious and bless us
    and let your face shed its light
        upon us.
So will your ways be known upon earth
    and all nations learn your
        salvation. ℟.

Let the nations be glad and shout for joy,
    with uprightness you rule the
        peoples;
you guide the nations on earth. ℟.

Let the peoples praise you, O God;
    let all the peoples praise you.
May God still give us his blessing
    that all the ends of the earth may
        revere him. ℟.

READING II   *Revelation 21:10–14, 22–23*

The angel took me in spirit to a great, high mountain and showed me the holy city Jerusalem coming down out of heaven from God. It gleamed with the splendor of God. Its radiance was like that of a precious stone, like jasper, clear as crystal. It had a massive, high wall, with twelve gates where twelve angels were stationed and on which names were inscribed, the names of the twelve tribes of the Israelites. There were three gates facing east, three north, three south, and three west. The wall of the city had twelve courses of stones as its foundation, on which were inscribed the twelve names of the twelve apostles of the Lamb.

    I saw no temple in the city for its temple is the Lord God almighty and the Lamb. The city had no need of sun or moon to shine on it, for the glory of God gave it light, and its lamp was the Lamb.

GOSPEL   *John 14:23–29*

Jesus said to his disciples: "Whoever loves me will keep my word, and my Father will love him, and we will come to him and make our dwelling with him. Whoever does not love me does not keep my words; yet the word you hear is not mine but that of the Father who sent me.

    "I have told you this while I am with you. The Advocate, the Holy Spirit, whom the Father will send in my name, will teach you everything and remind you of all that I told you. Peace I leave with you; my peace I give to you. Not as the world gives do I give it to you. Do not let your hearts be troubled or afraid. You heard me tell you, 'I am going away and I will come back to you.' If you loved me, you would rejoice that I am going to the Father; for the Father is greater than I. And now I have told you this before it happens, so that when it happens you may believe."

ASCENSION OF THE LORD / ABC 1180

READING I
Acts 1:1–11 / 58

In the first book, Theophilus, I dealt with all that Jesus did and taught until the day he was taken up, after giving instructions through the Holy Spirit to the apostles whom he had chosen. He presented himself alive to them by many proofs after he had suffered, appearing to them during forty days and speaking about the kingdom of God. While meeting with them, he enjoined them not to depart from Jerusalem, but to wait for "the promise of the Father about which you have heard me speak; for John baptized with water, but in a few days you will be baptized with the Holy Spirit."

When they had gathered together they asked him, "Lord, are you at this time going to restore the kingdom to Israel?" He answered them, "It is not for you to know the times or seasons that the Father has established by his own authority. But you will receive power when the Holy Spirit comes upon you, and you will be my witnesses in Jerusalem, throughout Judea and Samaria, and to the ends of the earth." When he had said this, as they were looking on, he was lifted up, and a cloud took him from their sight. While they were looking intently at the sky as he was going, suddenly two men dressed in white garments stood beside them. They said, "Men of Galilee, why are you standing there looking at the sky? This Jesus who has been taken up from you into heaven will return in the same way as you have seen him going into heaven."

RESPONSORIAL PSALM
Psalm 47:2–3, 6–7, 8–9

Or: Alleluia.

God mounts his throne to shouts of joy: a blare of trum-pets for the Lord.

All peoples, clap your hands.
  Cry to God with shouts of joy!
For the LORD, the Most High, is
    awesome,
  the great king over all the earth. ℟.

God goes up with shouts of joy.
  The LORD goes up with trumpet blast.

Sing praise for God; sing praise!
  Sing praise to our king; sing
    praise! ℟.

God is king of all the earth.
  Sing praise with all your skill.
God reigns over the nations.
  God sits upon his holy throne. ℟.

READING II
Ephesians 1:17–23

Brothers and sisters: May the God of our Lord Jesus Christ, the Father of glory, give you a Spirit of wisdom and revelation resulting in knowledge of him. May the eyes of your hearts be enlightened, that you may know what is the hope that belongs to his call, what are the riches of glory in his inheritance among the holy ones, and what is the surpassing greatness of his power for us who believe, in accord with the exercise of his great might, which he worked in Christ, raising him from the dead and seating him at his right hand in the heavens, far above every principality, authority, power, and dominion, and every name that is named not only in this age but also in the one to come. And he put all things beneath his feet and gave him as head over all things to the church, which is his body, the fullness of the one who fills all things in every way.

Or:

READING II / B   *Ephesians 4:1–13 or 4:1–7, 11–13*
For short form read only the parts in brackets.

[Brothers and sisters, I, a prisoner for the Lord, urge you to live in a manner worthy of the call you have received, with all humility and gentleness, with patience, bearing with one another through love, striving to preserve the unity of the spirit through the bond of peace: one body and one Spirit, as you were also called to the one hope of your call; one Lord, one faith, one baptism; one God and Father of all, who is over all and through all and in all.

But grace was given to each of us according to the measure of Christ's gift.] Therefore, it says:
He ascended on high and took prisoners captive;
he gave gifts to men.
What does "he ascended" mean except that he also descended into the lower regions of the earth? The one who descended is also the one who ascended far above all the heavens, that he might fill all things.

[And he gave some as apostles, others as prophets, others as evangelists, others as pastors and teachers, to equip the holy ones for the work of ministry, for building up the body of Christ, until we all attain to the unity of faith and knowledge of the Son of God, to mature manhood, to the extent of the full stature of Christ.]

Or:

READING II / C   *Hebrews 9:24–28; 10:19–23*
Christ did not enter into a sanctuary made by hands, a copy of the true one, but heaven itself, that he might now appear before God on our behalf. Not that he might offer himself repeatedly, as the high priest enters each year into the sanctuary with blood that is not his own; if that were so, he would have had to suffer repeatedly from the foundation of the world. But now once for all he has appeared at the end of the ages to take away sin by his sacrifice. Just as it is appointed that men and women die once, and after this the judgment, so also Christ, offered once to take away the sins of many, will appear a second time, not to take away sin but to bring salvation to those who eagerly await him.

Therefore, brothers and sisters, since through the blood of Jesus we have confidence of entrance into the sanctuary by the new and living way he opened for us through the veil, that is, his flesh, and since we have "a great priest over the house of God," let us approach with a sincere heart and in absolute trust, with our hearts sprinkled clean from an evil conscience and our bodies washed in pure water. Let us hold unwaveringly to our confession that gives us hope, for he who made the promise is trustworthy.

GOSPEL / A   *Matthew 28:16–20*

The eleven disciples went to Galilee, to the mountain to which Jesus had ordered them. When they saw him, they worshiped, but they doubted. Then Jesus approached and said to them, "All power in heaven and on earth has been given to me. Go, therefore, and make disciples of all nations, baptizing them in the name of the Father, and of the Son, and of the Holy Spirit, teaching them to observe all that I have commanded you. And behold, I am with you always, until the end of the age."

GOSPEL / B   *Mark 16:15–20*

Jesus said to his disciples: "Go into the whole world and proclaim the gospel to every creature. Whoever believes and is baptized will be saved; whoever does not believe will be condemned. These signs will accompany those who believe: in my name they will drive out demons, they will speak new languages. They will pick up serpents with their hands, and if they drink any deadly thing, it will not harm them. They will lay hands on the sick, and they will recover."

So then the Lord Jesus, after he spoke to them, was taken up into heaven and took his seat at the right hand of God. But they went forth and preached everywhere, while the Lord worked with them and confirmed the word through accompanying signs.

GOSPEL / C   *Luke 24:46–53*

Jesus said to his disciples: "Thus it is written that the Christ would suffer and rise from the dead on the third day and that repentance, for the forgiveness of sins, would be preached in his name to all the nations, beginning from Jerusalem. You are witnesses of these things. And behold I am sending the promise of my Father upon you; but stay in the city until you are clothed with power from on high."

Then he led them out as far as Bethany, raised his hands, and blessed them. As he blessed them he parted from them and was taken up to heaven. They did him homage and then returned to Jerusalem with great joy, and they were continually in the temple praising God.

SEVENTH SUNDAY OF EASTER / A   1181

READING I   *Acts 1:12–14 / 59*

After Jesus had been taken up to heaven the apostles returned to Jerusalem from the mount called Olivet, which is near Jerusalem, a sabbath day's journey away.

When they entered the city they went to the upper room where they were staying, Peter and John and James and Andrew, Philip and Thomas, Bartholomew and Matthew, James son of Alphaeus, Simon the Zealot, and Judas son of James. All these devoted themselves with one accord to prayer, together with some women, and Mary the mother of Jesus, and his brothers.

RESPONSORIAL PSALM

Psalm 27:1, 4, 7–8a

Or: Alleluia.

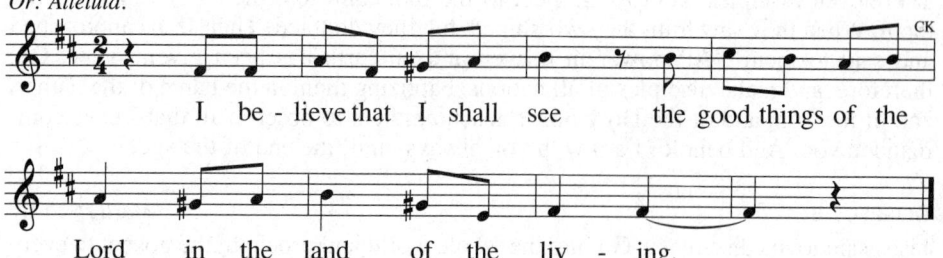

I be-lieve that I shall see the good things of the Lord in the land of the liv - ing.

The LORD is my light and my salvation;
    whom shall I fear?
The LORD is the stronghold of my life;
    whom should I dread? ℟.

There is one thing I ask of the LORD,
    only this do I seek:
to live in the house of the LORD

all the days of my life,
to gaze on the beauty of the LORD,
    to inquire at his temple. ℟.

O LORD, hear my voice when I call;
    have mercy and answer me.
Of you my heart has spoken,
    "Seek his face." ℟.

READING II

1 Peter 4:13–16

Beloved: Rejoice to the extent that you share in the sufferings of Christ, so that when his glory is revealed you may also rejoice exultantly. If you are insulted for the name of Christ, blessed are you, for the Spirit of glory and of God rests upon you. But let no one among you be made to suffer as a murderer, a thief, an evildoer, or as an intriguer. But whoever is made to suffer as a Christian should not be ashamed but glorify God because of the name.

GOSPEL

John 17:1–11a

Jesus raised his eyes to heaven and said, "Father, the hour has come. Give glory to your son, so that your son may glorify you, just as you gave him authority over all people, so that your son may give eternal life to all you gave him. Now this is eternal life, that they should know you, the only true God, and the one whom you sent, Jesus Christ. I glorified you on earth by accomplishing the work that you gave me to do. Now glorify me, Father, with you, with the glory that I had with you before the world began.

"I revealed your name to those whom you gave me out of the world. They belonged to you, and you gave them to me, and they have kept your word. Now they know that everything you gave me is from you, because the words you gave to me I have given to them, and they accepted them and truly understood that I came from you, and they have believed that you sent me. I pray for them. I do not pray for the world but for the ones you have given me, because they are yours, and everything of mine is yours and everything of yours is mine, and I have been glorified in them. And now I will no longer be in the world, but they are in the world, while I am coming to you."

SEVENTH SUNDAY OF EASTER / B   1182

READING I   *Acts 1:15–17, 20a, 20c–26 / 60*

Peter stood up in the midst of the brothers —there was a group of about one hundred and twenty persons in the one place—. He said, "My brothers, the Scripture had to be fulfilled which the Holy Spirit spoke beforehand through the mouth of David, concerning Judas, who was the guide for those who arrested Jesus. He was numbered among us and was allotted a share in this ministry.

"For it is written in the Book of Psalms:
May another take his office.

"Therefore, it is necessary that one of the men who accompanied us the whole time the Lord Jesus came and went among us, beginning from the baptism of John until the day on which he was taken up from us, become with us a witness to his resurrection." So they proposed two, Judas called Barsabbas, who was also known as Justus, and Matthias. Then they prayed, "You, Lord, who know the hearts of all, show which one of these two you have chosen to take the place in this apostolic ministry from which Judas turned away to go to his own place." Then they gave lots to them, and the lot fell upon Matthias, and he was counted with the eleven apostles.

RESPONSORIAL PSALM   *Psalm 103:1–2, 11–12, 19–20ab*

Or: Alleluia.

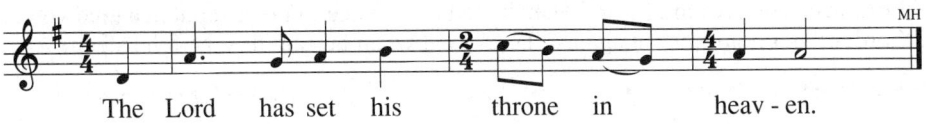

The Lord has set his throne in heav - en.

Bless the LORD, O my soul,
and all within me, his holy name.
Bless the LORD, O my soul,
and never forget all his benefits. ℟.

For as the heavens are high above the earth,
so strong his mercy for those who fear him.

As far as the east is from the west,
so far from us does he remove our transgressions. ℟.

The LORD has fixed his throne in heaven,
and his kingdom is ruling over all.
Bless the LORD, all you his angels,
mighty in power, fulfilling his word. ℟.

READING II   *1 John 4:11–16*

Beloved, if God so loved us, we also must love one another. No one has ever seen God. Yet, if we love one another, God remains in us, and his love is brought to perfection in us.

This is how we know that we remain in him and he in us, that he has given us of his Spirit. Moreover, we have seen and testify that the Father sent his Son as savior of the world. Whoever acknowledges that Jesus is the Son of God, God remains in him and he in God. We have come to know and to believe in the love God has for us.

God is love, and whoever remains in love remains in God and God in him.

GOSPEL   *John 17:11b–19*

Lifting up his eyes to heaven, Jesus prayed saying: "Holy Father, keep them in your name that you have given me, so that they may be one just as we are one. When I was with them I protected them in your name that you gave me, and I guarded them, and none of them was lost except the son of destruction, in order that the Scripture might be fulfilled. But now I am coming to you. I speak this in the world so that they may share my joy completely. I gave them your word, and the world hated them, because they do not belong to the world any more than I belong to the world. I do not ask that you take them out of the world but that you keep them from the evil one. They do not belong to the world any more than I belong to the world. Consecrate them in the truth. Your word is truth. As you sent me into the world, so I sent them into the world. And I consecrate myself for them, so that they also may be consecrated in truth."

1183 SEVENTH SUNDAY OF EASTER / C

READING I   *Acts 7:55–60 / 61*

Stephen, filled with the Holy Spirit, looked up intently to heaven and saw the glory of God and Jesus standing at the right hand of God, and Stephen said, "Behold, I see the heavens opened and the Son of Man standing at the right hand of God." But they cried out in a loud voice, covered their ears, and rushed upon him together. They threw him out of the city, and began to stone him. The witnesses laid down their cloaks at the feet of a young man named Saul. As they were stoning Stephen, he called out, "Lord Jesus, receive my spirit." Then he fell to his knees and cried out in a loud voice, "Lord, do not hold this sin against them"; and when he said this, he fell asleep.

RESPONSORIAL PSALM   *Psalm 97:1 and 2b, 6 and 7c, 9*

Or: Alleluia.

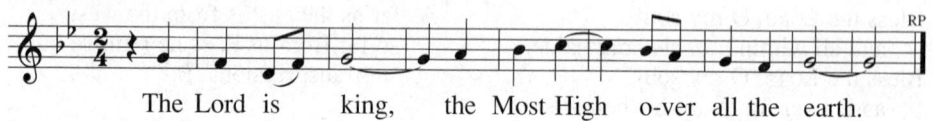

The Lord is king, the Most High o-ver all the earth.

The LORD is king, let earth rejoice;
  let the many islands be glad.
Justice and right are the foundation
    of his throne. ℟.

The skies proclaim his justice;

all peoples see his glory.
All you angels, worship him. ℟.

For you indeed are the LORD,
  most high above all the earth,
exalted far above all gods. ℟.

READING II   *Revelation 22:12–14, 16–17, 20*

I, John, heard a voice saying to me: "Behold, I am coming soon. I bring with me the recompense I will give to each according to his deeds. I am the Alpha and the Omega, the first and the last, the beginning and the end."

Blessed are they who wash their robes so as to have the right to the tree of life and enter the city through its gates.

"I, Jesus, sent my angel to give you this testimony for the churches. I am the root and offspring of David, the bright morning star."

The Spirit and the bride say, "Come." Let the hearer say, "Come." Let the one who thirsts come forward, and the one who wants it receive the gift of life-giving water.

The one who gives this testimony says, "Yes, I am coming soon." Amen! Come, Lord Jesus!

GOSPEL *John 17:20–26*

Lifting up his eyes to heaven, Jesus prayed saying: "Holy Father, I pray not only for them, but also for those who will believe in me through their word, so that they may all be one, as you, Father, are in me and I in you, that they also may be in us, that the world may believe that you sent me. And I have given them the glory you gave me, so that they may be one, as we are one, I in them and you in me, that they may be brought to perfection as one, that the world may know that you sent me, and that you loved them even as you loved me. Father, they are your gift to me. I wish that where I am they also may be with me, that they may see my glory that you gave me, because you loved me before the foundation of the world. Righteous Father, the world also does not know you, but I know you, and they know that you sent me. I made known to them your name and I will make it known, that the love with which you loved me may be in them and I in them."

PENTECOST SUNDAY—VIGIL MASS / ABC 1184

READING I *Genesis 11:1–9 / 62*

The whole world spoke the same language, using the same words. While the people were migrating in the east, they came upon a valley in the land of Shinar and settled there. They said to one another, "Come, let us mold bricks and harden them with fire." They used bricks for stone, and bitumen for mortar. Then they said, "Come, let us build ourselves a city and a tower with its top in the sky, and so make a name for ourselves; otherwise we shall be scattered all over the earth."

The LORD came down to see the city and the tower that the people had built. Then the LORD said: "If now, while they are one people, all speaking the same language, they have started to do this, nothing will later stop them from doing whatever they presume to do. Let us then go down there and confuse their language, so that one will not understand what another says." Thus the LORD scattered them from there all over the earth, and they stopped building the city. That is why it was called Babel, because there the LORD confused the speech of all the world. It was from that place that he scattered them all over the earth.

Or:

READING I *Exodus 19:3–8a, 16–20b*

Moses went up the mountain to God. Then the LORD called to him and said, "Thus shall you say to the house of Jacob; tell the Israelites: You have seen for yourselves how I treated the Egyptians and how I bore you up on eagle wings and brought you here to myself. Therefore, if you hearken to my voice and keep my covenant, you shall be my special possession, dearer to me than all other people, though all the earth is mine. You shall be to me a kingdom of priests, a holy nation. That is what you must tell the Israelites." So Moses went and summoned the elders of the people. When he set before them all that the LORD had ordered him to tell them, the people all answered together, "Everything the LORD has said, we will do."

On the morning of the third day there were peals of thunder and lightning, and a heavy cloud over the mountain, and a very loud trumpet blast, so that all the people in the camp trembled. But Moses led the people out of the camp to meet God, and they stationed themselves at the foot of the mountain. Mount Sinai was all wrapped in smoke, for the LORD came down upon it in fire. The smoke rose from it as though from a furnace, and the whole mountain trembled violently. The trumpet blast grew louder and louder, while Moses was speaking, and God answering him with thunder.

When the LORD came down to the top of Mount Sinai, he summoned Moses to the top of the mountain.

Or:

READING I   *Ezekiel 37:1–14*

The hand of the LORD came upon me, and he led me out in the spirit of the LORD and set me in the center of the plain, which was now filled with bones. He made me walk among the bones in every direction so that I saw how many they were on the surface of the plain. How dry they were! He asked me: Son of man, can these bones come to life? I answered, "Lord GOD, you alone know that." Then he said to me: Prophesy over these bones, and say to them: Dry bones, hear the word of the LORD! Thus says the Lord GOD to these bones: See! I will bring spirit into you, that you may come to life. I will put sinews upon you, make flesh grow over you, cover you with skin, and put spirit in you so that you may come to life and know that I am the LORD. I, Ezekiel, prophesied as I had been told, and even as I was prophesying I heard a noise; it was a rattling as the bones came together, bone joining bone. I saw the sinews and the flesh come upon them, and the skin cover them, but there was no spirit in them. Then the LORD said to me: Prophesy to the spirit, prophesy, son of man, and say to the spirit: Thus says the Lord GOD: From the four winds come, O spirit, and breathe into these slain that they may come to life. I prophesied as he told me, and the spirit came into them; they came alive and stood upright, a vast army. Then he said to me: Son of man, these bones are the whole house of Israel. They have been saying, "Our bones are dried up, our hope is lost, and we are cut off." Therefore, prophesy and say to them: Thus says the Lord GOD: O my people, I will open your graves and have you rise from them, and bring you back to the land of Israel. Then you shall know that I am the LORD, when I open your graves and have you rise from them, O my people! I will put my spirit in you that you may live, and I will settle you upon your land; thus you shall know that I am the LORD. I have promised, and I will do it, says the LORD.

Or:

READING I   *Joel 3:1–5*

Thus says the LORD:
I will pour out my spirit upon all flesh.
Your sons and daughters shall prophesy,
   your old men shall dream dreams,
   your young men shall see visions;
even upon the servants and the
     handmaids,
   in those days, I will pour out my
    spirit.
And I will work wonders in the
    heavens and on the earth,
   blood, fire, and columns of smoke;

the sun will be turned to darkness,
   and the moon to blood,
at the coming of the day of the LORD,
   the great and terrible day.
Then everyone shall be rescued
   who calls on the name of the LORD;
for on Mount Zion there shall be a
    remnant,
   as the LORD has said,
and in Jerusalem survivors
   whom the LORD shall call.

RESPONSORIAL PSALM   *Psalm 104:1–2a, 24 and 35c, 27–28, 29bc–30*

Or: Alleluia.

Lord, send out your Spir-it,   and re-new the face of the earth.

Bless the LORD, O my soul!
　O LORD my God, how great you are,
clothed in majesty and honor,
　wrapped in light as with a robe! ℟.

How many are your works, O LORD!
　In wisdom you have made them all.
The earth is full of your creatures.
　Bless the LORD, O my soul.
　　Alleluia! ℟.

All of these look to you

to give them their food in due season.
You give it, they gather it up;
　you open wide your hand, they are
　well filled. ℟.

You take away their breath, they die,
　returning to the dust from which they
　came.
You send forth your spirit, and they are
　created,
　and you renew the face of the earth. ℟.

READING II   *Romans 8:22–27*

Brothers and sisters: We know that all creation is groaning in labor pains even until now; and not only that, but we ourselves, who have the firstfruits of the Spirit, we also groan within ourselves as we wait for adoption, the redemption of our bodies. For in hope we were saved. Now hope that sees is not hope. For who hopes for what one sees? But if we hope for what we do not see, we wait with endurance.

In the same way, the Spirit too comes to the aid of our weakness; for we do not know how to pray as we ought, but the Spirit himself intercedes with inexpressible groanings. And the one who searches hearts knows what is the intention of the Spirit, because he intercedes for the holy ones according to God's will.

GOSPEL   *John 7:37–39*

On the last and greatest day of the feast, Jesus stood up and exclaimed, "Let anyone who thirsts come to me and drink. As Scripture says:
　Rivers of living water will flow from within him who believes in me."
He said this in reference to the Spirit that those who came to believe in him were to receive. There was, of course, no Spirit yet, because Jesus had not yet been glorified.

PENTECOST SUNDAY—MASS DURING THE DAY / ABC   1185

READING I   *Acts 2:1–11 / 63*

When the time for Pentecost was fulfilled, they were all in one place together. And suddenly there came from the sky a noise like a strong driving wind, and it filled the entire house in which they were. Then there appeared to them tongues as of fire, which parted and came to rest on each one of them. And they were all filled with the Holy Spirit and began to speak in different tongues, as the Spirit enabled them to proclaim.

Now there were devout Jews from every nation under heaven staying in Jerusalem. At this sound, they gathered in a large crowd, but they were confused because each one heard them speaking in his own language. They were astounded, and in amazement they asked, "Are not all these people who are speaking Galileans? Then how does each of us hear them in his native language? We are Parthians, Medes, and Elamites, inhabitants of Mesopotamia, Judea and Cappadocia, Pontus and Asia, Phrygia and Pamphylia, Egypt and the districts of Libya near Cyrene, as well as travelers from Rome, both Jews and converts to Judaism, Cretans and Arabs, yet we hear them speaking in our own tongues of the mighty acts of God."

RESPONSORIAL PSALM   *Psalm 104:1ab and 24ac, 29bc–30, 31 and 34*

Or: Alleluia.

Lord, send out your Spir-it,   and re-new the face of the earth.

Bless the LORD, O my soul!
   O LORD my God, how great you are.
How many are your works, O LORD!
   The earth is full of your creatures. ℟.

You take away their breath, they die,
   returning to the dust from which
     they came.
You send forth your spirit, and they are

   created,
   and you renew the face of the
     earth. ℟.

May the glory of the LORD last forever!
   May the LORD rejoice in his works!
May my thoughts be pleasing to him.
   I will rejoice in the LORD. ℟.

READING II / ABC   *1 Corinthians 12:3b–7, 12–13*
Brothers and sisters: No one can say, "Jesus is Lord," except by the Holy Spirit.
    There are different kinds of spiritual gifts but the same Spirit; there are different forms of service but the same Lord; there are different workings but the same God who produces all of them in everyone. To each individual the manifestation of the Spirit is given for some benefit.
    As a body is one though it has many parts, and all the parts of the body, though many, are one body, so also Christ. For in one Spirit we were all baptized into one body, whether Jews or Greeks, slaves or free persons, and we were all given to drink of one Spirit.

Or:

READING II / B   *Galatians 5:16–25*
Brothers and sisters, live by the Spirit and you will certainly not gratify the desire of the flesh. For the flesh has desires against the Spirit, and the Spirit against the flesh; these are opposed to each other, so that you may not do what you want. But if you are guided by the Spirit, you are not under the law. Now the works of the flesh are obvious: immorality, impurity, lust, idolatry, sorcery, hatreds, rivalry, jealousy, outbursts of fury, acts of selfishness, dissensions, factions, occasions of envy, drinking bouts, orgies, and the like. I warn you, as I warned you before, that those who do such things will not inherit the kingdom of God. In contrast, the fruit of the Spirit is love, joy,

peace, patience, kindness, generosity, faithfulness, gentleness, self-control. Against such there is no law. Now those who belong to Christ Jesus have crucified their flesh with its passions and desires. If we live in the Spirit, let us also follow the Spirit.

Or:

READING II / C
Romans 8:8–17

Brothers and sisters: Those who are in the flesh cannot please God. But you are not in the flesh; on the contrary, you are in the spirit, if only the Spirit of God dwells in you. Whoever does not have the Spirit of Christ does not belong to him. But if Christ is in you, although the body is dead because of sin, the spirit is alive because of righteousness. If the Spirit of the one who raised Jesus from the dead dwells in you, the one who raised Christ from the dead will give life to your mortal bodies also, through his Spirit that dwells in you. Consequently, brothers and sisters, we are not debtors to the flesh, to live according to the flesh. For if you live according to the flesh, you will die, but if by the Spirit you put to death the deeds of the body, you will live.

For those who are led by the Spirit of God are sons of God. For you did not receive a spirit of slavery to fall back into fear, but you received a Spirit of adoption, through whom we cry, "Abba, Father!" The Spirit himself bears witness with our spirit that we are children of God, and if children, then heirs, heirs of God and joint heirs with Christ, if only we suffer with him so that we may also be glorified with him.

SEQUENCE
1186

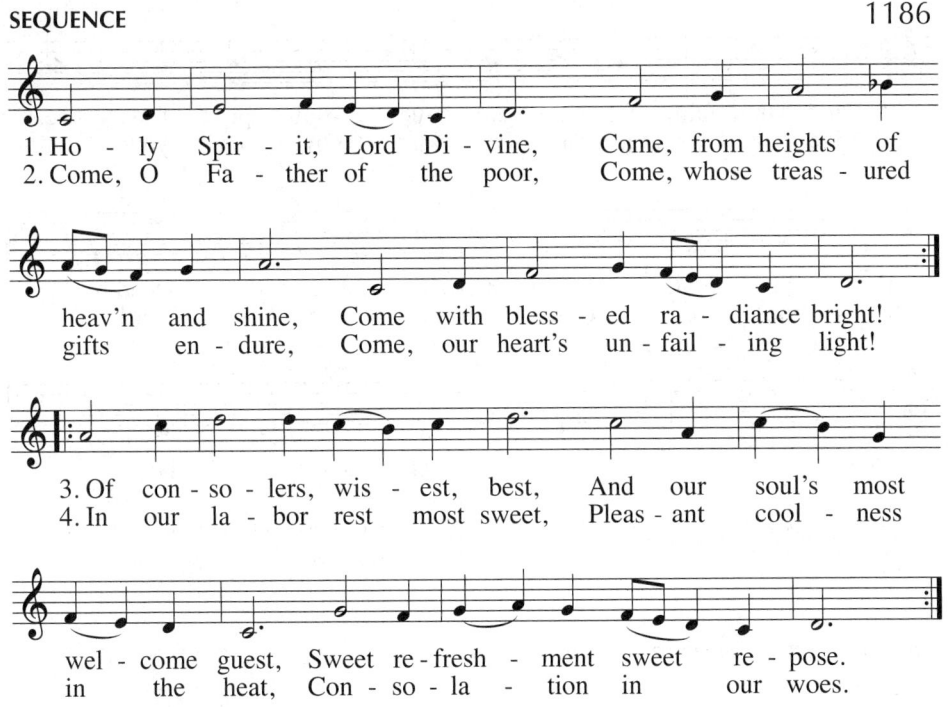

1. Ho - ly Spir - it, Lord Di - vine, Come, from heights of heav'n and shine, Come with bless - ed ra - diance bright!
2. Come, O Fa - ther of the poor, Come, whose treas - ured gifts en - dure, Come, our heart's un - fail - ing light!

3. Of con - so - lers, wis - est, best, And our soul's most wel - come guest, Sweet re - fresh - ment sweet re - pose.
4. In our la - bor rest most sweet, Pleas - ant cool - ness in the heat, Con - so - la - tion in our woes.

5. Light most bless - ed, shine with grace In our heart's most
6. Left with - out your pres - ence here, Life it - self would

se - cret place, Fill your faith - ful through and through.
dis - ap - pear, Noth - ing thrives a - part from you!

7. Cleanse our soil - ed hearts of sin, Ar - id souls re -
8. Bend the stub - born heart and will, Melt the fro - zen,

fresh with - in, Wound - ed lives to health re - store.
warm the chill, Guide the way - ward home once more!

9. On the faith - ful who are true And pro - fess their
10. Give us vir - tue's sure re - ward, Give us your sal -

faith in you, In your sev'n - fold gift de - scend!
va - tion, Lord, Give us joys that nev - er end!

A - men. Al - le - lu - ia.

Text: *Veni Sancte Spiritus*; attr. to Stephen Langton, c.1150–1228, et al.; tr. by Peter J. Scagnelli, b.1949, after Edward Caswall, 1814–1878, © 1983, Peter J. Scagnelli. Published by World Library Publications.
Tune: VENI SANCTE SPIRITUS, 7 7 7; Dublin *Troper*, c.1360; Mode I; acc. by Adriaan Engels, 1906–2003, © Interkerkelijke Stichting voor het Kerklied Den Haag

An alternate setting is found at no. 656.

GOSPEL / ABC   *John 20:19–23*

On the evening of that first day of the week, when the doors were locked, where the disciples were, for fear of the Jews, Jesus came and stood in their midst and said to them, "Peace be with you." When he had said this, he showed them his hands and his side. The disciples rejoiced when they saw the Lord. Jesus said to them again, "Peace be with you. As the Father has sent me, so I send you." And when he had said this, he breathed on them and said to them, "Receive the Holy Spirit. Whose sins you forgive are forgiven them, and whose sins you retain are retained."

Or:

GOSPEL / B   *John 15:26–27; 16:12–15*

Jesus said to his disciples: "When the Advocate comes whom I will send you from the Father, the Spirit of truth that proceeds from the Father, he will testify to me. And you also testify, because you have been with me from the beginning.

"I have much more to tell you, but you cannot bear it now. But when he comes, the Spirit of truth, he will guide you to all truth. He will not speak on his own, but he will speak what he hears, and will declare to you the things that are coming. He will glorify me, because he will take from what is mine and declare it to you. Everything that the Father has is mine; for this reason I told you that he will take from what is mine and declare it to you."

Or:

GOSPEL / C   *John 14:15–16, 23b–26*

Jesus said to his disciples: "If you love me, you will keep my commandments. And I will ask the Father, and he will give you another Advocate to be with you always.

"Whoever loves me will keep my word, and my Father will love him, and we will come to him and make our dwelling with him. Those who do not love me do not keep my words; yet the word you hear is not mine but that of the Father who sent me.

"I have told you this while I am with you. The Advocate, the Holy Spirit whom the Father will send in my name, will teach you everything and remind you of all that I told you."

1187 Ordinary Time

When the Church assembles, time is always given to the reading of Scripture. This is the book the Church esteems: the Law and the prophets, the books of wisdom and psalms, the letters and writings of Paul and of the other apostles, the gospels themselves. Throughout the history of the Church the readings from Scripture have been arranged so that the various Sundays have their assigned texts. This book of assigned scripture readings is the lectionary. In the present Roman lectionary the readings are ordered according to a cycle of three years.

Most of each year is called "Ordinary Time" or "Sundays of the Year." These are the weeks between the Christmas season and Lent, and the long period between Pentecost (the conclusion of the Easter season) and Advent (usually the first Sunday in December). On the Sundays of Ordinary Time, the lectionary has us read through the letters of the New Testament and the gospels. In the first year of the cycle, the gospel of Matthew is read from beginning to end; in the second year, Mark; in the third, Luke. Likewise, each Sunday finds the Church picking up the reading of one of the letters of the New Testament roughly where the previous week's reading concluded. At present, the first reading at Sunday Mass in Ordinary Time is chosen from the Hebrew Scriptures; these texts show the richness and the continuity of faith.

Sunday by Sunday, year after year, the Church reads through its book in the weeks of Ordinary Time. Each Christian, each local Church, each generation listens and so finds its own life in God's word.

The Church assembles around Scripture and around the Lord's table on Sunday. This day is called by Christians the Lord's Day. Whether the Church is in Ordinary Time or in the seasons of Advent/Christmas or Lent/Easter, the Lord's Day is kept holy; it is the original feast day. The rhythm of the weekdays and the Sunday is the basic rhythm of life in Christian churches. The practices with which a Church keeps the Lord's Day vary, but always and everywhere Christians assemble on this day so that the Church may listen to God's word. Through the days of the week, the Sunday's scripture readings are to be for reflection and nourishment as they are repeated and pondered in the households of the assembly.

MOST HOLY TRINITY / A 1188

READING I
Exodus 34:4b–6, 8–9 / 164

Early in the morning Moses went up Mount Sinai as the LORD had commanded him, taking along the two stone tablets.

Having come down in a cloud, the LORD stood with Moses there and proclaimed his name, "LORD." Thus the LORD passed before him and cried out, "The LORD, the LORD, a merciful and gracious God, slow to anger and rich in kindness and fidelity." Moses at once bowed down to the ground in worship. Then he said, "If I find favor with you, O LORD, do come along in our company. This is indeed a stiff-necked people; yet pardon our wickedness and sins, and receive us as your own."

RESPONSORIAL PSALM
Daniel 3:52, 53, 54, 55

Cantor or choir:

JG

You are blest, Lord God of our fa - thers.
Blest be your glo - ri - ous ho - ly name.
You are blest in the tem - ple of your glo - ry.
You are blest on the throne of your king - dom.
You are blest who gaze in - to the depths.
You are blest who sit a - bove the cher - u - bim.
You are blest in the firm - a - ment of heav - en.

Assembly:

To you glo - ry and praise for ev - er - more.

READING II
2 Corinthians 13:11–13

Brothers and sisters, rejoice. Mend your ways, encourage one another, agree with one another, live in peace, and the God of love and peace will be with you. Greet one another with a holy kiss. All the holy ones greet you.

The grace of the Lord Jesus Christ and the love of God and the fellowship of the Holy Spirit be with all of you.

GOSPEL
John 3:16–18

God so loved the world that he gave his only Son, so that everyone who believes in him might not perish but might have eternal life. For God did not send his Son into the world to condemn the world, but that the world might be saved through him. Whoever believes in him will not be condemned, but whoever does not believe has already been condemned, because he has not believed in the name of the only Son of God.

1189 MOST HOLY TRINITY / B

READING I *Deuteronomy 4:32–34, 39–40 / 165*

Moses said to the people: "Ask now of the days of old, before your time, ever since God created man upon the earth; ask from one end of the sky to the other: Did anything so great ever happen before? Was it ever heard of? Did a people ever hear the voice of God speaking from the midst of fire, as you did, and live? Or did any god venture to go and take a nation for himself from the midst of another nation, by testings, by signs and wonders, by war, with strong hand and outstretched arm, and by great terrors, all of which the LORD, your God, did for you in Egypt before your very eyes? This is why you must now know, and fix in your heart, that the LORD is God in the heavens above and on earth below, and that there is no other. You must keep his statutes and commandments that I enjoin on you today, that you and your children after you may prosper, and that you may have long life on the land which the LORD, your God, is giving you forever."

RESPONSORIAL PSALM *Psalm 33:4–5, 6 and 9, 18–19, 20 and 22*

Bless-ed the peo-ple the Lord has cho-sen to be his own.

The word of the LORD is faithful,
and all his works to be trusted.
The LORD loves justice and right,
and his merciful love fills the earth. ℟.

By the word of the LORD the heavens
were made,
by the breath of his mouth all their
host.
He spoke, and it came to be.
He commanded; it stood in place. ℟.

Yes, the LORD's eyes are on those who
fear him,
who hope in his merciful love,
to rescue their souls from death,
to keep them alive in famine. ℟.

Our soul is waiting for the LORD.
He is our help and our shield.
May your merciful love be upon us,
as we hope in you, O LORD. ℟.

READING II *Romans 8:14–17*

Brothers and sisters: Those who are led by the Spirit of God are sons of God. For you did not receive a spirit of slavery to fall back into fear, but you received a Spirit of adoption, through whom we cry, "Abba, Father!" The Spirit himself bears witness with our spirit that we are children of God, and if children, then heirs, heirs of God and joint heirs with Christ, if only we suffer with him so that we may also be glorified with him.

GOSPEL *Matthew 28:16–20*

The eleven disciples went to Galilee, to the mountain to which Jesus had ordered them. When they all saw him, they worshiped, but they doubted. Then Jesus approached and said to them, "All power in heaven and on earth has been given to me. Go, therefore, and make disciples of all nations, baptizing them in the name of the Father, and of the Son, and of the Holy Spirit, teaching them to observe all that I have commanded you. And behold, I am with you always, until the end of the age."

MOST HOLY TRINITY / C 1190

READING I
Proverbs 8:22–31 / 166

Thus says the wisdom of God:
"The LORD possessed me, the
   beginning of his ways,
 the forerunner of his prodigies of
   long ago;
from of old I was poured forth,
 at the first, before the earth.
When there were no depths I was
   brought forth,
 when there were no fountains or
   springs of water;
before the mountains were settled
   into place,
 before the hills, I was brought forth;
while as yet the earth and fields were
   not made,
 nor the first clods of the world.

"When the Lord established the heavens
   I was there,
 when he marked out the vault over
   the face of the deep;
when he made firm the skies above,
 when he fixed fast the foundations
   of the earth;
when he set for the sea its limit,
 so that the waters should not
   transgress his command;
then was I beside him as his craftsman,
 and I was his delight day by day,
playing before him all the while,
 playing on the surface of his earth;
and I found delight in the human
   race."

RESPONSORIAL PSALM
Psalm 8:4–5, 6–7, 8–9

JRC

O Lord, our God, how won-der-ful your name in all the earth!

When I see the heavens, the work of
   your fingers,
 the moon and the stars which you
   arranged,
what is man that you should keep him
   in mind,
 the son of man that you care for
   him? ℟.

Yet you have made him little lower
   than the angels;

with glory and honor you crowned
   him,
gave him power over the works of your
   hands:
 you put all things under his feet. ℟.

All of them, sheep and oxen,
 yes, even the cattle of the fields,
birds of the air, and fish of the sea
 that make their way through the
   waters. ℟.

READING II
Romans 5:1–5

Brothers and sisters: Therefore, since we have been justified by faith, we have peace with God through our Lord Jesus Christ, through whom we have gained access by faith to this grace in which we stand, and we boast in hope of the glory of God. Not only that, but we even boast of our afflictions, knowing that affliction produces endurance, and endurance, proven character, and proven character, hope, and hope does not disappoint, because the love of God has been poured out into our hearts through the Holy Spirit that has been given to us.

GOSPEL *John 16:12–15*

Jesus said to his disciples: "I have much more to tell you, but you cannot bear it now. But when he comes, the Spirit of truth, he will guide you to all truth. He will not speak on his own, but he will speak what he hears, and will declare to you the things that are coming. He will glorify me, because he will take from what is mine and declare it to you. Everything that the Father has is mine; for this reason I told you that he will take from what is mine and declare it to you."

1191 MOST HOLY BODY AND BLOOD OF CHRIST / A

READING I *Deuteronomy 8:2–3, 14b–16a / 167*

Moses said to the people: "Remember how for forty years now the LORD, your God, has directed all your journeying in the desert, so as to test you by affliction and find out whether or not it was your intention to keep his commandments. He therefore let you be afflicted with hunger, and then fed you with manna, a food unknown to you and your fathers, in order to show you that not by bread alone does one live, but by every word that comes forth from the mouth of the LORD.

"Do not forget the LORD, your God, who brought you out of the land of Egypt, that place of slavery; who guided you through the vast and terrible desert with its saraph serpents and scorpions, its parched and waterless ground; who brought forth water for you from the flinty rock and fed you in the desert with manna, a food unknown to your fathers."

RESPONSORIAL PSALM *Psalm 147:12–13, 14–15, 19–20*

Or: Alleluia.

Praise the Lord, Je - ru - sa - lem.

O Jerusalem, glorify the LORD!
O Sion, praise your God!
He has strengthened the bars of your
gates;
he has blessed your children within
you. ℟.

He established peace on your borders;
he gives you your fill of finest wheat.

He sends out his word to the earth,
and swiftly runs his command. ℟.

He reveals his word to Jacob;
to Israel, his decrees and judgments.
He has not dealt thus with other nations;
he has not taught them his
judgments. ℟.

READING II *1 Corinthians 10:16–17*

Brothers and sisters: The cup of blessing that we bless, is it not a participation in the blood of Christ? The bread that we break, is it not a participation in the body of Christ? Because the loaf of bread is one, we, though many, are one body, for we all partake of the one loaf.

SEQUENCE (Optional)
A metrical setting may be found at no. 667.

GOSPEL   *John 6:51–58*

Jesus said to the Jewish crowds: "I am the living bread that came down from heaven; whoever eats this bread will live forever; and the bread that I will give is my flesh for the life of the world."

The Jews quarreled among themselves, saying, "How can this man give us his flesh to eat?" Jesus said to them, "Amen, amen, I say to you, unless you eat the flesh of the Son of Man and drink his blood, you do not have life within you. Whoever eats my flesh and drinks my blood has eternal life, and I will raise him on the last day. For my flesh is true food, and my blood is true drink. Whoever eats my flesh and drinks my blood remains in me and I in him. Just as the living Father sent me and I have life because of the Father, so also the one who feeds on me will have life because of me. This is the bread that came down from heaven. Unlike your ancestors who ate and still died, whoever eats this bread will live forever."

MOST HOLY BODY AND BLOOD OF CHRIST / B   1192

READING I   *Exodus 24:3–8 / 168*

When Moses came to the people and related all the words and ordinances of the LORD, they all answered with one voice, "We will do everything that the LORD has told us." Moses then wrote down all the words of the LORD and, rising early the next day, he erected at the foot of the mountain an altar and twelve pillars for the twelve tribes of Israel. Then, having sent certain young men of the Israelites to offer holocausts and sacrifice young bulls as peace offerings to the LORD, Moses took half of the blood and put it in large bowls; the other half he splashed on the altar. Taking the book of the covenant, he read it aloud to the people, who answered, "All that the LORD has said, we will heed and do." Then he took the blood and sprinkled it on the people, saying, "This is the blood of the covenant that the LORD has made with you in accordance with all these words of his."

RESPONSORIAL PSALM   *Psalm 116:12–13, 15 and 16bc, 17–18*

Or: Alleluia.

I will take the cup of sal - va - tion,
and call on the name of the Lord.

How can I repay the LORD
   for all his goodness to me?
The cup of salvation I will raise;
   I will call on the name of the
      LORD. ℟.

How precious in the eyes of the LORD
   is the death of his faithful.
Your servant am I,

the son of your handmaid;
   you have loosened my bonds. ℟.

A thanksgiving sacrifice I make;
   I will call on the name of the
      LORD.
My vows to the LORD I will fulfill
   before all his people. ℟.

READING II   *Hebrews 9:11–15*

Brothers and sisters: When Christ came as high priest of the good things that have come to be, passing through the greater and more perfect tabernacle not made by hands, that is, not belonging to this creation, he entered once for all into the sanctuary, not with the blood of goats and calves but with his own blood, thus obtaining eternal redemption. For if the blood of goats and bulls and the sprinkling of a heifer's ashes can sanctify those who are defiled so that their flesh is cleansed, how much more will the blood of Christ, who through the eternal Spirit offered himself unblemished to God, cleanse our consciences from dead works to worship the living God.

For this reason he is mediator of a new covenant: since a death has taken place for deliverance from transgressions under the first covenant, those who are called may receive the promised eternal inheritance.

SEQUENCE   *A metrical setting may be found at no. 667.*

GOSPEL   *Mark 14:12–16, 22–26*

On the first day of the Feast of Unleavened Bread, when they sacrificed the Passover lamb, Jesus' disciples said to him, "Where do you want us to go and prepare for you to eat the Passover?" He sent two of his disciples and said to them, "Go into the city and a man will meet you, carrying a jar of water. Follow him. Wherever he enters, say to the master of the house, 'The Teacher says, "Where is my guest room where I may eat the Passover with my disciples?"' Then he will show you a large upper room furnished and ready. Make the preparations for us there." The disciples then went off, entered the city, and found it just as he had told them; and they prepared the Passover.

While they were eating, he took bread, said the blessing, broke it, gave it to them, and said, "Take it; this is my body." Then he took a cup, gave thanks, and gave it to them, and they all drank from it. He said to them, "This is my blood of the covenant, which will be shed for many. Amen, I say to you, I shall not drink again the fruit of the vine until the day when I drink it new in the kingdom of God." Then, after singing a hymn, they went out to the Mount of Olives.

1193   MOST HOLY BODY AND BLOOD OF CHRIST / C

READING I   *Genesis 14:18–20 / 169*

In those days, Melchizedek, king of Salem, brought out bread and wine, and being a priest of God Most High, he blessed Abram with these words:
    "Blessed be Abram by God Most High,
        the creator of heaven and earth;
    and blessed be God Most High,
        who delivered your foes into your hand."
Then Abram gave him a tenth of everything.

RESPONSORIAL PSALM

Psalm 110:1, 2, 3, 4

You are a priest for ev - er, in the line of Mel - chi-ze-dek.

The LORD's revelation to my lord:
   "Sit at my right hand,
   until I make your foes your
      footstool." ℟.

The LORD will send from Sion
   your scepter of power:
   rule in the midst of your foes. ℟.

With you is princely rule

on the day of your power.
In holy splendor, from the womb before
      the dawn,
   I have begotten you. ℟.

The LORD has sworn an oath he will
      not change:
   "You are a priest forever,
   in the line of Melchizedek." ℟.

READING II

1 Corinthians 11:23–26

Brothers and sisters: I received from the Lord what I also handed on to you, that the Lord Jesus, on the night he was handed over, took bread, and, after he had given thanks, broke it and said, "This is my body that is for you. Do this in remembrance of me." In the same way also the cup, after supper, saying, "This cup is the new covenant in my blood. Do this, as often as you drink it, in remembrance of me." For as often as you eat this bread and drink the cup, you proclaim the death of the Lord until he comes.

SEQUENCE   *A metrical setting may be found at no. 667.*

GOSPEL

Luke 9:11b–17

Jesus spoke to the crowds about the kingdom of God, and he healed those who needed to be cured. As the day was drawing to a close, the Twelve approached him and said, "Dismiss the crowd so that they can go to the surrounding villages and farms and find lodging and provisions; for we are in a deserted place here." He said to them, "Give them some food yourselves." They replied, "Five loaves and two fish are all we have, unless we ourselves go and buy food for all these people." Now the men there numbered about five thousand. Then he said to his disciples, "Have them sit down in groups of about fifty." They did so and made them all sit down. Then taking the five loaves and the two fish, and looking up to heaven, he said the blessing over them, broke them, and gave them to the disciples to set before the crowd. They all ate and were satisfied. And when the leftover fragments were picked up, they filled twelve wicker baskets.

MOST SACRED HEART OF JESUS / A   1194

READING I

Deuteronomy 7:6–11 / 170

Moses said to the people: "You are a people sacred to the LORD, your God; he has chosen you from all the nations on the face of the earth to be a people peculiarly his own. It was not because you are the largest of all nations that the LORD set his heart on you and chose you, for you are really the smallest of all nations. It was because the LORD loved you and because of his fidelity to the oath he had sworn to your fathers, that he brought you out with his strong hand from the place of slavery, and ransomed you from the hand of Pharaoh, king of Egypt. Understand, then, that the LORD, your God, is God indeed, the faithful God who keeps his merciful covenant down to the thousandth generation toward those who love him and keep his commandments, but who repays with destruction a person who hates him; he does not dally with such a one, but makes them personally pay for it. You shall therefore carefully observe the commandments, the statutes and the decrees that I enjoin on you today."

RESPONSORIAL PSALM   *Psalm 103:1–2, 3–4, 6–7, 8 and 10*

The Lord's kind - ness is ev - er - last - ing to those who fear him.

Bless the LORD, O my soul,
    and all within me, his holy name.
Bless the LORD, O my soul,
    and never forget all his benefits. ℟.

It is the Lord who forgives all your sins,
    who heals every one of your ills,
who redeems your life from the grave,
    who crowns you with mercy and
      compassion. ℟.

The LORD does just deeds,

gives full justice to all who are
    oppressed.
He made known his ways to Moses,
    and his deeds to the children of
      Israel. ℟.

The LORD is compassionate and gracious,
    slow to anger and rich in mercy.
He does not treat us according to our
    sins,
    nor repay us according to our
    faults. ℟.

READING II   *1 John 4:7–16*

Beloved, let us love one another, because love is of God; everyone who loves is begotten by God and knows God. Whoever is without love does not know God, for God is love. In this way the love of God was revealed to us: God sent his only Son into the world so that we might have life through him. In this is love: not that we have loved God, but that he loved us and sent his Son as expiation for our sins. Beloved, if God so loved us, we also must love one another. No one has ever seen God. Yet, if we love one another, God remains in us, and his love is brought to perfection in us.

This is how we know that we remain in him and he in us, that he has given us of his Spirit. Moreover, we have seen and testify that the Father sent his Son as savior of the world. Whoever acknowledges that Jesus is the Son of God, God remains in him and he in God. We have come to know and to believe in the love God has for us.

God is love, and whoever remains in love remains in God and God in him.

GOSPEL   *Matthew 11:25–30*

At that time Jesus exclaimed: "I give praise to you, Father, Lord of heaven and earth, for although you have hidden these things from the wise and the learned you have revealed them to little ones. Yes, Father, such has been your gracious will. All things have been handed over to me by my Father. No one knows the Son except the Father, and no one knows the Father except the Son and anyone to whom the Son wishes to reveal him.

"Come to me, all you who labor and are burdened, and I will give you rest. Take my yoke upon you and learn from me, for I am meek and humble of heart; and you will find rest for yourselves. For my yoke is easy, and my burden light."

MOST SACRED HEART OF JESUS / B   1195

READING I
Hosea 11:1, 3–4, 8c–9 / 171

Thus says the Lord:
When Israel was a child I loved him,
  out of Egypt I called my son.
Yet it was I who taught Ephraim to
  walk,
  who took them in my arms;
I drew them with human cords,
  with bands of love;
I fostered them like one
  who raises an infant to his cheeks;
Yet, though I stooped to feed my child,

they did not know that I was their
  healer.

My heart is overwhelmed,
  my pity is stirred.
I will not give vent to my blazing anger,
  I will not destroy Ephraim again;
For I am God and not a man,
  the Holy One present among you;
I will not let the flames consume you.

RESPONSORIAL PSALM
Isaiah 12:2–3, 4bcd, 5–6

You will draw wa - ter joy - ful - ly from the springs of sal - va - tion.

Truly, God is my salvation,
  I trust, I shall not fear.
For the Lord is my strength, my song,
  he became my savior.
With joy you will draw water
  from the wells of salvation. ℟.

Give thanks to the Lord,
  give praise to his name!
Make his mighty deeds

known to the peoples!
Declare the greatness of his name.
  Sing a psalm to the Lord! ℟.

For he has done glorious deeds,
  make them known to all the earth!
People of Zion,
  sing and shout for joy,
for great in your midst
  is the Holy One of Israel. ℟.

READING II
Ephesians 3:8–12, 14–19

Brothers and sisters: To me, the very least of all the holy ones, this grace was given, to preach to the Gentiles the inscrutable riches of Christ, and to bring to light for all what is the plan of the mystery hidden from ages past in God who created all things, so that the manifold wisdom of God might now be made known through the church to the principalities and authorities in the heavens. This was according to the eternal purpose that he accomplished in Christ Jesus our Lord, in whom we have boldness of speech and confidence of access through faith in him.

For this reason I kneel before the Father, from whom every family in heaven and on earth is named, that he may grant you in accord with the riches of his glory to be strengthened with power through his Spirit in the inner self, and that Christ may dwell in your hearts through faith; that you, rooted and grounded in love, may have strength to comprehend with all the holy ones what is the breadth and length and height and depth, and to know the love of Christ which surpasses knowledge, so that you may be filled with all the fullness of God.

GOSPEL *John 19:31–37*

Since it was preparation day, in order that the bodies might not remain on the cross on the sabbath, for the sabbath day of that week was a solemn one, the Jews asked Pilate that their legs be broken and they be taken down. So the soldiers came and broke the legs of the first and then of the other one who was crucified with Jesus. But when they came to Jesus and saw that he was already dead, they did not break his legs, but one soldier thrust his lance into his side, and immediately blood and water flowed out. An eyewitness has testified, and his testimony is true; he knows that he is speaking the truth, so that you also may come to believe. For this happened so that the Scripture passage might be fulfilled:

Not a bone of it will be broken.

And again another passage says:

They will look upon him whom they have pierced.

1196 MOST SACRED HEART OF JESUS / C

READING I *Ezekiel 34:11–16 / 172*

Thus says the Lord GOD: I myself will look after and tend my sheep. As a shepherd tends his flock when he finds himself among his scattered sheep, so will I tend my sheep. I will rescue them from every place where they were scattered when it was cloudy and dark. I will lead them out from among the peoples and gather them from the foreign lands; I will bring them back to their own country and pasture them upon the mountains of Israel in the land's ravines and all its inhabited places. In good pastures will I pasture them, and on the mountain heights of Israel shall be their grazing ground. There they shall lie down on good grazing ground, and in rich pastures shall they be pastured on the mountains of Israel. I myself will pasture my sheep; I myself will give them rest, says the Lord GOD. The lost I will seek out, the strayed I will bring back, the injured I will bind up, the sick I will heal, but the sleek and the strong I will destroy, shepherding them rightly.

RESPONSORIAL PSALM *Psalm 23:1–3a, 3b–4, 5, 6*

RP

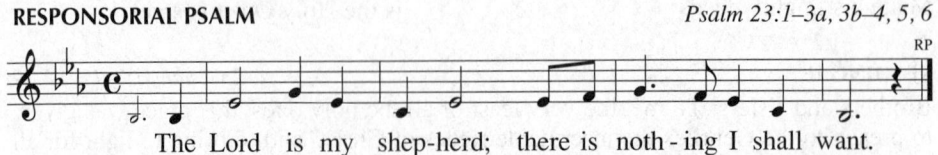

The Lord is my shep-herd; there is noth-ing I shall want.

The LORD is my shepherd;
   there is nothing I shall want.
Fresh and green are the pastures

where he gives me repose.
Near restful waters he leads me;
   he revives my soul. ℟.

He guides me along the right path,
for the sake of his name.
Though I should walk in the valley of
the shadow of death,
no evil would I fear, for you are
with me.
Your crook and your staff will give
me comfort. ℞.

You have prepared a table before me
in the sight of my foes.

My head you have anointed with oil;
my cup is overflowing. ℞.

Surely goodness and mercy shall follow
me
all the days of my life.
In the LORD's own house shall I dwell
for length of days unending. ℞.

READING II
Romans 5:5b–11

Brothers and sisters: The love of God has been poured out into our hearts through the Holy Spirit that has been given to us. For Christ, while we were still helpless, died at the appointed time for the ungodly. Indeed, only with difficulty does one die for a just person, though perhaps for a good person one might even find courage to die. But God proves his love for us in that while we were still sinners Christ died for us. How much more then, since we are now justified by his blood, will we be saved through him from the wrath. Indeed, if, while we were enemies, we were reconciled to God through the death of his Son, how much more, once reconciled, will we be saved by his life. Not only that, but we also boast of God through our Lord Jesus Christ, through whom we have now received reconciliation.

GOSPEL
Luke 15:3–7

Jesus addressed this parable to the Pharisees and scribes: "What man among you having a hundred sheep and losing one of them would not leave the ninety-nine in the desert and go after the lost one until he finds it? And when he does find it, he sets it on his shoulders with great joy and, upon his arrival home, he calls together his friends and neighbors and says to them, 'Rejoice with me because I have found my lost sheep.' I tell you, in just the same way there will be more joy in heaven over one sinner who repents than over ninety-nine righteous people who have no need of repentance."

SECOND SUNDAY IN ORDINARY TIME / A
1197

READING I
Isaiah 49:3, 5–6 / 64

The LORD said to me: You are my
servant,
Israel, through whom I show my
glory.
Now the LORD has spoken
who formed me as his servant
from the womb,
that Jacob may be brought back to him
and Israel gathered to him;
and I am made glorious in the sight

of the LORD,
and my God is now my strength!
It is too little, the LORD says, for you to
be my servant,
to raise up the tribes of Jacob,
and restore the survivors of Israel;
I will make you a light to the nations,
that my salvation may reach to the
ends of the earth.

RESPONSORIAL PSALM   *Psalm 40:2 and 4ab, 7–8a, 8b–9, 10*

Here am I, Lord; I come to do your will.

I waited, I waited for the LORD,
  and he stooped down to me; he
    heard my cry.
He put a new song into my mouth,
  praise of our God. ℟.

You delight not in sacrifice and
    offerings,
  but in an open ear.
You do not ask for holocaust and victim.
  Then I said, "See, I have come." ℟.

In the scroll of the book it stands
    written of me:
  "I delight to do your will, O my
    God;
  your instruction lies deep within
    me." ℟.

Your justice I have proclaimed
  in the great assembly.
My lips I have not sealed;
  you know it, O LORD. ℟.

READING II   *1 Corinthians 1:1–3*

Paul, called to be an apostle of Christ Jesus by the will of God, and Sosthenes our brother, to the church of God that is in Corinth, to you who have been sanctified in Christ Jesus, called to be holy, with all those everywhere who call upon the name of our Lord Jesus Christ, their Lord and ours. Grace to you and peace from God our Father and the Lord Jesus Christ.

GOSPEL   *John 1:29–34*

John the Baptist saw Jesus coming toward him and said, "Behold, the Lamb of God, who takes away the sin of the world. He is the one of whom I said, 'A man is coming after me who ranks ahead of me because he existed before me.' I did not know him, but the reason why I came baptizing with water was that he might be made known to Israel." John testified further, saying, "I saw the Spirit come down like a dove from heaven and remain upon him. I did not know him, but the one who sent me to baptize with water told me, 'On whomever you see the Spirit come down and remain, he is the one who will baptize with the Holy Spirit.' Now I have seen and testified that he is the Son of God."

1198 SECOND SUNDAY IN ORDINARY TIME / B

READING I   *1 Samuel 3:3b–10, 19 / 65*

Samuel was sleeping in the temple of the LORD where the ark of God was. The LORD called to Samuel, who answered, "Here I am." Samuel ran to Eli and said, "Here I am. You called me." "I did not call you," Eli said. "Go back to sleep." So he went back to sleep. Again the LORD called Samuel, who rose and went to Eli. "Here I am," he said. "You called me." But Eli answered, "I did not call you, my son. Go back to sleep."
    At that time Samuel was not familiar with the LORD, because the LORD had not revealed anything to him as yet. The LORD called Samuel again, for the third time.

Getting up and going to Eli, he said, "Here I am. You called me." Then Eli understood that the LORD was calling the youth. So he said to Samuel, "Go to sleep, and if you are called, reply, 'Speak, LORD, for your servant is listening.'" When Samuel went to sleep in his place, the LORD came and revealed his presence, calling out as before, "Samuel, Samuel!" Samuel answered, "Speak, for your servant is listening."

Samuel grew up, and the LORD was with him, not permitting any word of his to be without effect.

RESPONSORIAL PSALM   *Psalm 40:2 and 4ab, 7–8a, 8b–9, 10*

Here am I, Lord; I come to do your will.

I waited, I waited for the LORD,
   and he stooped down to me;
      he heard my cry.
He put a new song into my mouth,
   praise of our God. ℟.

You delight not in sacrifice and offerings,
   but in an open ear.
You do not ask for holocaust and
      victim.
   Then I said, "See, I have come." ℟.

In the scroll of the book it stands written
   of me:
   "I delight to do your will, O my God;
   your instruction lies deep within
      me." ℟.

Your justice I have proclaimed
   in the great assembly.
My lips I have not sealed;
   you know it, O LORD. ℟.

READING II   *1 Corinthians 6:13c–15a, 17–20*

Brothers and sisters: The body is not for immorality, but for the Lord, and the Lord is for the body; God raised the Lord and will also raise us by his power.

Do you not know that your bodies are members of Christ? But whoever is joined to the Lord becomes one Spirit with him. Avoid immorality. Every other sin a person commits is outside the body, but the immoral person sins against his own body. Do you not know that your body is a temple of the Holy Spirit within you, whom you have from God, and that you are not your own? For you have been purchased at a price. Therefore glorify God in your body.

GOSPEL   *John 1:35–42*

John was standing with two of his disciples, and as he watched Jesus walk by, he said, "Behold, the Lamb of God." The two disciples heard what he said and followed Jesus. Jesus turned and saw them following him and said to them, "What are you looking for?" They said to him, "Rabbi" —which translated means Teacher—, "where are you staying?" He said to them, "Come, and you will see." So they went and saw where Jesus was staying, and they stayed with him that day. It was about four in the afternoon. Andrew, the brother of Simon Peter, was one of the two who heard John and followed Jesus. He first found his own brother Simon and told him, "We have found the Messiah" —which is translated Christ. Then he brought him to Jesus. Jesus looked at him and said, "You are Simon the son of John; you will be called Cephas" —which is translated Peter.

1199 SECOND SUNDAY IN ORDINARY TIME / C

READING I

Isaiah 62:1–5 / 66

For Zion's sake I will not be silent,
> for Jerusalem's sake I will not be
> > quiet,
until her vindication shines forth like
> the dawn
> and her victory like a burning torch.

Nations shall behold your vindication,
> and all the kings your glory;
you shall be called by a new name
> pronounced by the mouth of the
> > LORD.
You shall be a glorious crown in the
hand of the LORD,
> a royal diadem held by your God.
No more shall people call you
> "Forsaken,"
> or your land "Desolate,"
but you shall be called "My Delight,"
> and your land "Espoused."
For the LORD delights in you
> and makes your land his spouse.
As a young man marries a virgin,
> your Builder shall marry you;
and as a bridegroom rejoices in his bride
> so shall your God rejoice in you.

RESPONSORIAL PSALM

Psalm 96:1–2a, 2b–3, 7–8a, 9–10a and c

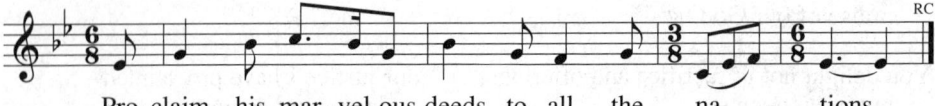

Pro-claim his mar-vel-ous deeds to all the na - tions.

O sing a new song to the LORD;
> sing to the LORD, all the earth.
> O sing to the LORD; bless his name. ℟.

Proclaim his salvation day by day.
> Tell among the nations his glory,
> and his wonders among all the
> > peoples. ℟.

Give the LORD, you families of peoples,
give the LORD glory and power;
give the LORD the glory of his
> name. ℟.

Worship the LORD in holy splendor.
> O tremble before him, all the earth.
Say to the nations, "The LORD is king."
> He will judge the peoples in
> > fairness. ℟.

READING II

1 Corinthians 12:4–11

Brothers and sisters: There are different kinds of spiritual gifts but the same Spirit; there are different forms of service but the same Lord; there are different workings but the same God who produces all of them in everyone. To each individual the manifestation of the Spirit is given for some benefit. To one is given through the Spirit the expression of wisdom; to another, the expression of knowledge according to the same Spirit; to another, faith by the same Spirit; to another, gifts of healing by the one Spirit; to another, mighty deeds; to another, prophecy; to another, discernment of spirits; to another, varieties of tongues; to another, interpretation of tongues. But one and the same Spirit produces all of these, distributing them individually to each person as he wishes.

GOSPEL

John 2:1–11

There was a wedding at Cana in Galilee, and the mother of Jesus was there. Jesus and his disciples were also invited to the wedding. When the wine ran short, the mother of Jesus said to him, "They have no wine." And Jesus said to her, "Woman, how does your concern affect me? My hour has not yet come." His mother said to the servers, "Do whatever he tells you." Now there were six stone water jars there for Jewish ceremonial washings, each holding twenty to thirty gallons. Jesus told them, "Fill the jars with water." So they filled them to the brim. Then he told them, "Draw some out now and take it to the headwaiter." So they took it. And when the headwaiter tasted the water that had become wine, without knowing where it came from —although the servers who had drawn the water knew—, the headwaiter called the bridegroom and said to him, "Everyone serves good wine first, and then when people have drunk freely, an inferior one; but you have kept the good wine until now." Jesus did this as the beginning of his signs at Cana in Galilee and so revealed his glory, and his disciples began to believe in him.

THIRD SUNDAY IN ORDINARY TIME / A 1200

READING I
Isaiah 8:23—9:3 / 67

First the Lord degraded the land of Zebulun and the land of Naphtali; but in the end he has glorified the seaward road, the land west of the Jordan, the District of the Gentiles.

Anguish has taken wing, dispelled is darkness:
　for there is no gloom where but now there was distress.
The people who walked in darkness
　have seen a great light;
upon those who dwelt in the land of gloom
　a light has shone.
You have brought them abundant joy
　and great rejoicing,
as they rejoice before you as at the harvest,
　as people make merry when dividing spoils.
For the yoke that burdened them,
　the pole on their shoulder,
and the rod of their taskmaster
　you have smashed, as on the day of Midian.

RESPONSORIAL PSALM
Psalm 27:1, 4, 13–14

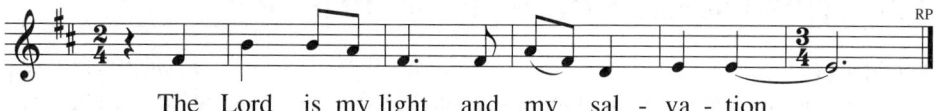

The Lord is my light and my sal - va - tion.

The LORD is my light and my salvation;
　whom shall I fear?
The LORD is the stronghold of my life;
　whom should I dread? R̸.

There is one thing I ask of the LORD,
　only this do I seek:
to live in the house of the LORD
　all the days of my life,

to gaze on the beauty of the LORD,
　to inquire at his temple. R̸.

I believe I shall see the LORD's goodness
　in the land of the living.
Wait for the LORD; be strong;
　be stouthearted, and wait for the
　LORD! R̸.

READING II   *1 Corinthians 1:10–13, 17*

I urge you, brothers and sisters, in the name of our Lord Jesus Christ, that all of you agree in what you say, and that there be no divisions among you, but that you be united in the same mind and in the same purpose. For it has been reported to me about you, my brothers and sisters, by Chloe's people, that there are rivalries among you. I mean that each of you is saying, "I belong to Paul," or "I belong to Apollos," or "I belong to Cephas," or "I belong to Christ." Is Christ divided? Was Paul crucified for you? Or were you baptized in the name of Paul? For Christ did not send me to baptize but to preach the gospel, and not with the wisdom of human eloquence, so that the cross of Christ might not be emptied of its meaning.

GOSPEL   *Matthew 4:12–23 or 4:12–17*

For short form read only the part in brackets.

[When Jesus heard that John had been arrested, he withdrew to Galilee. He left Nazareth and went to live in Capernaum by the sea, in the region of Zebulun and Naphtali, that what had been said through Isaiah the prophet might be fulfilled:

> *Land of Zebulun and land of Naphtali,*
> *the way to the sea, beyond the Jordan,*
> *Galilee of the Gentiles,*
> *the people who sit in darkness have seen a great light,*
> *on those dwelling in a land overshadowed by death*
> *light has arisen.*

From that time on, Jesus began to preach and say, "Repent, for the kingdom of heaven is at hand."]

As he was walking by the Sea of Galilee, he saw two brothers, Simon who is called Peter, and his brother Andrew, casting a net into the sea; they were fishermen. He said to them, "Come after me, and I will make you fishers of men." At once they left their nets and followed him. He walked along from there and saw two other brothers, James, the son of Zebedee, and his brother John. They were in a boat, with their father Zebedee, mending their nets. He called them, and immediately they left their boat and their father and followed him. He went around all of Galilee, teaching in their synagogues, proclaiming the gospel of the kingdom, and curing every disease and illness among the people.

1201   THIRD SUNDAY IN ORDINARY TIME / B

READING I   *Jonah 3:1–5, 10 / 68*

The word of the LORD came to Jonah, saying: "Set out for the great city of Nineveh, and announce to it the message that I will tell you." So Jonah made ready and went to Nineveh, according to the LORD's bidding. Now Nineveh was an enormously large city; it took three days to go through it. Jonah began his journey through the city, and had gone but a single day's walk announcing, "Forty days more and Nineveh shall be destroyed," when the people of Nineveh believed God; they proclaimed a fast and all of them, great and small, put on sackcloth.

When God saw by their actions how they turned from their evil way, he repented of the evil that he had threatened to do to them; he did not carry it out.

RESPONSORIAL PSALM *Psalm 25:4–5ab, 6 and 7bc, 8–9*

Teach me your ways, O Lord, teach me your ways.

O LORD, make me know your ways.
  Teach me your paths.
Guide me in your truth, and teach me;
  for you are the God of my salvation. R̂.

Remember your compassion, O LORD,
  and your merciful love,
  for they are from of old.

In your merciful love remember me,
  because of your goodness, O
  LORD. R̂.

Good and upright is the LORD;
  he shows the way to sinners.
He guides the humble in right judgment;
  to the humble he teaches his way. R̂.

READING II *1 Corinthians 7:29–31*

I tell you, brothers and sisters, the time is running out. From now on, let those having wives act as not having them, those weeping as not weeping, those rejoicing as not rejoicing, those buying as not owning, those using the world as not using it fully. For the world in its present form is passing away.

GOSPEL *Mark 1:14–20*

After John had been arrested, Jesus came to Galilee proclaiming the gospel of God: "This is the time of fulfillment. The kingdom of God is at hand. Repent, and believe in the gospel."

  As he passed by the Sea of Galilee, he saw Simon and his brother Andrew casting their nets into the sea; they were fishermen. Jesus said to them, "Come after me, and I will make you fishers of men." Then they abandoned their nets and followed him. He walked along a little farther and saw James, the son of Zebedee, and his brother John. They too were in a boat mending their nets. Then he called them. So they left their father Zebedee in the boat along with the hired men and followed him.

THIRD SUNDAY IN ORDINARY TIME / C 1202

READING I *Nehemiah 8:2–4a, 5–6, 8–10 / 69*

Ezra the priest brought the law before the assembly, which consisted of men, women, and those children old enough to understand. Standing at one end of the open place that was before the Water Gate, he read out of the book from daybreak till midday, in the presence of the men, the women, and those children old enough to understand; and all the people listened attentively to the book of the law. Ezra the scribe stood on a wooden platform that had been made for the occasion. He opened the scroll so that all the people might see it —for he was standing higher up than any of the people—; and, as he opened it, all the people rose. Ezra blessed the LORD, the great God, and all the people, their hands raised high, answered, "Amen, amen!" Then they bowed down and prostrated themselves before the LORD, their faces to the ground. Ezra read plainly from the book of the law of God, interpreting it so that all could understand what was read. Then Nehemiah, that is, His Excellency, and Ezra the priest-scribe and the Levites who were instructing the people said to all the people: "Today is holy to the LORD your God. Do not be sad, and do not weep"— for all the people were weeping as they heard the words of the law. He said further: "Go, eat rich foods and drink sweet drinks, and allot portions to those who had nothing prepared; for today is holy to our LORD. Do not be saddened this day, for rejoicing in the LORD must be your strength!"

RESPONSORIAL PSALM   *Psalm 19:8, 9, 10, 15*

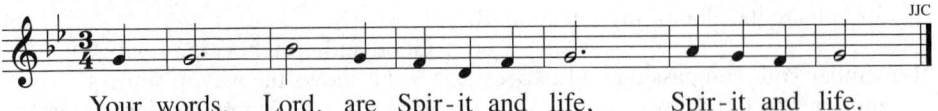

Your words, Lord, are Spir-it and life, Spir-it and life.

The law of the LORD is perfect;
  it revives the soul.
The decrees of the LORD are steadfast;
  they give wisdom to the simple. ℟.

The precepts of the LORD are right;
  they gladden the heart.
The command of the LORD is clear;
  it gives light to the eyes. ℟.

The fear of the LORD is pure,
  abiding forever.
The judgments of the LORD are true;
  they are, all of them, just. ℟.

May the spoken words of my mouth,
  the thoughts of my heart,
win favor in your sight, O LORD,
  my rock and my redeemer! ℟.

READING II   *1 Corinthians 12:12–30 or 12:12–14, 27*
For short form read only the parts in brackets.

[Brothers and sisters: As a body is one though it has many parts, and all the parts of the body, though many, are one body, so also Christ. For in one Spirit we were all baptized into one body, whether Jews or Greeks, slaves or free persons, and we were all given to drink of one Spirit.
  Now the body is not a single part, but many.] If a foot should say, "Because I am not a hand I do not belong to the body," it does not for this reason belong any less to the body. Or if an ear should say, "Because I am not an eye I do not belong to the body," it does not for this reason belong any less to the body. If the whole body were an eye, where would the hearing be? If the whole body were hearing, where would the sense of smell be? But as it is, God placed the parts, each one of them, in the body as he intended. If they were all one part, where would the body be? But as it is, there are many parts, yet one body. The eye cannot say to the hand, "I do not need you," nor again the head to the feet, "I do not need you." Indeed, the parts of the body that seem to be weaker are all the more necessary, and those parts of the body that we consider less honorable we surround with greater honor, and our less presentable parts are treated with greater propriety, whereas our more presentable parts do not need this. But God has so constructed the body as to give greater honor to a part that is without it, so that there may be no division in the body, but that the parts may have the same concern for one another. If one part suffers, all the parts suffer with it; if one part is honored, all the parts share its joy.

Now [you are Christ's body, and individually parts of it.] Some people God has designated in the church to be, first, apostles; second, prophets; third, teachers; then, mighty deeds; then gifts of healing, assistance, administration, and varieties of tongues. Are all apostles? Are all prophets? Are all teachers? Do all work mighty deeds? Do all have gifts of healing? Do all speak in tongues? Do all interpret?

GOSPEL   *Luke 1:1–4; 4:14–21*

Since many have undertaken to compile a narrative of the events that have been fulfilled among us, just as those who were eyewitnesses from the beginning and ministers of the word have handed them down to us, I too have decided, after investigating everything accurately anew, to write it down in an orderly sequence for you, most excellent Theophilus, so that you may realize the certainty of the teachings you have received.

Jesus returned to Galilee in the power of the Spirit, and news of him spread throughout the whole region. He taught in their synagogues and was praised by all.

He came to Nazareth, where he had grown up, and went according to his custom into the synagogue on the sabbath day. He stood up to read and was handed a scroll of the prophet Isaiah. He unrolled the scroll and found the passage where it was written:

The Spirit of the Lord is upon me,
  because he has anointed me
  to bring glad tidings to the poor.
He has sent me to proclaim liberty to captives
  and recovery of sight to the blind,
  to let the oppressed go free,
  and to proclaim a year acceptable to the Lord.

Rolling up the scroll, he handed it back to the attendant and sat down, and the eyes of all in the synagogue looked intently at him. He said to them, "Today this Scripture passage is fulfilled in your hearing."

FOURTH SUNDAY IN ORDINARY TIME / A   1203

READING I   *Zephaniah 2:3; 3:12–13 / 70*

Seek the LORD, all you humble of the earth,
  who have observed his law;
seek justice, seek humility;
  perhaps you may be sheltered
  on the day of the LORD's anger.

But I will leave as a remnant in your midst
  a people humble and lowly,

who shall take refuge in the name of the LORD:
  the remnant of Israel.
They shall do no wrong
  and speak no lies;
nor shall there be found in their mouths
  a deceitful tongue;
they shall pasture and couch their flocks
  with none to disturb them.

RESPONSORIAL PSALM   *Psalm 146:6c–7, 8–9a, 9bc–10*

Or: Alleluia.

Bless-ed are the poor in spir-it; the king-dom of heav-en is theirs!

It is the LORD who preserves fidelity
  forever,
  who does justice to those who are
  oppressed.
It is he who gives bread to the hungry,
  the LORD who sets prisoners free. ℟.

The LORD who opens the eyes of the
  blind,
  the LORD who raises up those who
  are bowed down.

It is the LORD who loves the just,
  the LORD who protects the
  stranger. ℟.

The LORD upholds the orphan and the
  widow,
  but thwarts the path of the wicked.
The LORD will reign forever,
  the God of Sion from age to age.
  Alleluia. ℟.

READING II   *1 Corinthians 1:26–31*

Consider your own calling, brothers and sisters. Not many of you were wise by human standards, not many were powerful, not many were of noble birth. Rather, God chose the foolish of the world to shame the wise, and God chose the weak of the world to shame the strong, and God chose the lowly and despised of the world, those who count for nothing, to reduce to nothing those who are something, so that no human being might boast before God. It is due to him that you are in Christ Jesus, who became for us wisdom from God, as well as righteousness, sanctification, and redemption, so that, as it is written, "Whoever boasts, should boast in the Lord."

GOSPEL   *Matthew 5:1–12a*

When Jesus saw the crowds, he went up the mountain, and after he had sat down, his disciples came to him. He began to teach them, saying:
  "Blessed are the poor in spirit,
    for theirs is the kingdom of heaven.
  Blessed are they who mourn,
    for they will be comforted.
  Blessed are the meek,
    for they will inherit the land.
  Blessed are they who hunger and thirst for righteousness,
    for they will be satisfied.
  Blessed are the merciful,
    for they will be shown mercy.
  Blessed are the clean of heart,
    for they will see God.
  Blessed are the peacemakers,
    for they will be called children of God.
  Blessed are they who are persecuted for the sake of righteousness,
    for theirs is the kingdom of heaven.

Blessed are you when they insult you and persecute you and utter every kind of evil against you falsely because of me. Rejoice and be glad, for your reward will be great in heaven."

FOURTH SUNDAY IN ORDINARY TIME / B   1204

READING I   *Deuteronomy 18:15–20 / 71*

Moses spoke to all the people, saying: "A prophet like me will the LORD, your God, raise up for you from among your own kin; to him you shall listen. This is exactly what you requested of the LORD, your God, at Horeb on the day of the assembly, when you said, 'Let us not again hear the voice of the LORD, our God, nor see this great fire any more, lest we die.' And the LORD said to me, 'This was well said. I will raise up for them a prophet like you from among their kin, and will put my words into his mouth; he shall tell them all that I command him. Whoever will not listen to my words which he speaks in my name, I myself will make him answer for it. But if a prophet presumes to speak in my name an oracle that I have not commanded him to speak, or speaks in the name of other gods, he shall die.'"

RESPONSORIAL PSALM   *Psalm 95:1–2, 6–7c, 7d–9*

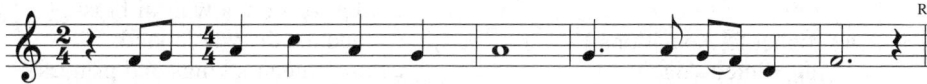

If to - day you hear his voice, hard - en not your hearts.

Come, let us ring out our joy to the LORD;
  hail the rock who saves us.
Let us come into his presence, giving thanks;
  let us hail him with a song of praise. ℟.

O come; let us bow and bend low.
  Let us kneel before the God who made us,
for he is our God and we
  the people who belong to his pasture,
  the flock that is led by his hand. ℟.

O that today you would listen to his voice!
  "Harden not your hearts as at Meribah,
  as on that day at Massah in the desert
when your forebears put me to the test;
  when they tried me, though they saw my work." ℟.

READING II   *1 Corinthians 7:32–35*

Brothers and sisters: I should like you to be free of anxieties. An unmarried man is anxious about the things of the Lord, how he may please the Lord. But a married man is anxious about the things of the world, how he may please his wife, and he is divided. An unmarried woman or a virgin is anxious about the things of the Lord, so that she may be holy in both body and spirit. A married woman, on the other hand, is anxious about the things of the world, how she may please her husband. I am telling you this for your own benefit, not to impose a restraint upon you, but for the sake of propriety and adherence to the Lord without distraction.

GOSPEL   *Mark 1:21–28*

Then they came to Capernaum, and on the sabbath Jesus entered the synagogue and taught. The people were astonished at his teaching, for he taught them as one having authority and not as the scribes. In their synagogue was a man with an unclean spirit; he cried out, "What have you to do with us, Jesus of Nazareth? Have you come to destroy us? I know who you are—the Holy One of God!" Jesus rebuked him and said, "Quiet! Come out of him!" The unclean spirit convulsed him and with a loud cry came out of him. All were amazed and asked one another, "What is this? A new teaching with authority. He commands even the unclean spirits and they obey him." His fame spread everywhere throughout the whole region of Galilee.

1205   FOURTH SUNDAY IN ORDINARY TIME / C

READING I   *Jeremiah 1:4–5, 17–19 / 72*

The word of the LORD came to me, saying:
> Before I formed you in the womb I
>   knew you,
>   before you were born I dedicated
>   you,
>   a prophet to the nations I
>   appointed you.

> But do you gird your loins;
>   stand up and tell them
>   all that I command you.
> Be not crushed on their account,
>   as though I would leave you

crushed before them;
> for it is I this day
>   who have made you a fortified
>   city,
> a pillar of iron, a wall of brass,
>   against the whole land:
> against Judah's kings and princes,
>   against its priests and people.
> They will fight against you but not
>   prevail over you,
>   for I am with you to deliver you,
>   says the LORD.

RESPONSORIAL PSALM   *Psalm 71:1–2, 3–4a, 5–6ab, 15ab and 17*

EE

I will sing of your sal - va - tion.

In you, O LORD, I take refuge;
> let me never be put to shame.
In your justice, rescue me, free me;
> incline your ear to me and save
> me. ℟.

Be my rock, my constant refuge,
> a mighty stronghold to save me,
for you are my rock, my stronghold.
> My God, free me from the hand of
> the wicked. ℟.

It is you, O Lord, who are my hope,
> my trust, O LORD, from my youth.
On you I have leaned from my birth;
> from my mother's womb, you have
> been my help. ℟.

My mouth will tell of your justice,
> and all the day long of your
> salvation.
O God, you have taught me from my
> youth,
> and I proclaim your wonders
> still. ℟.

READING II   *1 Corinthians 12:31—13:13 or 13:4–13*
For short form read only the parts in brackets.

[Brothers and sisters:] Strive eagerly for the greatest spiritual gifts. But I shall show you a still more excellent way.

If I speak in human and angelic tongues, but do not have love, I am a resounding gong or a clashing cymbal. And if I have the gift of prophecy, and comprehend all mysteries and all knowledge; if I have all faith so as to move mountains, but do not have love, I am nothing. If I give away everything I own, and if I hand my body over so that I may boast, but do not have love, I gain nothing.

[Love is patient, love is kind. It is not jealous, it is not pompous, it is not inflated, it is not rude, it does not seek its own interests, it is not quick-tempered, it does not brood over injury, it does not rejoice over wrongdoing but rejoices with the truth. It bears all things, believes all things, hopes all things, endures all things.

Love never fails. If there are prophecies, they will be brought to nothing; if tongues, they will cease; if knowledge, it will be brought to nothing. For we know partially and we prophesy partially, but when the perfect comes, the partial will pass away. When I was a child, I used to talk as a child, think as a child, reason as a child; when I became a man, I put aside childish things. At present we see indistinctly, as in a mirror, but then face to face. At present I know partially; then I shall know fully, as I am fully known. So faith, hope, love remain, these three; but the greatest of these is love.]

GOSPEL   *Luke 4:21–30*

Jesus began speaking in the synagogue, saying: "Today this Scripture passage is fulfilled in your hearing." And all spoke highly of him and were amazed at the gracious words that came from his mouth. They also asked, "Isn't this the son of Joseph?" He said to them, "Surely you will quote me this proverb, 'Physician, cure yourself,' and say, 'Do here in your native place the things that we heard were done in Capernaum.'" And he said, "Amen, I say to you, no prophet is accepted in his own native place. Indeed, I tell you, there were many widows in Israel in the days of Elijah when the sky was closed for three and a half years and a severe famine spread over the entire land. It was to none of these that Elijah was sent, but only to a widow in Zarephath in the land of Sidon. Again, there were many lepers in Israel during the time of Elisha the prophet; yet not one of them was cleansed, but only Naaman the Syrian." When the people in the synagogue heard this, they were all filled with fury. They rose up, drove him out of the town, and led him to the brow of the hill on which their town had been built, to hurl him down headlong. But Jesus passed through the midst of them and went away.

FIFTH SUNDAY IN ORDINARY TIME / A   1206

READING I   *Isaiah 58:7–10 / 73*

Thus says the LORD:
Share your bread with the hungry,
      shelter the oppressed and the homeless;
clothe the naked when you see them,
      and do not turn your back on your own.

Then your light shall break forth like the dawn,
    and your wound shall quickly be healed;
your vindication shall go before you,
    and the glory of the LORD shall be your rear guard.
Then you shall call, and the LORD will answer,
    you shall cry for help, and he will say: Here I am!
If you remove from your midst
    oppression, false accusation and malicious speech;
if you bestow your bread on the hungry
    and satisfy the afflicted;
then light shall rise for you in the darkness,
    and the gloom shall become for you like midday.

RESPONSORIAL PSALM

Psalm 112:4–5, 6–7, 8a and 9

Or: Alleluia.

The just man is a light in dark-ness to the up - right.

A light rises in the darkness for the
    upright;
    he is generous, merciful, and just.
It goes well for the man who deals
    generously and lends,
    who conducts his affairs with
      justice. ℟.

He will never be moved;
    forever shall the just be
    remembered.

He has no fear of evil news;
    with a firm heart, he trusts in the
    LORD. ℟.

With a steadfast heart he will not fear.
    Openhanded, he gives to the poor;
his justice stands firm forever.
    His might shall be exalted in
    glory. ℟.

READING II

1 Corinthians 2:1–5

When I came to you, brothers and sisters, proclaiming the mystery of God, I did not come with sublimity of words or of wisdom. For I resolved to know nothing while I was with you except Jesus Christ, and him crucified. I came to you in weakness and fear and much trembling, and my message and my proclamation were not with persuasive words of wisdom, but with a demonstration of Spirit and power, so that your faith might rest not on human wisdom but on the power of God.

GOSPEL

Matthew 5:13–16

Jesus said to his disciples: "You are the salt of the earth. But if salt loses its taste, with what can it be seasoned? It is no longer good for anything but to be thrown out and trampled underfoot. You are the light of the world. A city set on a mountain cannot be hidden. Nor do they light a lamp and then put it under a bushel basket; it is set on a lamp stand, where it gives light to all in the house. Just so, your light must shine before others, that they may see your good deeds and glorify your heavenly Father."

FIFTH SUNDAY IN ORDINARY TIME / B 1207

READING I
Job 7:1–4, 6–7 / 74

Job spoke, saying:
  Is not man's life on earth a drudgery?
    Are not his days those of hirelings?
  He is a slave who longs for the shade,
    a hireling who waits for his wages.
  So I have been assigned months of
    misery,
    and troubled nights have been
    allotted to me.

If in bed I say, "When shall I arise?"
  then the night drags on;
  I am filled with restlessness until the
    dawn.
My days are swifter than a weaver's
  shuttle;
  they come to an end without hope.
Remember that my life is like the wind;
  I shall not see happiness again.

RESPONSORIAL PSALM
Psalm 147:1–2, 3–4, 5–6

Or: Alleluia.

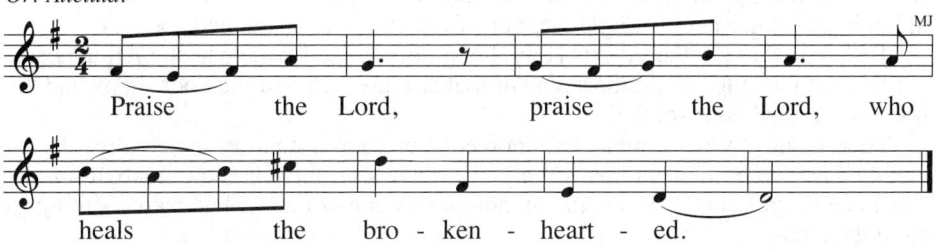

Praise the Lord, praise the Lord, who heals the bro - ken - heart - ed.

How good to sing psalms to our God;
  how pleasant to chant fitting praise!
The LORD builds up Jerusalem
  and brings back Israel's exiles; ℟.

He heals the brokenhearted;
  he binds up all their wounds.

He counts out the number of the stars;
  he calls each one by its name. ℟.

Our Lord is great and almighty;
  his wisdom can never be measured.
The LORD lifts up the lowly;
  he casts down the wicked to the
    ground. ℟.

READING II
1 Corinthians 9:16–19, 22–23

Brothers and sisters: If I preach the gospel, this is no reason for me to boast, for an obligation has been imposed on me, and woe to me if I do not preach it! If I do so willingly, I have a recompense, but if unwillingly, then I have been entrusted with a stewardship. What then is my recompense? That, when I preach, I offer the gospel free of charge so as not to make full use of my right in the gospel.

    Although I am free in regard to all, I have made myself a slave to all so as to win over as many as possible. To the weak I became weak, to win over the weak. I have become all things to all, to save at least some. All this I do for the sake of the gospel, so that I too may have a share in it.

GOSPEL
Mark 1:29–39

On leaving the synagogue Jesus entered the house of Simon and Andrew with James and John. Simon's mother-in-law lay sick with a fever. They immediately told him about her. He approached, grasped her hand, and helped her up. Then the fever left her and she waited on them.

When it was evening, after sunset, they brought to him all who were ill or possessed by demons. The whole town was gathered at the door. He cured many who were sick with various diseases, and he drove out many demons, not permitting them to speak because they knew him.

Rising very early before dawn, he left and went off to a deserted place, where he prayed. Simon and those who were with him pursued him and on finding him said, "Everyone is looking for you." He told them, "Let us go on to the nearby villages that I may preach there also. For this purpose have I come." So he went into their synagogues, preaching and driving out demons throughout the whole of Galilee.

1208 FIFTH SUNDAY IN ORDINARY TIME / C

READING I   *Isaiah 6:1–2a, 3–8 / 75*

In the year King Uzziah died, I saw the Lord seated on a high and lofty throne, with the train of his garment filling the temple. Seraphim were stationed above.

They cried one to the other, "Holy, holy, holy is the LORD of hosts! All the earth is filled with his glory!" At the sound of that cry, the frame of the door shook and the house was filled with smoke.

Then I said, "Woe is me, I am doomed! For I am a man of unclean lips, living among a people of unclean lips; yet my eyes have seen the King, the LORD of hosts!" Then one of the seraphim flew to me, holding an ember that he had taken with tongs from the altar.

He touched my mouth with it, and said, "See, now that this has touched your lips, your wickedness is removed, your sin purged."

Then I heard the voice of the Lord saying, "Whom shall I send? Who will go for us?" "Here I am," I said; "send me!"

RESPONSORIAL PSALM   *Psalm 138:1–2a, 2b–3, 4–5, 7c–8*

In the sight of the an-gels   I will sing   your prais-es,   Lord.

I thank you, LORD, with all my heart;
   you have heard the words of my
      mouth.
In the presence of the angels I praise you.
   I bow down toward your holy
      temple. ℟.

I give thanks to your name
   for your merciful love and your
      faithfulness.
You have exalted your name over all.
On the day I called, you answered me;
   you increased the strength of my
      soul. ℟.

All earth's kings shall thank you,
      O LORD,
   when they hear the words of your
      mouth.
They shall sing of the ways of the LORD,
   "How great is the glory of the
      LORD!" ℟.

With your right hand you save me;
   the LORD will accomplish this for
      me.
O LORD, your merciful love is eternal;
   discard not the work of your
      hands. ℟.

READING II   *1 Corinthians 15:1–11 or 15:3–8, 11*
For short form read only the parts in brackets.

I am reminding you, [brothers and sisters,] of the gospel I preached to you, which you indeed received and in which you also stand. Through it you are also being saved, if you hold fast to the word I preached to you, unless you believed in vain. For [I handed on to you as of first importance what I also received: that Christ died for our sins in accordance with the Scriptures; that he was buried; that he was raised on the third day in accordance with the Scriptures; that he appeared to Cephas, then to the Twelve. After that, he appeared to more than five hundred brothers at once, most of whom are still living, though some have fallen asleep. After that he appeared to James, then to all the apostles. Last of all, as to one born abnormally, he appeared to me.] For I am the least of the apostles, not fit to be called an apostle, because I persecuted the church of God. But by the grace of God I am what I am, and his grace to me has not been ineffective. Indeed, I have toiled harder than all of them; not I, however, but the grace of God that is with me. [Therefore, whether it be I or they, so we preach and so you believed.]

GOSPEL   *Luke 5:1–11*
While the crowd was pressing in on Jesus and listening to the word of God, he was standing by the Lake of Gennesaret. He saw two boats there alongside the lake; the fishermen had disembarked and were washing their nets. Getting into one of the boats, the one belonging to Simon, he asked him to put out a short distance from the shore. Then he sat down and taught the crowds from the boat. After he had finished speaking, he said to Simon, "Put out into deep water and lower your nets for a catch." Simon said in reply, "Master, we have worked hard all night and have caught nothing, but at your command I will lower the nets." When they had done this, they caught a great number of fish and their nets were tearing. They signaled to their partners in the other boat to come to help them. They came and filled both boats so that the boats were in danger of sinking. When Simon Peter saw this, he fell at the knees of Jesus and said, "Depart from me, Lord, for I am a sinful man." For astonishment at the catch of fish they had made seized him and all those with him, and likewise James and John, the sons of Zebedee, who were partners of Simon. Jesus said to Simon, "Do not be afraid; from now on you will be catching men." When they brought their boats to the shore, they left everything and followed him.

SIXTH SUNDAY IN ORDINARY TIME / A   1209

READING I   *Sirach 15:15–20 / 76*

If you choose you can keep the
    commandments, they will save
    you;
  if you trust in God, you too shall live;
he has set before you fire and water;
    to whichever you choose, stretch
    forth your hand.
Before man are life and death, good
    and evil,

whichever he chooses shall be given
    him.
Immense is the wisdom of the Lord;
  he is mighty in power, and all-seeing.
The eyes of God are on those who fear
    him;
  he understands man's every deed.
No one does he command to act unjustly,
  to none does he give license to sin.

RESPONSORIAL PSALM   *Psalm 119:1–2, 4–5, 17–18, 33–34*

Bless - ed are they   who fol - low the   law   of the Lord!

Blessed are those whose way is
  blameless,
who walk in the law of the LORD!
Blessed are those who keep his decrees!
  With all their hearts they seek him. ℟.

You have laid down your precepts
  to be carefully kept.
May my ways be firm
  in keeping your statutes. ℟.

Deal bountifully with your servant,
  that I may live and keep your word.
Open my eyes, that I may see
  the wonders of your law. ℟.

LORD, teach me the way of your
  statutes,
and I will keep them to the end.
Grant me insight that I may keep your
  law,
  and observe it wholeheartedly. ℟.

READING II   *1 Corinthians 2:6–10*

Brothers and sisters: We speak a wisdom to those who are mature, not a wisdom of this age, nor of the rulers of this age who are passing away. Rather, we speak God's wisdom, mysterious, hidden, which God predetermined before the ages for our glory, and which none of the rulers of this age knew; for, if they had known it, they would not have crucified the Lord of glory. But as it is written:

What eye has not seen, and ear has not heard,
  and what has not entered the human heart,
  what God has prepared for those who love him,

this God has revealed to us through the Spirit.
  For the Spirit scrutinizes everything, even the depths of God.

GOSPEL   *Matthew 5:17–37 or 5:20–22a, 27–28, 33–34a, 37*

For short form read only the parts in brackets.

[Jesus said to his disciples:] "Do not think that I have come to abolish the law or the prophets. I have come not to abolish but to fulfill. Amen, I say to you, until heaven and earth pass away, not the smallest letter or the smallest part of a letter will pass from the law, until all things have taken place. Therefore, whoever breaks one of the least of these commandments and teaches others to do so will be called least in the kingdom of heaven. But whoever obeys and teaches these commandments will be called greatest in the kingdom of heaven. [I tell you, unless your righteousness sur-passes that of the scribes and Pharisees, you will not enter the kingdom of heaven.

  "You have heard that it was said to your ancestors *You shall not kill; and whoever kills will be liable to judgment.* But I say to you, whoever is angry with his brother will be liable to judgment;] and whoever says to his brother, 'Raqa,' will be answer-able to the Sanhedrin; and whoever says, 'You fool,' will be liable to fiery Gehenna. Therefore, if you bring your gift to the altar, and there recall that your brother has anything against you, leave your gift there at the altar, go first and be reconciled with your brother, and then come and offer your gift. Settle with your opponent quickly while on the way to court. Otherwise your opponent will hand you over to the judge, and the judge will hand you over to the guard, and you will be thrown into prison. Amen, I say to you, you will not be released until you have paid the last penny.

["You have heard that it was said, *You shall not commit adultery.* But I say to you, everyone who looks at a woman with lust has already committed adultery with her in his heart.] If your right eye causes you to sin, tear it out and throw it away. It is better for you to lose one of your members than to have your whole body thrown into Gehenna. And if your right hand causes you to sin, cut it off and throw it away. It is better for you to lose one of your members than to have your whole body go into Gehenna.

"It was also said, *Whoever divorces his wife must give her a bill of divorce.* But I say to you, whoever divorces his wife —unless the marriage is unlawful— causes her to commit adultery, and whoever marries a divorced woman commits adultery.

["Again you have heard that it was said to your ancestors, *Do not take a false oath, but make good to the Lord all that you vow.* But I say to you, do not swear at all;] not by heaven, for it is God's throne; nor by the earth, for it is his footstool; nor by Jerusalem, for it is the city of the great King. Do not swear by your head, for you cannot make a single hair white or black. [Let your 'Yes' mean 'Yes,' and your 'No' mean 'No.' Anything more is from the evil one."]

SIXTH SUNDAY IN ORDINARY TIME / B   1210

READING I   *Leviticus 13:1–2, 44–46 / 77*

The Lord said to Moses and Aaron, "If someone has on his skin a scab or pustule or blotch which appears to be the sore of leprosy, he shall be brought to Aaron, the priest, or to one of the priests among his descendants. If the man is leprous and unclean, the priest shall declare him unclean by reason of the sore on his head.

"The one who bears the sore of leprosy shall keep his garments rent and his head bare, and shall muffle his beard; he shall cry out, 'Unclean, unclean!' As long as the sore is on him he shall declare himself unclean, since he is in fact unclean. He shall dwell apart, making his abode outside the camp."

RESPONSORIAL PSALM   *Psalm 32:1–2, 5, 11*

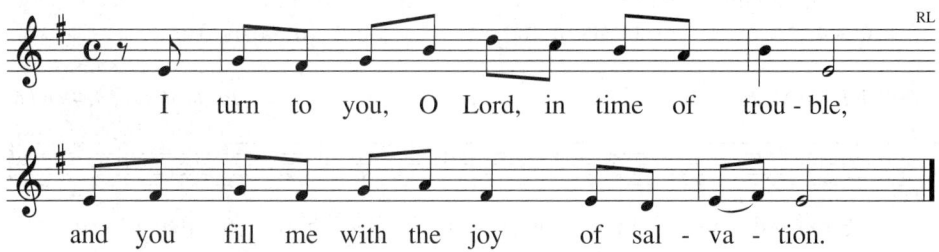

I turn to you, O Lord, in time of trou - ble,
and you fill me with the joy of sal - va - tion.

Blessed is he whose transgression is
    forgiven,
  whose sin is remitted.
Blessed the man to whom the Lord
    imputes no guilt,
  in whose spirit is no guile. ℟.

To you I have acknowledged my sin;
  my guilt I did not hide.
I said, "I will confess my transgression
    to the Lord."
  And you have forgiven the guilt of
    my sin. ℟.

Rejoice in the Lord; exult, you just!
Ring out your joy, all you upright of heart! ℟.

READING II   *1 Corinthians 10:31—11:1*

Brothers and sisters, whether you eat or drink, or whatever you do, do everything for the glory of God. Avoid giving offense, whether to the Jews or Greeks or the church of God, just as I try to please everyone in every way, not seeking my own benefit but that of the many, that they may be saved. Be imitators of me, as I am of Christ.

GOSPEL   *Mark 1:40–45*

A leper came to Jesus and kneeling down begged him and said, "If you wish, you can make me clean." Moved with pity, he stretched out his hand, touched him, and said to him, "I do will it. Be made clean." The leprosy left him immediately, and he was made clean. Then, warning him sternly, he dismissed him at once.

He said to him, "See that you tell no one anything, but go, show yourself to the priest and offer for your cleansing what Moses prescribed; that will be proof for them."

The man went away and began to publicize the whole matter. He spread the report abroad so that it was impossible for Jesus to enter a town openly. He remained outside in deserted places, and people kept coming to him from everywhere.

1211   SIXTH SUNDAY IN ORDINARY TIME / C

READING I   *Jeremiah 17:5–8 / 78*

Thus says the Lord:
Cursed is the one who trusts in
    human beings,
  who seeks his strength in flesh,
  whose heart turns away from the
    Lord.
He is like a barren bush in the desert
  that enjoys no change of season,
but stands in a lava waste,
  a salt and empty earth.
Blessed is the one who trusts in the
Lord.
  whose hope is the Lord.
He is like a tree planted beside the
  waters
  that stretches out its roots to the
    stream:
it fears not the heat when it comes;
  its leaves stay green;
in the year of drought it shows no
    distress,
  but still bears fruit.

RESPONSORIAL PSALM   *Psalm 1:1–2, 3, 4 and 6*

RJT

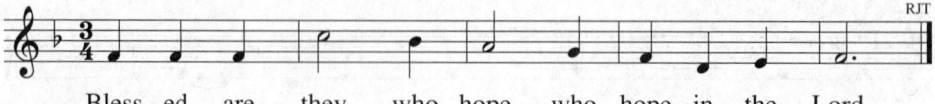

Bless - ed   are   they   who   hope,   who   hope   in   the   Lord.

Blessed indeed is the man
  who follows not the counsel of the
    wicked,
nor stands in the path with sinners,
nor abides in the company of scorners,
but whose delight is the law of the Lord,
and who ponders his law day and
    night. ℟.

He is like a tree that is planted
  beside the flowing waters,
  that yields its fruit in due season,
and whose leaves shall never fade;
  and all that he does shall prosper. ℟.

Not so are the wicked, not so!
  For they, like winnowed chaff,
  shall be driven away by the wind;
for the LORD knows the way of the just,
  but the way of the wicked will
    perish. ℟.

READING II   *1 Corinthians 15:12, 16–20*

Brothers and sisters: If Christ is preached as raised from the dead, how can some among you say there is no resurrection of the dead? If the dead are not raised, neither has Christ been raised, and if Christ has not been raised, your faith is vain; you are still in your sins. Then those who have fallen asleep in Christ have perished. If for this life only we have hoped in Christ, we are the most pitiable people of all.

But now Christ has been raised from the dead, the firstfruits of those who have fallen asleep.

GOSPEL   *Luke 6:17, 20–26*

Jesus came down with the Twelve and stood on a stretch of level ground with a great crowd of his disciples and a large number of the people from all Judea and Jerusalem and the coastal region of Tyre and Sidon. And raising his eyes toward his disciples he said:
  "Blessed are you who are poor,
    for the kingdom of God is yours.
  Blessed are you who are now hungry,
    for you will be satisfied.
  Blessed are you who are now weeping,
    for you will laugh.
  Blessed are you when people hate you,
    and when they exclude and insult you,
    and denounce your name as evil
    on account of the Son of Man.
Rejoice and leap for joy on that day! Behold, your reward will be great in heaven. For their ancestors treated the prophets in the same way.
  But woe to you who are rich,
    for you have received your consolation.
  Woe to you who are filled now,
    for you will be hungry.
  Woe to you who laugh now,
    for you will grieve and weep.
  Woe to you when all speak well of you,
    for their ancestors treated the false
      prophets in this way."

SEVENTH SUNDAY IN ORDINARY TIME / A   1212

READING I   *Leviticus 19:1–2, 17–18 / 79*

The LORD said to Moses, "Speak to the whole Israelite community and tell them: Be holy, for I, the LORD, your God, am holy.
  "You shall not bear hatred for your brother or sister in your heart. Though you may have to reprove your fellow citizen, do not incur sin because of him. Take no

revenge and cherish no grudge against any of your people. You shall love your neighbor as yourself. I am the LORD."

RESPONSORIAL PSALM *Psalm 103:1–2, 3–4, 8 and 10, 12–13*

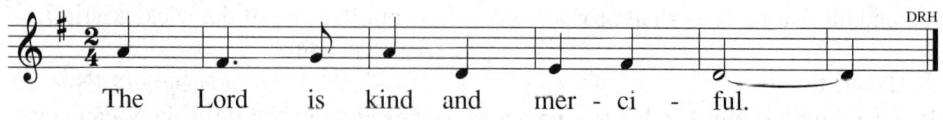

The Lord is kind and mer - ci - ful.

Bless the LORD, O my soul,
  and all within me, his holy name.
Bless the LORD, O my soul,
  and never forget all his benefits. ℟.

It is the Lord who forgives all your sins,
  who heals every one of your ills,
who redeems your life from the grave,
  who crowns you with mercy and
    compassion. ℟.

The LORD is compassionate and gracious,
  slow to anger and rich in mercy.

He does not treat us according to our
  sins,
  nor repay us according to our
    faults. ℟.

As far as the east is from the west,
  so far from us does he remove our
    transgressions.
As a father has compassion on his
  children,
  the LORD's compassion is on those
    who fear him. ℟.

READING II *1 Corinthians 3:16–23*

Brothers and sisters: Do you not know that you are the temple of God, and that the Spirit of God dwells in you? If anyone destroys God's temple, God will destroy that person; for the temple of God, which you are, is holy.

Let no one deceive himself. If any one among you considers himself wise in this age, let him become a fool, so as to become wise. For the wisdom of this world is foolishness in the eyes of God, for it is written:

God catches the wise in their own ruses,
and again:
The Lord knows the thoughts of the wise,
  that they are vain.

So let no one boast about human beings, for everything belongs to you, Paul or Apollos or Cephas, or the world or life or death, or the present or the future: all belong to you, and you to Christ, and Christ to God.

GOSPEL *Matthew 5:38–48*

Jesus said to his disciples: "You have heard that it was said, *An eye for an eye and a tooth for a tooth.* But I say to you, offer no resistance to one who is evil. When someone strikes you on your right cheek, turn the other one as well. If anyone wants to go to law with you over your tunic, hand over your cloak as well. Should anyone press you into service for one mile, go for two miles. Give to the one who asks of you, and do not turn your back on one who wants to borrow.

"You have heard that it was said, *You shall love your neighbor and hate your enemy.* But I say to you, love your enemies and pray for those who persecute you, that you may be children of your heavenly Father, for he makes his sun rise on the bad and the good, and causes rain to fall on the just and the unjust. For if you love those who love you, what recompense will you have? Do not the tax collectors do the same? And if you greet your brothers only, what is unusual about that? Do not the pagans do the same? So be perfect, just as your heavenly Father is perfect."

SEVENTH SUNDAY IN ORDINARY TIME / B   1213

READING I   *Isaiah 43:18–19, 21–22, 24b–25 / 80*

Thus says the LORD:
Remember not the events of the past,
    the things of long ago consider not;
see, I am doing something new!
    Now it springs forth, do you not
        perceive it?
In the desert I make a way,
    in the wasteland, rivers.
The people I formed for myself,
that they might announce my praise.
Yet you did not call upon me, O Jacob,
    for you grew weary of me, O Israel.
You burdened me with your sins,
    and wearied me with your crimes.
It is I, I, who wipe out,
    for my own sake, your offenses;
    your sins I remember no more.

RESPONSORIAL PSALM   *Psalm 41:2–3, 4–5, 13–14*

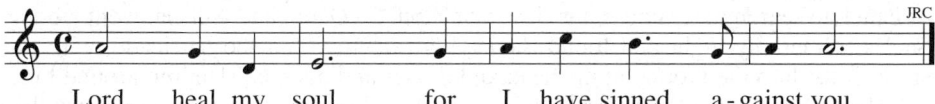

Lord, heal my soul, for I have sinned a-gainst you.

Blessed is he who has concern for the
        poor.
    In time of trouble, the LORD will
        rescue him.
The LORD will guard him, give him life,
    and make him blessed in the land,
    not give him up to the will of his
        foes. ℟.

The LORD will help him on his bed of
        pain;
    you will bring him back from
sickness to health.
As for me, I said, "LORD, have mercy
        on me;
    heal my soul, for I have sinned
        against you." ℟.

In my integrity you have upheld me,
    and have set me in your presence
        forever.
Blest be the LORD, the God of Israel,
    from age to age. Amen. Amen. ℟.

READING II   *2 Corinthians 1:18–22*

Brothers and sisters: As God is faithful, our word to you is not "yes" and "no." For the Son of God, Jesus Christ, who was proclaimed to you by us, Silvanus and Timothy and me, was not "yes" and "no," but "yes" has been in him. For however many are the promises of God, their Yes is in him; therefore, the Amen from us also goes through him to God for glory. But the one who gives us security with you in Christ and who anointed us is God; he has also put his seal upon us and given the Spirit in our hearts as a first installment.

GOSPEL   *Mark 2:1–12*

When Jesus returned to Capernaum after some days, it became known that he was at home. Many gathered together so that there was no longer room for them, not even around the door, and he preached the word to them. They came bringing to him a paralytic carried by four men. Unable to get near Jesus because of the crowd, they opened up the roof above him. After they had broken through, they let down the mat on which the paralytic was lying. When Jesus saw their faith, he said to the paralytic, "Child, your sins are forgiven." Now some of the scribes were sitting there asking themselves, "Why does this man speak that way? He is blaspheming. Who but God alone can forgive sins?" Jesus immediately knew in his mind what they were thinking to themselves, so he said, "Why are you thinking such things in your hearts? Which is easier, to say to the paralytic, 'Your sins are forgiven,' or to say, 'Rise, pick up your mat and walk?' But that you may know that the Son of Man has authority to forgive sins on earth" —he said to the paralytic, "I say to you, rise, pick up your mat, and go home." He rose, picked up his mat at once, and went away in the sight of everyone. They were all astounded and glorified God, saying, "We have never seen anything like this."

1214 SEVENTH SUNDAY IN ORDINARY TIME / C

READING I   *1 Samuel 26:2, 7–9, 12–13, 22–23 / 81*

In those days, Saul went down to the desert of Ziph with three thousand picked men of Israel, to search for David in the desert of Ziph. So David and Abishai went among Saul's soldiers by night and found Saul lying asleep within the barricade, with his spear thrust into the ground at his head and Abner and his men sleeping around him.

Abishai whispered to David: "God has delivered your enemy into your grasp this day. Let me nail him to the ground with one thrust of the spear; I will not need a second thrust!" But David said to Abishai, "Do not harm him, for who can lay hands on the LORD's anointed and remain unpunished?" So David took the spear and the water jug from their place at Saul's head, and they got away without anyone's seeing or knowing or awakening. All remained asleep, because the LORD had put them into a deep slumber.

Going across to an opposite slope, David stood on a remote hilltop at a great distance from Abner, son of Ner, and the troops.

He said: "Here is the king's spear. Let an attendant come over to get it. The LORD will reward each man for his justice and faithfulness. Today, though the LORD delivered you into my grasp, I would not harm the LORD's anointed."

RESPONSORIAL PSALM   *Psalm 103:1–2, 3–4, 8 and 10, 12–13*

DRH

The Lord is kind and mer-ci-ful.

Bless the LORD, O my soul,
    and all within me, his holy name.
Bless the LORD, O my soul,
    and never forget all his benefits. ℟.

It is the Lord who forgives all your sins,
    who heals every one of your ills,
who redeems your life from the grave,
    who crowns you with mercy and

compassion. ℟.

The LORD is compassionate and
    gracious,
    slow to anger and rich in mercy.
He does not treat us according to our
    sins,
nor repay us according to our
    faults. ℟.

As far as the east is from the west,
so far from us does he remove our
transgressions.

As a father has compassion on his
children,
the LORD's compassion is on those
who fear him. ℟.

READING II   *1 Corinthians 15:45–49*

Brothers and sisters: It is written, *The first man, Adam, became a living being,* the last Adam a life-giving spirit. But the spiritual was not first; rather the natural and then the spiritual. The first man was from the earth, earthly; the second man, from heaven. As was the earthly one, so also are the earthly, and as is the heavenly one, so also are the heavenly. Just as we have borne the image of the earthly one, we shall also bear the image of the heavenly one.

GOSPEL   *Luke 6:27–38*

Jesus said to his disciples: "To you who hear I say, love your enemies, do good to those who hate you, bless those who curse you, pray for those who mistreat you. To the person who strikes you on one cheek, offer the other one as well, and from the person who takes your cloak, do not withhold even your tunic. Give to everyone who asks of you, and from the one who takes what is yours do not demand it back. Do to others as you would have them do to you. For if you love those who love you, what credit is that to you? Even sinners love those who love them. And if you do good to those who do good to you, what credit is that to you? Even sinners do the same. If you lend money to those from whom you expect repayment, what credit is that to you? Even sinners lend to sinners, and get back the same amount. But rather, love your enemies and do good to them, and lend expecting nothing back; then your reward will be great and you will be children of the Most High, for he himself is kind to the ungrateful and the wicked. Be merciful, just as your Father is merciful.

"Stop judging and you will not be judged. Stop condemning and you will not be condemned. Forgive and you will be forgiven. Give, and gifts will be given to you; a good measure, packed together, shaken down, and overflowing, will be poured into your lap. For the measure with which you measure will in return be measured out to you."

EIGHTH SUNDAY IN ORDINARY TIME / A   1215

READING I   *Isaiah 49:14–15 / 82*

Zion said, "The LORD has
forsaken me;
my LORD has forgotten me."
Can a mother forget her infant,

be without tenderness for the child
of her womb?
Even should she forget,
I will never forget you.

RESPONSORIAL PSALM   *Psalm 62:2–3, 6–7, 8–9ab*

Rest in God a - lone,   rest in God a - lone,   my   soul,   my   soul.

In God alone is my soul at rest;
my salvation comes from him.

He alone is my rock, my salvation,
my fortress; never shall I falter. ℟.

In God alone be at rest, my soul,
  for my hope is from him.
He alone is my rock, my salvation,
  my fortress; never shall I falter. ℟.

In God is my salvation and glory,
  my rock of strength;
  in God is my refuge.
Trust him at all times, O people.
Pour out your hearts before him. ℟.

READING II
1 Corinthians 4:1–5

Brothers and sisters: Thus should one regard us: as servants of Christ and stewards of the mysteries of God. Now it is of course required of stewards that they be found trustworthy. It does not concern me in the least that I be judged by you or any human tribunal; I do not even pass judgment on myself; I am not conscious of anything against me, but I do not thereby stand acquitted; the one who judges me is the Lord. Therefore do not make any judgment before the appointed time, until the Lord comes, for he will bring to light what is hidden in darkness and will manifest the motives of our hearts, and then everyone will receive praise from God.

GOSPEL
Matthew 6:24–34

Jesus said to his disciples: "No one can serve two masters. He will either hate one and love the other, or be devoted to one and despise the other. You cannot serve God and mammon.

"Therefore I tell you, do not worry about your life, what you will eat or drink, or about your body, what you will wear. Is not life more than food and the body more than clothing? Look at the birds in the sky; they do not sow or reap, they gather nothing into barns, yet your heavenly Father feeds them. Are not you more important than they? Can any of you by worrying add a single moment to your life-span? Why are you anxious about clothes? Learn from the way the wild flowers grow. They do not work or spin. But I tell you that not even Solomon in all his splendor was clothed like one of them. If God so clothes the grass of the field, which grows today and is thrown into the oven tomorrow, will he not much more provide for you, O you of little faith? So do not worry and say, 'What are we to eat?' or 'What are we to drink?' or 'What are we to wear?' All these things the pagans seek. Your heavenly Father knows that you need them all. But seek first the kingdom of God and his righteousness, and all these things will be given you besides. Do not worry about tomorrow; tomorrow will take care of itself. Sufficient for a day is its own evil."

1216   EIGHTH SUNDAY IN ORDINARY TIME / B

READING I
Hosea 2:16b, 17b, 21–22 / 83

Thus says the LORD:
I will lead her into the desert
  and speak to her heart.
She shall respond there as in the days
    of her youth,
  when she came up from the land
    of Egypt.

I will espouse you to me forever:
  I will espouse you in right and in
    justice,
  in love and in mercy;
I will espouse you in fidelity,
  and you shall know the LORD.

RESPONSORIAL PSALM *Psalm 103:1–2, 3–4, 8 and 10, 12–13*

The Lord is kind and mer - ci - ful.

Bless the LORD, O my soul,
and all within me, his holy name.
Bless the LORD, O my soul,
and never forget all his benefits. ℟.

It is the Lord who forgives all your sins,
who heals every one of your ills,
who redeems your life from the grave,
who crowns you with mercy and
compassion. ℟.

The LORD is compassionate and
gracious,
slow to anger and rich in mercy.

He does not treat us according to our
sins,
nor repay us according to our
faults. ℟.

As far as the east is from the west,
so far from us does he remove our
transgressions.
As a father has compassion on his
children,
the LORD's compassion is on those
who fear him. ℟.

READING II *2 Corinthians 3:1b–6*

Brothers and sisters: Do we need, as some do, letters of recommendation to you or from you? You are our letter, written on our hearts, known and read by all, shown to be a letter of Christ ministered by us, written not in ink but by the Spirit of the living God, not on tablets of stone but on tablets that are hearts of flesh.

Such confidence we have through Christ toward God. Not that of ourselves we are qualified to take credit for anything as coming from us; rather, our qualification comes from God, who has indeed qualified us as ministers of a new covenant, not of letter but of spirit; for the letter brings death, but the Spirit gives life.

GOSPEL *Mark 2:18–22*

The disciples of John and of the Pharisees were accustomed to fast. People came to him and objected, "Why do the disciples of John and the disciples of the Pharisees fast, but your disciples do not fast?" Jesus answered them, "Can the wedding guests fast while the bridegroom is with them? As long as they have the bridegroom with them they cannot fast. But the days will come when the bridegroom is taken away from them, and then they will fast on that day. No one sews a piece of unshrunken cloth on an old cloak. If he does, its fullness pulls away, the new from the old, and the tear gets worse. Likewise, no one pours new wine into old wineskins. Otherwise, the wine will burst the skins, and both the wine and the skins are ruined. Rather, new wine is poured into fresh wineskins."

1217 EIGHTH SUNDAY IN ORDINARY TIME / C

READING I
Sirach 27:4–7 / 84

When a sieve is shaken, the husks
appear;
  so do one's faults when one speaks.
As the test of what the potter molds is
in the furnace,
  so in tribulation is the test of the just.

The fruit of a tree shows the care it has
had;
  so too does one's speech disclose the
bent of one's mind.
Praise no one before he speaks,
  for it is then that people are tested.

RESPONSORIAL PSALM
Psalm 92:2–3, 13–14, 15–16

Lord, it is good to give thanks to you.

It is good to give thanks to the LORD,
  to make music to your name,
    O Most High,
to proclaim your loving mercy in the
morning,
  and your truth in the watches of
the night. ℟.

The just will flourish like the palm tree,
  and grow like a Lebanon cedar.

Planted in the house of the LORD,
  they will flourish in the courts of
our God. ℟.

Still bearing fruit when they are old,
  still full of sap, still green,
to proclaim that the LORD is upright.
  In him, my rock, there is no
wrong. ℟.

READING II
1 Corinthians 15:54–58

Brothers and sisters: When this which is corruptible clothes itself with incorruptibility
and this which is mortal clothes itself with immortality, then the word that is written
shall come about:
  Death is swallowed up in victory.
  Where, O death, is your victory?
  Where, O death, is your sting?
The sting of death is sin, and the power of sin is the law. But thanks be to God who
gives us the victory through our Lord Jesus Christ.
  Therefore, my beloved brothers and sisters, be firm, steadfast, always fully devot-
ed to the work of the Lord, knowing that in the Lord your labor is not in vain.

GOSPEL
Luke 6:39–45

Jesus told his disciples a parable, "Can a blind person guide a blind person? Will not
both fall into a pit? No disciple is superior to the teacher; but when fully trained, every
disciple will be like his teacher. Why do you notice the splinter in your brother's eye,
but do not perceive the wooden beam in your own? How can you say to your brother,
'Brother, let me remove that splinter in your eye,' when you do not even notice the
wooden beam in your own eye? You hypocrite! Remove the wooden beam from your
eye first; then you will see clearly to remove the splinter in your brother's eye.
  "A good tree does not bear rotten fruit, nor does a rotten tree bear good fruit. For
every tree is known by its own fruit. For people do not pick figs from thornbushes,
nor do they gather grapes from brambles. A good person out of the store of goodness

in his heart produces good, but an evil person out of a store of evil produces evil; for from the fullness of the heart the mouth speaks."

NINTH SUNDAY IN ORDINARY TIME / A   1218

READING I   *Deuteronomy 11:18, 26–28, 32 / 85*

Moses told the people, "Take these words of mine into your heart and soul. Bind them at your wrist as a sign, and let them be a pendant on your forehead.

"I set before you here, this day, a blessing and a curse: a blessing for obeying the commandments of the LORD, your God, which I enjoin on you today; a curse if you do not obey the commandments of the LORD, your God, but turn aside from the way I ordain for you today, to follow other gods, whom you have not known. Be careful to observe all the statutes and decrees that I set before you today."

RESPONSORIAL PSALM   *Psalm 31:2–3a, 3bc–4, 17 and 25*

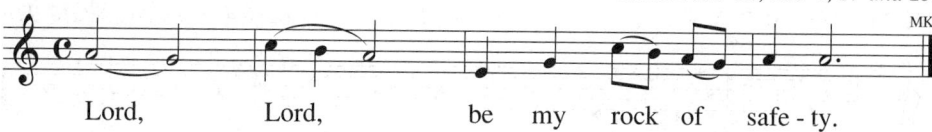

Lord, Lord, be my rock of safe-ty.

In you, O LORD, I take refuge.
    Let me never be put to shame.
In your justice, set me free;
      incline your ear to me, and speedily
        rescue me. ℟.

Be a rock of refuge for me,
    a mighty stronghold to save me.

For you are my rock, my stronghold!
    Lead me, guide me, for the sake of
      your name. ℟.

Let your face shine on your servant.
    Save me in your merciful love.
Be strong, let your heart take courage,
    all who hope in the LORD. ℟.

READING II   *Romans 3:21–25, 28*

Brothers and sisters, Now the righteousness of God has been manifested apart from the law, though testified to by the law and the prophets, the righteousness of God through faith in Jesus Christ for all who believe. For there is no distinction; all have sinned and are deprived of the glory of God. They are justified freely by his grace through the redemption in Christ Jesus, whom God set forth as an expiation, through faith, by his blood. For we consider that a person is justified by faith apart from works of the law.

GOSPEL   *Matthew 7:21–27*

Jesus said to his disciples: "Not everyone who says to me, 'Lord, Lord,' will enter the kingdom of heaven, but only the one who does the will of my Father in heaven. Many will say to me on that day, 'Lord, Lord, did we not prophesy in your name? Did we not drive out demons in your name? Did we not do mighty deeds in your name?' Then I will declare to them solemnly, 'I never knew you. Depart from me, you evildoers.'

"Everyone who listens to these words of mine and acts on them will be like a wise man who built his house on rock. The rain fell, the floods came, and the winds blew and buffeted the house. But it did not collapse; it had been set solidly on rock. And everyone who listens to these words of mine but does not act on them will be like a fool who built his house on sand. The rain fell, the floods came, and the winds blew and buffeted the house. And it collapsed and was completely ruined."

1219 NINTH SUNDAY IN ORDINARY TIME / B

READING I *Deuteronomy 5:12–15 / 86*

Thus says the LORD: "Take care to keep holy the sabbath day as the LORD, your God, commanded you. Six days you may labor and do all your work; but the seventh day is the sabbath of the LORD, your God. No work may be done then, whether by you, or your son or daughter, or your male or female slave, or your ox or ass or any of your beasts, or the alien who lives with you. Your male and female slave should rest as you do. For remember that you too were once a slave in Egypt, and the LORD, your God, brought you from there with his strong hand and outstretched arm. That is why the LORD, your God, has commanded you to observe the sabbath day."

RESPONSORIAL PSALM *Psalm 81:3–4, 5–6ab, 6c–8a, 10–11b*

RC

Sing with joy to God! Sing to God our help!

Raise a song and sound the timbrel,
  the sweet-sounding harp and the lute;
blow the trumpet at the new moon,
  when the moon is full, on our
    feast. ℟.

For this is a statute in Israel,
  a command of the God of Jacob.
He made it a decree for Joseph,
  when he went out from the land of
    Egypt. ℟.

A voice I did not know said to me:
  "I freed your shoulder from the

burden;
your hands were freed from the
    builder's basket.
You called in distress and I
    delivered you." ℟.

"Let there be no strange god among
    you,
  nor shall you worship a foreign god.
I am the LORD your God,
  who brought you up from the land
    of Egypt." ℟.

READING II *2 Corinthians 4:6–11*

Brothers and sisters: God who said, *Let light shine out of darkness,* has shone in our hearts to bring to light the knowledge of the glory of God on the face of Jesus Christ. But we hold this treasure in earthen vessels, that the surpassing power may be of God and not from us. We are afflicted in every way, but not constrained; perplexed, but not driven to despair; persecuted, but not abandoned; struck down, but not destroyed; always carrying about in the body the dying of Jesus, so that the life of Jesus may also be manifested in our body. For we who live are constantly being given up to death for the sake of Jesus, so that the life of Jesus may be manifested in our mortal flesh.

GOSPEL   *Mark 2:23—3:6 or 2:23—28*

For short form read only the part in brackets.

[As Jesus was passing through a field of grain on the sabbath, his disciples began to make a path while picking the heads of grain. At this the Pharisees said to him, "Look, why are they doing what is unlawful on the sabbath?" He said to them, "Have you never read what David did when he was in need and he and his companions were hungry? How he went into the house of God when Abiathar was high priest and ate the bread of offering that only the priests could lawfully eat, and shared it with his companions?" Then he said to them, "The sabbath was made for man, not man for the sabbath. That is why the Son of Man is lord even of the sabbath."]

Again he entered the synagogue. There was a man there who had a withered hand. They watched him closely to see if he would cure him on the sabbath so that they might accuse him. He said to the man with the withered hand, "Come up here before us." Then he said to them, "Is it lawful to do good on the sabbath rather than to do evil, to save life rather than to destroy it?" But they remained silent. Looking around at them with anger and grieved at their hardness of heart, he said to the man, "Stretch out your hand." He stretched it out and his hand was restored. The Pharisees went out and immediately took counsel with the Herodians against him to put him to death.

NINTH SUNDAY IN ORDINARY TIME / C   1220

READING I   *1 Kings 8:41–43 / 87*

In those days, Solomon prayed in the temple, saying, "To the foreigner, who is not of your people Israel, but comes from a distant land to honor you —since they will learn of your great name and your mighty hand and your outstretched arm—, when he comes and prays toward this temple, listen from your heavenly dwelling. Do all that foreigner asks of you, that all the peoples of the earth may know your name, may fear you as do your people Israel, and may acknowledge that this temple which I have built is dedicated to your honor."

RESPONSORIAL PSALM   *Psalm 117:1, 2*

Or: Alleluia.

Go out to all the world, and tell the Good News.

O praise the LORD, all you nations;
  acclaim him, all you peoples! ℟.

For his merciful love has prevailed
  over us;
  and the LORD's faithfulness endures
  forever. ℟.

READING II   *Galatians 1:1–2, 6–10*

Paul, an apostle not from human beings nor through a human being but through Jesus Christ and God the Father who raised him from the dead, and all the brothers who are with me, to the churches of Galatia.

I am amazed that you are so quickly forsaking the one who called you by the grace of Christ for a different gospel —not that there is another. But there are some who are disturbing you and wish to pervert the gospel of Christ. But even if we or an angel from heaven should preach to you a gospel other than the one that we preached to you, let that one be accursed! As we have said before, and now I say again, if anyone preaches to you a gospel other than what you have received, let that one be accursed!

Am I now currying favor with humans or with God? Or am I seeking to please people? If I were still trying to please people, I would not be a slave of Christ.

GOSPEL   *Luke 7:1–10*

When Jesus had finished all his words to the people, he entered Capernaum. A centurion there had a slave who was ill and about to die, and he was valuable to him. When he heard about Jesus, he sent elders of the Jews to him, asking him to come and save the life of his slave. They approached Jesus and strongly urged him to come, saying, "He deserves to have you do this for him, for he loves our nation and built the synagogue for us." And Jesus went with them, but when he was only a short distance from the house, the centurion sent friends to tell him, "Lord, do not trouble yourself, for I am not worthy to have you enter under my roof. Therefore, I did not consider myself worthy to come to you; but say the word and let my servant be healed. For I too am a person subject to authority, with soldiers subject to me. And I say to one, 'Go,' and he goes; and to another, 'Come here,' and he comes; and to my slave, 'Do this,' and he does it." When Jesus heard this he was amazed at him and, turning, said to the crowd following him, "I tell you, not even in Israel have I found such faith." When the messengers returned to the house, they found the slave in good health.

1221   TENTH SUNDAY IN ORDINARY TIME / A

READING I   *Hosea 6:3–6 / 88*

In their affliction, people will say:
"Let us know, let us strive to know
   the LORD;
    as certain as the dawn is his coming,
and his judgment shines forth like
   the light of day!
He will come to us like the rain,
    like spring rain that waters the earth."

What can I do with you, Ephraim?

What can I do with you, Judah?
Your piety is like a morning cloud,
   like the dew that early passes away.
For this reason I smote them through
   the prophets,
I slew them by the words of my
   mouth;
for it is love that I desire, not sacrifice,
   and knowledge of God rather than
   holocausts.

RESPONSORIAL PSALM   *Psalm 50:1 and 8, 12–13, 14–15*

To the up-right I will show the sav-ing pow'r of God.

The God of gods, the LORD,
   has spoken and summoned the earth,
   from the rising of the sun to its
   setting.

"I do not rebuke you for your sacrifices;
   your offerings are always before
   me." ℟.

"Were I hungry, I would not tell you,
  for the world and its fullness is mine.
Do I eat the flesh of bulls,
  or drink the blood of goats?" ℟.

"Give your praise as a sacrifice to God,
  and fulfill your vows to the
    Most High.
Then call on me in the day of distress.
  I will deliver you and you shall
    honor me." ℟.

READING II
Romans 4:18–25

Brothers and sisters: Abraham believed, hoping against hope, that he would become "the father of many nations," according to what was said, "Thus shall your descendants be." He did not weaken in faith when he considered his own body as already dead —for he was almost a hundred years old— and the dead womb of Sarah. He did not doubt God's promise in unbelief; rather, he was strengthened by faith and gave glory to God and was fully convinced that what he had promised he was also able to do. That is why *it was credited to him as righteousness*. But it was not for him alone that it was written that *it was credited to him;* it was also for us, to whom it will be credited, who believe in the one who raised Jesus our Lord from the dead, who was handed over for our transgressions and was raised for our justification.

GOSPEL
Matthew 9:9–13

As Jesus passed on from there, he saw a man named Matthew sitting at the customs post. He said to him, "Follow me." And he got up and followed him. While he was at table in his house, many tax collectors and sinners came and sat with Jesus and his disciples. The Pharisees saw this and said to his disciples, "Why does your teacher eat with tax collectors and sinners?" He heard this and said, "Those who are well do not need a physician, but the sick do. Go and learn the meaning of the words, 'I desire mercy, not sacrifice.' I did not come to call the righteous but sinners."

TENTH SUNDAY IN ORDINARY TIME / B
1222

READING I
Genesis 3:9–15 / 89

After the man, Adam, had eaten of the tree, the LORD God called to the man and asked him, "Where are you?" He answered, "I heard you in the garden; but I was afraid, because I was naked, so I hid myself." Then he asked, "Who told you that you were naked? You have eaten, then, from the tree of which I had forbidden you to eat!" The man replied, "The woman whom you put here with me— she gave me fruit from the tree, and so I ate it." The LORD God then asked the woman, "Why did you do such a thing?" The woman answered, "The serpent tricked me into it, so I ate it."

Then the LORD God said to the serpent:
    "Because you have done this, you shall be banned from
        all the animals
        and from all the wild creatures;
    on your belly shall you crawl,
        and dirt shall you eat
        all the days of your life.
    I will put enmity between you and the woman,
        and between your offspring and hers;
    he will strike at your head,
        while you strike at his heel."

RESPONSORIAL PSALM *Psalm 130:1–2, 3–4, 5–6ab and 7a, 7b–8*

JRC

With the Lord there is mer-cy, and full - ness of re - demp-tion.

Out of the depths I cry to you, O LORD;
    Lord, hear my voice!
O let your ears be attentive
    to the sound of my pleadings. ℟.

I long for you, O LORD,
    my soul longs for his word.
My soul hopes in the Lord
    more than watchmen for daybreak. ℟.

If you, O LORD, should mark iniquities,
    Lord, who could stand?
But with you is found forgiveness,
    that you may be revered. ℟.

Let Israel hope for the LORD.
For with the LORD there is mercy,
    in him is plentiful redemption.
It is he who will redeem Israel
    from all its iniquities. ℟.

READING II *2 Corinthians 4:13—5:1*

Brothers and sisters: Since we have the same spirit of faith, according to what is written, *I believed, therefore I spoke,* we too believe and therefore we speak, knowing that the one who raised the Lord Jesus will raise us also with Jesus and place us with you in his presence. Everything indeed is for you, so that the grace bestowed in abundance on more and more people may cause the thanksgiving to overflow for the glory of God. Therefore, we are not discouraged; rather, although our outer self is wasting away, our inner self is being renewed day by day. For this momentary light affliction is producing for us an eternal weight of glory beyond all comparison, as we look not to what is seen but to what is unseen; for what is seen is transitory, but what is unseen is eternal. For we know that if our earthly dwelling, a tent, should be destroyed, we have a building from God, a dwelling not made with hands, eternal in heaven.

GOSPEL *Mark 3:20–35*

Jesus came home with his disciples. Again the crowd gathered, making it impossible for them even to eat. When his relatives heard of this they set out to seize him, for they said, "He is out of his mind." The scribes who had come from Jerusalem said, "He is possessed by Beelzebul," and "By the prince of demons he drives out demons."

Summoning them, he began to speak to them in parables, "How can Satan drive out Satan? If a kingdom is divided against itself, that kingdom cannot stand. And if a house is divided against itself, that house will not be able to stand. And if Satan has risen up against himself and is divided, he cannot stand; that is the end of him. But no one can enter a strong man's house to plunder his property unless he first ties up the strong man. Then he can plunder the house. Amen, I say to you, all sins and all blasphemies that people utter will be forgiven them. But whoever blasphemes against the Holy Spirit will never have forgiveness, but is guilty of an everlasting sin." For they had said, "He has an unclean spirit."

His mother and his brothers arrived. Standing outside they sent word to him and called him. A crowd seated around him told him, "Your mother and your brothers and your sisters are outside asking for you." But he said to them in reply, "Who are my mother and my brothers?" And looking around at those seated in the circle he said, "Here are my mother and my brothers. For whoever does the will of God is my brother and sister and mother."

TENTH SUNDAY IN ORDINARY TIME / C 1223

READING I
1 Kings 17:17–24 / 90

Elijah went to Zarephath of Sidon to the house of a widow. The son of the mistress of the house fell sick, and his sickness grew more severe until he stopped breathing. So she said to Elijah, "Why have you done this to me, O man of God? Have you come to me to call attention to my guilt and to kill my son?" Elijah said to her, "Give me your son." Taking him from her lap, he carried the son to the upper room where he was staying, and put him on his bed. Elijah called out to the LORD: "O LORD, my God, will you afflict even the widow with whom I am staying by killing her son?" Then he stretched himself out upon the child three times and called out to the LORD: "O LORD, my God, let the life breath return to the body of this child." The LORD heard the prayer of Elijah; the life breath returned to the child's body and he revived. Taking the child, Elijah brought him down into the house from the upper room and gave him to his mother. Elijah said to her, "See! Your son is alive." The woman replied to Elijah, "Now indeed I know that you are a man of God. The word of the LORD comes truly from your mouth."

RESPONSORIAL PSALM
Psalm 30:2 and 4, 5–6, 11 and 12a and 13b

I will praise you, Lord, for you have res - cued me.

I will extol you, LORD, for you have
    raised me up,
    and have not let my enemies rejoice
      over me.
O LORD, you have lifted up my soul
    from the grave,
    restored me to life from those who
      sink into the pit. ℟.

Sing psalms to the LORD, you faithful
    ones;
    give thanks to his holy name.

His anger lasts a moment; his favor all
    through life.
    At night come tears, but dawn
      brings joy. ℟.

Hear, O LORD, and have mercy on me;
    be my helper, O LORD.
You have changed my mourning into
    dancing.
    O LORD my God, I will thank you
      forever. ℟.

READING II
Galatians 1:11–19

I want you to know, brothers and sisters, that the gospel preached by me is not of human origin. For I did not receive it from a human being, nor was I taught it, but it came through a revelation of Jesus Christ.

For you heard of my former way of life in Judaism, how I persecuted the church of God beyond measure and tried to destroy it, and progressed in Judaism beyond many of my contemporaries among my race, since I was even more a zealot for my ancestral traditions. But when God, who from my mother's womb had set me apart and called me through his grace, was pleased to reveal his Son to me, so that I might proclaim him to the Gentiles, I did not immediately consult flesh and blood, nor did I go up to Jerusalem to those who were apostles before me; rather, I went into Arabia and then returned to Damascus.

Then after three years I went up to Jerusalem to confer with Cephas and remained with him for fifteen days. But I did not see any other of the apostles, only James the brother of the Lord.

GOSPEL   *Luke 7:11–17*

Jesus journeyed to a city called Nain, and his disciples and a large crowd accompanied him. As he drew near to the gate of the city, a man who had died was being carried out, the only son of his mother, and she was a widow. A large crowd from the city was with her. When the Lord saw her, he was moved with pity for her and said to her, "Do not weep." He stepped forward and touched the coffin; at this the bearers halted, and he said, "Young man, I tell you, arise!" The dead man sat up and began to speak, and Jesus gave him to his mother. Fear seized them all, and they glorified God, exclaiming, "A great prophet has arisen in our midst," and "God has visited his people." This report about him spread through the whole of Judea and in all the surrounding region.

1224   ELEVENTH SUNDAY IN ORDINARY TIME / A

READING I   *Exodus 19:2–6a / 91*

In those days, the Israelites came to the desert of Sinai and pitched camp. While Israel was encamped here in front of the mountain, Moses went up the mountain to God. Then the LORD called to him and said, "Thus shall you say to the house of Jacob; tell the Israelites: You have seen for yourselves how I treated the Egyptians and how I bore you up on eagle wings and brought you here to myself. Therefore, if you hearken to my voice and keep my covenant, you shall be my special possession, dearer to me than all other people, though all the earth is mine. You shall be to me a kingdom of priests, a holy nation."

RESPONSORIAL PSALM   *Psalm 100:1–2, 3, 5*

MK

We are his peo-ple,   the sheep of his flock.

Cry out with joy to the LORD, all the
  earth.
  Serve the LORD with gladness.
  Come before him, singing for joy. ℟.

Know that he, the LORD, is God.
  He made us; we belong to him.

We are his people, the sheep of his
  flock. ℟.

Indeed, how good is the LORD,
  eternal his merciful love.
He is faithful from age to age. ℟.

READING II   *Romans 5:6–11*

Brothers and sisters: Christ, while we were still helpless, yet died at the appointed time for the ungodly. Indeed, only with difficulty does one die for a just person, though perhaps for a good person one might even find courage to die. But God proves his love for us in that while we were still sinners Christ died for us. How much more then, since we are now justified by his blood, will we be saved through him from the wrath. Indeed, if, while we were enemies, we were reconciled to God through the death of his Son, how much more, once reconciled, will we be saved by his life. Not only that, but we also boast of God through our Lord Jesus Christ, through whom we have now received reconciliation.

GOSPEL *Matthew 9:36—10:8*

At the sight of the crowds, Jesus' heart was moved with pity for them because they were troubled and abandoned, like sheep without a shepherd. Then he said to his disciples, "The harvest is abundant but the laborers are few; so ask the master of the harvest to send out laborers for his harvest."

Then he summoned his twelve disciples and gave them authority over unclean spirits to drive them out and to cure every disease and every illness. The names of the twelve apostles are these: first, Simon called Peter, and his brother Andrew; James, the son of Zebedee, and his brother John; Philip and Bartholomew, Thomas and Matthew the tax collector; James, the son of Alphaeus, and Thaddeus; Simon from Cana, and Judas Iscariot who betrayed him.

Jesus sent out these twelve after instructing them thus, "Do not go into pagan territory or enter a Samaritan town. Go rather to the lost sheep of the house of Israel. As you go, make this proclamation: 'The kingdom of heaven is at hand.' Cure the sick, raise the dead, cleanse lepers, drive out demons. Without cost you have received; without cost you are to give."

ELEVENTH SUNDAY IN ORDINARY TIME / B   1225

READING I *Ezekiel 17:22–24 / 92*

Thus says the Lord GOD:
    I, too, will take from the crest of the
        cedar,
            from its topmost branches tear
                off a tender shoot,
        and plant it on a high and lofty
            mountain;
            on the mountain heights of Israel
                I will plant it.
    It shall put forth branches and bear
        fruit,
        and become a majestic cedar.
    Birds of every kind shall dwell
        beneath it,
        every winged thing in the shade
            of its boughs.
And all the trees of the field shall
    know
        that I, the Lord,
    bring low the high tree,
        lift high the lowly tree,
    wither up the green tree,
        and make the withered tree
            bloom.
As I, the LORD, have spoken, so will I
    do.

RESPONSORIAL PSALM   *Psalm 92:2–3, 13–14, 15–16*

Lord, it is good to give thanks to you.

It is good to give thanks to the LORD,
  to make music to your name,
    O Most High,
to proclaim your loving mercy in the
      morning,
  and your truth in the watches of the
      night. ℟.

The just will flourish like the palm tree,
  and grow like a Lebanon cedar.

Planted in the house of the LORD,
  they will flourish in the courts of
      our God. ℟.

Still bearing fruit when they are old,
  still full of sap, still green,
to proclaim that the LORD is upright.
  In him, my rock, there is no
      wrong. ℟.

READING II   *2 Corinthians 5:6–10*

Brothers and sisters: We are always courageous, although we know that while we are at home in the body we are away from the Lord, for we walk by faith, not by sight. Yet we are courageous, and we would rather leave the body and go home to the Lord. Therefore, we aspire to please him, whether we are at home or away. For we must all appear before the judgment seat of Christ, so that each may receive recompense, according to what he did in the body, whether good or evil.

GOSPEL   *Mark 4:26–34*

Jesus said to the crowds: "This is how it is with the kingdom of God; it is as if a man were to scatter seed on the land and would sleep and rise night and day and through it all the seed would sprout and grow, he knows not how. Of its own accord the land yields fruit, first the blade, then the ear, then the full grain in the ear. And when the grain is ripe, he wields the sickle at once, for the harvest has come."

He said, "To what shall we compare the kingdom of God, or what parable can we use for it? It is like a mustard seed that, when it is sown in the ground, is the smallest of all the seeds on the earth. But once it is sown, it springs up and becomes the largest of plants and puts forth large branches, so that the birds of the sky can dwell in its shade." With many such parables he spoke the word to them as they were able to understand it. Without parables he did not speak to them, but to his own disciples he explained everything in private.

1226 ELEVENTH SUNDAY IN ORDINARY TIME / C

READING I   *2 Samuel 12:7–10, 13 / 93*

Nathan said to David: "Thus says the LORD God of Israel: 'I anointed you king of Israel. I rescued you from the hand of Saul. I gave you your lord's house and your lord's wives for your own. I gave you the house of Israel and of Judah. And if this were not enough, I could count up for you still more. Why have you spurned the Lord and done evil in his sight? You have cut down Uriah the Hittite with the sword; you took his wife as your own, and him you killed with the sword of the Ammonites. Now, therefore, the sword shall never depart from your house, because you have despised me and have taken the wife of Uriah to be your wife.'" Then David said to Nathan, "I have sinned against the LORD." Nathan answered David: "The LORD on his part has forgiven your sin: you shall not die."

RESPONSORIAL PSALM

Psalm 32:1–2, 5, 7, 11

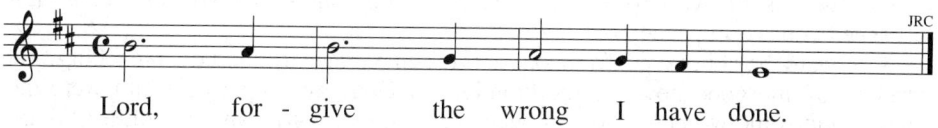

Lord, for-give the wrong I have done.

Blessed is he whose transgression is
   forgiven,
  whose sin is remitted.
Blessed the man to whom the LORD
   imputes no guilt,
  in whose spirit is no guile. ℟.

To you I have acknowledged my sin;
  my guilt I did not hide.
I said, "I will confess my transgression
  to the LORD."

And you have forgiven the guilt of
  my sin. ℟.

You are a hiding place for me;
  you keep me safe from distress;
  you surround me with cries of
   deliverance. ℟.

Rejoice in the LORD; exult, you just!
  Ring out your joy, all you upright of
   heart! ℟.

READING II

Galatians 2:16, 19–21

Brothers and sisters: We who know that a person is not justified by works of the law but through faith in Jesus Christ, even we have believed in Christ Jesus that we may be justified by faith in Christ and not by works of the law, because by works of the law no one will be justified. For through the law I died to the law, that I might live for God. I have been crucified with Christ; yet I live, no longer I, but Christ lives in me; insofar as I now live in the flesh, I live by faith in the Son of God who has loved me and given himself up for me. I do not nullify the grace of God; for if justification comes through the law, then Christ died for nothing.

GOSPEL

Luke 7:36—8:3 or 7:36–50

For short form read only the part in brackets.

[A Pharisee invited Jesus to dine with him, and he entered the Pharisee's house and reclined at table. Now there was a sinful woman in the city who learned that he was at table in the house of the Pharisee. Bringing an alabaster flask of ointment, she stood behind him at his feet weeping and began to bathe his feet with her tears. Then she wiped them with her hair, kissed them, and anointed them with the ointment. When the Pharisee who had invited him saw this he said to himself, "If this man were a prophet, he would know who and what sort of woman this is who is touching him, that she is a sinner." Jesus said to him in reply, "Simon, I have something to say to you." "Tell me, teacher," he said. "Two people were in debt to a certain creditor; one owed five hundred days' wages and the other owed fifty. Since they were unable to repay the debt, he forgave it for both. Which of them will love him more?" Simon said in reply, "The one, I suppose, whose larger debt was forgiven." He said to him, "You have judged rightly."

Then he turned to the woman and said to Simon, "Do you see this woman? When I entered your house, you did not give me water for my feet, but she has bathed them with her tears and wiped them with her hair. You did not give me a kiss, but she has not ceased kissing my feet since the time I entered. You did not anoint my head with oil, but she anointed my feet with ointment. So I tell you, her many sins have been forgiven because she has shown great love. But the one to whom little is forgiven, loves little." He said to her, "Your sins are forgiven." The others at table said to themselves, "Who is this who even forgives sins?" But he said to the woman, "Your faith has saved you; go in peace."]

Afterward he journeyed from one town and village to another, preaching and proclaiming the good news of the kingdom of God. Accompanying him were the Twelve and some women who had been cured of evil spirits and infirmities, Mary, called Magdalene, from whom seven demons had gone out, Joanna, the wife of Herod's steward Chuza, Susanna, and many others who provided for them out of their resources.

1227   TWELFTH SUNDAY IN ORDINARY TIME / A

READING I   *Jeremiah 20:10–13 / 94*

Jeremiah said:
"I hear the whisperings of many:
    'Terror on every side!
    Denounce! let us denounce him!'
All those who were my friends
    are on the watch for any misstep
        of mine.
'Perhaps he will be trapped; then we
    can prevail,
    and take our vengeance on him.'
But the LORD is with me, like a
    mighty champion:
    my persecutors will stumble,
    they will not triumph.

In their failure they will be put to
        utter shame,
    to lasting, unforgettable confusion.
O LORD of hosts, you who test the just,
    who probe mind and heart,
let me witness the vengeance you
        take on them,
    for to you I have entrusted my
        cause.
Sing to the LORD,
    praise the LORD,
for he has rescued the life of the poor
    from the power of the wicked!"

RESPONSORIAL PSALM   *Psalm 69:8–10, 14 and 17, 33–35*

CAP

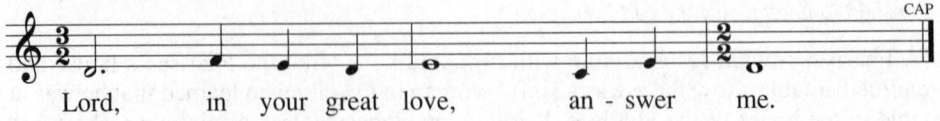

Lord,   in your great love,   an - swer   me.

It is for you that I suffer taunts,
    that shame has covered my face.
To my own kin I have become an
        outcast,
    a stranger to the children of my
        mother.
Zeal for your house consumes me,
    and taunts against you fall on me. ℟.

But I pray to you, O LORD,
    for a time of your favor.
In your great mercy, answer me, O God,
    with your salvation that never fails.
LORD, answer, for your mercy is kind;
    in your great compassion, turn
        toward me. ℟.

The poor when they see it will be glad,
and God-seeking hearts will revive;
for the LORD listens to the needy,
and does not spurn his own in their
chains.

Let the heavens and the earth give him
praise,
the seas and everything that moves
in them. ℟.

READING II
Romans 5:12–15

Brothers and sisters: Through one man sin entered the world, and through sin, death, and thus death came to all men, inasmuch as all sinned— for up to the time of the law, sin was in the world, though sin is not accounted when there is no law. But death reigned from Adam to Moses, even over those who did not sin after the pattern of the trespass of Adam, who is the type of the one who was to come.

But the gift is not like the transgression. For if by the transgression of the one the many died, how much more did the grace of God and the gracious gift of the one man Jesus Christ overflow for the many.

GOSPEL
Matthew 10:26–33

Jesus said to the Twelve: "Fear no one. Nothing is concealed that will not be revealed, nor secret that will not be known. What I say to you in the darkness, speak in the light; what you hear whispered, proclaim on the housetops. And do not be afraid of those who kill the body but cannot kill the soul; rather, be afraid of the one who can destroy both soul and body in Gehenna. Are not two sparrows sold for a small coin? Yet not one of them falls to the ground without your Father's knowledge. Even all the hairs of your head are counted. So do not be afraid; you are worth more than many sparrows. Everyone who acknowledges me before others I will acknowledge before my heavenly Father. But whoever denies me before others, I will deny before my heavenly Father."

TWELFTH SUNDAY IN ORDINARY TIME / B   1228

READING I
Job 38:1, 8–11 / 95

The Lord addressed Job out of the storm
and said:
Who shut within doors the sea,
when it burst forth from the womb;
when I made the clouds its garment
and thick darkness its swaddling
bands?

When I set limits for it
and fastened the bar of its door,
and said: Thus far shall you come but
no farther,
and here shall your proud waves be
stilled!

RESPONSORIAL PSALM
Psalm 107:23–24, 25–26, 28–29, 30–31

Or: Alleluia.

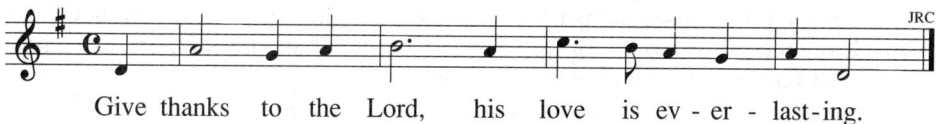

Give thanks to the Lord, his love is ev - er - last-ing.

Some went down to the sea in ships,
to trade on the mighty waters.

These have seen the deeds of the LORD,
the wonders he does in the deep. ℟.

For he spoke and raised up the
storm-wind,
tossing high the waves of the sea
that surged to heaven and dropped to
the depths.
Their souls melted away in their
distress. ℟.

Then they cried to the LORD in their
need,
and he rescued them from their
distress.

He stilled the storm to a whisper,
and the waves of the sea were
hushed. ℟.

They rejoiced because of the calm,
and he led them to the haven they
desired.
Let them thank the LORD for his mercy,
his wonders for the children of
men. ℟.

READING II   *2 Corinthians 5:14–17*

Brothers and sisters: The love of Christ impels us, once we have come to the conviction that one died for all; therefore, all have died. He indeed died for all, so that those
who live might no longer live for themselves but for him who for their sake died and
was raised.

Consequently, from now on we regard no one according to the flesh; even if we
once knew Christ according to the flesh, yet now we know him so no longer. So
whoever is in Christ is a new creation: the old things have passed away; behold, new
things have come.

GOSPEL   *Mark 4:35–41*

On that day, as evening drew on, Jesus said to his disciples: "Let us cross to the other
side." Leaving the crowd, they took Jesus with them in the boat just as he was. And
other boats were with him. A violent squall came up and waves were breaking over
the boat, so that it was already filling up. Jesus was in the stern, asleep on a cushion.
They woke him and said to him, "Teacher, do you not care that we are perishing?"
He woke up, rebuked the wind, and said to the sea, "Quiet! Be still!" The wind ceased
and there was great calm. Then he asked them, "Why are you terrified? Do you not
yet have faith?" They were filled with great awe and said to one another, "Who then
is this whom even wind and sea obey?"

1229   TWELFTH SUNDAY IN ORDINARY TIME / C

READING I   *Zechariah 12:10–11; 13:1 / 96*

Thus says the LORD: I will pour out on the house of David and on the inhabitants of
Jerusalem a spirit of grace and petition; and they shall look on him whom they have
pierced, and they shall mourn for him as one mourns for an only son, and they shall
grieve over him as one grieves over a firstborn.

On that day the mourning in Jerusalem shall be as great as the mourning of
Hadadrimmon in the plain of Megiddo.

On that day there shall be open to the house of David and to the inhabitants of
Jerusalem, a fountain to purify from sin and uncleanness.

RESPONSORIAL PSALM   *Psalm 63:2, 3–4, 5–6, 8–9*

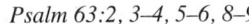

My soul is thirst-ing for you, O Lord, thirst - ing for you my God.

O God, you are my God; at dawn
    I seek you;
      for you my soul is thirsting.
For you my flesh is pining,
    like a dry, weary land without
      water. ℟.

I have come before you in the sanctuary,
    to behold your strength and your
      glory.
Your loving mercy is better than life;
    my lips will speak your praise. ℟.

I will bless you all my life;
    in your name I will lift up my hands.
My soul shall be filled as with a
    banquet;
    with joyful lips, my mouth shall
      praise you. ℟.

For you have been my strength;
    in the shadow of your wings I
      rejoice.
My soul clings fast to you;
    your right hand upholds me. ℟.

READING II   *Galatians 3:26–29*

Brothers and sisters: Through faith you are all children of God in Christ Jesus. For all of you who were baptized into Christ have clothed yourselves with Christ. There is neither Jew nor Greek, there is neither slave nor free person, there is not male and female; for you are all one in Christ Jesus. And if you belong to Christ, then you are Abraham's descendant, heirs according to the promise.

GOSPEL   *Luke 9:18–24*

Once when Jesus was praying in solitude, and the disciples were with him, he asked them, "Who do the crowds say that I am?" They said in reply, "John the Baptist; others, Elijah; still others, 'One of the ancient prophets has arisen.'" Then he said to them, "But who do you say that I am?" Peter said in reply, "The Christ of God." He rebuked them and directed them not to tell this to anyone.

He said, "The Son of Man must suffer greatly and be rejected by the elders, the chief priests, and the scribes, and be killed and on the third day be raised." Then he said to all, "If anyone wishes to come after me, he must deny himself and take up his cross daily and follow me. For whoever wishes to save his life will lose it, but whoever loses his life for my sake will save it."

1230 THIRTEENTH SUNDAY IN ORDINARY TIME / A

READING I   *2 Kings 4:8–11, 14–16a / 97*

One day Elisha came to Shunem, where there was a woman of influence, who urged him to dine with her. Afterward, whenever he passed by, he used to stop there to dine. So she said to her husband, "I know that Elisha is a holy man of God. Since he visits us often, let us arrange a little room on the roof and furnish it for him with a bed, table, chair, and lamp, so that when he comes to us he can stay there." Sometime later Elisha arrived and stayed in the room overnight.

Later Elisha asked, "Can something be done for her?" His servant Gehazi answered, "Yes! She has no son, and her husband is getting on in years." Elisha said, "Call her." When the woman had been called and stood at the door, Elisha promised, "This time next year you will be fondling a baby son."

RESPONSORIAL PSALM   *Psalm 89:2–3, 16–17, 18–19*

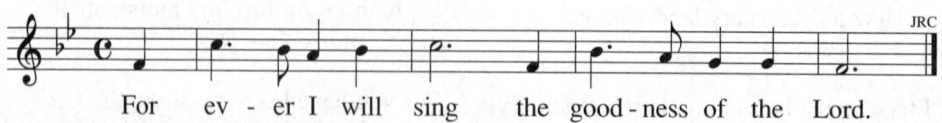

For ev - er I will sing the good - ness of the Lord.

I will sing forever of your mercies,
    O LORD;
  through all ages my mouth will
    proclaim your fidelity.
I have declared your mercy is
    established forever;
  your fidelity stands firm as the
    heavens. ℟.

How blessed the people who know your
    praise,
  who walk, O LORD, in the light of
    your face,
  who find their joy every day in your
    name,
  who make your justice their joyful
    acclaim. ℟.

For you are the glory of their strength;
  by your favor it is that our might is
    exalted.
Behold, the LORD is our shield;
  he is the Holy One of Israel, our
    king. ℟.

READING II   *Romans 6:3–4, 8–11*

Brothers and sisters: Are you unaware that we who were baptized into Christ Jesus were baptized into his death? We were indeed buried with him through baptism into death, so that, just as Christ was raised from the dead by the glory of the Father, we too might live in newness of life.

If, then, we have died with Christ, we believe that we shall also live with him. We know that Christ, raised from the dead, dies no more; death no longer has power over him. As to his death, he died to sin once and for all; as to his life, he lives for God. Consequently, you too must think of yourselves as dead to sin and living for God in Christ Jesus.

GOSPEL   *Matthew 10:37–42*

Jesus said to his apostles: "Whoever loves father or mother more than me is not worthy of me, and whoever loves son or daughter more than me is not worthy of me; and whoever does not take up his cross and follow after me is not worthy of me. Whoever finds his life will lose it, and whoever loses his life for my sake will find it.

"Whoever receives you receives me, and whoever receives me receives the one who sent me. Whoever receives a prophet because he is a prophet will receive a prophet's reward, and whoever receives a righteous man because he is a righteous man will receive a righteous man's reward. And whoever gives only a cup of cold water to one of these little ones to drink because the little one is a disciple— amen, I say to you, he will surely not lose his reward."

THIRTEENTH SUNDAY IN ORDINARY TIME / B   1231

READING I   *Wisdom 1:13–15; 2:23–24 / 98*

God did not make death,
  nor does he rejoice in the
    destruction of the living.
For he fashioned all things that they
    might have being;
  and the creatures of the world are
    wholesome,
and there is not a destructive drug
    among them
  nor any domain of the netherworld

on earth,
  for justice is undying.
For God formed man to be imperishable;
  the image of his own nature he
    made him.
But by the envy of the devil, death
    entered the world,
  and they who belong to his
    company experience it.

RESPONSORIAL PSALM   *Psalm 30:2 and 4, 5–6, 11 and 12a and 13b*

JRC

I will praise you, Lord, for you have res - cued me.

I will extol you, LORD, for you have
  raised me up,
  and have not let my enemies rejoice
    over me.
O LORD, you have lifted up my soul
    from the grave,
  restored me to life from those who
    sink into the pit. ℟.

Sing psalms to the LORD, you faithful
    ones;
  give thanks to his holy name.

His anger lasts a moment; his favor all
    through life.
  At night come tears, but dawn brings
    joy. ℟.

Hear, O LORD, and have mercy on me;
  be my helper, O LORD.
You have changed my mourning into
    dancing.
  O LORD my God, I will thank you
    forever. ℟.

READING II   *2 Corinthians 8:7, 9, 13–15*

Brothers and sisters: As you excel in every respect, in faith, discourse, knowledge, all earnestness, and in the love we have for you, may you excel in this gracious act also.

For you know the gracious act of our Lord Jesus Christ, that though he was rich, for your sake he became poor, so that by his poverty you might become rich. Not that others should have relief while you are burdened, but that as a matter of equality your abundance at the present time should supply their needs, so that their abundance may also supply your needs, that there may be equality. As it is written:
  Whoever had much did not have more,
    and whoever had little did not have less.

GOSPEL   *Mark 5:21–43 or 5:21–24, 35b–43*

For short form read only the parts in brackets.

[When Jesus had crossed again in the boat to the other side, a large crowd gathered around him, and he stayed close to the sea. One of the synagogue officials, named Jairus, came forward. Seeing him he fell at his feet and pleaded earnestly with him, saying, "My daughter is at the point of death. Please, come lay your hands on her that she may get well and live." He went off with him, and a large crowd followed him and pressed upon him.]

There was a woman afflicted with hemorrhages for twelve years. She had suffered greatly at the hands of many doctors and had spent all that she had. Yet she was not helped but only grew worse. She had heard about Jesus and came up behind him in the crowd and touched his cloak. She said, "If I but touch his clothes, I shall be cured." Immediately her flow of blood dried up. She felt in her body that she was healed of her affliction. Jesus, aware at once that power had gone out from him, turned around in the crowd and asked, "Who has touched my clothes?" But his disciples said to Jesus, "You see how the crowd is pressing upon you, and yet you ask, 'Who touched me?'" And he looked around to see who had done it. The woman, realizing what had happened to her, approached in fear and trembling. She fell down before Jesus and told him the whole truth. He said to her, "Daughter, your faith has saved you. Go in peace and be cured of your affliction."

[While he was still speaking, people from the synagogue official's house arrived and said, "Your daughter has died; why trouble the teacher any longer?" Disregarding the message that was reported, Jesus said to the synagogue official, "Do not be afraid; just have faith." He did not allow anyone to accompany him inside except Peter, James, and John, the brother of James. When they arrived at the house of the synagogue official, he caught sight of a commotion, people weeping and wailing loudly. So he went in and said to them, "Why this commotion and weeping? The child is not dead but asleep." And they ridiculed him. Then he put them all out. He took along the child's father and mother and those who were with him and entered the room where the child was. He took the child by the hand and said to her, *"Talitha koum,"* which means, "Little girl, I say to you, arise!" The girl, a child of twelve, arose immediately and walked around. At that they were utterly astounded. He gave strict orders that no one should know this and said that she should be given something to eat.]

1232 THIRTEENTH SUNDAY IN ORDINARY TIME / C

READING I   *1 Kings 19:16b, 19–21 / 99*

The LORD said to Elijah: "You shall anoint Elisha, son of Shaphat of Abel-Meholah, as prophet to succeed you."

Elijah set out and came upon Elisha, son of Shaphat, as he was plowing with twelve yoke of oxen; he was following the twelfth. Elijah went over to him and threw his cloak over him. Elisha left the oxen, ran after Elijah, and said, "Please, let me kiss my father and mother goodbye, and I will follow you." Elijah answered, "Go back! Have I done anything to you?" Elisha left him and, taking the yoke of oxen, slaughtered them; he used the plowing equipment for fuel to boil their flesh, and gave it to his people to eat. Then Elisha left and followed Elijah as his attendant.

RESPONSORIAL PSALM

Psalm 16:1–2a and 5, 7–8, 9–10, 11

You are my in - her - i - tance, O Lord, O Lord.

Preserve me, O God, for in you I take
  refuge.
  I say to the LORD, "You are my Lord."
O LORD, it is you who are my portion
  and cup;
  you yourself who secure my lot. ℟.

I will bless the LORD who gives me
  counsel,
  who even at night directs my heart.
I keep the LORD before me always;
  with him at my right hand,
  I shall not be moved. ℟.

And so, my heart rejoices, my soul is
  glad;
  even my flesh shall rest in hope.
For you will not abandon my soul to
  hell,
  nor let your holy one see
  corruption. ℟.

You will show me the path of life,
  the fullness of joy in your presence,
  at your right hand, bliss forever. ℟.

READING II

Galatians 5:1, 13–18

Brothers and sisters: For freedom Christ set us free; so stand firm and do not submit again to the yoke of slavery.

For you were called for freedom, brothers and sisters. But do not use this freedom as an opportunity for the flesh; rather, serve one another through love. For the whole law is fulfilled in one statement, namely, *You shall love your neighbor as yourself.* But if you go on biting and devouring one another, beware that you are not consumed by one another.

I say, then: live by the Spirit and you will certainly not gratify the desire of the flesh. For the flesh has desires against the Spirit, and the Spirit against the flesh; these are opposed to each other, so that you may not do what you want. But if you are guided by the Spirit, you are not under the law.

GOSPEL

Luke 9:51–62

When the days for Jesus' being taken up were fulfilled, he resolutely determined to journey to Jerusalem, and he sent messengers ahead of him. On the way they entered a Samaritan village to prepare for his reception there, but they would not welcome him because the destination of his journey was Jerusalem. When the disciples James and John saw this they asked, "Lord, do you want us to call down fire from heaven to consume them?" Jesus turned and rebuked them, and they journeyed to another village.

As they were proceeding on their journey someone said to him, "I will follow you wherever you go." Jesus answered him, "Foxes have dens and birds of the sky have nests, but the Son of Man has nowhere to rest his head."

And to another he said, "Follow me." But he replied, "Lord, let me go first and bury my father." But he answered him, "Let the dead bury their dead. But you, go and proclaim the kingdom of God." And another said, "I will follow you, Lord, but first let me say farewell to my family at home." To him Jesus said, "No one who sets a hand to the plow and looks to what was left behind is fit for the kingdom of God."

1233 FOURTEENTH SUNDAY IN ORDINARY TIME / A

READING I   *Zechariah 9:9–10 / 100*

Thus says the LORD:
Rejoice heartily, O daughter Zion,
 shout for joy, O daughter Jerusalem!
See, your king shall come to you;
 a just savior is he,
meek, and riding on an ass,
 on a colt, the foal of an ass.
He shall banish the chariot from Ephraim,
and the horse from Jerusalem;
the warrior's bow shall be banished,
 and he shall proclaim peace to the
 nations.
His dominion shall be from sea to sea,
 and from the River to the ends of
 the earth.

RESPONSORIAL PSALM   *Psalm 145:1–2, 8–9, 10–11, 13cd–14*

Or: Alleluia.

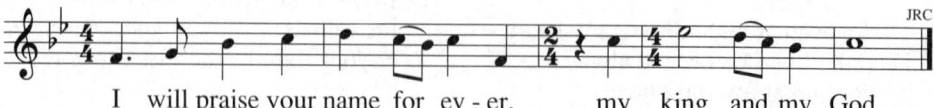

I will praise your name for ev-er, my king and my God.

I will extol you, my God and king,
 and bless your name forever and
 ever.
I will bless you day after day,
 and praise your name forever and
 ever. ℟.

All your works shall thank you,
 O LORD,
 and all your faithful ones bless you.
They shall speak of the glory of your
 reign,
 and declare your mighty deeds. ℟.

The LORD is kind and full of compassion,
 slow to anger, abounding in mercy.
How good is the LORD to all,
 compassionate to all his creatures. ℟.

The LORD is faithful in all his words,
 and holy in all his deeds.
The LORD supports all who fall,
 and raises up all who are bowed
 down. ℟.

READING II   *Romans 8:9, 11–13*

Brothers and sisters: You are not in the flesh; on the contrary, you are in the spirit, if only the Spirit of God dwells in you. Whoever does not have the Spirit of Christ does not belong to him. If the Spirit of the one who raised Jesus from the dead dwells in you, the one who raised Christ from the dead will give life to your mortal bodies also, through his Spirit that dwells in you. Consequently, brothers and sisters, we are not debtors to the flesh, to live according to the flesh. For if you live according to the flesh, you will die, but if by the Spirit you put to death the deeds of the body, you will live.

GOSPEL   *Matthew 11:25–30*

At that time Jesus exclaimed: "I give praise to you, Father, Lord of heaven and earth, for although you have hidden these things from the wise and the learned you have revealed them to little ones. Yes, Father, such has been your gracious will. All things have been handed over to me by my Father. No one knows the Son except the Father, and no one knows the Father except the Son and anyone to whom the Son wishes to reveal him."

"Come to me, all you who labor and are burdened, and I will give you rest. Take my yoke upon you and learn from me, for I am meek and humble of heart; and you will find rest for yourselves. For my yoke is easy, and my burden light."

FOURTEENTH SUNDAY IN ORDINARY TIME / B 1234

READING I
Ezekiel 2:2–5 / 101

As the LORD spoke to me, the spirit entered into me and set me on my feet, and I heard the one who was speaking say to me: Son of man, I am sending you to the Israelites, rebels who have rebelled against me; they and their ancestors have revolted against me to this very day. Hard of face and obstinate of heart are they to whom I am sending you. But you shall say to them: Thus says the Lord GOD! And whether they heed or resist —for they are a rebellious house— they shall know that a prophet has been among them.

RESPONSORIAL PSALM
Psalm 123:1–2a, 2bcd, 3–4

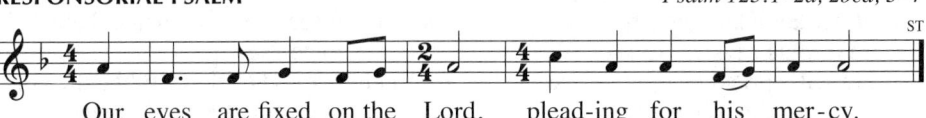

Our eyes are fixed on the Lord, plead-ing for his mer-cy.

To you have I lifted up my eyes,
  you who dwell in the heavens.
Behold, like the eyes of slaves
  on the hand of their lords. ℟.

Like the eyes of a servant
  on the hand of her mistress,
so our eyes are on the LORD our God,

till he show us his mercy. ℟.

Have mercy on us, LORD, have mercy.
  We are filled with contempt.
Indeed, all too full is our soul
  with the scorn of the arrogant,
  the disdain of the proud. ℟.

READING II
2 Corinthians 12:7–10

Brothers and sisters: That I, Paul, might not become too elated, because of the abundance of the revelations, a thorn in the flesh was given to me, an angel of Satan, to beat me, to keep me from being too elated. Three times I begged the Lord about this, that it might leave me, but he said to me, "My grace is sufficient for you, for power is made perfect in weakness." I will rather boast most gladly of my weaknesses, in order that the power of Christ may dwell with me. Therefore, I am content with weaknesses, insults, hardships, persecutions, and constraints, for the sake of Christ; for when I am weak, then I am strong.

GOSPEL
Mark 6:1–6

Jesus departed from there and came to his native place, accompanied by his disciples. When the sabbath came he began to teach in the synagogue, and many who heard him were astonished. They said, "Where did this man get all this? What kind of wisdom has been given him? What mighty deeds are wrought by his hands! Is he not the carpenter, the son of Mary, and the brother of James and Joses and Judas and Simon? And are not his sisters here with us?" And they took offense at him. Jesus said to them, "A prophet is not without honor except in his native place and among his own kin and in his own house." So he was not able to perform any mighty deed there, apart from curing a few sick people by laying his hands on them. He was amazed at their lack of faith.

1235 FOURTEENTH SUNDAY IN ORDINARY TIME / C

READING I *Isaiah 66:10–14c / 102*

Thus says the LORD:
Rejoice with Jerusalem and be glad
    because of her,
  all you who love her;
exult, exult with her,
  all you who were mourning over her!
Oh, that you may suck fully
  of the milk of her comfort,
that you may nurse with delight
  at her abundant breasts!
    For thus says the LORD:
Lo, I will spread prosperity over
    Jerusalem like a river,
  and the wealth of the nations like

an overflowing torrent.
As nurslings, you shall be carried in
    her arms,
  and fondled in her lap;
as a mother comforts her child,
  so will I comfort you;
  in Jerusalem you shall find your
    comfort.

When you see this, your heart shall
    rejoice
  and your bodies flourish like the grass;
the LORD's power shall be known to
  his servants.

RESPONSORIAL PSALM *Psalm 66:1–3a, 4–5, 6–7a, 16 and 20*

RMH

Let all the earth cry out, cry out to God with joy.

Cry out with joy to God, all the earth;
  O sing to the glory of his name.
O render him glorious praise.
  Say to God, "How awesome your
    deeds! ℟.

"Before you all the earth shall bow down,
  shall sing to you, sing to your name!"
Come and see the works of God:
  awesome his deeds among the
    children of men. ℟.

He turned the sea into dry land;
  they passed through the river on
    foot.
Let our joy, then, be in him;
  he rules forever by his might. ℟.

Come and hear, all who fear God;
  I will tell what he did for my soul.
Blest be God, who did not reject my
    prayer,
  nor withhold from me his merciful
    love. ℟.

READING II *Galatians 6:14–18*

Brothers and sisters: May I never boast except in the cross of our Lord Jesus Christ, through which the world has been crucified to me, and I to the world. For neither does circumcision mean anything, nor does uncircumcision, but only a new creation. Peace and mercy be to all who follow this rule and to the Israel of God.

From now on, let no one make troubles for me; for I bear the marks of Jesus on my body.

The grace of our Lord Jesus Christ be with your spirit, brothers and sisters. Amen.

GOSPEL *Luke 10:1–12, 17–20 or 10:1–9*
For short form read only the part in brackets.

[At that time the Lord appointed seventy-two others whom he sent ahead of him in pairs to every town and place he intended to visit. He said to them, "The harvest is abundant but the laborers are few; so ask the master of the harvest to send out labor-ers for his harvest. Go on your way; behold, I am sending you like lambs among wolves. Carry no money bag, no sack, no sandals; and greet no one along the way. Into whatever house you enter, first say, 'Peace to this household.' If a peaceful per-son lives there, your peace will rest on him; but if not, it will return to you. Stay in the same house and eat and drink what is offered to you, for the laborer deserves his payment. Do not move about from one house to another. Whatever town you enter and they welcome you, eat what is set before you, cure the sick in it and say to them, 'The kingdom of God is at hand for you.'] Whatever town you enter and they do not receive you, go out into the streets and say, 'The dust of your town that clings to our feet, even that we shake off against you.' Yet know this: the kingdom of God is at hand. I tell you, it will be more tolerable for Sodom on that day than for that town."

The seventy-two returned rejoicing, and said, "Lord, even the demons are subject to us because of your name." Jesus said, "I have observed Satan fall like lightning from the sky. Behold, I have given you the power to 'tread upon serpents' and scor-pions and upon the full force of the enemy and nothing will harm you. Nevertheless, do not rejoice because the spirits are subject to you, but rejoice because your names are written in heaven."

FIFTEENTH SUNDAY IN ORDINARY TIME / A   1236

READING I   *Isaiah 55:10–11 / 103*

Thus says the LORD:
Just as from the heavens
    the rain and snow come down
and do not return there
    till they have watered the earth,
    making it fertile and fruitful,
giving seed to the one who sows

and bread to the one who eats,
so shall my word be
    that goes forth from my mouth;
my word shall not return to me void,
    but shall do my will,
    achieving the end for which I sent it.

RESPONSORIAL PSALM   *Psalm 65:10abcd, 10e–11, 12–13, 14*

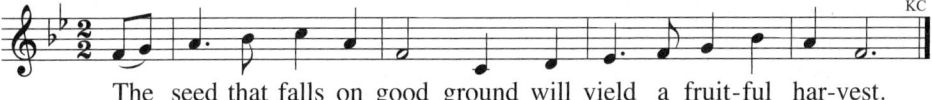

The seed that falls on good ground will yield a fruit-ful har-vest.

You visit the earth, give it water;
    you fill it with riches.
God's ever-flowing river brims over
    to prepare the grain. ℟.

And thus you provide for the earth:
    you drench its furrows;
you level it, soften it with showers;
    you bless its growth. ℟.

You crown the year with your bounty.
    Abundance flows in your pathways;
in pastures of the desert it flows.
    The hills are girded with joy. ℟.

The meadows clothed with flocks.
    The valleys are decked with wheat.
    They shout for joy; yes, they
        sing! ℟.

READING II   *Romans 8:18–23*

Brothers and sisters: I consider that the sufferings of this present time are as nothing compared with the glory to be revealed for us. For creation awaits with eager expectation the revelation of the children of God; for creation was made subject to futility, not of its own accord but because of the one who subjected it, in hope that creation itself would be set free from slavery to corruption and share in the glorious freedom of the children of God. We know that all creation is groaning in labor pains even until now; and not only that, but we ourselves, who have the firstfruits of the Spirit, we also groan within ourselves as we wait for adoption, the redemption of our bodies.

GOSPEL   *Matthew 13:1–23 or 13:1–9*
For short form read only the part in brackets.

[On that day, Jesus went out of the house and sat down by the sea. Such large crowds gathered around him that he got into a boat and sat down, and the whole crowd stood along the shore. And he spoke to them at length in parables, saying: "A sower went out to sow. And as he sowed, some seed fell on the path, and birds came and ate it up. Some fell on rocky ground, where it had little soil. It sprang up at once because the soil was not deep, and when the sun rose it was scorched, and it withered for lack of roots. Some seed fell among thorns, and the thorns grew up and choked it. But some seed fell on rich soil, and produced fruit, a hundred or sixty or thirtyfold. Whoever has ears ought to hear."]

The disciples approached him and said, "Why do you speak to them in parables?" He said to them in reply, "Because knowledge of the mysteries of the kingdom of heaven has been granted to you, but to them it has not been granted. To anyone who has, more will be given and he will grow rich; from anyone who has not, even what he has will be taken away. This is why I speak to them in parables, because *they look but do not see and hear but do not listen or understand.* Isaiah's prophecy is fulfilled in them, which says:

You shall indeed hear but not understand,
*   you shall indeed look but never see.*
Gross is the heart of this people,
*   they will hardly hear with their ears,*
*   they have closed their eyes,*
*   lest they see with their eyes*
*   and hear with their ears*
and understand with their hearts and be converted,
*   and I heal them.*

"But blessed are your eyes, because they see, and your ears, because they hear. Amen, I say to you, many prophets and righteous people longed to see what you see but did not see it, and to hear what you hear but did not hear it.

"Hear then the parable of the sower. The seed sown on the path is the one who hears the word of the kingdom without understanding it, and the evil one comes and steals away what was sown in his heart. The seed sown on rocky ground is the one who hears the word and receives it at once with joy. But he has no root and lasts only for a time. When some tribulation or persecution comes because of the word, he immediately falls away. The seed sown among thorns is the one who hears the word, but then worldly anxiety and the lure of riches choke the word and it bears no fruit. But the seed sown on rich soil is the one who hears the word and understands it, who indeed bears fruit and yields a hundred or sixty or thirtyfold."

FIFTEENTH SUNDAY IN ORDINARY TIME / B   1237

READING I   *Amos 7:12–15 / 104*

Amaziah, priest of Bethel, said to Amos, "Off with you, visionary, flee to the land of Judah! There earn your bread by prophesying, but never again prophesy in Bethel; for it is the king's sanctuary and a royal temple." Amos answered Amaziah, "I was no prophet, nor have I belonged to a company of prophets; I was a shepherd and a dresser of sycamores. The LORD took me from following the flock, and said to me, Go, prophesy to my people Israel."

RESPONSORIAL PSALM   *Psalm 85:9ab and 10, 11–12, 13–14*

Lord, let us see your kind-ness, and grant us your sal - va-tion.

I will hear what the LORD God speaks;
  he speaks of peace for his people
    and his faithful.
His salvation is near for those who fear
    him,
  and his glory will dwell in our land. ℟.

Merciful love and faithfulness have met;
  justice and peace have kissed.

Faithfulness shall spring from the earth,
  and justice look down from
    heaven. ℟.

Also the LORD will bestow his bounty,
  and our earth shall yield its increase.
Justice will march before him,
  and guide his steps on the way. ℟.

READING II   *Ephesians 1:3–14 or 1:3–10*

For short form read only the part in brackets.

[Blessed be the God and Father of our Lord Jesus Christ, who has blessed us in Christ with every spiritual blessing in the heavens, as he chose us in him, before the foundation of the world, to be holy and without blemish before him. In love he destined us for adoption to himself through Jesus Christ, in accord with the favor of his will, for the praise of the glory of his grace that he granted us in the beloved.

In him we have redemption by his blood, the forgiveness of transgressions, in accord with the riches of his grace that he lavished upon us. In all wisdom and insight, he has made known to us the mystery of his will in accord with his favor that he set forth in him as a plan for the fullness of times, to sum up all things in Christ, in heaven and on earth.]

In him we were also chosen, destined in accord with the purpose of the One who accomplishes all things according to the intention of his will, so that we might exist for the praise of his glory, we who first hoped in Christ. In him you also, who have heard the word of truth, the gospel of your salvation, and have believed in him, were sealed with the promised holy Spirit, which is the first installment of our inheritance toward redemption as God's possession, to the praise of his glory.

GOSPEL   *Mark 6:7–13*

Jesus summoned the Twelve and began to send them out two by two and gave them authority over unclean spirits. He instructed them to take nothing for the journey but a walking stick—no food, no sack, no money in their belts. They were, however, to wear sandals but not a second tunic. He said to them, "Wherever you enter a house, stay there until you leave. Whatever place does not welcome you or listen to you, leave there and shake the dust off your feet in testimony against them." So they went off and preached repentance. The Twelve drove out many demons, and they anointed with oil many who were sick and cured them.

1238 FIFTEENTH SUNDAY IN ORDINARY TIME / C

READING I *Deuteronomy 30:10–14 / 105*

Moses said to the people: "If only you would heed the voice of the LORD, your God, and keep his commandments and statutes that are written in this book of the law, when you return to the LORD, your God, with all your heart and all your soul.

"For this command that I enjoin on you today is not too mysterious and remote for you. It is not up in the sky, that you should say, 'Who will go up in the sky to get it for us and tell us of it, that we may carry it out?' Nor is it across the sea, that you should say, 'Who will cross the sea to get it for us and tell us of it, that we may carry it out?' No, it is something very near to you, already in your mouths and in your hearts; you have only to carry it out."

RESPONSORIAL PSALM *Psalm 69:14 and 17, 30–31, 33–34, 36ab and 37*

Turn to the Lord in your need, and you will live.

I pray to you, O LORD,
   for a time of your favor.
In your great mercy, answer me, O God,
   with your salvation that never fails.
LORD, answer, for your mercy is kind;
   in your great compassion, turn
     toward me. ℟.

As for me in my poverty and pain,
   let your salvation, O God, raise me up.
Then I will praise God's name with a
     song;
   I will glorify him with thanksgiving. ℟.

The poor when they see it will be glad,
   and God-seeking hearts will revive;
for the LORD listens to the needy,
   and does not spurn his own in their
     chains. ℟.

For God will bring salvation to Sion,
   and rebuild the cities of Judah.
The children of his servants shall
     inherit it;
   those who love his name shall dwell
     there. ℟.

Or:

RESPONSORIAL PSALM *Psalm 19:8, 9, 10, 11*

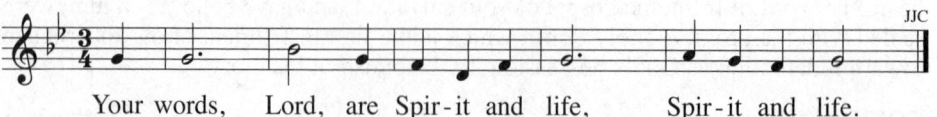

Your words, Lord, are Spir-it and life, Spir-it and life.

The law of the LORD is perfect;
   it revives the soul.

The decrees of the LORD are steadfast;
   they give wisdom to the simple. ℟.

The precepts of the LORD are right;
    they gladden the heart.
The command of the LORD is clear;
    it gives light to the eyes. ℟.

The fear of the LORD is pure,
    abiding forever.
The judgments of the LORD are true;

they are, all of them, just. ℟.

They are more to be desired than gold,
    than quantities of gold.
And sweeter are they than honey,
    than honey flowing from the
    comb. ℟.

READING II   *Colossians 1:15–20*

Christ Jesus is the image of the
    invisible God,
    the firstborn of all creation.
For in him were created all things in
    heaven and on earth,
    the visible and the invisible,
    whether thrones or dominions or
    principalities or powers;
    all things were created through him
    and for him.
He is before all things,
    and in him all things hold together.
He is the head of the body, the church.

He is the beginning, the firstborn from
    the dead,
    that in all things he himself might
    be preeminent.
For in him all the fullness was pleased to
    dwell,
    and through him to reconcile all
    things for him,
    making peace by the blood of his
    cross
    through him, whether those on earth
    or those in heaven.

GOSPEL   *Luke 10:25–37*

There was a scholar of the law who stood up to test him and said, "Teacher, what must I do to inherit eternal life?" Jesus said to him, "What is written in the law? How do you read it?" He said in reply, *"You shall love the Lord, your God, with all your heart, with all your being, with all your strength, and with all your mind, and your neighbor as yourself."* He replied to him, "You have answered correctly; do this and you will live."

But because he wished to justify himself, he said to Jesus, "And who is my neighbor?" Jesus replied, "A man fell victim to robbers as he went down from Jerusalem to Jericho. They stripped and beat him and went off leaving him half-dead. A priest happened to be going down that road, but when he saw him, he passed by on the opposite side. Likewise a Levite came to the place, and when he saw him, he passed by on the opposite side. But a Samaritan traveler who came upon him was moved with compassion at the sight. He approached the victim, poured oil and wine over his wounds and bandaged them. Then he lifted him up on his own animal, took him to an inn, and cared for him. The next day he took out two silver coins and gave them to the innkeeper with the instruction, 'Take care of him. If you spend more than what I have given you, I shall repay you on my way back.' Which of these three, in your opinion, was neighbor to the robbers' victim?" He answered, "The one who treated him with mercy." Jesus said to him, "Go and do likewise."

1239   SIXTEENTH SUNDAY IN ORDINARY TIME / A

READING I   *Wisdom 12:13, 16–19 / 106*

There is no god besides you who have the care of all,
   that you need show you have not unjustly condemned.
For your might is the source of justice;
   your mastery over all things makes you lenient to all.
For you show your might when the perfection of your power is disbelieved;
   and in those who know you, you rebuke temerity.
But though you are master of might, you judge with clemency,
   and with much lenience you govern us;
   for power, whenever you will, attends you.
And you taught your people, by these deeds,
   that those who are just must be kind;
and you gave your children good ground for hope
   that you would permit repentance for their sins.

RESPONSORIAL PSALM   *Psalm 86:5–6, 9–10, 15–16*

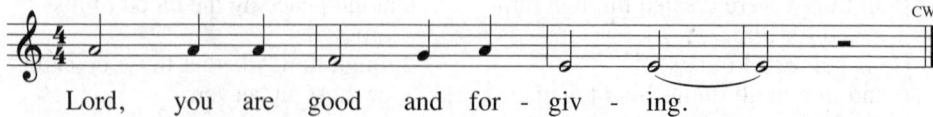

CW

Lord, you are good and for - giv - ing.

O Lord, you are good and forgiving,
   full of mercy to all who call to you.
Give ear, O LORD, to my prayer,
   and attend to my voice in
      supplication. ℟.

All the nations you have made shall
   come;
   they will bow down before you,
      O Lord,
   and glorify your name,

for you are great and do marvelous
   deeds,
   you who alone are God. ℟.

But you, O God, are compassionate and
   gracious,
   slow to anger, O Lord,
   abundant in mercy and fidelity;
   turn and take pity on me.
O give your strength to your servant. ℟.

READING II   *Romans 8:26–27*

Brothers and sisters: The Spirit comes to the aid of our weakness; for we do not know how to pray as we ought, but the Spirit himself intercedes with inexpressible groanings. And the one who searches hearts knows what is the intention of the Spirit, because he intercedes for the holy ones according to God's will.

GOSPEL   *Matthew 13:24–43 or 13:24–30*
For short form read only the part in brackets.

[Jesus proposed another parable to the crowds, saying: "The kingdom of heaven may be likened to a man who sowed good seed in his field. While everyone was asleep his enemy came and sowed weeds all through the wheat, and then went off. When the crop grew and bore fruit, the weeds appeared as well. The slaves of the householder came to him and said, 'Master, did you not sow good seed in your field? Where have the weeds come from?' He answered, 'An enemy has done this.' His slaves said to him, 'Do you want us to go and pull them up?' He replied, 'No, if you pull up the weeds you might uproot the wheat along with them. Let them grow together until harvest; then at harvest time I will say to the harvesters, "First collect the weeds and tie them in bundles for burning; but gather the wheat into my barn."''']

He proposed another parable to them. "The kingdom of heaven is like a mustard seed that a person took and sowed in a field. It is the smallest of all the seeds, yet when full-grown it is the largest of plants. It becomes a large bush, and the 'birds of the sky come and dwell in its branches.'"

He spoke to them another parable. "The kingdom of heaven is like yeast that a woman took and mixed with three measures of wheat flour until the whole batch was leavened."

All these things Jesus spoke to the crowds in parables. He spoke to them only in parables, to fulfill what had been said through the prophet:

I will open my mouth in parables,
I will announce what has lain hidden from the foundation of the world.

Then, dismissing the crowds, he went into the house. His disciples approached him and said, "Explain to us the parable of the weeds in the field." He said in reply, "He who sows good seed is the Son of Man, the field is the world, the good seed the children of the kingdom. The weeds are the children of the evil one, and the enemy who sows them is the devil. The harvest is the end of the age, and the harvesters are angels. Just as weeds are collected and burned up with fire, so will it be at the end of the age. The Son of Man will send his angels, and they will collect out of his kingdom all who cause others to sin and all evildoers. They will throw them into the fiery furnace, where there will be wailing and grinding of teeth. Then the righteous will shine like the sun in the kingdom of their Father. Whoever has ears ought to hear."

SIXTEENTH SUNDAY IN ORDINARY TIME / B   1240

READING I   *Jeremiah 23:1–6 / 107*

Woe to the shepherds who mislead and scatter the flock of my pasture, says the LORD. Therefore, thus says the LORD, the God of Israel, against the shepherds who shepherd my people: You have scattered my sheep and driven them away. You have not cared for them, but I will take care to punish your evil deeds. I myself will gather the remnant of my flock from all the lands to which I have driven them and bring them back to their meadow; there they shall increase and multiply. I will appoint shepherds for them who will shepherd them so that they need no longer fear and tremble; and none shall be missing, says the LORD.

Behold, the days are coming, says the LORD,
    when I will raise up a righteous shoot to David;
as king he shall reign and govern wisely,
    he shall do what is just and right in the land.
In his days Judah shall be saved,
    Israel shall dwell in security.
This is the name they give him:
    "The LORD our justice."

RESPONSORIAL PSALM *Psalm 23:1–3a, 3b–4, 5, 6*

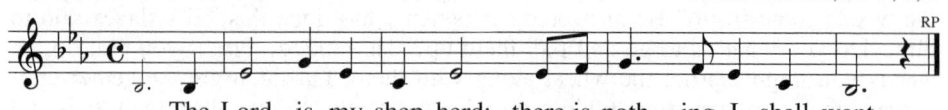

The Lord is my shep-herd; there is noth - ing I shall want.

The LORD is my shepherd;
  there is nothing I shall want.
Fresh and green are the pastures
  where he gives me repose.
Near restful waters he leads me;
  he revives my soul. ℟.

He guides me along the right path,
  for the sake of his name.
Though I should walk in the valley of
  the shadow of death,
  no evil would I fear, for you are
  with me.

Your crook and your staff will give
  me comfort. ℟.

You have prepared a table before me
  in the sight of my foes.
My head you have anointed with oil;
  my cup is overflowing. ℟.

Surely goodness and mercy shall
  follow me
  all the days of my life.
In the LORD's own house shall I dwell
  for length of days unending. ℟.

READING II *Ephesians 2:13–18*

Brothers and sisters: In Christ Jesus you who once were far off have become near by the blood of Christ.

For he is our peace, he who made both one and broke down the dividing wall of enmity, through his flesh, abolishing the law with its commandments and legal claims, that he might create in himself one new person in place of the two, thus establishing peace, and might reconcile both with God, in one body, through the cross, putting that enmity to death by it. He came and preached peace to you who were far off and peace to those who were near, for through him we both have access in one Spirit to the Father.

GOSPEL *Mark 6:30–34*

The apostles gathered together with Jesus and reported all they had done and taught. He said to them, "Come away by yourselves to a deserted place and rest a while." People were coming and going in great numbers, and they had no opportunity even to eat. So they went off in the boat by themselves to a deserted place. People saw them leaving and many came to know about it. They hastened there on foot from all the towns and arrived at the place before them.

When he disembarked and saw the vast crowd, his heart was moved with pity for them, for they were like sheep without a shepherd; and he began to teach them many things.

1241 SIXTEENTH SUNDAY IN ORDINARY TIME / C

READING I *Genesis 18:1–10a / 108*

The LORD appeared to Abraham by the terebinth of Mamre, as he sat in the entrance of his tent, while the day was growing hot. Looking up, Abraham saw three men standing nearby. When he saw them, he ran from the entrance of the tent to greet them; and bowing to the ground, he said: "Sir, if I may ask you this favor, please do not go on past your servant. Let some water be brought, that you may bathe your feet, and then rest yourselves under the tree. Now that you have come this close to your servant, let me bring you a little food, that you may refresh yourselves; and afterward you may go on your way." The men replied, "Very well, do as you have said."

Abraham hastened into the tent and told Sarah, "Quick, three measures of fine flour! Knead it and make rolls." He ran to the herd, picked out a tender, choice steer, and gave it to a servant, who quickly prepared it. Then Abraham got some curds and milk, as well as the steer that had been prepared, and set these before the three men; and he waited on them under the tree while they ate.

They asked Abraham, "Where is your wife Sarah?" He replied, "There in the tent." One of them said, "I will surely return to you about this time next year, and Sarah will then have a son."

RESPONSORIAL PSALM

Psalm 15:2–3a, 3bc–4ab, 5

The one who does jus-tice will live in the pres-ence of the Lord.

Whoever walks without fault;
  who does what is just,
and speaks the truth from his heart;
  whoever does not slander with his
    tongue. ℟.

Who does no wrong to a neighbor,
  who casts no slur on a friend,
who looks with scorn on the wicked,

but honors those who fear the
  Lord. ℟.

Who lends no money at interest,
  and accepts no bribes against the
    innocent.
  Such a one shall never be shaken. ℟.

READING II

Colossians 1:24–28

Brothers and sisters: Now I rejoice in my sufferings for your sake, and in my flesh I am filling up what is lacking in the afflictions of Christ on behalf of his body, which is the church, of which I am a minister in accordance with God's stewardship given to me to bring to completion for you the word of God, the mystery hidden from ages and from generations past. But now it has been manifested to his holy ones, to whom God chose to make known the riches of the glory of this mystery among the Gentiles; it is Christ in you, the hope for glory. It is he whom we proclaim, admonishing everyone and teaching everyone with all wisdom, that we may present everyone perfect in Christ.

GOSPEL

Luke 10:38–42

Jesus entered a village where a woman whose name was Martha welcomed him. She had a sister named Mary who sat beside the Lord at his feet listening to him speak. Martha, burdened with much serving, came to him and said, "Lord, do you not care that my sister has left me by myself to do the serving? Tell her to help me." The Lord said to her in reply, "Martha, Martha, you are anxious and worried about many things. There is need of only one thing. Mary has chosen the better part and it will not be taken from her."

1242 SEVENTEENTH SUNDAY IN ORDINARY TIME / A

READING I   *1 Kings 3:5, 7–12 / 109*

The LORD appeared to Solomon in a dream at night. God said, "Ask something of me and I will give it to you." Solomon answered: "O LORD, my God, you have made me, your servant, king to succeed my father David; but I am a mere youth, not knowing at all how to act. I serve you in the midst of the people whom you have chosen, a people so vast that it cannot be numbered or counted. Give your servant, therefore, an understanding heart to judge your people and to distinguish right from wrong. For who is able to govern this vast people of yours?"

The LORD was pleased that Solomon made this request. So God said to him: "Because you have asked for this— not for a long life for yourself, nor for riches, nor for the life of your enemies, but for understanding so that you may know what is right— I do as you requested. I give you a heart so wise and understanding that there has never been anyone like you up to now, and after you there will come no one to equal you."

RESPONSORIAL PSALM   *Psalm 119:57 and 72, 76–77, 127–128, 129–130*

Lord, I love your com-mands.

I have said, "O LORD, my portion
   is to obey your words."
The law from your mouth means more
   to me
    than large quantities of silver and
     gold. ℟.

Let your merciful love console me
   by your promise to your servant.
Show me compassion, that I may live,
   for your law is my delight. ℟.

That is why I love your commands
   more than finest gold,
why I rule my life by your precepts,
   and hate false ways. ℟.

Your decrees are wonderful indeed;
   therefore my soul obeys them.
The unfolding of your word gives light,
   and understanding to the simple. ℟.

READING II   *Romans 8:28–30*

Brothers and sisters: We know that all things work for good for those who love God, who are called according to his purpose. For those he foreknew he also predestined to be conformed to the image of his Son, so that he might be the firstborn among many brothers and sisters. And those he predestined he also called; and those he called he also justified; and those he justified he also glorified.

GOSPEL   *Matthew 13:44–52 or 13:44–46*

For short form read only the part in brackets.

[Jesus said to his disciples: "The kingdom of heaven is like a treasure buried in a field, which a person finds and hides again, and out of joy goes and sells all that he has and buys that field. Again, the kingdom of heaven is like a merchant searching for fine pearls. When he finds a pearl of great price, he goes and sells all that he has and buys it.] Again, the kingdom of heaven is like a net thrown into the sea, which collects fish of every kind. When it is full they haul it ashore and sit down to put what is good into buckets. What is bad they throw away. Thus it will be at the end of the age. The angels will go out and separate the wicked from the righteous and throw them into the fiery furnace, where there will be wailing and grinding of teeth.

"Do you understand all these things?" They answered, "Yes." And he replied, "Then every scribe who has been instructed in the kingdom of heaven is like the head of a household who brings from his storeroom both the new and the old."

SEVENTEENTH SUNDAY IN ORDINARY TIME / B   1243

READING I   *2 Kings 4:42–44 / 110*

A man came from Baal-shalishah bringing to Elisha, the man of God, twenty barley loaves made from the firstfruits, and fresh grain in the ear. Elisha said, "Give it to the people to eat." But his servant objected, "How can I set this before a hundred people?" Elisha insisted, "Give it to the people to eat. For thus says the LORD, 'They shall eat and there shall be some left over.'" And when they had eaten, there was some left over, as the LORD had said.

RESPONSORIAL PSALM   *Psalm 145:10–11, 15–16, 17–18*

The hand of the Lord feeds us; he an-swers all our needs.

All your works shall thank you,
    O LORD,
    and all your faithful ones bless you.
They shall speak of the glory of your
    reign,
    and declare your mighty deeds. ℟.

The eyes of all look to you,
    and you give them their food in
       due season.

You open your hand and satisfy
    the desire of every living thing. ℟.

The LORD is just in all his ways,
    and holy in all his deeds.
The LORD is close to all who call him,
    who call on him in truth. ℟.

READING II   *Ephesians 4:1–6*

Brothers and sisters: I, a prisoner for the Lord, urge you to live in a manner worthy of the call you have received, with all humility and gentleness, with patience, bearing with one another through love, striving to preserve the unity of the spirit through the bond of peace: one body and one Spirit, as you were also called to the one hope of your call; one Lord, one faith, one baptism; one God and Father of all, who is over all and through all and in all.

GOSPEL *John 6:1–15*

Jesus went across the Sea of Galilee. A large crowd followed him, because they saw the signs he was performing on the sick. Jesus went up on the mountain, and there he sat down with his disciples. The Jewish feast of Passover was near. When Jesus raised his eyes and saw that a large crowd was coming to him, he said to Philip, "Where can we buy enough food for them to eat?" He said this to test him, because he himself knew what he was going to do. Philip answered him, "Two hundred days' wages worth of food would not be enough for each of them to have a little." One of his disciples, Andrew, the brother of Simon Peter, said to him, "There is a boy here who has five barley loaves and two fish; but what good are these for so many?" Jesus said, "Have the people recline." Now there was a great deal of grass in that place. So the men reclined, about five thousand in number. Then Jesus took the loaves, gave thanks, and distributed them to those who were reclining, and also as much of the fish as they wanted. When they had had their fill, he said to his disciples, "Gather the fragments left over, so that nothing will be wasted." So they collected them, and filled twelve wicker baskets with fragments from the five barley loaves that had been more than they could eat. When the people saw the sign he had done, they said, "This is truly the Prophet, the one who is to come into the world." Since Jesus knew that they were going to come and carry him off to make him king, he withdrew again to the mountain alone.

1244 SEVENTEENTH SUNDAY IN ORDINARY TIME / C

READING I *Genesis 18:20–32 / 111*

In those days, the Lord said: "The outcry against Sodom and Gomorrah is so great, and their sin so grave, that I must go down and see whether or not their actions fully correspond to the cry against them that comes to me. I mean to find out."

While Abraham's visitors walked on farther toward Sodom, the Lord remained standing before Abraham. Then Abraham drew nearer and said: "Will you sweep away the innocent with the guilty? Suppose there were fifty innocent people in the city; would you wipe out the place, rather than spare it for the sake of the fifty innocent people within it? Far be it from you to do such a thing, to make the innocent die with the guilty so that the innocent and the guilty would be treated alike! Should not the judge of all the world act with justice?" The Lord replied, "If I find fifty innocent people in the city of Sodom, I will spare the whole place for their sake." Abraham spoke up again: "See how I am presuming to speak to my Lord, though I am but dust and ashes! What if there are five less than fifty innocent people? Will you destroy the whole city because of those five?" He answered, "I will not destroy it, if I find forty-five there." But Abraham persisted, saying "What if only forty are found there?" He replied, "I will forbear doing it for the sake of the forty." Then Abraham said, "Let not my Lord grow impatient if I go on. What if only thirty are found there?" He replied, "I will forbear doing it if I can find but thirty there." Still Abraham went on, "Since I have thus dared to speak to my Lord, what if there are no more than twenty?" The Lord answered, "I will not destroy it, for the sake of the twenty." But he still persisted: "Please, let not my Lord grow angry if I speak up this last time. What if there are at least ten there?" He replied, "For the sake of those ten, I will not destroy it."

RESPONSORIAL PSALM

Psalm 138:1–2a, 2bcd–3, 6–7ab, 7c–8

RCV

Lord, on the day I called for help, you an - swered me.

I thank you, LORD, with all my heart;
  you have heard the words of my
    mouth.
In the presence of the angels I praise you.
  I bow down toward your holy
    temple. ℟.

I give thanks to your name
  for your merciful love and your
    faithfulness.
You have exalted your name over all.
On the day I called, you answered me;
  you increased the strength of my
    soul. ℟.

The LORD is high, yet he looks on the
    lowly,
  and the haughty he knows from afar.
You give me life though I walk amid
    affliction;
  you stretch out your hand against
    the anger of my foes. ℟.

With your right hand you save me;
  the LORD will accomplish this for
    me.
O LORD, your merciful love is eternal;
  discard not the work of your
    hands. ℟.

READING II

Colossians 2:12–14

Brothers and sisters: You were buried with him in baptism, in which you were also raised with him through faith in the power of God, who raised him from the dead. And even when you were dead in transgressions and the uncircumcision of your flesh, he brought you to life along with him, having forgiven us all our transgressions; obliterating the bond against us, with its legal claims, which was opposed to us, he also removed it from our midst, nailing it to the cross.

GOSPEL

Luke 11:1–13

Jesus was praying in a certain place, and when he had finished, one of his disciples said to him, "Lord, teach us to pray just as John taught his disciples." He said to them, "When you pray, say:
    Father, hallowed be your name,
      your kingdom come.
      Give us each day our daily bread
      and forgive us our sins
      for we ourselves forgive everyone in debt to us,
      and do not subject us to the final test."

And he said to them, "Suppose one of you has a friend to whom he goes at midnight and says, 'Friend, lend me three loaves of bread, for a friend of mine has arrived at my house from a journey and I have nothing to offer him,' and he says in reply from within, 'Do not bother me; the door has already been locked and my children and I are already in bed. I cannot get up to give you anything.' I tell you, if he does not get up to give the visitor the loaves because of their friendship, he will get up to give him whatever he needs because of his persistence.

"And I tell you, ask and you will receive; seek and you will find; knock and the door will be opened to you. For everyone who asks, receives; and the one who seeks, finds; and to the one who knocks, the door will be opened. What father among you would hand his son a snake when he asks for a fish? Or hand him a scorpion when he asks for an egg? If you then, who are wicked, know how to give good gifts to your children, how much more will the Father in heaven give the Holy Spirit to those who ask him?"

1245 EIGHTEENTH SUNDAY IN ORDINARY TIME / A

READING I
Isaiah 55:1–3 / 112

Thus says the LORD:
All you who are thirsty,
   come to the water!
You who have no money,
   come, receive grain and eat;
Come, without paying and without cost,
   drink wine and milk!
Why spend your money for what is
   not bread;

your wages for what fails to satisfy?
Heed me, and you shall eat well,
   you shall delight in rich fare.
Come to me heedfully,
   listen, that you may have life.
I will renew with you the everlasting
   covenant,
   the benefits assured to David.

RESPONSORIAL PSALM
Psalm 145:8–9, 15–16, 17–18

The hand of the Lord feeds us; he an-swers all our needs.

The LORD is kind and full of compassion,
   slow to anger, abounding in mercy.
How good is the LORD to all,
   compassionate to all his creatures. ℟.

The eyes of all look to you,
   and you give them their food in due
   season.

You open your hand and satisfy
   the desire of every living thing. ℟.

The LORD is just in all his ways,
   and holy in all his deeds.
The LORD is close to all who call him,
   who call on him in truth. ℟.

READING II
Romans 8:35, 37–39

Brothers and sisters: What will separate us from the love of Christ? Will anguish, or distress, or persecution, or famine, or nakedness, or peril, or the sword? No, in all these things we conquer overwhelmingly through him who loved us. For I am convinced that neither death, nor life, nor angels, nor principalities, nor present things, nor future things, nor powers, nor height, nor depth, nor any other creature will be able to separate us from the love of God in Christ Jesus our Lord.

GOSPEL
Matthew 14:13–21

When Jesus heard of the death of John the Baptist, he withdrew in a boat to a deserted place by himself. The crowds heard of this and followed him on foot from their towns. When he disembarked and saw the vast crowd, his heart was moved with pity for them, and he cured their sick. When it was evening, the disciples approached him and said, "This is a deserted place and it is already late; dismiss the crowds so that they can go to the villages and buy food for themselves." Jesus said to them, "There is no need for them to go away; give them some food yourselves." But they said to him, "Five loaves and two fish are all we have here." Then he said, "Bring them here to me," and he ordered the crowds to sit down on the grass. Taking the five loaves and the two fish, and looking up to heaven, he said the blessing, broke the loaves, and gave them to the disciples, who in turn gave them to the crowds. They all ate and were satisfied, and they picked up the fragments left over— twelve wicker baskets full. Those who ate were about five thousand men, not counting women and children.

EIGHTEENTH SUNDAY IN ORDINARY TIME / B   1246

READING I
Exodus 16:2–4, 12–15 / 113

The whole Israelite community grumbled against Moses and Aaron. The Israelites said to them, "Would that we had died at the LORD's hand in the land of Egypt, as we sat by our fleshpots and ate our fill of bread! But you had to lead us into this desert to make the whole community die of famine!"

Then the LORD said to Moses, "I will now rain down bread from heaven for you. Each day the people are to go out and gather their daily portion; thus will I test them, to see whether they follow my instructions or not.

"I have heard the grumbling of the Israelites. Tell them: In the evening twilight you shall eat flesh, and in the morning you shall have your fill of bread, so that you may know that I, the LORD am your God."

In the evening quail came up and covered the camp. In the morning a dew lay all about the camp, and when the dew evaporated, there on the surface of the desert were fine flakes like hoarfrost on the ground. On seeing it, the Israelites asked one another, "What is this?" for they did not know what it was. But Moses told them, "This is the bread that the LORD has given you to eat."

RESPONSORIAL PSALM
Psalm 78:3 and 4bc, 23–24, 25 and 54

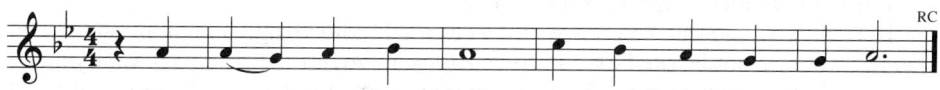

The Lord gave them bread, gave them bread from heav-en.

The things we have heard and
   understood,
   the things our fathers have told us,
   we will tell to the next generation:
The glories of the LORD and his might,
   and the marvelous deeds he has
     done. ℟.

He commanded the clouds above,

and opened the gates of heaven.
He rained down manna to eat,
   and gave them bread from heaven. ℟.

Man ate the bread of angels.
   He sent them abundance of food.
So he brought them to his holy land,
   to the mountain his right hand
     had won. ℟.

READING II
Ephesians 4:17, 20–24

Brothers and sisters: I declare and testify in the Lord that you must no longer live as the Gentiles do, in the futility of their minds; that is not how you learned Christ, assuming that you have heard of him and were taught in him, as truth is in Jesus, that you should put away the old self of your former way of life, corrupted through deceitful desires, and be renewed in the spirit of your minds, and put on the new self, created in God's way in righteousness and holiness of truth.

GOSPEL
John 6:24–35

When the crowd saw that neither Jesus nor his disciples were there, they themselves got into boats and came to Capernaum looking for Jesus. And when they found him across the sea they said to him, "Rabbi, when did you get here?" Jesus answered them and said, "Amen, amen, I say to you, you are looking for me not because you saw signs but because you ate the loaves and were filled. Do not work for food that perishes but for the food that endures for eternal life, which the Son of Man will give you. For on him the Father, God, has set his seal." So they said to him, "What can we do to accomplish the works of God?" Jesus answered and said to them, "This is the work of God, that you believe in the one he sent." So they said to him, "What sign can you do, that we may see and believe in you? What can you do? Our ancestors ate manna in the desert, as it is written:

He gave them bread from heaven to eat."

So Jesus said to them, "Amen, amen, I say to you, it was not Moses who gave the bread from heaven; my Father gives you the true bread from heaven. For the bread of God is that which comes down from heaven and gives life to the world."

So they said to him, "Sir, give us this bread always." Jesus said to them, "I am the bread of life; whoever comes to me will never hunger, and whoever believes in me will never thirst."

1247 EIGHTEENTH SUNDAY IN ORDINARY TIME / C

READING I
Ecclesiastes 1:2; 2:21–23 / 114

Vanity of vanities, says Qoheleth,
    vanity of vanities! All things are vanity!

Here is one who has labored with wisdom and knowledge and skill, and yet to another who has not labored over it, he must leave property. This also is vanity and a great misfortune. For what profit comes to man from all the toil and anxiety of heart with which he has labored under the sun? All his days sorrow and grief are his occupation; even at night his mind is not at rest. This also is vanity.

RESPONSORIAL PSALM
Psalm 90:3–4, 5–6, 12–13, 14 and 17

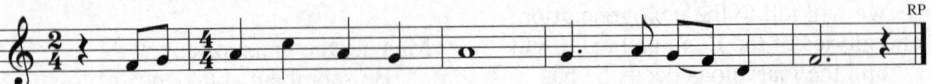

If to - day you hear his voice,   hard - en not your hearts.

You turn man back to dust,
    and say, "Return, O children of men."
To your eyes a thousand years

are like yesterday, come and gone,
or like a watch in the night. ℟.

You sweep them away like a dream,
   like grass which is fresh in the
      morning.
In the morning it sprouts and is fresh;
   by evening it withers and fades. ℟.

Then teach us to number our days,
   that we may gain wisdom of heart.
Turn back, O Lord! How long?

Show pity to your servants. ℟.

At dawn, fill us with your merciful love;
   we shall exult and rejoice all our days.
Let the favor of the Lord our God be
      upon us;
   give success to the work of our hands.
O give success to the work of our
      hands. ℟.

READING II   *Colossians 3:1–5, 9–11*

Brothers and sisters: If you were raised with Christ, seek what is above, where Christ is seated at the right hand of God. Think of what is above, not of what is on earth. For you have died, and your life is hidden with Christ in God. When Christ your life appears, then you too will appear with him in glory.

Put to death, then, the parts of you that are earthly: immorality, impurity, passion, evil desire, and the greed that is idolatry. Stop lying to one another, since you have taken off the old self with its practices and have put on the new self, which is being renewed, for knowledge, in the image of its creator. Here there is not Greek and Jew, circumcision and uncircumcision, barbarian, Scythian, slave, free; but Christ is all and in all.

GOSPEL   *Luke 12:13–21*

Someone in the crowd said to Jesus, "Teacher, tell my brother to share the inheritance with me." He replied to him, "Friend, who appointed me as your judge and arbitrator?" Then he said to the crowd, "Take care to guard against all greed, for though one may be rich, one's life does not consist of possessions."

Then he told them a parable. "There was a rich man whose land produced a bountiful harvest. He asked himself, 'What shall I do, for I do not have space to store my harvest?' And he said, 'This is what I shall do: I shall tear down my barns and build larger ones. There I shall store all my grain and other goods and I shall say to myself, "Now as for you, you have so many good things stored up for many years, rest, eat, drink, be merry!"' But God said to him, 'You fool, this night your life will be demanded of you; and the things you have prepared, to whom will they belong?' Thus will it be for all who store up treasure for themselves but are not rich in what matters to God."

NINETEENTH SUNDAY IN ORDINARY TIME / A   1248

READING I   *1 Kings 19:9a, 11–13a / 115*

At the mountain of God, Horeb, Elijah came to a cave where he took shelter. Then the Lord said to him, "Go outside and stand on the mountain before the Lord; the Lord will be passing by." A strong and heavy wind was rending the mountains and crushing rocks before the Lord— but the Lord was not in the wind. After the wind there was an earthquake— but the Lord was not in the earthquake. After the earthquake there was fire— but the Lord was not in the fire. After the fire there was a tiny whispering sound. When he heard this, Elijah hid his face in his cloak and went and stood at the entrance of the cave.

RESPONSORIAL PSALM *Psalm 85:9ab–10, 11–12, 13–14*

Lord, let us see your kind-ness, and grant us your sal - va-tion.

I will hear what the LORD God speaks;
   he speaks of peace for his people
      and his faithful.
His salvation is near for those who fear
      him,
   and his glory will dwell in our land. ℟.

Merciful love and faithfulness have met;
   justice and peace have kissed.

Faithfulness shall spring from the earth,
   and justice look down from
      heaven. ℟.

Also the LORD will bestow his bounty,
   and our earth shall yield its increase.
Justice will march before him,
   and guide his steps on the way. ℟.

READING II *Romans 9:1–5*

Brothers and sisters: I speak the truth in Christ, I do not lie; my conscience joins with the Holy Spirit in bearing me witness that I have great sorrow and constant anguish in my heart. For I could wish that I myself were accursed and cut off from Christ for the sake of my own people, my kindred according to the flesh. They are Israelites; theirs the adoption, the glory, the covenants, the giving of the law, the worship, and the promises; theirs the patriarchs, and from them, according to the flesh, is the Christ, who is over all, God blessed forever. Amen.

GOSPEL *Matthew 14:22–33*

After he had fed the people, Jesus made the disciples get into a boat and precede him to the other side, while he dismissed the crowds. After doing so, he went up on the mountain by himself to pray. When it was evening he was there alone. Meanwhile the boat, already a few miles offshore, was being tossed about by the waves, for the wind was against it. During the fourth watch of the night, he came toward them walking on the sea. When the disciples saw him walking on the sea they were terrified. "It is a ghost," they said, and they cried out in fear. At once Jesus spoke to them, "Take courage, it is I; do not be afraid." Peter said to him in reply, "Lord, if it is you, command me to come to you on the water." He said, "Come." Peter got out of the boat and began to walk on the water toward Jesus. But when he saw how strong the wind was he became frightened; and, beginning to sink, he cried out, "Lord, save me!" Immediately Jesus stretched out his hand and caught Peter, and said to him, "O you of little faith, why did you doubt?" After they got into the boat, the wind died down. Those who were in the boat did him homage, saying, "Truly, you are the Son of God."

1249 NINETEENTH SUNDAY IN ORDINARY TIME / B

READING I *1 Kings 19:4–8 / 116*

Elijah went a day's journey into the desert, until he came to a broom tree and sat beneath it. He prayed for death, saying: "This is enough, O LORD! Take my life, for I am no better than my fathers." He lay down and fell asleep under the broom tree, but then an angel touched him and ordered him to get up and eat. Elijah looked and there at his head was a hearth cake and a jug of water. After he ate and drank, he lay down again, but the angel of the LORD came back a second time, touched him, and ordered, "Get up and eat, else the journey will be too long for you!" He got up, ate, and drank; then strengthened by that food, he walked forty days and forty nights to the mountain of God, Horeb.

RESPONSORIAL PSALM   *Psalm 34:2–3, 4–5, 6–7, 8–9*

Taste and see the good - ness of the Lord.

I will bless the LORD at all times;
  praise of him is always in my mouth.
In the LORD my soul shall make its boast;
  the humble shall hear and be glad. ℟.

Glorify the LORD with me;
  together let us praise his name.
I sought the LORD, and he answered me;
  from all my terrors he set me free. ℟.

Look toward him and be radiant;
  let your faces not be abashed.

This lowly one called; the LORD heard,
  and rescued him from all his
  distress. ℟.

The angel of the LORD is encamped
  around those who fear him,
  to rescue them.
Taste and see that the LORD is good.
  Blessed the man who seeks refuge
  in him. ℟.

READING II   *Ephesians 4:30—5:2*
Brothers and sisters: Do not grieve the Holy Spirit of God, with which you were sealed for the day of redemption. All bitterness, fury, anger, shouting, and reviling must be removed from you, along with all malice. And be kind to one another, compassionate, forgiving one another as God has forgiven you in Christ.

So be imitators of God, as beloved children, and live in love, as Christ loved us and handed himself over for us as a sacrificial offering to God for a fragrant aroma.

GOSPEL   *John 6:41–51*
The Jews murmured about Jesus because he said, "I am the bread that came down from heaven," and they said, "Is this not Jesus, the son of Joseph? Do we not know his father and mother? Then how can he say, 'I have come down from heaven'?" Jesus answered and said to them, "Stop murmuring among yourselves. No one can come to me unless the Father who sent me draw him, and I will raise him on the last day. It is written in the prophets:
  They shall all be taught by God.
Everyone who listens to my Father and learns from him comes to me. Not that anyone has seen the Father except the one who is from God; he has seen the Father. Amen, amen, I say to you, whoever believes has eternal life. I am the bread of life. Your ancestors ate the manna in the desert, but they died; this is the bread that comes down from heaven so that one may eat it and not die. I am the living bread that came down from heaven; whoever eats this bread will live forever; and the bread that I will give is my flesh for the life of the world."

1250 NINETEENTH SUNDAY IN ORDINARY TIME / C

READING I   *Wisdom 18:6–9 / 117*

The night of the passover was known beforehand to our fathers,
    that, with sure knowledge of the oaths in which they put their faith,
    they might have courage.
Your people awaited the salvation of the just
    and the destruction of their foes.
For when you punished our adversaries,
    in this you glorified us whom you had summoned.
For in secret the holy children of the good were offering sacrifice
    and putting into effect with one accord the divine institution.

RESPONSORIAL PSALM   *Psalm 33:1 and 12, 18–19, 20 and 22*

Bless-ed the peo-ple the Lord has cho-sen to be his own.

Ring out your joy to the LORD, O you
    just;
    for praise is fitting for the upright.
Blessed the nation whose God is
        the LORD,
    the people he has chosen as his
        heritage. ℟.

Yes, the LORD's eyes are on those
    who fear him,

who hope in his merciful love,
    to rescue their souls from death,
    to keep them alive in famine. ℟.

Our soul is waiting for the LORD.
    He is our help and our shield.
May your merciful love be upon us,
    as we hope in you, O LORD. ℟.

READING II   *Hebrews 11:1–2, 8–19 or 11:1–2, 8–12*

For short form read only the part in brackets.

[Brothers and sisters: Faith is the realization of what is hoped for and evidence of things not seen. Because of it the ancients were well attested.

    By faith Abraham obeyed when he was called to go out to a place that he was to receive as an inheritance; he went out, not knowing where he was to go. By faith he sojourned in the promised land as in a foreign country, dwelling in tents with Isaac and Jacob, heirs of the same promise; for he was looking forward to the city with foundations, whose architect and maker is God. By faith he received power to generate, even though he was past the normal age —and Sarah herself was sterile— for he thought that the one who had made the promise was trustworthy. So it was that there came forth from one man, himself as good as dead, descendants as numerous as the stars in the sky and as countless as the sands on the seashore.]

    All these died in faith. They did not receive what had been promised but saw it and greeted it from afar and acknowledged themselves to be strangers and aliens on earth, for those who speak thus show that they are seeking a homeland. If they had been thinking of the land from which they had come, they would have had opportunity to return. But now they desire a better homeland, a heavenly one. Therefore, God is not ashamed to be called their God, for he has prepared a city for them.

By faith Abraham, when put to the test, offered up Isaac, and he who had received the promises was ready to offer his only son, of whom it was said, "Through Isaac descendants shall bear your name." He reasoned that God was able to raise even from the dead, and he received Isaac back as a symbol.

GOSPEL   *Luke 12:32–48 or 12:35–40*

For short form read only the parts in brackets.

[Jesus said to his disciples:] "Do not be afraid any longer, little flock, for your Father is pleased to give you the kingdom. Sell your belongings and give alms. Provide money bags for yourselves that do not wear out, an inexhaustible treasure in heaven that no thief can reach nor moth destroy. For where your treasure is, there also will your heart be.

["Gird your loins and light your lamps and be like servants who await their master's return from a wedding, ready to open immediately when he comes and knocks. Blessed are those servants whom the master finds vigilant on his arrival. Amen, I say to you, he will gird himself, have them recline at table, and proceed to wait on them. And should he come in the second or third watch and find them prepared in this way, blessed are those servants. Be sure of this: if the master of the house had known the hour when the thief was coming, he would not have let his house be broken into. You also must be prepared, for at an hour you do not expect, the Son of Man will come."]

Then Peter said, "Lord, is this parable meant for us or for everyone?" And the Lord replied, "Who, then, is the faithful and prudent steward whom the master will put in charge of his servants to distribute the food allowance at the proper time? Blessed is that servant whom his master on arrival finds doing so. Truly, I say to you, the master will put the servant in charge of all his property. But if that servant says to himself, 'My master is delayed in coming,' and begins to beat the menservants and the maidservants, to eat and drink and get drunk, then that servant's master will come on an unexpected day and at an unknown hour and will punish the servant severely and assign him a place with the unfaithful. That servant who knew his master's will but did not make preparations nor act in accord with his will shall be beaten severely; and the servant who was ignorant of his master's will but acted in a way deserving of a severe beating shall be beaten only lightly. Much will be required of the person entrusted with much, and still more will be demanded of the person entrusted with more."

TWENTIETH SUNDAY IN ORDINARY TIME / A   1251

READING I   *Isaiah 56:1, 6–7 / 118*

Thus says the LORD:
Observe what is right, do what is just;
    for my salvation is about to come,
    my justice, about to be revealed.

The foreigners who join themselves to
        the LORD,

ministering to him,
loving the name of the LORD,
    and becoming his servants—
all who keep the sabbath free from
        profanation
    and hold to my covenant,
them I will bring to my holy mountain

and make joyful in my house of
prayer;
their burnt offerings and sacrifices
will be acceptable on my altar,
for my house shall be called
a house of prayer for all peoples.

RESPONSORIAL PSALM   *Psalm 67:2–3, 5, 6 and 8*

O God, O God, let all the na-tions praise you!

O God, be gracious and bless us
  and let your face shed its light upon us.
So will your ways be known upon earth
  and all nations learn your salvation. ℟.

Let the nations be glad and shout for joy,
  with uprightness you rule the peoples;

you guide the nations on earth. ℟.

Let the peoples praise you, O God;
  let all the peoples praise you.
May God still give us his blessing
  that all the ends of the earth may
  revere him. ℟.

READING II   *Romans 11:13–15, 29–32*

Brothers and sisters: I am speaking to you Gentiles. Inasmuch as I am the apostle to the Gentiles, I glory in my ministry in order to make my race jealous and thus save some of them. For if their rejection is the reconciliation of the world, what will their acceptance be but life from the dead?

For the gifts and the call of God are irrevocable. Just as you once disobeyed God but have now received mercy because of their disobedience, so they have now disobeyed in order that, by virtue of the mercy shown to you, they too may now receive mercy. For God delivered all to disobedience, that he might have mercy upon all.

GOSPEL   *Matthew 15:21–28*

At that time, Jesus withdrew to the region of Tyre and Sidon. And behold, a Canaanite woman of that district came and called out, "Have pity on me, Lord, Son of David! My daughter is tormented by a demon." But Jesus did not say a word in answer to her. Jesus' disciples came and asked him, "Send her away, for she keeps calling out after us." He said in reply, "I was sent only to the lost sheep of the house of Israel." But the woman came and did Jesus homage, saying, "Lord, help me." He said in reply, "It is not right to take the food of the children and throw it to the dogs." She said, "Please, Lord, for even the dogs eat the scraps that fall from the table of their masters." Then Jesus said to her in reply, "O woman, great is your faith! Let it be done for you as you wish." And the woman's daughter was healed from that hour.

1252 TWENTIETH SUNDAY IN ORDINARY TIME / B

READING I   *Proverbs 9:1–6 / 119*

Wisdom has built her house,
  she has set up her seven columns;
she has dressed her meat, mixed her wine,
  yes, she has spread her table.

She has sent out her maidens; she calls
  from the heights out over the city:
"Let whoever is simple turn in here;

to the one who lacks understanding,
she says,
Come, eat of my food,
and drink of the wine I have mixed!

Forsake foolishness that you may live;
advance in the way of
understanding."

RESPONSORIAL PSALM *Psalm 34:2–3, 4–5, 6–7*

Taste and see the good - ness of the Lord.

I will bless the LORD at all times;
praise of him is always in my mouth.
In the LORD my soul shall make its boast;
the humble shall hear and be glad. ℟.

Glorify the LORD with me;
together let us praise his name.
I sought the LORD, and he answered me;

from all my terrors he set me free. ℟.

Look toward him and be radiant;
let your faces not be abashed.
This lowly one called; the LORD heard,
and rescued him from all his
distress. ℟.

READING II *Ephesians 5:15–20*

Brothers and sisters: Watch carefully how you live, not as foolish persons but as wise, making the most of the opportunity, because the days are evil. Therefore, do not continue in ignorance, but try to understand what is the will of the Lord. And do not get drunk on wine, in which lies debauchery, but be filled with the Spirit, addressing one another in psalms and hymns and spiritual songs, singing and playing to the Lord in your hearts, giving thanks always and for everything in the name of our Lord Jesus Christ to God the Father.

GOSPEL *John 6:51–58*

Jesus said to the crowds: "I am the living bread that came down from heaven; whoever eats this bread will live forever; and the bread that I will give is my flesh for the life of the world."

The Jews quarreled among themselves, saying, "How can this man give us his flesh to eat?" Jesus said to them, "Amen, amen, I say to you, unless you eat the flesh of the Son of Man and drink his blood, you do not have life within you. Whoever eats my flesh and drinks my blood has eternal life, and I will raise him on the last day. For my flesh is true food, and my blood is true drink. Whoever eats my flesh and drinks my blood remains in me and I in him. Just as the living Father sent me and I have life because of the Father, so also the one who feeds on me will have life because of me. This is the bread that came down from heaven. Unlike your ancestors who ate and still died, whoever eats this bread will live forever."

TWENTIETH SUNDAY IN ORDINARY TIME / C 1253

READING I *Jeremiah 38:4–6, 8–10 / 120*

In those days, the princes said to the king: "Jeremiah ought to be put to death; he is demoralizing the soldiers who are left in this city, and all the people, by speaking such things to them; he is not interested in the welfare of our people, but in their ruin." King Zedekiah answered: "He is in your power"; for the king could do nothing with them. And so they took Jeremiah and threw him into the cistern of Prince Malchiah, which was in the quarters of the guard, letting him down with ropes. There was no water in the cistern, only mud, and Jeremiah sank into the mud.

Ebed-melech, a court official, went there from the palace and said to him: "My lord king, these men have been at fault in all they have done to the prophet Jeremiah, casting him into the cistern. He will die of famine on the spot, for there is no more food in the city." Then the king ordered Ebed-melech the Cushite to take three men along with him, and draw the prophet Jeremiah out of the cistern before he should die.

RESPONSORIAL PSALM *Psalm 40:2, 3, 4, 18*

Lord, come to my aid!

I waited, I waited for the LORD,
and he stooped down to me;
he heard my cry. ℟.

He drew me from the deadly pit,
from the miry clay.
He set my feet upon a rock,
made my footsteps firm. ℟.

He put a new song into my mouth,
praise of our God.
Many shall see and fear
and shall trust in the LORD. ℟.

Wretched and poor though I am,
the Lord is mindful of me.
You are my rescuer, my help;
O my God, do not delay. ℟.

READING II *Hebrews 12:1–4*

Brothers and sisters: Since we are surrounded by so great a cloud of witnesses, let us rid ourselves of every burden and sin that clings to us and persevere in running the race that lies before us while keeping our eyes fixed on Jesus, the leader and perfecter of faith. For the sake of the joy that lay before him he endured the cross, despising its shame, and has taken his seat at the right of the throne of God. Consider how he endured such opposition from sinners, in order that you may not grow weary and lose heart. In your struggle against sin you have not yet resisted to the point of shedding blood.

GOSPEL *Luke 12:49–53*

Jesus said to his disciples: "I have come to set the earth on fire, and how I wish it were already blazing! There is a baptism with which I must be baptized, and how great is my anguish until it is accomplished! Do you think that I have come to establish peace on the earth? No, I tell you, but rather division. From now on a household of five will be divided, three against two and two against three; a father will be divided against his son and a son against his father, a mother against her daughter and a daughter against her mother, a mother-in-law against her daughter-in-law and a daughter-in-law against her mother-in-law."

TWENTY-FIRST SUNDAY IN ORDINARY TIME / A   1254

READING I   *Isaiah 22:19–23 / 121*

Thus says the LORD to Shebna, master
  of the palace:
"I will thrust you from your office
  and pull you down from your station.
On that day I will summon my servant
  Eliakim, son of Hilkiah;
I will clothe him with your robe,
  and gird him with your sash,
  and give over to him your authority.

He shall be a father to the inhabitants
  of Jerusalem,
  and to the house of Judah.
I will place the key of the House of
  David on Eliakim's shoulder;
  when he opens, no one shall shut,
  when he shuts, no one shall open.
I will fix him like a peg in a sure spot,
  to be a place of honor for his family."

RESPONSORIAL PSALM   *Psalm 138:1–2a, 2bc and 3, 6 and 8bc*

Lord, your love is e - ter-nal; do not for-sake the work of your hands.

I thank you, LORD, with all my heart;
  you have heard the words of my
    mouth.
In the presence of the angels I praise you.
  I bow down toward your holy
    temple. ℟.

I give thanks to your name
  for your merciful love and your
    faithfulness.

On the day I called, you answered me;
  you increased the strength of my
    soul. ℟.

The LORD is high, yet he looks on the
    lowly,
  and the haughty he knows from afar.
O LORD, your merciful love is eternal;
  discard not the work of your
    hands. ℟.

READING II   *Romans 11:33–36*

Oh, the depth of the riches and wisdom and knowledge of God! How inscrutable are
his judgments and how unsearchable his ways!
  For who has known the mind of the Lord
    or who has been his counselor?
  Or who has given the Lord anything
    that he may be repaid?
For from him and through him and for him are all things. To him be glory forever.
Amen.

GOSPEL   *Matthew 16:13–20*

Jesus went into the region of Caesarea Philippi and he asked his disciples, "Who do
people say that the Son of Man is?" They replied, "Some say John the Baptist, others Elijah, still others Jeremiah or one of the prophets." He said to them, "But who
do you say that I am?" Simon Peter said in reply, "You are the Christ, the Son of
the living God." Jesus said to him in reply, "Blessed are you, Simon son of Jonah.
For flesh and blood has not revealed this to you, but my heavenly Father. And so I
say to you, you are Peter, and upon this rock I will build my church, and the gates of

the netherworld shall not prevail against it. I will give you the keys to the kingdom of heaven. Whatever you bind on earth shall be bound in heaven; and whatever you loose on earth shall be loosed in heaven." Then he strictly ordered his disciples to tell no one that he was the Christ.

1255 TWENTY-FIRST SUNDAY IN ORDINARY TIME / B

READING I   *Joshua 24:1–2a, 15–17, 18b / 122*

Joshua gathered together all the tribes of Israel at Shechem, summoning their elders, their leaders, their judges, and their officers. When they stood in ranks before God, Joshua addressed all the people: "If it does not please you to serve the LORD, decide today whom you will serve, the gods your fathers served beyond the River or the gods of the Amorites in whose country you are now dwelling. As for me and my household, we will serve the LORD."

But the people answered, "Far be it from us to forsake the LORD for the service of other gods. For it was the LORD, our God, who brought us and our fathers up out of the land of Egypt, out of a state of slavery. He performed those great miracles before our very eyes and protected us along our entire journey and among the peoples through whom we passed. Therefore we also will serve the LORD, for he is our God."

RESPONSORIAL PSALM   *Psalm 34:2–3, 16–17, 18–19, 20–21*

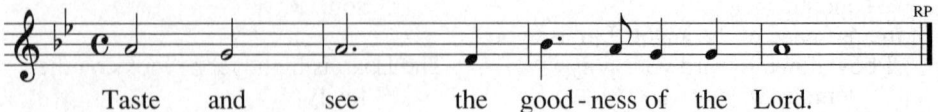

Taste and see the good-ness of the Lord.

I will bless the LORD at all times;
   praise of him is always in my mouth.
In the LORD my soul shall make its boast;
   the humble shall hear and be glad. ℟.

The LORD turns his eyes to the just,
   and his ears are open to their cry.
The LORD turns his face against the
      wicked
   to destroy their remembrance from
      the earth. ℟.

When the just cry out, the LORD hears,

and rescues them in all their distress.
The LORD is close to the
      brokenhearted;
   those whose spirit is crushed he will
      save. ℟.

Many are the trials of the just man,
   but from them all the LORD will
      rescue him.
He will keep guard over all his bones;
   not one of his bones shall be
      broken. ℟.

READING II   *Ephesians 5:21–32 or 5:2a, 25–32*
For long form, omit the phrase in double brackets; for short form read only the parts in brackets.

[Brothers and sisters:] [[Live in love, as Christ loved us.]] Be subordinate to one another out of reverence for Christ. Wives should be subordinate to their husbands as to the Lord. For the husband is head of his wife just as Christ is head of the church, he himself the savior of the body. As the church is subordinate to Christ, so wives should be subordinate to their husbands in everything. [Husbands, love your wives, even as Christ loved the church and handed himself over for her to sanctify her, cleansing her by the bath of water with the word, that he might present to himself the church in splendor, without spot or wrinkle or any such thing, that she might be holy and without blemish. So also husbands should love their wives as their own bodies. He who loves his wife loves himself. For no one hates his own flesh but rather nourishes and cherishes it, even as Christ does the church, because we are members of his body.

For this reason a man shall leave his father and his mother
and be joined to his wife,
and the two shall become one flesh.

This is a great mystery, but I speak in reference to Christ and the church.]

GOSPEL
John 6:60–69

Many of Jesus' disciples who were listening said, "This saying is hard; who can accept it?" Since Jesus knew that his disciples were murmuring about this, he said to them, "Does this shock you? What if you were to see the Son of Man ascending to where he was before? It is the spirit that gives life, while the flesh is of no avail. The words I have spoken to you are Spirit and life. But there are some of you who do not believe." Jesus knew from the beginning the ones who would not believe and the one who would betray him. And he said, "For this reason I have told you that no one can come to me unless it is granted him by my Father."

As a result of this, many of his disciples returned to their former way of life and no longer accompanied him. Jesus then said to the Twelve, "Do you also want to leave?" Simon Peter answered him, "Master, to whom shall we go? You have the words of eternal life. We have come to believe and are convinced that you are the Holy One of God."

TWENTY-FIRST SUNDAY IN ORDINARY TIME / C   1256

READING I
Isaiah 66:18–21 / 123

Thus says the LORD: I know their works and their thoughts, and I come to gather nations of every language; they shall come and see my glory. I will set a sign among them; from them I will send fugitives to the nations: to Tarshish, Put and Lud, Mosoch, Tubal and Javan, to the distant coastlands that have never heard of my fame, or seen my glory; and they shall proclaim my glory among the nations. They shall bring all your brothers and sisters from all the nations as an offering to the LORD, on horses and in chariots, in carts, upon mules and dromedaries, to Jerusalem, my holy mountain, says the LORD, just as the Israelites bring their offering to the house of the LORD in clean vessels. Some of these I will take as priests and Levites, says the LORD.

RESPONSORIAL PSALM
Psalm 117:1, 2

Or: Alleluia.

Go out to all the world, and tell the Good News.

O praise the LORD, all you nations;
    acclaim him, all you peoples! ℟.

For his merciful love has prevailed
    over us;
    and the LORD's faithfulness
    endures forever. ℟.

READING II   *Hebrews 12:5–7, 11–13*

Brothers and sisters, You have forgotten the exhortation addressed to you as children:
"My son, do not disdain the discipline of the Lord
    or lose heart when reproved by him;
for whom the Lord loves, he disciplines;
    he scourges every son he acknowledges."
Endure your trials as "discipline"; God treats you as sons. For what "son" is there whom his father does not discipline? At the time, all discipline seems a cause not for joy but for pain, yet later it brings the peaceful fruit of righteousness to those who are trained by it.

So strengthen your drooping hands and your weak knees. Make straight paths for your feet, that what is lame may not be disjointed but healed.

GOSPEL   *Luke 13:22–30*

Jesus passed through towns and villages, teaching as he went and making his way to Jerusalem. Someone asked him, "Lord, will only a few people be saved?" He answered them, "Strive to enter through the narrow gate, for many, I tell you, will attempt to enter but will not be strong enough. After the master of the house has arisen and locked the door, then will you stand outside knocking and saying, 'Lord, open the door for us.' He will say to you in reply, 'I do not know where you are from.' And you will say, 'We ate and drank in your company and you taught in our streets.' Then he will say to you, 'I do not know where you are from. Depart from me, all you evildoers!' And there will be wailing and grinding of teeth when you see Abraham, Isaac, and Jacob and all the prophets in the kingdom of God and you yourselves cast out. And people will come from the east and the west and from the north and the south and will recline at table in the kingdom of God. For behold, some are last who will be first, and some are first who will be last."

1257 TWENTY-SECOND SUNDAY IN ORDINARY TIME / A

READING I   *Jeremiah 20:7–9 / 124*

You duped me, O Lord, and I let
    myself be duped;
    you were too strong for me, and you
    triumphed.
All the day I am an object of laughter;
    everyone mocks me.

Whenever I speak, I must cry out,
    violence and outrage is my message;
the word of the Lord has brought me

derision and reproach all the day.

I say to myself, I will not mention him,
    I will speak in his name no more.
But then it becomes like fire burning in
    my heart,
    imprisoned in my bones;
I grow weary holding it in, I cannot
    endure it.

RESPONSORIAL PSALM *Psalm 63:2, 3–4, 5–6, 8–9*

My soul is thirst-ing for you, O Lord, thirst-ing for you my God.

O God, you are my God; at dawn I
 seek you;
 for you my soul is thirsting.
For you my flesh is pining,
 like a dry, weary land without
 water. ℟.

I have come before you in the sanctuary,
 to behold your strength and your
 glory.
Your loving mercy is better than life;
 my lips will speak your praise. ℟.

I will bless you all my life;
 in your name I will lift up my hands.
My soul shall be filled as with a
 banquet;
 with joyful lips, my mouth shall
 praise you. ℟.

For you have been my strength;
 in the shadow of your wings I
 rejoice.
My soul clings fast to you;
 your right hand upholds me. ℟.

READING II *Romans 12:1–2*

I urge you, brothers and sisters, by the mercies of God, to offer your bodies as a living sacrifice, holy and pleasing to God, your spiritual worship. Do not conform yourselves to this age but be transformed by the renewal of your mind, that you may discern what is the will of God, what is good and pleasing and perfect.

GOSPEL *Matthew 16:21–27*

Jesus began to show his disciples that he must go to Jerusalem and suffer greatly from the elders, the chief priests, and the scribes, and be killed and on the third day be raised. Then Peter took Jesus aside and began to rebuke him, "God forbid, Lord! No such thing shall ever happen to you." He turned and said to Peter, "Get behind me, Satan! You are an obstacle to me. You are thinking not as God does, but as human beings do."

Then Jesus said to his disciples, "Whoever wishes to come after me must deny himself, take up his cross, and follow me. For whoever wishes to save his life will lose it, but whoever loses his life for my sake will find it. What profit would there be for one to gain the whole world and forfeit his life? Or what can one give in exchange for his life? For the Son of Man will come with his angels in his Father's glory, and then he will repay all according to his conduct."

TWENTY-SECOND SUNDAY IN ORDINARY TIME / B 1258

READING I *Deuteronomy 4:1–2, 6–8 / 125*

Moses said to the people: "Now, Israel, hear the statutes and decrees which I am teaching you to observe, that you may live, and may enter in and take possession of the land which the LORD, the God of your fathers, is giving you. In your observance of the commandments of the LORD, your God, which I enjoin upon you, you shall not add to what I command you nor subtract from it. Observe them carefully, for thus will you give evidence of your wisdom and intelligence to the nations, who will hear of all these statutes and say, 'This great nation is truly a wise and intelligent people.' For what great nation is there that has gods so close to it as the LORD, our God, is to us whenever we call upon him? Or what great nation has statutes and decrees that are as just as this whole law which I am setting before you today?"

RESPONSORIAL PSALM   *Psalm 15:2–3a, 3bc–4ab, 5*

The one who does jus-tice will live in the pres-ence of the Lord.

Whoever walks without fault;
  who does what is just,
and speaks the truth from his heart;
  whoever does not slander with his
    tongue. ℟.

Who does no wrong to a neighbor,
  who casts no slur on a friend,
who looks with scorn on the wicked,

but honors those who fear the
  LORD. ℟.

Who lends no money at interest,
  and accepts no bribes against the
    innocent.
Such a one shall never be shaken. ℟.

READING II   *James 1:17–18, 21b–22, 27*
Dearest brothers and sisters: All good giving and every perfect gift is from above, coming down from the Father of lights, with whom there is no alteration or shadow caused by change. He willed to give us birth by the word of truth that we may be a kind of firstfruits of his creatures.

Humbly welcome the word that has been planted in you and is able to save your souls.

Be doers of the word and not hearers only, deluding yourselves.

Religion that is pure and undefiled before God and the Father is this: to care for orphans and widows in their affliction and to keep oneself unstained by the world.

GOSPEL   *Mark 7:1–8, 14–15, 21–23*
When the Pharisees with some scribes who had come from Jerusalem gathered around Jesus, they observed that some of his disciples ate their meals with unclean, that is, unwashed, hands. —For the Pharisees and, in fact, all Jews, do not eat without carefully washing their hands, keeping the tradition of the elders. And on coming from the marketplace they do not eat without purifying themselves. And there are many other things that they have traditionally observed, the purification of cups and jugs and kettles and beds.— So the Pharisees and scribes questioned him, "Why do your disciples not follow the tradition of the elders but instead eat a meal with unclean hands?" He responded, "Well did Isaiah prophesy about you hypocrites, as it is written:
  This people honors me with their lips,
    but their hearts are far from me;
  in vain do they worship me,
    teaching as doctrines human precepts.
You disregard God's commandment but cling to human tradition."

He summoned the crowd again and said to them, "Hear me, all of you, and understand. Nothing that enters one from outside can defile that person; but the things that come out from within are what defile.

"From within people, from their hearts, come evil thoughts, unchastity, theft, murder, adultery, greed, malice, deceit, licentiousness, envy, blasphemy, arrogance, folly. All these evils come from within and they defile."

TWENTY-SECOND SUNDAY IN ORDINARY TIME / C 1259

READING I *Sirach 3:17–18, 20, 28–29 / 126*

My child, conduct your affairs with
humility,
and you will be loved more than a
giver of gifts.
Humble yourself the more, the greater
you are,
and you will find favor with God.
What is too sublime for you, seek not,
into things beyond your strength
search not.
The mind of a sage appreciates proverbs,
and an attentive ear is the joy of the
wise.
Water quenches a flaming fire,
and alms atone for sins.

RESPONSORIAL PSALM *Psalm 68:4–5ac, 6–7ab, 10–11*

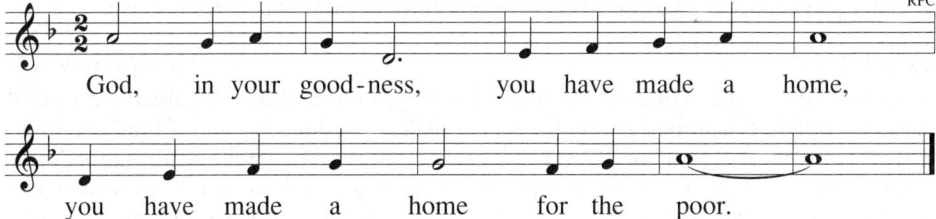

God, in your good-ness, you have made a home, you have made a home for the poor.

The just shall rejoice at the presence
of God;
they shall exult with glad rejoicing.
O sing to God; make music to his name.
The LORD is his name. ℟.

Father of orphans, defender of widows:
such is God in his holy place.
God gives the desolate a home to dwell in;
he leads the prisoners forth into
prosperity. ℟.

You poured down, O God, a generous
rain;
when your people languished, you
restored their inheritance.
It was there that your flock began to
dwell.
In your goodness, O God, you
provided for the poor. ℟.

READING II *Hebrews 12:18–19, 22–24a*

Brothers and sisters: You have not approached that which could be touched and a blazing fire and gloomy darkness and storm and a trumpet blast and a voice speaking words such that those who heard begged that no message be further addressed to them. No, you have approached Mount Zion and the city of the living God, the heavenly Jerusalem, and countless angels in festal gathering, and the assembly of the firstborn enrolled in heaven, and God the judge of all, and the spirits of the just made perfect, and Jesus, the mediator of a new covenant, and the sprinkled blood that speaks more eloquently than that of Abel.

GOSPEL *Luke 14:1, 7–14*

On a sabbath Jesus went to dine at the home of one of the leading Pharisees, and the people there were observing him carefully.

He told a parable to those who had been invited, noticing how they were choosing the places of honor at the table. "When you are invited by someone to a wedding banquet, do not recline at table in the place of honor. A more distinguished guest than you may have been invited by him, and the host who invited both of you may approach you and say, 'Give your place to this man,' and then you would proceed with embarrassment to take the lowest place. Rather, when you are invited, go and take the lowest place so that when the host comes to you he may say, 'My friend, move up to a higher position.' Then you will enjoy the esteem of your companions at the table. For everyone who exalts himself will be humbled, but the one who humbles himself will be exalted." Then he said to the host who invited him, "When you hold a lunch or a dinner, do not invite your friends or your brothers or your relatives or your wealthy neighbors, in case they may invite you back and you have repayment. Rather, when you hold a banquet, invite the poor, the crippled, the lame, the blind; blessed indeed will you be because of their inability to repay you. For you will be repaid at the resurrection of the righteous."

1260 TWENTY-THIRD SUNDAY IN ORDINARY TIME / A

READING I *Ezekiel 33:7–9 / 127*

Thus says the LORD: You, son of man, I have appointed watchman for the house of Israel; when you hear me say anything, you shall warn them for me. If I tell the wicked, "O wicked one, you shall surely die," and you do not speak out to dissuade the wicked from his way, the wicked shall die for his guilt, but I will hold you responsible for his death. But if you warn the wicked, trying to turn him from his way, and he refuses to turn from his way, he shall die for his guilt, but you shall save yourself.

RESPONSORIAL PSALM *Psalm 95:1–2, 6–7c, 7d–9*

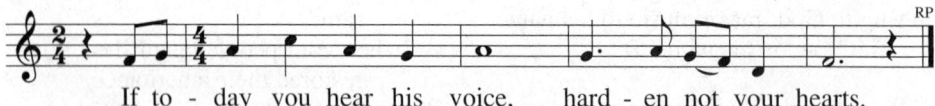

If to - day you hear his voice, hard - en not your hearts.

Come, let us ring out our joy to the LORD;
  hail the rock who saves us.
Let us come into his presence, giving
    thanks;
  let us hail him with a song of praise. ℟.

O come; let us bow and bend low.
  Let us kneel before the God who
    made us,
for he is our God and we
  the people who belong to his pasture,

the flock that is led by his hand. ℟.

O that today you would listen to his
  voice!
"Harden not your hearts as at
    Meribah,
as on that day at Massah in the
    desert
when your forebears put me to the test;
  when they tried me, though they saw
    my work." ℟.

READING II   *Romans 13:8–10*

Brothers and sisters: Owe nothing to anyone, except to love one another; for the one who loves another has fulfilled the law. The commandments, "You shall not commit adultery; you shall not kill; you shall not steal; you shall not covet," and whatever other commandment there may be, are summed up in this saying, namely, "You shall love your neighbor as yourself." Love does no evil to the neighbor; hence, love is the fulfillment of the law.

GOSPEL   *Matthew 18:15–20*

Jesus said to his disciples: "If your brother sins against you, go and tell him his fault between you and him alone. If he listens to you, you have won over your brother. If he does not listen, take one or two others along with you, so that 'every fact may be established on the testimony of two or three witnesses.' If he refuses to listen to them, tell the church. If he refuses to listen even to the church, then treat him as you would a Gentile or a tax collector. Amen, I say to you, whatever you bind on earth shall be bound in heaven, and whatever you loose on earth shall be loosed in heaven. Again, amen, I say to you, if two of you agree on earth about anything for which they are to pray, it shall be granted to them by my heavenly Father. For where two or three are gathered together in my name, there am I in the midst of them."

TWENTY-THIRD SUNDAY IN ORDINARY TIME / B   1261

READING I   *Isaiah 35:4–7a / 128*

Thus says the LORD:
  Say to those whose hearts are
    frightened:
    Be strong, fear not!
  Here is your God,
    he comes with vindication;
  with divine recompense
    he comes to save you.
  Then will the eyes of the blind be
    opened,

    the ears of the deaf be cleared;
  then will the lame leap like a stag,
    then the tongue of the mute will
      sing.
  Streams will burst forth in the desert,
    and rivers in the steppe.
  The burning sands will become
    pools,
    and the thirsty ground, springs of
    water.

RESPONSORIAL PSALM   *Psalm 146:6c–7, 8–9a, 9bc–10*
Or: Alleluia.

Praise the Lord, my soul! Praise the Lord!

It is the LORD who preserves fidelity
  forever,
  who does justice to those who are
  oppressed.
It is he who gives bread to the hungry,
  the LORD who sets prisoners free. ℟.

The LORD who opens the eyes of the
  blind,
  the LORD who raises up those who

  are bowed down.
It is the LORD who loves the just,
  the LORD who protects the stranger. ℟.

The LORD upholds the orphan and the
  widow,
  but thwarts the path of the wicked.
The LORD will reign forever,
  the God of Sion from age to age.
  Alleluia. ℟.

READING II *James 2:1–5*

My brothers and sisters, show no partiality as you adhere to the faith in our glorious Lord Jesus Christ. For if a man with gold rings and fine clothes comes into your assembly, and a poor person in shabby clothes also comes in, and you pay attention to the one wearing the fine clothes and say, "Sit here, please," while you say to the poor one, "Stand there," or "Sit at my feet," have you not made distinctions among yourselves and become judges with evil designs?

Listen, my beloved brothers and sisters. Did not God choose those who are poor in the world to be rich in faith and heirs of the kingdom that he promised to those who love him?

GOSPEL *Mark 7:31–37*

Again Jesus left the district of Tyre and went by way of Sidon to the Sea of Galilee, into the district of the Decapolis. And people brought to him a deaf man who had a speech impediment and begged him to lay his hand on him. He took him off by himself away from the crowd. He put his finger into the man's ears and, spitting, touched his tongue; then he looked up to heaven and groaned, and said to him, "*Ephphatha!*" —that is, "Be opened!"— And immediately the man's ears were opened, his speech impediment was removed, and he spoke plainly. He ordered them not to tell anyone. But the more he ordered them not to, the more they proclaimed it. They were exceedingly astonished and they said, "He has done all things well. He makes the deaf hear and the mute speak."

1262 TWENTY-THIRD SUNDAY IN ORDINARY TIME / C

READING I *Wisdom 9:13–18b / 129*

Who can know God's counsel,
  or who can conceive what the
    LORD intends?
For the deliberations of mortals are timid,
  and unsure are our plans.
For the corruptible body burdens the soul
  and the earthen shelter weighs
    down the mind that has many
      concerns.
And scarce do we guess the things on
earth,
and what is within our grasp we
  find with difficulty;
but when things are in heaven, who
  can search them out?
Or who ever knew your counsel, except
  you had given wisdom
and sent your holy spirit from on high?
And thus were the paths of those on
  earth made straight.

RESPONSORIAL PSALM *Psalm 90:3–4, 5–6, 12–13, 14 and 17*

CAP

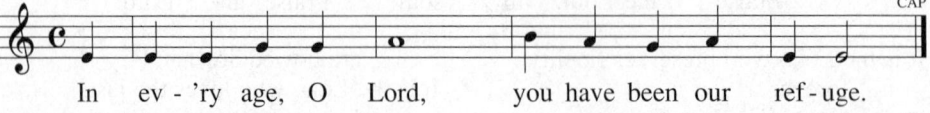

In ev-'ry age, O Lord, you have been our ref-uge.

You turn man back to dust,
  and say, "Return, O children of men."
To your eyes a thousand years
  are like yesterday, come and gone,
  or like a watch in the night. ℟.

You sweep them away like a dream,
  like grass which is fresh in the
    morning.
In the morning it sprouts and is fresh;
  by evening it withers and fades. ℟.

Then teach us to number our days,
   that we may gain wisdom of heart.
Turn back, O Lᴏʀᴅ! How long?
   Show pity to your servants. ℟.

At dawn, fill us with your merciful love;
   we shall exult and rejoice all our days.

Let the favor of the Lord our God be
   upon us;
give success to the work of our
   hands.
O give success to the work of our
   hands. ℟.

READING II   *Philemon 9–10, 12–17*

I, Paul, an old man, and now also a prisoner for Christ Jesus, urge you on behalf of my child Onesimus, whose father I have become in my imprisonment; I am sending him, that is, my own heart, back to you. I should have liked to retain him for myself, so that he might serve me on your behalf in my imprisonment for the gospel, but I did not want to do anything without your consent, so that the good you do might not be forced but voluntary. Perhaps this is why he was away from you for a while, that you might have him back forever, no longer as a slave but more than a slave, a brother, beloved especially to me, but even more so to you, as a man and in the Lord. So if you regard me as a partner, welcome him as you would me.

GOSPEL   *Luke 14:25–33*

Great crowds were traveling with Jesus, and he turned and addressed them, "If anyone comes to me without hating his father and mother, wife and children, brothers and sisters, and even his own life, he cannot be my disciple. Whoever does not carry his own cross and come after me cannot be my disciple. Which of you wishing to construct a tower does not first sit down and calculate the cost to see if there is enough for its completion? Otherwise, after laying the foundation and finding himself unable to finish the work the onlookers should laugh at him and say, 'This one began to build but did not have the resources to finish.' Or what king marching into battle would not first sit down and decide whether with ten thousand troops he can successfully oppose another king advancing upon him with twenty thousand troops? But if not, while he is still far away, he will send a delegation to ask for peace terms. In the same way, anyone of you who does not renounce all his possessions cannot be my disciple."

TWENTY-FOURTH SUNDAY IN ORDINARY TIME / A   1263

READING I   *Sirach 27:30—28:7 / 130*

Wrath and anger are hateful things,
   yet the sinner hugs them tight.
The vengeful will suffer the Lᴏʀᴅ's
   vengeance,
   for he remembers their sins in detail.
Forgive your neighbor's injustice;
   then when you pray, your own sins
   will be forgiven.
Could anyone nourish anger against
   another
   and expect healing from the Lᴏʀᴅ?
Could anyone refuse mercy to another
like himself,
   can he seek pardon for his own sins?
If one who is but flesh cherishes wrath,
   who will forgive his sins?
Remember your last days, set enmity
   aside;
   remember death and decay, and cease
   from sin!
Think of the commandments, hate not
   your neighbor;
   remember the Most High's covenant,
   and overlook faults.

RESPONSORIAL PSALM   *Psalm 103:1–2, 3–4, 9–10, 11–12*

The Lord is kind and mer-ci-ful; slow to an-ger, and rich in com-pas-sion.

Bless the Lord, O my soul,
    and all within me, his holy name.
Bless the Lord, O my soul,
    and never forget all his benefits. ℟.

It is the Lord who forgives all your sins,
    who heals every one of your ills,
who redeems your life from the grave,
    who crowns you with mercy and
        compassion. ℟.

He will not always find fault;
    nor persist in his anger forever.

He does not treat us according to our
    sins,
    nor repay us according to our
        faults. ℟.

For as the heavens are high above the
    earth,
    so strong his mercy for those who
        fear him.
As far as the east is from the west,
    so far from us does he remove our
        transgressions. ℟.

READING II   *Romans 14:7–9*
Brothers and sisters: None of us lives for oneself, and no one dies for oneself. For if we live, we live for the Lord, and if we die, we die for the Lord; so then, whether we live or die, we are the Lord's. For this is why Christ died and came to life, that he might be Lord of both the dead and the living.

GOSPEL   *Matthew 18:21–35*
Peter approached Jesus and asked him, "Lord, if my brother sins against me, how often must I forgive? As many as seven times?" Jesus answered, "I say to you, not seven times but seventy-seven times. That is why the kingdom of heaven may be likened to a king who decided to settle accounts with his servants. When he began the accounting, a debtor was brought before him who owed him a huge amount. Since he had no way of paying it back, his master ordered him to be sold, along with his wife, his children, and all his property, in payment of the debt. At that, the servant fell down, did him homage, and said, 'Be patient with me, and I will pay you back in full.' Moved with compassion the master of that servant let him go and forgave him the loan. When that servant had left, he found one of his fellow servants who owed him a much smaller amount. He seized him and started to choke him, demanding, 'Pay back what you owe.' Falling to his knees, his fellow servant begged him, 'Be patient with me, and I will pay you back.' But he refused. Instead, he had the fellow servant put in prison until he paid back the debt. Now when his fellow servants saw what had happened, they were deeply disturbed, and went to their master and reported the whole affair. His master summoned him and said to him, 'You wicked servant! I

forgave you your entire debt because you begged me to. Should you not have had pity on your fellow servant, as I had pity on you?' Then in anger his master handed him over to the torturers until he should pay back the whole debt. So will my heavenly Father do to you, unless each of you forgives your brother from your heart."

TWENTY-FOURTH SUNDAY IN ORDINARY TIME / B   1264

READING I
Isaiah 50:5–9a / 131

The Lord GOD opens my ear that I
    may hear;
and I have not rebelled,
    have not turned back.
I gave my back to those who beat me,
    my cheeks to those who plucked my
     beard;
my face I did not shield
    from buffets and spitting.

The Lord GOD is my help,

therefore I am not disgraced;
I have set my face like flint,
    knowing that I shall not be put to
     shame.
He is near who upholds my right;
    if anyone wishes to oppose me,
    let us appear together.
Who disputes my right?
    Let that man confront me.
See, the Lord GOD is my help;
    who will prove me wrong?

RESPONSORIAL PSALM
Psalm 116:1–2, 3–4, 5–6, 8–9

Or: Alleluia.

I will walk be - fore the   Lord   in the land of the liv - ing.

I love the LORD, for he has heard
    my voice, my appeal;
for he has turned his ear to me
    whenever I call. ℟.

They surrounded me, the snares of death;
    the anguish of the grave has found me;
    anguish and sorrow I found.
I called on the name of the LORD:
    "Deliver my soul, O LORD!" ℟.

How gracious is the LORD, and just;
    our God has compassion.
The LORD protects the simple;
    I was brought low, and he saved
     me. ℟.

He has kept my soul from death,
    my eyes from tears, and my feet
     from stumbling.
I will walk in the presence of the LORD
    in the land of the living. ℟.

READING II
James 2:14–18

What good is it, my brothers and sisters, if someone says he has faith but does not have works? Can that faith save him? If a brother or sister has nothing to wear and has no food for the day, and one of you says to them, "Go in peace, keep warm, and eat well," but you do not give them the necessities of the body, what good is it? So also faith of itself, if it does not have works, is dead.

    Indeed someone might say, "You have faith and I have works." Demonstrate your faith to me without works, and I will demonstrate my faith to you from my works.

GOSPEL   *Mark 8:27–35*

Jesus and his disciples set out for the villages of Caesarea Philippi. Along the way he asked his disciples, "Who do people say that I am?" They said in reply, "John the Baptist, others Elijah, still others one of the prophets." And he asked them, "But who do you say that I am?" Peter said to him in reply, "You are the Christ." Then he warned them not to tell anyone about him.

He began to teach them that the Son of Man must suffer greatly and be rejected by the elders, the chief priests, and the scribes, and be killed, and rise after three days. He spoke this openly. Then Peter took him aside and began to rebuke him. At this he turned around and, looking at his disciples, rebuked Peter and said, "Get behind me, Satan. You are thinking not as God does, but as human beings do."

He summoned the crowd with his disciples and said to them, "Whoever wishes to come after me must deny himself, take up his cross, and follow me. For whoever wishes to save his life will lose it, but whoever loses his life for my sake and that of the gospel will save it."

1265 TWENTY-FOURTH SUNDAY IN ORDINARY TIME / C

READING I   *Exodus 32:7–11, 13–14 / 132*

The LORD said to Moses, "Go down at once to your people, whom you brought out of the land of Egypt, for they have become depraved. They have soon turned aside from the way I pointed out to them, making for themselves a molten calf and worshiping it, sacrificing to it and crying out, 'This is your God, O Israel, who brought you out of the land of Egypt!' I see how stiff-necked this people is," continued the LORD to Moses. "Let me alone, then, that my wrath may blaze up against them to consume them. Then I will make of you a great nation."

But Moses implored the LORD, his God, saying, "Why, O LORD, should your wrath blaze up against your own people, whom you brought out of the land of Egypt with such great power and with so strong a hand? Remember your servants Abraham, Isaac, and Israel, and how you swore to them by your own self, saying, 'I will make your descendants as numerous as the stars in the sky; and all this land that I promised, I will give your descendants as their perpetual heritage.'" So the LORD relented in the punishment he had threatened to inflict on his people.

RESPONSORIAL PSALM   *Psalm 51:3–4, 12–13, 17 and 19*

I will rise and go to my fa - ther.

Have mercy on me, O God,
    according to your merciful love;
according to your great compassion,
    blot out my transgressions.
Wash me completely from my iniquity,
    and cleanse me from my sin. ℟.

Create a pure heart for me, O God;
    renew a steadfast spirit within me.
Do not cast me away from your
    presence;
    take not your holy spirit from me. ℟.

O Lord, open my lips
and my mouth shall proclaim your
praise.

My sacrifice to God, a broken spirit:
a broken and humbled heart,
O God, you will not spurn. ℟.

READING II
1 Timothy 1:12–17

Beloved: I am grateful to him who has strengthened me, Christ Jesus our Lord, because he considered me trustworthy in appointing me to the ministry. I was once a blasphemer and a persecutor and arrogant, but I have been mercifully treated because I acted out of ignorance in my unbelief. Indeed, the grace of our Lord has been abundant, along with the faith and love that are in Christ Jesus. This saying is trustworthy and deserves full acceptance: Christ Jesus came into the world to save sinners. Of these I am the foremost. But for that reason I was mercifully treated, so that in me, as the foremost, Christ Jesus might display all his patience as an example for those who would come to believe in him for everlasting life. To the king of ages, incorruptible, invisible, the only God, honor and glory forever and ever. Amen.

GOSPEL
Luke 15:1–32 or 15:1–10

For short form read only the part in brackets.

[Tax collectors and sinners were all drawing near to listen to Jesus, but the Pharisees and scribes began to complain, saying, "This man welcomes sinners and eats with them." So to them he addressed this parable. "What man among you having a hundred sheep and losing one of them would not leave the ninety-nine in the desert and go after the lost one until he finds it? And when he does find it, he sets it on his shoulders with great joy and, upon his arrival home, he calls together his friends and neighbors and says to them, 'Rejoice with me because I have found my lost sheep.' I tell you, in just the same way there will be more joy in heaven over one sinner who repents than over ninety-nine righteous people who have no need of repentance.

"Or what woman having ten coins and losing one would not light a lamp and sweep the house, searching carefully until she finds it? And when she does find it, she calls together her friends and neighbors and says to them, 'Rejoice with me because I have found the coin that I lost.' In just the same way, I tell you, there will be rejoicing among the angels of God over one sinner who repents."]

Then he said, "A man had two sons, and the younger son said to his father, 'Father give me the share of your estate that should come to me.' So the father divided the property between them. After a few days, the younger son collected all his belongings and set off to a distant country where he squandered his inheritance on a life of dissipation. When he had freely spent everything, a severe famine struck that country, and he found himself in dire need. So he hired himself out to one of the local citizens who sent him to his farm to tend the swine. And he longed to eat his fill of the pods on which the swine fed, but nobody gave him any. Coming to his senses he thought, 'How many of my father's hired workers have more than enough food to eat, but here am I, dying from hunger. I shall get up and go to my father and I shall say to him, "Father, I have sinned against heaven and against you. I no longer deserve to be called your son; treat me as you would treat one of your hired workers."' So he got up and went back to his father. While he was still a long way off, his father caught sight of him, and was filled with compassion. He ran to his son, embraced him and kissed him. His son said to him, 'Father, I have sinned against heaven and against you; I no longer deserve to be called your son.' But his father ordered his servants, 'Quickly bring the finest robe and put it on him; put a ring on his finger and sandals on his feet. Take the fattened calf and slaughter it. Then let us celebrate with a feast, because this son of mine was dead, and has come to life again; he was lost, and has been found.' Then the celebration began. Now the older son had been out in the field and, on his way back, as he neared the house, he heard the sound of music and dancing. He called one of the servants and asked what this might mean. The servant said to him, 'Your brother has returned and your father has slaughtered the fattened calf because he has him back safe and sound.' He became angry, and when he refused to enter the house, his father came out and pleaded with him. He said to his father in reply, 'Look, all these years I served you and not once did I disobey your orders; yet you never gave me even a young goat to feast on with my friends. But when your son returns, who swallowed up your property with prostitutes, for him you slaughter the fattened calf.' He said to him, 'My son, you are here with me always; everything I have is yours. But now we must celebrate and rejoice, because your brother was dead and has come to life again; he was lost and has been found.'"

1266   TWENTY-FIFTH SUNDAY IN ORDINARY TIME / A

READING I   *Isaiah 55:6–9 / 133*

Seek the LORD while he may be found,
  call him while he is near.
Let the scoundrel forsake his way,
  and the wicked his thoughts;
let him turn to the LORD for mercy;
  to our God, who is generous in
    forgiving.
For my thoughts are not your thoughts,

nor are your ways my ways, says the
  LORD.
As high as the heavens are above the
  earth,
so high are my ways above your
  ways
and my thoughts above your
  thoughts.

RESPONSORIAL PSALM   *Psalm 145:2–3, 8–9, 17–18*

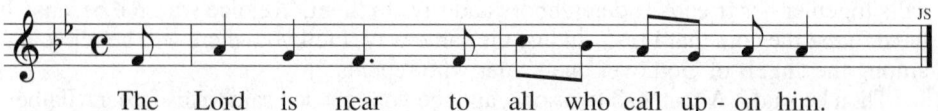

The Lord is near to all who call up-on him.

I will bless you day after day,
  and praise your name forever and
    ever.
The LORD is great and highly to be
    praised;
  his greatness cannot be measured. ℟.

The LORD is kind and full of compassion,
  slow to anger, abounding in mercy.

How good is the LORD to all,
  compassionate to all his creatures. ℟.

The LORD is just in all his ways,
  and holy in all his deeds.
The LORD is close to all who call him,
  who call on him in truth. ℟.

READING II   *Philippians 1:20c–24, 27a*

Brothers and sisters: Christ will be magnified in my body, whether by life or by death. For to me life is Christ, and death is gain. If I go on living in the flesh, that means fruitful labor for me. And I do not know which I shall choose. I am caught between the two. I long to depart this life and be with Christ, for that is far better. Yet that I remain in the flesh is more necessary for your benefit.

Only, conduct yourselves in a way worthy of the gospel of Christ.

GOSPEL   *Matthew 20:1–16a*

Jesus told his disciples this parable: "The kingdom of heaven is like a landowner who went out at dawn to hire laborers for his vineyard. After agreeing with them for the usual daily wage, he sent them into his vineyard. Going out about nine o'clock, the landowner saw others standing idle in the marketplace, and he said to them, 'You too go into my vineyard, and I will give you what is just.' So they went off. And he went out again around noon, and around three o'clock, and did likewise. Going out about five o'clock, the landowner found others standing around, and said to them, 'Why do you stand here idle all day?' They answered, 'Because no one has hired us.' He said to them, 'You too go into my vineyard.' When it was evening the owner of the vineyard said to his foreman, 'Summon the laborers and give them their pay, beginning with the last and ending with the first.' When those who had started about five o'clock came, each received the usual daily wage. So when the first came, they thought that they would receive more, but each of them also got the usual wage. And on receiving it they grumbled against the landowner, saying, 'These last ones worked only one hour, and you have made them equal to us, who bore the day's burden and the heat.' He said to one of them in reply, 'My friend, I am not cheating you. Did you not agree with me for the usual daily wage? Take what is yours and go. What if I wish to give this last one the same as you? Or am I not free to do as I wish with my own money? Are you envious because I am generous?' Thus, the last will be first, and the first will be last."

TWENTY-FIFTH SUNDAY IN ORDINARY TIME / B   1267

READING I   *Wisdom 2:12, 17–20 / 134*

The wicked say:
    Let us beset the just one, because he is obnoxious to us;
        he sets himself against our doings,
    reproaches us for transgressions of the law
        and charges us with violations of our training.
    Let us see whether his words be true;
        let us find out what will happen to him.
    For if the just one be the son of God, God will defend him
        and deliver him from the hand of his foes.
    With revilement and torture let us put the just one to the test
        that we may have proof of his gentleness
        and try his patience.
    Let us condemn him to a shameful death;
        for according to his own words, God will take care of him.

RESPONSORIAL PSALM *Psalm 54:3–4, 5, 6 and 8*

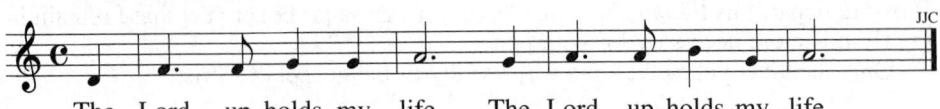

JJC

The Lord up-holds my life. The Lord up-holds my life.

O God, save me by your name;
   by your power, defend my cause.
O God, hear my prayer;
   give ear to the words of my mouth. ℟.

For the proud have risen against me,
   and the ruthless seek my life.
   They have no regard for God. ℟.

See, I have God for my help.
   The Lord sustains my soul.
I will sacrifice to you with willing
   heart,
   and praise your name, for it is
   good. ℟.

READING II *James 3:16—4:3*

Beloved: Where jealousy and selfish ambition exist, there is disorder and every foul practice. But the wisdom from above is first of all pure, then peaceable, gentle, compliant, full of mercy and good fruits, without inconstancy or insincerity. And the fruit of righteousness is sown in peace for those who cultivate peace.

Where do the wars and where do the conflicts among you come from? Is it not from your passions that make war within your members? You covet but do not possess. You kill and envy but you cannot obtain; you fight and wage war. You do not possess because you do not ask. You ask but do not receive, because you ask wrongly, to spend it on your passions.

GOSPEL *Mark 9:30–37*

Jesus and his disciples left from there and began a journey through Galilee, but he did not wish anyone to know about it. He was teaching his disciples and telling them, "The Son of Man is to be handed over to men and they will kill him, and three days after his death the Son of Man will rise." But they did not understand the saying, and they were afraid to question him.

They came to Capernaum and, once inside the house, he began to ask them, "What were you arguing about on the way?" But they remained silent. They had been discussing among themselves on the way who was the greatest. Then he sat down, called the Twelve, and said to them, "If anyone wishes to be first, he shall be the last of all and the servant of all." Taking a child, he placed it in the their midst, and putting his arms around it, he said to them, "Whoever receives one child such as this in my name, receives me; and whoever receives me, receives not me but the One who sent me."

1268 TWENTY-FIFTH SUNDAY IN ORDINARY TIME / C

READING I *Amos 8:4–7 / 135*

Hear this, you who trample upon the
   needy
   and destroy the poor of the land!
"When will the new moon be over,"
   you ask,

"that we may sell our grain,
   and the sabbath, that we may display
   the wheat?
We will diminish the ephah,
   add to the shekel,

and fix our scales for cheating!
We will buy the lowly for silver,
  and the poor for a pair of sandals;
  even the refuse of the wheat we will
    sell!"

The LORD has sworn by the pride of
    Jacob:
  Never will I forget a thing they
    have done!

RESPONSORIAL PSALM
Psalm 113:1–2, 4–6, 7–8

Or: Alleluia.

Praise the Lord who lifts up the poor.

Praise, O servants of the LORD,
  praise the name of the LORD!
May the name of the LORD be blest
  both now and forevermore! ℟.

High above all nations is the LORD,
  above the heavens his glory.
Who is like the LORD, our God,
  who dwells on high,

who lowers himself to look down
  upon heaven and earth? ℟.

From the dust he lifts up the lowly,
  from the ash heap he raises the
    poor,
to set them in the company of princes,
  yes, with the princes of his
    people. ℟.

READING II
1 Timothy 2:1–8

Beloved: First of all, I ask that supplications, prayers, petitions, and thanksgivings be offered for everyone, for kings and for all in authority, that we may lead a quiet and tranquil life in all devotion and dignity. This is good and pleasing to God our savior, who wills everyone to be saved and to come to knowledge of the truth.
  For there is one God.
  There is also one mediator between God and men,
  the man Christ Jesus,
  who gave himself as ransom for all.
This was the testimony at the proper time. For this I was appointed preacher and apostle —I am speaking the truth, I am not lying—, teacher of the Gentiles in faith and truth.
  It is my wish, then, that in every place the men should pray, lifting up holy hands, without anger or argument.

GOSPEL
Luke 16:1–13 or 16:10–13

For short form read only the parts in brackets.

[Jesus said to his disciples,] "A rich man had a steward who was reported to him for squandering his property. He summoned him and said, 'What is this I hear about you? Prepare a full account of your stewardship, because you can no longer be my steward.' The steward said to himself, 'What shall I do, now that my master is taking the position of steward away from me? I am not strong enough to dig and I am ashamed to beg. I know what I shall do so that, when I am removed from the stewardship, they may welcome me into their homes.' He called in his master's debtors one by one. To the first he said, 'How much do you owe my master?' He replied, 'One hundred measures of olive oil.' He said to him, 'Here is your promissory note. Sit down and quickly write one for fifty.' Then to another the steward said, 'And you, how much do you owe?' He replied, 'One hundred kors of wheat.' The steward said to him, 'Here is your promissory note; write one for eighty.' And the master commended that dishonest steward for acting prudently. "For the children of this world are more prudent in dealing with their own generation than are the children of light. I tell you, make friends for yourselves with dishonest wealth, so that when it fails, you will be welcomed into eternal dwellings. [The person who is trustworthy in very small matters is also trustworthy in great ones; and the person who is dishonest in very small matters is also dishonest in great ones. If, therefore, you are not trustworthy with dishonest wealth, who will trust you with true wealth? If you are not trustworthy with what belongs to another, who will give you what is yours? No servant can serve two masters. He will either hate one and love the other, or be devoted to one and despise the other. You cannot serve both God and mammon."]

1269 TWENTY-SIXTH SUNDAY IN ORDINARY TIME / A

READING I *Ezekiel 18:25–28 / 136*

Thus says the LORD: You say, "The LORD's way is not fair!" Hear now, house of Israel: Is it my way that is unfair, or rather, are not your ways unfair? When someone virtuous turns away from virtue to commit iniquity, and dies, it is because of the iniquity he committed that he must die. But if he turns from the wickedness he has committed, and does what is right and just, he shall preserve his life; since he has turned away from all the sins that he has committed, he shall surely live, he shall not die.

RESPONSORIAL PSALM *Psalm 25:4–5ab, 6–7, 8–9*

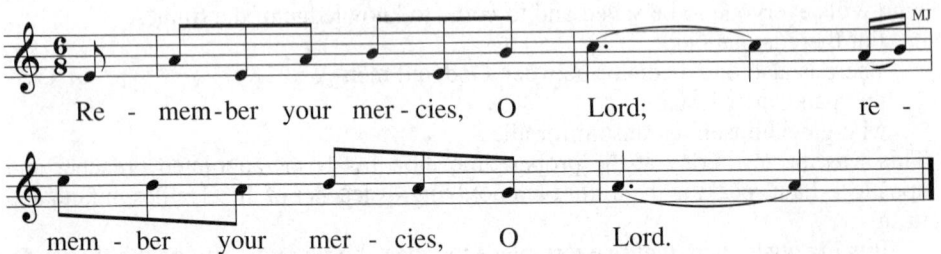

Re - mem-ber your mer - cies, O Lord; re -
mem - ber your mer - cies, O Lord.

O LORD, make me know your ways.
    Teach me your paths.
Guide me in your truth, and teach me;
    for you are the God of my salvation. ℟.

Remember your compassion, O LORD,
    and your merciful love,
    for they are from of old.
Do not remember the sins of my youth,
    nor my transgressions.

In your merciful love remember me,
    because of your goodness,
    O LORD. ℟.

Good and upright is the LORD;
    he shows the way to sinners.
He guides the humble in right judgment;
    to the humble he teaches his
    way. ℟.

READING II

Philippians 2:1–11 or 2:1–5

For short form read only the part in brackets.

[Brothers and sisters: If there is any encouragement in Christ, any solace in love, any participation in the Spirit, any compassion and mercy, complete my joy by being of the same mind, with the same love, united in heart, thinking one thing. Do nothing out of selfishness or out of vainglory; rather, humbly regard others as more important than yourselves, each looking out not for his own interests, but also for those of others.

Have in you the same attitude that is also in Christ Jesus,]

Who, though he was in the form of God,
did not regard equality with God
something to be grasped.
Rather, he emptied himself,
taking the form of a slave,
coming in human likeness;
and found human in appearance,
he humbled himself,
becoming obedient to the point of death,
even death on a cross.
Because of this, God greatly exalted him
and bestowed on him the name
which is above every name,
that at the name of Jesus
every knee should bend,
of those in heaven and on earth and under the earth,
and every tongue confess that
Jesus Christ is Lord,
to the glory of God the Father.

GOSPEL

Matthew 21:28–32

Jesus said to the chief priests and elders of the people: "What is your opinion? A man had two sons. He came to the first and said, 'Son, go out and work in the vineyard today.' He said in reply, 'I will not,' but afterwards changed his mind and went. The man came to the other son and gave the same order. He said in reply, 'Yes, sir,' but did not go. Which of the two did his father's will?" They answered, "The first." Jesus said to them, "Amen, I say to you, tax collectors and prostitutes are entering the kingdom of God before you. When John came to you in the way of righteousness, you did not believe him; but tax collectors and prostitutes did. Yet even when you saw that, you did not later change your minds and believe him."

TWENTY-SIXTH SUNDAY IN ORDINARY TIME / B   1270

READING I

Numbers 11:25–29 / 137

The LORD came down in the cloud and spoke to Moses. Taking some of the spirit that was on Moses, the LORD bestowed it on the seventy elders; and as the spirit came to rest on them, they prophesied.

Now two men, one named Eldad and the other Medad, were not in the gathering but had been left in the camp. They too had been on the list, but had not gone out to the tent; yet the spirit came to rest on them also, and they prophesied in the camp.

So, when a young man quickly told Moses, "Eldad and Medad are prophesying in the camp," Joshua, son of Nun, who from his youth had been Moses' aide, said, "Moses, my lord, stop them." But Moses answered him, "Are you jealous for my sake? Would that all the people of the LORD were prophets! Would that the LORD might bestow his spirit on them all!"

RESPONSORIAL PSALM   *Psalm 19:8, 10, 12–13, 14*

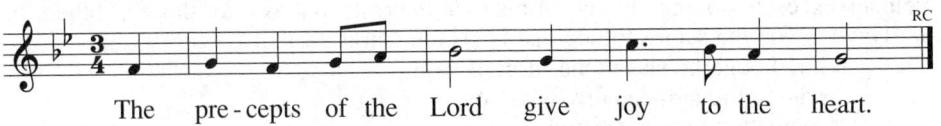

The pre-cepts of the Lord give joy to the heart.

The law of the LORD is perfect;
   it revives the soul.
The decrees of the LORD are steadfast;
   they give wisdom to the simple. ℟.

The fear of the LORD is pure,
   abiding forever.
The judgments of the LORD are true;
   they are, all of them, just. ℟.

So in them your servant finds
   instruction;
   great reward is in their keeping.
But who can detect their own errors?
   From hidden faults acquit me. ℟.

From presumption restrain your servant;
   may it not rule me.
Then shall I be blameless,
   clean from grave sin. ℟.

READING II   *James 5:1–6*

Come now, you rich, weep and wail over your impending miseries. Your wealth has rotted away, your clothes have become moth-eaten, your gold and silver have corroded, and that corrosion will be a testimony against you; it will devour your flesh like a fire. You have stored up treasure for the last days. Behold, the wages you withheld from the workers who harvested your fields are crying aloud; and the cries of the harvesters have reached the ears of the Lord of hosts. You have lived on earth in luxury and pleasure; you have fattened your hearts for the day of slaughter. You have condemned; you have murdered the righteous one; he offers you no resistance.

GOSPEL   *Mark 9:38–43, 45, 47–48*

At that time, John said to Jesus, "Teacher, we saw someone driving out demons in your name, and we tried to prevent him because he does not follow us." Jesus replied, "Do not prevent him. There is no one who performs a mighty deed in my name who can at the same time speak ill of me. For whoever is not against us is for us. Anyone who gives you a cup of water to drink because you belong to Christ, amen, I say to you, will surely not lose his reward.

   "Whoever causes one of these little ones who believe in me to sin, it would be better for him if a great millstone were put around his neck and he were thrown into the sea. If your hand causes you to sin, cut it off. It is better for you to enter into life maimed than with two hands to go into Gehenna, into the unquenchable fire. And if your foot causes you to sin, cut if off. It is better for you to enter into life crippled than with two feet to be thrown into Gehenna. And if your eye causes you to sin, pluck it out. Better for you to enter into the kingdom of God with one eye than with two eyes to be thrown into Gehenna, where 'their worm does not die, and the fire is not quenched.'"

TWENTY-SIXTH SUNDAY IN ORDINARY TIME / C   1271

READING I   *Amos 6:1a, 4–7 / 138*

Thus says the LORD the God of hosts:
Woe to the complacent in Zion!
Lying upon beds of ivory,
    stretched comfortably on their
    couches,
they eat lambs taken from the flock,
    and calves from the stall!
Improvising to the music of the harp,
    like David, they devise their own
    accompaniment.

They drink wine from bowls
    and anoint themselves with the best
    oils;
yet they are not made ill by the
    collapse of Joseph!
Therefore, now they shall be the first to
    go into exile,
    and their wanton revelry shall be
    done away with.

RESPONSORIAL PSALM   *Psalm 146:6c–7, 8–9a, 9bc–10*

Or: Alleluia.

Praise   the Lord,   my   soul!   Praise   the   Lord!

It is the LORD who preserves
    fidelity forever,
who does justice to those who are
    oppressed.
It is he who gives bread to the hungry,
    the LORD who sets prisoners free. ℟.

The LORD who opens the eyes of the blind,
    the LORD who raises up those who
    are bowed down.

It is the LORD who loves the just,
    the LORD who protects the
    stranger. ℟.

The LORD upholds the orphan and the
    widow,
    but thwarts the path of the wicked.
The LORD will reign forever,
    the God of Sion from age to age.
    Alleluia. ℟.

READING II   *1 Timothy 6:11–16*

But you, man of God, pursue righteousness, devotion, faith, love, patience, and gentleness. Compete well for the faith. Lay hold of eternal life, to which you were called when you made the noble confession in the presence of many witnesses. I charge you before God, who gives life to all things, and before Christ Jesus, who gave testimony under Pontius Pilate for the noble confession, to keep the commandment without stain or reproach until the appearance of our Lord Jesus Christ that the blessed and only ruler will make manifest at the proper time, the King of kings and Lord of lords, who alone has immortality, who dwells in unapproachable light, and whom no human being has seen or can see. To him be honor and eternal power. Amen.

GOSPEL   *Luke 16:19–31*

Jesus said to the Pharisees: "There was a rich man who dressed in purple garments and fine linen and dined sumptuously each day. And lying at his door was a poor man named Lazarus, covered with sores, who would gladly have eaten his fill of the scraps that fell from the rich man's table. Dogs even used to come and lick his sores. When the poor man died, he was carried away by angels to the bosom of Abraham. The rich man also died and was buried, and from the netherworld, where he was in torment, he raised his eyes and saw Abraham far off and Lazarus at his side. And he cried out, 'Father Abraham, have pity on me. Send Lazarus to dip the tip of his finger in water and cool my tongue, for I am suffering torment in these flames.' Abraham replied, 'My child, remember that you received what was good during your lifetime while Lazarus likewise received what was bad; but now he is comforted here, whereas you are tormented. Moreover, between us and you a great chasm is established to prevent anyone from crossing who might wish to go from our side to yours or from your side to ours.' He said, 'Then I beg you, father, send him to my father's house, for I have five brothers, so that he may warn them, lest they too come to this place of torment.' But Abraham replied, 'They have Moses and the prophets. Let them listen to them.' He said, 'Oh no, father Abraham, but if someone from the dead goes to them, they will repent.' Then Abraham said, 'If they will not listen to Moses and the prophets, neither will they be persuaded if someone should rise from the dead.'"

1272   TWENTY-SEVENTH SUNDAY IN ORDINARY TIME / A

READING I   *Isaiah 5:1–7 / 139*

Let me now sing of my friend,
  my friend's song concerning his
    vineyard.
My friend had a vineyard
  on a fertile hillside;
he spaded it, cleared it of stones,
  and planted the choicest vines;
within it he built a watchtower,
  and hewed out a wine press.
Then he looked for the crop of grapes,
  but what it yielded was wild grapes.

Now, inhabitants of Jerusalem and
    people of Judah,
  judge between me and my vineyard:
What more was there to do for my
    vineyard
  that I had not done?
Why, when I looked for the crop of grapes,

did it bring forth wild grapes?
Now, I will let you know
  what I mean to do with my vineyard:
take away its hedge, give it to grazing,
  break through its wall, let it be
    trampled!
Yes, I will make it a ruin:
  it shall not be pruned or hoed,
  but overgrown with thorns and
    briers;
I will command the clouds
  not to send rain upon it.
The vineyard of the LORD of hosts is the
    house of Israel,
  and the people of Judah are his
    cherished plant;
he looked for judgment, but see,
    bloodshed!
  for justice, but hark, the outcry!

RESPONSORIAL PSALM   *Psalm 80:9 and 12, 13–14, 15–16, 19–20*

RC

The vine-yard of the Lord is the house of Is - ra - el.

You brought a vine out of Egypt;
  you drove out the nations and
    planted it.
It stretched out its branches to the sea;
  to the River it stretched out its
    shoots. ℟.

Then why have you broken down its
    walls?
  It is plucked by all who pass by the
    way.
  It is ravaged by the boar of the forest,
  devoured by the beasts of the field. ℟.

God of hosts, turn again, we implore;
  look down from heaven and see.
Visit this vine and protect it,
    the vine your right hand has planted,
    the son of man you have claimed
      for yourself. ℟.

And we shall never forsake you again;
  give us life that we may call upon
  your name.
O Lord God of hosts, bring us back;
  let your face shine forth, and we
  shall be saved. ℟.

READING II   *Philippians 4:6–9*

Brothers and sisters: Have no anxiety at all, but in everything, by prayer and petition, with thanksgiving, make your requests known to God. Then the peace of God that surpasses all understanding will guard your hearts and minds in Christ Jesus.

Finally, brothers and sisters, whatever is true, whatever is honorable, whatever is just, whatever is pure, whatever is lovely, whatever is gracious, if there is any excellence and if there is anything worthy of praise, think about these things. Keep on doing what you have learned and received and heard and seen in me. Then the God of peace will be with you.

GOSPEL   *Matthew 21:33–43*

Jesus said to the chief priests and the elders of the people: "Hear another parable. There was a landowner who planted a vineyard, put a hedge around it, dug a wine press in it, and built a tower. Then he leased it to tenants and went on a journey. When vintage time drew near, he sent his servants to the tenants to obtain his produce. But the tenants seized the servants and one they beat, another they killed, and a third they stoned. Again he sent other servants, more numerous than the first ones, but they treated them in the same way. Finally, he sent his son to them, thinking, 'They will respect my son.' But when the tenants saw the son, they said to one another, 'This is the heir. Come, let us kill him and acquire his inheritance.' They seized him, threw him out of the vineyard, and killed him. What will the owner of the vineyard do to those tenants when he comes?" They answered him, "He will put those wretched men to a wretched death and lease his vineyard to other tenants who will give him the produce at the proper times." Jesus said to them, "Did you never read in the Scriptures:

The stone that the builders rejected
  has become the cornerstone;
by the Lord has this been done,
  and it is wonderful in our eyes?

Therefore, I say to you, the kingdom of God will be taken away from you and given to a people that will produce its fruit."

TWENTY-SEVENTH SUNDAY IN ORDINARY TIME / B   1273

READING I   *Genesis 2:18–24 / 140*

The Lord God said: "It is not good for the man to be alone. I will make a suitable partner for him." So the Lord God formed out of the ground various wild animals and various birds of the air, and he brought them to the man to see what he would call them; whatever the man called each of them would be its name. The man gave names to all the cattle, all the birds of the air, and all wild animals; but none proved to be the suitable partner for the man.

So the LORD God cast a deep sleep on the man, and while he was asleep, he took out one of his ribs and closed up its place with flesh. The LORD God then built up into a woman the rib that he had taken from the man. When he brought her to the man, the man said:

"This one, at last, is bone of my bones
    and flesh of my flesh;
this one shall be called 'woman,'
    for out of 'her man' this one has been taken."

That is why a man leaves his father and mother and clings to his wife, and the two of them become one flesh.

RESPONSORIAL PSALM   *Psalm 128:1–2, 3, 4–5, 6*

AGM

May the Lord bless and pro-tect us   all the   days of our lives.

Blessed are all who fear the LORD,
    and walk in his ways!
By the labor of your hands you shall eat.
    You will be blessed and prosper. ℟.

Your wife like a fruitful vine
    in the heart of your house;
your children like shoots of the olive
    around your table. ℟.

Indeed thus shall be blessed
    the man who fears the LORD.
May the LORD bless you from Sion.
    May you see Jerusalem prosper
    all the days of your life! ℟.

May you see your children's children.
    On Israel, peace! ℟.

READING II   *Hebrews 2:9–11*

Brothers and sisters: He "for a little while" was made "lower than the angels," that by the grace of God he might taste death for everyone.

For it was fitting that he, for whom and through whom all things exist, in bringing many children to glory, should make the leader to their salvation perfect through suffering. He who consecrates and those who are being consecrated all have one origin. Therefore, he is not ashamed to call them "brothers."

GOSPEL   *Mark 10:2–16 or 10:2–12*
For short form read only the part in brackets.

[The Pharisees approached Jesus and asked, "Is it lawful for a husband to divorce his wife?" They were testing him. He said to them in reply, "What did Moses command you?" They replied, "Moses permitted a husband to write a bill of divorce and dismiss her." But Jesus told them, "Because of the hardness of your hearts he wrote you this commandment. But from the beginning of creation, *God made them male and female. For this reason a man shall leave his father and mother and be joined to his wife, and the two shall become one flesh.* So they are no longer two but one flesh. Therefore what God has joined together, no human being must separate." In the house the disciples again questioned Jesus about this. He said to them, "Whoever divorces his wife and marries another commits adultery against her; and if she divorces her husband and marries another, she commits adultery."]

And people were bringing children to him that he might touch them, but the disciples rebuked them. When Jesus saw this he became indignant and said to them, "Let the children come to me; do not prevent them, for the kingdom of God belongs to such as these. Amen, I say to you, whoever does not accept the kingdom of God like a child will not enter it." Then he embraced them and blessed them, placing his hands on them.

TWENTY-SEVENTH SUNDAY IN ORDINARY TIME / C   1274

READING I
Habakkuk 1:2–3; 2:2–4 / 141

How long, O LORD? I cry for help
   but you do not listen!
I cry out to you, "Violence!"
   but you do not intervene.
Why do you let me see ruin;
   why must I look at misery?
Destruction and violence are before me;
   there is strife, and clamorous discord.
Then the LORD answered me and said:
   Write down the vision clearly upon
the tablets,
   so that one can read it readily.
For the vision still has its time,
   presses on to fulfillment, and will
   not disappoint;
if it delays, wait for it,
   it will surely come, it will not be late.
The rash one has no integrity;
   but the just one, because of his faith,
   shall live.

RESPONSORIAL PSALM
Psalm 95:1–2, 6–7c, 7d–9

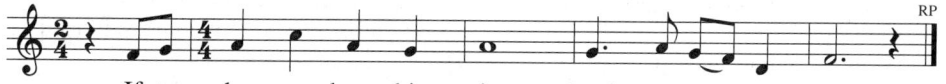

If to-day you hear his voice, hard-en not your hearts.

Come, let us ring out our joy to the
   LORD;
   hail the rock who saves us.
Let us come into his presence, giving
   thanks;
   let us hail him with a song of
   praise. ℟.

O come; let us bow and bend low.
   Let us kneel before the God who
   made us,
for he is our God and we
   the people who belong to his

pasture,
   the flock that is led by his hand. ℟.

O that today you would listen to his
   voice!
   "Harden not your hearts as at
   Meribah,
   as on that day at Massah in the
   desert
when your forebears put me to the test;
   when they tried me, though they
   saw my work." ℟.

READING II *2 Timothy 1:6–8, 13–14*

Beloved: I remind you to stir into flame the gift of God that you have through the imposition of my hands. For God did not give us a spirit of cowardice but rather of power and love and self-control. So do not be ashamed of your testimony to our Lord, nor of me, a prisoner for his sake; but bear your share of hardship for the gospel with the strength that comes from God.

Take as your norm the sound words that you heard from me, in the faith and love that are in Christ Jesus. Guard this rich trust with the help of the Holy Spirit that dwells within us.

GOSPEL *Luke 17:5–10*

The apostles said to the Lord, "Increase our faith." The Lord replied, "If you have faith the size of a mustard seed, you would say to this mulberry tree, 'Be uprooted and planted in the sea,' and it would obey you.

"Who among you would say to your servant who has just come in from plowing or tending sheep in the field, 'Come here immediately and take your place at table'? Would he not rather say to him, 'Prepare something for me to eat. Put on your apron and wait on me while I eat and drink. You may eat and drink when I am finished'? Is he grateful to that servant because he did what was commanded? So should it be with you. When you have done all you have been commanded, say, 'We are unprofitable servants; we have done what we were obliged to do.'"

1275 TWENTY-EIGHTH SUNDAY IN ORDINARY TIME / A

READING I *Isaiah 25:6–10a / 142*

On this mountain the Lord of hosts
    will provide for all peoples
a feast of rich food and choice wines,
    juicy, rich food and pure, choice
        wines.
On this mountain he will destroy
    the veil that veils all peoples,
the web that is woven over all nations;
    he will destroy death forever.
The Lord God will wipe away
    the tears from every face;
the reproach of his people he will

remove
from the whole earth; for the Lord
    has spoken.
On that day it will be said:
"Behold our God, to whom we looked to
    save us!
This is the Lord for whom we
    looked;
    let us rejoice and be glad that he has
        saved us!"
For the hand of the Lord will rest on
    this mountain.

RESPONSORIAL PSALM *Psalm 23:1–3a, 3b–4, 5, 6*

RJB

I shall live in the house of the Lord   all the   days of my life.

The Lord is my shepherd;
    there is nothing I shall want.
Fresh and green are the pastures

where he gives me repose.
Near restful waters he leads me;
he revives my soul. ℟.

He guides me along the right path,
for the sake of his name.
Though I should walk in the valley of
the shadow of death,
no evil would I fear, for you are
with me.
Your crook and your staff will give
me comfort. ℟.

You have prepared a table before me

in the sight of my foes.
My head you have anointed with oil;
my cup is overflowing. ℟.

Surely goodness and mercy shall
follow me
all the days of my life.
In the LORD's own house shall I dwell
for length of days unending. ℟.

READING II   *Philippians 4:12–14, 19–20*

Brothers and sisters: I know how to live in humble circumstances; I know also how
to live with abundance. In every circumstance and in all things I have learned the
secret of being well fed and of going hungry, of living in abundance and of being in
need. I can do all things in him who strengthens me. Still, it was kind of you to share
in my distress.

My God will fully supply whatever you need, in accord with his glorious riches
in Christ Jesus. To our God and Father, glory forever and ever. Amen.

GOSPEL   *Matthew 22:1–14 or 22:1–10*
For short form read only the part in brackets.

[Jesus again in reply spoke to the chief priests and elders of the people in parables,
saying, "The kingdom of heaven may be likened to a king who gave a wedding feast
for his son. He dispatched his servants to summon the invited guests to the feast,
but they refused to come. A second time he sent other servants, saying, 'Tell those
invited: "Behold, I have prepared my banquet, my calves and fattened cattle are
killed, and everything is ready; come to the feast."' Some ignored the invitation and
went away, one to his farm, another to his business. The rest laid hold of his servants,
mistreated them, and killed them. The king was enraged and sent his troops, destroyed
those murderers, and burned their city. Then he said to his servants, 'The feast is
ready, but those who were invited were not worthy to come. Go out, therefore, into
the main roads and invite to the feast whomever you find.' The servants went out into
the streets and gathered all they found, bad and good alike, and the hall was filled
with guests.] But when the king came in to meet the guests, he saw a man there not
dressed in a wedding garment. The king said to him, 'My friend, how is it that you
came in here without a wedding garment?' But he was reduced to silence. Then the
king said to his attendants, 'Bind his hands and feet, and cast him into the darkness
outside, where there will be wailing and grinding of teeth.' Many are invited, but few
are chosen."

TWENTY-EIGHTH SUNDAY IN ORDINARY TIME / B   1276

READING I   *Wisdom 7:7–11 / 143*

I prayed, and prudence was given me;
I pleaded, and the spirit of wisdom came to me.
I preferred her to scepter and throne,

and deemed riches nothing in comparison with her,
    nor did I liken any priceless gem to her;
because all gold, in view of her, is a little sand,
    and before her, silver is to be accounted mire.
Beyond health and comeliness I loved her,
and I chose to have her rather than the light,
    because the splendor of her never yields to sleep.
Yet all good things together came to me in her company,
    and countless riches at her hands.

RESPONSORIAL PSALM

Psalm 90:12–13, 14–15, 16–17

RJB

Fill us with your love, O Lord, and we will sing for joy!

Teach us to number our days,
    that we may gain wisdom of heart.
Turn back, O LORD! How long?
    Show pity to your servants. ℟.

At dawn, fill us with your merciful love;
    we shall exult and rejoice all our days.
Give us joy for the days of our affliction,
    for the years when we looked upon
        evil. ℟.

Let your deed be seen by your servants,
    and your glorious power by their
    children.
Let the favor of the Lord our God be
    upon us;
give success to the work of our
    hands.
O give success to the work of our
    hands. ℟.

READING II

Hebrews 4:12–13

Brothers and sisters: Indeed the word of God is living and effective, sharper than any two-edged sword, penetrating even between soul and spirit, joints and marrow, and able to discern reflections and thoughts of the heart. No creature is concealed from him, but everything is naked and exposed to the eyes of him to whom we must render an account.

GOSPEL

Mark 10:17–30 or 10:17–27

For short form read only the part in brackets.

[As Jesus was setting out on a journey, a man ran up, knelt down before him, and asked him, "Good teacher, what must I do to inherit eternal life?" Jesus answered him, "Why do you call me good? No one is good but God alone. You know the commandments: *You shall not kill; you shall not commit adultery; you shall not steal; you shall not bear false witness; you shall not defraud; honor your father and your mother.*" He replied and said to him, "Teacher, all of these I have observed from my youth." Jesus, looking at him, loved him and said to him, "You are lacking in one thing. Go, sell what you have, and give to the poor and you will have treasure in heaven; then come, follow me." At that statement his face fell, and he went away sad, for he had many possessions.

Jesus looked around and said to his disciples, "How hard it is for those who have wealth to enter the kingdom of God!" The disciples were amazed at his words. So Jesus again said to them in reply, "Children, how hard it is to enter the kingdom of God! It is easier for a camel to pass through the eye of a needle than for one who is rich to enter the kingdom of God." They were exceedingly astonished and said among themselves, "Then who can be saved?" Jesus looked at them and said, "For human beings it is impossible, but not for God. All things are possible for God."] Peter began to say to him, "We have given up everything and followed you." Jesus said, "Amen, I say to you, there is no one who has given up house or brothers or sisters or mother or father or children or lands for my sake and for the sake of the gospel who will not receive a hundred times more now in this present age: houses and brothers and sisters and mothers and children and lands, with persecutions, and eternal life in the age to come."

TWENTY-EIGHTH SUNDAY IN ORDINARY TIME / C   1277

READING I
2 Kings 5:14–17 / 144

Naaman went down and plunged into the Jordan seven times at the word of Elisha, the man of God. His flesh became again like the flesh of a little child, and he was clean of his leprosy.

Naaman returned with his whole retinue to the man of God. On his arrival he stood before Elisha and said, "Now I know that there is no God in all the earth, except in Israel. Please accept a gift from your servant."

Elisha replied, "As the LORD lives whom I serve, I will not take it;" and despite Naaman's urging, he still refused. Naaman said: "If you will not accept, please let me, your servant, have two mule-loads of earth, for I will no longer offer holocaust or sacrifice to any other god except to the LORD."

RESPONSORIAL PSALM
Psalm 98:1, 2–3ab, 3cd–4

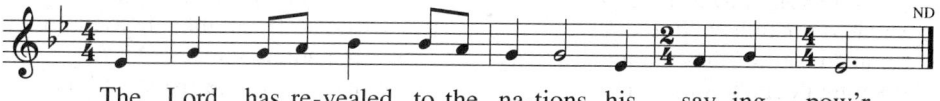

The Lord has re-vealed to the na-tions his sav-ing pow'r.

O sing a new song to the LORD,
    for he has worked wonders.
His right hand and his holy arm
    have brought salvation. ℟.

The LORD has made known his salvation,
    has shown his deliverance to the
      nations.
He has remembered his merciful love

and his truth for the house of
    Israel. ℟.

All the ends of the earth have seen
    the salvation of our God.
Shout to the LORD, all the earth;
    break forth into joyous song,
    and sing out your praise. ℟.

READING II
2 Timothy 2:8–13

Beloved: Remember Jesus Christ, raised from the dead, a descendant of David: such is my gospel, for which I am suffering, even to the point of chains, like a criminal. But the word of God is not chained. Therefore, I bear with everything for the sake of

those who are chosen, so that they too may obtain the salvation that is in Christ Jesus, together with eternal glory. This saying is trustworthy:
If we have died with him
we shall also live with him;
if we persevere
we shall also reign with him.
But if we deny him
he will deny us.
If we are unfaithful
he remains faithful,
for he cannot deny himself.

GOSPEL *Luke 17:11–19*

As Jesus continued his journey to Jerusalem, he traveled through Samaria and Galilee. As he was entering a village, ten lepers met him. They stood at a distance from him and raised their voices, saying, "Jesus, Master! Have pity on us!" And when he saw them, he said, "Go show yourselves to the priests." As they were going they were cleansed. And one of them, realizing he had been healed, returned, glorifying God in a loud voice; and he fell at the feet of Jesus and thanked him. He was a Samaritan. Jesus said in reply, "Ten were cleansed, were they not? Where are the other nine? Has none but this foreigner returned to give thanks to God?" Then he said to him, "Stand up and go; your faith has saved you."

1278 TWENTY-NINTH SUNDAY IN ORDINARY TIME / A

READING I *Isaiah 45:1, 4–6 / 145*

Thus says the LORD to his anointed,
Cyrus,
whose right hand I grasp,
subduing nations before him,
and making kings run in his service,
opening doors before him
and leaving the gates unbarred:
For the sake of Jacob, my servant,
of Israel, my chosen one,
I have called you by your name,
giving you a title, though you

knew me not.
I am the LORD and there is no other,
there is no God besides me.
It is I who arm you, though you know
me not,
so that toward the rising and the
setting of the sun
people may know that there is none
besides me.
I am the LORD, there is no other.

RESPONSORIAL PSALM *Psalm 96:1 and 3, 4–5, 7–8, 9–10a and c*

Give the Lord glo - ry, glo-ry and hon - or.

O sing a new song to the LORD;
sing to the LORD, all the earth.
Tell among the nations his glory,

and his wonders among all the
peoples. ℟.

For the LORD is great and highly to be
  praised,
to be feared above all gods.
For the gods of the nations are naught.
  It was the LORD who made the
  heavens. ℟.

Give the LORD, you families of peoples,
  give the LORD glory and power;

give the LORD the glory of his name.
  Bring an offering and enter his
  courts. ℟.

Worship the LORD in holy splendor.
  O tremble before him, all the earth.
  Say to the nations, "The LORD is king."
  He will judge the peoples in
  fairness. ℟.

READING II   *1 Thessalonians 1:1–5b*

Paul, Silvanus, and Timothy to the church of the Thessalonians in God the Father and
the Lord Jesus Christ: grace to you and peace. We give thanks to God always for all
of you, remembering you in our prayers, unceasingly calling to mind your work of
faith and labor of love and endurance in hope of our Lord Jesus Christ, before our
God and Father, knowing, brothers and sisters loved by God, how you were chosen.
For our gospel did not come to you in word alone, but also in power and in the Holy
Spirit and with much conviction.

GOSPEL   *Matthew 22:15–21*

The Pharisees went off and plotted how they might entrap Jesus in speech. They sent
their disciples to him, with the Herodians, saying, "Teacher, we know that you are a
truthful man and that you teach the way of God in accordance with the truth. And you
are not concerned with anyone's opinion, for you do not regard a person's status. Tell
us, then, what is your opinion: Is it lawful to pay the census tax to Caesar or not?"
Knowing their malice, Jesus said, "Why are you testing me, you hypocrites? Show
me the coin that pays the census tax." Then they handed him the Roman coin. He said
to them, "Whose image is this and whose inscription?" They replied, "Caesar's." At
that he said to them, "Then repay to Caesar what belongs to Caesar and to God what
belongs to God."

TWENTY-NINTH SUNDAY IN ORDINARY TIME / B   1279

READING I   *Isaiah 53:10–11 / 146*

The LORD was pleased
  to crush him in infirmity.

If he gives his life as an offering
    for sin,
  he shall see his descendants in a
    long life,
  and the will of the LORD shall be

accomplished through him.

Because of his affliction
  he shall see the light in fullness
    of days;
through his suffering, my servant shall
    justify many,
  and their guilt he shall bear.

RESPONSORIAL PSALM   *Psalm 33:4–5, 18–19, 20 and 22*

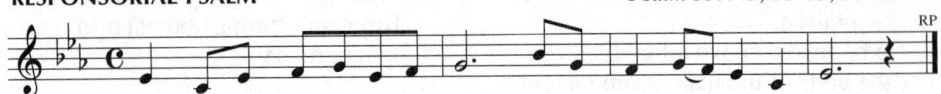

Lord, let your mer-cy be on us,   as we place our trust in you.

The word of the LORD is faithful,
   and all his works to be trusted.
The LORD loves justice and right,
   and his merciful love fills the earth. ℟.

Yes, the LORD's eyes are on those who
   fear him,
   who hope in his merciful love,

to rescue their souls from death,
   to keep them alive in famine. ℟.

Our soul is waiting for the LORD.
   He is our help and our shield.
May your merciful love be upon us,
   as we hope in you, O LORD. ℟.

READING II   *Hebrews 4:14–16*
Brothers and sisters: Since we have a great high priest who has passed through the heavens, Jesus, the Son of God, let us hold fast to our confession. For we do not have a high priest who is unable to sympathize with our weaknesses, but one who has similarly been tested in every way, yet without sin. So let us confidently approach the throne of grace to receive mercy and to find grace for timely help.

GOSPEL   *Mark 10:35–45 or 10:42–45*
For short form read only the part in brackets.

James and John, the sons of Zebedee, came to Jesus and said to him, "Teacher, we want you to do for us whatever we ask of you." He replied, "What do you wish me to do for you?" They answered him, "Grant that in your glory we may sit one at your right and the other at your left." Jesus said to them, "You do not know what you are asking. Can you drink the cup that I drink or be baptized with the baptism with which I am baptized?" They said to him, "We can." Jesus said to them, "The cup that I drink, you will drink, and with the baptism with which I am baptized, you will be baptized; but to sit at my right or at my left is not mine to give but is for those for whom it has been prepared." When the ten heard this, they became indignant at James and John. [Jesus summoned *them and said to them, "You know that those who are recognized as rulers over the Gentiles lord it over them, and their great ones make their authority over them felt. But it shall not be so among you. Rather, whoever wishes to be great among you will be your servant; whoever wishes to be first among you will be the slave of all. For the Son of Man did not come to be served but to serve and to give his life as a ransom for many."]

In the short form: the Twelve

1280 TWENTY-NINTH SUNDAY IN ORDINARY TIME / C

READING I   *Exodus 17:8–13 / 147*
In those days, Amalek came and waged war against Israel. Moses, therefore, said to Joshua, "Pick out certain men, and tomorrow go out and engage Amalek in battle. I will be standing on top of the hill with the staff of God in my hand." So Joshua did as Moses told him: he engaged Amalek in battle after Moses had climbed to the top of the hill with Aaron and Hur. As long as Moses kept his hands raised up, Israel had

the better of the fight, but when he let his hands rest, Amalek had the better of the fight. Moses' hands, however, grew tired; so they put a rock in place for him to sit on. Meanwhile Aaron and Hur supported his hands, one on one side and one on the other, so that his hands remained steady till sunset. And Joshua mowed down Amalek and his people with the edge of the sword.

RESPONSORIAL PSALM   *Psalm 121:1–2, 3–4, 5–6, 7–8*

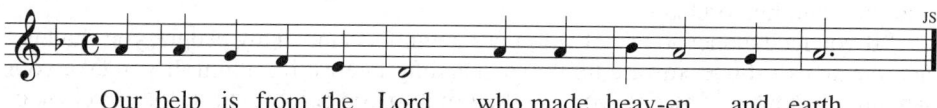

Our help is from the Lord   who made heav-en   and earth.

I lift up my eyes to the mountains;
    from where shall come my help?
My help shall come from the LORD,
    who made heaven and earth. ℟.

    your shade
    at your right hand.
By day the sun shall not smite you,
    nor the moon in the night. ℟.

He will keep your foot from stumbling.
    Your guard will never slumber.
No, he sleeps not nor slumbers,
    Israel's guard. ℟.

The LORD will guard you from evil;
    he will guard your soul.
The LORD will guard your going and
    coming,
    both now and forever. ℟.

The LORD your guard, the LORD

READING II   *2 Timothy 3:14—4:2*
Beloved: Remain faithful to what you have learned and believed, because you know from whom you learned it, and that from infancy you have known the sacred Scriptures, which are capable of giving you wisdom for salvation through faith in Christ Jesus. All Scripture is inspired by God and is useful for teaching, for refutation, for correction, and for training in righteousness, so that one who belongs to God may be competent, equipped for every good work.

    I charge you in the presence of God and of Christ Jesus, who will judge the living and the dead, and by his appearing and his kingly power: proclaim the word; be persistent whether it is convenient or inconvenient; convince, reprimand, encourage through all patience and teaching.

GOSPEL   *Luke 18:1–8*
Jesus told his disciples a parable about the necessity for them to pray always without becoming weary. He said, "There was a judge in a certain town who neither feared God nor respected any human being. And a widow in that town used to come to him and say, 'Render a just decision for me against my adversary.' For a long time the judge was unwilling, but eventually he thought, 'While it is true that I neither fear God nor respect any human being, because this widow keeps bothering me I shall deliver a just decision for her lest she finally come and strike me.'" The Lord said, "Pay attention to what the dishonest judge says. Will not God then secure the rights of his chosen ones who call out to him day and night? Will he be slow to answer them? I tell you, he will see to it that justice is done for them speedily. But when the Son of Man comes, will he find faith on earth?"

1281   THIRTIETH SUNDAY IN ORDINARY TIME / A

READING I   *Exodus 22:20–26 / 148*

Thus says the LORD: "You shall not molest or oppress an alien, for you were once aliens yourselves in the land of Egypt. You shall not wrong any widow or orphan. If ever you wrong them and they cry out to me, I will surely hear their cry. My wrath will flare up, and I will kill you with the sword; then your own wives will be widows, and your children orphans.

"If you lend money to one of your poor neighbors among my people, you shall not act like an extortioner toward him by demanding interest from him. If you take your neighbor's cloak as a pledge, you shall return it to him before sunset; for this cloak of his is the only covering he has for his body. What else has he to sleep in? If he cries out to me, I will hear him; for I am compassionate."

RESPONSORIAL PSALM   *Psalm 18:2–3a, 3bc–4, 47 and 51ab*

I love you, I love you, Lord, my strength.

I love you, LORD, my strength;
  O LORD, my rock, my fortress,
    my savior. ℟.

My God, my rock where I take refuge;
  my shield, my saving strength, my
    stronghold.
I cry out, "Praised be the LORD!"
  and see, I am saved from my foes. ℟.

The LORD lives, and blest be my Rock!
  May the God of my salvation be
    exalted.
The LORD gives great victories to his
  king,
and shows merciful love for his
  anointed. ℟.

READING II   *1 Thessalonians 1:5c–10*

Brothers and sisters: You know what sort of people we were among you for your sake. And you became imitators of us and of the Lord, receiving the word in great affliction, with joy from the Holy Spirit, so that you became a model for all the believers in Macedonia and in Achaia. For from you the word of the Lord has sounded forth not only in Macedonia and in Achaia, but in every place your faith in God has gone forth, so that we have no need to say anything. For they themselves openly declare about us what sort of reception we had among you, and how you turned to God from idols to serve the living and true God and to await his Son from heaven, whom he raised from the dead, Jesus, who delivers us from the coming wrath.

GOSPEL   *Matthew 22:34–40*

When the Pharisees heard that Jesus had silenced the Sadducees, they gathered together, and one of them, a scholar of the law, tested him by asking, "Teacher, which commandment in the law is the greatest?" He said to him, "You shall love the Lord, your God, with all your heart, with all your soul, and with all your mind. This is the greatest and the first commandment. The second is like it: You shall love your neighbor as yourself. The whole law and the prophets depend on these two commandments."

THIRTIETH SUNDAY IN ORDINARY TIME / B 1282

READING I

Jeremiah 31:7–9 / 149

Thus says the LORD:
Shout with joy for Jacob,
    exult at the head of the nations;
    proclaim your praise and say:
The LORD has delivered his people,
    the remnant of Israel.
Behold, I will bring them back
    from the land of the north;
I will gather them from the ends of the
    world,
    with the blind and the lame in their
    midst,

the mothers and those with child;
    they shall return as an immense
    throng.
They departed in tears,
    but I will console them and guide
    them;
I will lead them to brooks of water,
    on a level road, so that none shall
    stumble.
For I am a father to Israel,
Ephraim is my first-born.

RESPONSORIAL PSALM

Psalm 126:1–2ab, 2cd–3, 4–5, 6

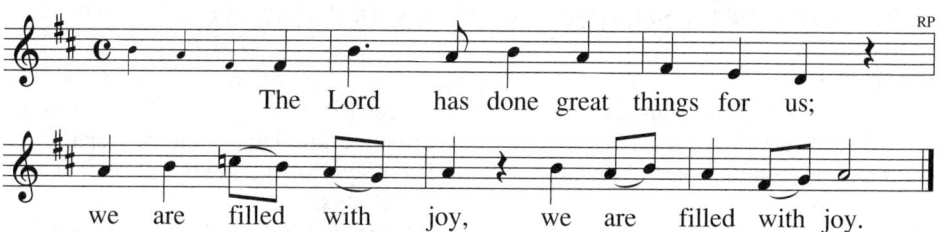

The Lord has done great things for us;
we are filled with joy, we are filled with joy.

When the LORD brought back the
    exiles of Sion,
we thought we were dreaming.
Then was our mouth filled with laughter;
    on our tongues, songs of joy. ℟.

Then the nations themselves said,
    "What great deeds
the LORD worked for them!"
What great deeds the LORD worked for us!
    Indeed, we were glad. ℟.

Bring back our exiles, O LORD,
    as streams in the south.
Those who are sowing in tears
    will sing when they reap. ℟.

They go out, they go out, full of tears,
    bearing seed for the sowing;
they come back, they come back with
    a song,
bearing their sheaves. ℟.

READING II

Hebrews 5:1–6

Brothers and sisters: Every high priest is taken from among men and made their representative before God, to offer gifts and sacrifices for sins. He is able to deal patiently with the ignorant and erring, for he himself is beset by weakness and so, for this reason, must make sin offerings for himself as well as for the people. No one takes this honor upon himself but only when called by God, just as Aaron was. In the same way, it was not Christ who glorified himself in becoming high priest, but rather the one who said to him:

You are my son:
    this day I have begotten you;

just as he says in another place:
*You are a priest forever
according to the order of Melchizedek.*

GOSPEL
Mark 10:46–52

As Jesus was leaving Jericho with his disciples and a sizable crowd, Bartimaeus, a blind man, the son of Timaeus, sat by the roadside begging. On hearing that it was Jesus of Nazareth, he began to cry out and say, "Jesus, son of David, have pity on me." And many rebuked him, telling him to be silent. But he kept calling out all the more, "Son of David, have pity on me." Jesus stopped and said, "Call him." So they called the blind man, saying to him, "Take courage; get up, Jesus is calling you." He threw aside his cloak, sprang up, and came to Jesus. Jesus said to him in reply, "What do you want me to do for you?" The blind man replied to him, "Master, I want to see." Jesus told him, "Go your way; your faith has saved you." Immediately he received his sight and followed him on the way.

1283 THIRTIETH SUNDAY IN ORDINARY TIME / C

READING I
Sirach 35:12–14, 16–18 / 150

The LORD is a God of justice,
who knows no favorites.
Though not unduly partial toward the weak,
yet he hears the cry of the oppressed.
The Lord is not deaf to the wail of the orphan,
nor to the widow when she pours out her complaint.
The one who serves God willingly is heard;
his petition reaches the heavens.
The prayer of the lowly pierces the clouds;
it does not rest till it reaches its goal,
nor will it withdraw till the Most High responds,
judges justly and affirms the right,
and the Lord will not delay.

RESPONSORIAL PSALM
Psalm 34:2–3, 17–18, 19 and 23

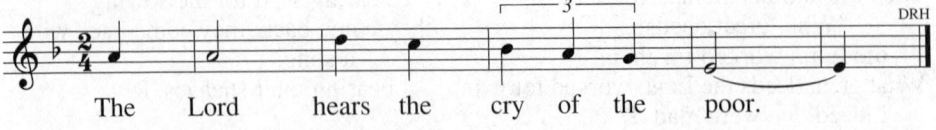

The Lord hears the cry of the poor.

I will bless the LORD at all times;
praise of him is always in my mouth.
In the LORD my soul shall make its boast;
the humble shall hear and be glad. ℟.

The LORD turns his face against the wicked
to destroy their remembrance from the earth.
When the just cry out, the LORD hears,
and rescues them in all their distress. ℟.

The LORD is close to the brokenhearted;
those whose spirit is crushed he will save.
The LORD ransoms the souls of his servants.
All who trust in him shall not be condemned. ℟.

READING II   *2 Timothy 4:6–8, 16–18*

Beloved: I am already being poured out like a libation, and the time of my departure is at hand. I have competed well; I have finished the race; I have kept the faith. From now on the crown of righteousness awaits me, which the Lord, the just judge, will award to me on that day, and not only to me, but to all who have longed for his appearance.

At my first defense no one appeared on my behalf, but everyone deserted me. May it not be held against them! But the Lord stood by me and gave me strength, so that through me the proclamation might be completed and all the Gentiles might hear it. And I was rescued from the lion's mouth. The Lord will rescue me from every evil threat and will bring me safe to his heavenly kingdom. To him be glory forever and ever. Amen.

GOSPEL   *Luke 18:9–14*

Jesus addressed this parable to those who were convinced of their own righteousness and despised everyone else. "Two people went up to the temple area to pray; one was a Pharisee and the other was a tax collector. The Pharisee took up his position and spoke this prayer to himself, 'O God, I thank you that I am not like the rest of humanity—greedy, dishonest, adulterous—or even like this tax collector. I fast twice a week, and I pay tithes on my whole income.' But the tax collector stood off at a distance and would not even raise his eyes to heaven but beat his breast and prayed, 'O God, be merciful to me a sinner.' I tell you, the latter went home justified, not the former; for whoever exalts himself will be humbled, and the one who humbles himself will be exalted."

THIRTY-FIRST SUNDAY IN ORDINARY TIME / A   1284

READING I   *Malachi 1:14b–2:2b, 8–10 / 151*

A great King am I, says the LORD
    of hosts,
    and my name will be feared
    among the nations.
And now, O priests, this
    commandment is for you:
    If you do not listen,
if you do not lay it to heart,
    to give glory to my name, says
    the LORD of hosts,
I will send a curse upon you
    and of your blessing I will make
    a curse.
You have turned aside from the way,

and have caused many to falter by
    your instruction;
you have made void the covenant of
    Levi,
    says the LORD of hosts.
I, therefore, have made you contemptible
    and base before all the people,
since you do not keep my ways,
    but show partiality in your decisions.
Have we not all the one father?
    Has not the one God created us?
Why then do we break faith with one
    another,
    violating the covenant of our fathers?

RESPONSORIAL PSALM   *Psalm 131:1, 2, 3*

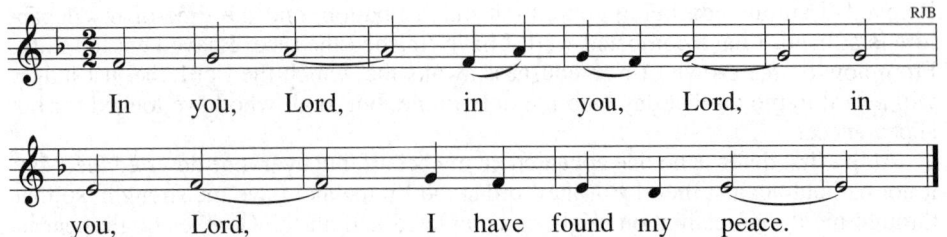

In you, Lord, in you, Lord, in you, Lord, I have found my peace.

O LORD, my heart is not proud,
  nor haughty my eyes.
I have not gone after things too great,
  nor marvels beyond me. ℟.

Truly, I have set my soul
  in tranquility and silence.

As a weaned child on its mother,
  as a weaned child is my soul within
  me. ℟.

O Israel, wait for the LORD,
  both now and forever. ℟.

READING II   *1 Thessalonians 2:7b–9, 13*

Brothers and sisters: We were gentle among you, as a nursing mother cares for her children. With such affection for you, we were determined to share with you not only the gospel of God, but our very selves as well, so dearly beloved had you become to us. You recall, brothers and sisters, our toil and drudgery. Working night and day in order not to burden any of you, we proclaimed to you the gospel of God.

And for this reason we too give thanks to God unceasingly, that, in receiving the word of God from hearing us, you received not a human word but, as it truly is, the word of God, which is now at work in you who believe.

GOSPEL   *Matthew 23:1–12*

Jesus spoke to the crowds and to his disciples, saying, "The scribes and the Pharisees have taken their seat on the chair of Moses. Therefore, do and observe all things whatsoever they tell you, but do not follow their example. For they preach but they do not practice. They tie up heavy burdens hard to carry and lay them on people's shoulders, but they will not lift a finger to move them. All their works are performed to be seen. They widen their phylacteries and lengthen their tassels. They love places of honor at banquets, seats of honor in synagogues, greetings in marketplaces, and the salutation 'Rabbi.' As for you, do not be called 'Rabbi.' You have but one teacher, and you are all brothers. Call no one on earth your father; you have but one Father in heaven. Do not be called 'Master'; you have but one master, the Christ. The greatest among you must be your servant. Whoever exalts himself will be humbled; but whoever humbles himself will be exalted."

1285 THIRTY-FIRST SUNDAY IN ORDINARY TIME / B

READING I   *Deuteronomy 6:2–6 / 152*

Moses spoke to the people, saying: "Fear the LORD, your God, and keep, throughout the days of your lives, all his statutes and commandments which I enjoin on you, and thus have long life. Hear then, Israel, and be careful to observe them, that you may grow and prosper the more, in keeping with the promise of the LORD, the God of your fathers, to give you a land flowing with milk and honey.

"Hear, O Israel! The LORD is our God, the LORD alone! Therefore, you shall love the LORD, your God, with all your heart, and with all your soul, and with all your strength. Take to heart these words which I enjoin on you today."

RESPONSORIAL PSALM   *Psalm 18:2–3a, 3bc–4, 47 and 51ab*

I love you, I love you, Lord, my strength.

I love you, LORD, my strength;
 O LORD, my rock, my fortress,
  my savior. ℟.

My God, my rock where I take refuge;
 my shield, my saving strength, my
  stronghold.
I cry out, "Praised be the LORD!"
 and see, I am saved from my foes. ℟.

The LORD lives, and blest be my Rock!
 May the God of my salvation be
  exalted.
The LORD gives great victories to his
  king,
 and shows merciful love for his
  anointed. ℟.

READING II   *Hebrews 7:23–28*

Brothers and sisters: The levitical priests were many because they were prevented by death from remaining in office, but Jesus, because he remains forever, has a priesthood that does not pass away. Therefore, he is always able to save those who approach God through him, since he lives forever to make intercession for them.

It was fitting that we should have such a high priest: holy, innocent, undefiled, separated from sinners, higher than the heavens. He has no need, as did the high priests, to offer sacrifice day after day, first for his own sins and then for those of the people; he did that once for all when he offered himself. For the law appoints men subject to weakness to be high priests, but the word of the oath, which was taken after the law, appoints a son, who has been made perfect forever.

GOSPEL   *Mark 12:28b–34*

One of the scribes came to Jesus and asked him, "Which is the first of all the commandments?" Jesus replied, "The first is this: *Hear, O Israel! The Lord our God is Lord alone! You shall love the Lord your God with all your heart, with all your soul, with all your mind, and with all your strength.* The second is this: *You shall love your neighbor as yourself.* There is no other commandment greater than these." The scribe said to him, "Well said, teacher. You are right in saying, 'He is One and there is no other than he.' And 'to love him with all your heart, with all your understanding, with all your strength, and to love your neighbor as yourself' is worth more than all burnt offerings and sacrifices." And when Jesus saw that he answered with understanding, he said to him, "You are not far from the kingdom of God." And no one dared to ask him any more questions.

1286   THIRTY-FIRST SUNDAY IN ORDINARY TIME / C

READING I   *Wisdom 11:22—12:2 / 153*

Before the Lord the whole universe is as a grain
    from a balance
  or a drop of morning dew come down upon the earth.
But you have mercy on all, because you can do all things;
  and you overlook people's sins that they may repent.
For you love all things that are
  and loathe nothing that you have made;
  for what you hated, you would not have fashioned.
And how could a thing remain, unless you willed it;
  or be preserved, had it not been called forth by you?
But you spare all things, because they are yours,
  O Lord and lover of souls,
  for your imperishable spirit is in all things!
Therefore you rebuke offenders little by little,
  warn them and remind them of the sins
    they are committing,
  that they may abandon their wickedness
    and believe in you, O Lord!

RESPONSORIAL PSALM   *Psalm 145:1–2, 8–9, 10–11, 13cd–14*

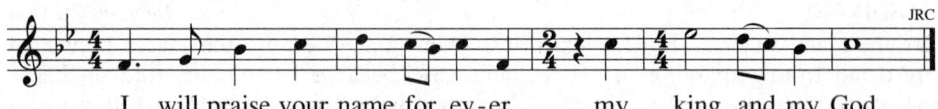

I will praise your name for ev-er, my king and my God.

I will extol you, my God and king,
  and bless your name forever and
    ever.
I will bless you day after day,
  and praise your name forever and
    ever. ℟.

The Lord is kind and full of
  compassion,
  slow to anger, abounding in mercy.
How good is the Lord to all,
  compassionate to all his creatures. ℟.

All your works shall thank you, O
  Lord,
  and all your faithful ones bless you.
They shall speak of the glory of your
  reign,
  and declare your mighty deeds. ℟.

The Lord is faithful in all his words,
  and holy in all his deeds.
The Lord supports all who fall,
  and raises up all who are bowed
  down. ℟.

READING II   *2 Thessalonians 1:11—2:2*

Brothers and sisters: We always pray for you, that our God may make you worthy of
his calling and powerfully bring to fulfillment every good purpose and every effort
of faith, that the name of our Lord Jesus may be glorified in you, and you in him, in
accord with the grace of our God and Lord Jesus Christ.

    We ask you, brothers and sisters, with regard to the coming of our Lord Jesus
Christ and our assembling with him, not to be shaken out of your minds suddenly, or
to be alarmed either by a "spirit," or by an oral statement, or by a letter allegedly from
us to the effect that the day of the Lord is at hand.

GOSPEL   *Luke 19:1–10*

At that time, Jesus came to Jericho and intended to pass through the town. Now a man there named Zacchaeus, who was a chief tax collector and also a wealthy man, was seeking to see who Jesus was; but he could not see him because of the crowd, for he was short in stature. So he ran ahead and climbed a sycamore tree in order to see Jesus, who was about to pass that way. When he reached the place, Jesus looked up and said, "Zacchaeus, come down quickly, for today I must stay at your house." And he came down quickly and received him with joy. When they all saw this, they began to grumble, saying, "He has gone to stay at the house of a sinner." But Zacchaeus stood there and said to the Lord, "Behold, half of my possessions, Lord, I shall give to the poor, and if I have extorted anything from anyone I shall repay it four times over." And Jesus said to him, "Today salvation has come to this house because this man too is a descendant of Abraham. For the Son of Man has come to seek and to save what was lost."

THIRTY-SECOND SUNDAY IN ORDINARY TIME / A   1287

READING I   *Wisdom 6:12–16 / 154*

Resplendent and unfading is wisdom,
　and she is readily perceived by
　　those who love her,
　and found by those who seek her.
She hastens to make herself known
　in anticipation of their desire;
　whoever watches for her at dawn
　　shall not be disappointed,
　for he shall find her sitting by his
　　gate.

For taking thought of wisdom is the
　perfection of prudence,
　and whoever for her sake keeps vigil
　shall quickly be free from care;
because she makes her own rounds,
　seeking those worthy of her,
　and graciously appears to them in
　　the ways,
　and meets them with all solicitude.

RESPONSORIAL PSALM   *Psalm 63:2, 3–4, 5–6, 7–8*

My soul is thirst-ing for you, O Lord, thirst-ing for you my God.

O God, you are my God; at dawn I seek
　you;
　for you my soul is thirsting.
For you my flesh is pining,
　like a dry, weary land without
　　water. ℟.

I have come before you in the sanctuary,
　to behold your strength and your
　　glory.
Your loving mercy is better than life;
　my lips will speak your praise. ℟.

I will bless you all my life;
    in your name I will lift up my hands.
My soul shall be filled as with a
        banquet;
    with joyful lips, my mouth shall
        praise you. ℟.

When I remember you upon my bed,
    I muse on you through the watches
        of the night.
For you have been my strength;
    in the shadow of your wings I
        rejoice. ℟.

READING II   *1 Thessalonians 4:13–18 or 4:13–14*
For short form read only the part in brackets.

[We do not want you to be unaware, brothers and sisters, about those who have fallen asleep, so that you may not grieve like the rest, who have no hope. For if we believe that Jesus died and rose, so too will God, through Jesus, bring with him those who have fallen asleep.] Indeed, we tell you this, on the word of the Lord, that we who are alive, who are left until the coming of the Lord, will surely not precede those who have fallen asleep. For the Lord himself, with a word of command, with the voice of an archangel and with the trumpet of God, will come down from heaven, and the dead in Christ will rise first. Then we who are alive, who are left, will be caught up together with them in the clouds to meet the Lord in the air. Thus we shall always be with the Lord. Therefore, console one another with these words.

GOSPEL   *Matthew 25:1–13*
Jesus told his disciples this parable: "The kingdom of heaven will be like ten virgins who took their lamps and went out to meet the bridegroom. Five of them were foolish and five were wise. The foolish ones, when taking their lamps, brought no oil with them, but the wise brought flasks of oil with their lamps. Since the bridegroom was long delayed, they all became drowsy and fell asleep. At midnight, there was a cry, 'Behold, the bridegroom! Come out to meet him!' Then all those virgins got up and trimmed their lamps. The foolish ones said to the wise, 'Give us some of your oil, for our lamps are going out.' But the wise ones replied, 'No, for there may not be enough for us and you. Go instead to the merchants and buy some for yourselves.' While they went off to buy it, the bridegroom came and those who were ready went into the wedding feast with him. Then the door was locked. Afterwards the other virgins came and said, 'Lord, Lord, open the door for us!' But he said in reply, 'Amen, I say to you, I do not know you.' Therefore, stay awake, for you know neither the day nor the hour."

1288   THIRTY-SECOND SUNDAY IN ORDINARY TIME / B

READING I   *1 Kings 17:10–16 / 155*
In those days, Elijah the prophet went to Zarephath. As he arrived at the entrance of the city, a widow was gathering sticks there; he called out to her, "Please bring me a small cupful of water to drink." She left to get it, and he called out after her, "Please bring along a bit of bread." She answered, "As the LORD, your God, lives, I have nothing baked; there is only a handful of flour in my jar and a little oil in my jug. Just now I was collecting a couple of sticks, to go in and prepare something for myself and my son; when we have eaten it, we shall die." Elijah said to her, "Do not be afraid. Go and do as you propose. But first make me a little cake and bring it to me. Then you can prepare something for yourself and your son. For the LORD, the God of Israel, says,

'The jar of flour shall not go empty, nor the jug of oil run dry, until the day when the LORD sends rain upon the earth.'" She left and did as Elijah had said. She was able to eat for a year, and he and her son as well; the jar of flour did not go empty, nor the jug of oil run dry, as the LORD had foretold through Elijah.

RESPONSORIAL PSALM
Psalm 146:6c–7, 8–9a, 9bc–10

Or: Alleluia.

Praise the Lord, my soul! Praise the Lord!

It is the LORD who preserves
    fidelity forever,
  who does justice to those who are
    oppressed.
It is he who gives bread to the hungry,
  the LORD who sets prisoners free. ℟.

The LORD who opens the eyes of the blind,
  the LORD who raises up those who
    are bowed down.

It is the LORD who loves the just,
  the LORD who protects the
    stranger. ℟.

The LORD upholds the orphan and the
  widow,
but thwarts the path of the wicked.
The LORD will reign forever,
  the God of Sion from age to age.
  Alleluia. ℟.

READING II
Hebrews 9:24–28

Christ did not enter into a sanctuary made by hands, a copy of the true one, but heaven itself, that he might now appear before God on our behalf. Not that he might offer himself repeatedly, as the high priest enters each year into the sanctuary with blood that is not his own; if that were so, he would have had to suffer repeatedly from the foundation of the world. But now once for all he has appeared at the end of the ages to take away sin by his sacrifice. Just as it is appointed that human beings die once, and after this the judgment, so also Christ, offered once to take away the sins of many, will appear a second time, not to take away sin but to bring salvation to those who eagerly await him.

GOSPEL
Mark 12:38–44 or 12:41–44

For short form read only the parts in brackets. The word in parentheses is omitted in the long form.

In the course of his teaching Jesus said to the crowds, "Beware of the scribes, who like to go around in long robes and accept greetings in the marketplaces, seats of honor in synagogues, and places of honor at banquets. They devour the houses of widows and, as a pretext recite lengthy prayers. They will receive a very severe condemnation."

He [(Jesus) sat down opposite the treasury and observed how the crowd put money into the treasury. Many rich people put in large sums. A poor widow also came and put in two small coins worth a few cents. Calling his disciples to himself, he said to them, "Amen, I say to you, this poor widow put in more than all the other contributors to the treasury. For they have all contributed from their surplus wealth, but she, from her poverty, has contributed all she had, her whole livelihood."]

1289 THIRTY-SECOND SUNDAY IN ORDINARY TIME / C

READING I   *2 Maccabees 7:1–2, 9–14 / 156*

It happened that seven brothers with their mother were arrested and tortured with whips and scourges by the king, to force them to eat pork in violation of God's law. One of the brothers, speaking for the others, said: "What do you expect to achieve by questioning us? We are ready to die rather than transgress the laws of our ancestors."

At the point of death he said: "You accursed fiend, you are depriving us of this present life, but the King of the world will raise us up to live again forever. It is for his laws that we are dying."

After him the third suffered their cruel sport. He put out his tongue at once when told to do so, and bravely held out his hands, as he spoke these noble words: "It was from Heaven that I received these; for the sake of his laws I disdain them; from him I hope to receive them again." Even the king and his attendants marveled at the young man's courage, because he regarded his sufferings as nothing.

After he had died, they tortured and maltreated the fourth brother in the same way. When he was near death, he said, "It is my choice to die at the hands of men with the hope God gives of being raised up by him; but for you, there will be no resurrection to life."

RESPONSORIAL PSALM   *Psalm 17:1, 5–6, 8 and 15*

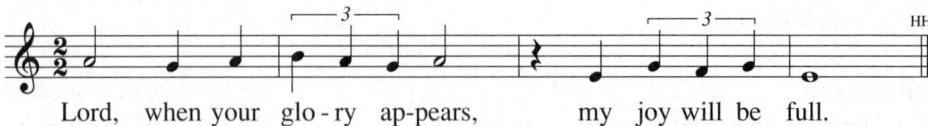

Lord, when your glo-ry ap-pears,   my joy will be full.

O LORD, hear a cause that is just,
    pay heed to my cry.
Turn your ear to my prayer:
    no deceit is on my lips. ℟.

I kept my steps firmly in your paths.
    My feet have never faltered.
To you I call; for you will surely heed
        me, O God.
    Turn your ear to me; hear my
        words. ℟.

Guard me as the apple of your eye.
Hide me in the shadow of your
    wings.
As for me, in justice I shall behold your
    face;
    when I awake I shall be filled with
        the vision of your presence. ℟.

READING II   *2 Thessalonians 2:16—3:5*

Brothers and sisters: May our Lord Jesus Christ himself and God our Father, who has loved us and given us everlasting encouragement and good hope through his grace, encourage your hearts and strengthen them in every good deed and word.

Finally, brothers and sisters, pray for us, so that the word of the Lord may speed forward and be glorified, as it did among you, and that we may be delivered from perverse and wicked people, for not all have faith. But the Lord is faithful; he will strengthen you and guard you from the evil one. We are confident of you in the Lord that what we instruct you, you are doing and will continue to do. May the Lord direct your hearts to the love of God and to the endurance of Christ.

GOSPEL   *Luke 20:27–38 or 20:27, 34–38*
For short form read only the parts in brackets.

[Some Sadducees, those who deny that there is a resurrection, came forward] and put this question to Jesus, saying, "Teacher, Moses wrote for us, *If someone's brother dies leaving a wife but no child, his brother must take the wife and raise up descendants for his brother.* Now there were seven brothers; the first married a woman but died childless. Then the second and the third married her, and likewise all the seven died childless. Finally the woman also died. Now at the resurrection whose wife will that woman be? For all seven had been married to her." [Jesus said to them, "The children of this age marry and remarry; but those who are deemed worthy to attain to the coming age and to the resurrection of the dead neither marry nor are given in marriage. They can no longer die, for they are like angels; and they are the children of God because they are the ones who will rise. That the dead will rise even Moses made known in the passage about the bush, when he called out 'Lord,' the God of Abraham, the God of Isaac, and the God of Jacob; and he is not God of the dead, but of the living, for to him all are alive."]

THIRTY-THIRD SUNDAY IN ORDINARY TIME / A   1290

READING I   *Proverbs 31:10–13, 19–20, 30–31 / 157*

When one finds a worthy wife,
  her value is far beyond pearls.
Her husband, entrusting his heart to her,
  has an unfailing prize.
She brings him good, and not evil,
  all the days of her life.
She obtains wool and flax
  and works with loving hands.
She puts her hands to the distaff,

and her fingers ply the spindle.
She reaches out her hands to the poor,
  and extends her arms to the needy.
Charm is deceptive and beauty fleeting;
  the woman who fears the Lord is to
  be praised.
Give her a reward for her labors,
  and let her works praise her at the
  city gates.

RESPONSORIAL PSALM   *Psalm 128:1–2, 3, 4–5*

Bless-ed are those who fear the Lord.

Blessed are all who fear the Lord,
  and walk in his ways!
By the labor of your hands you shall eat.
  You will be blessed and prosper. ℟.

Your wife like a fruitful vine
  in the heart of your house;
your children like shoots of the olive
  around your table. ℟.

Indeed thus shall be blessed
  the man who fears the Lord.
May the Lord bless you from Sion.
  May you see Jerusalem prosper
  all the days of your life! ℟.

READING II   *1 Thessalonians 5:1–6*

Concerning times and seasons, brothers and sisters, you have no need for anything to be written to you. For you yourselves know very well that the day of the Lord will come like a thief at night. When people are saying, "Peace and security," then sudden disaster comes upon them, like labor pains upon a pregnant woman, and they will not escape.

But you, brothers and sisters, are not in darkness, for that day to overtake you like a thief. For all of you are children of the light and children of the day. We are not of the night or of darkness. Therefore, let us not sleep as the rest do, but let us stay alert and sober.

GOSPEL   *Matthew 25:14–30 or 25:14–15, 19–21*

For short form read only the parts in brackets.

[Jesus told his disciples this parable: "A man going on a journey called in his servants and entrusted his possessions to them. To one he gave five talents; to another, two; to a third, one—to each according to his ability. Then he went away.] Immediately the one who received five talents went and traded with them, and made another five. Likewise, the one who received two made another two. But the man who received one went off and dug a hole in the ground and buried his master's money.

["After a long time the master of those servants came back and settled accounts with them. The one who had received five talents came forward bringing the additional five. He said, 'Master, you gave me five talents. See, I have made five more.' His master said to him, 'Well done, my good and faithful servant. Since you were faithful in small matters, I will give you great responsibilities. Come, share your master's joy.'] Then the one who had received two talents also came forward and said, 'Master, you gave me two talents. See, I have made two more.' His master said to him, 'Well done, my good and faithful servant. Since you were faithful in small matters, I will give you great responsibilities. Come, share your master's joy.' Then the one who had received the one talent came forward and said, 'Master, I knew you were a demanding person, harvesting where you did not plant and gathering where you did not scatter; so out of fear I went off and buried your talent in the ground. Here it is back.' His master said to him in reply, 'You wicked, lazy servant! So you knew that I harvest where I did not plant and gather where I did not scatter? Should you not then have put my money in the bank so that I could have got it back with interest on my return? Now then! Take the talent from him and give it to the one with ten. For to everyone who has, more will be given and he will grow rich; but from the one who has not, even what he has will be taken away. And throw this useless servant into the darkness outside, where there will be wailing and grinding of teeth.'"

1291   THIRTY-THIRD SUNDAY IN ORDINARY TIME / B

READING I   *Daniel 12:1–3 / 158*

In those days, I Daniel,
   heard this word of the Lord:
"At that time there shall arise
   Michael, the great prince,
   guardian of your people;

it shall be a time unsurpassed in distress
   since nations began until that time.
At that time your people shall escape,
   everyone who is found written in the
   book.

"Many of those who sleep in the dust of
the earth shall awake;
some shall live forever,
others shall be an everlasting horror
and disgrace.

"But the wise shall shine brightly
like the splendor of the firmament,
and those who lead the many to justice
shall be like the stars forever."

RESPONSORIAL PSALM   *Psalm 16:5 and 8, 9–10, 11*

You are my in-her-i-tance, O Lord, O Lord.

O LORD, it is you who are my portion
and cup;
you yourself who secure my lot.
I keep the LORD before me always;
with him at my right hand, I shall
not be moved. ℟.

And so, my heart rejoices, my soul is
glad;
even my flesh shall rest in hope.

For you will not abandon my soul to
hell,
nor let your holy one see
corruption. ℟.

You will show me the path of life,
the fullness of joy in your presence,
at your right hand, bliss forever. ℟.

READING II   *Hebrews 10:11–14, 18*

Brothers and sisters: Every priest stands daily at his ministry, offering frequently those same sacrifices that can never take away sins. But this one offered one sacrifice for sins, and took his seat forever at the right hand of God; now he waits until his enemies are made his footstool. For by one offering he has made perfect forever those who are being consecrated.

Where there is forgiveness of these, there is no longer offering for sin.

GOSPEL   *Mark 13:24–32*

Jesus said to his disciples: "In those days after that tribulation
the sun will be darkened,
and the moon will not give its light,
and the stars will be falling from the sky,
and the powers in the heavens will be shaken.

"And then they will see 'the Son of Man coming in the clouds' with great power and glory, and then he will send out the angels and gather his elect from the four winds, from the end of the earth to the end of the sky.

"Learn a lesson from the fig tree. When its branch becomes tender and sprouts leaves, you know that summer is near. In the same way, when you see these things happening, know that he is near, at the gates. Amen, I say to you, this generation will not pass away until all these things have taken place. Heaven and earth will pass away, but my words will not pass away.

"But of that day or hour, no one knows, neither the angels in heaven, nor the Son, but only the Father."

1292 THIRTY-THIRD SUNDAY IN ORDINARY TIME / C

READING I   *Malachi 3:19–20a / 159*

Lo, the day is coming, blazing like an
    oven,
  when all the proud and all evildoers
    will be stubble,
  and the day that is coming will set
    them on fire,

leaving them neither root nor branch,
  says the LORD of hosts.
But for you who fear my name, there
    will arise
  the sun of justice with its healing
    rays.

RESPONSORIAL PSALM   *Psalm 98:5–6, 7–9a, 9bc*

RC

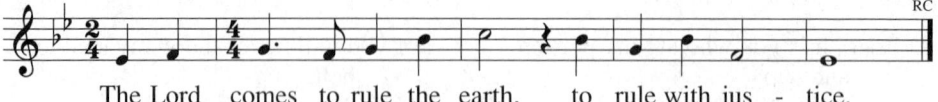

The Lord comes to rule the earth, to rule with jus - tice.

Sing psalms to the LORD with the harp,
  with the harp and the sound of song.
With trumpets and the sound of the horn,
  raise a shout before the King,
    the LORD. ℟.

Let the sea and all within it thunder;
  the world, and those who dwell in it.

Let the rivers clap their hands,
  and the hills ring out their joy
  at the presence of the LORD, for he
    comes. ℟.

He comes to judge the earth.
  He will judge the world with justice,
  and the peoples with fairness. ℟.

READING II   *2 Thessalonians 3:7–12*

Brothers and sisters: You know how one must imitate us. For we did not act in a disorderly way among you, nor did we eat food received free from anyone. On the contrary, in toil and drudgery, night and day we worked, so as not to burden any of you. Not that we do not have the right. Rather, we wanted to present ourselves as a model for you, so that you might imitate us. In fact, when we were with you, we instructed you that if anyone was unwilling to work, neither should that one eat. We hear that some are conducting themselves among you in a disorderly way, by not keeping busy but minding the business of others. Such people we instruct and urge in the Lord Jesus Christ to work quietly and to eat their own food.

GOSPEL   *Luke 21:5–19*

While some people were speaking about how the temple was adorned with costly stones and votive offerings, Jesus said, "All that you see here—the days will come when there will not be left a stone upon another stone that will not be thrown down."

Then they asked him, "Teacher, when will this happen? And what sign will there be when all these things are about to happen?" He answered, "See that you not be deceived, for many will come in my name, saying, 'I am he,' and 'The time has come.' Do not follow them! When you hear of wars and insurrections, do not be terrified; for such things must happen first, but it will not immediately be the end." Then he said to them, "Nation will rise against nation, and kingdom against kingdom. There will be powerful earthquakes, famines, and plagues from place to place; and awesome sights and mighty signs will come from the sky.

"Before all this happens, however, they will seize and persecute you, they will hand you over to the synagogues and to prisons, and they will have you led before kings and governors because of my name. It will lead to your giving testimony. Remember, you are not to prepare your defense beforehand, for I myself shall give you a wisdom in speaking that all your adversaries will be powerless to resist or refute. You will even be handed over by parents, brothers, relatives, and friends, and they will put some of you to death. You will be hated by all because of my name, but not a hair on your head will be destroyed. By your perseverance you will secure your lives."

OUR LORD JESUS CHRIST, KING OF THE UNIVERSE / A   1293

READING I   *Ezekiel 34:11–12, 15–17 / 160*

Thus says the Lord GOD: I myself will look after and tend my sheep. As a shepherd tends his flock when he finds himself among his scattered sheep, so will I tend my sheep. I will rescue them from every place where they were scattered when it was cloudy and dark. I myself will pasture my sheep; I myself will give them rest, says the Lord GOD. The lost I will seek out, the strayed I will bring back, the injured I will bind up, the sick I will heal, but the sleek and the strong I will destroy, shepherding them rightly.

As for you, my sheep, says the Lord GOD, I will judge between one sheep and another, between rams and goats.

RESPONSORIAL PSALM   *Psalm 23:1–2a, 2b–3, 5–6*

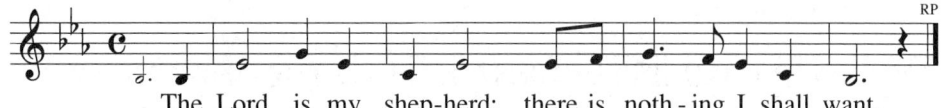

The Lord is my shep-herd; there is noth-ing I shall want.

The LORD is my shepherd;
    there is nothing I shall want.
Fresh and green are the pastures
    where he gives me repose. ℟.

Near restful waters he leads me;
    he revives my soul.
He guides me along the right path,
    for the sake of his name. ℟.

You have prepared a table before me
    in the sight of my foes.
My head you have anointed with oil;
    my cup is overflowing. ℟.

Surely goodness and mercy shall
    follow me
all the days of my life.
In the LORD's own house shall I dwell
    for length of days unending. ℟.

READING II   *1 Corinthians 15:20–26, 28*

Brothers and sisters: Christ has been raised from the dead, the firstfruits of those who have fallen asleep. For since death came through man, the resurrection of the dead came also through man. For just as in Adam all die, so too in Christ shall all be brought to life, but each one in proper order: Christ the firstfruits; then, at his coming, those who belong to Christ; then comes the end, when he hands over the kingdom to his God and Father, when he has destroyed every sovereignty and every authority and power. For he must reign until he has put all his enemies under his feet. The last enemy to be destroyed is death. When everything is subjected to him, then the Son himself will also be subjected to the one who subjected everything to him, so that God may be all in all.

GOSPEL *Matthew 25:31–46*

Jesus said to his disciples: "When the Son of Man comes in his glory, and all the angels with him, he will sit upon his glorious throne, and all the nations will be assembled before him. And he will separate them one from another, as a shepherd separates the sheep from the goats. He will place the sheep on his right and the goats on his left. Then the king will say to those on his right, 'Come, you who are blessed by my Father. Inherit the kingdom prepared for you from the foundation of the world. For I was hungry and you gave me food, I was thirsty and you gave me drink, a stranger and you welcomed me, naked and you clothed me, ill and you cared for me, in prison and you visited me.' Then the righteous will answer him and say, 'Lord, when did we see you hungry and feed you, or thirsty and give you drink? When did we see you a stranger and welcome you, or naked and clothe you? When did we see you ill or in prison, and visit you?' And the king will say to them in reply, 'Amen, I say to you, whatever you did for one of the least brothers of mine, you did for me.' Then he will say to those on his left, 'Depart from me, you accursed, into the eternal fire prepared for the devil and his angels. For I was hungry and you gave me no food, I was thirsty and you gave me no drink, a stranger and you gave me no welcome, naked and you gave me no clothing, ill and in prison, and you did not care for me.' Then they will answer and say, 'Lord, when did we see you hungry or thirsty or a stranger or naked or ill or in prison, and not minister to your needs?' He will answer them, 'Amen, I say to you, what you did not do for one of these least ones, you did not do for me.' And these will go off to eternal punishment, but the righteous to eternal life."

1294 OUR LORD JESUS CHRIST, KING OF THE UNIVERSE / B

READING I *Daniel 7:13–14 / 161*

As the visions during the night continued, I saw
  one like a Son of man coming,
    on the clouds of heaven;
  when he reached the Ancient One
    and was presented before him,
  the one like a Son of man received
    dominion, glory, and kingship;

all peoples, nations, and
  languages serve him.
His dominion is an everlasting
  dominion
that shall not be taken away,
his kingship shall not be
  destroyed.

RESPONSORIAL PSALM *Psalm 93:1ab, 1c–2, 5*

RJB

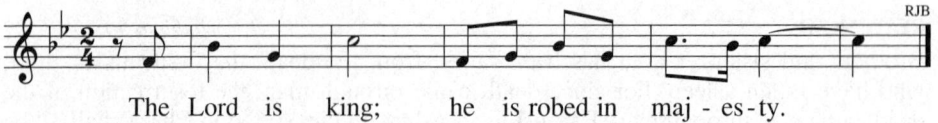

The Lord is king; he is robed in maj - es - ty.

The LORD is king, with majesty enrobed.
  The LORD has robed himself with
    might;
  he has girded himself with power. ℟.

The world you made firm, not to be
  moved;
  your throne has stood firm from of
    old.
    From all eternity, O LORD, you are. ℟.

Truly your decrees are to be trusted.
    Holiness is fitting to your house,
    O Lᴏʀᴅ, until the end of time. ℟.

READING II   *Revelation 1:5–8*

Jesus Christ is the faithful witness, the firstborn of the dead and ruler of the kings of the earth. To him who loves us and has freed us from our sins by his blood, who has made us into a kingdom, priests for his God and Father, to him be glory and power forever and ever. Amen.
    Behold, he is coming amid the clouds,
        and every eye will see him,
        even those who pierced him.
    All the peoples of the earth will lament him.
        Yes. Amen.
    "I am the Alpha and the Omega," says the Lord God, "the one who is and who was and who is to come, the almighty."

GOSPEL   *John 18:33b–37*

Pilate said to Jesus, "Are you the King of the Jews?" Jesus answered, "Do you say this on your own or have others told you about me?" Pilate answered, "I am not a Jew, am I? Your own nation and the chief priests handed you over to me. What have you done?" Jesus answered, "My kingdom does not belong to this world. If my kingdom did belong to this world, my attendants would be fighting to keep me from being handed over to the Jews. But as it is, my kingdom is not here." So Pilate said to him, "Then you are a king?" Jesus answered, "You say I am a king. For this I was born and for this I came into the world, to testify to the truth. Everyone who belongs to the truth listens to my voice."

OUR LORD JESUS CHRIST, KING OF THE UNIVERSE / C   1295

READING I   *2 Samuel 5:1–3 / 162*

In those days, all the tribes of Israel came to David in Hebron and said: "Here we are, your bone and your flesh. In days past, when Saul was our king, it was you who led the Israelites out and brought them back. And the Lᴏʀᴅ said to you, 'You shall shepherd my people Israel and shall be commander of Israel.'" When all the elders of Israel came to David in Hebron, King David made an agreement with them there before the Lᴏʀᴅ, and they anointed him king of Israel.

RESPONSORIAL PSALM   *Psalm 122:1–2, 3–4ab, 4cd–5*

RJB

Let us go re-joic-ing to the house, to the house of the Lord.

I rejoiced when they said to me,   And now our feet are standing
    "Let us go to the house of the Lᴏʀᴅ."   within your gates, O Jerusalem. ℟.

Jerusalem is built as a city
   bonded as one together.
It is there that the tribes go up,
   the tribes of the LORD. ℞.

For Israel's witness it is
   to praise the name of the LORD.
There were set the thrones for
      judgment,
   the thrones of the house of
   David. ℞.

READING II *Colossians 1:12–20*

Brothers and sisters: Let us give thanks to the Father, who has made you fit to share in the inheritance of the holy ones in light. He delivered us from the power of darkness and transferred us to the kingdom of his beloved Son, in whom we have redemption, the forgiveness of sins.
   He is the image of the invisible God,
      the firstborn of all creation.
   For in him were created all things in heaven and on earth,
      the visible and the invisible,
      whether thrones or dominions or principalities or powers;
      all things were created through him and for him.
   He is before all things,
      and in him all things hold together.
   He is the head of the body, the church.
   He is the beginning, the firstborn from the dead,
      that in all things he himself might be preeminent.
   For in him all the fullness was pleased to dwell,
      and through him to reconcile all things for him,
      making peace by the blood of his cross
      through him, whether those on earth or those in heaven.

GOSPEL *Luke 23:35–43*

The rulers sneered at Jesus and said, "He saved others, let him save himself if he is the chosen one, the Christ of God." Even the soldiers jeered at him. As they approached to offer him wine they called out, "If you are King of the Jews, save yourself." Above him there was an inscription that read, "This is the King of the Jews."
   Now one of the criminals hanging there reviled Jesus, saying, "Are you not the Christ? Save yourself and us." The other, however, rebuking him, said in reply, "Have you no fear of God, for you are subject to the same condemnation? And indeed, we have been condemned justly, for the sentence we received corresponds to our crimes, but this man has done nothing criminal." Then he said, "Jesus, remember me when you come into your kingdom." He replied to him, "Amen, I say to you, today you will be with me in Paradise."

Other Feasts and Celebrations

FEBRUARY 2: PRESENTATION OF THE LORD — 1296

Forty days after the celebration of Christmas, this feast tells of how Mary and Joseph brought the child to the Temple. There the aged Simeon took the baby in his arms and proclaimed that Jesus would be "a light to the Gentiles, the glory of Israel." These words have been sung for centuries on February 2 as Christians have blessed and carried lighted candles in procession.

BLESSING OF CANDLES AND PROCESSION

As the candles are lighted, this antiphon (with optional verses) may be sung:

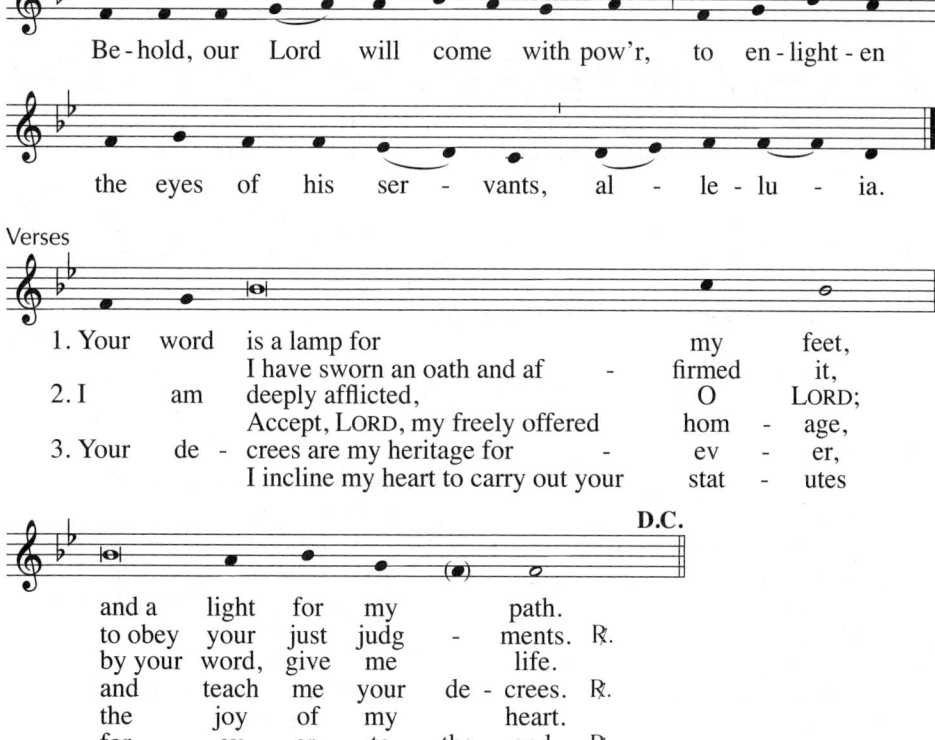

Antiphon

Be - hold, our Lord will come with pow'r, to en - light - en the eyes of his ser - vants, al - le - lu - ia.

Verses

1. Your word is a lamp for my feet,
and a light for my path.
I have sworn an oath and af - firmed it,
to obey your just judg - ments. ℟.
2. I am deeply afflicted, O LORD;
by your word, give me life.
Accept, LORD, my freely offered hom - age,
and teach me your de - crees. ℟.
3. Your de - crees are my heritage for - ev - er,
the joy of my heart.
I incline my heart to carry out your stat - utes
for - ev - er, to the end. ℟.

Text: Psalm 119:105–108, 111–112, *The Revised Grail Psalms,* © 2010, Conception Abbey and The Grail, admin. by GIA Publications, Inc.; antiphon, ICEL, © 2010
Music: Chant Mode VIII; acc. by Richard Proulx, © 1985, GIA Publications, Inc.; antiphon, ICEL, © 2010

When the candles have been blessed, the priest sings:

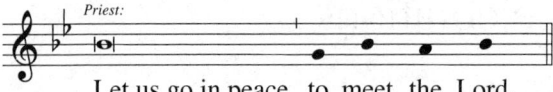

Let us go in peace to meet the Lord.

Or:

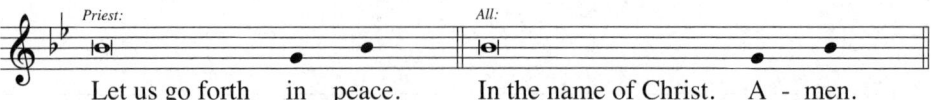

Let us go forth in peace. In the name of Christ. A - men.

1297 *During the procession, the following may be sung:*

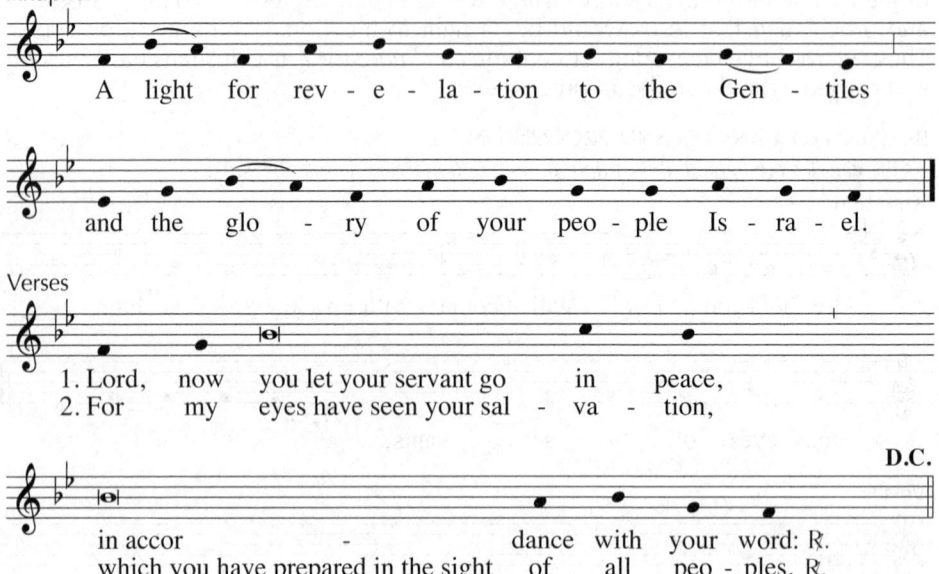

Antiphon

A light for rev - e - la - tion to the Gen - tiles

and the glo - ry of your peo - ple Is - ra - el.

Verses

1. Lord, now you let your servant go in peace,
2. For my eyes have seen your sal - va - tion,

D.C.

in accor - dance with your word: ℟.
which you have prepared in the sight of all peo - ples. ℟.

Text: Luke 2:29–32, trans. ICEL, © 2010
Music: Chant Mode VIII; acc. by Richard Proulx, © 1985, GIA Publications, Inc.; antiphon, ICEL, © 2010

READING I *Malachi 3:1–4 / 524*

Thus says the Lord God:
Lo, I am sending my messenger
　to prepare the way before me;
And suddenly there will come to the
　temple
　the LORD whom you seek,
And the messenger of the covenant
　whom you desire.
　Yes, he is coming, says the LORD of
　hosts.
But who will endure the day of his
　coming?
　And who can stand when he appears?

For he is like the refiner's fire,
　or like the fuller's lye.
He will sit refining and purifying silver,
　and he will purify the sons of Levi,
Refining them like gold or like silver
　that they may offer due sacrifice to
　the LORD.
Then the sacrifice of Judah and
　Jerusalem
　will please the LORD,
　as in the days of old, as in years
　gone by.

RESPONSORIAL PSALM

Psalm 24:7, 8, 9, 10

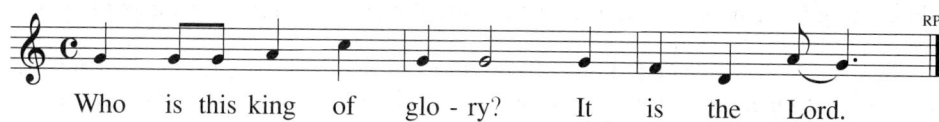

Who is this king of glo - ry? It is the Lord.

O gates, lift high your heads;
   grow higher, ancient doors.
   Let him enter, the king of glory! ℟.

Who is this king of glory?
   The LORD, the mighty, the valiant;
   the LORD, the valiant in war. ℟.

O gates, lift high your heads;
   grow higher, ancient doors.
   Let him enter, the king of glory! ℟.

Who is this king of glory?
   He, the LORD of hosts,
   he is the king of glory. ℟.

READING II

Hebrews 2:14–18

Since the children share in blood and flesh, Jesus likewise shared in them, that through death he might destroy the one who has the power of death, that is, the Devil, and free those who through fear of death had been subject to slavery all their life. Surely he did not help angels but rather the descendants of Abraham; therefore, he had to become like his brothers and sisters in every way, that he might be a merciful and faithful high priest before God to expiate the sins of the people. Because he himself was tested through what he suffered, he is able to help those who are being tested.

GOSPEL

Luke 2:22–40 or 2:22–32

For short form, read only the part in brackets.

[When the days were completed for their purification according to the law of Moses, Mary and Joseph took Jesus up to Jerusalem to present him to the Lord, just as it is written in the law of the Lord, *Every male that opens the womb shall be consecrated to the Lord,* and to offer the sacrifice of *a pair of turtledoves or two young pigeons,* in accordance with the dictate in the law of the Lord.

Now there was a man in Jerusalem whose name was Simeon. This man was righteous and devout, awaiting the consolation of Israel, and the Holy Spirit was upon him. It had been revealed to him by the Holy Spirit that he should not see death before he had seen the Christ of the Lord. He came in the Spirit into the temple; and when the parents brought in the child Jesus to perform the custom of the law in regard to him, he took him into his arms and blessed God, saying:

"Now, Master, you may let your servant go
   in peace, according to your word,
for my eyes have seen your salvation,
   which you prepared in sight of all the peoples,
a light for revelation to the Gentiles,
   and glory for your people Israel."]

The child's father and mother were amazed at what was said about him; and Simeon blessed them and said to Mary his mother, "Behold, this child is destined for the fall and rise of many in Israel, and to be a sign that will be contradicted —and you yourself a sword will pierce— so that the thoughts of many hearts may be revealed." There was also a prophetess, Anna, the daughter of Phanuel, of the tribe of Asher. She was advanced in years, having lived seven years with her husband after her marriage, and then as a widow until she was eighty-four. She never left the temple, but worshipped night and day with fasting and prayer. And coming forward at that very time, she gave thanks to God and spoke about the child to all who were awaiting the redemption of Jerusalem.

When they had fulfilled all the prescriptions of the law of the Lord, they returned to Galilee, to their own town of Nazareth. The child grew and became strong, filled with wisdom; and the favor of God was upon him.

1298 MARCH 19: JOSEPH, HUSBAND OF MARY

READING I   *2 Samuel 7:4–5a, 12–14a, 16 / 543*

The LORD spoke to Nathan and said: "Go, tell my servant David, 'When your time comes and you rest with your ancestors, I will raise up your heir after you, sprung from your loins, and I will make his kingdom firm. It is he who shall build a house for my name. And I will make his royal throne firm forever. I will be a father to him, and he shall be a son to me. Your house and your kingdom shall endure forever before me; your throne shall stand firm forever.'"

RESPONSORIAL PSALM   *Psalm 89:2–3, 4–5, 27 and 29*

The Son of Da - vid will live for ev - er.

I will sing forever of your mercies,
O LORD;
   through all ages my mouth will
   proclaim your fidelity.
I have declared your mercy is
   established forever;
   your fidelity stands firm as the
   heavens. ℟.

"With my chosen one I have made a
   covenant;
   I have sworn to David my servant:

I will establish your descendants forever,
   and set up your throne through all
   ages." ℟.

"He will call out to me, 'You are my
   father,
   my God, the rock of my salvation.'
I will keep my faithful love for him
   always;
   with him my covenant shall last." ℟.

READING II   *Romans 4:13, 16–18, 22*

Brothers and sisters: It was not through the law that the promise was made to Abraham and his descendants that he would inherit the world, but through the righteousness that comes from faith. For this reason, it depends on faith, so that it may be a gift, and the promise may be guaranteed to all his descendants, not to those who only adhere to the law but to those who follow the faith of Abraham, who is the father of all of us, as it is written, *I have made you father of many nations.* He is our father in the sight of God, in whom he believed, who gives life to the dead and calls into being what does not exist. He believed, hoping against hope, that he would become *the father of many nations,* according to what was said, *Thus shall your descendants be.* That is why *it was credited to him as righteousness.*

GOSPEL

Matthew 1:16, 18–21, 24a

Jacob was the father of Joseph, the husband of Mary. Of her was born Jesus who is called the Christ.

Now this is how the birth of Jesus Christ came about. When his mother Mary was betrothed to Joseph, but before they lived together, she was found with child through the Holy Spirit. Joseph her husband, since he was a righteous man, yet unwilling to expose her to shame, decided to divorce her quietly. Such was his intention when, behold, the angel of the Lord appeared to him in a dream and said, "Joseph, son of David, do not be afraid to take Mary your wife into your home. For it is through the Holy Spirit that this child has been conceived in her. She will bear a son and you are to name him Jesus, because he will save his people from their sins." When Joseph awoke, he did as the angel of the Lord had commanded him and took his wife into his home.

Or:

GOSPEL

Luke 2:41–51a

Each year Jesus' parents went to Jerusalem for the feast of Passover, and when he was twelve years old, they went up according to festival custom. After they had completed its days, as they were returning, the boy Jesus remained behind in Jerusalem, but his parents did not know it. Thinking that he was in the caravan, they journeyed for a day and looked for him among their relatives and acquaintances, but not finding him, they returned to Jerusalem to look for him. After three days they found him in the temple, sitting in the midst of the teachers, listening to them and asking them questions, and all who heard him were astounded at his understanding and his answers. When his parents saw him, they were astonished, and his mother said to him, "Son, why have you done this to us? Your father and I have been looking for you with great anxiety." And he said to them, "Why were you looking for me? Did you not know that I must be in my Father's house?" But they did not understand what he said to them. He went down with them and came to Nazareth, and was obedient to them.

MARCH 25: ANNUNCIATION OF THE LORD   1299

READING I

Isaiah 7:10–14; 8:10 / 545

The LORD spoke to Ahaz, saying: Ask for a sign from the LORD, your God; let it be deep as the nether world, or high as the sky! But Ahaz answered, "I will not ask! I will not tempt the LORD!" Then Isaiah said: Listen, O house of David! Is it not enough for you to weary people, must you also weary my God? Therefore the Lord himself will give you this sign: the virgin shall conceive, and bear a son, and shall name him Emmanuel, which means "God is with us!"

RESPONSORIAL PSALM

Psalm 40:7–8a, 8b–9, 10, 11

Here am I, Lord; I come to do your will.

You delight not in sacrifice and offerings,   You do not ask for holocaust and victim.
   but in an open ear.   Then I said, "See, I have come." ℟.

In the scroll of the book it stands
    written of me:
       "I delight to do your will, O my God;
       your instruction lies deep within
       me." ℟.

Your justice I have proclaimed
    in the great assembly.
My lips I have not sealed;

you know it, O LORD. ℟.

Your saving help I have not hidden in
    my heart;
of your faithfulness and salvation I
    have spoken.
I made no secret of your merciful love
    and your faithfulness to the great
    assembly. ℟.

READING II
Hebrews 10:4–10

Brothers and sisters: It is impossible that the blood of bulls and goats takes away sins. For this reason, when Christ came into the world, he said:

"Sacrifice and offering you did not desire,
    but a body you prepared for me;
in holocausts and sin offerings you took no delight.
Then I said, 'As is written of me in the scroll,
behold, I come to do your will, O God.'"

First he says, "Sacrifices and offerings, holocausts and sin offerings, you neither desired nor delighted in." These are offered according to the law. Then he says, "Behold, I come to do your will." He takes away the first to establish the second. By this "will," we have been consecrated through the offering of the Body of Jesus Christ once for all.

GOSPEL
Luke 1:26–38

The angel Gabriel was sent from God to a town of Galilee called Nazareth, to a virgin betrothed to a man named Joseph, of the house of David, and the virgin's name was Mary. And coming to her, he said, "Hail, full of grace! The Lord is with you." But she was greatly troubled at what was said and pondered what sort of greeting this might be. Then the angel said to her, "Do not be afraid, Mary, for you have found favor with God. Behold, you will conceive in your womb and bear a son, and you shall name him Jesus. He will be great and will be called Son of the Most High, and the Lord God will give him the throne of David his father, and he will rule over the house of Jacob forever, and of his Kingdom there will be no end." But Mary said to the angel, "How can this be, since I have no relations with a man?" And the angel said to her in reply, "The Holy Spirit will come upon you, and the power of the Most High will overshadow you. Therefore the child to be born will be called holy, the Son of God. And behold, Elizabeth, your relative, has also conceived a son in her old age, and this is the sixth month for her who was called barren; for nothing will be impossible for God." Mary said, "Behold, I am the handmaid of the Lord. May it be done to me according to your word." Then the angel departed from her.

1300 JUNE 24: NATIVITY OF ST. JOHN THE BAPTIST—VIGIL MASS

READING I
Jeremiah 1:4–10 / 586

In the days of King Josiah, the word of the LORD came to me, saying:

    Before I formed you in the womb I
       knew you,

before you were born I dedicated you,
a prophet to the nations I appointed
    you.

"Ah, Lord God!" I said,
"I know not how to speak; I am too
young."
But the Lord answered me,
Say not, "I am too young."
To whomever I send you, you shall
go;
whatever I command you, you shall
speak.
Have no fear before them,
because I am with you to deliver

you, says the Lord.

Then the Lord extended his hand and
touched my mouth, saying,

See, I place my words in your mouth!
This day I set you
over nations and over kingdoms,
to root up and to tear down,
to destroy and to demolish,
to build and to plant.

RESPONSORIAL PSALM   *Psalm 71:1–2, 3–4a, 5–6ab, 15ab and 17*

Since my moth-er's womb, you have been my strength.

In you, O Lord, I take refuge;
let me never be put to shame.
In your justice, rescue me, free me;
incline your ear to me and save me. ℟.

Be my rock, my constant refuge,
a mighty stronghold to save me,
for you are my rock, my stronghold.
My God, free me from the hand
of the wicked. ℟.

It is you, O Lord, who are my hope,
my trust, O Lord, from my youth.
On you I have leaned from my birth;
from my mother's womb, you have
been my help. ℟.

My mouth will tell of your justice,
and all the day long of your salvation.
O God, you have taught me from my youth,
and I proclaim your wonders still. ℟.

READING II   *1 Peter 1:8–12*

Beloved: Although you have not seen Jesus Christ you love him; even though you do
not see him now yet believe in him, you rejoice with an indescribable and glorious
joy, as you attain the goal of your faith, the salvation of your souls.

Concerning this salvation, prophets who prophesied about the grace that was to be
yours searched and investigated it, investigating the time and circumstances that the
Spirit of Christ within them indicated when he testified in advance to the sufferings
destined for Christ and the glories to follow them. It was revealed to them that they
were serving not themselves but you with regard to the things that have now been
announced to you by those who preached the good news to you through the Holy
Spirit sent from heaven, things into which angels longed to look.

GOSPEL   *Luke 1:5–17*

In the days of Herod, King of Judea, there was a priest named Zechariah of the priestly division of Abijah; his wife was from the daughters of Aaron, and her name was
Elizabeth. Both were righteous in the eyes of God, observing all the commandments
and ordinances of the Lord blamelessly. But they had no child, because Elizabeth
was barren and both were advanced in years. Once when he was serving as priest in
his division's turn before God, according to the practice of the priestly service, he

was chosen by lot to enter the sanctuary of the Lord to burn incense. Then, when the whole assembly of the people was praying outside at the hour of the incense offering, the angel of the Lord appeared to him, standing at the right of the altar of incense. Zechariah was troubled by what he saw, and fear came upon him. But the angel said to him, "Do not be afraid, Zechariah, because your prayer has been heard. Your wife Elizabeth will bear you a son, and you shall name him John. And you will have joy and gladness, and many will rejoice at his birth, for he will be great in the sight of the Lord. John will drink neither wine nor strong drink. He will be filled with the Holy Spirit even from his mother's womb, and he will turn many of the children of Israel to the Lord their God. He will go before him in the spirit and power of Elijah to turn their hearts toward their children and the disobedient to the understanding of the righteous, to prepare a people fit for the Lord."

1301 JUNE 24: NATIVITY OF ST. JOHN THE BAPTIST–MASS DURING THE DAY

READING I   *Isaiah 49:1–6 / 587*

Hear me, O coastlands
   listen, O distant peoples.
The LORD called me from birth,
   from my mother's womb he gave
   me my name.
He made of me a sharp-edged sword
   and concealed me in the shadow of
   his arm.
He made me a polished arrow,
   in his quiver he hid me.
You are my servant, he said to me,
   Israel, through whom I show my
   glory.

Though I thought I had toiled in vain,
   and for nothing, uselessly, spent my
   strength,

yet my reward is with the LORD,
   my recompense is with my God.
For now the LORD has spoken
   who formed me as his servant from
   the womb,
that Jacob may be brought back to him
   and Israel gathered to him;
and I am made glorious in the sight of
   the LORD,
   and my God is now my strength!
It is too little, he says, for you to be my
   servant,
   to raise up the tribes of Jacob,
   and restore the survivors of Israel;
I will make you a light to the nations,
   that my salvation may reach to the
   ends of the earth.

RESPONSORIAL PSALM   *Psalm 139:1–3, 13–14ab, 14c–15*

I praise you, O Lord, for I am won-der-ful-ly made.

O LORD, you search me and you know
   me.
   You yourself know my resting and
   my rising;
   you discern my thoughts from afar.
You mark when I walk or lie down;
   you know all my ways through and
   through. ℟.

For it was you who formed my inmost
   being,
   knit me together in my mother's
   womb.
I thank you who wonderfully made me;
   how wonderful are your works,
   which my soul knows well! ℟.

My frame was not hidden from you,
   when I was being fashioned in
     secret

and molded in the depths of the
   earth. ℟.

READING II   *Acts 13:22–26*

In those days, Paul said: "God raised up David as their king; of him he testified,
*I have found David, son of Jesse, a man after my own heart; he will carry out my
every wish.* From this man's descendants God, according to his promise, has brought
to Israel a savior, Jesus. John heralded his coming by proclaiming a baptism of
repentance to all the people of Israel; and as John was completing his course, he
would say, 'What do you suppose that I am? I am not he. Behold, one is coming after
me; I am not worthy to unfasten the sandals of his feet.'

"My brothers, children of the family of Abraham, and those others among you
who are God-fearing, to us this word of salvation has been sent."

GOSPEL   *Luke 1:57–66, 80*

When the time arrived for Elizabeth to have her child she gave birth to a son. Her
neighbors and relatives heard that the Lord had shown his great mercy toward her,
and they rejoiced with her. When they came on the eighth day to circumcise the child,
they were going to call him Zechariah after his father, but his mother said in reply,
"No. He will be called John." But they answered her, "There is no one among your
relatives who has this name." So they made signs, asking his father what he wished
him to be called. He asked for a tablet and wrote, "John is his name," and all were
amazed. Immediately his mouth was opened, his tongue freed, and he spoke blessing
God. Then fear came upon all their neighbors, and all these matters were discussed
throughout the hill country of Judea. All who heard these things took them to heart,
saying, "What, then, will this child be?" For surely the hand of the Lord was with him.
The child grew and became strong in spirit, and he was in the desert until the day of
his manifestation to Israel.

JUNE 29: STS. PETER & PAUL, APOSTLES—VIGIL MASS   1302

READING I   *Acts 3:1–10 / 590*

Peter and John were going up to the temple area for the three o'clock hour of prayer.
And a man crippled from birth was carried and placed at the gate of the temple called
"the Beautiful Gate" every day to beg for alms from the people who entered the
temple. When he saw Peter and John about to go into the temple, he asked for
alms. But Peter looked intently at him, as did John, and said, "Look at us." He paid
attention to them, expecting to receive something from them. Peter said, "I have
neither silver nor gold, but what I do have I give you: in the name of Jesus Christ the
Nazorean, rise and walk." Then Peter took him by the right hand and raised him up,
and immediately his feet and ankles grew strong. He leaped up, stood, and walked
around, and went into the temple with them, walking and jumping and praising God.
When all the people saw the man walking and praising God, they recognized him as
the one who used to sit begging at the Beautiful Gate of the temple, and they were
filled with amazement and astonishment at what had happened to him.

RESPONSORIAL PSALM   *Psalm 19:2–3, 4–5*

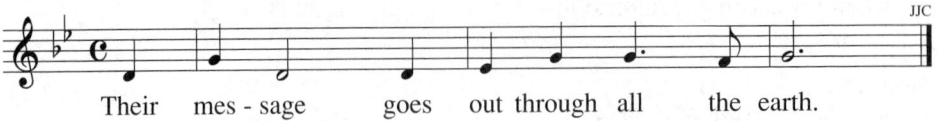

Their mes-sage goes out through all the earth.

The heavens declare the glory of God,
and the firmament proclaims the
work of his hands.
Day unto day conveys the message,
and night unto night imparts the
knowledge. ℟.

No speech, no word, whose voice goes
unheeded;
their sound goes forth through all
the earth,
their message to the utmost bounds
of the world. ℟.

READING II   *Galatians 1:11–20*

I want you to know, brothers and sisters, that the gospel preached by me is not of
human origin. For I did not receive it from a human being, nor was I taught it, but it
came through a revelation of Jesus Christ.

For you heard of my former way of life in Judaism, how I persecuted the church
of God beyond measure and tried to destroy it, and progressed in Judaism beyond
many of my contemporaries among my race, since I was even more a zealot for my
ancestral traditions. But when God, who from my mother's womb had set me apart
and called me through his grace, was pleased to reveal his Son to me, so that I might
proclaim him to the Gentiles, I did not immediately consult flesh and blood, nor did I
go up to Jerusalem to those who were apostles before me; rather, I went into Arabia
and then returned to Damascus.

Then after three years I went up to Jerusalem to confer with Cephas and remained with
him for fifteen days. But I did not see any other of the apostles, only James the brother of
the Lord. —As to what I am writing to you, behold, before God, I am not lying.

GOSPEL   *John 21:15–19*

Jesus revealed himself to his disciples and, when they had finished breakfast, said to
Simon Peter, "Simon, son of John, do you love me more than these?" He answered
him, "Yes, Lord, you know that I love you." Jesus said to him, "Feed my lambs." He
then said to him a second time, "Simon, son of John, do you love me?" He answered
him, "Yes, Lord, you know that I love you." He said to him, "Tend my sheep." He
said to him the third time, "Simon, son of John, do you love me?" Peter was dis-
tressed that Jesus had said to him a third time, "Do you love me?" and he said to him,
"Lord, you know everything; you know that I love you." Jesus said to him, "Feed
my sheep. Amen, amen, I say to you, when you were younger, you used to dress
yourself and go where you wanted; but when you grow old, you will stretch out your
hands, and someone else will dress you and lead you where you do not want to go."
He said this signifying by what kind of death he would glorify God. And when he had
said this, he said to him, "Follow me."

1303 JUNE 29: STS. PETER & PAUL, APOSTLES–MASS DURING THE DAY

READING I   *Acts 12:1–11 / 591*

In those days, King Herod laid hands upon some members of the church to harm
them. He had James, the brother of John, killed by the sword, and when he saw that

this was pleasing to the Jews he proceeded to arrest Peter also. —It was the feast of Unleavened Bread.— He had him taken into custody and put in prison under the guard of four squads of four soldiers each. He intended to bring him before the people after Passover. Peter thus was being kept in prison, but prayer by the church was fervently being made to God on his behalf.

On the very night before Herod was to bring him to trial, Peter, secured by double chains, was sleeping between two soldiers, while outside the door guards kept watch on the prison. Suddenly the angel of the Lord stood by him and a light shone in the cell. He tapped Peter on the side and awakened him, saying, "Get up quickly." The chains fell from his wrists. The angel said to him, "Put on your belt and your sandals." He did so. Then he said to him, "Put on your cloak and follow me." So he followed him out, not realizing that what was happening through the angel was real; he thought he was seeing a vision. They passed the first guard, then the second, and came to the iron gate leading out to the city, which opened for them by itself. They emerged and made their way down an alley, and suddenly the angel left him. Then Peter recovered his senses and said, "Now I know for certain that the Lord sent his angel and rescued me from the hand of Herod and from all that the Jewish people had been expecting."

RESPONSORIAL PSALM

Psalm 34:2–3, 4–5, 6–7, 8–9

The an-gel of the Lord will res-cue those who fear him.

I will bless the LORD at all times;
  praise of him is always in my mouth.
In the LORD my soul shall make its boast;
  the humble shall hear and be glad. ℟.

Glorify the LORD with me;
  together let us praise his name.
I sought the LORD, and he answered me;
  from all my terrors he set me free. ℟.

Look toward him and be radiant;

let your faces not be abashed.
This lowly one called; the LORD heard,
  and rescued him from all his
  distress. ℟.

The angel of the LORD is encamped
  around those who fear him,
  to rescue them.
Taste and see that the LORD is good.
Blessed the man who seeks refuge
  in him. ℟.

READING II

2 Timothy 4:6–8, 17–18

I, Paul, am already being poured out like a libation, and the time of my departure is at hand. I have competed well; I have finished the race; I have kept the faith. From now on the crown of righteousness awaits me, which the Lord, the just judge, will award to me on that day, and not only to me, but to all who have longed for his appearance.

The Lord stood by me and gave me strength, so that through me the proclamation might be completed and all the Gentiles might hear it. And I was rescued from the lion's mouth. The Lord will rescue me from every evil threat and will bring me safe to his heavenly kingdom. To him be glory forever and ever. Amen.

GOSPEL   *Matthew 16:13–19*

When Jesus went into the region of Caesarea Philippi he asked his disciples, "Who do people say that the Son of Man is?" They replied, "Some say John the Baptist, others Elijah, still others Jeremiah or one of the prophets." He said to them, "But who do you say that I am?" Simon Peter said in reply, "You are the Christ, the Son of the living God." Jesus said to him in reply, "Blessed are you, Simon son of Jonah. For flesh and blood has not revealed this to you, but my heavenly Father. And so I say to you, you are Peter, and upon this rock I will build my Church, and the gates of the netherworld shall not prevail against it. I will give you the keys to the Kingdom of heaven. Whatever you bind on earth shall be bound in heaven; and whatever you loose on earth shall be loosed in heaven."

1304   JULY 4: INDEPENDENCE DAY

RESPONSORIAL PSALM   *Psalm 85:9ab and 10, 11–12, 13–14*

The Lord speaks of peace to his peo - ple.

I will hear what the LORD God speaks;
  he speaks of peace for his people
    and his faithful.
His salvation is near for those who fear
    him,
  and his glory will dwell in our
    land. ℟.

Merciful love and faithfulness have met;
  justice and peace have kissed.

Faithfulness shall spring from the earth,
  and justice look down from
    heaven. ℟.

Also the LORD will bestow his bounty,
  and our earth shall yield its increase.
Justice will march before him,
  and guide his steps on the way. ℟.

1305   AUGUST 6: TRANSFIGURATION OF THE LORD

READING I   *Daniel 7:9–10, 13–14 / 614*

As I watched:
  Thrones were set up
    and the Ancient One took his throne.
  His clothing was bright as snow,
    and the hair on his head as white as wool;
  his throne was flames of fire,
    with wheels of burning fire.
  A surging stream of fire
    flowed out from where he sat;
  Thousands upon thousands were ministering to him,
    and myriads upon myriads attended him.
The court was convened and the books were opened.

As the visions during the night continued, I saw

> One like a Son of man coming,
>   on the clouds of heaven;
> When he reached the Ancient One
>   and was presented before him,
> The one like a Son of man received dominion, glory, and kingship;
>   all peoples, nations, and languages serve him.
> His dominion is an everlasting dominion
>   that shall not be taken away,
>   his kingship shall not be destroyed.

RESPONSORIAL PSALM   *Psalm 97:1–2, 5–6, 9*

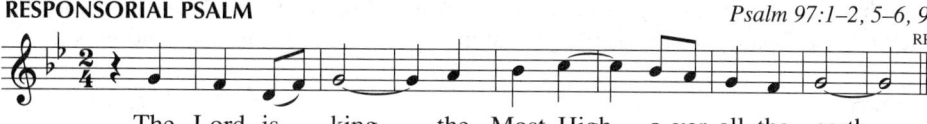

The Lord is king, the Most High o-ver all the earth.

The LORD is king, let earth rejoice;
  let the many islands be glad.
Cloud and darkness surround him;
  justice and right are the foundation
  of his throne. ℟.

The mountains melt like wax
  before the face of the LORD,

before the face of the Lord of all the
  earth.
The skies proclaim his justice;
  all peoples see his glory. ℟.

For you indeed are the LORD,
  most high above all the earth,
  exalted far above all gods. ℟.

READING II   *2 Peter 1:16–19*

Beloved: We did not follow cleverly devised myths when we made known to you the power and coming of our Lord Jesus Christ, but we had been eyewitnesses of his majesty. For he received honor and glory from God the Father when that unique declaration came to him from the majestic glory, "This is my Son, my beloved, with whom I am well pleased." We ourselves heard this voice come from heaven while we were with him on the holy mountain. Moreover, we possess the prophetic message that is altogether reliable. You will do well to be attentive to it, as to a lamp shining in a dark place, until day dawns and the morning star rises in your hearts.

GOSPEL / A   *Matthew 17:1–9*

Jesus took Peter, James, and his brother, John, and led them up a high mountain by themselves. And he was transfigured before them; his face shone like the sun and his clothes became white as light. And behold, Moses and Elijah appeared to them, conversing with him. Then Peter said to Jesus in reply, "Lord, it is good that we are here. If you wish, I will make three tents here, one for you, one for Moses, and one for Elijah." While he was still speaking, behold, a bright cloud cast a shadow over them, then from the cloud came a voice that said, "This is my beloved Son, with whom I am well pleased; listen to him." When the disciples heard this, they fell prostrate and were very much afraid. But Jesus came and touched them, saying, "Rise, and do not be afraid." And when the disciples raised their eyes, they saw no one else but Jesus alone.

As they were coming down from the mountain, Jesus charged them, "Do not tell the vision to anyone until the Son of Man has been raised from the dead."

GOSPEL / B *Mark 9:2–10*

Jesus took Peter, James, and John and led them up a high mountain apart by themselves. And he was transfigured before them, and his clothes became dazzling white, such as no fuller on earth could bleach them. Then Elijah appeared to them along with Moses, and they were conversing with Jesus. Then Peter said to Jesus in reply, "Rabbi, it is good that we are here! Let us make three tents: one for you, one for Moses, and one for Elijah." He hardly knew what to say, they were so terrified. Then a cloud came, casting a shadow over them; from the cloud came a voice, "This is my beloved Son. Listen to him." Suddenly, looking around, they no longer saw anyone but Jesus alone with them.

As they were coming down from the mountain, he charged them not to relate what they had seen to anyone, except when the Son of Man had risen from the dead. So they kept the matter to themselves, questioning what rising from the dead meant.

GOSPEL / C *Luke 9:28b–36*

Jesus took Peter, John, and James and went up a mountain to pray. While he was praying his face changed in appearance and his clothing became dazzling white. And behold, two men were conversing with him, Moses and Elijah, who appeared in glory and spoke of his exodus that he was going to accomplish in Jerusalem. Peter and his companions had been overcome by sleep, but becoming fully awake, they saw his glory and the two men standing with him. As they were about to part from him, Peter said to Jesus, "Master, it is good that we are here; let us make three tents, one for you, one for Moses, and one for Elijah." But he did not know what he was saying. While he was still speaking, a cloud came and cast a shadow over them, and they became frightened when they entered the cloud. Then from the cloud came a voice that said, "This is my chosen Son; listen to him." After the voice had spoken, Jesus was found alone. They fell silent and did not at that time tell anyone what they had seen.

1306 AUGUST 15: ASSUMPTION OF MARY—VIGIL MASS

READING I *1 Chronicles 15:3–4, 15–16; 16:1–2 / 621*

David assembled all Israel in Jerusalem to bring the ark of the LORD to the place that he had prepared for it. David also called together the sons of Aaron and the Levites.

The Levites bore the ark of God on their shoulders with poles, as Moses had ordained according to the word of the LORD.

David commanded the chiefs of the Levites to appoint their kinsmen as chanters, to play on musical instruments, harps, lyres, and cymbals, to make a loud sound of rejoicing.

They brought in the ark of God and set it within the tent which David had pitched for it. Then they offered up burnt offerings and peace offerings to God. When David had finished offering up the burnt offerings and peace offerings, he blessed the people in the name of the LORD.

RESPONSORIAL PSALM   *Psalm 132:6–7, 9–10, 13–14*

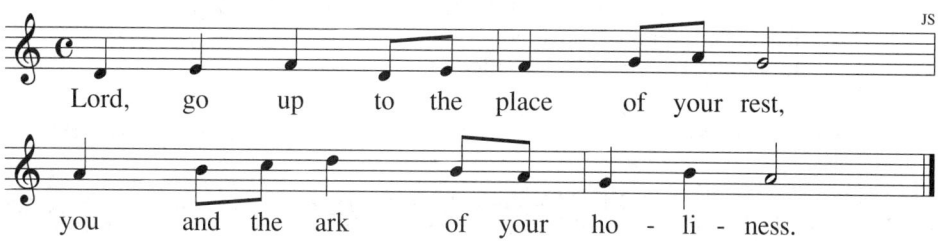

Lord, go up to the place of your rest, you and the ark of your ho-li-ness.

At Ephrata we heard of it;
  we found it in the plains of Yearim.
"Let us go to the place of his dwelling;
  let us bow down at his footstool." ℟.

Your priests shall be clothed with justice;
  your faithful shall ring out their joy.
For the sake of David your servant,

do not reject your anointed. ℟.

For the LORD has chosen Sion;
  he has desired it for his dwelling:
"This is my resting place from age to
  age;
here have I chosen to dwell." ℟.

READING II   *1 Corinthians 15:54b–57*

Brothers and sisters: When that which is mortal clothes itself with immortality, then the word that is written shall come about:

  Death is swallowed up in victory.
  Where, O death, is your victory?
  Where, O death, is your sting?

The sting of death is sin, and the power of sin is the law. But thanks be to God who gives us the victory through our Lord Jesus Christ.

GOSPEL   *Luke 11:27–28*

While Jesus was speaking, a woman from the crowd called out and said to him, "Blessed is the womb that carried you and the breasts at which you nursed." He replied, "Rather, blessed are those who hear the word of God and observe it."

AUGUST 15: ASSUMPTION OF MARY—MASS DURING THE DAY 1307

READING I   *Revelation 11:19a; 12:1–6a, 10ab / 622*

God's temple in heaven was opened, and the ark of his covenant could be seen in the temple.

  A great sign appeared in the sky, a woman clothed with the sun, with the moon beneath her feet, and on her head a crown of twelve stars. She was with child and wailed aloud in pain as she labored to give birth. Then another sign appeared in the sky; it was a huge red dragon, with seven heads and ten horns, and on its heads were seven diadems. Its tail swept away a third of the stars in the sky and hurled them down to the earth. Then the dragon stood before the woman about to give birth, to devour her child when she gave birth. She gave birth to a son, a male child, destined to rule all the nations with an iron rod. Her child was caught up to God and his throne. The woman herself fled into the desert where she had a place prepared by God.

Then I heard a loud voice in heaven say:
"Now have salvation and power come,
and the Kingdom of our God
and the authority of his Anointed One."

RESPONSORIAL PSALM   *Psalm 45:10, 11, 12ab, 16*

The queen stands at your right hand, ar-rayed in gold.

The daughters of kings are those whom
you favor.
On your right stands the queen in
gold of Ophir. ℟.

Listen, O daughter; pay heed and give ear:
forget your own people and your
father's house. ℟.

So will the king desire your beauty.
He is your lord, pay homage to
him. ℟.

They are escorted amid gladness and
joy;
they pass within the palace of the
king. ℟.

READING II   *1 Corinthians 15:20–27*
Brothers and sisters: Christ has been raised from the dead, the firstfruits of those
who have fallen asleep. For since death came through man, the resurrection of the
dead came also through man. For just as in Adam all die, so too in Christ shall all
be brought to life, but each one in proper order: Christ the firstfruits; then, at his
coming, those who belong to Christ; then comes the end, when he hands over the
Kingdom to his God and Father, when he has destroyed every sovereignty and every
authority and power. For he must reign until he has put all his enemies under his feet.
The last enemy to be destroyed is death, for "he subjected everything under his feet."

GOSPEL   *Luke 1:39–56*
Mary set out and traveled to the hill country in haste to a town of Judah, where she
entered the house of Zechariah and greeted Elizabeth. When Elizabeth heard Mary's
greeting, the infant leaped in her womb, and Elizabeth, filled with the Holy Spirit,
cried out in a loud voice and said, "Blessed are you among women, and blessed is
the fruit of your womb. And how does this happen to me, that the mother of my Lord
should come to me? For at the moment the sound of your greeting reached my ears,
the infant in my womb leaped for joy. Blessed are you who believed that what was
spoken to you by the Lord would be fulfilled."

And Mary said:
"My soul proclaims the greatness of the Lord;
my spirit rejoices in God my Savior
for he has looked upon his lowly servant.
From this day all generations will call me blessed:
the Almighty has done great things for me,
and holy is his Name.

He has mercy on those who fear him
  in every generation.
He has shown the strength of his arm,
  and has scattered the proud in their conceit.
He has cast down the mighty from their thrones,
  and has lifted up the lowly.
He has filled the hungry with good things,
  and the rich he has sent away empty.
He has come to the help of his servant Israel
  for he has remembered his promise of mercy,
  the promise he made to our fathers,
  to Abraham and his children for ever."

Mary remained with her about three months and then returned to her home.

FIRST MONDAY IN SEPTEMBER: LABOR DAY   1308

RESPONSORIAL PSALM   *Psalm 90:2, 3–4, 12–13, 14 and 16*

Lord, give suc - cess to the work of our hands.

Before the mountains were born,
  or the earth or the world were
    brought forth,
  you are God, from age to age. ℟.

You turn man back to dust,
  and say, "Return, O children of men."
To your eyes a thousand years
  are like yesterday, come and gone,
  or like a watch in the night. ℟.

Then teach us to number our days,
  that we may gain wisdom of heart.
Turn back, O LORD! How long?
  Show pity to your servants. ℟.

At dawn, fill us with your merciful love;
  we shall exult and rejoice all our
    days.
Let your deed be seen by your servants,
  and your glorious power by their
    children. ℟.

SEPTEMBER 14: EXALTATION OF THE HOLY CROSS   1309

READING I   *Numbers 21:4b–9 / 638*

With their patience worn out by the journey, the people complained against God and Moses, "Why have you brought us up from Egypt to die in this desert, where there is no food or water? We are disgusted with this wretched food!"

In punishment the LORD sent among the people saraph serpents, which bit the people so that many of them died. Then the people came to Moses and said, "We have sinned in complaining against the LORD and you. Pray the LORD to take the serpents from us." So Moses prayed for the people, and the LORD said to Moses, "Make a saraph and mount it on a pole, and if any who have been bitten look at it, they will live." Moses accordingly made a bronze serpent and mounted it on a pole, and whenever anyone who had been bitten by a serpent looked at the bronze serpent, he lived.

RESPONSORIAL PSALM *Psalm 78:1bc–2, 34–35, 36–37, 38*

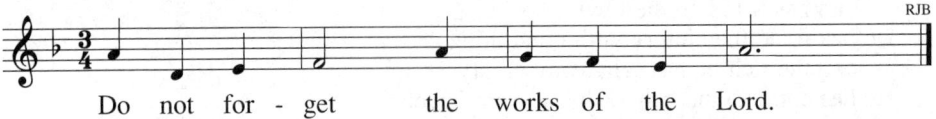

RJB

Do not for-get the works of the Lord.

Give ear, my people, to my teaching;
    incline your ear to the words of my
        mouth.
I will open my mouth in a parable
    and utter hidden lessons of the
        past. ℟.

When he slew them, then they sought
        him,
    repented and earnestly sought God.
They would remember that God was
        their rock,
    God the Most High their
        redeemer. ℟.

Yet they deceived him with their
        mouths;
    they lied to him with their tongues.
For their hearts were not steadfast
        toward him;
    they were not faithful to his
        covenant. ℟.

Yet he who is full of compassion
    forgave them their sin and spared
        them.
So often he held back his anger,
    and did not stir up all his rage. ℟.

READING II *Philippians 2:6–11*

Brothers and sisters:
    Christ Jesus, though he was in the
        form of God,
        did not regard equality with God
            something to be grasped.
    Rather, he emptied himself,
        taking the form of a slave,
        coming in human likeness;
        and found human in appearance,
        he humbled himself,
        becoming obedient to the point
            of death,

        even death on a cross.
Because of this, God greatly exalted
        him
    and bestowed on him the name
    which is above every name,
    that at the name of Jesus
    every knee should bend,
    of those in heaven and on earth
        and under the earth,
    and every tongue confess that
    Jesus Christ is Lord,
    to the glory of God the Father.

GOSPEL *John 3:13–17*

Jesus said to Nicodemus: "No one has gone up to heaven except the one who has come down from heaven, the Son of Man. And just as Moses lifted up the serpent in the desert, so must the Son of Man be lifted up, so that everyone who believes in him may have eternal life."

    For God so loved the world that he gave his only Son, so that he who believes in him might not perish but might have eternal life. For God did not send his Son into the world to condemn the world, but that the world might be saved through him.

NOVEMBER 1: ALL SAINTS   1310

READING I   *Revelation 7:2–4, 9–14 / 667*

I, John, saw another angel come up from the East, holding the seal of the living God. He cried out in a loud voice to the four angels who were given power to damage the land and the sea, "Do not damage the land or the sea or the trees until we put the seal on the foreheads of the servants of our God." I heard the number of those who had been marked with the seal, one hundred and forty-four thousand marked from every tribe of the children of Israel.

After this I had a vision of a great multitude, which no one could count, from every nation, race, people, and tongue. They stood before the throne and before the Lamb, wearing white robes and holding palm branches in their hands. They cried out in a loud voice:

"Salvation comes from our God,
> who is seated on the throne,
and from the Lamb."

All the angels stood around the throne and around the elders and the four living creatures. They prostrated themselves before the throne, worshipped God, and exclaimed:

"Amen. Blessing and glory, wisdom and thanksgiving,
> honor, power, and might
be to our God forever and ever. Amen."

Then one of the elders spoke up and said to me, "Who are these wearing white robes, and where did they come from?" I said to him, "My lord, you are the one who knows." He said to me, "These are the ones who have survived the time of great distress; they have washed their robes and made them white in the Blood of the Lamb."

RESPONSORIAL PSALM   *Psalm 24:1bc–2, 3–4ab, 5–6*

Lord, this is the peo-ple that longs to see your face.

The LORD's is the earth and its fullness,
> the world, and those who dwell in it.
It is he who set it on the seas;
> on the rivers he made it firm. ℟.

Who shall climb the mountain of the
> LORD?
> Who shall stand in his holy place?
The clean of hands and pure of heart,

whose soul is not set on vain
> things. ℟.

Blessings from the LORD shall he receive,
> and right reward from the God who
> saves him.
Such are the people who seek him,
> who seek the face of the God of
> Jacob. ℟.

READING II   *1 John 3:1–3*

Beloved: See what love the Father has bestowed on us that we may be called the children of God. Yet so we are. The reason the world does not know us is that it did not know him. Beloved, we are God's children now; what we shall be has not yet been revealed. We do know that when it is revealed we shall be like him, for we shall see him as he is. Everyone who has this hope based on him makes himself pure, as he is pure.

GOSPEL *Matthew 5:1–12a*

When Jesus saw the crowds, he went up the mountain, and after he had sat down, his disciples came to him. He began to teach them, saying:

"Blessed are the poor in spirit,
  for theirs is the Kingdom of heaven.
Blessed are they who mourn,
  for they will be comforted.
Blessed are the meek,
  for they will inherit the land.
Blessed are they who hunger and thirst for righteousness,
  for they will be satisfied.
Blessed are the merciful,
  for they will be shown mercy.
Blessed are the clean of heart,
  for they will see God.
Blessed are the peacemakers,
  for they will be called children of God.
Blessed are they who are persecuted for the sake of righteousness,
  for theirs is the Kingdom of heaven.

Blessed are you when they insult you and persecute you and utter every kind of evil against you falsely because of me. Rejoice and be glad, for your reward will be great in heaven."

1311 NOVEMBER 2: ALL SOULS' DAY

RESPONSORIAL PSALM *Psalm 23:1–3a, 3b–4, 5, 6 / 668*

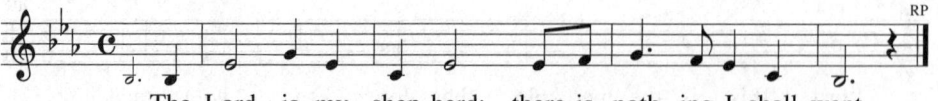

The Lord is my shep-herd; there is noth-ing I shall want.

or:

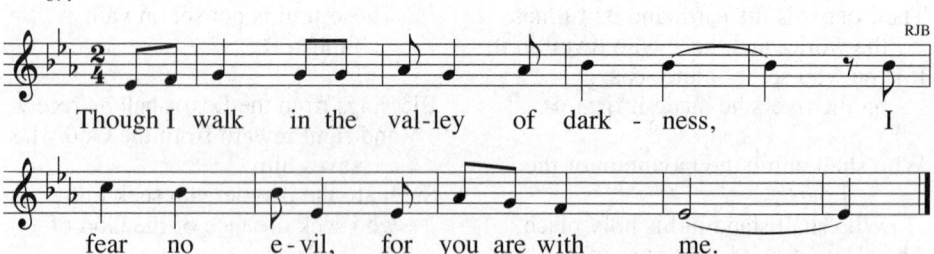

Though I walk in the val-ley of dark - ness, I
fear no e-vil, for you are with me.

The LORD is my shepherd;
  there is nothing I shall want.
Fresh and green are the pastures
  where he gives me repose.
Near restful waters he leads me;
  he revives my soul. ℟.

He guides me along the right path,
  for the sake of his name.
Though I should walk in the valley of
  the shadow of death,
  no evil would I fear, for you are
  with me.
Your crook and your staff will give
  me comfort. ℟.

You have prepared a table before me
    in the sight of my foes.
My head you have anointed with oil;
    my cup is overflowing. ℟.

Surely goodness and mercy shall follow
    me
    all the days of my life.
In the LORD's own house shall I dwell
    for length of days unending. ℟.

Or:

RESPONSORIAL PSALM   *Psalm 25:6–7bc, 17–18, 20–21*

To you, O Lord, I lift my soul.

or:

No one who waits for you, O Lord, will ev-er be put to shame.

Remember your compassion, O LORD,
    and your merciful love,
    for they are from of old.
In your merciful love remember me,
    because of your goodness, O LORD. ℟.

Relieve the anguish of my heart,
    and set me free from my distress.

See my lowliness and suffering,
    and take away all my sins. ℟.

Preserve my life and rescue me.
    Let me not be put to shame,
    for in you I trust.
May integrity and virtue protect me,
    for I have hoped in you, O LORD. ℟.

Or:

RESPONSORIAL PSALM   *Psalm 27:1, 4, 7 and 8b and 9a, 13–14*

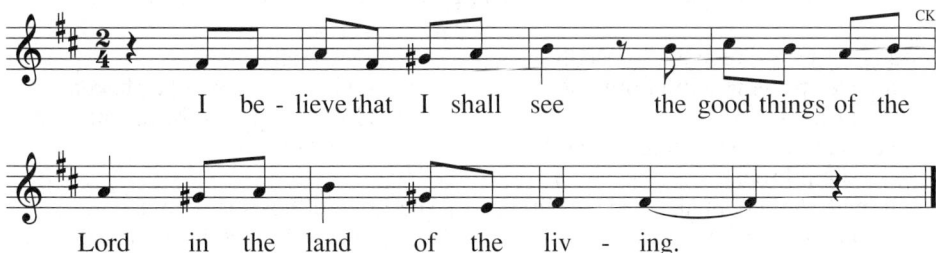

The Lord is my light and my sal - va - tion.

or:

I be - lieve that I shall see the good things of the

Lord in the land of the liv - ing.

The LORD is my light and my salvation;
    whom shall I fear?

The LORD is the stronghold of my life;
    whom should I dread? ℟.

There is one thing I ask of the Lord,
  only this do I seek:
to live in the house of the Lord
  all the days of my life,
to gaze on the beauty of the Lord,
  to inquire at his temple. ℟.

O Lord, hear my voice when I call;
  have mercy and answer me.

It is your face, O Lord, that I seek;
  hide not your face from me. ℟.

I believe I shall see the Lord's
  goodness
  in the land of the living.
Wait for the Lord; be strong;
  be stouthearted, and wait for the
  Lord! ℟.

1312   NOVEMBER 9: DEDICATION OF THE LATERAN BASILICA

READING I   *Ezekiel 47:1–2, 8–9, 12 / 671*

The angel brought me back to the entrance of the temple, and I saw water flowing out
from beneath the threshold of the temple toward the east, for the façade of the temple
was toward the east; the water flowed down from the southern side of the temple,
south of the altar. He led me outside by the north gate, and around to the outer gate
facing the east, where I saw water trickling from the southern side. He said to me,
"This water flows into the eastern district down upon the Arabah, and empties into the
sea, the salt waters, which it makes fresh. Wherever the river flows, every sort of living creature that can multiply shall live, and there shall be abundant fish, for wherever
this water comes the sea shall be made fresh. Along both banks of the river, fruit trees
of every kind shall grow; their leaves shall not fade, nor their fruit fail. Every month
they shall bear fresh fruit, for they shall be watered by the flow from the sanctuary.
Their fruit shall serve for food, and their leaves for medicine."

RESPONSORIAL PSALM   *Psalm 46:2–3, 5–6, 8–9*

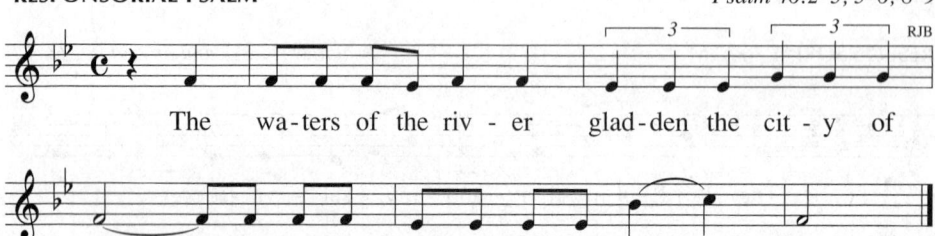

God is for us a refuge and strength,
  an ever-present help in time of
    distress:
so we shall not fear though the earth
    should rock,
  though the mountains quake to the
    heart of the sea. ℟.

The waters of a river give joy to God's
    city,
  the holy place, the dwelling of the

Most High.
God is within, it cannot be shaken;
  God will help it at the dawning of
    the day. ℟.

The Lord of hosts is with us:
  the God of Jacob is our stronghold.
Come and behold the works of the
    Lord,
  the awesome deeds he has done on
    the earth. ℟.

READING II   *1 Corinthians 3:9c–11, 16–17*

Brothers and sisters: You are God's building. According to the grace of God given to me, like a wise master builder I laid a foundation, and another is building upon it. But each one must be careful how he builds upon it, for no one can lay a foundation other than the one that is there, namely, Jesus Christ.

Do you not know that you are the temple of God, and that the Spirit of God dwells in you? If anyone destroys God's temple, God will destroy that person; for the temple of God, which you are, is holy.

GOSPEL   *John 2:13–22*

Since the Passover of the Jews was near, Jesus went up to Jerusalem. He found in the temple area those who sold oxen, sheep, and doves, as well as the money changers seated there. He made a whip out of cords and drove them all out of the temple area, with the sheep and oxen, and spilled the coins of the money changers and overturned their tables, and to those who sold doves he said, "Take these out of here, and stop making my Father's house a marketplace." His disciples recalled the words of Scripture, *Zeal for your house will consume me.* At this the Jews answered and said to him, "What sign can you show us for doing this?" Jesus answered and said to them, "Destroy this temple and in three days I will raise it up." The Jews said, "This temple has been under construction for forty-six years, and you will raise it up in three days?" But he was speaking about the temple of his body. Therefore, when he was raised from the dead, his disciples remembered that he had said this, and they came to believe the Scripture and the word Jesus had spoken.

THANKSGIVING DAY   1313

RESPONSORIAL PSALM   *Psalm 138:1–2a, 2bc and 3, 4–5*

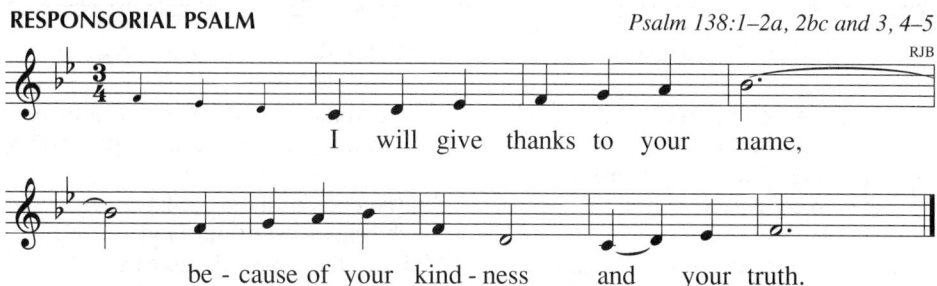

I will give thanks to your name, be-cause of your kind-ness and your truth.

I thank you, LORD, with all my heart;
  you have heard the words of my
    mouth.
In the presence of the angels I praise you.
  I bow down toward your holy
    temple. ℞.

I give thanks to your name
  for your merciful love and your
    faithfulness.
On the day I called, you answered me;

you increased the strength of my
  soul. ℞.

All earth's kings shall thank you,
  O LORD,
  when they hear the words of your
    mouth.
They shall sing of the ways of the LORD,
  "How great is the glory of the
    LORD!" ℞.

1314 DECEMBER 8: IMMACULATE CONCEPTION

READING I   *Genesis 3:9–15, 20 / 689*

After the man, Adam, had eaten of the tree, the LORD God called to the man and asked
him, "Where are you?" He answered, "I heard you in the garden; but I was afraid,
because I was naked, so I hid myself." Then he asked, "Who told you that you were
naked? You have eaten, then, from the tree of which I had forbidden you to eat!" The
man replied, "The woman whom you put here with me— she gave me fruit from the
tree, and so I ate it." The LORD God then asked the woman, "Why did you do such a
thing?" The woman answered, "The serpent tricked me into it, so I ate it."

> Then the LORD God said to the serpent:
> "Because you have done this, you shall be banned
>   from all the animals
>   and from all the wild creatures;
> on your belly shall you crawl,
>   and dirt shall you eat
>   all the days of your life.
> I will put enmity between you and the woman,
>   and between your offspring and hers;
> he will strike at your head,
>   while you strike at his heel."

The man called his wife Eve, because she became the mother of all the living.

RESPONSORIAL PSALM   *Psalm 98:1, 2–3ab, 3cd–4*

JRC

Sing to the Lord a new song, for he has done mar-vel-ous deeds.

O sing a new song to the LORD,
    for he has worked wonders.
His right hand and his holy arm
    have brought salvation. ℟.

The LORD has made known his salvation,
    has shown his deliverance to the
    nations.

He has remembered his merciful love
    and his truth for the house of Israel. ℟.

All the ends of the earth have seen
    the salvation of our God.
Shout to the LORD, all the earth;
    break forth into joyous song,
    and sing out your praise. ℟.

READING II   *Ephesians 1:3–6, 11–12*

Brothers and sisters: Blessed be the God and Father of our Lord Jesus Christ, who has
blessed us in Christ with every spiritual blessing in the heavens, as he chose us in him,
before the foundation of the world, to be holy and without blemish before him. In love
he destined us for adoption to himself through Jesus Christ, in accord with the favor
of his will, for the praise of the glory of his grace that he granted us in the beloved.

In him we were also chosen, destined in accord with the purpose of the One who
accomplishes all things according to the intention of his will, so that we might exist
for the praise of his glory, we who first hoped in Christ.

GOSPEL *Luke 1:26–38*

The angel Gabriel was sent from God to a town of Galilee called Nazareth, to a virgin betrothed to a man named Joseph, of the house of David, and the virgin's name was Mary. And coming to her, he said, "Hail, full of grace! The Lord is with you." But she was greatly troubled at what was said and pondered what sort of greeting this might be. Then the angel said to her, "Do not be afraid, Mary, for you have found favor with God. Behold, you will conceive in your womb and bear a son, and you shall name him Jesus. He will be great and will be called Son of the Most High, and the Lord God will give him the throne of David his father, and he will rule over the house of Jacob forever, and of his Kingdom there will be no end." But Mary said to the angel, "How can this be, since I have no relations with a man?" And the angel said to her in reply, "The Holy Spirit will come upon you, and the power of the Most High will overshadow you. Therefore the child to be born will be called holy, the Son of God. And behold, Elizabeth, your relative, has also conceived a son in her old age, and this is the sixth month for her who was called barren; for nothing will be impossible for God." Mary said, "Behold, I am the handmaid of the Lord. May it be done to me according to your word." Then the angel departed from her.

DECEMBER 12: OUR LADY OF GUADALUPE 1315

READING I *Zechariah 2:14–17 / 690A*

Sing and rejoice, O daughter Zion! See, I am coming to dwell among you, says the LORD. Many nations shall join themselves to the LORD on that day, and they shall be his people, and he will dwell among you, and you shall know that the LORD of hosts has sent me to you. The LORD will possess Judah as his portion in the holy land, and he will again choose Jerusalem. Silence, all mankind, in the presence of the LORD! For he stirs forth from his holy dwelling.

Or:

READING I *Revelation 11:19a; 12:1–6a, 10ab*

God's temple in heaven was opened, and the ark of his covenant could be seen in the temple.

A great sign appeared in the sky, a woman clothed with the sun, with the moon under her feet, and on her head a crown of twelve stars. She was with child and wailed aloud in pain as she labored to give birth. Then another sign appeared in the sky; it was a huge red dragon, with seven heads and ten horns, and on its head were seven diadems. Its tail swept away a third of the stars in the sky and hurled them down to the earth. Then the dragon stood before the woman about to give birth, to devour her child when she gave birth. She gave birth to a son, a male child, destined to rule all the nations with an iron rod. Her child was caught up to God and his throne. The woman herself fled into the desert where she had a place prepared by God.
Then I heard a loud voice in heaven say:
    "Now have salvation and power come,
        and the Kingdom of our God
        and the authority of his Anointed."

RESPONSORIAL PSALM   *Judith 13:18bcde, 19*

KC

You are the high - est hon - or of our race.
Tú e - res el or - gu - llo de nues - tra ra - za.

Blessed are you, daughter, by the Most
    High God,
  above all the women on earth;
  and blessed be the Lord God,
  the creator of heaven and earth. ℟.

Your deed of hope will never be
    forgotten
  by those who tell of the might of
    God. ℟.

GOSPEL   *Luke 1:26–38*

The angel Gabriel was sent from God to a town of Galilee called Nazareth, to a virgin betrothed to a man named Joseph, of the house of David, and the virgin's name was Mary. And coming to her, he said, "Hail, full of grace! The Lord is with you." But she was greatly troubled at what was said and pondered what sort of greeting this might be. Then the angel said to her, "Do not be afraid, Mary, for you have found favor with God. Behold, you will conceive in your womb and bear a son, and you shall name him Jesus. He will be great and will be called Son of the Most High, and the Lord God will give him the throne of David his father, and he will rule over the house of Jacob forever, and of his Kingdom there will be no end." But Mary said to the angel, "How can this be, since I have no relations with a man?" And the angel said to her in reply, "The Holy Spirit will come upon you, and the power of the Most High will overshadow you. Therefore the child to be born will be called holy, the Son of God. And behold, Elizabeth, your relative, has also conceived a son in her old age, and this is the sixth month for her who was called barren; for nothing will be impossible for God." Mary said, "Behold, I am the handmaid of the Lord. May it be done to me according to your word." Then the angel departed from her.

Or:

GOSPEL   *Luke 1:39–47*

Mary set out and traveled to the hill country in haste to a town of Judah, where she entered the house of Zechariah and greeted Elizabeth. When Elizabeth heard Mary's greeting, the infant leaped in her womb, and Elizabeth, filled with the Holy Spirit, cried out in a loud voice and said, "Most blessed are you among women, and blessed is the fruit of your womb. And how does this happen to me, that the mother of my Lord should come to me? For at the moment the sound of your greeting reached my ears, the infant in my womb leaped for joy. Blessed are you who believed that what was spoken to you by the Lord would be fulfilled."

And Mary said:
  "My soul proclaims the greatness of the Lord;
    my spirit rejoices in God my Savior."

Alternate Lectionary Psalm Refrains

The following psalm refrains are from Michel Guimont's Lectionary Psalms.

Psalm 1   1316

Bless-ed are they, bless-ed are they who hope in the Lord.

Psalm 4   1317

Lord, let your face shine on us.

Psalm 8   1318

O Lord, our God, how won-der-ful your name in all the earth!

Psalm 15   1319

He who does jus-tice will live in the pres-ence of the Lord.

Psalm 15   1320

One who does jus-tice will live in the pres-ence of the Lord.

Psalm 16   1321

You are my in-her-i-tance, O Lord.

Psalm 16   1322

Lord, you will show us the path of life.

Psalm 16   1323

You are my in-her-i-tance, O Lord.

Psalm 17   1324

Lord, when your glo-ry ap-pears, my joy will be full.

1325 Psalm 18

I love you, Lord, my strength, my strength.

1326 Psalm 19

Lord, you have the words of ev - er - last - ing life.

1327 Psalm 19

Your words, O Lord, are Spir - it and life.

1328 Psalm 19

The pre-cepts of the Lord give joy to the heart.

1329 Psalm 19

Their mes - sage goes out through all the earth.

1330 Psalm 22

My God, my God, why have you a - ban - doned me?

1331 Psalm 22

I will praise you, Lord, in the as - sem - bly of your peo - ple.

1332 Psalm 23

The Lord is my shep-herd; there is noth - ing I shall want.

1333 Psalm 23

Though I walk in the val - ley of dark - ness, I fear no

Psalm 23   1334

Psalm 24   1335

Psalm 24   1336

Psalm 24   1337

Psalm 25   1338

Psalm 25   1339

Psalm 25   1340

Psalm 25   1341

1342 Psalm 25

No one who waits for you, O Lord, will ev-er be put to shame.

1343 Psalm 27

The Lord is my light and my sal-va-tion.

1344 Psalm 27

I be-lieve that I shall see the good things of the Lord in the land of the liv-ing.

1345 Psalm 27

I be-lieve that I shall see the good things of the Lord in the land of the liv-ing.

1346 Psalm 29

The Lord will bless his peo-ple with his peace.

1347 Psalm 30

I will praise you, Lord, for you have res-cued me.

1348 Psalm 31

Fa-ther, in-to your hands I com-mend my spir-it.

1349 Psalm 31

Lord, be my rock of safe-ty.

Psalm 32   1350

I turn to you, O Lord, in time of trou - ble, and you fill me with the joy of sal - va - tion.

Psalm 32   1351

Lord, for - give the wrong I have done.

Psalm 33   1352

Lord, let your mer - cy be on us, as we place our trust in you.

Psalm 33   1353

The earth is full of the good-ness of the Lord, the good-ness of the Lord.

Psalm 33   1354

Bless - ed the peo-ple the Lord has cho - sen to be his own.

Psalm 34   1355

Taste and see the good - ness of the Lord.

Psalm 34   1356

The Lord hears the cry of the poor.

Psalm 34   1357

The an - gel of the Lord will res - cue those who fear him.

1358 Psalm 40

Here am I, Lord; here am I, Lord; I come to do your will.

1359 Psalm 40

Lord, come to my aid, Lord, come to my aid!

1360 Psalm 41

Lord, heal my soul, for I have sinned a - gainst you.

1361 Psalm 42

Like a deer that longs for run - ning streams, my

soul longs for you, my God; my soul longs for you, my God.

1362 Psalm 45

The queen stands at your right hand, ar - rayed in gold.

1363 Psalm 46

The wa - ters of the riv - er glad - den the cit - y of

God, the ho - ly dwell-ing of the Most High.

1364 Psalm 47

God mounts his throne to shouts of joy: a blare of

trum - pets for the Lord.

Psalm 50   1365

To the up-right I will show the sav-ing pow'r of God.

Psalm 51   1366

Be mer-ci-ful, O Lord, for we have sinned.

Psalm 51   1367

Cre-ate in me, cre-ate in me a clean heart, O God.

Psalm 51   1368

I will rise and go to my fa-ther.

Psalm 54   1369

The Lord up-holds my life.

Psalm 62   1370

Rest in God a-lone, rest in God a-lone, my soul.

Psalm 63   1371

My soul is thirst-ing for you, O Lord, thirst-ing for you my God.

Psalm 65   1372

The seed that falls on good ground will yield a fruit-ful har-vest.

Psalm 66   1373

Let all the earth cry out to God with joy.

1374 Psalm 67

May God bless us in his mer - cy,

may God bless us in his mer - cy.

1375 Psalm 67

O God, O God, let all the na-tions praise you!

1376 Psalm 68

God, in your good-ness, you have made a home for the poor.

1377 Psalm 69

Lord, in your great love, an-swer me.

1378 Psalm 69

Turn to the Lord in your need, and you will live.

1379 Psalm 71

I will sing of your sal - va - tion.

1380 Psalm 71

Since my moth-er's womb, you have been my strength.

1381 Psalm 72

Jus-tice shall flour-ish in his time, and full-ness of peace for ev - er.

1391 Psalm 86

Lord, you are good and for - giv - ing.

1392 Psalm 89

For - ev - er I will sing the good - ness of the Lord.

1393 Psalm 89

The son of Da - vid will live for ev - er.

1394 Psalm 90

In ev-'ry age, O Lord, you have been our ref - uge.

1395 Psalm 90

Fill us with your love, O Lord, and we will sing for joy!

1396 Psalm 90

Lord, give suc - cess to the work of our hands, to the work of our hands.

1397 Psalm 91

Be with me, Lord, when I am in trou - ble.

1398 Psalm 92

Lord, it is good to give thanks to you, to give thanks to you.

1399 Psalm 93

The Lord is king; he is robed in maj - es - ty.

Psalm 95   1400

If to-day you hear his voice, hard-en not your hearts.

Psalm 96   1401

To-day, to-day, to-day is born our Sav-ior, Christ the Lord.

Psalm 96   1402

Pro-claim his mar-vel-ous deeds to all the na - tions.

Psalm 96   1403

Give the Lord glo-ry and hon - or.

Psalm 97   1404

A light will shine on us this day: the Lord is born for us.

Psalm 97   1405

The Lord is king, the Lord Most High o-ver all the earth.

Psalm 98   1406

All the ends of the earth have seen the sav - ing pow'r of God.

Psalm 98   1407

The Lord has re-vealed to the na - tions his sav-ing pow'r, his

sav - ing pow'r.

1408 Psalm 98

The Lord comes to rule the earth with jus - tice.

1409 Psalm 98

Sing to the Lord a new song, for he has done mar-vel-ous deeds.

1410 Psalm 100

We are his peo - ple, the sheep of his flock.

1411 Psalm 103

The Lord is kind and mer-ci-ful; the Lord is kind and mer-ci-ful.

1412 Psalm 103

The Lord has set his throne in heav - en.

1413 Psalm 103

The Lord's kind - ness is ev-er - last - ing to those who fear him.

1414 Psalm 103

The Lord is kind and mer - ci - ful, slow to an - ger, and

rich in com-pas - sion.

1415 Psalm 104

O bless the Lord, my soul, O bless the Lord.

Psalm 104   1416

Lord, send out your Spir - it, and re - new the face of the earth.

Psalm 105   1417

The Lord re - mem - bers his cov - e - nant for ev - er.

Psalm 107   1418

Give thanks to the Lord, his love is ev - er - last - ing.

Psalm 110   1419

You are a priest for ev - er, in the line of Mel - chi - ze - dek.

Psalm 112   1420

The just man is a light in dark - ness to the up - right.

Psalm 113   1421

Praise the Lord, praise the Lord who lifts up the poor.

Psalm 116   1422

I will walk be - fore the Lord, in the land of the liv - ing.

Psalm 116   1423

Our bless - ing - cup is a com - mun - ion with the Blood of Christ.

Psalm 116   1424

I will take the cup of sal - va - tion, and call on the name of the Lord.

1425 Psalm 117

Go out to all the world and tell the Good News.

1426 Psalm 118

Al - le - lu - ia, al - le - lu - ia, al - le - lu - ia!

1427 Psalm 118

This is the day the Lord has made; let us re - joice and be glad.

1428 Psalm 118

Give thanks to the Lord, for he is good, his love is ev - er - last - ing.

1429 Psalm 118

The stone re - ject - ed by the build - ers has be - come the cor - ner - stone.

1430 Psalm 119

Bless - ed are they who fol - low the law of the Lord!

1431 Psalm 119

Lord, I love your com - mands, I love your com - mands.

1432 Psalm 121

Our help is from the Lord, who made heav - en and earth.

1433 Psalm 122

Let us go re - joic - ing to the house of the Lord.

1443 Psalm 138

In the sight of the an - gels,   I will sing your prais-es, O Lord.

1444 Psalm 138

Lord, on the day I called for help,   you an - swered me.

1445 Psalm 138

Lord, your love is e - ter - nal;   do not for-sake the work of your hands.

1446 Psalm 139

I   praise you, O Lord,   for   I   am won-der-ful-ly made.

1447 Psalm 145

I will praise your name for ev - er,   my king and my   God.

1448 Psalm 145

The hand of the Lord   feeds   us;   he an - swers all our needs.

1449 Psalm 145

The   Lord   is near   to   all who call on him.

1450 Psalm 146

Lord,   come and   save   us.

1451 Psalm 146

Bless-ed the poor in spir-it;   the king-dom of heav-en is   theirs!

Psalm 146 — 1452
Praise the Lord, my soul! Praise the Lord!

Psalm 147 — 1453
O praise the Lord, Je - ru - sa - lem.

Psalm 147 — 1454
Praise the Lord, praise the Lord, who heals the bro-ken-heart-ed.

Exodus 15 — 1455
Let us sing to the Lord; he has cov-ered him-self in glo - ry.

1 Chronicles 29 — 1456
O God, O God, let all the na-tions praise you!

Isaiah 12 — 1457
Cry out with joy and glad-ness: for a - mong you is the great and
Ho - ly One of Is - ra - el.

Isaiah 12 — 1458
You will draw wa-ter joy-ful-ly from the springs of sal - va - tion.

Daniel 3 — 1459
Glo - ry and praise for ev - er-more.

Luke 1 — 1460
My soul re - joic - es in my God, my soul re - joic - es in my God.

1461 Acknowledgments

SERVICE MUSIC

All music found at nos. 1–491 is copyright or administered by GIA Publications, Inc., with the exception of those items specified below. Please refer to these numbers for exact copyright dates. For more complete information regarding copyrights of ICEL and other entities, please see the copyright page at the beginning of this edition. The composers of lectionary psalm refrains are identified by their initials. They are: Robert J. Batastini (RJB), J. Robert Carroll (JRC), James J. Chepponis (JJC), Rory P. Cooney (RPC), Kyle Cothern (KC), Patricia Craig (PC), Randolph Currie (RC), Norah Duncan IV (ND), Eugene Englert (EE), Joseph Gelineau, SJ (JG), David R. Haas (DRH), Marty Haugen (MH), Howard Hughes, SM (HH), Robert M. Hutmacher, OFM (RMH), Michael Joncas (MJ), Columba Kelly, OSB (CK), Marie Kremer (MK), Ronald F. Krisman (RFK), Robert LeBlanc (RL), A. Gregory Murray, OSB (AGM), C. Alexander Peloquin (CAP), Richard Proulx (RP), John Schiavone (JS), Frank Schoen (FS), Robert J. Thompson (RJT), Suzanne Toolan (ST), Ralph C. Verdi (RCV), Chrysogonus Waddell, OCSO (CW).

5 Text © 1969, James Quinn, SJ. Published by OCP, 5536 NE Hassalo, Portland, OR 97213. All rights reserved. Used with permission.
6 Psalm tone © Downside Abbey
15 Text tr. © William G. Storey
25 Text © 1967, Benedictine Nuns of St. Mary's Abbey, West Malling, Kent
31 Psalm tone © Downside Abbey
40 Spanish text © 1970, Conferencia Episcopal Española
45 Psalm tone © 1969, Ampleforth Abbey Trustees
52 © 1978, John B. Foley, SJ, and OCP, 5536 NE Hassalo, Portland, OR 97213. All rights reserved. Used with permission.
53 Verses text and music © 1971, 1991, OCP, 5536 NE Hassalo, Portland, OR 97213. All rights reserved. Used with permission.
55 © 1988, Bob Hurd. Published by OCP, 5536 NE Hassalo, Portland, OR 97213. All rights reserved. Used with permission.
58 Antiphon III music © 1969, Geoffrey Chapman Ltd.
62 Psalm tone © Gethsemani Abbey
63 Verses text adapt. © 1970, Confraternity of Christian Doctrine, Inc.
64 Music © 1985, Michael Joncas. Published by OCP, 5536 NE Hassalo, Portland, OR 97213. All rights reserved. Used with permission.
65 Spanish text © 1970, 1972, Conferencia Episcopal Española
78 Verses tr. © 1970, Confraternity of Christian Doctrine.
90 Spanish refrain tr. © 1970, Conferencia Episcopal Española
96 Verses text © Confraternity of Christian Doctrine, Inc. Music © 1988, Jan Michael Joncas Trust. Published by OCP, 5536 NE Hassalo, Portland, OR 97213. All rights reserved. Used with permission.
100 Verses music © 1984, Benedictine Sisters of Stanbrook Abbey
104 © 1983, OCP, 5536 NE Hassalo, Portland, OR 97213. All rights reserved. Used with permission.
109 Spanish refrain tr. © 1981, Comisión Episcopal Española de Liturgia
116 © 1964, World Library Publications, wlpmusic.com
118 Text © 1970, Confraternity of Christian Doctrine, Inc.
121 Text © 1970, Confraternity of Christian Doctrine, Inc. Music © 2002, World Library Publications, wlpmusic.com
122 Text © 1970, Confraternity of Christian Doctrine, Inc.
130 Text © 1991, Owen Alstott. Music © 1993, Bernadette Farrell. Published by OCP, 5536 NE Hassalo, Portland, OR 97213. All rights reserved. Used with permission.
132 Text © 1969, 1989, James Quinn, SJ. Published by OCP, 5536 NE Hassalo, Portland, OR 97213. All rights reserved. Used with permission.
134 Text © 1970, Confraternity of Christian Doctrine, Inc.
135 Text © 1970, Confraternity of Christian Doctrine, Inc.
145 Music © 1991, Birnamwood Publications, a div. of MorningStar Music Publishers, Inc.
181 Text © 1969, James Quinn, SJ. Published by OCP, 5536 NE Hassalo, Portland, OR 97213. All rights reserved. Used with permission.
224 Text © 2000, World Library Publications, wlpmusic.com
403 Music © 2011, World Library Publications, wlpmusic.com
411 Refrain music © 1958, World Library Publications, wlpmusic.com
413 © 1985, Fintan O'Carroll and Christopher Walker. Published by OCP, 5536 NE Hassalo, Portland, OR 97213. All rights reserved. Used with permission.
414 Music © 1999, MorningStar Music Publishers
428 Refrain music © 1965, 1966, 1968, 1973, World Library Publications, wlpmusic.com
435 Music © 1994, World Library Publications, wlpmusic.com
438 Music © 2001, World Library Publications, wlpmusic.com
458 Music © 1970, 1987, 2010, World Library Publications, wlpmusic.com

459 Music © 2010, World Library Publications, wlpmusic.com
460 Music © 1970, 1973, 2011, World Library Publications, wlpmusic.com
462 Music © 2010, World Library Publications, wlpmusic.com
463 Music © 2010, World Library Publications, wlpmusic.com
464 Music © 2010, World Library Publications, wlpmusic.com
469 Music © 2007, 2009, Daniel L. Schutte. Published by OCP, 5536 NE Hassalo, Portland, OR 97213. All rights reserved. Used with permission.
470 Music © 2007, 2009, Daniel L. Schutte. Published by OCP, 5536 NE Hassalo, Portland, OR 97213. All rights reserved. Used with permission.
471 Music © 2007, 2009, Daniel L. Schutte. Published by OCP, 5536 NE Hassalo, Portland, OR 97213. All rights reserved. Used with permission.
487 Arr. © 2006, World Library Publications, wlpmusic.com
492 Acc. © 1975, GIA Publications, Inc.
493 Acc. © 1981, ICEL
494 © 2007, GIA Publications, Inc.
495 Tr. © 1985, The Church Pension Fund. Acc. © 1986, GIA Publications, Inc.
496 Text © 1982, The Jubilate Group (admin. Hope Publishing Company, Carol Stream, IL 60188). All rights reserved. Used by permission.
498 St. 4 text © 2006, Augsburg Fortress
499 © 1982, tr. © 2005, GIA Publications, Inc.
501 Text © David Higham Assoc. Ltd. Harm. (from *The Oxford Book of Carols*) © 1928, Oxford University Press. Reproduced by permission. All rights reserved.
502 © 1984, Les Presses de Taizé, GIA Publications, Inc., agent
504 Arr. © 1994, GIA Publications, Inc.
505 Text © 2006, Arr. © 2008, GIA Publications, Inc.
506 © 2011, GIA Publications, Inc.
507 © 1984, Les Presses de Taizé, GIA Publications, Inc., agent
508 © 2001, World Library Publications, wlpmusic.com
509 © 2005, GIA Publications, Inc.
510 © 2012, GIA Publications, Inc.
511 Text adapt., Tune © 2001, Iona Community, GIA Publications, Inc., agent
512 Tr., adapt. © 1982, The Jubilate Group (admin. Hope Publishing Company, Carol Stream, IL 60188). All rights reserved. Used by permission.
513 Music © 2010, Conception Abbey, admin. GIA Publications, Inc.
514 Text © 1995, Tune © 2003, GIA Publications, Inc.
516 © 2000, GIA Publications, Inc.
517 © 1983, GIA Publications, Inc.
519 Tr. © 2011, Acc. © 1986, GIA Publications, Inc.
522 Harm. © 1994, GIA Publications, Inc.
526 Alt. text © 1992, GIA Publications, Inc.
528 © 1984, GIA Publications, Inc.
529 Acc. © 1985, GIA Publications, Inc.
530 Harm. © Walton Music Corp., a div. of GIA Publications, Inc.
532 © 2002, GIA Publications, Inc.
533 Arr. © 1987, GIA Publications, Inc.
534 Text © 1996, LNWhymns.com, admin. Music Services. All rights reserved. International copyright secured. Used by permission. Harm. © 2011, GIA Publications, Inc.
535 Tune transcr., arr. © 1990, Iona Community, GIA Publications, Inc., agent
536 Text adapt. © 2011, GIA Publications, Inc. Harm. © Oxford University Press. Reproduced by permission. All rights reserved.
537 Music © 1979, 1988, Les Presses de Taizé, GIA Publications, Inc., agent
538 © 2009, GIA Publications, Inc.
539 © 1996, GIA Publications, Inc.
540 Text, Arr. © 2014, GIA Publications, Inc.

Acknowledgments/*continued*

Acknowledgments/*continued*

Acknowledgments/*continued*

Scripture Passages Related to Hymns/*continued*

Scripture Passages Related to Hymns/*continued*

MALACHI

3:1	Love Divine, All Loves Excelling 806
3:1	On Jordan's Bank 503
3:6	Abide With Me 949
4:2	Hark! The Herald Angels Sing 520
4:2	Jesus, the Light of the World 550

MATTHEW

1:23	Love Has Come 534
1:23	Praise We the Lord This Day 973
1:23–24	The Hands that First Held Mary's Child 970
2:1–2	O Little Town of Bethlehem 523
2:1–11	Good Christian Friends, Rejoice 526
2:1–12	A Child Is Born in Bethlehem / Puer Natus in Bethlehem 519
2:1–12	As with Gladness Men of Old 551
2:1–12	Songs of Thankfulness and Praise 548
2:1–12	The First Nowell 554
2:1–12	We Three Kings of Orient Are 547
2:2–10	What Star Is This 553
2:9–11	Sing We Now of Christmas 536
2:10–11	Gentle Mary Laid Her Child 546
2:10–11	O Come, All Ye Faithful / Venid, Fieles Todos / Adeste Fideles 521
2:11	What Child Is This 552
2:12–18	Mary, First among Believers 1004
2:13–23	Jesus Entered Egypt 909
2:16–18	By All Your Saints Still Striving 986
3:3	On Jordan's Bank 503
3:13–17	Songs of Thankfulness and Praise 548
3:13–17	To Jordan Jesus Humbly Came 556
3:13–17	When Jesus Came to Jordan 975
3:13–17	When John Baptized by Jordan's River 555
4:1–2	Forty Days and Forty Nights 565
4:1–2	The Glory of These Forty Days 570
4:1–4	Led by the Spirit 576
4:1–11	Lord, Who throughout These Forty Days 564
4:1–11	Tree of Life 581
4:12–23	Two Fishermen 892
4:16	Comfort, Comfort, O My People 497
4:18–20	Those Who Love and Those Who Labor 891
4:18–22	Pescador de Hombres / Lord, When You Came 884
4:23	Lord Jesus Christ, Lover of All 1056
5:1–6	Jerusalem, My Destiny 568
5:3	Glorify the Lord by Our Lives 878
5:3	O Breathe on Me, O Breath of God 649
5:3–12	Blest Are They 839
5:3–12	Jesus Entered Egypt 909
5:3–12	O Blessed Are the Poor in Spirit 857
5:6	We Are Called 902
5:9	Dona Nobis Pacem Domine 917
5:13–14	Gather Us In 929
5:14	We Are Called 902
5:14–16	As a Fire Is Meant for Burning 850
5:14–16	God, Bless Your Church with Strength! 849
5:21–24	Forgive Our Sins 1062
5:38–48	Lord of All Nations, Grant Me Grace 810
6:1–6	Again We Keep This Solemn Fast 566
6:9–13	This Is My Song 1086
6:9–15	Forgive Our Sins 1062
6:10	Mayenziwe / Your Will Be Done 785
6:16–18	Again We Keep This Solemn Fast 566
6:25–34	Lord of All Hopefulness 758
6:25–34	Peace, Be Not Anxious 916

6:25–34	Praise and Thanksgiving 753
6:26	Do Not Be Afraid 829
6:33	Seek Ye First 800
6:33	Wait for the Lord 502
6:34	Do Not Be Afraid 829
7:7	Seek Ye First 800
7:7	Wait for the Lord 502
7:24	How Can I Keep from Singing? 802
8:23–27	Stand by Me 835
9:1–2	I Danced in the Morning 887
9:9	By All Your Saints Still Striving 986
9:9–13	Come, You Sinners, Poor and Needy 1061
9:9–13	For the Faithful Who Have Answered 990
9:11–13	The Master Came to Bring Good News 1067
10:9–12	Jesus Entered Egypt 909
10:32	Jesus, Lead the Way 824
10:34	God, Whose Purpose Is to Kindle 905
10:34	You, Lord, Are Both Lamb and Shepherd 708
10:37–39	The Summons 886
10:37–42	Take Up Your Cross 890
11:11	By All Your Saints Still Striving 986
11:11	The Great Forerunner of the Morn 974
11:25–30	How Blessed Is This Place 998
11:25–30	I Heard the Voice of Jesus Say 821
11:28	Come, Bring Your Burdens to God / Woza Nomthwalo Wakho 837
11:28	Come to Me 836
11:28	Softly and Tenderly Jesus Is Calling 1060
11:28–30	Come to Me, All Pilgrims Thirsty 1039
11:28–30	Come to Me, O Weary Traveler 823
11:28–30	Come to the Water 690
11:29–30	We Shall Rise Again 962
13:	Christ's Church Shall Glory 851
13:1–23	Word of God, Come Down on Earth 701
13:21–43	Come, You Thankful People, Come 752
13:24–33	The Reign of God 841
13:44–49	The Reign of God 841
14:14	Love Divine, All Loves Excelling 806
14:15–21	O Blessed Savior 1045
14:22–32	Stand by Me 835
14:22–33	How Can I Keep from Singing? 802
14:22–33	How Firm a Foundation 793
14:22–33	Precious Lord, Take My Hand 826
15:32–38	O Blessed Savior 1045
16:24–25	Take Up Your Cross 890
17:1–9	How Good, Lord, to Be Here! 978
17:1–9	Transform Us 977
17:2	From Ashes to the Living Font 562
17:2	You, Lord, Are Both Lamb and Shepherd 708
18:10–14	My Shepherd, You Supply My Need 827
18:10–14	The King of Love My Shepherd Is 820
18:20	Draw Us in the Spirit's Tether 1047
18:20	The God of All Eternity 1088
18:20	Vamos Todos al Banquete / Let Us Go Now to the Banquet 941
18:20	Where Two or Three Are Gathered 936
19:13–15	Wash, O God, Our Sons and Daughters 1014
19:30	To You Who Bow 675
20:1–16	For the Fruits of All Creation 750
20:16	To You Who Bow 675
20:17–28	Lord, Help Us Walk Your Servant Way 888
20:25–28	Lord, Whose Love in Humble Service 868

Scripture Passages Related to Hymns/*continued*

16:1–7	Christ Has Arisen, Alleluia / Mfurahini, Haleluya 633
16:3–4	Were You There 600
16:5–6	Surrexit Christus 624
16:6	I Danced in the Morning 887
16:15–20	Go Make of All Disciples 866

LUKE

1:11–20	The Great Forerunner of the Morn 974
1:26–33	Mary, First among Believers 1004
1:26–35	Como Estrella en Claro Cielo / As a Star on Cloudless Evenings 1006
1:26–37	Ave Maria 1001
1:26–38	For All the Faithful Women 985
1:26–38	I Sing a Maid 1008
1:26–38	Immaculate Mary 993
1:26–38	No Wind at the Window 971
1:26–38	Praise We the Lord This Day 973
1:26–38	Sing We of the Blessed Mother 1003
1:26–38	The Angel Gabriel from Heaven Came 972
1:26–45	Savior of the Nations, Come 498
1:28	Buenos Días, Paloma Blanca / Fairest Dove, Most Lovely Maiden 996
1:28	Mañanitas a la Virgen de Guadalupe / Morning Praises to the Virgin of Guadalupe 995
1:37	Nothing Is Impossible with God 801
1:38	Mary, First among Believers 1004
1:38	Now Let Us from This Table Rise 872
1:40–42	Hail, Holy Queen Enthroned Above 979
1:41	The Great Forerunner of the Morn 974
1:46	Como Estrella en Claro Cielo / As a Star on Cloudless Evenings 1006
1:46	Magnificat 713
1:46	The Angel Gabriel from Heaven Came 972
1:46–47	Let Us Sing to the Lord 678
1:46–55	All Who Claim the Faith of Jesus 1005
1:46–58	Canticle of the Turning 728
1:48	Buenos Días, Paloma Blanca / Fairest Dove, Most Lovely Maiden 996
1:49	Let Us Sing to the Lord 678
1:49	Nothing Is Impossible with God 801
1:57–64	The Great Forerunner of the Morn 974
1:78	As Stars Adorn the Night-Veiled Sky 983
1:78–79	O Come, Divine Messiah! 500
1:78–79	O Come, O Come, Emmanuel 492
2:1–7	Hacia Belén / Mary Journeyed with Her Husband 541
2:1–10	The First Nowell 554
2:1–20	A Child Is Born in Bethlehem / Puer Natus in Bethlehem 519
2:6–7	Savior of the Nations, Come 498
2:6–14	Awake! Awake, and Greet the New Morn 517
2:6–14	Silent Night / Noche de Paz 527
2:6–18	Gentle Mary Laid Her Child 546
2:6–18	Go Tell It on the Mountain 530
2:6–18	God Rest You Merry, Gentlemen 525
2:6–18	What Child Is This 552
2:7	Away in a Manger 522
2:7	Good Christian Friends, Rejoice 526
2:7	Lo, How a Rose E'er Blooming 515
2:7	Once in Royal David's City 543
2:7	Sing of Mary, Pure and Lowly 545
2:10–11	Good Christian Friends, Rejoice 526
2:10–11	It Came upon the Midnight Clear 531
2:10–11	O Come, All Ye Faithful / Venid, Fieles Todos / Adeste Fideles 521
2:10–14	Immaculate Mary 993
2:10–16	Sing We Now of Christmas 536
2:11–16	Love Has Come 534
2:13–14	Everything That Has Voice 914
2:13–15	O Come, All Ye Faithful / Venid, Fieles Todos / Adeste Fideles 521
2:13–18	Angels We Have Heard on High 524
2:14	Gloria, Gloria 537
2:15–19	Mary, First among Believers 1004
2:19	Como Estrella en Claro Cielo / As a Star on Cloudless Evenings 1006
2:22–24	In His Temple Now Behold Him 967
2:22–40	Long-Awaited Holy One 968
2:25	Como Estrella en Claro Cielo / As a Star on Cloudless Evenings 1006
2:40	Sing of Mary, Pure and Lowly 545
2:41–51	Mary, First among Believers 1004
3:4–5	Prepare! Prepare! 494
3:4–6	On Jordan's Bank 503
3:4–6	Prepare the Way of the Lord 507
3:15–16	To Jordan Jesus Humbly Came 556
3:15–16	When John Baptized by Jordan's River 555
3:21–22	Songs of Thankfulness and Praise 548
3:21–22	To Jordan Jesus Humbly Came 556
3:21–22	When John Baptized by Jordan's River 555
4:1–2	Lord, Who throughout These Forty Days 564
4:1–2	The Glory of These Forty Days 570
4:1–13	Forty Days and Forty Nights 565
4:16–22	The Spirit Sends Us Forth to Serve 871
4:18	Hold Us in Your Mercy: Penitential Litany 583
4:18	Song of the Body of Christ / Canción del Cuerpo de Cristo 1042
4:18–19	God Has Chosen Me 867
4:19	Heaven Is Singing for Joy / El Cielo Canta Alegría 731
4:21–30	God Has Spoken by the Prophets 699
4:41	We Cannot Measure How You Heal 1057
5:1–11	Pescador de Hombres / Lord, When You Came 884
5:1–11	Two Fishermen 892
5:17	Lord Jesus Christ, Lover of All 1056
5:27	Two Fishermen 892
6:17	O Blessed Are the Poor in Spirit 857
6:20	Be Not Afraid 797
6:20	Glorify the Lord by Our Lives 878
6:20–26	O Blessed Are the Poor in Spirit 857
6:27–38	Lord of All Nations, Grant Me Grace 810
8:	Christ's Church Shall Glory 851
8:1–2	Lord Jesus Christ, Lover of All 1056
8:22–25	How Firm a Foundation 793
8:22–25	Stand by Me 835
9:11–17	We Come with Joy in Jesus Christ 879
9:12–17	O Blessed Savior 1045
9:23–24	Take Up Your Cross 890
9:25	The Love of the Lord 893
9:28–36	How Good, Lord, to Be Here! 978
9:28–36	Transform Us 977
11:1–13	Seek Ye First 800
11:2	Song of the Body of Christ / Canción del Cuerpo de Cristo 1042
11:2–4	This Is My Song 1086
11:9–10	A Prayer Canticle 769
11:9–13	If You Believe and I Believe 904
12:22–28	Peace, Be Not Anxious 916
12:32	This Is My Song 1086
12:32–40	God, Whose Giving Knows No Ending 870

Scripture Passages Related to Hymns/*continued*

Scripture Passages Related to Hymns/*continued*

2:4–6	Christ's Church Shall Glory 851
2:4–7	For Builders Bold 997
2:5	Take and Eat 1025
2:9–10	God Is Here! As We His People 927
2:9–10	Sing a New Church 848
2:24	Perdona a Tu Pueblo, Señor / Forgive Us, Your People, O Lord 579
3:11	O Day of Peace 911

2 PETER

1:16–18	Transform Us 977
1:19	Take and Eat 1025
1:19	The King Shall Come When Morning Dawns 504
2:4–8	O Christ the Great Foundation 854

1 JOHN

1:	Now We Remain 889
1:5	I Want to Walk as a Child of the Light 693
1:5	O Radiant Light 16
1:5	Our Darkness 950
1:9	Softly and Tenderly Jesus Is Calling 1060
2:27	Come, Holy Ghost 648
2:27	Veni Creator Spiritus 650
3:14	We Glory in the Cross 596
3:16	Holy Spirit, Come to Us 644
3:17	God, Whose Purpose Is to Kindle 905
3:18	A Living Faith 787
3:18	Now Let Us from This Table Rise 872
3:23	We Glory in the Cross 596
4:	Ubi Caritas (Hurd) 815
4:	Ubi Caritas (Taizé) 808
4:	Where Charity and Love Prevail 809
4:7–17	Love Divine, All Loves Excelling 806
4:10	Holy Spirit, Come to Us 644
4:10–16	Where True Love and Charity Are Found / Ubi Caritas 589
4:12	Heaven Is Singing for Joy / El Cielo Canta Alegría 731
4:12	Ubi Caritas (Hurd) 815
4:12	Ubi Caritas (Taizé) 808
4:16	Holy Spirit, Come to Us 644
4:16	Ubi Caritas (Hurd) 815
4:16	Ubi Caritas (Taizé) 808
5:13	Good Christians All 634
9:12–16	Easter Alleluia 629

REVELATION

1:8	Of the Father's Love Begotten 529
1:9	By All Your Saints Still Striving 986
1:15	He Comes to Us as One Unknown 786
1:18	The Strife Is O'er 617
2:10	By All Your Saints Still Striving 986
2:10	For All the Saints 984
3:20	Somebody's Knockin' at Your Door 573
4:	God, We Praise You! 703
4:	Holy God, We Praise Thy Name 705
4:	Holy, Holy, Holy! Lord God Almighty! 659
4:6	Alleluia! Sing to Jesus! 1030

4:8	Of the Father's Love Begotten 529
4:10	Love Divine, All Loves Excelling 806
4:11	You, Lord, Are Both Lamb and Shepherd 708
5:	This Is the Feast of Victory 618
5:9	Alleluia! Sing to Jesus! 1030
5:9	At the Lamb's High Feast We Sing 613
5:9	Crown Him with Many Crowns 669
5:9	To Jesus Christ, Our Sovereign King 671
5:11–12	Alabaré 720
5:11–14	All Hail the Power of Jesus' Name! 672
5:13	All Glory, Laud, and Honor 585
5:13	Palm Sunday Processional 586
6:9–11	All Hail the Power of Jesus' Name! 672
6:9–11	Holy God, We Praise Thy Name 705
6:12–17	My Lord, What a Morning! 955
7:2–4	By All Your Saints Still Striving 986
7:2–4	For All the Saints 984
7:9–14	By All Your Saints Still Striving 986
7:9–14	For All the Saints 984
7:9–17	Blessed Feasts of Blessed Martyrs 987
8:3–4	How Blessed Is This Place 998
12:1	Buenos Días, Paloma Blanca / Fairest Dove, Most Lovely Maiden 996
12:1	Mañanitas a la Virgen de Guadalupe / Morning Praises to the Virgin of Guadalupe 995
15:4	Holy, Holy, Holy! Lord God Almighty! 659
18:23	O Radiant Light 16
19:4	Come, Christians, Join to Sing 733
19:6–9	Wake, O Wake, and Sleep No Longer 512
19:11–16	Let All Mortal Flesh Keep Silence 717
19:12	Crown Him with Many Crowns 669
19:16	Christ the Lord Is Risen! 621
21:1–4	Jerusalem, My Happy Home 963
21:1–4	O Holy City, Seen of John 957
21:1–7	Alleluia! Jesus Is Risen! 622
21:6	Jesus Christ, Yesterday, Today, and Forever / Jesucristo Ayer 723
21:9	O Lord, You Died That All Might Live 1081
21:9–13	Wake, O Wake, and Sleep No Longer 512
21:23	I Want to Walk as a Child of the Light 693
21:23	O Radiant Light 16
21:27	For the Healing of the Nations 898
22:	Jerusalem, My Happy Home 963
22:	O Holy City, Seen of John 957
22:1	Shall We Gather at the River 960
22:5	Our Darkness 950
22:16	As Stars Adorn the Night-Veiled Sky 983
22:17	I Heard the Voice of Jesus Say 821
22:17	Let All Who Are Thirsty, Come 768
22:17	We Know That Christ Is Raised 1019
22:20	Soon and Very Soon 954
22:20	The King Shall Come When Morning Dawns 504

Liturgical Index   1463

Liturgical Index/*continued*

Liturgical Index/*continued*

Liturgical Index/*continued*

Liturgical Index/*continued*

Topical Index/*continued*

Topical Index/*continued*

Topical Index/*continued*

Topical Index/*continued*

1079 God of Love, Whose Mercies
    Daily
778 How Long, O God
744 In the Lord I'll Be Ever Thankful
695 Lord Jesus Chris
825 Nada Te Turbe
801 Nothing Is Impossible with God
889 Now We Remain
795 On Eagle's Wings
816 Shall Tribulation or Distress
1088 The God of All Eternity
886 The Summons
767 Turn My Heart, O God
1057 We Cannot Measure How You
    Heal
906 We Shall Overcome
962 We Shall Rise Again
832 Within Our Darkest Night
822 You Are Mine

FEAST
853 A House of Prayer
925 All Are Welcome
1032 All Who Hunger
931 All Who Hunger, Gather Gladly
924 As We Gather at Your Table
613 At the Lamb's High Feast We Sing
1051 At the Table of Jesus
593 Called to the Supper
509 Come, Emmanuel
761 Come, My Way, My Truth, My
    Life
1039 Come to Me, All Pilgrims Thirsty
625 Day of Delight
1070 God, in the Planning
833 Heart of a Shepherd
869 Here I Am, Lord
682 Light Dawns on a Weary World
506 Like a Bird
1073 Love Has Brought Us Here
    Together
813 Love Is His Word
937 Making Their Way
1040 Many and Great
1049 May We Be One (Communion
    Hymn)
1048 May We Be One (Communion
    Litany)
667 Praise, O Zion, Voices Raising
939 Risen Lord, We Gather Round
    You
1025 Take and Eat
618 This Is the Feast of Victory
941 Vamos Todos al Banquete / Let Us
    Go Now to the Banquet
936 Where Two or Three Are Gathered
845 Within the Reign of God

FOOD
1032 All Who Hunger
931 All Who Hunger, Gather Gladly
1030 Alleluia! Sing to Jesus!
1035 Bread of Life from Heaven / Pan
    de Vida Eterna
692 Christ, Be Our Light!
1033 Eat This Bread
745 Father, We Thank You, Who Have
    Planted
750 For the Fruits of All Creation
738 Halleluya! We Sing Your Praises
676 I Sing the Mighty Power of God
682 Light Dawns on a Weary World
827 My Shepherd, You Supply My
    Need
753 Praise and Thanksgiving
667 Praise, O Zion, Voices Raising
935 Prepare a Room for Me
1036 This Is the Body of Christ

941 Vamos Todos al Banquete / Let Us
    Go Now to the Banquet
845 Within the Reign of God

FORGIVENESS
See Mercy, Reconciliation

FREEDOM
519 A Child Is Born in Bethlehem /
    Puer Natus in Bethlehem
566 Again We Keep This Solemn Fast
1087 America the Beautiful
1020 Baptized in Water
728 Canticle of the Turning
633 Christ Has Arisen, Alleluia /
    Mfurahini, Haleluya
851 Christ's Church Shall Glory
876 City of God
509 Come, Emmanuel
923 Come Now, O Prince of Peace
493 Come, O Long-Expected Jesus
610 Come, You Faithful, Raise the
    Strain
495 Creator of the Stars of Night
829 Do Not Be Afraid
898 For the Healing of the Nations
1062 Forgive Our Sins
903 Freedom Is Coming
591 Glory in the Cross
867 God Has Chosen Me
1044 Gusten y Vean / Taste and See
738 Halleluya! We Sing Your Praises
1065 Help Us Forgive, Forgiving Lord
583 Hold Us in Your Mercy:
    Penitential Litany
934 I Come with Joy
1023 I Receive the Living God
904 If You Believe and I Believe
723 Jesus Christ, Yesterday, Today,
    and Forever / Jesucristo Ayer
858 Journey of Faith
576 Led by the Spirit
943 Let Us Rise
726 Lift Every Voice and Sing
1048 May We Be One (Communion
    Litany)
558 Merciful God
575 Mercy, O God
500 O Come, Divine Messiah!
503 On Jordan's Bank
763 Open My Eyes
737 Praise the One Who Breaks the
    Darkness
702 Praise to You, O Christ, Our
    Savior
736 Soli Deo Gloria
954 Soon and Very Soon
1025 Take and Eat
1031 Taste and See
569 The Cross of Jesus
538 The People Who Walked in
    Darkness
755 There's a Wideness in God's
    Mercy
603 Way of the Cross
902 We Are Called
879 We Come with Joy in Jesus Christ
906 We Shall Overcome
627 We Walk His Way / Ewe, Thina
496 When the King Shall Come Again
936 Where Two or Three Are Gathered
845 Within the Reign of God
822 You Are Mine

FRIENDSHIP
951 At Evening
656 Come, Holy Spirit, on Us Shine
1016 Covenant Hymn

922 Diverse in Culture, Nation, Race
1047 Draw Us in the Spirit's Tether
734 For the Beauty of the Earth
1074 God of Love, Embrace Your
    People
1065 Help Us Forgive, Forgiving Lord
934 I Come with Joy
897 I Will Be the Vine
723 Jesus Christ, Yesterday, Today,
    and Forever / Jesucristo Ayer
1073 Love Has Brought Us Here
    Together
812 No Greater Love
831 There Is a Balm in Gilead
879 We Come with Joy in Jesus Christ
883 We Have Been Told
845 Within the Reign of God

GATHERING
853 A House of Prayer
925 All Are Welcome
928 All People That on Earth Do
    Dwell
1032 All Who Hunger
931 All Who Hunger, Gather Gladly
1026 As the Bread of Life Is Broken
924 As We Gather at Your Table
855 Bless These Walls
692 Christ, Be Our Light!
852 Christ Is Made the Sure Founda-
    tion
621 Christ the Lord Is Risen!
722 Christians, Lift Up Your Hearts
510 Come, Lord Jesus
930 Come, Rejoice before Your Maker
752 Come, You Thankful People,
    Come
669 Crown Him with Many Crowns
922 Diverse in Culture, Nation, Race
1047 Draw Us in the Spirit's Tether
929 Gather Us In
577 Gather Us in Mercy, Lord
940 Gather Your People
927 God Is Here! As We His People
698 God Is Still Speaking
1074 God of Love, Embrace Your
    People
1079 God of Love, Whose Mercies
    Daily
705 Holy God, We Praise Thy Name
938 Holy Manna
998 How Blessed Is This Place
934 I Come with Joy
715 I Just Came to Praise the Lord
932 I Rejoiced When I Heard Them
    Say
723 Jesus Christ, Yesterday, Today,
    and Forever / Jesucristo Ayer
712 Jubilate, Servite
506 Like a Bird
868 Lord, Whose Love in Humble Ser-
    vice
937 Making Their Way
1040 Many and Great
780 May the Road Rise to Meet You
558 Merciful God
575 Mercy, O God
714 Praise to the Lord, the Almighty
935 Prepare a Room for Me
939 Risen Lord, We Gather Round
    You
960 Shall We Gather at the River
848 Sing a New Church
775 The Steadfast Love of the Lord
926 Uyai Mose / Come All You People
941 Vamos Todos al Banquete / Let Us
    Go Now to the Banquet
879 We Come with Joy in Jesus Christ
746 We Gather Together

Topical Index/*continued*

HEALING
853 A House of Prayer
517 Awake! Awake, and Greet the New Morn
882 Christ Has No Body Now But Yours
862 Christ in Me Arise
656 Come, Holy Spirit, on Us Shine
544 Come, Sing a Home and Family
836 Come to Me
922 Diverse in Culture, Nation, Race
898 For the Healing of the Nations
878 Glorify the Lord by Our Lives
772 God Weeps with Us Who Weep and Mourn
661 God, Whose Almighty Word
870 God, Whose Giving Knows No Ending
1066 Healer of Our Every Ill
765 Healing River of the Spirit
560 Hear Us, Almighty Lord / Attende Domine
583 Hold Us in Your Mercy: Penitential Litany
1054 Hold Us, Jesus
778 How Long, O God
838 In the Arms of God
568 Jerusalem, My Destiny
1059 Jesus, Heal Us
580 Kyrie
576 Led by the Spirit
1056 Lord Jesus Christ, Lover of All
810 Lord of All Nations, Grant Me Grace
1048 May We Be One (Communion Litany)
558 Merciful God
827 My Shepherd, You Supply My Need
1053 O Christ, the Healer
668 O Christ, Your Heart Compassionate
776 O God, Why Are You Silent?
503 On Jordan's Bank
579 Perdona a Tu Pueblo, Señor / Forgive Us, Your People, O Lord
737 Praise the One Who Breaks the Darkness
563 Return to God / Volvamos Hoy a Nuestro Dios
939 Risen Lord, We Gather Round You
704 Sing Praise to God Who Reigns Above
1042 Song of the Body of Christ / Canción del Cuerpo de Cristo
548 Songs of Thankfulness and Praise
592 Stay Here and Keep Watch
1052 Stop By, Lord
792 Surely It Is God Who Saves Me
1058 The God of Second Chances
831 There Is a Balm in Gilead
771 There Is a Longing
1080 There Is a Place
755 There's a Wideness in God's Mercy
1036 This Is the Body of Christ
675 To You Who Bow
604 Tree of Life and Glory
767 Turn My Heart, O God
650 Veni Creator Spiritus
1022 Wade in the Water
952 Watch, O Lord
1057 We Cannot Measure How You Heal
784 We Remember
496 When the King Shall Come Again
832 Within Our Darkest Night
701 Word of God, Come Down on Earth
822 You Are Mine

HEAVEN
949 Abide With Me
983 As Stars Adorn the Night-Veiled Sky
1051 At the Table of Jesus
986 By All Your Saints Still Striving
608 Christ the Lord Is Risen Today
733 Come, Christians, Join to Sing
752 Come, You Thankful People, Come
946 Day Is Done
828 Do Not Let Your Hearts Be Troubled
942 Father, We Praise You
984 For All the Saints
1079 God of Love, Whose Mercies Daily
966 God, Who Made the Earth and Heaven
731 Heaven Is Singing for Joy / El Cielo Canta Alegría
705 Holy God, We Praise Thy Name
938 Holy Manna
998 How Blessed Is This Place
965 How Bright Is the Day
1029 I Am the Bread of Life / Yo Soy el Pan de Vida
611 I Know That My Redeemer Lives! (DUKE STREET)
1084 I Know That My Redeemer Lives (Hughes)
693 I Want to Walk as a Child of the Light
219 In Paradisum / May Choirs of Angels
963 Jerusalem, My Happy Home
824 Jesus, Lead the Way
901 Jesus, Our Divine Companion
842 Jesus, Remember Me
707 Joyful, Joyful, We Adore You
806 Love Divine, All Loves Excelling
961 Lux Aeterna Litany
1082 May Holy Angels Lead You
220 May Saints and Angels Lead You On
1078 May the Angels Lead You into Paradise
780 May the Road Rise to Meet You
827 My Shepherd, You Supply My Need
825 Nada Te Turbe
743 Now Thank We All Our God
910 O God of Love, O King of Peace
957 O Holy City, Seen of John
179 O Saving Victim / O Salutaris
543 Once in Royal David's City
916 Peace, Be Not Anxious
847 Plenty Good Room
826 Precious Lord, Take My Hand
834 Quietly, Peacefully
1000 Salve Regina / Hail, Queen of Heaven
960 Shall We Gather at the River
1003 Sing We of the Blessed Mother
609 Sing with All the Saints in Glory
1085 Song of Farewell
954 Soon and Very Soon
959 Steal Away to Jesus
964 Take Me Home
740 Te Deum
970 The Hands that First Held Mary's Child
540 The Table of Emmanuel
1080 There Is a Place

512 Wake, O Wake, and Sleep No Longer
962 We Shall Rise Again
783 We Walk by Faith
589 Where True Love and Charity Are Found / Ubi Caritas
936 Where Two or Three Are Gathered
685 Who Can Measure Heaven and Earth
822 You Are Mine

HOLINESS
991 A Great Cloud of Witnesses
999 Among All
983 As Stars Adorn the Night-Veiled Sky
855 Bless These Walls
839 Blest Are They
996 Buenos Días, Paloma Blanca / Fairest Dove, Most Lovely Maiden
646 Come Down, O Love Divine
544 Come, Sing a Home and Family
1006 Como Estrella en Claro Cielo / As a Star on Cloudless Evenings
929 Gather Us In
659 Holy, Holy, Holy! Lord God Almighty!
662 Let There Be Light
1011 Litany of Mary / Letanía de la Santísima Virgen María
992 Litany of the Saints
696 Love, Burn Bright
995 Mañanitas a la Virgen de Guadalupe / Morning Praises to the Virgin of Guadalupe
881 Moved by the Gospel, Let Us Move
649 O Breathe on Me, O Breath of God
1053 O Christ, the Healer
1002 O Sanctissima / O Most Holy One
847 Plenty Good Room
798 Pues Si Vivimos / If We Are Living
1007 Stainless the Maiden / Serdeczna Matko
974 The Great Forerunner of the Morn
1014 Wash, O God, Our Sons and Daughters
809 Where Charity and Love Prevail
1018 Who Calls You by Name
811 With Great Love

HOLY SPIRIT
853 A House of Prayer
769 A Prayer Canticle
622 Alleluia! Jesus Is Risen!
1020 Baptized in Water
658 Be Present, Spirit of the Lord
1013 Blessed Be God, Who Chose You in Christ
655 By the Waking of Our Hearts
1012 Come and Be Sealed
646 Come Down, O Love Divine
648 Come, Holy Ghost
656 Come, Holy Spirit, on Us Shine
510 Come, Lord Jesus
762 Come to Us, Creative Spirit
922 Diverse in Culture, Nation, Race
1021 Easter Vigil Initiation Acclamations
562 From Ashes to the Living Font
577 Gather Us in Mercy, Lord
940 Gather Your People
878 Glorify the Lord by Our Lives
927 God Is Here! As We His People
1079 God of Love, Whose Mercies Daily

Topical Index/*continued*

Topical Index/*continued*

Topical Index/*continued*

Topical Index/*continued*

Topical Index/*continued*

Topical Index/*continued*

Topical Index/*continued*

Topical Index/*continued*

Topical Index/*continued*

Topical Index/*continued*

Topical Index/*continued*

Topical Index/*continued*

Topical Index/*continued*

Index of Composers, Authors and Sources/*continued*

Index of Composers, Authors and Sources/*continued*

Index of Composers, Authors and Sources/*continued*

Metrical Index/*continued*

66 4 666 4
ITALIAN HYMN 661

666 4 WITH REFRAIN
GIVE ME JESUS 686

6 6 6 6 4 44 4
LOVE UNKNOWN 599

666 66 WITH REFRAIN
PERSONENT HODIE 721

6 6 6 6 66 6 6
MADRID (SPANISH HYMN) 733

66 77 78 55
IN DULCI JUBILO 526

66 89 66
STILLE NACHT 527

66 9 D
PRECIOUS LORD 826

66 10 66 10 14 14 66 10
ANTHEM 726

66 11 D
DOWN AMPNEY 646

66 11 66 11 D
ASH GROVE 747 880

6 7 6 7 6 6 6 6
NUN DANKET 743

6 7 6 7 WITH REFRAIN
VREUCHTEN 606

6 8 8 6 WITH REFRAIN
UNLESS A GRAIN 895

7 5 7 6 WITH REFRAIN
HEAVENLY FEAST 936

7 6 6 7 8 WITH REFRAIN
TEMPLE OF PEACE 682

7 6 7 6
DE EERSTEN ZIJN DE LAATSTEN 975

7 6 7 6 6 7 6
ES IST EIN' ROS' ENTSPRUNGEN 515

7 6 7 6 777 6
KELVINGROVE 886

7 6 8 6 8 6
ALDINE 679

7 7 7
VENI SANCTE SPIRITUS 1186

77 7 4 D WITH REFRAIN
HERE I AM, LORD 869

77 77 77
DIX 551 685 734

77 77 D WITH REFRAIN
MENDELSSOHN 520

7 7 7 9 D WITH REFRAIN
CARITAS DOMINI 893

7 7 9 WITH REFRAIN
CHEREPONI 595

7 7 9 7 WITH REFRAIN
THE HOLLY AND THE IVY 540

7 8 7 6 WITH REFRAIN
VENEZ, DIVIN MESSIE 500

7 8 7 7 WITH REFRAIN
WHAT A MORNING 955

7 8 7 8 77
GROSSER GOTT 705

7 8 7 8 88
LIEBSTER JESU 701

7 8 8 8 WITH REFRAIN
WADE IN THE WATER 1022

7 10 12 WITH REFRAIN
WE REMEMBER 784

8 3 8 3 77 8 3
STAND BY ME 835

8 4 8 4 777 4 5
SALVE REGINA COELITUM 979

8 4 8 4 888 4
AR HYD Y NOS 946 966

8 5 8 4 7
REGINA CAELI 616

8 5 8 5 84 3
CASTLEWOOD 762

8 6 8 6 7 6 8 6
ST. LOUIS 523

8 6 8 6 8 6 WITH REFRAIN
GOD REST YOU MERRY 525

8 6 8 6 11 9
AIKENHEAD 878

8 6 88 66
REPTON 786 658

8 7 8 7 44 7
UNION SEMINARY 1047

8 7 8 7 66 66 7
EIN' FESTE BURG 851

8 7 8 77
THOMAS 581

8 7 8 7 77
IRBY 543

8 7 8 7 77 88
GENEVA 42 497

8 7 8 7 8 7 7
DIVINUM MYSTERIUM 529

Metrical Index/*continued*

8 7 8 7 D WITH REFRAIN
WE GIVE YOU THANKS 751

8 7 8 7 88 7
MIT FREUDEN ZART 704

8 7 8 7 888 4
AR HYD Y NOS 750

87 98 87
BESANÇON 501

88 WITH ALLELUIAS AND REFRAIN
PUER NATUS 519

8 8 WITH REFRAIN
ALLELUIA NO. 1 620

88 44 6 WITH REFRAIN
KINGS OF ORIENT 547

88 7
STABAT MATER 224

888 WITH REFRAIN
VICTORY 617

888 4 WITH REFRAIN
O FILII ET FILIAE 626 656

8 8 8 4 4 8 8
ROMANS 8 816

8 8 8 8 WITH ALLELUIAS
CH THREE 511

8 8 8 8 8 8
ST. CATHERINE 787

8 8 8 8 D
YE BANKS AND BRAES 1057

88 9 WITH REFRAIN
HEALER OF OUR EVERY ILL 1066

8 8 12 7 WITH REFRAIN
ISAIAH 9 538

89 8 89 8 66 4 44 8
WACHET AUF 512

8 10 8 10
FOUNTAIN OF LIFE 864

8 10 10 WITH REFRAIN
PESCADOR DE HOMBRES 884

9 6 8 5
NEW BEGINNING 1058

9 6 8 6 8 7 10 WITH REFRAIN
TWO OAKS 925

9 8 9 6 WITH REFRAIN
CHRIST, BE OUR LIGHT 692

9 8 9 8
ST. CLEMENT 953

9 8 9 8 WITH REFRAIN
SAWYER'S EXIT 965

9 8 9 8 D
RENDEZ À DIEU 555 745

9 8 9 8 8 7 8 9
REJOICE, REJOICE 517

9 8 9 8 9 66
KOMT NU MET ZANG 933 937

9 8 10 10 WITH REFRAIN
LIFE-GIVING BREAD 1038

99 999 77
SOLI DEO GLORIA 736

9 9 10 9 9 8
UN FLAMBEAU 534

9 10 WITH REFRAIN
PRODIGAL 1069

9 10 9 10 WITH REFRAIN
ABINGTON 532

9 10 10 9 10 5 9
LET US RISE 943

10 7 10 8 WITH REFRAIN
HOUSTON 693

10 9 10 9 WITH REFRAIN
SUNRISE SONG 691

10 9 10 10 D
GATHER US IN 929

10 10 9 D WITH REFRAIN
IN DIR IST FREUDE 625

10 10 10 WITH ALLELUIA
ENGELBERG 716 1019

10 10 10 4
CAMACUÁ 756

10 10 10 10 10 10
UNDE ET MEMORES 1024

10 10 10 11 WITH REFRAIN
BRAINTREE 539

10 10 11 11
LAUDATE DOMINUM 840

10 10 12 10
GABRIEL'S MESSAGE 972

10 10 12 11 D
APARACIONES GUADALUPANAS 994

10 11 6 10 11 4
JE LOUERAI L'ÉTERNE 727

10 11 11 12
SLANE 758

11 10 11 4
DUNBLANE PRIMARY 1080

11 10 11 10 WITH REFRAIN
HOW GREAT THOU ART 730

Metrical Index/*continued*

Tune Index   1467

Tune Index/*continued*

Index of Service Music/*continued*

Index of Service Music/*continued*

A light will shine on us this day: the Lord is born for us. 1104 1404

All power is yours, Lord God, our mighty King, alleluia! 136

All the ends of the earth have seen the power of God. 80

All the ends of the earth have seen the saving power of God. 1105 1406

Alleluia, alleluia, alleluia! 83 94 116 1160 1426

And holy is your name through all generations! Everlasting is your mercy to the people you have chosen, and holy is your name. 123

Arise, come to your God, sing him your songs of rejoicing. 83

As morning breaks I look to you; I look to you, O Lord, to be my strength this day, as morning breaks, as morning breaks. 64

As the deer longs for running streams, so I long, so I long, so I long for you. 55

Be gracious, O Lord! Let my prayer rise like incense, my hands like an evening sacrifice. 111

Be merciful, O Lord; be merciful, O Lord. Be merciful, O Lord, for we have sinned. 61

Be merciful, O Lord, for we have sinned. 62 1115 1116 1366

Be merciful, O Lord, for we have sinned; be merciful, O Lord, for we have sinned. 60

Be with me, Lord, when I am in trouble. 1118 1397

Be with me, Lord, when I am in trouble, be with me Lord, I pray. 75

Blessed are the poor in spirit; the kingdom of heaven is theirs! 1203

Blessed are they, blessed are they who hope in the Lord. 1316

Blessed are they who dwell in your house, O Lord. 1388

Blessed are they who follow the law of the Lord! 1209 1430

Blessed are they who hope in the Lord, who hope in the Lord. 30

Blessed are they who hope, who hope in the Lord. 1211

Blessed are those who fear the Lord. 1290 1438

Blessed are those who fear the Lord and walk in his ways. 103 1436

Blessed be the Lord, for he has come to his people and set them free. 8

Blessed, blessed are they who dwell in your house, O Lord. 1108

Blessed the people the Lord has chosen to be his own. 1189 1250 1354

Blessed the poor in spirit; the kingdom of heaven is theirs! 1451

Blest are those who love you, happy those who follow you, blest are those who seek you, O God. 102

By your wounds, O Christ, we have been healed. 135

Call upon the Lord and he will hear you. 74

Christ is born for us; come, let us adore him. 3

Christ is the light of the nations, to bring salvation to the ends of the earth. 58

Come, let us worship the Lord, the King who is to come. 3

Create a clean heart, a clean heart in me, O God. 1129 1159

Create in me, create in me a clean heart, O God. 1367

Cry out with joy and gladness: for among you is the great and Holy One of Israel. 1098 1457

Cry out with joy to the Lord, all the earth; serve the Lord with gladness. 3

Dichoso el pueblo que el Señor se escogió como heredad. 49

Do not forget the works of the Lord! 1309 1384

El Señor es mi pastor, nada me falta. El Señor es mi pastor, nada me faltará. 40

Éste es el día que hizo el Señor: sea nuestra alegría y gozo. 94

Every nation on earth will adore you, Lord. 68

Father, into your hands I commend my spirit. 47 1348

Father, into your hands I commend my spirit, my spirit. 1146

Fill us with your love, O Lord, and we will sing for joy! 1276 1395

Fill us with your love, O Lord, and we will sing for joy, we will sing for joy! 73

For ever I will sing the goodness of the Lord. 1100 1102 1230 1392

For ever I will sing the goodness of the Lord, the goodness of the Lord. 72

From the voices of children, Lord, comes the sound of your praise. 33

Give back to me the joy of your salvation. 62

Give him/her eternal rest, O Lord, and may your light shine on him/her for ever. 211

Give thanks to the Lord for he is good, his love is everlasting. 94 1167 1428

Give thanks to the Lord, his love is everlasting. 1228 1418

Give the Lord glory and honor. 79 1403

Give the Lord glory, glory and honor. 1278

Glory and praise for evermore. 1459

Go out to all the world, and tell the Good News. 1220 1256 1425

God is praised and exalted above all forever. 121

God mounts his throne to shouts of joy: a blare of trumpets for the Lord. 57 59 1180 1364

God mounts his throne to shouts of joy, to shouts, to shouts of joy. 58

God, in your goodness, you have made a home for the poor. 1376

God, in your goodness, you have made a home, you have made a home for the poor. 1259

Happy are the people the Lord has chosen, chosen to be his own. 49

Happy are they who dwell in your house, O Lord, who dwell in your house, O Lord. 70

Have mercy, Lord, and hear my prayer. 31

Have mercy, Lord, cleanse me from all my sins. 62

He who does justice will live in the presence of the Lord. 1319

Here am I, Lord, here am I; I come to do your will. 54

Here am I, Lord; here am I, Lord; I come to do your will. 1358

Here am I, Lord; I come to do your will. 1197 1198 1299

Here I am, Lord, here I am. I come to do your will. 53

His goodness shall follow me always to the end of my days. 41

How great is your name, O Lord our God, through all the earth! 33

I am the living bread come down from heaven; anyone who eats this bread will live for ever, alleluia. 41

I believe that I shall see the good things of the Lord in the land of the living. 45 1181 1311 1344 1345

I believe that I shall see the good things of the Lord in the land of the living, in the land of the living. 44

I love you, I love you, Lord, my strength. 1281 1285

I love you, Lord, my strength, my strength. 1325

I praise you, O Lord, for I am wonderfully made. 1301 1446

I shall live in the house of the Lord all the days of my life. 1275 1334

I turn to you, Lord, in time of trouble, and you fill me with the joy of salvation. 48

I turn to you, O Lord, in time of trouble, and you fill me with the joy of salvation. 1210 1350

I will bless the Lord at all times. 51

I will give thanks to your name, because of your kindness and your truth. 1313

I will praise the Lord all my days, make music to my God while I live. 115

I will praise you, Lord, for you have rescued me. 46 1156 1170 1223 1231 1347

I will praise you, Lord, in the assembly of your people. 1175 1331

I will praise your name for ever, my King and my God. 113 114 1176 1233 1286 1447

I will praise your name, my King and my God. 112

I will rise and go to my father. 1265 1368

I will sing and make music for the Lord. 45

I will sing, I will sing to the God who sets me free! Pharaoh's army and his chariots God cast into the sea! 117

I will sing of your salvation. 67 1205 1379

I will take the cup of life, I will call God's name all my days. 91

I will take the cup of salvation, and call on the name of the Lord. 93 1192 1424

I will walk before the Lord, in the land of the living. 1120 1264 1422

If today, if today you hear his voice, harden not your hearts. 77

If today you hear God's voice, harden not your hearts. 76

If today you hear his voice, harden not your hearts. 1122 1204 1247 1260 1274 1400

In every age, O Lord, you have been our refuge. 1262 1394

In his days justice will flourish; in his days fullness of peace forevermore. 68

In the land of the living, I will walk with God all my days. 91

In the morning I will sing, will sing glad songs of praise to you. 6

In the sight of the angels I will sing your praises, Lord. 1208

In the sight of the angels I will sing, sing your praises, sing your praises, I will sing your praises, Lord. 108

In the sight of the angels, I will sing your praises, O Lord. 1443

In the silent hours of night, bless the Lord. 26

In you, Lord, in you, Lord, in you, Lord, I have found my peace. 1284

In you, O Lord, I have found my peace. 1440

In you, O Lord, I have found my peace, I have found my peace. 106

Justice shall flourish in his time, and fullness of peace for ever. 1093 1381

La misericordia de nuestro Dios llena la tierra. 49

Let all the earth cry out, cry out to God with joy. 1177 1235

Let all the earth cry out to God with joy. 1373

Let my prayer rise up like incense in your presence, the raising of my hands, an offering to you. 109

Let my tongue be silenced, if I ever forget you! 107 1126 1442

Let the Lord enter; he is king of glory. 1099 1335

Let us go rejoicing to the house of the Lord. 99 1433

Let us go rejoicing to the house of the Lord, to the house of the Lord. 100

Let us go rejoicing to the house, to the house of the Lord. 1090 1295

Let us sing to the Lord; he has covered himself in glory! 118 1155 1455

Let your mercy be on us, O God, as we place our trust in you. 49

Like a deer that longs for running streams, my soul longs for you, my God. 1159

Like a deer that longs for running streams, my soul longs for you, my God; my soul longs for you, my God. 1361

Lord, be my rock of safety. 1349

Lord, come and save us. 1096 1450

Lord, come to my aid! 1253

Lord, come to my aid, Lord, come to my aid! 1359

Lord, every nation on earth will adore you. 1110 1382

Lord, forgive the wrong I have done. 1226 1351

Lord, forgive the wrong I have done, forgive the wrong I have done. 48

Lord, give success to the work of our hands. 1308

Lord, give success to the work of our hands, to the work of our hands. 1396

Lord, go up to the place of your rest, you and the ark of your holiness. 1306 1441

Lord, heal my soul, for I have sinned against you. 1213 1360

Lord, I love your commands. 1242

Lord, I love your commands, I love your commands. 1431

Lord, I thank you for your faithfulness and love. 108

Lord, if you will, you can make me clean. 62

Lord, in your great love, answer me. 1227 1377

Lord, it is good to give thanks to you. 1217 1225

Lord, it is good to give thanks to you, to give thanks to you. 1398

Lord, let us see your kindness. 71

Lord, let us see your kindness, and grant us your salvation. 1094 1237 1248 1389

Lord, let your face shine on us. 1169 1317

Lord, let your mercy be on us, as we place our trust in you. 1119 1174 1279 1352

Lord, Lord, be my rock of safety. 1218

Lord, make us turn to you; let us see your face and we shall be saved. 1091 1101 1385

Lord, make us turn to you, Lord, make us turn to you; let us see your face and we shall be saved. 69

Lord, on the day I called for help, you answered me. 1244 1444

Lord, on the day I called for help, you answered me, you answered me. 108

Lord, send out your Spirit, and renew the face of the earth. 86 169 1153 1184 1185 1416

Lord, send out your Spirit on us; renew the face of the earth. 87

Lord, this is the people that longs to see your face. 1310 1337

Lord, when your glory appears, my joy will be full. 1289 1324

Lord, you are good and forgiving. 1239 1391

Lord, you have the words of everlasting life. 35 36 1123 1158 1326

Lord, you will show us the path of life. 34 1168 1322

Lord, your love is eternal; do not forsake the work of your hands. 1254 1445

Lord, your love is eternal, Lord, your love is eternal; do not forsake the work of your hands, Lord, your love is eternal. 108

Magnificat, Magnificat ánima mea Dóminum. 127

May God bless us in his mercy. 66

May God bless us in his mercy, may God bless us in his mercy. 1109 1374

May the Lord bless and protect us all the days of our lives. 1273 1437

May the Lord bless us all the days of our lives. 103

May the Lord bless us, may the Lord protect us, all the days, all the days of our life. 102

Mi alma está sedienta de ti, Señor, Dios mío. My soul is thirsting for you, O Lord, my God. 65

My God, my God, come quickly to help me. 193

My God, my God, O why have you abandoned me? 38

My God, my God, why have you abandoned me? 37 1138 1330

My prayers rise like incense, my hands like an evening offering. 17

My prayers rise like incense, my hands like the evening offering. 110

My refuge, my stronghold, my God in whom I trust! 74

My shepherd is the Lord, I want for nothing. My shepherd is the Lord, nothing more shall I need. 40

My shepherd is the Lord, nothing indeed shall I want. 41

My soul, give thanks to the Lord, and bless God's holy name. 85

My soul is thirsting for you, O Lord, thirsting for you my God. 1229 1257 1287 1371

My soul is thirsting, my soul is thirsting, my soul is thirsting for you, O Lord my God. 63

My soul rejoices in my God, my soul rejoices in my God. 1460

My soul rejoices, my soul rejoices in my God. 1097

Night holds no terrors for me sleeping under God's wings. 74

No one who waits for you, O Lord, will ever be put to shame. 1311 1342

O bless the Lord, bless the Lord, my soul, O my soul. 1113

O bless the Lord, my soul, O bless the Lord. 1415

O blessed are those who fear the Lord and walk in his ways. 1106

O God, let all the nations praise you! 66

O God, O God, let all the nations praise you! 1179 1251 1375 1456

O Lord, our God, how glorious is your name! How glorious is your name over all the earth! 32

O Lord, our God, how wonderful your name in all the earth! 1190 1318

O praise the Lord, Jerusalem. 1453

One who does justice will live in the presence of the Lord. 1320

Our blessing-cup is a communion with the Blood of Christ. 91 1143 1423

Our blessing-cup is a communion with the Blood of Christ the Lord. El cáliz que bendecimos es la comunión de la sangre de Cristo. 90

Our blessing-cup is a communion with the Blood of the Lord. 92

Our eyes are fixed on the Lord, pleading for his mercy. 1234 1434

Our help comes from the Lord, the maker of heaven and earth. 98
Our help is from the Lord who made heaven and earth. 1280 1432

Praise and exalt him for ever, O praise and exalt him for ever. 122
Praise the Lord and call upon his name. 190
Praise the Lord, Jerusalem. 1191
Praise the Lord, my soul! Praise the Lord! 1261 1271 1288 1452
Praise the Lord, praise the Lord, who heals the bro-kenhearted. 1207 1454
Praise the Lord, praise the Lord who lifts up the poor. 1421
Praise the Lord who lifts up the poor. 1268
Proclaim his marvelous deeds to all the nations. 1199 1402
Proclaim the greatness of God; rejoice in God, my Savior! 126
Proclaim to all the nations the marvelous deeds of the Lord! 79
Protect us, Lord, as we stay awake; watch over us as we sleep, that awake we may keep watch with Christ, and, asleep, rest in his peace. 28
Put your hope in the Lord; take courage and be strong. 45

Remember your mercies, O Lord. 1341
Remember your mercies, O Lord; remember your mercies, O Lord. 1269
Rest in God alone, rest in God alone, my soul. 1370
Rest in God alone, rest in God alone, my soul, my soul. 1215

Send forth your spirit, O God, send forth your spirit, O God, and renew the earth, renew the earth, send forth your spirit, O God. 88
Señor, que tu misericordia venga sobre nosotros. 49
Shepherd me, O God, beyond my wants, beyond my fears, from death into life. 39
Since my mother's womb, you have been my strength. 1300 1380
Since my mother's womb, you have been my strength, you have been my strength. 67
Sing praise to our king, sing praise: for God is king of all the earth. 58
Sing to the Lord a new song, for God has done won-derful deeds. 80
Sing to the Lord a new song, for he has done marvel-ous deeds. 1314 1409
Sing with joy to God! Sing to God our help! 1219 1387
Suba mi oración como incienso en tu presencia, el alzar de mis manos como ofrenda de la tarde. 109

Taste and see, taste and see the goodness of the Lord. 51
Taste and see the goodness of the Lord. 51 200 1127 1249 1252 1255 1355

Taste and see the goodness of the Lord, the goodness of the Lord. 50
Teach me your ways, O Lord, teach me your ways. 1201 1340
The Almighty has done great things for me, and holy is his Name. 19
The angel of the Lord will rescue those who fear him. 1303 1357
The earth is full of the goodness of God, the good-ness of our God. 49
The earth is full of the goodness of the Lord, the goodness of the Lord. 1353
The earth is full of the goodness, the goodness of the Lord. 1153
The hand of the Lord feeds us; he answers all our needs. 1243 1245 1448
The hand of the Lord feeds us; he answers all our needs, he answers all our needs. 114
The just man is a light in darkness to the upright. 1206 1420
The Lord comes to rule the earth, to rule with jus-tice. 1292
The Lord comes to rule the earth with justice. 1408
The Lord comes to the earth to rule the earth with justice. 80
The Lord gave them bread from heaven. 1383
The Lord gave them bread, gave them bread from heaven. 1246
The Lord has done great things for us; we are filled with joy. 1435
The Lord has done great things for us; we are filled with joy, we are filled with joy. 101 1095 1130 1282
The Lord has revealed to the nations his saving power. 1277
The Lord has revealed to the nations his saving power, his saving power. 1407
The Lord has revealed to the nations, revealed his saving power. 1178
The Lord has set his throne in heaven. 1182 1412
The Lord hears the cry of the poor. 1283 1356
The Lord hears the cry of the poor. Blessed be the Lord. 52
The Lord is kind and merciful. 85 1124 1212 1214 1216
The Lord is kind and merciful, slow to anger, and rich in compassion. 1263 1414
The Lord is kind and merciful; the Lord is kind and merciful. 1411
The Lord is kind and merciful; the Lord is kind and merciful. Slow to anger, rich in kindness, the Lord is kind and merciful. 84
The Lord is king; he is robed in majesty. 1294 1399
The Lord is king, the Lord Most High over all the earth. 1405
The Lord is king, the Most High over all the earth. 1183 1305
The Lord is my light and my salvation. 45 158 206 1121 1200 1311 1343

Psalm Refrains Set to Music/*continued*

The Lord is my light and my salvation, of whom should I be afraid, of whom should I be afraid? 43

The Lord is my light, my light and my salvation. The Lord is my light and my salvation. 44

The Lord is my shepherd, nothing shall I want: he leads me by safe paths, nothing shall I fear. 41

The Lord is my shepherd; there is nothing I shall want. 41 212 1125 1171 1196 1240 1293 1311 1332

The Lord is near to all who call on him. 1449

The Lord is near to all who call upon him. 1266

The Lord is near to all who call upon him, the Lord is near, the Lord is near. 114

The Lord is risen, alleluia. 3

The Lord remembers his covenant for ever. 1107 1417

The Lord said to my lord: "Sit at my right hand." 89

The Lord speaks of peace, peace, peace to his people. 1390

The Lord speaks of peace to his people. 1304

The Lord upholds my life. 1369

The Lord upholds my life. The Lord upholds my life. 1267

The Lord will bless his people with his peace. 1346

The Lord will bless his people with peace. 1111

The Lord's kindness is everlasting to those who fear him. 1194 1413

The one who does justice will live in the presence of the Lord. 1241 1258

The precepts of the Lord give joy to the heart. 35 1270 1328

The queen stands at your right hand, arrayed in gold. 1307 1362

The queen stands at your right hand, arrayed in gold, arrayed in gold. 56

The Rising Sun of joy and justice lights the way that leads to peace. As the day descends from heaven, so does love that sets us free. 129

The seed that falls on good ground will yield a fruitful harvest. 1236 1372

The son of David will live for ever. 1298 1393

The stone rejected by the builders has become the cornerstone. 1172 1429

The vineyard of the Lord is the house of Israel. 1272 1386

The waters of the river gladden the city of God, the holy dwelling of the Most High. 1312 1363

Their message goes out through all the earth. 1302 1329

This is the day the Lord has made; let us rejoice and be glad. 94 95 96 1427

This is the day the Lord has made; let us rejoice and be glad in it! 97

This is the day the Lord has made; let us rejoice, let us rejoice, let us rejoice and be glad. 1165

Though I walk in the valley of darkness, I fear no evil, for you are with me. 1311 1333

To the upright I will show the saving power of God. 1221 1365

To you glory and praise for evermore. 1188

To you, O Lord, I lift my soul. 1092 1311

To you, O Lord, I lift my soul, to you I lift my soul. 42 1338

Today if you hear the voice of the Lord, harden not your hearts. 3

Today is born our Savior, Christ the Lord. 78 1103

Today, today, today is born our Savior, Christ the Lord. 1401

Tú eres el orgullo de nuestra raza. 1315

Turn to the Lord in your need, and you will live. 1238 1378

We are God's people, the flock of the Lord. 81

We are his people, the sheep of his flock. 82 1173 1224 1410

Who is this king of glory? It is the Lord! 1297 1336

With the Lord there is mercy, and fullness of redemption. 105 185 1128 1222 1439

With the Lord there is mercy and the fullness of redemption, call to him in your trials, he will answer whenever you call. 104

You are a priest for ever, in the line of Melchizedek. 89 1193 1419

You are my inheritance, O Lord. 34 1321 1323

You are my inheritance, O Lord, O Lord. 1154 1232 1291

You are the highest honor of our race. 1315

You will draw water joyfully from the springs of salvation. 1112 1157 1159 1195 1458

You will draw water joyfully from the springs of salvation. Sacarán aguas con alegría de last fuentes de salvación. 119

Your ways, O Lord, are love and truth, to those who keep your covenant. 42 1117 1339

Your words, Lord, are Spirit and life, Spirit and life. 1202 1238

Your words, Lord, are Spirit and life, your words are Spirit and life. 35

Your words, O Lord, are Spirit and life. 1327

Index of First Lines and Common Titles/*continued*

Index of First Lines and Common Titles/*continued*

Index of First Lines and Common Titles/*continued*

Index of First Lines and Common Titles/*continued*

Index of First Lines and Common Titles/*continued*

Index of First Lines and Common Titles/*continued*